INCUNABULA AND AMERICANA

INCUNABULA
AND AMERICANA
1450-1800

A KEY TO BIBLIOGRAPHICAL STUDY

BY

MARGARET BINGHAM STILLWELL

LIBRARIAN OF THE
ANNMARY BROWN MEMORIAL

COOPER SQUARE PUBLISHERS, INC.

New York • *1961*

Printed in U.S.A. by
NOBLE OFFSET PRINTERS, INC.
NEW YORK 3, N. Y.

TO THE LATE
RUSH CHRISTOPHER HAWKINS
WHO IN FOUNDING THE
ANNMARY BROWN MEMORIAL
CREATED A CHAIR
FOR BIBLIOGRAPHICAL RESEARCH

PREFACE

To anyone undertaking the study of incunabula or of Americana, I offer ready sympathy and, I hope, a helping hand. I remember the feeling of bewilderment with which I first turned to the study of early printing. I felt myself surrounded by a veritable wilderness of books — ancient books, ponderous, fascinating, beautiful to be sure, but shrouded deep in mystery; a mass of bibliographies full of signs and symbols, dealing with infinite minutiæ; a seemingly endless number of monographs on incunabula, histories of early presses, discussions of types, and essays on a thousand aspects of the subject. Twenty years ago, when I took my first plunge into the study of Americana, I passed through much the same ordeal. Even under the guidance of bibliographers seasoned in the work, I felt often haunted by a questioning fear. Had I not overlooked the obvious? Were there not other mysterious rites to have been performed in the name of the meticulous god called Collation?

From confessions made by bookmen of the older school and from the questions asked me by the younger set, I feel convinced that others pass through similar ordeals in entering either subject, and experience oftentimes the same bibliographical quakings deep within their souls. So, having blazed something of a trail through two forests, alluring although impenetrable to my youthful eyes, I have now gone back in memory, reëxamining the trails and marking them for whomsoever may wish to go by a similar route.

One thing I can promise. Beyond the maze of the forest, one comes to the sunshine. The ancient books, seemingly so reticent, yield their secrets more and more joyously. Bibliographical lists and monographs become daily the stoutest of allies. And among other workers in the field, the owners of rare books, and the scholars devoted to the theme, one finds coöperation and a friendly spirit. Of this, the present volume gives ample proof. As with everyone who undertakes a project within the realms of booklore, the courtesies extended have been legion. Beginning with five good neighbors in the John Carter Brown Library who have given gracious and unending service, and my Trustee, Mr. Walter F. Angell, whose interest, help, and understanding have been an unfailing inspiration — my indebtedness to kindly correspondents and co-workers includes many in America and in foreign lands.

To Mr. Alfred W. Pollard and Mr. Victor Scholderer of the British Museum; Dr. Konrad Haebler of Dresden; M. Seymour de Ricci of Paris; Dr. Ernst Crous, Dr. Max Josef Husung, and Dr. Rudolf Juchhoff of the *Gesamtkatalog* headquarters; Mr. E. P. Goldschmidt and Mr. G. D. Hobson of London; Dr. Wieruszowski of Berlin; Mr. Taeuber of Munich; Dr. Rodolfo R. Schuller of Vienna; Dr. J. Martini of Florence; Dr. Arnold C. Klebs of Nyon; Dr. Max Fleuiss of Rio de Janeiro; and Dr. Bernardo Rubio of Barcelona, grateful acknowledgment is made for their courtesy in verifying data and in submitting criticisms. To all of these, Sr. José Toribio Medina of Santiago de Chile included, is due a tribute for the store of knowledge comprised within their writings, through which channel the results of their insistent research have become the property of the bookish world.

Among American librarians and collectors, Mr. Wilberforce Eames, Mr. H. M. Lydenberg, and Mr. Victor H. Paltsits of the New York Public Library; Dr. Alexander Marx of the Jewish Theological Seminary of America; Mr. Lathrop C. Harper of New York; Mr. Charles Martel of the Library of Congress; Mr. William E. Foster of the Providence Public Library; Professor R. C. Archibald and Professor J. F. Green of Brown University; Mr. Andrew Keogh of the Yale University Library; Mr. F. M. Cushman of the Annmary Brown Memorial; Mr. Leslie E. Bliss and Mr. H. R. Mead of the Henry E. Huntington Library; and in particular Mr. Lawrence C. Wroth of the John Carter Brown Library, have aided the project in a wide variety of ways, verifying data, reading copy, supplying rare reference works, even lending me treasures from their private shelves. To all of these good bookmen, and to Dr. William MacDonald, historian and critic, my sincerest thanks are given. And the account cannot be closed without grateful recognition of the years of training in an earlier decade, under George Parker Winship and Wilberforce Eames.

Portions of the text of the present volume and the general scheme of its chapters correspond to the lectures prepared by the writer for the course in advanced cataloguing in the graduate School of Library Service at Columbia University. For the interest which originally prompted this project, my thanks are due to the Director of the School of Library Service, Dr. Charles C. Williamson, and I deeply appreciate the keen interest throughout the project, of Miss Minnie E. Sears of the School of Library Service, Miss Isadore G. Mudge, Reference Librarian of Columbia University, and Mr. Frederick Coykendall and Miss Georgia W. Read of the Columbia University Press.

Within this volume, in the two subjects of which it treats, bibliography is considered in its actual and in its subsidiary aspects. In five of its eight textual divisions, the effort is made from time to time to indicate certain contributions of bibliography to our knowledge of civilization, through the fifteenth century books which introduced the use of movable metal types, thus making possible the quick transmission of thought, and through those whose subject matter beginning in 1492 relates to the discovery, conquest, colonization, and early development of the New World. In the remaining chapters — and in the notes, definitions, tables, and lists of the Reference Sections — a means is provided for entering upon the technical study and the analysis of the books comprised within these two fields of research. Bibliographical analysis, however, and the fine points in the technique of the game, should not be mistaken for bibliography itself. Behind the physical make-up and the questions involved in determining the physical origin of a book are an understanding and evaluation of its subject matter. Behind these is the personality of its author. Behind that is the relation of the book and of its writer to the thought of the times. Technical analysis is but a means to an end. It is the chemical analysis through which — in its accurate identification of author, place, date, printer, edition, etc. — each printed work is given its rightful place among the records of the past. It is in this final aspect that bibliography appears in its true light, and it is through sources and methods such as these herein indicated that the bibliographical study of incunabula and Americana may be undertaken.

It may seem odd to treat of incunabula and Americana within a single volume. But, are they not America's heritage in booklore, strongly knit by the bonds of our proudly polyglot origin? Furthermore, there is a precedent in the writings of Baptista Fulgosus. On June 22, 1509, in his book *De Dictis Factisque*, that worthy Doge included a section on Gutenberg in which he paid high tribute to the inventor of mechanically printed metal letters. On the same page, and directly beneath this eulogy, he placed a paragraph in praise of Columbus — two men of the fifteenth century who, in the ever-widening spheres of influence emanating from their achievements, altered the course of history more effectively than anyone since the birth of Christ.

With this thought in mind a page from the Strabo *Geographia*, Rome [1469], has been reproduced in the Incunabula section, show-ing the fine Rome type used by the first of the German printers who were responsible for the spreading of the printing art through west-ern Europe. The title-page carries the contemporary picture of the 'Santa Maria' at anchor in the New World, reproduced without lettering from Columbus' account of his discovery, in the *De Insulis inuentis. Epistola Cristoferi Colom.* [Basel, 1493.] And the end-paper — a reproduction from one of the three known illustrated copies of Stobnicza's *Introductio in Ptholomei Cosmographia*, Cracow, 1512 — represents the Western Hemisphere, in the re-rendering of the insert in the Waldseemüller map of 1507 which, because of its convenient size, was doubtless more influential in spreading knowledge of the new discoveries than the huge wall map which was its source.

As for incunabula, it has been truthfully said that a final word on the beginnings of printing cannot be written until after the com-pleted publication of the *Gesamtkatalog der Wiegendrucke*. It has also been said, with possibly some degree of truth, that womankind enjoys a final word. If one were to wait, however, the necessary twelve to fifteen years in a state of suspended animation, who knows if in the end speech itself might not be lacking? I am offering there-fore an intermediary word, for there is much to be learned and much still to be said in these years of pleasant waiting.

MARGARET BINGHAM STILLWELL

The Annmary Brown Memorial
Providence, Rhode Island
June 22, 1930

CONTENTS

INTRODUCTION

THE PURPOSE AND PLAN OF THE BOOK

In compiling his *Bibliotheca Lusitana* in 1741, Barbosa Machado chose as his motto, *Nihil sine te lucet.* The same golden truth prevails with regard to this key to bibliographical study. Beyond the subject as it is here presented lie two broad fields of investigation, incunabula and Americana. In either of these, the student of booklore may spend years of productive study. If this book, with its discussions and explanations, its tables prepared to aid his early investigations and its lists of selected reference works, shall have fortified him in some measure for his task, it will have served its purpose. In its text and in its Reference Sections, it is intended as an answer to many of the questions that surge through the mind of a beginner in the lore of rare books, and as a guide to the reference books in which the answers to other questions may be found. It is offered, furthermore, as a contribution toward a source book for students of incunabula and Americana, and as a handbook for the librarians and collectors who may find it convenient to have, in compressed form, information of a bibliographical nature relating to the two subjects most commonly found upon the rare-book shelves of America.

To this end, it is divided into three parts. The first relates to incunabula and its study. The second relates to Americana from 1492 to 1700, with notes on later Americana through the Revolutionary periods, chapters on the introduction of printing into the two Americas, and a preliminary chapter on methods of study. The third, the Reference Sections, the result of research in this country and abroad, provides accompanying definitions, foreign bibliographical terms and their equivalents, Latin place-names employed in early books, tables of abbreviations, and lists of selected reference works of bibliographical importance, the latter comprising twelve hundred, or more, numbered titles.

In the section on incunabula (*i.e.,* on the printed books of the fifteenth century, at the time when modern bookmaking methods came into being), I have endeavored to give a brief description of the books themselves; to call to mind the trend of events and the influences at work during the period of early printing; to indicate the spread of the art through western Europe from 1450 to 1500; to trace the evolution of bookmaking during the first fifty years in which movable metal type was used, with a slight but insistent emphasis upon the beginnings of things; and finally to indicate some of the libraries and special collections in which copies of early printed books are to be found today. Then I have endeavored to describe the various steps and processes by which a bibliographer undertakes to identify and to collate a fifteenth century book; to describe the methods of arrangement in each of the two main groups of bibliographies, the alphabetical, and the chronological or 'natural history' groups; and to suggest opportunities for studying incunabula with the aid of specialized bibliographies and monographs. The selected list of such reference works, six hundred or more in number, given at the end of the book in the Reference Sections, further includes a brief selected list of works on the allied topic of early illustration and engraving.

Although various lists of Latin place-names have been compiled from time to time, recording the names found in inscriptions and in manuscripts, from the days of the Caesars to the Renaissance, very little regard has been paid to grouping such place-names according to the usage of a given period. It seemed advisable to build a table giving only the forms actually found in the printed books of the fifteenth century. The table of Place-Names of Fifteenth Century Printing Towns comprises, therefore, such forms as have been seen (in the course of the present compilation) in the printed colophons or incipits of incunabula. The parallel columns of modern place-names, following the usage of the British Museum and of the *Gesamtkatalog der Wiegendrucke,* have been submitted respectively to Mr. Victor Scholderer of the British Museum and to Dr. M. J. Husung and Dr. R. Juchhoff of *Gesamtkatalog* headquarters, each of whom in addition to the courtesy of verifying their respective columns, sent me several rare fifteenth century forms. The Hebrew printing towns according to fifteenth century usage, which are listed at the end of the table, have been very kindly contributed by Dr.

Alexander Marx, Librarian of the Jewish Theological Seminary of America.

The list of Latin Contractions and Abbreviations, also a part of the Reference Sections, comprises a selection of abbreviations taken from fifteenth century printed colophons and incipits, and chosen to aid the student's first contact with these early texts. Longer lists, suitable for more extensive textual deciphering, are indicated at the end of the section. The facsimile showing a paragraph from a fifteenth century book, transliterated according to the usage of the *Gesamtkatalog,* and expanded into modern Latin, is reproduced through the courtesy of Dr. Ernst Crous. The remaining portion of the section relating to abbreviations comprises those employed in Hain's *Repertorium,* listed alphabetically under the first term of the phrases most frequently used by Hain, together with their Latin and English equivalents.

In the Americana section, the original plan included in its scope the years 1492 to 1700, since at the latter date the various European colonies had become firmly implanted upon American shores and the art of bookmaking had not only been introduced into both North and South America, but it had become an established and influential factor in colonial life. At the solicitation of various students, however, the book has now been made to include a series of bibliographical notes covering the later colonial and Revolutionary periods, thus moving the final date, in the discussion of North American and South American bibliography, to 1800 and 1824 respectively. Throughout the Americana text, I have endeavored to maintain three lines of thought, interweaving a thread of historical narrative into the account of the books printed within each period, together with the discussion of parallel bibliographical reference sources. The material is grouped more or less chronologically, in chapters which relate to the century of maritime discovery, 1492–1600; the two centuries of colonial growth, in South and in North America, 1500–1700; later Americana and the Revolutionary periods. A final note relates to bibliographical material on the introduction of printing into Hispanic America and British America; and a separate chapter, placed at the beginning of the section, discusses bibliographical treatment. The six hundred or more selected

titles of bibliographies and bibliographical monographs relating to
early Americana, included in the Reference Sections, provide a
means through which the specialized study of its various periods
may be carried to any length.

The two subjects, incunabula and Americana, share in common
the remaining data comprised within the Reference Sections. The
Notes and Definitions which make up the opening division relate,
for the most part, to both subjects. Similarly, the list of foreign
bibliographical terms is intended as a general aid to students in
consulting foreign works of reference. Each column of foreign
terms within the table has been submitted for verification to one
or more of the leading bookmen of the country cited; and the position of the French, German, Italian and Spanish terms with their
English equivalents may be found in the parallel columns of the
table, through the numbers quoted in the alphabetical index comprising its final column. At the close of the volume is the list of
Selected Bibliographies to which reference has been made. This
treats of incunabula and Americana in separate sections, with a
few entries at the end of each relative to topics of closely allied
interest. A table giving the order of arrangement introduces each
main section. Within each subdivision are the general and important works with which a beginner must first become familiar.
Following these general titles are subject lists of specialized bibliographies and bibliographical monographs, selected in order to
illustrate the almost innumerable avenues of approach to the study
of incunabula and Americana, as well as to afford an introductory
guide to bibliographical study. At the end of the volume are listed
monographs descriptive of certain rare-book collections in America,
and tributes to bibliographers of incunabula and Americana.

A book about books must, of necessity, rest upon those which
its text concerns. Relatively few of those mentioned in the book
proved of unobtainable rarity. Through a combination of favorable circumstances, a large majority of the original, contemporary
works referred to in the text and of the works cited in the Reference
Sections have passed through the hands of the writer in the course
of its preparation, thus yielding of their abundant wealth to its
conceived design.

INCUNABULA

1450–1500

Eptimuſ liber:reliquaſEurope parteſexplicat. Sunt autem quæ orientem
ſpectant ultra Rhenum:uſq; Tanain:& Meotidiſ paludiſoſtium.   Quæ
inter ſinū Adriaticum:& ſiniſtraſmariſpōtici parteſ:Iſter accipit:ad Auſtrū
uſq; in Greciam atq; Propontidem. In hiſtota Macedonia continetur.

Vm a nobiſde Hiſpania:deq; Galliciſq; gētibuſ:cū uiciniſ
Inſuliſdictū ſic: Deincepſ relique parteſ Europe uidentur enar/
rande:quo ſe modo facultaſobtulerit partiendo.Reſtant autem:
que ad orientem tranſ Rhenum: uſq; Tanain loca ſpectant. &
Meotice paludiſoſtiū. Queq; inter Adriaticum ſinum: & ſiniſtraſ
pontici mariſoraſIſter capit in Auſtrū:uſq; in Greciam atq; Pro/
pontidem. Iſter enim duaſin parteſ proxime terram predictam
diuidit uniuerſam.Cunctoſ Europe fluuioſmagnitudine ſuperanſ. A primordio ſu
in Auſtrū labitur. Inde ab occidente ſtatim ad orientem curuatur in pontū. Oritur
autem ab extremiſGermanie partibuſab occaſu:prope ſinum Adriaticū:procul ab
illo ſtad: circiter mille. Finitur autem in ponto:non longe admodū ab Tyre ac Bo/
ryſtheniſeruptionibuſ: paululum in ſeptentrionem uergenſ. Spectanteſ quidem in
ſeptentrionē Iſtri parteſ:ſunt tranſRhenum regioeſ.& Gallie. que ſunt gallice gēteſ:
& germanice:uſq; ad Baſtarnaſ.&Tyrrhengetaſ:& Boryſtheni adiacēteſ ore:que iter
hunc:&Tanain:& paludiſoſtiū Meotidiſ locantur.Itaq; mediterraneā ad Oceanū
extendit. Et mari alluitur pontico. In Auſtrum uergentia ſunt Illyrica:&Thracia.
& quecunq; de Galliciſiſtiſadmixta ſunt.ſeu de pleriſq; aliiſuſq; ad oraſGreciæ:De
tractu igitur extra Iſtrum primū dicamuſ. Multo enim q̃ cetere: que ad alterutram
partem iacent:ſimplicioraſūt. Statim igitur regionē tranſRhenū ad ortū uergentē
Germani colunt:nationem Gallicam pauliſper imitanteſ:& feritatiſabundantia:et
pro ceritate corporum.& colore flauo: cum reliquiſin rebuſ& forma:& moribuſ:et
uiuendi ritibuſ:pareſexiſtant.qualeſGalloſdiximuſ.Ideo Romani hoc illiſnomen
iure ſdidiſſe:mihi uident. Perinde ac eoſfratreſlegittimoſſane Galliſeloq uoluerit.
Legittimi nāq; fratreſRomano ſermone Germani intelligunt. Prime huiuſregióiſ
parteſ ſunt Rheno proxime:ab ipſiuſ fere fontiſinitio:quoad in pelaguſinfundit.
Et hec eſt occidētaliſplage latitudo uniuerſa.quā flumen alluit.Eiuſaūt portionē
quandam ad Galliam traduxere Romani. Quedam uero in profundam regionem
tranſmigranſperuenit.ſicut & Marſi.Ceteri pauci ſunt. & Sugambroɤ portio. Poſt
uicinoſautem amni accolaſ:& alie genteſ ſunt:inter Rhenum & Albin fluuium:qui
ubiq; pariter ab eo diſtanſ fluit in Oceanum: non minorem illo perlabenſ agrum.
Interſunt & amneſalii:nauigiſpermeabileſ.E quibuſeſt Hamaſia.In quo Druſuſ
Bructeroſnauali prelio ſuperauit. Hi ſimiliter ab Auſtro ad Aquilonem in Oceanū
elabuntur. Regio hec uerſuſAuſtrum extenſa:quoddam continenſAlpibuſdorſum
efficit:ad orientem protenſum:quaſi quedam Alpium particula exiſtat. Pleriq; autē
hunc in modum oſtenderunt:& propter ſitum antedictum:& cum eandem efferat
materiam. Huiuſtamen tractuſparteſnequāim in tam ſublime extolluntur. In hoc
tractu ſita eſt Hercynia ſilua.& Sueuorum natio. Ex quibuſnonnulli intra: aliqui
extra ſiluam habitant. Sicut & Colduorum pleriq;.In quibuſ& Buhiemū:Marobudi
Regia. Quem in locum ipſe: cum alioſpluriſtraduceret incolaſ: ſuoſconterraneoſ
Marcómanoſadegit. Iſ.n.ex humiliori gradu maioreſad reſconſtitutuſ fuit: Poſt q̃

*The superb Roman type employed by Sweynheim and Pannartz: reproduction
of a page (reduced) of Strabo's Geographia, Rome [1469]*

Chapter I

THE PRINTED BOOKS OF THE FIFTEENTH CENTURY

The Books Themselves

The first thing to do in introducing oneself to a fifteenth century book is to see if it has, at the end of its text, a paragraph called a colophon. The majority of the early printers — if they signed and dated their books — signed and dated them at the end, as an artist would sign a portrait after he had completed it. It is for this reason that, in seeking to identify an early printed book, one turns first of all to its final page, in search of its colophon, the finishing stroke. Happily for the lover of beautiful books, one need not feel compelled to do this quickly. That would be a sacrilege. A fine old book is often frail with age. One should turn its pages gently and with a reverent hand. There is thus excuse enough to loiter and to absorb something of its personality and its beauty, before taking up the task of finding out just what it is, a task which in itself is often a matter of hours or days.

As in the manuscripts of the period, one finds upon opening an early printed book that its opposite pages are invariably planned to balance one another; and the ample margins, extending around the whole, give to the two pages the appearance of a single decorative unit. In its combination of utility with beauty the slightly wider margin, or tail, at the base of each printed page allows space for the hands that hold the book; and, to the eye, supplies a base on which the printed text seems to stand at rest. Illuminated initials in the blank spaces frequently left at the beginning of each new section of text, often at the beginning of each paragraph, for the insertion of painted letters, give to the printed page the richness of color to which the patrons of bookmaking had already long been accustomed.

The form of handwriting used by the scribes of various localities quite naturally became the basis of design for the fonts of type cast

in that locality. Since Latin was the working language of the day,
the majority of the early printed books are likewise in Latin, and
since every printed book was in the first instance set up from a
manuscript, the abbreviations employed by the scribes appear freely
in the early printed texts. In the writing of manuscripts, speed
could be gained and paper saved by shortening the written word;
and the full spelling of a word, or again an abbreviated form of it,
afforded a certain adaptability in keeping the margins clear and
even. Consequently a special sign language developed, with various
marks to indicate the omission of one or more vowels, the omission
of a prefix, the abbreviation of a case ending, a conjunction, or a
preposition. These marks were adopted bodily by the early printers.
In studying their books, therefore, one should know not only Latin
but the usual abbreviations as well.

Sometimes one finds in early printed books the medieval
numerals 1 2 3 5 7 6 7 8 9 — or possibly a transitional form,
with the *seven* beginning to turn to its modern position and the *five*
like a modern *five* save for its final stroke. In the colophons, a Saint's
Day or a festival often appears in place of a calendar date. Sometimes the year is given in a combination of numerals and words.
Sometimes the day is recorded according to the Roman method,
in which the days are counted backward from and including the
Kalends, often abbreviated as Kal. or Kl., and indicating the first
day of the month; the Ides (Id.), the 15th day of March, May,
July, and October, and the 13th day of other months; or the Nones
(Non.), the 9th day preceding the Ides. Thus, each book bears
one mark or another of its traditional heritage.

During the half century preceding the invention of printing,
northern Europe had enjoyed a period of considerable peace and
prosperity. In the Netherlands, the religious order had been formed
called the Brothers of the Common Life. In Germany, the reaction from the great schism in the Church occasioned a reform of
the Benedictine houses. Both of these religious orders promoted
the reading and copying of books, which for the most part were in
Latin. There developed, in consequence, an increased interest in
the Latin language and a renewed demand for the Latin grammar
of Aelius Donatus, a work which, although written in the fourth

century, was still in use throughout Europe. The continued popularity of this booklet and the simplicity of its makeup account for the fact that a 'Donatus' was often among the first products of an early press. The hard usage which such a book would naturally receive accounts in large measure for the extreme rarity of these early pieces today. Whoever can discover a copy of the 'Donatus' from Italy's first press, for instance, will write his name indelibly in the annals of collecting.

According to the testimony of Ulrich Zel, the first printer of Cologne, given in later life to the compiler of the Cologne Chronicle, 'Donatuses' were printed in some inferior way in Holland even before printing began at Mainz. If so, nothing more came of these early efforts. In Mainz, however, the 'Donatus' which Gutenberg printed among his early experimental pieces was followed, in 1454 and 1455, by the printing of two grants of indulgences, broadsides in neat small types quite unlike those previously used; and, simultaneously with these, by the printing of the two volumes of the *42-line Bible*, the so-called *Gutenberg Bible*, of about 1455. There is a grandeur about this Bible, a superb air of finality, that stands in curious contrast to the fact that it is the first book to have been printed with movable metal types, and thus the starting point in the history of modern bookmaking.

In Germany, the needs which the art of printing was invented to satisfy were mainly religious and moral. The production, within seven or eight years, of four huge Bibles and two magnificent Psalters abundantly proves this setting to have been favorable not only for the birth of the new invention but for its tenacious growth.

In Italy, where the interest in humanism had been developing for a century or more, the demand was for the Latin classics. Latin epistolography was in vogue and the Latin classics were assiduously studied for their style. Years before this, Petrarch and Boccaccio had inspired the search for classical literature. In 1447, Tommaso Parentucelli, a learned humanist, became Pope Nicholas V. It is said that his efforts to increase the Papal Library left it, at the time of his death in 1455, with eight hundred and twenty-four manuscripts. Subsequently, the Duke of Urbino gathered his scribes about him, binding their manuscripts in crimson and silver, and allowing no printed book to profane his shelves, thus — according to his trusted agent, Vespasiano da Bisticci of Florence — exemplifying the patrician hatred of the new mechanical art. Academies were founded under patronage, for study and discussion; and the Medici, with agencies throughout Europe and the Levant, made every effort to secure magnificent copies of the classics, thus bringing to medieval Italy a heritage enriched, through preceding centuries, by alternate contributions from East and West.

When printing was introduced into Italy, a decade after the death of Nicholas V, it encountered a period rich in beauty. Brunelleschi had revitalized the principles of classic architecture. Cathedral building as in Gothic France, the painting of tryptich and altar pieces, the intricacies of mosaic, the jewel-like designs of stained glass and illuminated manuscripts had reached, or in the growing Renaissance were close upon the zenith of their beauty. The scribes, making their copies from dictation, had developed a surety of execution which lent legibility and charm to their hand-printed words. The influence of artistic environment showed immediately in the products of the Italian press. No books since issued have surpassed those produced by Sweynheim and Pannartz, and Jenson; and few have equalled them.

Meantime, while Gutenberg was working to perfect the casting of metal type, the Vatican Library, which was presently to house so many of the products of his invention, was founded. Regiomontanus, the great German astronomer and the first of the humanists of the North, was at work upon his computations. Perugino, destined to become Raphael's teacher and the founder of the Roman school of painting, was, like the printing art itself, an infant. Athens was soon to yield to the aggression of the Turks. The days of the Crusades were over. In spite of the fall of Constantinople in 1453, the ever-present fear caused by subsequent encroachments of the Turks, and the efforts of the Pope, and Diets, Europe refused to be aroused to a Holy War. Venice held concessions from Mohammed. And Bruges and Ghent, at the height of their prosperity, were busy trading with the world — a world that did not know that it was round, nor that vast treasure-lands lay midway across the seas. The invention of printing, in the midst of all this, had much to do with accelerating the Renaissance; and at the end of the century, it was the printing press that spread the news of Columbus's discovery, thus sending navigator after navigator to explore the new-found world.

The controversy that raged fitfully and intensively, fifty years ago, as to whether Gutenberg of Mainz or Coster of Haarlem originated and introduced into Europe the idea of printing with separate letters, seems now to rest with the odds in favor of Gutenberg, although not incontrovertibly so. One would wish to give full credit to the inventor, or to each participant in the invention, as the case may be. But the fact which really matters is that movable type was finally invented. Like Shakespeare's plays, it is the achievement itself that counts. Controversialists may wrangle and savants ponder. The achievement transcends controversy.

Even if, through means unknown to us, the idea of printing individual characters might have been transmitted from the East, the credit for the invention of casting metal type may be claimed by Europe. It may be that the idea of casting type was suggested by the goldsmiths' method of testing delicately wrought designs in metal; or by the practice of the bookbinders in embossing intricate patterns with a variety of separate tools. Or, as shown by the reconstruction of type recently attempted at Frankfort-on-the-Main, the idea may have developed through experimentation, in making sand moulds from the wooden models of separate letters and using these moulds for casting metal type. Whatever its source, the idea of casting movable metal types was one of the greatest factors in the progress of modern civilization. In that respect, Gutenberg may be looked upon unequivocally as the Father of the Printing Art.

The Origin and Spread of the Art of Printing

Gutenberg's policy was one of secrecy. When he returned to his native town of Mainz (by 1448), he had been working for some years at Strassburg, presumably at experimental printing. At Mainz, he continued his experiments and organized a printing shop. The loans made him by Johann Fust, a local goldsmith, for the purpose of printing books, were apparently called in before the great *42-line Bible* was completed; and Fust appears to have secured the aid of Gutenberg's efficient workman, Peter Schoeffer, in completing it. Thus the monopoly of the secret process passed from Gutenberg's control.

In August, 1457, the new firm of Fust and Schoeffer produced a superbly printed *Psalter* for choir use, with large and small initial letters printed in red and blue. To this book was appended, for the first time, a colophon giving the printers' names and date of printing — an innovation which was repeated in their *Psalter* of 1459 and in the handsome *Bible* of 1462.

To Gutenberg himself may be attributed a number of experimental pieces in addition to several small books, and the great Latin dictionary, the *Catholicon* of Johannes Balbus. This has a colophon which, while dated 1460 and glorifying Mainz as the birthplace of the craft, still withholds its printer's name. It contains, however, a rather pathetic reference to 'God's revelation to his little ones of the secrets denied to the proud' which reads as if it came from the hand of the disappointed inventor, and places the *Catholicon* almost without question among the products attributed to Gutenberg's anonymous press. In October, 1462, the city of Mainz was sacked. Save for the undated publication of a Papal Bull, with a first attempt at a title-page, we know of no printing there for the next two years, although by 1465 Fust and Schoeffer resumed their work with vigor.

Printing, meantime, had been practised in two or three instances outside of Mainz, each of these instances seeming to be traceable to Gutenberg himself. The so-called *36-line Bible,* probably printed at Bamberg about 1458, is in the larger experimental type of the *Calendar* of " 1448 " — a type which Gutenberg apparently discarded for the perfected type of his *42-line Bible,* and which appeared subsequently in the hands of Albrecht Pfister at Bamberg. The third of the four great Bibles of the first decade was printed by Johann Mentelin in or about 1460, at Strassburg, the city in which Gutenberg is believed to have made his first experiments. There is a possibility that a life of Christ was printed in Italy by a pupil of Gutenberg's, as early as 1462. Mainz, however, had remained in the meantime the headquarters for the mysterious new method of making books.

After the disasters of 1462, some of the apprenticed printers seem to have left Mainz, seeking to establish themselves elsewhere, and thus inadvertently bringing about a gradual diffusion of the arts of casting type and printing. Each of these outgoing printers had of necessity to design and cast his own type. Each had to construct his heavy-framed presses, to supply himself with paper, and to make his ink, in addition to determining upon a town that seemed a favorable place in which to market his products, and upon a first book that would sell. After the fall of Mainz, it took about three years before any of the printers who are believed to have come from there had established themselves elsewhere. By 1465, two of these printers had settled at the monastery of Subiaco, about forty miles from Rome, and in that year they issued Italy's first known printed books, the first of these to bear a date being the Lactantius of October 29th. During that same year a press at Cologne was started by Ulrich Zel, ' clericus diocesis Moguntinensis,' a clerk from the diocese of Mainz.

Within the next five years, five towns admitted German printers —Rome, where Sweynheim and Pannartz, coming down from Subiaco in 1467, found themselves confronted by a rival press; Eltvil, 1467; Augsburg, 1468, where the local guild of wood-engravers forced Günther Zainer to agree to employ its members to illustrate his printed books; Basel [1468]; and Venice, 1469, destined with Rome and Florence to contribute a full measure of beauty to the bookmaking of the world. Thus the knowledge of the hitherto mysterious process moved gradually from Germany to Italy, and touched one town in what now is Switzerland.

In 1470 there came a sudden awakening of interest, the beginning of the 'triumphal march of the printing art.' Eight towns, possibly ten, opened presses within that year, the one in the Sorbonne at Paris having the distinction of being the world's first private press. Throughout that decade, the art spread rapidly. By 1480 Venice, Nuremberg, Basel, and Lyons ranked as centers of distribution for the growing trade; and Paris, Frankfort, Antwerp, and Milan were likewise becoming active centers of book commerce.

At the end of the fifteenth century, the processes of casting and of printing with metal type were known throughout practically all of western Europe. Reviewed chronologically, the production of books by mechanical printing, established in Germany by 1455 after a decade or more of experimentation, was introduced into Italy in 1465, or possibly a little earlier, and into Switzerland about 1468. It appeared in France in 1470. The year 1473 witnessed the introduction of the art into Hungary and Belgium, the southern Netherlands; and the first dated book printed in Holland was issued in 1473, although it is probable that at least some of a group of anonymous books, assigned to the 'Printer of the Speculum Humanae Saluationis,' were issued earlier than this. Spain and Poland had printing in 1474; Austria and possibly Bohemia in 1475; England in 1476; Denmark in 1482; Sweden the following year; Moravia in 1486; Portugal in 1487; and Montenegro in 1493.

In some towns the printing art took immediate root and prospered. In others, a printer came and went, sometimes invited to perform a single stipulated task, sometimes driven elsewhere by circumstance and hardship, sometimes impelled apparently by his own nomadic spirit, as in the case of Heinrich of Cologne, who worked in eight Italian towns in less than twenty years.

There has been considerable divergence of theory as to whether type-founding existed as a specialized industry before the end of the fifteenth century. It is known that a knowledge of type-casting was often considered an essential part of a printer's equipment, and that certain master printers and men within the printing shops became expert in the craft. About fifty documentary sources dating from 1470 to 1500 have been brought to light by Dr. Konrad Haebler[1] which tend to show that, although printers were hired because of their skill in casting type and that types were sometimes sold by one printing house to another, type-founding as an industry apart from the printing shop was apparently unknown during the fifteenth century.

[1] *Ars Typographica*, New York, July 1926.

The Development of the Printed Book, 1450–1500

Although Gutenberg is known to have been at work upon various pieces of experimental printing for ten years and more, it is interesting to note that the first book printed in Germany — aside from the experimental 'Donatus,' etc. — at the almost unquestionable date of 1455, was the *Bible* — the *42-line Bible* (so called as a means of unmistakable identification). The first book now known from an Italian press, printed ten years later, was a classic — Cicero's *De Oratore* issued at Subiaco during [1465]. Ten years later still, Caxton printed his translation of the *Recueil des Histoires de Troye* — a romance, the first book printed by an Englishman. This was brought out at Bruges, in [1475], where he was Governor of the English Nation over the Company of Merchant Adventurers. A distinction must be made, however, between this and the first dated book issued *in* England, the *Dictes or Sayengis of the Philosophhres,* printed by Caxton two years later at his press in Westminster where, not later than the 13th of December 1476, he had printed for the Papal commissary an indulgence to contributors toward the expenses of resisting the Turks.

Something over thirty-five thousand separate editions of fifteenth century printing are still in existence. We shall never know how many other works have been lost to us through the ages. The subject matter of the books that survive, however, may serve to indicate the intellectual life of their original readers. Since a goodly proportion of the educated persons of the day were ecclesiastical in their interests, it is not surprising to find that more than fifty percent of the incunabula that survive is of a religious nature. The remainder relates to a wide variety of subjects: as law, proclamations, almanacs, music, medicine and allied subjects, cosmography, the classics, geometry, geography, astronomy, Latin grammar, romance, a sprinkling of fables, farces and poetry, and various ponderous chronicles.

Beginning with Boner's *Edelstein,* printed in German at Bamberg on St. Valentine's Day 1461, there was an occasional and a gradually increasing number of books printed in the vernacular. The earliest book in Italian, found in the course of the present

survey, was issued in 1470. The first book printed entirely in
Greek appeared at Milan on January 30, 1476 (although anticipated by Greek phrases in movable type in Cicero's *Officia et Para-
doxa,* printed at Mainz in 1465, as well as by similar phrases in the
Lactantius issued at Subiaco that same year, and in various books
printed during the intervening decade). In Spain, printing in the
vernacular began at once with the [1473] *Indulgencias* and with the
Obres e trobes en lahors de la verge Maria, assigned to 1474, after
February the eleventh. The first printing in Hebrew was done in
1475. In January 1476 [1477], the first dated book in French was
issued in Paris, *Les croniques de France,* although possibly preceded by two undated works assigned to Lyon in 1476. The *Old
Testament* in Dutch appeared in 1477, the first book in Swedish in
Stockholm in 1495, and during that same year the first book in
Danish was issued in Copenhagen and a handsome volume in Portuguese was printed in Lisbon. Cyrillic type was used as early as
1491, and a license for printing music by a new method with metal
type was granted to Ottaviano Petrucci, at Venice, in 1498.

During the fifty years comprising the so-called period of incunabula or 'cradle-printing,' [1450]-1500, a process of evolution in
methods of bookmaking was under way which, at the end of the
period, left the printed book with substantially all of its present elements. Color printing, attempted by Gutenberg in the introductory
pages of the *42-line Bible,* was mastered by Schoeffer in the beautiful *Psalter* of 1457, experimented with at Strassburg, and re-
mastered by Ratdolt at his Venetian and Augsburg presses. The
first printed book to be illustrated with woodcuts was the *Edelstein*
already mentioned as appearing at Bamberg in 1461. In 1470,
the first book bearing leaf numbers was issued at Cologne. And
this same book—Rolewinck's *Sermo in festo praesentationis
beatae Virginis*—has also the distinction of being the first dated
book in which the colophon was transferred bodily to a preliminary
leaf. Thus the so-called label-title (first used by Schoeffer in the
undated Papal Bull of 1463) became the precursor of the modern
title-page. In 1476, in the Italian edition of the calendar of
Regiomontanus which Ratdolt issued at Venice, he and his partners
split the information comprised within the customary colophon and

produced the first title-page in modern form — with the imprint, " Venetijs, 1476," and the names of the three printers given at the base of the page.

Like the color printing achieved by Schoeffer in 1457 and 1459, and later by Ratdolt, these innovations did not immediately make their existence felt. They were destined, however, to survive. Color printing became relatively common by 1490. Leaf-numbering reappeared after an interval and gradually developed into the page numbering that has survived through the intervening centuries. Similarly, the label-title came into occasional use after 1480 and gradually merged, after the close of the century, into the modern form of title-page which had in reality been conceived in 1476.

Meanwhile, the use of signatures — already employed by manuscript makers as an aid to the binder, and introduced into printed books by Johann Koelhoff the Elder, in Nider's *Expositio Decalogi*, Cologne, 1472 — was maintained in the majority of the hundred and fifty works issued by his press. The device appeared at Speier in December, 1472, and was at once adopted by other printers. Catchwords, for the similar purpose of aiding the binder, appeared during that same year in a book issued in Bologna, and possibly appeared a year earlier in Venice.

Soon after 1470 the use of pictures became general. Augsburg, Ulm, Florence, and Venice presently assumed prominent places in the annals of early book illustration and decoration. The earliest pictures were simple woodcuts, printed with the expectation that they would be colored by hand. Metal engraving appeared in 1477, possibly as early as 1476; and when cross-hatching was introduced as a means of shading in black and white, the custom of painting the engravings and cuts gradually died out. In the middle period of incunabula, a small guide-letter printed in the square left for the insertion of a hand-painted initial letter informed the scribe or illuminator what letter should be painted in. It was but a logical step for a woodcut initial, often of exquisite tracery, to usurp the privileged square, and presently for woodcut borders to adorn the margins. Folded plates were used in 1486. Meanwhile, as early as 1474, a usable form of index had been introduced, with a dot before or after the leaf number to indicate the recto or verso of the leaf. And there in all its essential features, save the use of footnotes, we have the conception of bookmaking from which the modern book is a lineal descendant.

Thus we may follow the evolution of the printed book. In the course of fifty years — prior to which the intellectual world had held its store of knowledge in manuscripts written by scribes and embellished by illuminators — the printed book emerged, at the end of the fifteenth century, substantially in its modern and accepted form, with a title-page bearing the author's name, title, place of printing, printer's name, and date; with numbered leaves; with signatures or catchwords; with woodcut or metal engraved initial letters and ornaments; with illustrations in which arrangements of black and white were employed, instead of color, in giving decorative effect; and with an index giving page references to the text. But when the work of the illuminators upon the *Books of Hours* (the *Horae*), which meantime had had tremendous vogue in Paris, was brought to its end by the highly ornamented *Horae* printed by Pigouchet and his rival engravers in the last decade of the fifteenth century, a new era, that of commercialism, began.

Evolution viewed in retrospect seems to be a continuous passing from stage to stage, and in a sense that is the truth. On the other hand, events, when various countries and towns are concerned, do not move forward at a uniform pace. In the present instance, by the end of the century, methods of bookmaking were fairly stabilized; but in the course of the years preceding, the innovations attempted by the bookbuilders of one town were not necessarily known to those of another. The exchange of books from one printer to another, thus adding bookselling to the offices of the printing shop and eventually developing organized book-trading agencies in the great commercial centers, doubtless had much to do with the ultimate standardization of mode. But throughout the fifteenth century, the details of book-building were in a period of flux and flow, a circumstance that adds much of charm to their study. The presence or absence of innovations and changes in the method of book-building adds the zest of discovery to the otherwise dry task of collation.

LIBRARIES AND COLLECTIONS OF INCUNABULA

One would turn naturally to Europe as the place for the study of incunabula: to the vast resources of the British Museum; the Bibliothèque Nationale in Paris; the mammoth collection of books in the Staatsbibliothek, formerly the Royal Library, in Munich; the Library of the Vatican in Rome; and the great libraries of Berlin, Vienna, Milan, Manchester, Brussels, and The Hague. Representative collections may, however, be found in America. Specimens of fifteenth century printing, a dozen or more, were at Harvard in 1723 when the library issued its first printed catalogue. These unhappily were lost in the fire of 1764, the foundation of the present Harvard collection having been laid between that year and 1774. Various rare items found their way to the shelves of a number of American college libraries early in the last century. The Lenox Collection, which is now incorporated in the New York Public Library, contained in the first days of its formation specimens of incunabula. Mr. John Carter Brown secured the 1493 Paris edition of the Columbus *Letter* in 1846, and in the following year Mr. James Lenox secured a copy of the *42-line Bible* at the 'mad price' of nearly $3,000! General Rush C. Hawkins, whose collection of first issues is at the Annmary Brown Memorial, purchased his first fifteenth century book in 1855. Mr. John Boyd Thacher's collection, brought together in the last years of the nineteenth century, is now in the Library of Congress.[2]

Since about 1880, and more especially since 1920, interest both in the study of incunabula and in their acquisition has greatly increased in America. Within recent years, a number of European collections formerly in private hands have come upon the market. Several thousand copies of incunabula have been brought into the United States within this decade alone, and European booksellers have done everything possible to stimulate American interest. The United States thus affords a potential field for the study of incunabula and many notable collections exist in addition to those already mentioned. Some of the finest treasures of booklore are to be

[2] While this book was in press, the bill was passed for the purchase of the Vollbehr collection of incunabula for the Library of Congress.

found in the Pierpont Morgan Library in New York; the Henry E. Huntington Library in San Marino, California; the Hispanic Society of America; at Columbia University; Yale; Cornell; the University of Michigan; the Chapin Library at Williams College; the New-berry Library and the John Crerar Library in Chicago; the University of Chicago; the Widener Branch of the Free Library of Philadelphia; the Library of the Surgeon General's Office in Washington; the Boston Athenaeum; the Grolier Club in New York; various theological seminaries, and so on. Isolated volumes of early printing, as well as those in specialized collections, are frequently to be met with throughout the country; and there are numerous fine collections in private hands. The list of libraries in the first volume of the *Gesamtkatalog der Wiegendrucke* (1925), recorded one hundred and fifty public institutions in America which possess incunabula, and this list took no account of the collections, great and small, that were at that time in private ownership.

In the wording of the preceding paragraphs there was no thought of comparing American collections as to their size or value. Many of them are so specialized in scope that comparison would be largely futile. The New York Public Library, for instance, has the Lenox Bibles. The General Theological Seminary in New York is likewise rich in its collection of Bibles. The Pierpont Morgan Library, among liturgical works, classics and other treasures, has the *Indulgence* of 1455, the rare Italian *Bible,* 1471, on vellum, and some Coster pieces. Harvard is especially strong in Savonarola tracts; both Harvard and the Library of Congress in the representation of presses; and the Riant-Harvard collection in matters pertaining to the relations between the European powers and the Turks. A notable collection of Caxton is at the Pierpont Morgan Library and another at the Henry E. Huntington Library. Spanish incunabula is to be found in the library of the Hispanic Society, in New York. The Newberry Library, in Chicago, has been enriched through its Ayer collection of Ptolemy's geographies; similar collections are to be found at the John Carter Brown Library in Providence, the New York Public Library, and the William L. Clements Library at Ann Arbor. Early medical books form the nucleus of the fifteenth century collections in the John Crerar Library in Chicago, the Library of the Surgeon General's Office in Washington, the Boston Medical Society, and the New York Academy of Medicine; Virgil, of the collection at Princeton; and Petrarch and Dante, of that at Cornell. None of these libraries, excepting possibly the medical, are limited to the collections mentioned. Frequently the various libraries supplement one another in these and other interests. The friendly spirit of coöperation existing affords every possible facility for research and collation.

A student working at the Huntington Library upon its mass of fifteenth century material, something over five thousand titles, of which many are of the utmost rarity, could not fail to gain perspective upon the intellectual life of that epoch-making period. A visit to the Pierpont Morgan Library would give a conception of the splendor of environment which has frequently surrounded these fine old books, as they have passed from one generation of wealthy collectors to another. A pilgrimage to the Annmary Brown Memorial in Providence and, across the seas, to the Plantin-Moretus Museum in Antwerp would together afford opportunity to visualize fifteenth century printing methods and the principles which underlie the canons of fine bookmaking. From the several hundred selected books which are displayed, opened, in the gallery of incunabula at the Annmary Brown Memorial one may visualize typographically the diffusion of the printing art as it spread from town to town after the sack of Mainz, and compare variations of type and composition. At the Plantin-Moretus Museum in Antwerp, the visitor is received in a venerable printing house with hand-presses and equipment closely identical, it is said, with the presses and equipment used by the earliest printers.

Christopher Plantin, the founder of a house of printers whose work continued more than three centuries, secured his license to print in Antwerp just fifty years after the close of the period of incunabula. At the present day, a lapse of fifty years would mean inevitable changes in method, but in those earlier times changes came more slowly. Printing methods, having virtually established themselves by the end of the fifteenth century, continued to thrive under much the same process year in and year out. The principles and theories of book-building at the end of the sixteenth century were not unlike those that had virtually established themselves by the end of the fifteenth. The methods employed by Christopher Plantin were in turn continued by his son-in-law Jean Moretus, and the latter's conservative descendants.

Consequently, in the quaint old printing house, taken over in recent years by the Belgian government as a museum, one sees a shop equipped for business, much as in the early days of the printing art. Here one may wander at will among the cases of types and initial blocks, among hand presses that seem at rest only that the early printers themselves may enjoy a well earned holiday. The editorial and composers' rooms overlook a charming courtyard. A bookshop well stocked for prospective customers opens upon a lane leading from the main thoroughfare. The shelves of the great and little library are crowded with interesting, timeworn books. Family portraits adorn the walls. Across the court, the tile-floored kitchen is still replete with polished copper cooking utensils. Whether viewed as a home or as a printing house, the Plantin-Moretus Museum is of incomparable charm.

At the Bibliothèque Nationale in Paris, at Munich, or at the British Museum, one might spend a lifetime to advantage, so inexhaustible are the opportunities for the study of incunabula. The same might be said of the libraries of Berlin, Rome, Milan, or of any of the world's largest collections. But because of facility of arrangement and the representative quality of their treasures, at the Annmary Brown Memorial and at the Plantin-Moretus Museum one might spend even so short a time as a day and still carry away a visualized conception of early printing that would endure for a lifetime.

IDENTIFICATION AND COLLATION

IDENTIFICATION

As pointed out in the preceding chapter, the first step in identifying a fifteenth century book is to search for a colophon at the end of its text. The colophon, if present, may be brief in its statements, or it may be long and involved. It is counted as complete if it comprises five factors: the author's name, the title of the book or a statement regarding its subject, the name of the place of printing, the printer's name, and the date of printing.

The first points for consideration are the place, printer, and date. Here the cataloguer's troubles begin, for the colophon is almost invariably in Latin and the place-name is therefore frequently in a form with which we are not familiar. Mainz, for instance, may appear as Maguntina; Strassburg, as Argentine; Milan, as Mediolani; and so on. As it is often difficult to recognize the place-names if one is not familiar with these forms, the table of Place-names of Fifteenth Century Printing Towns taken from the colophons of incunabula, which forms Reference Section IV of this volume, may prove helpful.

The interpretation of the date also presents its difficulties. The year may be recorded in medieval numerals: I 2 3 4 5 6 7 8 9. In place of the customary M of the Roman notation, there may be a symbol made up of an I between two C's, the latter C being inverted. This gives an unusual appearance to a Roman date, until one realizes that it was an effort on the part of the printer to reproduce the actual strokes of a brush. The date may be written out in full, or abbreviated, or partially omitted, as explained below in Reference Section III, under Latin Contractions and Abbreviations.

The day of the book's completion may have been a Saint's Day. Or the date may have to be computed according to the Roman calendar, the specified day being found by counting backward (and including) the Kalends, the Ides, or the Nones. New Year's Day is quite often given, and that is a date more or less variable according to the locality.

It is not necessary, in the first instance, to interpret the date. The first need is merely to find it. When the place and date of printing have been found, they should be noted upon a slip of paper; and the printer's name, or that of the printing firm, which may be found in conjunction with the place and date, should be added to the tentative note.

The next points for consideration are the author's name and the title. Here the cataloguer is frequently aided by the fact that the names of many authors are already familiar. If the colophon is so involved that the name cannot easily be found, it may be that a caption at the beginning of the text, giving the author's name and title in briefer form, will supplement and verify one's findings in the colophon. This heading is sometimes designated as the title-caption but more often as the *incipit*, since the word 'incipit,' meaning *here begins*, commonly begins or is included within it. The author's name and a brief rendering of the title should be added to the note recording the place, printer, and date. Armed with this note, the cataloguer is then prepared to consult both the bibliographies that list incunabula by place of printing, and those that list incunabula by author-entries.

When an author-entry bibliography is consulted, a comparison should be made between the title-entries under the author's name, and the data already worked out from the book. The aim, of course, is to find first the work in question and then the particular edition wherein the place, printer, and date agree with those of the copy in hand. The original project, which was to note for oneself everything possible regarding the five points of preliminary identification, is now replaced by the effort to identify the book, by means of comparing this data with the statements found in the author-entry bibliographies. If the memorandum made from the book is found to agree with a bibliographical entry, then the memorandum should temporarily be laid aside. The colophon itself should be compared with that recorded in the bibliography, word for word and line for line. A full collation should then be made (as explained below under Collation and Verification); and a further comparison should be made with the place-entry bibliographies.

If, however, the memorandum does not agree with any of the bibliographical entries in the author-entry group, one of two things must be true: either the memorandum is in error, or the edition is not recorded in the particular bibliographies consulted. It may be that, in the first reading of the colophon, a commentator's name was mistaken for that of the author; or, the place from which the printer came, his birthplace, may have been mistaken for the place in which the book was printed; one may have been upon the wrong trail all the while. Or it may be that the colophon was not correctly analyzed for printer or date, in which case a direct comparison of the colophon with all those quoted under the given author and title may reveal both the error and the desired entry. When all possibilities have been exhausted, if the book cannot be found in any of the author-entry bibliographies, the search must be carried elsewhere.

The place-entry bibliographies almost invariably list imprints under *countries* in the order in which the art of printing was introduced (*i.e.*, Germany, Italy, Switzerland, France, Holland, Belgium, Austria-Hungary,[1] Spain, England, Denmark, Sweden, Portugal, and Montenegro); and then chronologically under *towns* in the order in which printing was established within them. The project is then, under a given town, to locate the section devoted to the products of the desired *printer* (also presumably listed according to the date of the opening of his press), and there to find the *author-entry* and *title* of one's book. Here, one should seek to verify the colophon with the entry found in the bibliography and, if the two agree point by point, should go forward with the remainder of the collation.

If, in consulting a place-entry bibliography, there is no table of

---

[1] In bibliographies of the old order, which comprise the greater part of our bibliographic source material, the early imprints of Hungary, Poland, Austria, Bohemia and Moravia are grouped together under Austria-Hungary. In certain of the more modern bibliographical works these countries are treated independently, in which case Hungary is assigned the place formerly assigned to the empire, and the countries are listed as follows: Germany, Italy, Switzerland, France, Holland, Belgium, Hungary, Spain, Poland, Austria, Bohemia, England, Denmark, Sweden, Moravia, Portugal, and Montenegro.

contents and one is at a loss as to the order in which the town or
printer may be listed, the order may be worked out by consulting
Proctor's *Index to the Early Printed Books in the British Museum,*
London, 1898. At the beginning of each section devoted to countries, Proctor's *Index* gives a chronological list of towns; and subsequently under each town, a chronological list of printers. In the
majority of instances, it will be found that Proctor's order prevails
in whatever place-entry bibliography one may wish to consult.

Having found what is apparently the record of one's book, in the
author-entry or place-entry bibliographies — or, better still, in *both*
— one may not consider the book as identified until not only the
author's name, title, place, printer, and date have been verified, but
every bibliographical factor within the book has been thoroughly
collated and found to be identical with the recorded data. Such
data will normally comprise the size, or format, of the book according to the folding of the paper on which the book was printed; the
exact number of leaves comprising the book; the number of leaves,
or folios, comprised within its various signatures; the number of
columns to the page; the average number of lines to a page, the
exact number on a definite page, etc. These all-important bibliographical factors must be considered, in addition to the exact
wording of the colophon, the incipit and other captions, their alignment, abbreviations, and punctuation.

For a moment we must pause to consider the not infrequent
instances in which the colophon fails to give the full information, or
when the colophon itself is lacking. In the first instance, if not all
of the five desirable facts are given by the colophon, it will doubtless be possible in the course of time to work out one's data from
the author-entry or place-entry bibliographies, according to whatever information may be afforded by the colophon or incipit. That
is, the investigator assembles every scrap of data that the book itself may yield, and with that in hand uses his intelligence to find
his book in the type of bibliography to which his data leads him.
In which process the data regarding size, the number of leaves and
of lines to the page, the presence of a printer's mark at the end of the
text, the identification of the type through the use of Haebler's
M-table of types, etc., may be used as factors in identifying the

book. When there is no colophon, or when the colophon is lacking because of the book's imperfection, then the cataloguer must exercise his full ingenuity to find some clue — any clue — that will start him upon the road to identification.

When unquestionable identification has been made, information as to place of printing, the printer, or the date which may have been supplied by an authoritative bibliography may be added to the cataloguer's note, enclosed in square brackets, [ ], and the source of this information should be recorded. If no place of printing, no printer or date, is known, the phrase [n.p., n.pr., n.d.] may be used.

The rule for bracketing such data is well stated in the *Introduction* to volume III of the *Gesamtkatalog der Wiegendrucke*: When the name of the printer and the place of printing are not specified in the book, but are indirectly ascertained, they are quoted in square brackets; when they cannot be determined with certainty, a note of interrogation enclosed within round brackets (?) is added, which here as elsewhere refers only to the statement immediately preceding it. Printers and places of printing are regarded as unspecified if their identity is merely ascertained from printers' devices or addresses; . . . if the date can be established within certain limits, the words *before, not before, after* [*vor, nicht vor,* or *nach*] are prefixed; when no limit can be fixed, the approximate date preceded by *about* [*um*] is given. In some bibliographies, the Latin equivalents of these terms, or their abbreviations, are used instead of the vernacular: see below, in Reference Section III, under: Latin Abbreviations Employed in Hain's *Repertorium Bibliographicum*.

It sometimes happens that a previous owner of the book may have pencilled a bibliographical reference number upon a fly-leaf, or may have laid in a bookseller's description of the volume. Old books such as these have passed through many hands in the course of time and it seldom occurs that a volume which is without its identifying factors will have entirely escaped annotation. Whether accurate or inaccurate, such an annotation offers something to work with. It is for the investigator to discover whether or not the designation is correct. In the course of the comparisons and collations which this task will involve, even though the annotation itself may

not have been altogether accurate, other factors will often come to
light that will furnish a clue to the book's identity. It has been well
stated that bibliography is a matter of dissection, accuracy, and
minute observation. Every scrap of evidence is of value, even the
height, in millimeters, of the different kinds of type.

There is danger in annotations, however, the danger of accepting them, of relying upon them to be correct. Today, we do not write
in incunabula, because such books are far too precious. Instead,
we lay a typewritten record within the book or file the record
for future reference. Annotations such as are cut from a bookseller's catalogue, even though they are oftentimes excellent; or such
as may be found written on a fly-leaf, may serve as a point of departure but should never be accepted as an established fact. The
attitude of the true bibliographer is always to question and to verify.
One might truly say that every clue to a bibliographic source is
acceptable and yet none is accepted. That is, none is accepted until
in a thorough and complete investigation of every conceivable point,
the book in hand and the bibliographic source have been found to
agree.

Collation

Having now established the probable identity of the book by
a line-for-line collation of its colophon with the colophon quoted in
one or more of the authoritative bibliographies (and usually marked
off with two vertical strokes at the end of each line) we may turn
to the bibliographic factors involved.

The first of these is the *format* or *size* of the book. Size in this
connection has nothing whatever to do with a ruler or with linear
measurement. The size of an early printed book is determined according to the manner in which its paper was originally folded for
printing. According to Mr. Pollard's definition, in his article on
Bibliography and Bibliology (*Encyclopædia Britannica*), size was
'originally a technical expression for the relation of the individual
leaves to the sheet of paper of which they formed a part.' By that is
meant that when the original sheet has been folded once, making
two leaves, the book composed of such folded sheets is called a *folio*.
When the original sheets have been folded twice, making four leaves,

the book is designated as a *quarto*. And when folded once again, making eight leaves, it is an *octavo*.

The heavy linen paper used in the majority of these old books is similar to our so-called laid paper. As you hold a sheet to the light, you find a series of parallel lines embedded in the substance of the paper and rather widely spaced. These are called the *chain-lines;* whereas the smaller, uneven, compact lines that cross them are *wire-lines* resulting from the combing of the pulp over the wire mould, in the process of paper making.

A full sized sheet, of whatever dimensions it may have been, is taken always as the basis of computation in determining the make-up of a volume. This single sheet, such as one sees in a proclamation or a large single-sheet almanac, is termed a *broadside*. Ordinarily a broadside is printed in a vertical position, with the chain-lines running horizontally from side to side. If this sheet were to be folded parallel to the shorter diameter, and the fold held as in the binding of a book, the chain-lines would assume a vertical position and a watermark located in the upper portion of the broadside would, in this *folio*, appear in the center of one of the folio's two leaves. If the folio were folded, and the fold held as if for binding, the chain-lines would then become horizontal and the watermark would find itself divided by the fold, in a *quarto*. Folding this once again would bring the folded watermark into an upper corner of an *octavo*, with the chain-lines in a vertical position.

Perhaps the best way is to demonstrate this by taking a sheet of paper, with the shorter edge up, drawing upon each side of it a few parallel horizontal lines to represent the chain-lines, and placing a circle in the center of its upper half to represent the watermark. By folding this sheet and turning it once, twice, and thrice one can produce a miniature *folio, quarto,* or *octavo,* and study at leisure the varying arrangements of chain-lines and watermark. In R. B. McKerrow's *Introduction to Bibliography for Literary Students,*[2] there are diagrams to represent these three sizes; and also the more complicated system where the original, full sheet is folded into three areas, and turned and folded again to produce a 12mo, and so on to produce a 24mo and a 48mo. The latter system, however, is not

---

[2] Oxford, 1927, pp. 167–71.

found in fifteenth century books, excepting in an occasional *Book of Prayer* or *Breviary* printed toward the end of the century.

One point must always be borne in mind in analyzing the size of an early printed book. In order to save time in the sewing of the folds on to the bands at the back of the binding, the printers often planned to print several folds to be laid together as in a quire. This quire is variously spoken of as the *sewed fold* or the *gathering*. It is not uncommon to find a folio volume whose signatures show six or ten leaves to the sewed fold. This is then called a *folio in 6s*, or a *folio in 10s*. In the same way, a quarto volume in which two quarto folds are laid one within the other, is described as a *quarto in 8s*. Since an octavo would naturally have eight leaves in the fold, the distinction between quarto and octavo often rests upon the direction of the chain-lines, the position of the watermark, and the relative height and width of the volume.

When the size of the book has been determined, it should be compared with the size stated in the various bibliographical entries, to see if they agree. If not, it may be that one's conclusions are wrong, or that some factor has been forgotten. All the points should therefore be reviewed and re-valued with utmost care. If one's conclusion is still at variance with that in the bibliographies, the data upon which one has based the conclusion should be carefully noted and also the fact that such and such bibliographies describe a copy which is of another format. One is never expected to agree with a bibliography for the sake of agreement. Our knowledge of incunabula would not progress far by that means. On the other hand, one should never disagree with a bibliographical description unless one is convinced that one's data are accurate and one's reasoning sound.

In determining the *foliation*, or total number of leaves within a fifteenth century printed book, the unit for counting is the single *leaf*, or *folio*. Paging rarely has to be considered. These books, if numbered at all, are invariably numbered leaf by leaf. Page references are indicated according to the location of the reference on the leaf, either according to the leaf number or its signature mark. That is, since the upper side of a leaf is called the *recto*, and the lower side *verso*, a page reference may be indicated by the folio number (as, F

54a), or by the signature mark (as, Eij b), the *a* or *b* indicating the recto or verso of the leaf.

In counting the foliation, if the folios or leaves have been numbered by hand, as is frequently the case, that fact may be disregarded in the collation, the total being given according to actual count (as, 642 *ff*.). If the folio numbers have been printed on the recto of each leaf and collation has proved the notation to be correct, the total may be stated as 642 *ff*. numbered. But if, as is more frequently the case, the printed notation is inaccurate, that fact may be indicated by quoting in parenthesis the inaccurate, printed, final number, as 642 (" 593 ") *ff*.

Since many incunabula are of considerable bulk, the difficulty of counting the leaves may be lessened by inserting small, temporary slips at every sixtieth leaf. It is helpful to keep these markers in place until the count by signatures, the next step in collation, has been completed and the total has been found to equal that of the foliation. If a discrepancy occurs between the two totals, the presence of these markers will aid in locating the miscounted section. In such a dilemma, each group of sixty leaves may be counted by folios and by signatures, and the totals balanced as if each section were a separate book. In most instances, the difficulty will prove to have been caused by an error in counting. But it occasionally happens that an *extra printed leaf* has been inserted by one of the several printers working simultaneously upon the book, whose assignment of text exceeded his paper. Or it may be that, because more paper was allowed than text in one of the assignments of copy, the surplus *blank leaf* [3] has since been torn out. Since every leaf is half or part of a folded sheet, each has its conjugate leaf, and the total was originally an even number. Mr. McKerrow, however, has pointed out that for reasons of economy a brief preliminary section might have been printed as a leaf or two of the last signature and subsequently cut out and transposed to the front of the book. In such an event, an uneven number of preliminary leaves might seem to the unwary to indicate that a missing conjugate, possibly a blank leaf, had been torn out.

The total number of leaves should of course be compared with

---

[3] For a discussion of the blank leaf, see Reference Section I, under: Notes and Definitions.

the total given in various bibliographies, but it is perhaps better to wait until one's own total has been verified by adding together the number of leaves within each signature of the book. Obviously these two totals, the number of leaves according to actual count and the added totals of the leaves within the signatures, should equal one another.

Before it is possible to secure this latter total, it is necessary to analyze the *registration* or *signaturing* of the book. Since each book is made up of a series of folded sheets laid together in gatherings, so that they may be sewed to the bands of the binding, these gatherings frequently vary in the number of folded sheets which they contain; and sometimes, according to the manuscript tradition, they will be found to have been signed with a letter. If the signature marks or letters are printed, they are usually in the lower margins of the recto of the first leaves of the signature but not usually on their conjugates which, however, are counted in the total of the leaves within the gathering. Such signature marks as appear will presumably be found accompanied by the number of the leaf within the signature as: A, Aij, Aiij, or A, A_2, A_3, etc.

If the book contains a sufficient number of signatures, or gatherings, to exhaust the alphabet, it is presumable that only twenty-three letters will be found. In the Latin alphabet *i* was interchangeable with *j*, *u* with *v*, and *w* was omitted. If the gatherings more than exhaust the Latin alphabet, the remaining signatures may be found designated by double letters or even triple letters. Or, if the preliminary section were set up after the main portion of the book had been printed, the asterisk and other symbols may have been used as signature marks for the preliminary leaves. In recording the signatures, the symbols or letters are given just as they are found printed in the book.

Whenever any of the leaves within the gathering have a *printed* signature letter or mark, that letter or symbol is used in the final equation to denote the entire gathering, its total number of leaves being given as an exponent or superior number, as: A^{10}, B^6. The first leaf of signature A is often unsigned; but, if other leaves within the signature are signed, the signature itself may be designated as A, without brackets. But when no signature marks have been printed, a letter may be supplied and with its exponent enclosed in brackets, as: [A ^{10},] B ^{6}. If all of the signatures are unsigned, *i.e.*, if the entire signaturing for the book has to be supplied, it is customary to use the Latin alphabet of twenty-three letters, and to enclose the whole equation in brackets. The fact that signature marks may have been supplied in manuscript in the book may be disregarded. Although signature marks in manuscript may prove helpful in analyzing the gathering, the latter is never counted as signed unless the signature marks are actually printed as a part of the book.

Mr. Pollard is quoted as saying that it does not much matter what form you give to your bibliographical statement provided you make your intentions perfectly clear. No hard and fast rule can be given regarding the writing of the signature equation. It depends largely upon circumstance. In a first collation it is well to record each gathering and its number of leaves independently, as it is then a simple matter to check an inaccuracy in the count. In the final equation written upon the memorandum, however, it is generally possible to group the statements. Thus a ^{10}, b ^{12}, c ^{12}, d ^{12}, e ^{10}, f ^{12}, g ^{12}, h ^{12} may be reduced to a ^{10}, b-d ^{12}, e ^{10}, f-h ^{12}. If it had happened that the 10s and 12s had alternated, the equation might even have been stated as briefly as, a-h $^{10.12}$. Although the exponent is almost always used to denote the total number of leaves within the gathering, some writers prefer, especially if the statement is to be type-written, to keep the equation on a single line. In this case the equation might be written as: a in 10; b-d in 12s; e in 10; f-h in 12s.

The purpose of this minute analysis is to determine the exact way in which the book was built, an important factor when comparing it with other copies. This analysis furnishes also a method of proving the completeness of the book, and of verifying the count of the total number of leaves. If the total should prove to be an uneven number, the gathering having an uneven number of leaves must be sought out and its make-up carefully analyzed. Either the gathering lacks a leaf, printed or blank; or it contains an inserted leaf which may or may not be a continuation of the text. If a leaf is lacking, the equation is given as if the book were perfect, with a statement in parentheses regarding the imperfection, as: a ^{10}, b-d ^{12},

e ^{10}, f-h ^{12} (b$_6$ lacking). If, however, a leaf had been inserted in signature b, and examination had proved its subject matter to be a
continuation of the text, the equation should read: a ^{10}, b $^{12\,+\,1}$, c-d ^{12},
e ^{10}. The resultant equation should be carefully collated, point by
point, with the signaturing recorded in the various bibliographies.
The totals of the number of leaves within each gathering should then
be added together, and the grand total thus obtained should be used
to verify the foliation which was previously determined by the counting of the leaves from cover to cover. If these two totals balance
one another, the temporary markers inserted in the book may be
removed.

The next two factors, although important, are relatively simple.
The number of columns in the text should be noted, if the text has
been so printed; and the number of lines to a page. In counting the
latter, it is necessary to count the lines on various pages throughout
the book to be sure that the number quoted is truly that of a typical
page. Sometimes the number of lines to the page varies, in which
case the note may read *31–35 lines;* or, if the majority of the pages
comprise a given number but a few pages were differently set, the
note might read *33 (34) lines.* The British Museum *Catalogue*
(1908, etc.) secures accuracy by giving the number of lines on a
definite page, with the measurement in millimeters of the type-block
upon that page, as: 2 ^{a}: 33 lines, 145 x 90 mm. The *Gesamtkatalog
der Wiegendrucke* prefers the more general method indicated above,
with the initial Z for " Zeilen," and the addition of the word " wech-
selnd " (variable) when the occurrence of different types makes it
impossible to gauge the number of lines on certain pages.

The question of type is a difficult one. It is really an independent
study in itself. Through association, one learns to distinguish between the heavy characters of *gothic* type and the clear faced, *roman*
type; but an ability to recognize transitional types containing elements of both, or to pick out the new and old types employed by a
given printer, can be acquired only through a long and intensive
study of the subject. It is not necessary to attempt more in cataloguing than to indicate the general character of the type and then
to give in millimeters the space occupied by twenty lines of type
(measured, according to Dr. Haebler's system, from the base of the

lowest line, not counting descenders, up to the base of the twenty-first line from the bottom). Thus, in British Museum practice, the phrase " 117R, denotes a roman type of which twenty lines measure 117 mm.; 117G., a gothic type of the same measurement. In the same way SG. denotes semi-gothic, and Gk, Greek." The type-measurement given is the result of a comparison of the type-measurement of all available specimens; and it is suggested that the relation to the type-measurement of a particular book (which may vary because of shrinkage or the quality of the paper) may be found by ascertaining the height of the type-page in millimeters, multiplying by twenty, and dividing the total by the number of lines on the page. The value of this method, which makes it possible to visualize approximately the size of the type, as compared with Proctor's method of numbering the various types of each printer chronologically according to the latter's adoption of each font, is discussed on pages xix–xxi of the Introduction to Volume I of the *Catalogue of Books Printed in the XVth Century now in the British Museum* (1908, etc.). The *Gesamtkatalog der Wiegendrucke*, beginning with its third volume, holds to both schools, giving first the press number of the type according to Haebler's enumeration, and then the twenty-line measurement in millimeters. Thus, the phrase " Typen:1:130G, 2:69G " would indicate that two gothic types are to be found in the book, the first measuring 130 millimeters to twenty lines and listed as the printer's first type in Haebler's *Typenrepertorium der Wiegendrucke*, and the other measuring 69 millimeters and listed by Haebler as the printer's second type. In measuring the twenty lines of type in millimeters, some leeway must be allowed for the variable shrinkage of the paper. Provided that all other bibliographical factors tally, and twenty lines of the type of an average page of one copy occupy the same or approximately the same number of millimeters as twenty lines in another copy, it is reasonably safe to assume that the type in both copies is the same. Unless one has originals at hand for comparison, and an eye trained to all the niceties of type design, it is not necessary in general to pursue the matter beyond the twenty-line measurement and its approximate accuracy.

The presence of a printer's device or of woodcut initials should be noted; also the presence of small letters printed as guides in the squares left for the insertion of painted letters, with an exponent or superior number indicating the number of lines indented for the insertion. In the *Gesamtkatalog*, " printed initials are indicated by round brackets [*i.e.*, parentheses]; spaces by square brackets; guide-letters are reproduced in their original form within round brackets." The presence of engravings, maps, and printed marginal notes should also be recorded. All of these bibliographical factors, size, foliation, registration, the number of columns, the number of lines, the character of the type and its twenty-line measurement, the presence of a printer's device, of initials, etc., should be added, point by point, to the cataloguer's note.

Following these entries should come the assignment of the bibliographical reference numbers which, through the collations described above, have been found to correspond to the copy in hand; and, in a final paragraph, a statement giving the provenance of the volume. The constant checking of the items in this note with the data found in the bibliographies, and oftentimes their revision, will doubtless make a reworking necessary. A verification of the final typewritten copy with the entries in the various bibliographies should leave the record in shape for filing as an analysis of the copy.

A discussion of all these points, according to British Museum usage, will be found in the introductions to the respective volumes of that library's *Catalogue of Books Printed in the XVth Century,* (1908, etc.). *Suggestions for the Cataloguing of Incunabula,* compiled and tabulated by Mr. Henry Guppy, and based largely upon the British Museum practice, appeared in the *Bulletin* of the John Rylands Library in July, 1924, and was separately printed later in that year. A provisional recommendation of nine briefly stated rules was compiled by a committee of the American Library Association and printed in the *Papers and Proceedings* of the Association in 1925, under the title *Rules for Cataloguing Incunabula, simplified form.* A statement of the method of describing incunabula which is being employed in the *Gesamtkatalog* will be found, in English, in the preliminary pages of Volume III of the *Gesamtkatalog der Wiegendrucke.*

If a catalogue card is desired in addition to the typewritten analysis (whose filing number, or location, should be written on the verso of the card), the card itself should bear only the simplest of statements: Author entry; brief title; place, printer, date (each or all of these facts to be included in square brackets, if supplied from a source other than the colophon) ; size (according to format) ; and a block of brief notes including: Bibliographical reference numbers (qualified or unqualified, as the case may require) ; a brief statement of edition, or of issue (if the status of the copy has become known through bibliographic study and comparison) ; imperfections in the copy (if a brief statement seems desirable) ; provenance (the names of successive owners of the book, so far as they are known). Although the collation by signatures and the foliation may of course be noted after the size, and the statement of diagrams, woodcuts, etc., such information ordinarily complicates the matter. These points may be given in detail on the typewritten record. (An outline indicating the application of these points to books of varying periods will be found below, in Reference Section I, Notes and Definitions: Cataloguing: Card Entries; and a discussion of the distinction between edition and issue will be found in the same section under: Bibliographical Points, Edition and Issue.)

It must be remembered that the assignment of a bibliographical reference number is always taken to mean that the collation quoted in that entry corresponds in every particular to that of the book to which the reference number is assigned. If a minor difference exists, a number may sometimes be assigned with a qualifying phrase as: Hain 2858, with variant alignment in colophon. If, however, the variations are important and yet the titles so similar that confusion may arise between them, it is well to state that the book is: Not Hain 2825. A definite statement is more helpful in such an instance than the usual: Not in Hain.

The recording of imperfections is a matter of judgment. If the copy is without an important or a rare map, the fact that the map is wanting should of course be stated on the card. Similarly, if an integral part of the book is missing, that also should be stated, as: Commentary, ff. 62–125, lacking. On the other hand, if occasional leaves or portions of leaves have been torn out, it is generally sufficient to say: Imperfect; or, Slightly imperfect. The exact nature of the deficiency and the leaf numbers should appear in the typewritten record of collation which is filed elsewhere.

In collating our data with the entry for the same edition in various bibliographies and in assigning appropriate reference numbers, the results are twofold. The status and condition of our copy becomes known, and, in determining whether our copy is perfect and our data correct, we provide also a concise means of identification; for, by consulting a bibliography under the number assigned, our co-workers have immediately before them the bibliographic description of our book, while in the typewritten analysis of our copy, filed for future reference, we have the proof that the assignment of this and other bibliographical reference numbers is correct.

VERIFICATION

Having outlined the main processes and purpose of collation, we may now turn to the bibliographic tools which make bibliographic comparison possible. The first step in verifying one's data is to consult the *Repertorium Bibliographicum* published by Ludwig Hain at Stuttgart just a century ago. This work lists, alphabetically by authors, over sixteen thousand titles of fifteenth century books, and gives ordinarily a bibliographical description of each title. It is usually personified as *Hain* as if it were a living thing, and indeed it is.

Hain's order of description under each entry is simple and logical. After an assigned heading, comprising the author-entry and a brief title, the description begins with a transcript of the incipit, the important caption-headings, and the colophon. Following this is a statement of the collation and bibliographic characteristics of the book. There are certain points, however, which need explanation to a person not familiar with the Hain symbols. Consulting Hain number 1099 as a sample, we find first of all that the number is preceded by an asterisk. This indicates that the volume was seen by Hain himself in the Royal Library at Munich. We may thus expect to find a comparatively full bibliographical description and, barring the frailties of human nature, an accurate one. Directly after the number 1099, comes the author-entry which, if another work by the same author had preceded this upon the page, would have been represented by a dash. Then comes the title-entry which, if another edition of the same work had preceded it, would have been indicated by a second dash.

Following the author- and title-heading, we come to the description of the book itself. First comes the italicised phrase *F. 1 a tit.*, followed by a colon and a series of Latin words. Thus we are informed that on *Folio 1, recto*, we shall find the title-caption, which is quoted after the colon. Subsequently, the italicised phrases *F 1. B* and *F 2 b incipit opus*, inform us that the words quoted after the former, will be found on *Folio 1, verso*, and that on *Folio 2, recto*, the work itself, or the text, begins.

Between the captions noted above and the technical collation, Hain invariably gives a long quotation introduced by the italicised words, *In fine*, at the end of the work. Here we have the colophon — or, in this instance, an explicit or author's colophon — word for word and line for line as it appears in the volume, a double vertical bar being inserted by Hain to indicate the termination of each line in the original. It is necessary that each word should be checked with Hain and every variation noted, even the misspelling of words in the original, which are indicated by the insertion of the Latin word (*sic*), meaning *thus*, so it stands in the original. Minor differences such as these do not affect the identity of a work as a whole, being indicative merely of a variant issue; but, if any of the factors of identification are found to vary, a description of our volume must be searched for under some other entry.

Printed beneath the Hain transcript of the explicit is the technical collation which in this instance appears as the mystical phrase: *s.l.a. et typ. n. 4. g. ch. c. s. 33 l. 16 ff.* By supplying the Latin words indicated by the abbreviations and then translating into English, this phrase resolves itself into the following statement: Without place, year, and printer's name; quarto; gothic characters; with signatures; 33 lines to the page; 16 folios. (For an explanation of these abbreviations, see Reference Section III below, under: *Abbreviations Employed in Hain's Repertorium Bibliographicum.*)

The fact that the author's colophon, quoted in full in Hain, although replete with information regarding the author, yields nothing with regard to place, date, and printer, is here indicated in the collation by the phrase *s.l.a. et typ. n.* — *sine loco, anno, et typographici nomine.* According to Hain, then, the Munich copy is a quarto. Its text is printed in gothic type; each series of leaves within the gatherings bear signature-marks; its pages have an average of thirty-three lines; and the volume itself contains sixteen leaves.

All of these points must be carefully verified and found to be correct before we may say that our volume is Hain 1099. And even after this detailed verification has been completed, there are still other bibliographic reference books to be consulted with similar attention to detail, before one can have completed the triple task of identification, collation, and verification. Hain's *Repertorium* was compiled a hundred years ago and, although his descriptions still rank as the first point of departure, much has been learned in the intervening century regarding these rare old books. More modern bibliographies must be consulted also.

When the author-entry falls under *A*, as in this instance, or is in the first part of *B*, the task is a simple one. If the same form of entry has been retained, the work will be found very fully described in one of the first volumes [4] of the forthcoming *Gesamtkatalog der Wiegendrucke* (1925, etc.), the general catalogue of incunabula. Otherwise it will be necessary to seek means of verification in the bibliographies suggested in the following chapter of this book. Happily for present needs, our title is in the second volume of the *Gesamtkatalog.*

This catalogue, the *GW* as it is called in bibliographical slang, has reached its third volume, A-Bernardus. The work as a whole aims to give a complete and authentic description of all of the books issued during the fifteenth century which are now in existence. The German Commission which conceived this project began its work in 1904 by registering all of the incunabula to be found in Germany. More recently, through the coöperation of incunabulists in various countries, the Commission expanded its program until at the time of the issuing of the first volume in 1925, the *Gesamtkatalog* took its place as an international catalogue undertaking to

---

[4] Volume IV of the *Gesamtkatalog* has appeared since this book went to press.

comprise, within its twelve or more folio volumes, a full biblio-graphical record of the thirty-five thousand or more incunabula (separate editions, not duplicate copies) that have survived the passing centuries.

Like Hain, the *Gesamtkatalog* is arranged alphabetically by author-entries. However, the *Gesamtkatalog* in the end will have listed over twice as many titles as those known to Hain, and in many instances the Commission has found it desirable to alter the form of author-entry. The Hain and *GW* numbers are therefore *not* interchangeable, a difficulty which is overcome by the insertion in each volume of the *Gesamtkatalog* of a table giving parallel references from Hain to the *Gesamtkatalog* numbers. A search in this table shows that our specimen title, Hain 1099, is *GW* 1891. And a study of the collation given under *GW* 1891 reveals several important and interesting facts added to the information previously found in Hain.

A brief biographical statement regarding the author precedes the full entry. Then after the author-entry and brief title of the assigned heading, there appears in brackets the statement that the volume (*sine loco, anno, et typographici nomine*, in Hain) has since been assigned to the press of Albrecht Kunne at Memmingen, " um 1490," at about the year 1490. To the collation giving size and foliation has been added the actual make-up of the book by signatures, a⁶, b⁴, c⁶, thus making it possible to check our copy signature by signature and, if the copy chance to be imperfect or in any way irregular, to determine the nature of its imperfection or variation. The text is again described as having been printed in 33 lines to the page. The types, according to Haebler's enumeration of the types employed by Albrecht Kunne, are noted as being numbers 2 and 6.[5] It is further noted that lower-case guide-letters, *Minus-*

---

[5] A typographical bypath may be followed by comparing the statements regarding Kunne's types at Memmingen in Haebler's *Typenrepertorium* with the notes regarding them in the British Museum *Catalogue*. In the latter, Vol. II, p. 608, the *Tractatus* of Jacobus Angeli is described as being in types occupying 115 mm. and 87 mm. in the 20-line measurement; and the note on Kunne's types, at the beginning of the section devoted to him, states that variations of the 115 type, due to filing, sometimes appear as low as 102 mm. to 20 lines. In Haebler, *Typenrepertorium*, Kunne's types 2 and 6, in which the *Gesamtkatalog* copy of the *Tractatus* is said to be printed, are listed as 105 mm. and 88 mm. From which it would seem that the *Gesamtkatalog* copy has one of the variations of the 115 type noted in the British

keln für Initialen, are printed in the capital spaces; and that rubrics (agreeing with the third form noted by Haebler, under Kunne's press) occur in the copy described. That is, in the *Gesamtkatalog,* whenever a symbol occurs after *Init:* or *Rubr:,* it refers to the symbol used in Haebler's *Typenrepertorium* in describing initials or rubrication employed by a given printer. Since, in this instance, no reference is made to the number of columns to a page [2 Sp. or 3 Sp.], it is to be assumed that the work is printed in a one-column page; also, since the phrase *Kol. Tit.* is not given, it is to be assumed that the book has no running titles.

Beneath the collation paragraph are quotations from various captions and from the termination of the book, the final paragraph being an explicit, giving an account of the author, rather than a complete colophon giving the five desirable factors. Accompanying these quotations are the leaf numbers, or the leaf numbers with signatures; and, in the final instance, the number of the line at which the quotation begins. In the course of the quotation from the recto of leaf 2 with signature a₂, it is further noted that a capital space, or square, five lines in height contains the guide-letter ' m.' The paragraph ends with the statement that the verso of leaf 16 is blank, *Blatt 16b leer.*

Of keen interest to the conscientious student is the subsequent list of bibliographic sources which make it possible to follow out the increase in the knowledge of the book, during the century between the publication of Hain and of the *Gesamtkatalog.* The source-paragraph in this instance reads as follows: Hain-Copinger 1099 = Hain 5541. Proctor 2807. Pellechet 758. Census S. 13. BMC.II.-608.IA.11,134.[6] Being interpreted, the first note informs us that Hain 1099 is again entered as Hain 5541, and that further information will be found under the original Hain number, 1099, in Part I of Copinger's *Supplement to Hain's Repertorium Bibliographicum.* Proctor's *Index to the Early Printed Books in the British Museum* (1898), is said to list the title under 2807, an entry which, more than

---

Museum *Catalogue;* whereas its other type, noted as 88 mm. (versus 87), is merely the inconsequential matter of a millimeter due to the shrinkage of the paper, and therefore negligible in its variation.

[6] For a discussion of these and other works of reference, see the following chapter, on: Bibliographical Reference Material.

likely, will be found to have been responsible for the assignment of place, printer, and date. Mlle. Pellechet's *Catalogue* of incunabula in the public libraries of France, it seems, records the title under number 758; and the *Census of Fifteenth Century Books Owned in America* (1918), records the work on page 13. The final rather cryptic entry refers both to the volume and page of the *Catalogue of Books printed in the XVth Century now in the British Museum* (1908), where a full description will be found; and, in its latter portion, to the British Museum press or call-number.

The thoroughgoing student will range all these reference sources on the table before him and will painstakingly check and collate his data or the volume itself, point by point, with each and every one of the recorded collations. Such a procedure is not a waste of time. Although there is necessarily a certain amount of repetition in each comparison, the collector or cataloguer is meantime becoming better and better acquainted with the volume he has been seeking to analyze. It is only when the main facts about a book have been so thoroughly verified as to cease to concern him that he is free to notice whatever minor variations his copy may have. And it is only after attaining a thorough understanding of his own copy, in its relation to the bibliographic descriptions of other copies, that he can know whether his own data comprises anything which adds to the accumulated knowledge of the book.

A final paragraph in the *Gesamtkatalog* records nineteen copies of the book in various libraries, that are listed alphabetically by place, the libraries being indicated by the initials or abbreviated forms that are explained in the preliminary pages of Volume I of the *Gesamtkatalog*.

It might seem that the pursuit of all these technical matters would become wearisome. After all, they are much like the fine points of a game. The according of due credit to one another's discoveries and the hauling down of one's colors, especially when a volume believed to be unique, or outstanding in some bibliographical feature, may no longer claim that distinction, requires good sporting blood on the part of librarian or collector. It is no doubt this element of good sportsmanship that has tended to make bibliographers the world over so willing to coöperate in one another's interest.

It is with an inward thought of questioning and of verifying that one bibliographer checks the work of another. This attitude of mind, however, is quite impersonal, without thought of being unkindly critical; neither does one gloat, even inwardly, over an error discovered in another's work. In work of this character, each participant is striving for accuracy, yet so many are the pitfalls along the way that no one can be infallible. The correcting of an error, if it chance that an error exists, is just so much accomplished toward the desired and common goal. The correction is made, and received, in the spirit of simple hearted coöperation.

For this reason, it is often considered good form to write an annotation in the margin of a bibliography, correcting an error or recording the existence of a copy variant from the one described. Such a note should be concise and straight to the point. It requires not a little intelligence to give, in the fewest possible words, the exact information which will be useful. Such a note should be a little masterpiece in precision.

THE ULTIMATE GOAL

The matter of collation and identification is not an end in itself. It is a means to an end. Given the critical assignment of author, place, and date, and a tabulated record of the technical points essential to its exact bibliographical status, the ultimate goal is the subject analysis of the work, that the book may take its place in the history of human thought and progress. In his recent introduction to Harper's *Selection of Incunabula,* Mr. Winship notes the present revival of interest in medieval studies; and Dr. Arnold C. Klebs urged coöperation in an essay on *Desiderata in the cataloguing of incunabula,* contributed to the *Papers* of the Bibliographical Society of America in 1916. His appeal resolved itself into four desiderata: a greater emphasis upon the subject-content of incunabula; the use of the family or given name of an author, rather than the town-name or the epithets not infrequently found in early printed books; a synoptic title-entry indicating the subject of the book, rather than

a transcript of its involved and oftentimes obscurely worded incipit;
and, finally, uniformity in the author- and title-entries of all editions and issues of a given work, even if modified by commentators
or translators.   Here he speaks both as medical man and bookman,
for his own collection of medical incunabula is catalogued with due
regard to its technical and its medico-historical aspects.

In the history of medicine the subject-content of incunabula
plays an interesting and important part; in mathematics also, and
in music, which originally ranked as a department of mathematics;
in theology; in literature; law; cosmography, architecture; the
Renaissance; and so on almost *ad infinitum* — dull reading, perhaps, according to modern standards, yet teeming with interest in
the perspective of history.   Various specialized bibliographies and
monographs treating of incunabula according to subject matter
have made a beginning in this department of research: the Boston
Public Library has begun the publication of an annotated catalogue
of its collection of incunabula; Dr. Klebs has a forthcoming book
on medical incunabula which will doubtless add much to books
already treating of this subject; Professor E. R. A. Seligman of
Columbia University is gathering a collection of incunabula relating to the field of economics; excellent contributions have been
made by various European booksellers in their annotated catalogues
of incunabula; and Mr. Steele's serial on *What fifteenth century
books are about,* which ran intermittently in *The Library* from 1903
through 1907, affords an excellent survey.

The British Museum *Catalogue* and the *Gesamtkatalog der
Wiegendrucke,* in their critical assignment of author-entries and
the latter in its biographical paragraphs, are making a definite and
valuable contribution toward this ideal.   In their assignment of
hitherto undated works through the identification of types and the
intercollation of copies, still another contribution is being made.
If, in addition, the *Gesamtkatalog* Commission eventually issues a
subject index to the titles listed within this catalogue of all the
known editions of incunabula, then the broad way will be open for
historians and students of literature and the history of science.

Meantime, every owner of incunabula and every cataloguer may
do much: first, by paying close heed to the bibliographical analysis

of each book within his keeping, thus helping to clear the field of its technical problems; and secondly, by contributing as much as lies within his power to an understanding of its subject matter. Even though its highly contracted Latin text may render it temporarily a closed book to him, the owner of an early printed book should look upon it with veneration not only because of its age, or its beauty, or its rarity, or the interest of fine points in its bibliographical analysis, but because it is a record of human thought, an integral part of the history of mankind. And he should welcome the day when either his own researches, or those of another worker in the field, may hand him the key to whatever of interest lies hidden between its covers.

It is through these first printed books that, in a sense, we of the modern age go back to the source of our being. For the invention of the arts of casting and employing metal types unknowingly achieved a dual purpose. Through the printed page it preserved to us much of the best that had survived of the cultural thought of earlier centuries, at the same time making possible the quick interchange and dissemination of thought that ultimately brought about the civilization of our day.

CHAPTER III

BIBLIOGRAPHICAL REFERENCE MATERIAL

Whoever would study the subject of incunabula must set himself the task of mastering its historical and technical aspects. He must know the facts regarding the development of fifteenth century bookmaking; the introduction and early history of printing in each country; the status of the printers; and, as opportunity permits of intensive and individual study, the characteristics of each press. He must understand the bibliographical or technical analysis of the books themselves; the methods employed in the bibliographies and monographs devoted to the subject; and, in his own work, he must develop accuracy and simplicity of technique, that whoever uses his notes may find within them the precise data which the analysis should contain. First of all, he must know what authoritative, bibliographical reference material exists, a subject which is almost a special study in itself.

In the technical treatment of incunabula the aims of the student are precision of knowledge and precision of statement, and precision can be achieved only through constant and unending verification. As it is seldom possible to collate various copies of these rare books with one another, the verifying and checking must be done through the skillful use of bibliographical works. These divide into two schools: those listing titles alphabetically under author-entries; and those listing them chronologically by countries, towns, and printers. The former method, the alphabetical, is doubtless to be preferred in studying incunabula as books among books; the latter, the chronological, in studying incunabula with regard to the early history of the printing art, and the products of given localities and presses.

Alphabetical Author-Entry Group

Hain's *Repertorium*, with its alphabetical arrangement of author-entries discussed in the latter portion of the preceding chapter, was followed seventy years after its publication by Copinger's *Supplement* and, ten years later still by Reichling's *Appendices*, a supplement to both. Alphabetical listing of authors was employed by Mlle. Pellechet in her *Catalogue général des incunables des bibliothèques publiques de France* (1897), and adopted in both the *Census of Fifteenth Century Books Owned in America* and in the *Gesamtkatalog der Wiegendrucke*. In their respective notations, the American *Census* follows Hain implicitly; Copinger and Reichling follow Hain's notation whenever possible; and Pellechet and the *Gesamtkatalog*, although alphabetical by author-entries, have individual systems of numbering.

The statement that Copinger and Reichling follow Hain's notation whenever possible, sounds innocent enough, but it involves a tale of considerable complexity. Copinger, in his *Supplement to Hain's Repertorium*,[1] follows Hain's numbering in Part I, which is devoted to additions and corrections to Hain's collations. In Part II, works not known to Hain, Copinger had of necessity to develop a notation of his own, although whenever possible he used Hain's author forms (and *Addenda* to Parts I and II are at the end of the volume). His arrangement of undated titles differs somewhat from Hain's, as explained in his introductory note (Volume I, page ix); collations by signatures are given; and the British Museum's and other copies are cited for works not seen by Hain (with a supplementary list of British Museum titles in the *Addenda*). A list of abbreviations precedes the first part and addenda to both parts are given at the end of the second. In quoting and in consulting Copinger, one must keep the two parts and their dual notations clearly in mind.

A bibliographical reference to Hain-Copinger 419, for instance, refers to an entirely different title than Copinger 419. The former reference (which one may find recorded also in abbreviated form, as HC 419) means that a title described in Hain's *Repertorium* un-

---

[1] (Two parts in 3 vols.) London, 1895, 1898, 1902.

der 419 will be found corrected or amplified in Copinger's Part I, under number 419. Whereas the second reference (which may also appear as Cop. 419, or C 419) indicates that Copinger, in his Part II, gives the collation of a title not known to Hain. With a little practice, one learns to discriminate easily between references to Part I and Part II. In building up one's own references for an unidentified book, it is well to search both parts. An incomplete entry in Hain, insufficient for identification, may be amplified in Copinger's Part I. Or the work, entirely unknown to Hain, may be described by Copinger in his second part. One of the most important features of Copinger's series, as described below, is the index by Konrad Burger of *The Printers and Publishers of the XV. Century, with lists of their works.*

Reichling's *Appendices* to Hain-Copinger is a more difficult work to cope with than Copinger's. It comprises a series of seven thin volumes published at Munich between 1905 and 1911, followed in 1914 by a *Supplement.* Each volume is designated as a *Fasciculus,* the seventh volume containing several helpful indexes, and the *Supplement,* an *Index auctorum generalis.* The difficulty lies in the fact that each of the six main volumes consists of two sections. The first in each instance comprises works not known to Hain or Copinger; these are listed alphabetically in each volume but numbered consecutively throughout the six *Fasciculi* as numbers 1–1,920, with additional titles in the *Supplement,* 1–223. The second section, within each *Fasciculus,* comprises additions to titles listed in Hain, Hain-Copinger, or Copinger as the case may be, the distinction being shown by the initials H, H(C), or C, printed so as to precede each of the reference numbers used by Hain or by Copinger in one of the other of his parts. The seventh volume (1911), containing indexes to both sections, is a saving grace. Otherwise a conscientious worker would have to search each of the six *Fasciculi,* and sometimes both sections of each. Even with the help afforded by the 1911 volume, it must be remembered that a Reichling reference in Arabic numerals (not preceded by a Roman numeral or by an initial) refers to the first section in each volume, in which the notation is one continuous series throughout the six volumes. Whereas a Reichling reference, comprising both Roman and Arabic numerals, refers to the second section within each; the Roman number indicates the volume; the Arabic numeral, the page within the volume; and a subordinate number with the initials H, H(C), or C, the title listed upon the page. In the *Supplement*, 1914, the *Index auctorum generalis* combines in one alphabet the items listed in the preceding parts, and maintains the dual system of numbering.

The *Gesamtkatalog* in its references to Reichling endeavors to disentangle these complications by using the term *Reichling* with Arabic numerals to indicate the consecutively numbered titles within the first section of each *Fasciculus;* and the phrases *Hain-Reichling,* or *Hain-Copinger-Reichling* or *Copinger-Reichling* for titles within the second, which may then be traced through the author index in Reichling's supplementary volume or in the second part of his seventh volume. This is cumbersome; yet, after all, it is but an expansion of Reichling's own idea, and it gives at a glance the history of each case. An *Index urbium et typographorum* is also given in Reichling's seventh volume, with additions in the *Supplement* of 1914.

The *Catalogue général des incunables des bibliothèques publiques de France,* the first volume of which was issued by Mlle. Pellechet in 1897, is arranged alphabetically under authors. Whenever possible the Hain number is given after each collation. The notation is entirely independent of Hain. The *Catalogue* comprises a census with collations of the early printed books, Abano-Gregorius, that were to be found in French public libraries during the course of its compilation. A key to the abbreviations, on a preliminary page of each volume, makes it easy to check the collations. Although the death of Mlle. Pellechet brought the series temporarily to a halt, it is to be hoped that M. Polain, who took over the editing in 1900, will eventually complete its publication.

The *Census of Fifteenth Century Books Owned in America,* which was compiled in 1918 by a committee of the Bibliographical Society of America, with George Parker Winship as editor, follows Hain implicitly both in author-entries and in its numbering. The title-entries and collations are purposely made very brief, for the Hain numbers which precede the titles whenever possible and the references to other bibliographies which follow the titles, direct one to the sources where more ample information may be found. Without duplication of information, the *Census* achieves its purpose of being a handbook supplementing Hain and of giving the record of American ownership up to the date of its compilation. Its lapses in notation correspond to the absence at that time of various titles from America's bookshelves, and the titles unknown to Hain are inserted in their respective places without numbers. For the latter reason, references to the *Census* are customarily made by pages.

A *Second Census of Fifteenth Century Books Owned in America* is now in process of compilation. Its manuscript files comprise the record of approximately nine thousand copies of incunabula registered in this country since the *Census* of 1918. As in the earlier instance, the *Second Census* is being compiled under the auspices of the Bibliographical Society of America, but with the curator of the Annmary Brown Memorial as compiler and general editor. Since 1924, the Memorial has been serving in the dual capacity of national headquarters for the census files, and as the American secretarial office for the *Gesamtkatalog der Wiegendrucke*.

Just as Ludwig Hain in his *Repertorium*, 1826–1838, brought to a focus the results of the bibliographical researches of Cornelius van Beughem (1688), Maittaire (1719, etc.), Denis (1789), and Panzer (1793, etc.), so the Commission for the *Gesamtkatalog*, through its comparative study of fifteenth century printing on the one hand, and of the mass of bibliographical data on the other has brought to a focus the results of the researches of Hain, Copinger, Reichling, Proctor, Burger, and the incunabulists of the passing century. Until the *Gesamtkatalog* is completed, all of these references must be consulted. After its completion, they will doubtless merge gradually into the historical background of bibliography; and new works, monographs, specialized bibliographies, etc., based upon the findings of the *Gesamtkatalog*, will contribute still further to our knowledge of early printed books. Exhaustive research is much like evolution. Each successive period of investigation carries the resultant knowledge forward to another plane. For the incunabulist of the future, ample tools will be at hand with which to ply his trade, but the great foundation will have been laid, unquestionably, for all time.

As a project, the *Gesamtkatalog* is as broadly and as scientifically conceived as can well be imagined. Although originating in Germany, compiled in Germany, issued through a German commission and under a German title, the *Gesamtkatalog der Wiegendrucke* through the coöperation of many scholars has been made an international affair. That is, the work as a whole, as noted in the preceding chapter, will comprise a full, bibliographical description of the thirty-five thousand or more fifteenth century books which are now to be found in Austria, Hungary, Denmark, Sweden, part of Russia, Belgium, Holland, Switzerland, the United States, Mexico, Spain, Portugal, Great Britain, Ireland, France, Italy, and Germany. In fact, Volume I in its preliminary pages lists 2,177 libraries (in public institutions alone) whose early printed books are to be described.

The arrangement of its data is so logical and simple that it practically speaks for itself. The text comprises a straightforward alphabetical arrangement of authors' names, with a brief biographical note under the name of each; or with cross references to the new form whenever the author-entry has been changed from that in Hain. Then, in general, follow the author's works chronologically arranged. In the case of works augmented and edited by various commentators, special systems of arrangement have been developed; and in such instances, an index or key to the arrangement follows directly after the biographical note. It takes but a little browsing, therefore, to be able to pick one's way.

The entry for each title in general comprises five paragraphs, varying in length according to circumstance. The first (giving the *Gesamtkatalog* number, the author, brief title, place of printing, printer, date, and size) is in Roman type clearly spaced. The second (giving foliation, registration, and other factors in collation) is in small italic type. The third (quoting caption headings and colophon) is in black letter or small Roman, according to which type was employed in the book described. The fourth (giving the Hain number, references to other bibliographies, facsimiles, and the American *Census*) is again in small italic. And the fifth (giving an alphabetical place-list of libraries owning the book) uses small Roman for place, and italic for the library or collection. This varied use of type looks well upon the open page. It is decorative in effect; but far more important than effect is the utilitarian advantage thus gained. Each paragraph, by reason of its type and careful spacing, stands as a definite and clearcut unit, a fact which is of incalculable value in the oftentimes difficult process of checking a bibliographical description with a fifteenth century printed book. (For a more detailed account of a *Gesamtkatalog* entry, see the third section of the preceding chapter.)

The *Gesamtkatalog* will more than double Hain's 16,299 titles and, in addition to the present researches of its Commission, it brings to a focus the combined research of a hundred years. The bookish world, however, has used Hain for a century as the point of departure in its study of early printed books. The Hain number [2] is the accustomed and quick form of identification. A transition period of some years must necessarily elapse before custom will yield completely to the *Gesamtkatalog*. The older generation will consult Hain always, from sheer force of habit if nothing more. It is in wise acknowledgment of this transition that the Commission has issued a concordance as an insert for each volume, giving the Hain and the corresponding *Gesamtkatalog* numbers in parallel columns.

These, then, are the general bibliographies to which one turns in the first effort to identify and collate a fifteenth century book according to the author-entry method of approach.

CHRONOLOGICAL PLACE-ENTRY GROUP

In the century which intervened between Hain and the *Gesamtkatalog,* certain milestones have been erected which cannot be passed unnoted. About 1870 Henry Bradshaw, Librarian of the University of Cambridge (influenced by Panzer who had worked three quarters of a century before him, and possibly by his own contemporaries Blades and Holtrop), introduced what he whimsi-

[2] For a comparison of a Hain entry and the same entry in the *Gesamtkatalog,* see the third section of the preceding chapter.

cally called the natural history method of studying early printing. It is true that this method of arrangement — first, by *countries* (in the order in which printing was introduced); then, under each country, by *towns* (in the chronological order of the opening of the first press); then, under towns, by *presses* (in the chronological order of their establishment); and finally, under each press, chronologically by *imprints* — is analogous to classification by family and species.

This system, which is remarkably well adapted to the historical study of early printing and to the identification of types, became definitely established in 1898, when the late Robert Proctor applied it in his *Index to the Early Printed Books in the British Museum . . . with Notes of those in the Bodleian Library.* In the study of types, made possible under this method of arrangement, Proctor identified and placed a large number of unsigned and undated books, this enabling him to make his invaluable contribution to the subject of early printing. The chronological place-entry system has since been almost universally adopted in Great Britain and in America, and in varying instances by bibliographers of other countries. The present *Catalogue of Books Printed in the XVth Century now in the British Museum* (started in 1908 and still in process of publication) is the leading exponent of the 'natural history method' today. By means of this system, plus Proctor's and Haebler's type-systems and the type facsimiles issued by learned societies in various European countries, a large percent of the early printed books from anonymous presses have now been assigned to definite printers, or places and periods. It is excellently suited to the purposes of specialized bibliographies. Even those scholars who believe in the alphabetical author-entry arrangement for general purposes, agree that the 'natural history' or chronological place-entry method is better suited to the study of the history of printing. Fortunately, for the student of incunabula, there is abundance of bibliographical data arranged according to both systems.

Perhaps the best way in which to gain an understanding of the place-entry system is to spend an hour or more browsing in Proctor's *Index*. The fact that Proctor gives short title-entries, not more than a line or two to a work, affords an opportunity to study the arrangement in skeleton form; after which survey, it is a relatively simple matter to find one's way about among the fuller entries of the numerous bibliographies and catalogues using the place-entry method. The British Museum *Catalogue* (1908), for instance, is based upon Proctor's arrangement but it is both an amplification and a critique. That is, its entries and collations are given with abundant detail, followed by whatever annotations may be helpful; its paragraphs regarding the date of each press and its type descriptions (given at the beginning of the section devoted to each press) and its assignments of unsigned or undated books are a critical verification, or if necessary a rectification, of Proctor's assignments. This invaluable catalogue, happily, is in our own tongue and in need of little explanation, for its methods of giving author-entries, anonymous title-entries, collations, etc., are described in Mr. Pollard's *Introduction* to Part I.

It often happened that the year when printing was introduced into various European towns and the year of the first known, dated issue in a given town were not identical. In some instances, contemporary records show that the license for printing was granted some time before the first dated product of the newly established press; and circumstantial evidence may show that one or more undated pieces antedated the first dated issue of the press. The searchlights of scholarly research have long been focussed upon such points as these. It was Robert Proctor who brought together the accumulated knowledge of his time and added to it his own broad scholarship, thus introducing a new era in the knowledge of the history of early printing. Since his *Index* was published, thirty years have passed. Through a group of scholars, often using Proctor's research as a basis for new investigation — Pollard, Haebler, Voulliéme, Collijn, etc. — much information has been gained. And now more recently Dr. Crous and Dr. Husung in the *Gesamtkatalog der Wiegendrucke* and Mr. Scholderer in the *Catalogue* of the British Museum have brought a critical analysis to bear upon the intensive studies of these thirty years.

Monographs and Specialized Bibliographies

The reference works that have been cited are the general bibliographies to which one turns in seeking to identify and collate the books of the fifteenth century, Hain, Copinger, Reichling, Pellechet, the American *Census*, and the *Gesamtkatalog* being among those most frequently used in the alphabetical author-entry group; and Proctor, and the British Museum *Catalogue* being indicative of the 'natural history' or chronological place-entry group.

Another entrance to the subject may be made through Burger's *Printers and Publishers of the XV. Century, with Lists of their Works*, already spoken of as an invaluable part of Copinger's *Supplement*. It is an alphabetical list of printers and publishers, with a chronological list of their imprints under each, followed by their undated publications listed alphabetically by titles. Thus it is especially valuable in bringing together in brief form the chronological record of each press, and helpful in the fact that the varying forms of dating employed in the early printed books are here converted into the dates of our present calendar system. The works in which no printer's name is given — *s. typ. n.*, in Hain or Copinger — are listed under the Latinized place-names, thus affording still another avenue of approach.

In seeking to identify and to study incunabula, it is as if the reference material might be thought of as a wheel. The point that one is seeking to verify becomes the hub; and the data in hand may be moved about the rim, until some portion of it coincides with whatever type of reference material will lead on into the quest. This is fanciful, no doubt. Yet it illustrates the fact that the reference material is sufficiently varied so that, if lack of data prohibits an approach to solution in one way, another may not be wanting.

For instance, Dr. Haebler's *Typenrepertorium der Wiegendrucke* gives the measurements of the types used by each printer, with a graphic representation of the outstanding features of the capital letter *M*, in each case, if the type is gothic; and *qu* if the type is Roman. The *Typenrepertorium* is the most difficult and, at the same time, one of the most helpful, of the bibliographical handbooks. It is a highly technical classification of the types of the fifteenth century, gothic and roman, by means of which either the types used by a given press in a given book may be described, or a fragment of unknown origin may be identified. The classification, in the main, rests upon two factors: the number of millimeters covered by twenty lines of closely set type measured from the base of the bottom line, not counting descenders, up to the base of the twenty-first line; and the outstanding characteristics of the particular type in question. Described in its very broadest terms the work, which comprises several compact volumes of signs and symbols, is divided into two sections. The first relates to the types, etc., of Germany and the countries influenced by early German types or geographically near at hand. The second relates to the types of Italy, the Netherlands, France, Spain, Portugal and England. In both sections, or their subdivisions, the towns are listed alphabetically under countries, and the printers chronologically under the towns according to Proctor's order. Under each printer, the varied symbols and numbers indicate the various types used by the press, and the number of millimeters to the twenty-line measurement (unless otherwise specified), with additional notes and symbols representative of the initials, rubrics, and printer's signs. And also in both sections, or their subdivisions, there are tables dependent upon 101 M-forms if the types are gothic, or upon the *qu* and other outstanding letter forms if the types are roman, by means of which with the aid of the twenty-line measurements, etc., unsigned type may be identified. The fact that many of the specimen sheets of gothic types, appended to each volume of the British Museum *Catalogue,* 1908, have been selected with a view to Dr. Haebler's M-forms affords an excellent illustration of the coöperation and interrelation of one bibliographical work with another.

The so-called Woolley Facsimiles, issued by Mr. George Dunn in 1899–1905, entitled *Photographs of Fifteenth-Century Types;* the publications of the Type Facsimile Society (Oxford, 1900, etc.) ; and of the Gesellschaft für Typenkunde des 15. Jahrhunderts (Leipzig, 1907, etc.), are also invaluable both in identifying types and as a means of learning to recognize the niceties of type design. Two volumes entitled *Printing Types: Their History, Forms and Use* by Mr. Berkeley Updike of the Merrymount Press, discuss the subject of early types from the combined point of view of the connoisseur and of the practical printer.

Reproductions of French provincial types will be found in Thierry-Poux's *Premiers Monuments de l'imprimerie en France au XVe siècle* (Paris, 1890); and of the types of Paris and Lyons in Claudin's *Histoire de l'imprimerie en France* (Paris, 1900, etc.), which was continued in 1926 by M. Seymour de Ricci under the title *Documents sur la typographie et la gravure en France, aux XVe et XVie siècles*. Certain German and Italian types are reproduced in Burger's *Monumenta Germaniae et Italiae Typographica* (Berlin, 1892, etc.); those of the Low Countries in Holtrop's *Monuments typographiques des pays bas* (La Haye, 1857); those of Spain and Portugal in Haebler's *Typographie ibérique* (La Haye, 1901–02); and all of the fifteenth century English types used at home and abroad, in Mr. E. Gordon Duff's *Early English Printing. A Series of Facsimiles* (London, 1896). Printers' marks will be found in Berjeau's *Early Dutch, German, and English Printers' Marks*, London, 1866, and in numerous later works, some of which are listed in the reference sections of this volume. The watermarks found in fifteenth century paper are reproduced, according to subject, in Briquet's *Les Filigranes* (Paris, 1907); and various essays deal with early paper making which was a not uncommon industry when the art of printing was introduced.

Two hundred and eighty-three monographs on separate towns or individual printers are listed in R. A. Peddie's *Fifteenth Century Books* (London, 1913), and the list was intended as a guide rather than as a survey. In the sixteen years since it was published, especially since 1920, many important monographs and bibliographical reference books have been written. The number of monographs upon fifteenth century printing is of surprising magnitude. One often wishes for a general periodical index of the essays and notes, on one phase or another of the subject, that have appeared in the *Zentralblatt für Bibliothekswesen, The Library, Bibliographica,* the *Gutenberg-Festschrift;* and various journals of bibliography which have flourished from time to time. The forthcoming lists from the Wiegendruck-Gesellschaft, two of which have been already issued, promise to be of immense help in this particular. In Reference Section V of the present *Key* to the bibliographical study of incunabula, the list of six hundred titles is highly selective. It comprises perhaps not more than a quarter of the monographs which might be listed. Its titles have been selected, however, as an introduction to the subject and, if used thoughtfully (in following out all the clues afforded in the list and in the texts or footnotes of the works whose titles are included within it), it may be made to lead far into the field of research.

As one becomes familiar with these monographs and the bibliographies of early printing, there are certain names that one learns to associate with particular phases of the subject: Haebler, with Spanish and Portuguese printing, with books produced by German printers outside their native land, and the classification and identification of type; Proctor, with the dating and identifying of anonymously printed books; Steinschneider, Amram, Schwab, Freimann, and Marx, with books in Hebrew type; Proctor, and Scholderer, with early Greek type; Duff, Madan, Steele, and Plomer, with fifteenth century English printing; Voulliéme, with German incunabula; Collijn and Nielsen, with Scandinavian and Danish; Claudin, Thierry-Poux, and Seymour de Ricci, with French incunabula; Fumagalli, with Italian; Campbell, with that of the Netherlands; Schwenke, Zedler, and Seymour de Ricci, with books printed in Mainz; and among the notable names in such a list is that of Mr. Alfred W. Pollard, former Keeper of Printed Books at the British Museum, and the present dean among English-speaking incunabulists.

Mr. Pollard's range of knowledge, like Dr. Haebler's, seems to extend over the entire field of incunabula. His introductions to Parts I–IV of the *Catalogue of Books Printed in the XVth Century now in the British Museum* (1908, etc.), are packed with information on early printing and on bibliographical method. The British Museum *Catalogue* will eventually comprise, no doubt, a dozen volumes or more. Those on early German printing, on German-speaking Switzerland, on Austria-Hungary, and part of those on the products of the Italian presses, have already been issued. It is presumable, and most earnestly to be hoped, that the introductory paragraphs inaugurated by Mr. Pollard and continued by Mr.

Scholderer will be maintained throughout. Meantime, Mr. Pollard's notes in his *Catalogue* of the Annmary Brown Memorial brings together in brief form a series of authoritative statements outlining the skeleton of the history of incunabula. His paragraphs on the printing of each country, town, and printer are thumb-nail histories of the topic to which each section relates.

Mr. Pollard's rather large volume entitled *Fine Books* (1912), contains a pleasantly written history of early printing, and its index makes it possible to put one's finger on a hundred and one important bibliographical facts. In addition, he has published numerous books and essays on numerous aspects of incunabula: *Last Words on the History of the Titlepage; Early Illustrated Books,* etc. A wide variety of notes, reviews, and essays signed with his name, or more often by his initials, " A. W. P.," will be found in *Bibliographica,* and in *The Library* which has become the official organ of the Bibliographical Society. His article on *Bibliography and Bibliology* in the *Encyclopaedia Britannica* should be consulted by any one undertaking bibliographical study.

Special effort has been devoted by various bibliographers to periods and practices in early bookmaking, and to monographic studies by subjects according to those dealt with in the fifteenth century books themselves. Dr. Crous, in the chapter assigned him in Peddie's *Printing: A Short History of the Art,* gives an account of the inter-relation of the early experimental pieces; and in *Die gotischen Schriftarten,* a classification of the Gothic handscripts of the Middle Ages that were taken over by the early printers as a basis for their type designs. Mr. Winship, in his *Gutenberg to Plantin,* traces the history of bookmaking through its first century and a quarter. Dr. Haebler, in his *Handbuch der Inkunabelkunde,* discusses many of the processes in the evolution of the printed book. Miss Lone has taken up the study of 'Firsts.' Schreiber, Heitz, Muther, Pollard, Prince d'Essling, Kristeller, and Lyell, have specialized in the work of the early wood engravers. Schramm, in 1920, began a series of twenty-eight volumes of reproductions of early book illustrations, of which twelve volumes have already seen the light. Bohatta treats of liturgies and of Books of Hours; Choulant, Sudhoff, Osler, and Klebs, of the fifteenth century printed works on medical subjects, anatomy, and pestilence. And so on, indefinitely, through astronomy, music, mathematics, even to an elaborate bibliography of early books on human thirst and one on the notices of fifteenth century rifle matches, we find an infinite number of writers on an infinite number of subjects, each one contributing not only to our knowledge of these early books but to our understanding of the background of modern civilization. In addition to works such as these (which are listed more fully in the Reference Sections of this volume) there are innumerable general histories and surveys of early printing; and finally, the catalogues, the Pierpont Morgan, the Perrins, the Fairfax Murray, the John Rylands, the Walters, and that of the collection of Manuel, King of Portugal. For the titles which they comprise, these catalogues are often rich in bibliographical data. Such in brief are the tools of the incunabulist, a matter of several thousand helpful works of reference, if the full tale were to be told. And, through Dr. George Sarton's *Introduction to the History of Science,* in its present and forthcoming volumes may be traced the factors which influenced the thought and literature of the fifteenth century.

As has been said earlier in the chapter, a comprehensive knowledge of the first fifty years of printing can be gained only through familiarity with its authoritative bibliographies and monographs. The aims of the incunabulist are precision of knowledge and precision of statement. Precision can be achieved only through constant and unending verification. It is more important in studying incunabula to know where to find a fact accurately stated, than it is at first to try to learn the fact itself.

This may sound like heresy. But the student's attitude toward his gradually increasing knowledge should be that it is approximately true. There are too many things to be considered, too many qualifications, to permit an immediate and accurate grasp of all the details — unless, steeped in the subject through the passing decades, after half a century one has become a saturated solution! In all intermediate stages, and perhaps even then, one's data should be verified and re-verified. Memory is treacherous. If it fails to function at the crucial moment, the offender goes on his way ignorant, not innocent, of error. If his mental effort, however, has been con-

centrated upon his reference sources, and memory plays him unexpected tricks, then the very fact that he fails to find what he is
looking for advises him of error. He thus has opportunity to search
elsewhere for the needful points by which to verify his data. And
even then, a single source is not sufficient. Every conceivable source
of verification should be consulted — always.

AMERICANA

1492–1800

CHAPTER I

PRELIMINARY SURVEY OF SOURCES AND METHODS

Just at the end of the fifteenth century, America loomed suddenly and unexpectedly upon the European horizon. Learned men had long suspected that the world might be capable of circumnavigation. No one had imagined, however, the existence of the vast treasure lands lying midway between western Europe and the Orient. The news brought by each returning voyageur spread from town to town. The news-sheets, or brief pamphlets, by means of which the news was spread, were read and re-read by an eager public; and the comparatively few copies which have survived take rank today among the rarest items in the realms of booklore.

Americana, in the restrictive sense of colonial Americana, covers the three centuries which, although preceded by books expounding the theories of early cosmographers, actually began with the various editions of the Columbus *Letter*, in 1493 — in its Latin version, the *Epistola Christofori Colom: cui etas nostra multū debet: de Insulis Indie, super Gangem nuper inuentis.* In scope, colonial Americana comprises all of the source material printed within the three centuries relative to the discovery, exploration and colonial expansion of the two Americas; that is, all of the books written or printed in or about the two Americas from the year 1492 to the beginning of the nineteenth century. The phrase, the beginning of the nineteenth century, is used advisedly. The final date is variable. Bibliographers dealing with books relating to North America frequently close the period of study with the year 1800, at which time the United States had become established as a nation. Early Canadian bibliography, however, is sometimes continued to 1820. Bibliographers treating of Spanish America usually continue their study until 1824, by which time the Spanish colonies had revolted one by one and their independence, threatened by the restoration of monarchy in 1823, was aided by the enunciation of the Monroe Doctrine

later in that year. From that time onward, with the exception of
Canada, the New World was free of the surveillance of the Old.

There are countless angles from which the geographical, economic, political, and literary growth of the colonies may be studied.
Bibliographies dealing with these three centuries of growth and expansion are almost innumerable. Yet there are a few works that
stand out above all others as bibliographical sources for the study
of colonial Americana: for the period of discovery, the works of
Henri Harrisse; for works printed in Mexico from 1539 to 1600,
the *Bibliografía Mexicana* by Garcia Icazbalceta; for works relating to Spanish-American possessions from 1493 to 1824, the remarkable series of bibliographies by José Toribio Medina; for French
Americana, a group of more or less specialized bibliographies in
which the names of Harrisse, Paltsits, Dionne, Gagnon, Atkinson,
and Biggar are eminent; for works published in the area now occupied by the United States, from 1639 to 1820, the *American Bibliography* of Charles Evans which, now completed to the year 1796,
lists its 30,832 titles chronologically by their imprints; and for a
general bibliography, the *Dictionary of Books Relating to America*
by Joseph Sabin, now being continued by Wilberforce Eames. In
addition to the library catalogues that rank as bibliographies, each
of these general works, whatever the field that it covers, is supported
by bibliographical material from these and other pens, devoted to
specialized topics.[1]

The bibliographical treatment and analysis of colonial Americana is, in its earlier years, practically the same as that of incunabula. In fact the principles of bibliographical investigation which
are described above in Incunabula, Chapter II: Identification
and Collation are applicable throughout, excepting that, as the
dates of imprint advance, the books become more and more stand-
ardized in their form and more simple in their make-up, until certain bibliographical factors characteristic of the earliest books, one
by one, drop from sight or cease to be of bibliographical value.

As in the case of incunabula, the collator is advised to assemble
his data directly from the book and then to verify each point of his

---

[1] For a selective list of such titles, see below, Reference Section VII under: Selected Bibliographies and Bibliographical Monographs, Americana, nos. 650–1250.

collation with such bibliographical descriptions of the book as are available. That is, it is suggested that attention be focussed first upon the five factors of preliminary identification: the author and title of the book, its printer, and the place and date of printing. Sabin's *Dictionary* and occasional bibliographies list their titles by author-entries. The majority of the bibliographies and monographs relating to Americana, however, arrange their titles chronologically according to their year of printing. Special attention should therefore be given to finding the date of printing, either in the colophon at the end of the book, or more often in the imprint on the title-page. Having found the five factors of preliminary identification in the book (or whatever regarding them may be there revealed), the collator will doubtless find it helpful to note these factors on a temporary record sheet, and to use this data in the effort to locate the entry for the book in one of the leading bibliographies in which a full entry may appropriately be sought. Then, having found what is apparently the proper entry, he should carefully compare the title-page or title-caption of his book, and the imprint or colophon, word for word and line for line with these sections as they are recorded in the bibliography. If the bibliographical entry still seems to be the correct one for the book, its reference number may be noted tentatively on a record sheet. Attention should then be turned to the collation which, in accord with the method previously suggested, should be built directly from the book itself. Its size should be determined according to its format, that is, according to the folding and gathering of its paper. Its signatures should be analyzed for the number of leaves in each, and the signature equation recorded. Its foliation should be counted, or the pagination if the pages are numbered, and the total so obtained should be used to balance the total obtained from the addition of the groups of leaves recorded in the signature-equation (the latter, of course, being doubled if the former count is of pages instead of leaves). The presence of maps, charts, diagrams, etc., should be noted. Then, in checking this record with the corresponding factors in the bibliography already consulted, the size, signaturing, foliation or pagination, etc., each serve in the dual capacity of identifying the book and of checking one's accuracy in building the collation from the book. Whatever factors fail to agree should be carefully re-collated in the book. If the factors continue to be at variance with those recorded in the bibliography, and the variation is of bibliographical importance, the entry should be abandoned and another entry should be sought, in which case the entire process of identification should be repeated from the beginning. If, however, the variation is of minor import, the bibliographical reference may be assigned with the addition of a qualifying clause. That is, a bibliographical reference number should never be assigned outright, unless the collation of the book and the bibliographical description agree throughout.

The assignment of a reference number does not end the matter. Entries should be sought in other bibliographies if possible; and the record re-collated and verified with each. It is only through this repeated intercollation of the book with its bibliographical descriptions, and if possible also with other copies of the book itself, that one becomes free to notice little things about the book which may prove of importance in its further study.

It is seldom possible in the case of incunabula to bring two copies of a book together for collation. One must rely almost entirely upon the detailed descriptions given in the bibliographies. In the case of Americana, however, it is often possible to place two copies side by side and to collate them page for page. Books which are offered for sale, and which seem ostensibly to be duplicates of those already shelved, may often be kept over night. Intercollation may reveal them to be of different issues, or possibly even of different editions. In this intercollation, the books should first be compared for format, to see if both are folios, or both quartos. Title-pages, or title-captions, should then be compared slowly, word for word. Imprints, or colophons, should be given the same minute scrutiny. Each of the respective pages within the books should be compared by the first word at the top of the page and the last word at the bottom. Leaf or page numbers should be watched, and also signature marks and catchwords. The moment any variation is noticed — such as a change in the first or last word on a page, in the type, or in the appearance of the type page — the intercollation should immediately become more intensive. The suspicious page and several following it should be collated line for line, and often word for word, to find just what it is, bibliographically, that has happened. Often the variations detected are of little consequence, and the mere recording of their existence is sufficient. But if a portion of the text has been reset, the collator should ascertain exactly what portion, or portions, and should note this specifically in his statement regarding each issue.

If the entire book has been reset, each copy may be rated as a separate edition. One must often resort to extreme measures, however, before maintaining a complete resetting of types which are similar in size and design. At intervals, throughout the copies, one may measure the length of a given number of words on a given line, with the corresponding words in the corresponding line. One may even swing a ruler from a corner of the page tangent to the end of a word, and from the opposite corner (on the same edge of the page) tangent to the beginning of the word, to see what letters are cut through in the lines above and below. To indulge in such practices often, might easily result in ' bibliographobia,' but occasionally there are books important enough to warrant this scrutiny. Such matters pertain rather to the advanced stages of the lore of rare books, than to our introductory study of Americana.

The various steps comprised in the general process of identification, verification, and bibliographic study may at first seem complex. The theory underlying the suggested procedure is simple enough. The object is, first of all, to identify the book through its title and imprint; secondly, to collate the book and verify the factors of its collation with corresponding bibliographic descriptions of the book; and thirdly, while making this collation and assigning the respective reference numbers as the result of the verification, to learn all that can be learned regarding its edition, its relation to other editions of the book, its relation to contemporary source material, and its similarity to or variations from other recorded copies or issues.

In deciding how intensively a book should be collated, one must consider its relative age and importance. The points selected for collation, whether they be many or few, should each in itself be minute and exact. In a late imprint, it is generally not necessary

to consider as many factors in the collation as in a book of an earlier
century. The outline given under the heading Collation [2] in Reference Section I of this volume may serve, in general, both as a guide
in the collating of books of varying periods, and as a key to the
various methods of collation which are discussed in further detail
above, in Incunabula: Chapter II, Identification and Collation.
For instance, since it seemed unnecessary to discuss twice within
one volume the value of the chain-lines in paper and of watermarks,
in determining the format, or size, of a book; the methods of recording the signature equation; of noting inserted leaves or leaves that
are lacking, etc., the sections that pertain respectively to Americana
of the sixteenth, seventeenth and eighteenth centuries may be located through this outline of Collation. Similarly the entry, in
Reference Section I of this volume, under Cataloguing: Card
Entries, may afford a suggestion as to how much of the collation
record, for books of these varying centuries, need be put upon the
final catalogue card.

[2] See below Reference Section I, Notes and Definitions. 2. Collation: Tabulated Record.

THE CENTURY OF MARITIME DISCOVERY, 1492–1600

NEWS OF THE FIRST DISCOVERIES

In a survey of the century of maritime discovery, imagination thrills at the daring of Columbus; at the exploits of Vespuccius credited with discovering the Western mainland; of Cabot who discovered North America and cruised along its Atlantic coast; of Nuñez de Balboa who crossed the Isthmus of Panama; of Magellan, the returning of whose shattered fleet proved to the popular mind the roundness of the world; of Cortés, who conquered Mexico; of Pizarro, who added Peru to the Spanish dominion; of Ponce de Leon, Nuñez Cabeza de Vaca, Coronado, and Soto who ventured into Florida or plunged across the wilderness lying to the west; of Cartier, who found the Gulf of St. Lawrence; of Drake, and Frobisher, who explored far northern coasts; and of Drake, again, who explored the coast of California and then sailed on and on toward the setting sun 'round about the whole globe of the earth.' As Europe watched, in the course of the sixteenth century, two great continents grew as if by magic before her eyes. No wonder then that, as the panorama of the New World unfolded, the books describing the deeds of these hardy adventurers were read with avidity and reprinted year by year.

In 1493, there appeared a news-sheet of two leaves, folio, the Barcelona edition of the Columbus *Letter* announcing to the Spanish Court the discovery of the 'islands of the Indies.' Few events have caused a quicker stir. Twelve editions were printed within the year. Three editions in Latin were issued in Rome and one in Italian verse. Three Latin editions appeared in Paris. Antwerp and Basel each produced a Latin version, and Florence two editions of the metrical version in Italian. In 1494, Bergman de Olpe of Basel issued the *Letter* together with a drama by Verardus. The demand for the metrical version in 1495 occasioned two other Florentine editions. Two years later the Spanish original was re-issued at Valladolid and during that year the first German translation appeared at Strassburg. Thus, from the bibliographical study of the unique or rare copies of the Columbus *Letter* which are extant today, it is known that within five years of Columbus' first voyage the report of his discovery had been printed in at least seventeen editions, issued in four languages, in the leading cities of six countries. That the news was read with stirring effect may be judged from the fact that authentic traces of eighty trans-Atlantic crossings within the decade after Columbus' first return were found by Henri Harrisse, bibliographer and historian of the Columbus period, and Harrisse believed these to be only about a quarter of the number of crossings made within those years, many of them secretly made in quest of gold.

Meanwhile, the Nuremberg *Chronicle* of 1493, in the misplaced zeal of local pride, endeavored to claim precedence of discovery for Martin Behaim of Nuremberg in company with Joseph Cam, a Portuguese. Nicolò Syllacio of Pavia, hearing from Spain of Columbus' second voyage, published the news sent him by Guglielmo Coma, a member of the expedition. His *De Insulis Meridiani* formed the basis of knowledge regarding the second voyage until Fernández de Navarrete, in 1825, published an account by Dr. Chanca who also was with Columbus on the expedition. So eager was the Spanish Court to establish its claim to the Western World and to secure profits therefrom, that Ferdinand and Isabella in 1494 are said to have ordered a ship to sail every month and another to return. During that same year, Sebastian Brandt in his *Narrenschiff* poked fun at Ptolemy and Pliny for their misconceptions of the world — in his *Ship of Fools* which, in its numerous editions both authentic and pirated, was destined to become perhaps the most popular book of its time. References to the discovery appeared in other current works and the account of Columbus' first three voyages was printed, in April 1504, in the famous *Libretto*, now known in two copies only, an unauthorized translation of Peter Martyr's unpublished Latin letters. Sabellicus, in the second part of *Enneades* published at Venice in October of that year, contributes the interesting statement that " a great many Spaniards desirous of glory, by permission of the King, fitted out ships at private expense and in the hope of gain explored many places to the south."

During the preceding year, on May 10, 1503, Americus Vespuccius had weighed anchor for his fourth and last voyage to the New World. The account of his third voyage, written prior to that date, ran into at least twenty-four separate editions or variants before 1508, fifteen in Latin, eight in German, and one in Dutch. An Italian version appeared, together with the *Libretto* version of the first three voyages of Columbus, in the *Paesi Nouamente Retrouati* put together by Fracan da Montalboddo and printed at Vicenza, November 3, 1507 — a forerunner of their frequent inclusion in the collections of voyages which, introduced by the *Libretto* and the *Paesi*, became characteristic of the sixteenth century.

Earlier in 1507 there had appeared at Saint Dié, in Lorraine, the first of the editions of Martin Waldseemüller's *Cosmographiae Introdvctio* which inadvertently misnamed two continents. This small book of far-reaching consequence is a quarto of fifty-two unnumbered leaves, comprising two parts: the first, an essay on cosmography designed to accompany the engraved wall map issued simultaneously with it; and the second, an account of the four voyages made by Vespuccius. It is in the first part, on the verso of leaf xv, that Waldseemüller made the suggestion which in translation reads: " But now that these parts have been more extensively examined, and another fourth part has been discovered by Americus Vespuccius (as will be seen in the sequel) I do not see why we should rightly refuse to name it America, namely the land of Amerigen or America, after its discoverer Americus, a man of sagacious mind, since both Europe and Asia took their names from women." The word *America* is printed in the margin of the page and the name appears again in the delineation of the New World, on the great Waldseemüller map. The suggestion, offered by this kindly exponent of the rights of man, was destined to survive. There is no question that his little book was read, for two continents were erroneously baptized on the day that it was issued, April 25, 1507, at Saint Dié far away " among the crags of the Vosges."

Seven early, printed maps, that are more or less interrelated in their cartography and bibliography, show delineations of the new found world: the 'Stevens-John Carter Brown map' of possibly 1505 or 1506, known only in the copy at the latter Library; the unique print of the Contarini map of 1506, at the British Museum; the huge wall map (already spoken of) completed by Martin Waldseemüller in 1507, known only in the copy in Wolfegg Castle, Württemberg; the Ruysch map included in the 1508 edition of Ptolemy's *Geographia;* the Stobnicza map in the edition of Ptolemy printed at Cracow in 1512; and two 'new maps' in the 1513 Ptolemy, both of which are attributed to Waldseemüller. Among these, the undated 'Stevens-John Carter Brown' map and the great wall map of 1507 bear the name *America*.

As one stands in a treasure room of Americana, one is struck by the magnetic power of the earliest pieces: a few maps; hardly a handful of pamphlets by Columbus, Vespuccius, and Waldseemüller; meager in bulk in the midst of hundreds of choice books. Yet, are they not responsible in their diligent spreading of news for a rounding century of adventure, enacted and told by men passionate in their bravery, astounding in their exploits — an unending tale, replete now with the glamour of ancient civilizations and now with the blood and lust of conquest or the rush for gold, told and retold with increasing volume throughout the century, in books which at the time flooded the book markets of the Old World and which today are among the coveted book treasures of the New?

Like a train of satellites throughout the century came the works of the narrators, historians, compilers, cosmographers, and publishers who followed and told of the great adventures across the seas: Peter Martyr, who published accounts of the first discoveries; Varthema, who published the travels of Grijalva in Yucatan; Pigafetta, who accompanied and described the Magellan expedition; Fernández de Oviedo, official Chronicler of the Indies, who faithfully recorded colonial affairs up to the middle of the century; Ramusio; Ortelius; Eden; Hakluyt; Hulsius; De Bry.

Sometimes the leaders themselves wrote the tale of their adventures, as Cortés in his annual *Carta* reported the conquering of Mexico. Sometimes a member of an expedition became its chronicler, as Xerés, secretary to Pizarro, wrote the *Conquista del Perú;* or some one who heard news at court, as when Columbus talked with Peter Martyr, made haste to write and publish the first-hand information thus received. Frequently the narratives were printed, or reprinted, in the compilations of voyages which tended to increase in bulk as the century drew near its end. In studying sixteenth century Americana, therefore, one must become familiar with the names of those who recounted and published the events of each discovery, or who described the new found land. Bibliography is concerned, not with the deeds of men, but with the books that recount and preserve the record of their deeds: for example, the voyages of

COLUMBUS	NARRATED BY, OR PUBLISHED UNDER THE TITLE OF
I. Aug. 3, 1492– Mar. 15, 1493 II. Sept. 25, 1493– June 11, 1496 III. May 30, 1498– Nov. 1500 IV. May 1502– Nov. 7, 1504	I. Columbus, *Epistola* [1493], etc. II. Syllacio, *De insulis meridiani* [1494]. I–III. [Martyr] *Libretto*, 1504. IV. Columbus, *Copia de la lettera*, 1505. I–III. Fracan da Montalboddo, *Paesi*, 1507, etc. I–III. Martyr, *Occeani decas*, 1511, *De nouo Decades*, 1516, 1530, etc.
VESPUCCIUS	
I. May 1497– Oct. 15, 1498–99 II. May 16, 1499– Sept. 8, 1500 III. May 1501– Sept. 1502 IV. May 10, 1503– June 1504	III. Vespuccius, *Mundus Novus* [1502], etc. I–IV. Vespuccius, *Lettera* [1505–6]. I–IV. Waldseemüller, *Cosmographiae*, 1507. III. Fracan da Montalboddo, *Paesi*, 1507, etc. I–IV. *Diss Büchlin*, 1509., etc.

CABOT	NARRATED BY, OR PUBLISHED UNDER THE TITLE OF

I. May 1497–
    July 1497
II. [?June] 1498–
    [before June 1501]
	II. de la Cosa [MS. map] 1500. I–II. Martyr, *De orbe nouo Decades* iii, lib. vi, 1516, 1530, etc. I–II. Ramusio, ed., *Svmmario, f.* 65 [1534], with map. I. Cabot, S. *Retulo del autor* [map with legend relative to the voyage, engraved in or after 1544]. I–II. Ramusio, *Navigationi*, i, *f.* 402b, 1550, etc.; iii, *ff.* 35–36, etc.

Contemporary with the expanding conquest of the New World came accounts of its colonization and descriptions of its climate, natural history, the curious customs of its natives and their wholesale conversion to the Christian faith. For the aggrandizement of the King of Spain and his agents, vast wealth was dug from the mines of Mexico and Peru, riches which the enemies of Spain strove to capture in their transit across the sea. And while Europe rejoiced in the masterpieces of Raphael, Titian, Correggio, and Michelangelo; thrilled to the wonders of the New World; followed or opposed the political doctrines of Machiavelli and Wolsey, the Papal defiance of Henry VIII, the religious questionings of Luther, Erasmus, and Calvin; or witnessed the struggles between the Huguenots of France and the Catholics, the Church, whose power had been challenged at home, sought with the aid of the printing press to spread the Gospel on foreign shores. By the middle of the century, the glamour of the first discoveries in America had passed. Yet during its latter half, the mother countries of Europe heard tales of Soto at the Mississippi, of Frobisher in uncharted northern seas, of Drake sailing round the world, of Ribault and Laudonnière in Florida, of the founding of the Spanish stronghold at St. Augustine, of Raleigh's attempted settlement in Virginia, and, finally, of the destruction of Spain's Armada. More effective than hearsay were the tales read and re-read in the published accounts of these and earlier voyages to the Americas and to the remote corners of the earth.

Collected Narratives of Early Voyages

As far as the dates of occurrence allow, the majority of the narratives of adventure by sea and by land will be found in one or more of the great collections: in the works of Peter Martyr, Ramusio, Eden, Hakluyt, De Bry, and Hulsius.

Peter Martyr (Pietro Martire d'Anghiera), the first historian of America, obtaining direct information from the early navigators, embodied this in his *De Orbe Nouo Decades*. It is known that it was Peter Martyr who wrote the accounts of Columbus's voyages published anonymously and surreptitiously in 1504, in the *Libretto de tutta la Nauigatione de Re de Spagna de le Isole et Terreni nouamente trouati*. The Latin version of the text from which the *Libretto* was translated appeared again as Martyr's first *Decade*, printed at Seville in 1511. Three *Decades* were issued at Alcala in 1516, and the completed series of eight *Decades* was issued in his *De Orbe Nouo* of 1530. This work was partially re-issued in a French translation in 1532, and at Basel in 1533, being frequently re-translated, summarized, or republished. A translation into English by Richard Eden appeared in 1555; in 1577, it was re-issued with alterations under the title *History of Trauayle;* and in 1587, the complete work was printed at Paris under the editorship of Richard Hakluyt, with an excellent map showing British discoveries to within a few years of its publication. It is said that this and the English translations so whetted Britain's appetite for adventure that Peter Martyr's *Decades* are largely responsible for her subsequent dominion of the seas. Martyr's letters, the *Opvs Epistolarū*, issued in 1530, include one written at Barcelona, May 14, 1493, mentioning the return of Columbus, and throughout the compilation provide oftentimes an actual contemporary record of events.

Giovanni Battista Ramusio, whose collections and translations are likewise among the fundamental sources of historical knowledge, was a geographer and historian of note. His *Svmmario,* a compilation from several works, attributed to him and printed in 1534, was intended to have been accompanied by a map (now known in two copies only), giving an excellent delineation of the West Indies and of the eastern coasts of North and South America. His *Delle Navigationi et Viaggi*, first issued at Venice in 1550, appeared in amplified form in 1554, 1563, 1588, 1606, and 1613. It is partially devoted to America and comprises sections relating to Vespuccius' third and fourth voyages and Pigafetta's account of Magellan's circumnavigation of the world, with references in the text to Cabot, Cartier, and Coronado. The second volume, of the series started in 1554, contains nothing of American interest. The third, however, issued in 1556, 1565, and again in 1606 is devoted almost entirely to the Western Hemisphere. Its sections on Columbus, Cabot, and Balboa taken from the writings of Peter Martyr, and a summary of Oviedo's *Historia* are followed by the second, third, and fourth relations of Cortés, the account of Alvar Nuñez Cabeza de Vaca's thrilling exploits in Paraguay, sections relating to Nuño de Guzman, Ulloa, Coronado, Pizarro, Verrazzano, and the first and second relations of Cartier in New France. The frequency with which these huge volumes were reprinted affords some idea of the eagerness with which their tales of adventure were devoured by the reading public of the day.

Richard Hakluyt's narratives entitled *Divers Voyages touching the Discouerie of America,* issued at London in 1582 and properly containing two rare maps, sets forth the British claims based upon the Cabot discoveries, those of France based upon Verrazzano's explorations along the coast from South Carolina to Nova Scotia, and the 'last discouerie' of Florida by Ribault. In 1589 Hakluyt issued *The Principall Navigations, Voiages, and Discoveries of the English Nation.* Its third part describes England's searchings into 'almost all the corners of the vaste and new world of America' — Newfoundland, Virginia, Brazil, Chili, Peru, the Gulf of California, and Nova Albion back of Canada — 'further then euer any Christian hitherto hath pierced,' and a complete copy should contain the rare six leaves printed for insertion after page 643, 'The famous voyage of Sir Francis Drake into the South Sea, and there hence about the whole globe of the earth, begun in the yeere of our Lord, 1577.'

Hakluyt's work was subsequently enlarged into three sumptuous volumes and issued between 1598 ano 1600 under a similar title, *The Principal Navigations, Voiages, Traffiqves and Discoueries of the English Nation.* Corresponding to the third part of the original edition, the third volume relates to America and comprises eighty-one voyages with accompanying documents, letters, etc., ranging from the period of discovery to the voyages of the last decades of the sixteenth century. Here we find ringing tales of achievement, the collective accounts of the Cabots, Verrazzano, Cartier, Ulloa, Coronado, Ribault, Laudonnière, Espejo, Sir John Hawkins, Frobisher, Sir Humphrey Gilbert, Raleigh, the enlarged account of Drake's voyage, and Candish. It is this edition that contains the famous 'Wright-Molyneux map,' which first made Mercator's projection practicable for the use of the mariner, thus providing one of the greatest instruments leading to intercourse between the nations.

The position which is rightfully accorded Richard Hakluyt in the annals of British scholarship is demonstrated in the prodigious series of voyages reprinted from time to time in his honor by the Hakluyt Society. Each of these modern reprints, amounting in their total to not far from two hundred volumes, contains an introduction prepared by a scholar who is oftentimes both a historian and a bibliographer. In seeking to study or to catalogue an original voyage it is well to see if it has been included among the Hakluyt Society reprints, in which case the accompanying introduction will undoubtedly prove helpful to the purpose. The recently published account of *Richard Hakluyt and the English Voyages* by G. B. Parks (1928), gives a valuable list of Hakluyt's own publications, among them not only the collected voyages issued under his name but also the separate accounts of voyages published at his instance. Hakluyt himself died before all the papers in his possession had been printed. These papers, rather unintelligently edited by an Englishman named Samuel Purchas, were issued between 1613 and 1626 under the respective titles *Purchas his Pilgrimage, Hakluytus Posthumus,* and *Purchas his Pilgrimes.* If one would set himself a task of intriguing difficulty, there is opportunity in unravelling the bibliographical tangle which surrounds these later volumes, although doubtless it is a task whose reward would lie largely in the consciousness of work well done.

Another complex problem is presented by the works of Theodor De Bry and his family, a group of engravers and publishers, who issued two series of voyages between the years 1590 and 1634. As one consults these sets of voyages in any of the great collections of Americana, they fill a section of wide shelves with tall, thin, tightly pressed volumes. Frequently they are handsomely bound, for each set has been for years a collector's hobby; always they seem permeated with an air of dignity and aloofness. The New York Public Library, according to its *Bulletin* of May 1904, has over three hundred parts and variants.

It happened that while the later parts of the De Bry series were being issued, the first parts ran out of print. Such was their popularity, owing to interest in the subject of their narratives and to the engraved illustrations of Indian life and of the customs of strange nations, that new parts were struck off and made up with the remnants of the former issue. Because of this and other complicating features, the various De Bry sets present such an intermingling of the old and the new that probably every set in existence is variant from every other. Disregarding the multiplicity of variations, the voyages consist of two main series. These are designated according to their respective sizes, as the *Grands Voyages* which relate entirely to North and South America; and the *Petits Voyages* which relate to Africa and the East Indies but contain sections relating to Henry Hudson, to Linschoten in the north, and to the third and fourth voyages of Vespuccius. Editions were issued in Latin and in German, and beginnings were made upon a French and an English series. Despite heroic efforts on the part of students and collectors of De Bry, from 1742 to 1924, the technical, bibliographical side of the question has not even yet been fully solved.

A much less complicated series and one of greater historical import was started just at the close of the sixteenth century. In 1598, Levinus Hulsius of Ghent, who had settled at Frankfort, brought out the first of a series of twenty-six voyages, his interests being largely

Dutch and English. The work was even more popular than that of De Bry. Some of the narratives among those relating to America appeared in as many as five editions. According to a recent count of the known editions and variants, a complete set is said to comprise sixty-nine volumes. These are in small quarto and many are very rare. The object of the Hulsius series, which was completed in 1663, is said to have been to bring out material not hitherto printed. Hulsius's worthy purpose, and its achievement, form a fitting close to the century of maritime discovery.

CHAPTER III

TWO CENTURIES OF COLONIAL GROWTH, 1500–1700

SOUTH AMERICA AND THE SPANISH COLONIES OF THE NORTH, 1500–1700

The sixteenth century found Spain exploiting her island colonies and seeking a passage to the Orient. Within a few years, both interests became largely eclipsed by the conquests of Mexico and Peru, and the tales of fabulous wealth in the books describing America. The discovery of Mexico — announced in the *Itinerario* of Grijalva, which appeared as an appendix to the Eastern voyages of Varthema — was heralded throughout the Old World, between 1520 and 1522, by nine known news-sheets issued in Spanish, Latin, German, French, and Italian; and Cortes' official account of its conquest fired the imagination of adventure-loving and avaricious men. Of his four *Cartas*, fourteen editions printed between 1522 and 1532 have survived; and the fact that these were issued in Antwerp, Seville, Nuremberg, Cologne, Venice, Paris, Toledo, and Valencia indicates the wide interest in and outside of Spain which the news created. Fernández de Oviedo's description of the strange new continent, better known under its secondary title as the *Sumario de la natural y general Istoria de las Indias,* which appeared in 1526, and his great chronicle, the *Historia general de las Indias,* first issued in 1535, added fuel to Europe's enthusiasm. The accounts of the conquest of Peru — by Xeres, Oviedo, and the dependable Cieza de Leon — brought an invasion of explorers and colonists. In fact, the account published by Ramusio was even accompanied by a map (now known in only two copies), in which is shown the approach to Peru. To many of the stirring men of the age, the call of the New World proved irresistible.

To the publishers also, the accounts of the New World proved irresistible. For instance, *La Istoria de las Indias* of Lopez de

Gomara, based like Oviedo's history upon governmental records, was reissued again and again after its publication in 1552; and a description of these editions, with a discussion of the possible attempt at suppression on the part of the Spanish government, is given in Wagner's bibliography of the *Spanish Southwest*. Only the *Breuissima Relacion* and the tracts giving Las Casas' arraignment of the *Conquistadores* strikes a discordant note in the onsweep of Spain's passionate and cruel aggression, forever attaching thoughts of horror to tales of Spanish conquest. The discoveries of Soto (partially told by Oviedo in 1547 and more fully told a decade later by the anonymous Gentleman of Elvas), even though they brought no news of gold, awoke Spain and her enemies to a knowledge of the great river and the fruitful region lying west of Florida. Meantime, the publication in 1542 of Nuñez Cabeza de Vaca's *Relacion* of his years of wandering from Gulf to Gulf across the base of North America, turned the attention of Spain's hardy explorers to the wilderness north of Mexico. The news of the resulting expeditions in search of treasure was announced by Ramusio, in his third volume, 1556, in which appears the narratives of Fr. Marcos' preliminary search for Cíbola, reputed to be agleam with turquoises and silver; of the elaborate expedition under Coronado, setting out with all the pomp of pageantry in search of the nebulous riches of Quivira; and of Alarcon's auxiliary expedition ' which went by sea to discover the Kingdom of the Seven Cities.' Never was there a more thorough search in a more futile quest. A map, depicting in graphic outline the *Exploration and Settlement of Northern New Spain* (in Bolton's *Spanish Borderlands*, 1921) affords a means of visualizing Spain's great thrust north of Mexico.

With the return of Coronado's haggard band in 1542, the first period of exploration passed. Colonization had begun. New towns were springing up in the mining and agricultural districts of Mexico and Peru, and even in the remote regions of the South. The majestic sweep of conquest, the hazards of guerrilla warfare, and the hardships of pioneer life were each in turn to yield to the elaborate, and in a sense the deadening, system of colonial government organized by the King and the Council of the Indies. The discovery in 1557 of the amalgam of quicksilver, in extracting silver from the ore, resulted in a large-scale development of the mining industry. The exploitation of the labor of the Indians brought wealth to the Viceroys and high officials and to the proprietors, or *encomenderos*, favored by the Crown with grants of land and with allotted numbers of Indian laborers. And the work of conversion went on apace, both among the natives thus bound to servitude, and in the mission centers of the outlying districts. Although the Indians of Mexico and Peru succumbed eventually to the advance of civilization, its imposed Christianity, and the cruel labor in the mines, the Indians of Florida and the Great Plains of North America were of hardier stuff; and from far to the south came Ercilla y Zuñiga's epic poem, *La Araucana*, eulogizing the valor of the Araucanian Indians in maintaining their independence, and painting in brilliant colors the events of the Chilean frontier. By the end of the sixteenth century, the Spanish flag had been planted in vast regions north and south of the Equator. But Spain, crippled by the loss of her Armada, found herself confronted with the problem of holding the territory which her valiant explorers had won. The dozen or more editions of Acosta's *Historia natural y moral de las Indias* issued in the last decade of the century indicate Europe's thirst for accounts of the industrial activities and the government of the Indies, as well as of the customs of the natives, the climate of the New World, and its strange plant and animal life which had been described throughout the century.

If books such as these stirred the peoples of Europe with a desire to colonize, in spite of the tales of hardship which they told, it is small wonder that, reread after the passing of the centuries, they seem freighted with the glamour of romance. Many of the early books were written by the officials sent out by the Court of Spain. Others were the narratives of the leaders of expeditions, or were chronicled by the local heads of the religious orders piously seeking to convert the aborigines. A few were written by men from the ranks, bold soldiers of fortune, seeking what adventures the world might hold. Such a man was Cieza de Leon, who wrote his great history of Peru after seventeen years of service in the army; and the sturdy Bernal Diaz del Castillo who, late in life, described events which he had witnessed in Mexico and Yucatan. Of similar type were the foreign free lances. Girolamo Benzoni from Milan, an impartial traveller through the islands, New Spain and Peru, wrote untouched by the pride of patriotism or by its inherent responsibilities. Hans Stade, a Hessian, described with vivid pen his life in the wilds of eastern Brazil; and Ulrich Schmidel, a Bavarian, who enlisted for service under the Spanish flag, published in Sebastian Franck's *Weltbuch* of 1567 the thrilling account of his twenty years in Paraguay and southern Brazil — for Portugal's right to Brazil, by virtue of the 1494 Treaty of Tordesillas and her Captaincies established east of the Line of Demarcation to the sea, was early contested by the Spaniards and later by the French and Dutch. In the sixteenth century the tang of adventure scented the air, and America offered untold possibilities to the ambitious nations of the world.

Furthermore, Spain was in proselyting mood. The discovery of America, in the year which had ended her seven centuries of conflict with the Mohammedans, gave impetus to her overwhelming zeal in making Christian converts. Added to the crusading spirit was Spain's insatiable desire for power, more dominant in her, perhaps, than in any other nation at that time. During her colonial régime, benevolence and greed seem alternately to have struggled for control, each cause supported by able partisans and each faction favored by the Crown, now in its laws intended for the protection of the natives, now in its demand for increased revenue. Eastbound ships must go laden low with treasure, regardless of what pressure was put upon the natives who worked the mines. Through her fleets of armed merchantmen, Spain must keep complete monopoly of trade — and, trade and treasure being first assured, the Viceroys were left to see that justice should be done to a conquered race. The ships which carried grasping officials, explorers, and soldiers to America, carried also colonists, equipped with the essentials of pioneer life, and missionaries. The latter found themselves often in conflict with the heartless greed of the officials, who connived in the exploitation of the natives for private gain.

The issuing of the *Doctrina Christiana en Lengua Mexicana y Castellana* of 1539 for the instruction and information of the natives — the first book known to have been printed on American soil — was the forerunner of a prolific series of booklets prepared for the religious training of the Indians, and now valued not so much for their pious intent or for their extreme rarity as because of the fact that in their texts, as in the grammars and *Vocabularios* prepared by the missionaries, are preserved the native languages and dialects of Mexico and provinces of South America. Nearly two hundred and fifty linguistic works — sermons, grammars, catechisms and service books printed before the year 1700 — are listed by Viñaza in his *Bibliografia española de Lenguas indigenas de America*. The subject of the books in native languages, printed contemporaneously with the expansion of the mission field, is also treated by Garcia Icazbalceta in his brief *Apuntes* and in his bibliography of Zumárraga, the first Bishop of Mexico who, at his own expense, published the *Doctrina* of 1539. An interesting monograph was written by Pilling on *The Writings of Padre Andres de Olmos in the Mexican Languages*, and the titles of various works of Peruvian and Brazilian linguistics will be found in Fumagalli's *Bibliografia Italiana* in the sixth volume of the *Raccolta*, and also in various scholarly monographs by Dr. Rodolfo R. Schuller relative to Spanish and Portuguese Americana.

The majority of the sixteenth century works on Spanish America, and all of those on Portuguese America, are of European imprint. They may be studied bibliographically through the entries in Sabin's *Dictionary of Books relating to America* and in the catalogues of the John Carter Brown Library and of the Church collection, which is now a part of the Henry E. Huntington Library. For the period up to 1550, Harrisse's *Bibliotheca Americana Vetustissima* is a standard authority, and there are numerous specialized bibliographies and monographs treating of this century, a selection of which is given in the Reference Sections at the end of this volume.

The introduction of printing into Mexico in 1539 and into Lima in 1584 adds about two hundred titles to the bibliography of this early period. The first sixty years of Mexican printing, of books issued largely to meet local needs, are described in Garcia Icazbalceta's *Bibliografia Mexicana del Siglo XVI*. This exemplary bibliography, together with the entries in Medina's *Imprenta en Mexico*, which carries the record through the colonial period, provides opportunity for a thorough study of early Mexicana. This is further aided by the census of *Sixteenth-Century Mexican Imprints* in thirty or more foreign and American libraries, prepared in 1924 by Mr. H. R. Wagner and published during that year in the 'Eames volume.' A survey of the books listed within these reference works reveals the fact that, in addition to the numerous linguistic works and the topics common to all early Spanish American literature, there was in Mexico a marked interest in philosophical and scientific matters. This was due largely no doubt to the influence of the University of Mexico, which may be counted responsible for the first arithmetic printed in the New World, the *Sumario Cōpēdioso* of 1556. The first book of physical science printed in America, the *Phisica Specvlatio* of Fr. Alonso de la Veracruz, which came out the following year, is a work of outstanding importance in the history of American science. In the field of medicine and surgery Bravo's *Opera Medicinalia* of 1570 was followed, in 1578, by the *Svmma y Recopilacion de Chirvgia* of Lopez de Hinojoso (known in only one copy), and in 1579 by a treatise on surgery by Augustin Farfán, sometimes confused with the latter's *Tractado brebē* which appeared in 1592. An account of the medical writers of the sixteenth century is given in Garcia Icazbalceta's *Bibliografia Mexicana,* and a survey of the numerous works of astronomy which were written by the mathematicians of New Spain is briefly given in Dr. H. I. Priestley's recent volume on *The Coming of the White Man;* an account of the contact of colonial bookmen with the Inquisition will be found in the monograph compiled by Fernández del Castillo on *Libros y Libreros del Siglo XVI;* and the question of the books which were permitted to circulate or were smuggled into New Spain is discussed in Dr. Priestley's work just cited and, with regard to South America, in the various works of Dr. Bernard Moses.

It must not be thought that the production of books of a scholarly nature is typical of the first two centuries of Spanish Americana, excepting occasionally in the university centers. The legal restrictions placed by Spain upon all importations into the colonies, the importation of books included; and the rigid censorship of manuscripts for publication, combined to hold the rather prolific output of colonial literature to certain prescribed channels. Historical works reflecting the glory of Spain were acceptable alike to the

Council of the Indies, to the officials of the Inquisition, and to the reading public of Spain and her colonies. Descriptions of the physical geography of the New World were likewise permitted, unless in the eyes of the authorities they divulged facts to the advantage of Spain's jealous and equally avaricious enemies. Mystical works on the saints — Santa Teresa, Santa Rosa de Lima, and Santa Maria de Guadeloupe included; biographies of the Church Fathers and martyred missionaries; grammatical works in the native languages of Mexico, New Mexico, and South America; reports and petitions; funeral sermons lauding local officials; historical poems; laws; legal treatises interpreting the laws of the Indies; and works equally satisfactory to the censors, were produced in increasing volume as the decades passed into the seventeenth century. Chapters on the historical poems written in imitation of *La Araucana,* and on contemporary works relating to the government and laws of the colonies will be found in Dr. Bernard Moses' monograph on *Spanish Colonial Literature in South America* (its appendix giving a list of titles by means of which one may determine whether or not the works of prose and poetry discussed within its pages were among those contemporaneously printed, and hence within the realm of sixteenth and seventeenth century bibliography).

According to Jesuit custom, a *Carta* was submitted annually to the European head of the order, by the local commissary of each American province. These reports, frequently collected annually and printed at Rome or at Naples, Florence, Lyons, or Antwerp as *Litteræ Annuæ,* afford one of the main sources of historical research and they are bibliographically described in the works of Sommervogel and Backer. A hitherto unknown account of the life of Father Francisco de Borja, the third General of the Jesuit order in America, is described in De Puy's brief monograph on *An early Account of the Establishment of the Jesuit Missions in America.* Chronicles such as this — written by the heads of the various mission centers and describing the successes of the Jesuits and Augustinians in Mexico, New Granada, Peru, Paraguay, and Chile; of the Franciscans in Florida and New Mexico; and, late in the seventeenth century, of the Jesuits in Lower California, reveal, in their optimistic tone, the pathetic eagerness with which the friars carried on their efforts to convert the Indians, often in the face of most cruel martyrdom. Devotional works of all sorts were prepared for the instruction of the natives, actuated by the common belief, almost fanatical, that baptism and instruction in the doctrines of the Church brought about a spiritual conversion from paganism, or even from cannibalism, and a mental revolt from barbarism to the European mode of life. The occasional account of an auto-da-fé, from the pen of an eyewitness, gives proof of the frightful power of the Inquisition.

In view of the strict censorship of manuscripts and the difficulties incident to having a book issued in a far distant town, as was frequently the case, the surprisingly large number of contemporary publications bespeaks a determined literary energy on the part of the early colonists and explorers. For instance, Medina's *Biblioteca Hispano-Americana* and *Biblioteca Hispano-Chilena,* comprising Americana of European imprint, relating in the first instance to South America as a whole and in the latter to colonial Chile, list together nearly twenty-three hundred works issued during the two centuries after the discovery of America. His *Imprenta en Mexico* lists seventeen hundred printed in the City of Mexico between the introduction of printing in 1539 and the year 1700 and his *Imprenta en Lima* records seven hundred issued after 1584 in the capital of Peru, 'La Ciudad de los Reyes.' The *Bibliotheca Lusitana*[1] of Barbosa Machado includes works relating to Brazil during the period of the Portuguese 'Captivity,' 1580–1640, when Portugal, broken by the disasters of the Moorish wars, came under Spain's control; and Wagner's *Spanish Southwest,* a bibliography devoted to Spanish interests north and west of Mexico, adds still others to this total of approximately five thousand Spanish Americana printed before 1700 — a total, however, which omits special account of Spanish

---

[1] Barbosa Machado in his *Bibliotheca Lusitana* (in Index III, *Das Patrias*) lists under *America* ninety-one authors whose works were published before 1759; and authors of interest in the study of Americana are included among those listed in the sections entitled *Historia ecclesiastica, Historia secular,* etc. Various early Brazilian titles are given by Garraux, and in the *Catalogo* of the Biblioteca Nacional of Brazil. Winsor, in the eighth volume of his *Narrative and Critical History of America,* gives a note on early Braziliana; quotations from many of these works are given in Southey's *History of Brazil* which, although written a century ago, is, with the exception of its first two or three chapters, a standard authority on Brazil; and many important titles are listed in the bibliography appended to the modern edition of the *Historia* of Pedro de Magalhanes, edited by J. B. Stetson, Jr.

Florida, the island colonies, or of the titles entered in Medina's minor bibliographies treating of this early period. The lethargizing effect of Spain's restrictive policy became more evident as time went on.

Three outstanding works ushered in the seventeenth century: Herrera Tordesillas' *Historia general de los Hechos de los Castellanos;* Garcilasso de la Vega's *Commentarios reales, que tratan del Origen de los Yncas;* and Torquemada's *Monarchia Yndiana* — the first, reviewing the history of Spanish conquest; the second, setting forth an Inca's inherited knowledge of the rich traditions of his race; and the third, conveying in the course of its ponderous pages the news of Vizcaino's discovery of a portion of the coast of Upper California. Vizcaino's explorations along the Pacific coast and Oñate's expedition into Arizona, both a renewal of the quest for a waterway from sea to sea, brought the first century of Spain's colonial expansion to a close. With it passed the thrill of the first discoveries. Yet Spain's thirst for the rehearsal of her glories remained unquenched. The numerous editions of Antonio de Solis's *Historia de la Conquista de Mexico,* twenty-seven or more between 1684 and 1800, indicate that tales of the golden realms were popular in Spain, and also at the hearthsides of her enemies. Apparently picturesque stories were more in vogue than the simple soldier's narrative of the *Historia verdadera* of Bernal Diaz del Castillo, which is credited with only five editions in the long years between 1632 and 1800. Yet it has subsequently been reprinted a dozen times in the interests of later scholarship.

As the pressure of Spain's restrictive policy became more and more felt, the autocratic character of the government of the colonies made essential a clear understanding of Spain's colonial laws. León Pinelo, the first bibliographer of America, is said to have urged the need of an official compilation of all the laws of the Indies, a need which in the earlier century had been met by the 'New Laws' for the protection of the Indians (issued by the Council of the Indies in 1543), by various *Pragmaticas,* and by the *Ordenanças* issued by Mendoza and succeeding Viceroys. A summary of the laws was published by Aguiar y Acuña in 1628. Solorzano Pereira's *Disputationem de Indiarum Jure* of 1629 was followed by a 'Tomum alterum ' in 1639 and, in 1648, by his even greater work, the *Politica Indiana*. The official *Recopilacion de Leyes de los Reynos de las Indias* finally appeared in 1681 in four handsomely printed volumes. And Escalona Aguero's *Gazophilatium Regium Perubicum*, printed at Madrid in 1647 and again in 1675, treating of the function of Royal officials and of matters of judicial and civil law, taxation, and economic affairs, gives a comprehensive picture in its legal aspects of the elaborate political structure built up by the Court of Spain for the government of the colonies.

The interminable wars between the Araucanian Indians and the frontiersmen pushing southward into Chile furnished another important theme for seventeenth century colonial writers, as did the establishment and vicissitudes of the colonies of Florida and New Mexico. The famous chronicle of Friar Alonso de Benavides, describing the annexation of New Mexico, ' espirituales y temporales,' was issued at Madrid by the Royal press in 1630. Within five years, translations appeared in French, Dutch, Latin, and German. In fact, the jealous interest of other European nations in Spain's colonial expansion, territorial and religious, may often be followed bibliographically through the translations and contemporary foreign reprints of works published primarily for the consumption of Spanish readers. For instance, the Las Casas ' Tracts ' (regardless of the ' New Laws ' for the protection of the natives which he had called into being), were reprinted during the seventeenth century in Italian, Dutch, French, English, German, and Latin, in thirty-five editions or more, variously printed at Venice, Amsterdam, Antwerp, Paris, Rouen, Lyon, London, Oppenheim, Heidelberg, and Frankfort. The enemies of Spain and of the Church found good reading in Las Casas' early plea for a cessation of atrocities.

Furthermore, the destruction of the great Armada had given comparative freedom of the seas. Henceforth Spain's hold upon her American colonies and their wealth was somewhat weakened, and foreign publishers continued assiduously to reprint the books describing the riches of Mexico and Peru. Even the account of Espejo's discovery of fifteen provinces and the distant mines of Arizona, disclosed in the 1586 Gerardo issue of Gonzales de Mendoza's *Historia de las Cosas mas notables,* was seized upon by Richard Hakluyt and

immediately reprinted as a ' separate.' French and English translations appeared within a year. In 1609, Hakluyt published an English version of the ' Elvas ' narrative of Soto's expedition, as a bit of
propaganda, under the suggestive title *Virginia richly valued: By the
Description of the maine land of Florida, her next Neighbour.* In
view of Hakluyt's interest, which mirrored that of his time, it is not
surprising that the line of Spanish outposts, originally extending
from South Carolina to West Florida, was presently forced back by
the English into Georgia and eventually, in 1686, down to St. Mary's
River. Meanwhile, foreign pirates alternately attacked Spanish
argosies upon the seas, and smuggled foreign goods to the colonists
under the noses of the Spanish officials.

In the West, the explorations of La Salle aroused the French.
A translation of the ' Elvas ' narrative was issued in Paris in 1686.
A century and a quarter after its publication, this still contained the
fullest description of the basin of the Mississippi, although interest
was further stimulated by the three French editions issued between
1670 and 1710 of Garcillasso de la Vega's *Florida del Ynca* based
upon three other accounts of Soto's expedition. An account of the
French colony attempted by La Salle at the mouth of the Mississippi
and of his death is given in Le Clercq's *Etablissement de la Foy dans
la Nouvelle France,* 1691, occasionally found with the rare map
' compris la Lovisiane Gaspesie et la Nouueau Mexique.' A Spanish
version of the episode is given in the rare work of Sigüenza y Gon-
zora, the *Trofeo de la Jvsticia Española* of the same year; and a
single copy is known of the nine-page report of Spain's counter-
project, in the expedition sent out under Alonso de Leon to frustrate
further attempts by Louis XIV to found a colony (to be called
Louisiana) in the territory west of Florida. Thus the Spaniards of
the North found themselves involved in conflict with both the English and the French, for possession of Florida and the mouth of the
Mississippi. A constant guerrilla warfare was meantime being
waged with the Indians of the plains. In fact, for eighteen years
toward the end of the century the Indians held New Mexico. It
was only through the expeditions of Diego de Vargas — described
in the *Mercurio volante,* 1693, of Sigüenza y Gongora, and in Vetan-
curt's *Chronica,* 1697 — that New Mexico was rewon by the Span-

iards. Similar uprisings by the Indians of the Mexican and Peruvian mines were quelled with appalling consequences to the rebels.

The dangers of foreign invasion and of the expected inroads of the Dutch in Chile in 1643, had occasioned the writing of Aguirre's *Poblacion* which, in the course of its pages, provides posterity with the record of a century of Dutch and English depredations along the South American coast. The account of the beginning of the thirty years' struggle for possession of Brazil is told respectively in Dutch, Spanish, and Portuguese publications of 1624 and 1625. The points of view of the contending nations may be further traced in the numerous contemporary tracts listed in Medina's *Biblioteca Hispano Americana,* in Asher's *Bibliographical . . . Essay on the Dutch Books . . . relating to . . . the Dutch West-India Company and to its Possessions in Brazil,* in the *Catalogo* of the National library of Brazil and in Knuttel's *Catalogus van de Pamfletten-Verzameling berustende in de Koninklijke Bibliotheek.* Contemporary imprints relative to the conflict between the Portuguese and the Dutch, after Portugal was free of Spanish rule, are listed in the two catalogues just cited and in the final volume of Winsor's *Narrative and Critical History of America.* It said that the rarity of the early books relating to Brazil is due to suppression by the authorities, who feared that the enemies of Spain or Portugal might profit by the information which they contained. The return of Brazil to Portugal in 1640, at the moment of the publication of Acuña's *Nvevo Descvbrimiento* describing Spanish explorations in the basin of the Amazon, is thus held responsible for the official suppression of the Madrid edition in 1641. Friar Barba's important work on the method of refining silver by quicksilver is said also to have been suppressed because of information of possible value to Spain's eager rivals. Yet in spite of this precaution, like Acuña's description of the Amazon, it was eventually translated and published in English and French. British publishers sought to stir adventure-loving souls to action by reprinting the accounts of Drake's successes, in various books, the best known of which is *Sir Francis Drake reuiued: Calling vpon this Dull or Effeminate Age to folowe his Noble Steps for Golde and Siluer.* Still another side to the picture of Spain's troubles with her enemies is depicted in the stirring tales of plunder told by Alexander Olivier Exquemelin, a buccaneer, also called John. His narrative, *De Americaensche Zee-Roovers*, was first published in Dutch in 1678, in an edition now of considerable rarity. It was subsequently translated into Spanish, English, French (and possibly into German), and reprinted in numerous editions — the first Spanish edition, 1681, the *Piratas de la America, y luz à la Defensa de las Costas de Indias Occidentales*, being the source of the hair-raising *Bucaniers of America: Or, a true Account of the most remarkable Assaults Committed of late years upon the Coasts of the West-Indies, By the Bucaniers of Jamaica and Tortuga, both English and French. Wherein are contained more especially, the unparallel'd Exploits of Sir Henry Morgan, our English Jamaican Hero who sack'd Puerto Velo, burnt Panama, &c. Written originally in Dutch by John Esquemeling, one of the Bucaniers, who was present at those Tragedies: and thence translated into Spanish.* It seems as if the hands of all Europe stretched out toward the Spanish colonies. The extremely detailed maps of the Spanish Southwest and of South America, designed by Sanson, cartographer to the French King, and published all during the latter half of the seventeenth century, are indicative of the keen interest taken by France in the regions claimed by Spain.

In spite of the efforts of Spain's eager enemies, her argosies continued to sail homeward freighted with the products of the deep mines of Mexico and Peru; and the great fairs for the sale of imported Spanish merchandise were held annually at Vera Cruz and Porto Bello, the licensed ports of entrance for the twin Viceroyalties of Mexico and Peru. It was only at the turning of the century, when a grandson of Louis XIV for a few years occupied the throne of Spain, that commercial restrictions were lessened and the stimulus of foreign influence was permitted to reach the colonies. For an interval, at the beginning of the eighteenth century, French scientists and French merchantmen crossed to South American ports. Before Louis XIV's death in 1715, France had been permitted to establish a colony in Louisiana, as a means — so it was argued — of offsetting the aggressions of the English in the territory west of Florida.

THE NORTHERN COLONIES OF NORTH AMERICA, 1600–1700

The seventeenth century found the French and the British skirting the Atlantic coast of North America, with the Dutch soon to join in the search for the long-desired passage to the Orient. Within five years, Brereton's and Rosier's *Relations* made known to the British public the explorations of Gosnold, Gilbert, and Waymouth along the present New England coast; and the account of Champlain's first voyage to the regions discovered by Cartier, and which he was soon to know so well, appeared in Paris under the title *Des Savvages, ov Voyage de Samvel Champlain, de Brovage, fait en la France Nouuelle, l'an mil six cens trois.* During the sixteenth century, apparently, the auspices had not been favorable for colonization in North America. Laudonnière and Ribault had each failed to gain a footing in Florida, and Roberval in Canada. The colonies attempted by Gilbert and Raleigh had met with lamentable failure. Only the Spaniards, in their stronghold at St. Augustine, held territory by right of continued occupation.

Permanent colonization in the north, however, was soon to follow. Before the first forty years of the century had passed, France, England, Holland, and Sweden had succeeded in planting colonies in North America. Although gold was sought at first, the futility of the quest became self-evident. As the hope of finding a passage to the Orient also vanished, the colonies settled down to the sturdy business of conquering the wilderness and its fierce inhabitants and of fishing along the northern Banks, trading for furs with the Indians and, in the south, raising larger and larger crops of tobacco and corn. Before the end of the century, the Dutch had captured the Swedish colony and the British in turn had absorbed the Dutch. Thus, the British and the French found themselves the sole contestants for the vast area north of the Spanish outposts in Florida and New Mexico, with a combined frontier stretching down the Atlantic coast to Charleston and down the valley of the Mississippi to the Gulf. Three general bibliographical works treat of this conquest of a continent — Sabin's *Dictionary of Books Relating to America*, the John Carter Brown and the Church Collection catalogues; various essays relating to this period are included in Winsor's *Narrative and Critical History of America;* and contemporary imprints are further treated in the innumerable monographs relating bibliographically to one or another of the four seventeenth century colonies, north of the Spanish line.

The first French settlers, the so-called De Monts colony, had arrived in 1604. After a distressing winter at Ste. Croix, the colonists moved to Port Royal (near the present site of Annapolis in Nova Scotia), making there the first permanent settlement in Canada. In the following year, new colonists arrived from France, among them Marc Lescarbot, a lawyer and writer. It is a pleasant picture of Acadian life that Lescarbot gives in his *Histoire de la Novvelle France,* of days spent in planting and in testing the quality of the soil and of evenings passed in the quiet of meditation or of writing. It was under such circumstances that he wrote the first play enacted in North America, *Les Mvses de la Novvelle France,* which appeared with each of the five editions and issues of his *Histoire* that were printed between 1609 and 1618. A description of these editions, together with a translation of the *Histoire de la Novvelle France,* will be found among the publications of The Champlain Society.

The idyllic conditions of Lescarbot's year in the North were destined not to prevail. Champlain's *Voyages . . . ou Iovrnal tres-fidele* recounts the great fight with the Iroquois on Lake Champlain in 1609, an event which the Iroquois neither forgot nor forgave. Champlain, the 'Father of New France,' was a man who was both the chief actor in the midst of stirring events and the narrator of those events. His works, numerous in themselves and frequently reprinted and translated, include not only his accounts of the founding of Quebec and the expansion of the French colony toward the West, but maps based upon actual surveys, descriptions of Indian life and accounts of the natural history of the regions which he explored from northern New England to the Great Lakes. A definitive modern edition of his works will be found in the publications of The Champlain Society, with a critical estimate of his maps in the translator's preface.

The printed story of British colonization in North America begins with Captain John Smith's *Trve Relation of such occurrences and accidents of noate as hath hapned in Virginia,* London, 1608, so

far as known, the first narrative in English to be written in the territory of the British colonies, although Hariot's *Briefe and true Report*
of the preceding century has the distinction of being the first book in
English written about that region. Smith's *Trve Relation* stands
also as the first item in the bibliographical history of colonial Virginia. The first permanent British settlement on the continent had
been made at Jamestown in the preceding year — a fact which, no
doubt, brought mingled feelings of chagrin and pleasure to Sir
Walter Raleigh when news of the eventual success of the colony
reached his prison room in the Tower of London.

It was an age of great commercial companies, as well as of endless warfare in Europe. A third European power, the greatest commercial factor during the first decades of the century, a nation of
sturdy people of the type whom Rembrandt painted, was destined
for a time to control a portion of the Indian trade in pelts and skins.
In 1609, just after the signing of the truce between Spain and the
revolting Netherlands, Henry Hudson, an Englishman employed by
the Dutch East India Company, inadvertently discovered Manhattan and proceeded up the river as far as the present Troy. In a
similarly vain attempt to find a passage to the East, Hudson is
known to have entered Delaware Bay and the Delaware River of
which, so far as known, he was the discoverer. The account of his
explorations appeared in Emanuel van Meteren's *Commentarien
ofte Memorien van den Nederlandtsen Staet* of 1610. His journal,
now lost, is believed to have been the basis of the account published
and subsequently amplified by Joannes de Laet; and the journal
kept by Robert Juet, a member of the expedition, was later published
in *Purchas his Pilgrimes*. In 1615, the year following the explorations of Adriaen Block along the coast north of Manhattan, and of
Hendricks in Delaware River, Jacob Franck took note of their
return to Holland in his *Relationis historicae*, giving to the region
' beyond Virginia and not far from New France ' the name ' Nouam
Hollandiam.' This term, in its more appropriate Dutch form of
' Nieu Nederlant,' appeared on the first printed map of the region,
Blaeu's *Paskaart* of about 1617. During the preceding year, the
publication in London of Smith's *Description of New England*, had
christened for all time the land lying to the north to which Captain

John Smith had been sent to develop the fish and fur trade with the Indians, six years after the failure of the Popham colony on the coast of Maine. The colonization of New England, however, was to come about some years later and in another way.

Through the charter printed both in Dutch and in English in 1621, the newly organized Dutch West India Company was granted trade and colonization monopolies in New Netherland. In the *Briefe Relation of the Discovery of . . . New England,* issued the following year, mention is made of 'certaine Hollanders who had a trade in Hudsons riuer some yeares before that time.' Yet it was not until 1624 — just a century after Verrazzano, in the employ of France, had dipped into New York's outer harbor — that the first family settlement was made along the Hudson River. This was at Fort Orange, the Albany of today; but, although new settlers came to the support of the infant colony, the site was abandoned except as a trading post when the island of Manhattan was purchased two years later from the Indians. A critical analysis of the records of alleged voyages to this region is given in Victor H. Paltsits's monograph on the *Founding of New Amsterdam in 1626.* A detailed and vivid account of events centering around New Amsterdam, and of the seven administrations of the Dutch régime, is given in the first volume of I. N. Phelps Stokes's *Iconography of Manhattan Island.* The second volume of this scholarly work relates to the cartography of the region. The fourth contains a minute chronology of events. And Mr. Paltsits's invaluable *Bibliography,* in the sixth volume of the *Iconography,* affords a key to both original and reference sources. The work of the student is also furthered by the translated excerpts from early sources in Jameson's *Narratives of New Netherland,* and by the analyses in Asher's *Bibliographical and historical Essay on the Dutch Books . . . relating to New Netherland,* although certain of the annotations in the two works last named have now been superseded by the results of later research.

The printed story of New England's colonization begins most fittingly with the *Sermon preached* [by Robert Cushman] *at Plimmoth in Nevv-England, December 9, 1621. In an assemblie of his Maiesties faithfull Subiects, there inhabiting . . . Together vvith a Preface, shewing the state of the Country and Condition of the Sav-*

ages, London, 1622. This was followed, within the year, by the publication of two tracts — *A Briefe Relation of the . . . Plantation of New England,* and the so-called Mourt's *Relation.* The incidents of founding the Plymouth colony are still further set forth in Edward Winslow's little tract entitled *Good News from New England,* London, 1624. It is curious that Winslow should have hit upon the very title employed eleven years before by Alexander Whitaker in his *Good Newes from Virginia.* Both tracts were doubtless written with the desire of drawing colonists and of offsetting the stories of hardship and loss which the first settlers had perforce sent home to their relatives in England. The optimism thus expressed, if perhaps not well founded, became eventually a reality. The beginning of tobacco culture in 1617 was a turning point in the history of Virginia. Five years later, the year of the first Indian massacre, sixty thousand pounds of tobacco are said to have been exported from the colony. The emigration of the Puritans to New England in 1630, bringing the strength of numbers, proved to be a similar turning point in the history of the northern colony. In each instance, by the end of the first decade of their existence, the permanence of Virginia and of New England seemed assured. In 1634, at St. Mary's, Lord Baltimore founded the first settlement on his great land grant in Maryland, his efforts to secure emigration being disclosed to us in the single known copy of *A Declaration of the Lord Baltemore's Plantation in Mary-land,* London, 1633. Before 1640, the eve of the Civil War in England, the early settlements in the present states of New Hampshire and Maine had been strengthened; Connecticut had been founded; Rhode Island, colonized in the name of religious freedom; Harvard College, founded; and Captain John Mason had brought the Pequot War to a bloody finish. Numerous records of these events, sent to the mother country, were printed as small tracts and read by friends and countrymen eagerly waiting for news. The literary value of these writings and the charm which they oftentimes possess are described in Moses Coit Tyler's *History of American Literature, 1607–1765,* with liberal quotations from their texts.

These early tracts, 1608 to 1640, written spontaneously during the quick march of events, are well worth the reading, not only for their historical content but for their style. They mark the beginning of English-American literature and this, it must be remembered, was born under the influence of, and contemporary with, the writings of Ben Jonson, Shakespeare, and Milton. The Elizabethan knack of writing pungent English is evident in the writings of Captain John Smith; of William Strachey, whose *True Repository of the Wrack and Redemption of Sir Thomas Gates, Kt.,* is said to have suggested to Shakespeare the idea of *The Tempest;* of Sandys's translation of Ovid, made among troublesome days in Virginia and described by Professor Tyler as ' the first monument of English poetry, of classical scholarship, and of deliberate literary art, reared on these shores '; of William Bradford's *History of the Plimouth Plantation* (not printed in full until over two hundred years after it was penned); of John Winthrop's *History of New England,* begun as he sailed from England in 1630 and likewise destined to tardy publication; and similarly, although lacking the judicial temper of Winthrop's writings, *The Wonder-working Providence of Zion's Saviour in New England,* 1654, by Edward Johnson, a selectman of Woburn, Massachusetts, who had the skill to ' rough-hew a handful of sentences ' in total oblivion of the bombast and formalism which already in his day were beginning to eliminate literary value from British colonial writings of the latter part of the century. Many of these early pieces are bibliographically described in Sabin's *Dictionary* which, happily for present needs, is being continued. The nineteen volumes which appeared between 1868 and 1891 comprise author-entries from *A* through *Sim,* coming to a pause when the editor found himself confronted by the Smiths. Mr. Wilberforce Eames has now carried the data part way through the Smiths, and the section relating to the works of Captain John Smith is therefore complete and authoritative. The John Carter Brown Library *Catalogue* and the Church *Catalogue* are especially rich in tracts relating to New England and Virginia. The *Check-list or Brief Catalogue of the Library of Henry E. Huntington (English literature to 1640)* affords a survey of this period, as it includes Americana and the titles of the Church Collection books, now the property of that library. A study of the *Maryland colonization tracts, 1632–1646* was contributed by Mr. L. C. Wroth, to the volume of *Essays offered to*

Herbert Putnam; a facsimile of the *Declaration of the Lord Baltemore's Plantation in Mary-land* has just been issued with a bibliographical introduction; and 'A moderate and safe expedient to remove jealousies,' a Maryland tract of 1646, urging that Parliament authorize the removal of Roman Catholics to Maryland, was treated by Mr. L. C. Harper in the 'Eames volume.' Contemporary maps have been treated by Mr. P. Lee Phillips. *The Colonial Mind 1620–1800* is ably discussed by V. L. Parrington, and various bibliographical monographs devoted to subjects treated by colonial writers, will be found below in the selective list of bibliographies, those of this early and virile period among them.

Another series of contemporary works, resonant with the life of the times, is the so-called *Jesuit Relations* recounting the expansion of the French colony in the North and West. After the capture of Quebec by the English and its restoration to the French in 1632, the Jesuits had been given control over the spiritual life of New France. Quebec became the great mission center and from that time until the imperialistic development of New France under Louis XIV toward the end of the century, the expansion of French territory in North America was due largely to the efforts of the missionaries. Undeterred by the loneliness and the perils of the wilderness, the Jesuit Fathers zealously pursued their work far removed from the turmoil occasioned in Europe by the Thirty Years' War, and priests of the Recollect and Sulpician orders joined in the work of gaining Christian converts. To quote from Dr. Thwaites, one of the foremost students of this period, the missionaries 'left the most highly civilized country of their times, to plunge at once into the heart of the American wilderness, and attempt to win to the Christian faith the fiercest savages known to history,' the story making in its totality 'one of the most thrilling chapters in human history.' It is a chapter that, for the most part, can be read and studied exactly as it happened. The early achievements in making converts and in unceasing exploration were described by Gabriel Sagard in *Le grand Voyage dv Pays des Hvrons,* 1632, together with a dictionary in the Huron language, and the disasters of the British invasion in his *Histoire dv Canada* of 1636. From 1632 a report was sent annually to the superior of the Jesuit order in France, and immediately published. The only complete collection of these *Jesuit Relations* known is in the New York Public Library, although notable collections exist in the great libraries of Americana, and various reprints have been issued. The definitive modern edition is the complete reprint in seventy-three volumes, edited by Dr. Reuben G. Thwaites under the title, *The Jesuit Relations and Allied Documents. Travels and Explorations of the Jesuit Missionaries in New France, 1610–1791.* The original texts are given with translations into English and notes; and the critical, bibliographical data compiled by Mr. Victor H.-Paltsits and comprised within these volumes supersedes all other records of the editions and variants. Brief bibliographical accounts of the *Relations* will be found, however, in the bibliographies of Backer, Carayon, and Sommervogel, and entries in Sabin's *Dictionary* under ' Relation de ce qvi s'est passé en la Nouvelle France.' There is no general bibliographical counterpart for French Americana corresponding to Medina's *Biblioteca Hispano-Americana.* Harrisse's *Notes pour servir à l'histoire, à la bibliographie et à la cartographie de la Nouvelle-France* covers the period from 1545 to 1700, together with its supplement by Marcel. Pilling's *Bibliography of the Iroquoian Languages* relates to the general region of New France. And two works, Dionne's *Québec et Nouvelle France. Bibliographie . . . 1534–1906,* and Gagnon's *Essai de Bibliographie Canadienne,* comprise early imprints as well as those of later date.

The activities of the French did not center solely in the conversion of the Indians. Commercial interests had from the beginning urged their traders to push farther and farther into the West. It was due to the pioneer work of the fur traders as well as of the missionaries, in advancing the frontier from year to year, that the French later won the region of the Great Lakes and the basin of the Mississippi. The Dutch colonists likewise carried on a lively fur trade with the Indians. In 1638 Swedish colonists arrived at Delaware Bay, sent out by the New Sweden Company under the leadership of Peter Minuit, formerly Director-General of New Netherland, and financed by both Swedish and Dutch commercial interests. The development of this colony (until the cessation of friendly relations between the Dutch and Swedish nations, the capture of the colony by Peter Stuyvesant in 1655, and its absorption by the English in 1664) is described in detail in Amandus Johnson's *Swedish Settlements on the Delaware, their History and Relation to the Indians, Dutch and English, 1638–1664,* and in the fourth volume of Winsor's *Narrative and Critical History of America.* The latter account, in its critical essay on the sources of information, lists various Dutch works relating to the Swedish colony, and Dr. J. Franklin Jameson's monograph on *Willem Usselinx* records the writings of that highly international figure, who was instrumental in promoting the commercial interests of northern Europe. A chapter on ' Life among the Dutch and Swedes ' is given in Professor H. I. Priestley's recent work on *The Coming of the White Man.* The *Catechismvs Lutheri Lingva Svecico,* the translation of the Lutheran Catechism into the local Indian language by Johan Campanius, contains a copper engraved map of ' Nova Svecia ' probably by Lindeström, a geographer who was among the early settlers of New Sweden.

The first map pertaining solely to New Netherland had appeared in 1630 in Joannes de Laet's *Beschrijvinghe van West Indien.* In that same year, the Dutch West India Company issued the ' Freedoms and Exemptions,' the *Vryheden By de Vergaderinghe,* which has the double distinction of marking the beginning of the patroon system of colonization in New Netherland and of being the first separate publication relating to that colony. British colonists were presently admitted to New Netherland upon taking the oath of allegiance and it is said that within twenty years of its founding eighteen languages were current in New Amsterdam. One of these alien residents, Captain John Underhill, in his *Newes from America,* issued one of the first descriptions in English of the region occupied by the Dutch, and this no doubt played its part in the interest which the British subsequently took in that region. The year 1644, following the outbreak of the Indians in retaliation for the treachery of Director-General Kieft, saw the publication of *Een kort Ontwerp vande Mahakuase Indiaenen* by Johannes Megapolensis. This interesting description of the customs and life of the Mohawks, written by the first Protestant missionary to the Indians, was reprinted in 1651 in the *Beschrijvinghe van Virginia, Nieuw Nederlandt* published by Hartgers, a volume containing what some consider and others deny to be the first known engraving of New Amsterdam. The earliest publication devoted to the internal affairs of the colony, the anonymous *Breeden-Raedt* was issued at Antwerp in 1649. This was followed the next year by the stirring appeal, *Vertoogh van Nieu-Nederland,* by Van der Donck and others who sought redress from the arbitrary acts of Kieft and Stuyvesant. It was during this year, or very soon afterward, that the famous ' Janssonius-Visscher ' map appeared, the so-called ' Prototype Map,' made from actual surveys of the coast from Maine to Chesapeake Bay. In 1655, the year of Van der Donck's death, his *Beschryvinge van Nieuw-Nederlant,* an important work, now a collector's nugget, was issued, and its popularity caused it to be reprinted the next year.

As the relations between the Dutch colonists and their neighbors became more and more unfriendly, boundary disputes arose with the English and the dangers of invasion were averted by the Hartford Treaty of 1650 and England's temporary alliance with Holland in 1654. Rivalry was keen in trading with the Indians. This, and the jealousy of Holland over Sweden's rise to prominence in northern Europe, led to the capture of the Swedish colony on the Delaware. Realizing the precariousness of their position, the Dutch colonists sought to strengthen their numbers by additional laborers from Holland. Jacob Steendam's ' Complaint of New Amsterdam to her Mother ' — the *Klacht van Nieuw-Amsterdam in Nieuw-Nederlandt tot haar Moeder* — was printed in 1659. This quaint handbill bears the first poem known to have been written in the colony. A tract entitled *Korte Verhael,* setting forth the advantages of New Netherland for colonization was issued in 1662, and reissued in 1663 as *Zeekere Vrye-Voorslagen.* Like the majority of Dutch Americana, this is now of excessive rarity, only one copy being known. The frequent breaking of the restrictions of the British Navigation Acts, by both the English and Dutch colonials, finally aroused in the British government a determination to secure control of the coast between New England and Virginia. In 1663, following the great Dutch campaign against the Esopus Indians, there came the publication of a *Remonstrantie* against aggressions of the English and a further remonstrance, *Naeder Klagh-Vertoogh,* was issued the following year. Although the renewal of the privileges of the

Dutch West India Company in January 1664 bespoke a certain optimism, before the summer had gone the colony of New Netherland, and with it the former Swedish colony, had passed into the hands of the British. The *Hollandsche Mercurius* of 1664 records the events of the year; and Dutch Americana relative to the region around New York (all of which imprints are European) ends with the broadside which announced to the people of Holland the terms of colonial surrender, the *Artykelen, van't Overgaen van Nieuw-Nederlandt. Op den 27 Augustij, Oude Stijl, Anno 1664.* The birth of the new era is recorded in Denton's *Brief Description of New York: formerly called New-Netherlands*, London, 1670.

In the British colonies, with the establishment of a printing press at Cambridge (Massachusetts), in 1639, a new factor entered the field of Americana. To the mass of books printed in Europe about the North American colonies must be added those printed in the colonies after 1639, a matter of nearly a thousand titles. Similarly, the list of general bibliographies must include the *American Bibliography* of Mr. Charles Evans, the text of which begins with the first issues of the Cambridge press and proceeds chronologically.[2] The first step in treating a book printed in British America is always to 'search Evans' under the appropriate entry. The preface to the first volume is a charmingly written account of the earliest books printed in North America. In addition to this, specialized bibliographical works relative to British Americana exist almost without number. Some of the more important of these are listed below in the section of Selected Bibliographies, numbers 791–800, 940–1073, and 1241–1284a, and the references contained within these works will lead to other monographs and a complete survey of the field.

The titles of the first broadside and of the first book from the

---

[2] The ten volumes already issued bring the record into the year 1796 and comprise a total of 30,832 titles. Appended to each volume are three indexes. These include an author index with a brief title-list beneath each entry; a classified subject index (invaluable in indicating in a general way the trend of thought throughout a given period); and a list of printers and publishers arranged chronologically by towns, according to the date of the first imprint in each. The fact that addresses are given with dates, in instances when the printers were at a stated location, is often helpful in assigning a year to an undated work in which the printer's address appears. For instance, a supplied date is ordinarily a multiple of five: that is, if the printer were at a certain address from 1683 to 1688, an undated tract on which that address appears would normally be assigned to [1685?].

Cambridge press, ' The Freeman's Oath ' and *The VVhole Booke of Psalmes* (commonly called the Bay Psalm Book), seem curiously enough to have struck the keynotes of British American colonial life during its first century. The ideal of liberty set forth in ' *The Freeman's Oath* ' was destined not only to endure throughout the years of colonization, but to strengthen until eventually independence had been won. The religious absorption suggested by the Bay Psalm Book grew in intensity until it culminated in the witchcraft trials at the end of the seventeenth century, after which time various broadening interests gradually claimed the colonists' attention.

Doubtless peace reigned in the hearts of many men, but during the early years of British colonization, peace was not the subject of which men wrote. From 1640 to 1700, colonial literature (both European and local imprints) dealt largely with the trials of Indian warfare, and with the controversies waged by dominant religious sects, Congregationalists, Baptists, Quakers, and Catholics, against the Anglican Church and each and every form of divergent faith. A considerable number of peace-abiding almanacs were published, to be sure — and laws, local histories in the making, occasional poems and elegies of 'dismal excellence' — but religious dogma, boundary disputes, and governmental questions involved in charters and patents were the topics of more absorbing interest. There was, however, one fine exception in the midst of unending controversy, the altruistic intent expressed in the translation of sermons, church service books and primers into the Indian languages. John Eliot, Roger Williams, and Thomas Shepard stood foremost in the small group of religious leaders who made every effort to convert and to make friends with their Indian neighbors. Roger Williams's *Key into the Language of America,* so he states in its preface, was written on shipboard on his way to England ' as a private helpe to my owne memory, that I might not by my present absence [for the purpose of securing from Parliament a Rhode Island charter] lightly lose what I had so dearly bought in some few yeares hardship, and charges among the barbarians.' Eliot's translation of the New and Old Testaments was an undertaking little short of the heroic. Pilling's *Bibliography of the Algonquian Languages* treats of this period. Mr. Eames's bibliography, which appeared in Pilling, has also been printed as a separate. An essay on the *Eliot Indian tracts* was contributed to the 'Eames volume' by George Parker Winship. And De Puy's *Bibliography of the English Colonial Treaties* with the American Indians, begins with the 'Articles of Peace' of 1677.

Although far removed from the civil and religious affairs of England, denominational interests played a large part, particularly in Maryland, in the attitude of the colonists during the vicissitudes of Cromwell's rule, the Restoration and the Revolution of the Whigs. With the establishing of constitutional monarchy in England, reorganization of the colonial governments gradually followed. Trade was given minute supervision. Committees, oftentimes offensive to the colonial governors, were appointed by the Privy Council and officials; and from time to time, Navigation Acts were passed as a means of strengthening Britain's commercial position, without particular regard to the well-being of the colonies. Following the capture of New Amsterdam, the province of New Jersey or Nova Caesaria was granted to Carteret and Berkeley. Emigrants arrived in 1665. Meantime local colonists had moved unbidden into East New Jersey which became, in some respects, a replica of dogma-bound New England. 'Religion stands on Tip-toe in Our Land' wrote a settler of New Jersey in *An Abstract or Abbreviation of some Few of the Many . . . Testimonys from the Inhabitants,* London, 1681. Colonization tracts such as this were the order of the day. When Charleston was founded in 1670 by proprietaries from Barbadoes and England, its advantages had already been set forth by a previous and less fortunate colony, in *A Brief Description of the Province of Carolina on the Coasts of Floreda. And more perticularly of a New-Plantation begun by the English at Cape-Feare . . . the 29th of May, 1664. Wherein is set forth the Healthfulness of the Air . . . Together with a most accurate Map of the whole Province.* The attractions of Maryland were also advertised in the tract entitled the *Character of the Province of Mary-land, wherein is described . . . I. The Scituation, and plenty of the Province.*

In 1677, British colonists arrived at West New Jersey [Delaware], under a charter of Concessions and Agreements said to be 'the broadest, sanest, and most equitable charter draughted for any body of colonists up to this time' of varied and inadequate forms of

British colonial administration. It was upon this that William Penn based his *Frame of Government* in 1682, on the eve of the founding of the Quaker colony of Pennsylvania. Meantime, the arbitrary rule of Governor Berkeley of Virginia led to the famous Bacon Rebellion of 1676; and, a decade later, Andros's attempt to establish an aristocratic form of government in Massachusetts occasioned a fierce though bloodless rebellion, the viewpoint of the colonists being expressed in Increase Mather's *Narrative of the Miseries of New-England, by reason of an Arbitrary Government Erected there,* 1688 or 1689. The growing demand of the various British colonists throughout the seventeenth century for representation in their government, reached a crisis at this time, and these radical principles reappeared intensified in the pre-Revolutionary discussions of later days. It was a period of petty stress and storm, of heated controversies, and sonorous phrases taken seriously to heart, during the century when men's concerns, both civil and religious, were practically dominated by the pulpit — a period which reached its liveliest exponent in the person of Cotton Mather. The century ended true to form. The witchcraft trials in Massachusetts and Connecticut, like the far swing of the pendulum, marked the end of the period characterized by over-religious zeal. And ceaseless boundary disputes, jealousy, retaliation for Indian raids, and the general hostility between France and England, precipitated King William's War, in which Acadia twice changed hands and Schenectady and Haverhill were razed.

The development of New France, which was partially responsible for the jealousy of the English, had begun twenty-five years or so before the war. Although the daring *coureurs de bois* under the agency of trading companies, and the Recollect, the Jesuit, and the Sulpician missionaries had continually pushed into the wilderness, the years following 1664 are counted as the great period of French exploration in the West. The imperialistic policy of expansion in New France began with the appointment of Colbert as Controller-General of French finance. While France was at the zenith of her power, Louis XIV resolved upon a policy of colonial paternalism. Bibliographically, the publication of Monsieur Denys's *Description geographique et historique des Costes de l'Ameriqve Septen-*

trionale in 1672, five years after a periodic return of Acadia by the English, marks the end of the old régime. The powerful order of the Jesuits sought to obviate certain evils by securing the prohibition of trade with the Indians; on the other hand Frontenac, the great provincial governor, favored territorial expansion through increased trade; and these two parties, each with supporting factions at Court, naturally occasioned a somewhat vacillating colonial policy. Yet both parties favored expansion and both interests came together in the expedition of Marquette and Joliet, sent out in 1674 into the great Northwest. The record of the expedition, as told by Father Marquette himself, was included in 1681 in Thevenot's *Recueil de Voyages,* and separately issued that same year under the title *Voyage et Découverte de quelques Pays et Nations . . . par le P. Marquette et Sr. Joliet.* The death of the beloved Father in 1675, brought to an end not only his explorations, but a missionary career as successful in its relations with the Indian converts as the missions far to the south in Lower California and Paraguay.

Frontenac, bent on territorial expansion and the aggrandizement of France, then sent La Salle into the West in 1679, accompanied by Tonti and Joutel. In 1682, after infinite adventure and misadventure (described in Alvord's *Illinois Country, 1673–1818,* and with a wealth of detail in the works of Francis Parkman), the party reached the mouth of the Mississippi, taking formal possession of the vast Mississippi Valley in the name of France. Frontenac's temporary recall, however, withdrew the necessary support for La Salle's elaborate plans for organizing the fur trade and colonizing the West. La Salle hurried to France and it is said that, to his surprise, he found himself a famous man. Father Hennepin, a Recollect priest who had started with the expedition but had become separated from it, had worked his way back to civilization and had already published his *Description de la Louisiane, nouvellement decouverte.* Another account of La Salle and his discoveries was published by Father LeClercq in 1691 in his *Etablissement de la Foy dans la Nouvelle France. . . . Avec une Relation exacte des Expeditions . . . entrepris pour la Découverte du Fleuve Mississipi,* with a map, known in a few copies only, 'compris La Lovisiane Gaspesie et le Nouueau Mexique.' The fate of La Salle's little colony, which had inadvertently landed on the coast of Texas and of La Salle's death by treachery, as he again sought the mouth of the Mississippi, was learned by the Spanish expedition sent out in 1689 for its destruction and described in Sigüenza y Gongora's *Trofeo de la Jvsticia Española* of 1691. Tonti's account of the *Dernieres Decouvertes* appeared in 1697, and Joutel's *Journal Historique du dernier Voyage que feu M. de la Sale* in 1713. The complete records of the first and second expeditions, kept by La Salle and Joutel, were not published, however, until 1879 when the manuscripts were printed by Pierre Margry in his *Découvertes et Établissements des Français.* The authenticity of Margry's sources was questioned at the time, but the records published by him have always to be taken into consideration by students of the period.

More than a decade after La Salle's assassination, Hennepin published a *Nouvelle Decouverte,* Utrecht, 1697, and a *Nouveau Voyage,* Utrecht, 1698. A combination of the two appeared in English in *A new Discovery of a vast Country in America,* printed in London in 1698, thus apprising the English of the broad prairies and the deep forests back of the British colonies on the Atlantic coast. The veracity of Hennepin's assertions was attacked nearly half a century later by the able historian Charlevoix. A careful estimate of Hennepin's statements is given by Dr. Reuben G. Thwaites in his 1903 reprint of Hennepin's *New Discovery* and in this work [also separately printed], Mr. Victor H. Paltsits's essay on ' Bibliographical Data ' gives a critical survey of Hennepin's titles and the works relating to them. An important bio-bibliographical sketch of Hennepin was issued by Father Goyens in 1925. Two works by the French bibliographer Gravier, issued in 1871 and 1872 respectively, also treat of the discovery and exploration of the Mississippi.

In the year in which the first of the so-called French and Indian Wars between the French and British colonials and their Indian allies came to an end, the publication of Father LeClercq's *Nouvelle Relation de la Gaspesie, qui contient les Moeurs et la Religion des Sauvages Gaspesiens* turned the attention of the reading public once more to the region above Acadia southeast of the St. Lawrence, depicting the home life and customs of the Indians with a power which still makes one feel its reality. Six years later, the century of European wars, with its parallel series of minor conflicts in the colonies, came to a close with the Treaty of Ryswick. Acadia, temporarily in the hands of the British, was once again returned to the French. In the Middle West, peace was made in 1701 with the Iroquois, thus leaving the French in control of the upper Mississippi and averting the dreaded alliance of the British, the Iroquois, and the Indians farther west. In the South, the erection of the Spanish fort at Pensacola in 1698, as the result of the consternation aroused in Mexico over La Salle's attempted settlement near the mouth of the Mississippi, was answered by the erection of a French fort at Biloxi. The moment was at hand, however, for the alliance of French and Spanish interests so greatly feared by British statesmen. With the accession of a grandson of Louis XIV to the throne of Spain in 1701, the great French monarch's dream of a Louisiana was destined to come true.

CHAPTER IV

LATER AMERICANA AND THE REVOLUTIONARY PERIODS

NORTH AMERICA, 1700–1763–1800

1. *British and French Colonies, 1700–1763*

The fifty years following 1700 are frequently passed over so quickly in general historical narrative that the period has been called the 'forgotten half century' of American history. Up to the Seven Years' War, to be sure, events were neither so striking as those which were to follow, nor so romantic as those of the first days of discovery and exploration. Yet there were certain great movements astir which have occasioned careful historical and bibliographical study.

The eighteenth century found the French on the eve of the strategic development of the Illinois country and Louisiana. By the Treaty of Utrecht, following Queen Anne's War — the American phase of the War of the Spanish Succession 1701–1713 — Acadia, Hudson's Bay and Newfoundland were lost to the French. France and Spain became separated, and Great Britain stood at the beginning of her naval and colonial supremacy. France immediately turned her attention to the development of the West, for the dual purpose of securing Spanish trade and access to the mines, and of offsetting the danger of a British thrust beyond the Alleghanies. By 1720, John Law had developed (and pricked) the 'Mississippi Bubble' — the gigantic speculation which for several years drained the money markets of Europe and brought five thousand settlers of various nationalities to the valleys of the Middle West. Scrupulous care was taken that the peace made with the Iroquois at the turning of the century should not be broken. The great Natchez massacre, however, occurred in 1729 and guerrilla warfare, instigated more or less by the English colonists, raged intermittently with other tribes. While the mother countries participated in the War of the Austrian

Succession (1740–1748), their rival colonies joined in King George's War, which was fought for the most part in the northern reaches. By 1750, French traders had penetrated New Mexico to Santa Fé and trading posts had been established far beyond Lake Superior.

In the British colonies, the Anglican Church gained in power as the hold of Puritanism on church and state, in certain regions, gradually relaxed. New England, suffering from Indian raids instigated by the French in Canada, maintained that efforts to take Quebec must be renewed; and from the Middle and Southern Colonies settlers pushed over into the territory beyond the Alleghany Mountains. Following the repulse of the Spanish attack upon Charleston and the Indian raids of the first part of the century, the South settled to agricultural life, and the increased importation of negro slaves, and the North in general to trading, fishing, and ship-building. Immigrating Germans arrived in Pennsylvania and New Jersey; and in 1732 Georgia was founded as a buffer colony against the Spaniards, and as a philanthropic enterprise. As in the earlier century, various colonies became involved in boundary disputes. Endless discussions arose regarding charters and forms of government, and the irritating restrictions imposed by England upon commerce and colonial currency.

By 1750, boundary questions had been largely settled; and New Hampshire had separated from Massachusetts. The results of Peter Zenger's trial for libel in 1735 had won the freedom of the press for the British American colonies — more than fifty years before the same privilege was secured for the press of the mother country. In 1756, midway in the course of the Seven Years' War, William Pitt came into office, with a full realization of the importance of securing Canada. In 1759, Quebec fell before the English attack; and in 1763, to quote from Alvord's *Illinois Country,* 'France ceded to Great Britain all its possessions on the continent east of the Mississippi, with the exception of a small strip at the mouth of the river where New Orleans was situated; it retained certain islands on the Canadian coast and in the West Indies, and the fishery rights near Newfoundland and Nova Scotia. In compensation for the loss of Florida to Great Britain, the French territory west of the Mississippi, together with the eastern strip at its mouth, was ceded to Spain

by separate agreement.' It is a curious fact that the year in which
Great Britain acquired a second empire in America should rank,
bibliographically, as the beginning of the controversial period in the
course of which, through her ill-advised colonial policy, she was
destined to lose her original holding.

Sabin's *Dictionary of Books relating to America,* the John Carter Brown Library *Catalogue* and the Church *Catalogue* are general
sources for American bibliography of the eighteenth century.
Dionne's and Gagnon's works include the books of this important
period in French colonial history. Mr. Lawrence C. Wroth and
Miss Gertrude L. Annan have compiled a list of the *Acts of French
royal Administration concerning Canada . . . and Louisiana* from
1540 to 1791, whose publication began in the *Bulletin* of the New
York Public Library in November 1929. This is based upon Mr.
Worthington C. Ford's *French royal edicts, etc., on America* which
appeared in the *Proceedings* of the Massachusetts Historical Society
in April, 1927. In 1901, Doughty and Middleton issued a *Bibliography of the Siege of Quebec,* with a list of plans of Quebec by P.
Lee Phillips. Backer, Carayon, Sommervogel, and Thwaites's
Jesuit Relations [with bibliographical data by V. H. Paltsits] record
the works describing Jesuit missions and explorations in the West.
An exhaustive bibliography of the writings of Baron Lahontan is
given by Mr. Paltsits in the Thwaites reprint of Lahontan's works,
and is also separately published. Chailley-Bert's *Compagnies de
colonisation sous l'ancien régime* contains a chronological record
of French colonization companies from 1599 until after the loss of
the North American colonies. The regions occupied by the French,
British and Spanish colonies in 1715, and the territories disputed by
them, are graphically shown in a map of *Eastern North America
1715,* in Professor Evarts B. Greene's *Provincial America.*

Evans's *American Bibliography* of British colonial and later imprints has now progressed beyond the Revolution and the Constitutional period, into 1796. The Newberry Library has issued a list
of three hundred or more titles of original editions and reprints
of the narratives of Indian captivities, largely of the eighteenth century. Pilling's extensive works relating to the American Indians,
the Algonquians, Iroquois, Muskhogean, etc., cover Indian relations

with the English and French colonials. De Puy's *Bibliography of the English Colonial Treaties with the American Indians* gives a synopsis of each treaty. Dexter's *Congregationalism* lists many of the works of controversial New England. Dr. A. S. W. Rosenbach has recently issued an American Jewish bibliography; and Joseph Smith's two Quaker bibliographies include works relative to Quakerism and anti-Quakerism in America. Tyler's history of American literature, 1607–1765, discusses British colonial writings and Professor Parrington's *Colonial Mind,* although not a bibliographical work, provides an excellent background for the study of colonial literature. Sacred music and its publication are discussed by F. J. Metcalf; the music of the Ephrata Cloister, by J. F. Sachse; and secular music, by O. G. Sonneck. Prize causes tried before the Commissioners of Appeals of the Privy council, 1736–1758, have been listed by Paul Leicester Ford.

The southern frontier from 1670 to 1732, and the promotion literature of Georgia have been ably discussed both historically and bibliographically by Professor V. W. Crane. New York from 1664 to 1763 has been covered in the first volume of Mr. I. N. Phelps Stokes's *Iconography of Manhattan Island,* with bibliographical data by Mr. Paltsits in the final volume; and tracts relating to North and South Carolina have been treated by W. K. Boyd and E. L. Whitney respectively. Virginia material, listed by periods, appeared in the *Bulletin* of the New York Public Library, February–April, 1907. Numerous monographs listing the products of the various presses, thus recording colonial history and interests year by year, are mentioned below in the note on the establishment of printing in the American colonies. The catalogue of the Charlemagne Tower Collection of American Colonial Laws, and compilations by Mr. C. F. D. Belden and Miss Adelaide R. Hasse, treat of colonial printed documents. MacDonald's *Documentary Source Book,* although not bibliographical, is an essential handbook in studying British colonial government. The laws of Connecticut, Massachusetts, New York, Pennsylvania, Rhode Island, and Virginia have been made the subjects of bibliographical monographs or reprints by a variety of authors. Similarly, colonial almanacs have been listed in numerous regional monographs. Mr. Andrew McFarland

Davis has made an exhaustive study of *Colonial Currency Reprints,
1682–1751,* including a chronological list of pamphlets checked for
the location of copies. Dramas published between 1714 and 1830,
and American poetry from 1650 to 1820 have been listed by Mr.
Oscar Wegelin. And juvenile literature — *The History of the Holy
Jesus,* New England catechisms, *The New-England Primer,* and *The
Royal Primer* — has been treated by Mr. Eames and by other bibliographers.

One of the most essential and fruitful sources in the study of this
period is provided by the contemporary newspapers. Of the bibliographies of newspapers, the definitive work is Mr. Clarence S.
Brigham's *Bibliography of American Newspapers, 1690–1820.* His
list, which approximates nine thousand titles, appeared between
1913 and 1927 in the *Proceedings* of the American Antiquarian Society, and its publication as a work in two volumes is expected in the
near future. Mr. J. v. N. Ingram in 1912 issued a check list of American newspapers in the Library of Congress; a 'Want-list' appeared
in 1909. Mr. George Parker Winship has written on eighteenth
century newspapers of Newport; Mr. C. C. Crittenden, North Carolina newspapers before 1790; Mr. Stokes, early New York newspapers from 1725 to 1811; and Mr. William Beer in 1922 prepared
for the American Antiquarian Society a *Checklist of American Periodicals, 1741–1800.* Nelson's *Notes toward a History of the American Newspaper* appeared in 1918.

In the British colonies of the eighteenth century, the products
of the colonial press, even more than contemporary Americana of
European imprint, reflect the life and incidents of the passing
decades. In literary value, few have the force of the tracts written
before 1640. On the other hand, comparatively few after the death of
Cotton Mather, in 1728, have the naïve intensity of the controversial
tracts written between 1640 and 1700. After the latter date, although controversies continued on the relation of church and state
and the payment of taxes for church support by communicants of
another faith, Puritanism ceased to have a fanatic hold upon its
supporters. The Church of England sought to gain in power through
the Society for the Propagation of the Gospel in Foreign Parts.
Minor controversies centered around Catholicism, Methodism, the

Moravians, the Ephrata Community, the Quakers, and such strange doctrines as those set up by the Rogerenes and Antinomians. By March 1764, seven colleges had been founded — Harvard, William and Mary, Yale, the present University of Pennsylvania, Princeton, King's College (Columbia), and Brown, the last named being incorporated as 'the College or University in the English colony of Rhode Island and Providence Plantations.'

A survey of the output of the colonial presses shows that this was a period in which the colonists were settling down to established law and order, and to the discussion (already mentioned) of charter rights and commercial regulations. There was a noticeable outburst of local histories — not now of history in the making and the events of the hour as in earlier days, but of local history in retrospect. The laws of the colonies were, as a rule, regularly published, as were proclamations, charters, and acts of Assembly. As interest in governmental questions and in politics increased, there were not infrequent criticisms of the home government and of its colonial governors and customs officials. The colonies were still isolated and individual. Yet, as one surveys the products of their many presses, one finds a certain continuity of thought, a growth of self-dependence which were no doubt among the first steps toward independence.

2. The Revolution and the United States, 1763–1800

The books and pamphlets of the American Revolution deal more with principles and convictions than with military affairs. As in any war troops fought and bled, but the real battles of the American Revolution were fought in the minds of stern, upstanding men who in the decade prior to the Declaration of Independence, and simultaneous with it, turned one by one from loyalty and allegiance to avowed rebellion. Upon his own bookshelves, the collector of Americana may witness the battles of mind against mind, as they were waged in hundreds of pamphlets — an overwhelming mass of controversy, fired by the eloquence of conviction which was ultimately to burn into the very hearts of men.

The expenses of the Seven Years' War (of which the so-called

French and Indian War was the American phase) left Great
Britain involved in debt. The accession of Canada necessitated the
maintenance of a military force in America. Directly after Town-
shend's appointment as first lord of trade, it was announced that
expenses would be met by the taxation of the colonies and a new
policy was inaugurated. The Sugar Act of 1764 was followed in
1765 by the Stamp Act, levying a series of taxes upon all legal documents, almanacs, and a wide variety of papers; and by the Quarter-
ing Act for the housing of the standing army. For ten years and
more, the colonies were subjected to a series of arbitrary acts at the
hands of the British foreign ministry. Concern gave way to anxiety.
Anxiety finally gave way to alarm. The repeal of the Stamp Act
marked only a cessation of the threatening policy. New York's refusal to quarter troops was followed by an act suspending the New
York Assembly. The Boston Massacre of 1770 caused wide appre-
hension. The Boston 'Tea Party,' in which tea was thrown from
the ships in Boston harbor as a demonstration against the tax on
imports, resulted in the official closing of the port, the removal of
the Massachusetts seat of government to Salem, and the arrival of
General Gage with troops and power to enforce the retaliatory acts
of Parliament. It is small wonder that the thirteen colonies,
hitherto acting independently of one another, should have resolved
to come together. In October, 1774, the First Continental Congress drew up a declaration of rights calling for the principles of
fair play in matters of taxation, representation, and judicial procedure.

Meanwhile, during all these years, a veritable war of pamphlets
had been waged between conflicting parties. A considerable faction
in England supported the rights of the colonists; and the colonists
who later participated in the Revolution at first did their utmost to
bring the home government to reason. Under cover of pseudonyms,
men spoke their minds freely. Every side of every question was
worn threadbare by discussion. The output of the colonial press
was astonishing. Evans lists over fifty-three hundred works printed
in the colonies and this number takes no account of the pamphlets
written and printed abroad, nor of the mass of colonial writings
reprinted there. In England, a group of forceful orators and writers

such as Burke, Fox, Pitt, Pownall, Bryan Edwards, James Callander, maintained sympathy with the stand taken by the colonists; whereas Lord Grenville, supported by Jenyns, Hutchinson, and others equally blind to inevitable consequences, remained firm in upholding the policy of Parliament. In America certain of the controversialists — Samuel Seabury, Joseph Galloway, Daniel Leonard, Isaac Wilkins, Jonathan Odell, Daniel Dulany, and John Joachim Zubly among them — at first opposed Great Britain's policy; yet, when it came to the moment of final decision, they remained true in their allegiance to the Crown. Henceforth, they took their stand as Loyalists or Tories. Alexander Hamilton, Jefferson, Franklin, and John Adams assumed a natural leadership among the patriot writers, their political theories being largely influenced by the philosophy of John Locke and, in some instances, by the writings of Voltaire and Rousseau.

Political tracts were scattered broadcast, and newspaper columns were filled with anonymous letters. Satire often proved a keen-edged weapon. Samuel Seabury, under the name of 'A Westchester Farmer,' attacked the proceedings of the Continental Congress and was in turn attacked by Alexander Hamilton, a 'Sincere Friend to America.' Daniel Leonard as 'Massachusettensis' found an able opponent in John Adams as 'Novanglus.' Martin Howard's *Defence of the Letter from a Gentleman at Halifax to his friend in Rhode-Island*, was in answer to anonymous attacks upon his *Letter* by Stephen Hopkins (to whom it had been addressed in reply to Hopkins's *Rights of the Colonies examined*) and by James Otis's *Vindication of the British Colonies against the Aspersions of the Halifax Gentleman.* John Dickinson, the 'Pennsylvania Farmer,' wrote *Letters from a Farmer in Pennsylvania*, first published in the *Pennsylvania Chronicle* and re-issued in innumerable separates. Charles Carroll of Maryland, as the 'First Citizen,' took up the gauntlet thrown down by Daniel Dulany as 'Antilon' in an imaginary dialogue between a first and second citizen which had appeared in the *Maryland Gazette* of January 3, 1773. From January, 1775 through October 1776, the weekly issues of *The Crisis* provided English readers with a series of dynamic political essays. The turning point of the whole affair was the publication, on January 8,

1776, of Thomas Paine's *Common Sense*. This boldly advocated a stand for independence. The enormous sale of this little tract, a hundred thousand copies, crystallized public opinion. It was a time of deep pondering, of excitement and of decision, the latter sometimes dividing families and friends. Thomas Jefferson's task, assigned him by the Continental Congress on May 15, of drawing up a proclamation of independence was but the logical result of the trend of affairs.

The years between 1776 and 1783 stand as the period of conviction and action — a period which Moses Coit Tyler has described as ' a time of immense hope, of immense wrath, of immense despair.' On July 8, 1776, four days after the Declaration of Independence, official printing was ordered of the *Rules and Articles for the Better Government of the Troops raised, or to be raised . . . at the Expence of the United States*, Philadelphia, 1776. Two years later, France decided to throw her weight against Great Britain, in an effort to establish trade relations with the colonies and somewhat in retaliation for her recent loss of Canada; and a Philadelphia press issued the *Treaties of Amity and Commerce, and of Alliance eventual and defensive between His Most Christian Majesty and the Thirteen United States of America.* Colonial newspapers published the news from the front. Early in 1783, a London publisher issued *Authentic Copies of the provisional and preliminary Articles of Peace signed between Great Britain, France, Spain and the United States of America.* On September third the Treaty of Paris was signed.

The great problems which now confronted the new republic were the drafting and ratifying of a Constitution. In September, 1787, about sixty copies of a tentative draft were printed for the use of convention members. Fortunately, it was a time of great leaders, the talents of each reacting upon the others and uniting to weld the new experiment in democracy into lasting form. The official edition of the final draft of the Constitution appeared later in the year, a remarkable series of eighty-six essays written in its support by Jay, Hamilton, and Madison being issued the following year under the title of *The Federalist: A Collection of Essays written in Favour of the New Constitution.* It has been said that there is probably no work 'in so small a compass that contains so much political information.'

From the Constitutional period to the end of the century, the products of the printing presses of the United States mirror the problems, the interests and, occasionally, the recreations of the new-born nation. The annual sermons commemorating the Boston Massacre, characteristic of the war period, gave place to annual Fourth of July orations. Magazines and newspapers flourished. A marked interest in literary matters became evident. Poetry and juvenile books were popular. In 1790, Royall Tyler's comedy, *The Contrast*, was printed in Philadelphia, "the first American play acted by an established company of comedians." Occasionally books of religious controversy were published, as were local church histories, theological discussions, and ordination sermons. The writings which particularly characterize the first days of the United States, however, are the almost innumerable works on law, political science, civil government, the new Constitution, political methods, political rights, commerce and trade, finance, taxation, crime, slavery, insurance, yellow fever, the Society of the Cincinnati, and Freemasonry. John Fitch's map of 1785 with its graphic details and the *Ordinance for the Government of the Territory of the United States, Northwest of the River Ohio* were together largely responsible for subsequent occupation of the Northwest Territory. As one approaches the end of the century, there seems to have been the taking of a general account of stock. Biographical books were written and histories were compiled. Books of travel appeared upon the market. And in the winter of 1799–1800 a flood of eulogistic sermons and orations was printed in memory of George Washington.

In addition to the general works of reference and the specialized bibliographies mentioned earlier in this note, the majority of which extend into the latter half of the eighteenth century, there are various monographs devoted solely to the bibliography of the Revolutionary and Constitutional periods. Monsieur Bernard Faÿ's *Bibliographie critique des Ouvrages français relatifs aux Etats-Unis, 1700–1800* was issued in Paris in 1925, and Mr. A. P. C. Griffin has published a *List* of works relating to the French alliance in the American Revolution.   Professor Alvord's introduction to the reprint of the *Invitation sérieuse aux Habitants des Illinois* (Philadelphia, 1772) discusses the relation of the French and English colonists from 1763 to 1774, and the desire on the part of the former for a release from British military rule.   European imprints, particularly those issued in England, will be found in the British Museum *Catalogue*.   The *Literary History of the American Revolution, 1763–1783*, is discussed in two volumes by Moses Coit Tyler.   Sabine's *Biographical Sketches of Loyalists* relates to the men who suffered disgrace, exile and oftentimes-poverty for the sake of loyalty to the Crown.   Mr. Stokes's *Revolutionary Period 1763–1783*, in the first volume of his *Iconography of Manhattan Island*, describes the fate of New York newspapers during the War; and his *Period of Adjustment and Reconstruction*, in the same volume, contains reference to the controversy involving Citizen Genet.   A series of essays on *French Newspapers in the United States before 1800* was edited by G. P. Winship in the fifteenth volume of the *Papers* of the Bibliographical Society of America.   Mr. Brigham's comprehensive bibliography, already mentioned, records American newspapers up to 1820. Philip Freneau's newspapers and his poetry of the Revolution have been studied bibliographically by Victor H. Paltsits.   Harbeck's *Contribution to the Bibliography of the History of the United States Navy* begins with privateering during this period.   The pamphlets relative to the Constitution of the United States and the papers and journals of the Continental Congress have been treated by Paul Leicester Ford; and the latter subject, more recently, by Mr. Worthington C. Ford and Mr. Gaillard Hunt.   As one of the Acorn Club publications, Mr. A. C. Bates issued a list of the official publications of Connecticut from 1774 to 1788; and Mr. J. B. Wilbur contributed to the ' Eames volume ' a *Note on the Laws of the Republic of Vermont, 1779–1791*.   Mr. S. J. Buck, in his volume on *Travel and Description, 1765–1865*, has recorded the laws passed northwest of the Ohio River and printed between 1792 and 1800.   The public documents of the first fourteen Congresses, 1789–1817, have been listed by General A. W. Greely; and the Treasury Reports of Alexander Hamilton, 1789–1795, by Paul Leicester Ford.   Finotti's *Bibliographia Catholica Americana* relates, in its first part, to the works of Catholic authors published in the United States between 1784 and 1820. The controversy over the proposition for an American Episcopate before the outbreak of the Revolution has been made the subject of a monograph by Nelson; and a list of the early editions and reprints of the General Convention Journals, 1785–1814, was published by Trinity College, Hartford, in its *Bulletin* for April, 1908. Benson's *American Revisions of Watts's Psalms* begins with the Mycall Revision printed in Newburyport in 1781. The poetry of Phillis Wheatley, a negro servant whose writings date from 1770, has been listed by Heartman; and Wegelin has brought together the titles of early American fiction from 1774 to 1830. The Thwaites reprints of *Early Western Travels, 1748–1846,* relate to the Middle and the Far West. Monographs giving bibliographical data on the maps of the late eighteenth century will be found below, in the section of Selected Bibliographies, under Cartography. Mr. J. T. Lee has issued two works on the travels of Captain Jonathan Carver, and Mr. S. C. Williams one on travels in the Tennessee country before 1800. A list of books on architecture printed in America between 1775 and 1830, was contributed by Mr. Wall to the 'Eames volume,' but from the humble character of its titles — *The British Architect or, the Builders Treasury of Stair-Cases; The Practical Builder; The Carpenter's Pocket Directory* — one would hardly recognize this to be the period of the beautiful buildings designed by Thomas Jefferson and Bulfinch. Although Tompkins' *Bibliotheca Jeffersoniana* has no reference to Jefferson's architectural masterpieces, it records his various statesmanlike contributions to the making of the nation. Hamilton, and *The Federalist* have been treated by Paul Leicester Ford, and *Hamilton's 'Publius'* was made the subject of a brief essay by Worthington C. Ford; a bibliography of Weems's *Life and memorable Actions of George Washington,* begun by the former, is completed in *Mason Locke Weems — His Works and Ways* edited by Emily E. Ford Skeel. Franklin and his works have been studied by a variety of bibliographers. The period ends bibliographically, and not inappropriately with Washingtoniana, variously described by Hough, Baker, and Griffin; and the *Washington Eulogies,* a check list of eulogies and funeral orations on the death of George Washington, December,

1799–February, 1800, published in the *Bulletin* of the New York Public Library, February–May, 1916.

Because of the chronological arrangement of Evans's *American Bibliography*, it is possible, in the course of its pages, to follow the writings of the times parallel with the march of events. Although Mr. Evans lists only American imprints, many of the writings of English pamphleteers were reprinted in America and are consequently included among his entries. From the records of these reprints, it is possible to work back to the original issues by searching their author-entries in Sabin, thus ascertaining the original sequence. The cross-references in Sabin are particularly helpful in tracing the pseudonyms employed by various controversialists. Many of the outstanding works are described in the Church *Catalogue*. Further contributions to the subject may be expected from the William L. Clements Library and the Henry E. Huntington Library. The former, which contains the collection of Revolutionary material brought together by Mr. Henry N. Stevens, has already devoted a section to this period in the important volume on the William L. Clements Library, Ann Arbor, 1923. When the *Catalogue* of the John Carter Brown Library reaches the period of the eighteenth century, a bibliographical contribution of great worth may be expected, for the library is likewise rich in the controversial pamphlets of the Revolutionary and Constitutional periods.

SPANISH AMERICAN COLONIES, 1700–1778–1824

1. *Florida and the Spanish Southwest, 1700–1783*

On the Atlantic coast, the eighteenth century found the English in control of the territory north of the Savannah River. An interesting account of the region, known at the time as Florida, appeared in the letter of the Franciscan Friar Andres Quiles Galindo, *Al Exc.*[mo] *Señor Conde de Frigiliana*, printed probably at Madrid in 1707. During 1709 and two years later, French translations of Garcilasso de la Vega's *Florida del Ynca* were issued; and Gonzales Barcia's *Ensayo Cronologico para la historia general de la Florida* [1723], which describes not only Florida and the Spanish colonies of the

North, but the neighboring French and English colonies as well, serves to illustrate the fact that the interest of Spain and of her rivals in one another's territory was a reciprocal affair.

In fact by 1721, the British had forced the Spanish frontier down to the Altamaha River. Spanish missions were destroyed in the interior of Tallahassee; and the founding of Oglethorpe's colony in Georgia as a refuge for the destitute and as a bulwark against Spanish aggression, occasioned border conflicts between the British colonists and their Spanish neighbors. The *Relacion de los Meritos y Servicios del Coronel Don Diego Ortiz Parrilla,* [1770], records the delivery of Pensacola to the British in 1763. For, by the Treaty of Paris, Spain, beset by the hostility of the Florida Indians and pressed by the English on the North and the French on the West, ceded her claim to Florida in exchange for Cuba, which had been captured by the British. A London publisher was quick to take advantage of this turn of affairs. Before the year was out, London bookdealers were selling *An Account of the First Discovery and Natural History of Florida. With a Particular Detail of the several Expeditions and Descents made on that Coast. Collected from the best authorities, by William Roberts. Illustrated by a general Map, and some particular Plans, together with a geographical Description of that Country, By T. Jefferys, Geographer to His Majesty.* The ownership of Florida, however, was not settled even then. In 1781, Pensacola was captured by the Spanish; and, in 1783, Florida was retroceded to Spain, in whose hands it was destined to remain for the next thirty-six years.

West Florida. — In the region west of Florida, the seventeenth century had ended with the erection in 1698 of a Spanish fort on the Florida frontier and, simultaneously, with the erection of a French fort at Biloxi, for the protection of the colony which Louis XIV desired to plant in Louisiana. The death of the Spanish king, however, prevented the outbreak of hostilities, for his successor to the throne, a grandson of Louis XIV, became convinced (under French influence) that the establishment of a French colony in Louisiana would be a desirable means of offsetting the aggressions of the English. The alarm of the British was expressed in the tract originally sold for 6 d., and now of utmost rarity, entitled *A Letter to a Mem-*

ber of the P——t of G——t = B——n, Occasion'd by the Priviledge granted by the French King to Mr. Crozat, and issued in London in 1713. Simultaneously, as a bit of colonization propaganda, Joutel's *Journal Historique du Dernier Voyage que feu M. de la Sale fit* was printed at Paris in 1713 together with a map, the *Carte Nouvelle de la Louisiane, et de la Riviere de Missisipi . . . et de plusieurs autres Rivieres, jusqu'icy inconnuës, qui tombent dans la Baye de St. Loüis; Dressée par le Sr. Joutel, qui êtoit de ce Voyage.* This work was immediately translated for the benefit of the British public, and published at London with the map in 1714, under the title *A Journal of the Last Voyage Perform'd by Monsr. de la Sale, To the Gulph of Mexico, To find out the Mouth of the Missisipi River.* Evidently it found a good sale, for another London publisher brought out the same work in 1719 with the title *Mr. Joutel's Journal of his Voyage to Mexico: His Travels Eight hundred Leagues through Forty Nations of Indians in Lovisiana to Canada: His Account of the great River Missasipi. To which is Added A Map of that Country; with a Description of the great Water-Falls in the River Misouris.*

Following the Treaty of Utrecht, and the death of Louis XIV (and under the influence of Franciscans who were desirous of extending the mission field), the Viceroy of Mexico in 1716 sent out a colony which settled in Louisiana in rather close proximity to the outposts of the French. Another colony, sent out in 1718, settled San Antonio. The French simultaneously founded New Orleans. Peace reigned during the remainder of the year, but, with the outbreak of a European war between the mother countries, hostilities were inevitable. Spanish missions were destroyed and the frontier forts changed hands repeatedly. The account of the expedition under the Marques de San Miguel de Aguayo against the French is told by a member of the expedition, Juan Antonio de la Peña, whose *Derrotero de la Expedicion en la Provincia de los Texas* was printed in Mexico in 1722. Under Aguayo, and apparently at his expense, new missions were built and new forts erected. A governor for the province was appointed; and Friar Mathias Saenz de San Antonio (who had been one of the founders of the missions in northeastern Texas) in 1724 addressed an appeal to the King for increased coloni-

zation. In this, he gives an inviting description of Texas and of
its possibilities, the first of the sort to be published. An account of
the new missions erected by Fernando Perez de Almazan, the first
Governor of Texas, and of improvements in the frontier forts, is
given in the *Relacion de los Meritos, y Servicios de Don Fernando
Perez de Almazan*, printed at Madrid after October 17, 1729 and
known only in one copy at Seville. Ladron de Guevara's *Noticias*
of 1739 contains a critical account of the administration of the missions and forts of Mexico and along the northern frontier into Texas;
and the prime authority regarding the Franciscans in Texas is the
Chronica Apostolica, 1746. This was written by Fray Espinosa,
who had been in the expeditionary force of 1716 and among the missionaries who, under the leadership of Father Antonio Margil de
Jesus, had founded the missions far to the northeast.

In 1760, the Mexican press operated by the heirs of Doña Maria
de Rivera, issued Garcia's *Manual para administrar los santos
Sacramentos*, said to be the only work on the polyglot languages
of the Texas Indians issued during the period of the Spanish
occupation. As relatively peaceful relations had prevailed between the French and Spanish colonists, French traders had
utilized the opportunity to invade Spanish territory. Contraband
goods were smuggled to the colonists and trade was carried on
surreptitiously with the Indians. In 1763, just before the Treaty
of Paris, France ceded Louisiana to Spain to save it from their
mutual enemy. The Spanish colonists thus found themselves face
to face with their hated British rivals across the Mississippi, and
the Spanish governor sent to New Orleans in 1766 — Juan
Antonio de Ulloa, the scientist — found himself confronted
by the unfriendly attitude of his French subjects in Louisiana.
New Orleans revolted in 1768. By the end of the following year, the Spaniards had regained control. The rebel leaders
were punished and one of the seditious publications of the revolt, the
Mémoire contre les Républicans, was ordered to be destroyed by the
'executioner'; no copy is known to have survived. The recommendations resulting from a rather elaborate survey of frontier conditions in 1766 and 1767 occasioned the publication (at Madrid in
1772, and at Mexico in 1773) of the *Reglamento*, the official edition

of the *Instruccion* which had been tentatively published in Mexico in 1771 for the regulation of the frontier provinces. British interest in these regions was evidenced in the publication of the first and only known volume of Captain Bernard Romans's *Concise Natural History of East and West Florida; Containing an Account of the Natural Produce of all the Southern Part of British America*, printed in New York in 1775, reprinted in 1776 — and usually assigned to the press of James Rivington, Royalist printer, on the eve of the troublous times of the Revolution.

In 1779, Spain, the traditional enemy of the British, joined with the American colonists in the hope of territorial gain. The Spanish frontier was pushed northward into Michigan. Gálvez, Governor of Louisiana, captured Mississippi forts and trading stations. Pensacola, as already stated, was recaptured by the Spanish in 1781; and in 1783 Florida and this region of West Florida again came under Spanish rule. As stated by Dr. Bolton in his *Spanish Borderlands*, Spain's ' Anglo-American frontier now stretched all the way from St. Mary's River on the Atlantic coast to the head of the Mississippi.' Until 1800, when Napoleon took over Louisiana and until he subsequently sold it, Spain endeavored to hold this territory against the inroads of American and Canadian traders.

New Mexico. — In the century-old colony of New Mexico, the year 1700 found the Pueblo Indians subdued and crushed in their valiant effort to regain their independence, and their conqueror, Don Diego de Vargas, involved in a lawsuit with the city of Santa Fé. The document accusing him of misdemeanors and an improper auditing of accounts was presumably printed in Mexico in 1703, the year in which the King, in recognition of his services in putting down the rebellion, reappointed him to the governorship of New Mexico. In the following year Vargas died while on an expedition against the Apaches. Although the uprising of the local natives had been completely quelled, leaving the survivors subject to exploitation at the hand of their conquerors, the wild tribes of the North were still untamed. The officials of New Mexico were apparently a questionable lot, as shown by the *Breve Memorial* addressed in 1720 to the Viceroy of Mexico by the soldiers of Santa Fé who, through their representative, Joseph Mendez, brought suit against the lawyers employed to collect their overdue pay.

Antagonism, traditional from the earliest times, prevailed between the officials and the *custodio* of the missions. In the region originally called Cibola, the Franciscans had planted nineteen missions and a chain of mission stations extending toward the south. In 1731, in answer to a serious criticism of the *custodio's* administration, Fray Gonzales published a defence giving an account of the Franciscans in the province and reiterating their desire that a bishopric should be erected there. This marked the beginning of a dispute which ultimately was carried to the Council of the Indies. Events in the guerrilla warfare with the Indians are recounted in the *Relacion de Servicios de Don Antonio Perez Velarde,* dated 1732 and presumably issued by a Mexican press. The most valuable of the printed accounts of affairs in the frontier provinces, however, is contained in the *Diario* of Pedro de Rivera, official inspector of the frontier forts of New Spain, New Mexico and Texas. The maps of the frontier boundaries made by Alvarez y Barreyro, an engineer who accompanied the expedition, were unfortunately not printed with the *Diario* in 1736, but six are said to exist in manuscript in the archives of Seville. The results of a general survey of Spanish America, ordered by the King in 1740, appeared six years later in the *Theatro Americano* of Villa-Señor y Sanchez, in the latter pages of which due reference is made to the towns and missions of New Mexico.

Outside of the cities of Santa Fé, Santa Cruz, Albuquerque and El Paso, and in addition to the mission settlements, there were plantations and ranches of varying size and importance, devoted to agriculture and the raising of live stock. Even the early expeditions had carried seeds and stock into the wilderness, together with the equipment for soldiers and the inevitable missionaries. Wool and cotton were woven to some extent and the vineyards produced good wine. The commercial policy of relentless restriction which had dominated the colonies had dulled the enterprise of the colonists, a state of affairs which in New Mexico was enlivened by Indian trade, as far north as Utah, and by the smuggling of imports from the French in Louisiana. Spain's acquisition of this territory in

1763 enabled the New Mexicans to extend their trading to the Indians of the Plains. During the efficient reign of Charles III, economic changes altered conditions somewhat for the better in the
South American colonies, affecting the northern borderland as well,
and under this able monarch the Jesuits were expelled from Spain
and her colonies as a means of maintaining the power of the state,
undisputed by that hitherto powerful organization within the
church.

In 1781, a *Breve Apostólico,* issued by the Pope, was printed in
Madrid, conveying instructions for the administration of the Franciscan *custodias* in New Mexico, California, and New Spain; five
years later the Conde de Gálvez issued an *Instruccion Formada* (in
two issues, known in two and three copies respectively) which relates
to trade relations with the Indians and provisions necessary to the
conquest of the Apaches. Traffic in merchandise had thus replaced
the original gallant quest for gold, but the conquest and conversion
of the aborigines remained a steadfast purpose to the end. In 1821,
New Mexico as a province of Mexico, became independent of the
mother country and its population north of the present Mexican
border is said at that time to have comprised thirty thousand
settlers.

California. — At the beginning of the eighteenth century, the name
California was applied to the peninsula now known as Lower California, and the name Alta, or Nueva, California to the relatively unknown region now called California. The probable origin of the
name and the history of its early use are charmingly told by Miss
Ruth Putnam in a monograph included in volume IV of the University of California's *Publications in History* (1917). For over a
hundred and fifty years after Vizcaino explored San Diego Bay,
California (as we know it) remained a land of mystery, save as certain points along the coast were sighted from time to time by the
ships following the homeward trade routes from the Philippines to
Acapulco in Mexico. The dangers which beset these galleons may
be inferred from the rather jubilant title of Captain Cooke's *Voyage
to the South Sea . . . Containing a Journal of . . . the taking of
the Towns of Puna and Guayaquil and several Prizes, one of which
a rich Acapulco Ship,* issued in London in 1712 and containing, in its

second volume, a translation of valuable Spanish Coasting Pilots hitherto in manuscript and presumably found upon the captured ship.

Within the next decade, Behring's discovery (in the interests of Russia) of a strait at the far north introduced a new foe upon the Pacific. The publication, in 1750 and following years, of the maps of Philippe Buache and Monsieur De l'Isle of the discoveries of the Russians, and of Torrubia's *I Moscoviti nella California* of 1759, no doubt awakened the various rivals in the Pacific to this new danger. When Charles III ascended the throne in the latter year, full of plans for the reform and the development of Spain's colonial system, Russian trading posts had been erected at far northern points and Russian ships were sailing southward along the Pacific coast. After Spain had accepted Louisiana, defensive measures were decided upon for the far West. In 1769, expeditions by both land and sea were fitted out to erect fortresses and mission stations at San Diego and Monterey. After untold hardship Portolá, Rivera, Crespi, and the Franciscan leader, Junípero Serra, eventually arrived at San Diego. Part of the expedition, pushing on to Monterey, by happy accident discovered San Francisco Bay — which the few known copies of the *Navegacion especvlativa y practica*, describing the trade routes of the Pacific and the coastline of California, prove to have been unknown to Spanish navigators as late as 1734. For want of food the colonists turned back. In 1770, however, the fortress and mission of San Carlos were founded on Monterey Bay, henceforth the headquarters of Junípero Serra, California's famous missionary to the Indians. The account of this expedition was published contemporaneously in the *Diario* of Miguel Costansó and officially announced in the *Estracto de Noticias del Puerto de Monterrey . . . y del sucesso de las dos Expediciones de Mar, y Tierra que à este fin se despacharon en el año proximo anterior de 1769,* which was twice printed in small editions by the Mexican government during 1770. The map prepared by Costansó is said to have been issued in 1771, the year in which the mission of San Gabriel was founded.

Four years later, as a preliminary to colonization, a trail to San Francisco Bay was blazed by Anza and his intrepid band of frontiers-

men. Upon their return, the first colonists for San Francisco started
on their way, accompanied by Pedro Font, diarist and astronomer,
a march of a thousand miles or more fraught with peril and fatigue.
The fortress and mission of San Francisco were founded in the
autumn of 1776. Five years later, Los Angeles was founded; and
within the decade, Santa Barbara. Meantime Spanish ships, pushing along the Pacific coast, were watchful of the Russians and the
British. By a strange anomaly of fate, Mourelle's *Journal* of an expedition toward the North is known only in its English translation.
This was issued in 1780 or 1781, with a map, and entitled *Journal of
a Voyage in 1775. To explore the coast of America, Northward of
California, By the second Pilot of the Fleet, Don Francisco Antonio
Maurelle, in the King's Schooner, called the Sonora.* In 1784, the
Reglamento para el Gobierno de la Provincia de Californias promulgated the official regulations for the Californias which obtained, it is
said, until some time after Mexico and her provinces had gained
their independence. The history of California and its missions up
to 1784 is recounted in Friar Paloú's *Relacion Historica de la Vida
. . . del Venerable Padre Fray Junipero Serra y de las Misiones
que fundó en la California Septentrional*, Mexico, 1787. By the end
of the century, eighteen Franciscan missions had been established,
the last of which was San Luis Rey.

Wagner's *Spanish Southwest, 1542–1794,* many of whose titles
and annotations have been used in writing these notes, is the prime
authority on the bibliography of the Spanish frontier colonies. Parallel to it is Bolton's monograph on the history of the *Spanish
Borderlands.* Priestley's *Coming of the White Man* contains a
chapter on ' The Last Cycle of New Spain ' describing economic conditions which ultimately became factors of more or less importance
in the revolutionary movement, and a final chapter giving a critical
survey of reference works, bibliographical and otherwise, relative to
the Spanish colonies in North America. Among the numerous
works here cited, as bearing upon the subject from a variety of
angles, are the works of Bancroft, Bolton, Richman, and Chapman,
occasional original sources, society and university publications,
J. L. Mecham's *Northern Expansion of New Spain, 1522–1822; a
selected descriptive bibliographical List,* and R. E. Cowan's *Bib-*

*liography of the History of California and the Pacific West, 1510–
1906.* A list of reference works is also given at the end of Wagner's
Spanish Southwest.

2. *The Southern Spanish Colonies, 1700–1778*

Under the influence of the French at the opening of the eighteenth
century, the restrictions imposed for nearly two centuries upon the
Spanish colonies by the Crown and the Casa de Contratacion were
temporarily broken down. Ostensibly the broadening influences,
experienced in this period of intercourse with French scientists and
merchantmen, passed when Spain once more closed her colonial
ports and set in motion the complicated workings of her hierarchic
system. In reality, the leaven of new ideas introduced into the
colonies within these years and the influence of travel upon certain
of the wealthy Creoles, continued quietly at work and increased in
strength throughout the century. With the growth of the colonies,
the Viceroyalty of Mexico was extended to the North and West, and
the jurisdiction of the Viceroy of Peru was curtailed by the establishment of the Viceroyalty of New Granada in 1717 (reorganized in
1739), and by the creation of the Viceroyalty of Buenos Aires in
1776.

Until after the promulgation of the laws of 1778, lessening restrictions on trade between the colonies and Spain, and the consequent growth of colonial activities and revolutionary ideas, the
general trend of colonial writings and of those about the Spanish
colonies was much the same as in the seventeenth century. A possible exception to this was the anonymously published *Estado
politico del Reino del Peru* printed at Madrid in 1747. Earlier
works had undertaken to explain the laws or to describe the existent
system of government. This anonymous work was frankly critical.
Although written in a spirit of loyalty, and addressed to the King, it
proposed reforms in the military and commercial affairs of the
colony.

Poetry, biography, lives of the saints and martyrs, accounts of
Indian conversions and rebellions, linguistics, religious works, proclamations, laws, histories, and descriptions of the country as in

earlier days, fell within the range of interest permitted by the official censors. It is largely works of this character that make up the several thousand titles listed in the bibliographies of Medina and Dr. Nicolas León. In 1705, a Paris editor included in the *Lettres Edifiantes et Curieuses, ecrites des Missions Etrangeres par quelques Missionaires de la Compagnie de Jesus* Father Kino's map of Lower California and a translation into French of Picolo's *Informe del Estado de la Nueva Christiandad* — both works being described in bibliographical detail in Wagner's *Spanish Southwest*. Zamora's ecclesiastical history of New Granada had appeared at the turning of the century, and the first volume of Oviedo y Baños's valuable history of Caracas was brought out at Madrid in 1723. Catalogues of the Jesuits in the province of Mexico were issued in 1751 and 1758, and again in 1764. The latter, which brings the record close to the expulsion of the Jesuits in 1767 by order of the energetic Charles III, now ranks as an unknown work although, as Mr. Wagner notes, it was evidently seen by Dr. León, since it has been printed in full in the third volume of his *Bibliografia Mexicana del Siglo XVIII*. The *Noticia* of 1757 written by Andres Marcos Burriel, and based more or less upon a manuscript of Venegas describing the missions of Lower California, brought that region into prominence in the book world of Europe. An English translation was issued in 1759 as *A Natural and Civil History of California;* a Dutch version appeared in 1761; a French translation in 1766; and one in German in 1769. Gamboa's *Comentarios a las Ordenanzas de Minas,* Madrid, 1761, although written with regard to the organization of a company for draining the Mexican mines, comprises an important account of metallurgy and the mining industry in Mexico, midway in the century. Cisneros's *Descripcion* (printed in 1764 with the debatable imprint, Valencia) recounts the economic history of Venezuela. It is written from the practical standpoint of an agent of the Royal Guipuzcoa Company, the only South American trading agency permitted outside the privileged port of Porto Bello. Gumilla's *El Orinoco,* 1741 (re-issued in 1745 and translated into French in 1758) suggests the works of the earlier century, for it describes the 'natural, civil, and geographical history of this great river with new and useful accounts of animals, trees, fruits, oils, resins, herbs, and medical roots.'

From the southern reaches, came the *Historia de la Compañia de Jesus en la Provincia del Paraguay*, 1754–1755, whose author — Pedro Lozano, official historian of the Jesuits — is said to have been an impartial archivist, a zealous student of nature, and of the languages and religion of the aborigines. His *Descripcion . . . del gran Chaco, Gualamba*, previously issued at Cordoba, describes in detail the customs of the Indians of the interior. Charlevoix's *Histoire du Paraguay*, 1756, was variously reprinted and translated; and the additional matter supplied in the translation of Muriel (1779) carries the history of Paraguay down to 1767, the memorable year of the Jesuit expulsion. Two belated Jesuit accounts of the far south were published even after that event — Thomas Falkner's *Description of Patagonia*, printed at Hereford in 1774, and later translated into French and German; and Dobrizhoffer's *Historia de Abiponibus*, published in Latin in 1784 and in German, the authors in each instance being foreigners who had labored in the American mission field. Under the Jesuits in Paraguay, and also in the region of the Orinoco, an effort had been made to teach the natives by practical methods to adapt themselves to European modes of life, one of the products of their industry being, in Paraguay, the casting of type. The products of their printing press — dictionaries and devotional books in their native tongue — have a certain rude strength which makes them a point of especial interest in the collecting of Americana.

The outstanding feature of the century, however, from a bibliographical point of view, is the series of scientific works relating to South America which were published after 1714. In that year, Louis Feuillée, ' mathematicien et botaniste de sa Majesté,' issued in Paris his *Journal des Observations physiques, mathematiques et botaniques, faites . . . sur les Côtes Orientales de l'Amerique Meridionale . . . depuis l'année 1707 jusques en 1712*. In 1716, there appeared Frezier's *Relation du Voyage . . . aux Côtes du Chily et du Perou* in which the author — engineer in ordinary to the King of France — was at some pains to explain that his findings were at variance with those of Feuillée. In 1725, the latter brought forth a new volume of the *Journal* with a ' Preface contenant des Reflexions critiques sur . . . M. Frezier.' In reply, Frezier's *Rela-*

tion reappeared in 1732 with fifty-six pages in ' Réponse a la Preface.' As it happened, the English, French, Dutch, and German editions of Frezier's *Relation* (London 1717, Amsterdam 1717 and 1718, and Hamburg 1718) were issued too early to be party to the controversy. Later editions (London, Hamburg, etc.) apparently follow the early tradition. Frezier's *Réponse,* however, is on record as having been separately published in 1727, a probability which would seem to be substantiated by the repetition of page numbers and signaturing and by other bibliographical factors in the *Réponse* as it appeared in the 1732 edition of the *Relation.*

The difficulties and the consequent inaccuracies in charting the region of the Amazon, in the map valiantly made by Padre Fritz ' sans pendule et sans lunette ' (engraved at Quito in 1707), are discussed in Monsieur de La Condamine's *Relation abrégée d'un Voyage fait dans l'Interieur de l'Amérique Méridionale,* Paris 1745. The map itself is reproduced in section one hundred and eleven of Stocklein's *Allerhand so Lehr-als Geist-reiche Brief, Schrifften und Reis-Beschreibungen,* the so-called *Welt-Bott deren Missionarien Soc. Iesu* of 1726. It is said by both La Condamine and Backer to have been reproduced in the Jesuit *Lettres édifiantes.* According to Stocklein, the Fritz map based upon extensive explorations was the first map of the valley of the Amazon. In 1751, the official account of the scientific expeditions to South America, made by French scientists fifteen years before — for the purpose of measuring the arc of the Meridian and computing the dimensions of the globe — and partially sponsored by the Spanish crown, was published in La Condamine's *Mesure des trois premiers Degrés du Méridien dans l'Hémisphere Austral, tirée des Observations de M.rs de l'Académie Royale des Sciences, envoyés par le Roi sous l'Équateur.* The reports of Jorge Juan y Santacilia and Antonio de Ulloa, who had represented Spanish interests in the expedition, were made in their *Observaciones astronomicas y phisicas* printed at Madrid in 1748 and again in 1773. A further report was given in their *Relacion historica del Viage . . . en conocimiento de la verdadera Figura y Magnitud de la Tierra* printed at Madrid in 1748, and translated into French, Dutch, and English. When the earthquake of 1746 demolished the city of Lima, it was one of the

Academicians, it is said, who helped to rebuild the city and its great cathedral.

Although these scientific works introduce a new element into Spanish Americana of the eighteenth century, they form a group distinct from other works and of contemporary interest to the savants of Europe and a small group of scientists in America, rather than to the colonists in general. Their importance today, however, is inversely proportional to that of the popular works of their day. An attempt to bridge the chasm at the time is shown in the change of emphasis on the title-pages of the French and English translations of Juan and Ulloa's *Relacion*. In the French version of Amsterdam, 1752, it is stated that the *Voyage historique*, as it is renamed, contains ' une Histoire des Yncas du Perou, Et les Observations Astronomiques et Physiques, faites pour déterminer la Figure et la Grandeur de la Terre.' In the English title-page of 1758 merely the human interest prevails, and the book appears as *A Voyage to South-America describing at large the Spanish Cities, Towns, Provinces, &c., on that extensive Continent. Interspersed throughout with Reflections on the Genius, Customs, Manners and Trade of the Inhabitants; Together with . . . An Account of their Gold and Silver Mines*.

Many important works, written contemporaneously with colonial events, remained in manuscript until after the colonial era. For instance, the *Noticias secretas* of Juan and Ulloa, the critique of colonial affairs prepared by them for the King directly after their participation in the measuring of the arc of the Meridian, remained in the Spanish archives until its publication in 1826. From the point of view of the archivist, such a work falls under the date when it was written. From the viewpoint of the bibliographer, who treats of printed matter in the order in which its context comes into circulation in printed form, such a work lies outside the period of colonial Americana. The historian must of necessity take both factors into consideration — the time and circumstances under which a book was written, and the time and circumstance under which its information first became available to the world. Both factors play a part of constantly varying importance in the trend and interrelation of affairs.

Compared with Spanish Americana of the sixteenth century, brimming with news of discovery, conquest, and early exploration in the New Found World, even the descriptions of territory hitherto unexplored, or tales of robbery on the high sea and plundering along the coast, leave the books of two succeeding centuries relatively lacking in the spirit of romance. Yet their intense historic interest has held José Toribio Medina to his lifelong task of recording and describing Spanish Americana in bibliographical detail. The monograph on *Spanish Colonial Literature* by Bernard Moses gives a critique of both the printed and the manuscript material of the period. An author list with brief titles, at the end of the book, enables one to pick out those of bibliographical interest. By considering merely the titles comprised in Medina's major works covering the period between the years 1600 and 1778, some idea may be gained of the vast number of works relative to Spanish America which were published during these years. For instance, in his bibliography of Lima, 1,448 titles are listed between these dates; in the bibliography of Mexico, 6,856; Chile, 534; Puebla de los Angeles (during and after 1640), 1,025; Guatemala (1660), 431. To these should be added the works in his *Biblioteca Hispano-Americana,* 4,488 imprints within these years — making a total (not including undated works nor titles listed in his minor works)[1] of over fourteen thousand works, of which over ten thousand are Spanish Americana printed between 1700 and December 1778.

3. *The Revolutionary Period, 1778–1824*

Although the period of British Americana ends usually at the year 1800, Spanish Americana continues until 1824, by which time a series of new republics had been born. In the British colonies, intellectually and spiritually independent of the mother country long before the days of political revolution, the colonists had from the first participated in civic control. The pressure later brought to bear by England's mistaken colonial policy had been every man's affair. Each had of necessity to stand by the policy or to oppose it;

---

[1] See below in the Reference Section, under: Selected Bibliographies — Americana, nos. 844–847, 878–895, 901–904: a; and under: Tributes to Bibliographers, no. 1291.

and, in the period of indecision, the political opinions of both parties had found expression in hundreds of pamphlets, their prolific output being made possible by the fact that the means for printing were already at hand.

In South America, the hierarchic structure of the social order had created two groups as widely separated as the poles. The subsidized officials and proprietors, vastly satisfied with their lot, were desirous of maintaining it, and a larger group comprised of Creoles and mestizos had either stagnated beneath social repression and the economic restrictions imposed by Spain, or were restive beneath the yoke. The latter comprised a small minority. The code of 1778 lessened commercial restrictions to a considerable extent, permitting a certain expansion and marking the beginning of a new commercial era; but it failed to open the ports to foreign wares and, psychologically, it came too late. The horrible execution of Tupac Amaru, after the rebellion of the Peruvian natives in 1781, sounded 'the death knell of Spanish colonial dominion,' as Sir Clements Markham has justly stated, 'the first stroke of that bell which was to toll for forty years.' In spite of the censored news issued for nearly thirty years in the *Gaçeta de Lima,* for the deliberate purpose of counteracting revolutionary influence, the ideas gained during the revolutions in North America and in France were gradually accepted by a limited number of thinkers. In the latter days of the century, a small group stood opposed to the established order. Their absorbing thought was for emancipation. Beyond that they had no thought, and no experience to guide their thought. Until the later phases of the Spanish-American Revolution, the clergy and the majority of the colonists (a decreasing majority, to be sure) remained true to the old régime. It was the new order, however, that was destined to prevail.

The new intellectual movement first found expression in the North. In New Granada, schools were established to replace those closed in 1767, after the expulsion of the Jesuit order. Books gathered from the Jesuit colleges were formed into a Royal Library at Bogotá. New and more liberal subjects were introduced into the curriculum of the universities. Literary societies were formed under the influence of the Botanical Expedition led by José Celestino

Mutis, and of the Creoles who had travelled abroad or who had been educated there. Articles on disease and on the virtues of quinine, the result of this and other expeditions, appeared in the *Mercurio Peruano*, issued at Lima from 1791 to 1795.

The political leaders in this group of intellectuals were Francisco Antonio Zea and Antonio Nariño, both of whom fell under suspicion and were arrested by the authorities — the latter because of his impolitic translation of the *Rights of Man*. In Venezuela, new recruits were added to the group of revolutionary thinkers after 1797, by the gradual importation of books. After the alliance between England and Spain, English books entered without restriction. In Buenos Aires, *El Telegrafo Mercantil*, founded in 1801 for the advancement of learning, was suppressed by the authorities after its fifth volume. From 1808, matters moved with considerable rapidity. The triumphs of Napoleon in Spain intensified the fear of possible French control of the colonies and furnished an opportune moment for the preaching of revolutionary doctrines. The bonds of allegiance were weakened, since the sentiment of loyalty which had bound the clergy and many of the conservatives to the person of the King, would not necessarily endure for Spain in the hands of a foreign power. The year 1810 brought a declaration of independence by the Creoles of New Granada; it marked the beginning of the Mexican revolution under Hidalgo; and it saw the organization of the revolutionary congress in Chile. The fact that the colonies were presently allowed representation in the temporary, constituent congress of Spain, which framed the Constitution of 1812, gave its colonial members experience in organization. When monarchy was restored, the clergy renewed their allegiance to the King. Otherwise, the obvious contrast between the two systems of government worked to the advantage of the revolutionary faction, in spreading its propaganda.

The inevitable revolution, however, was of slow growth and it was frequently through newspapers and periodicals, sponsored by the small but growing party, that its ideas were spread. In Argentina, the writings of Bernardo Monteagudo filled the pages of the *Gazeta de Buenos-Ayres* from 1810 to 1812, and those of *El Mártir ó Libre* and *El Independiente* until his exile in 1815. An even more radical journal, *La Aurora de Chile*, was issued from February 13, 1812 to April 1, 1813, a veritable 'trumpet call to liberty' in whose columns appeared not only fiery exhortations by Camilo Henríquez, its editor, but translations of addresses by Washington, Jefferson, Madison, and other leaders of the northern republic, and of Raynal's letter to the National Assembly of France.

Beyond the actual attainment of freedom lay the problem of government. Unlike the British colonists, who had had merely to continue a form of government already existent, the Spanish colonists were faced by the necessity of deciding upon and establishing a new governmental system. Should the new government be a monarchy, a dictatorship, or a democracy? What relationship should exist between the capitals of the former viceroyalties and the provinces? These were paramount among the questions which confronted the colonists and which, while their military leaders fought to secure their emancipation from Spanish rule, absorbed many of them in debate and political writing. The revolutionists of the North and of the South had thus the triple tasks of freeing the colonies from Spain's control, of wresting the government from the hands of the royalists, and of establishing a new governmental system. After temporary defeat, Bolívar met with military success in Venezuela and New Granada, and San Martín succeeded in winning Chile. Peru, the great royalist stronghold, yet remained.

The first move of the revolutionists was to disseminate liberal ideas through the press. San Martín, in his proclamation of November 1818, *A los Limeños y Habitantes de todo el Perú*, suggested the union of Buenos Aires, Chile, and Peru in the cause of liberty. Monteagudo, upon his return to Santiago de Chile from exile, founded in 1820 a new periodical, *El Censor de la Revolución*, aimed especially at the royalists of Peru. In July 1821, San Martín and his expeditionary forces arrived in Peru, and the following month a provisional government was organized in which he became Supreme Protector; and Monteagudo, the Minister of War and of the Navy. The latter, however, turned his attention to political writing, editing two short-lived journals, the *Boletín del Ejército* and *El Pacificador del Perú*, both advocating a monarchial form for the new government. In September, the revolutionists entered Mexico City, where Iturbide was destined for an interval to rule as emperor.

Directly after the New Year, the Sociedad Patriótica de Lima was organized for political discussion and debate. Two periodicals were subsequently developed, a weekly issued as a means of aiding the educational program of the society, and a quarterly issued as an organ for the publication of addresses and articles on political or scientific subjects. The securing of independence, the establishment of a proper form of government based upon humane principles, and the education of the people were, here and elsewhere, the problems of the hour. Patriotic societies were formed throughout the colonies. The revolutionary leaders, with the exception of Bolívar, generally favored monarchy as the safest measure for a people untutored in the art of self-government. With the awakening and development of public interest in political matters, however, there arose an overwhelming sentiment in favor of democracy — and this party carried the day. The tribute to Bolívar in Olmedo's poem, *La Victoria de Junín* (started, it is said, soon after the battle of Junín and completed after the final victory at Ayacucho) is a song 'of triumph, of exhortation, and of prophecy.' The Monroe Doctrine promulgated in 1823 — which had been suggested by Canning, Great Britain's foreign minister, and developed into an American policy by John Quincy Adams and President Monroe in order to check the plans of the Holy Alliance — assured the South American republics of security from European interference. The year 1824, therefore, is accepted by some bibliographers as the final date for Spanish Americana. By others, the bibliographies relating to revolutionary imprints within each colony are brought to a close respectively at the dates of independence.

Practically all of Medina's works, following the latter method, extend through the Revolutionary period of the various colonies. His *Imprenta en Mexico,* for instance, extends through the year 1821; his *Biblioteca Hispano-Chilena,* through 1817; and his *Imprenta en Lima,* through 1824. His minor works relating to Spanish American imprints likewise close at variable dates, according to the progress of the revolution in their respective regions. Many of these early presses, in fact, owe their origin to the revolutionary movement. As will be shown in the tentative table of ' firsts ' given below, presses were started in Santiago de Chile in 1776 and in Buenos Aires in 1780; and the history of printing in Montevideo begins in 1807, in Caracas in 1808, in Cartagena de las Indias in 1809, in Mérida in Yucatan in 1813, and in various towns of Peru between 1820 and 1825. The titles within these works are of the newspapers and pamphlets of the revolutionary period. Dr. Bernard Moses's scholarly works, upon which this note has been more or less based, include a monograph on *The Intellectual Background of the Revolution in South America, 1810–1824.* His monograph on *Spanish Colonial Literature in South America* contains two chapters on ' Late eighteenth century Historians ' and ' The Outlook towards Emancipation.' Keniston's *List of Works for the Study of Hispanic American History,* published by the Hispanic Society of America in 1920, devotes a section to imprints contemporary with the colonial revolution. And the *Bibliografía Venezolanista,* of works relative to Venezuela printed or reprinted during the nineteenth century, describes the Sanchez collection which was dispersed in 1913 and divided between Harvard University, Northwestern University, and the John Crerar, Libraries.

CHAPTER V

EARLY PRINTING IN AMERICA

NOTES ON BIBLIOGRAPHICAL MATERIAL

Hispanic America, 1539–1823

Less than twenty years after the conquest of Mexico and the overthrow of its ancient culture, Juan Cromberger, the foremost printer of Spain, sent a representative to America to introduce the art of printing into the Western World. An attempt may even have been made as early as 1532 to establish a printing press in Mexico; but Juan Pablos, financed by Cromberger and his heirs from 1539 to 1547, is the first American printer whose works have survived. No copy is extant of the first work known to have been printed, the *Breve y más compendiosa Doctrina Christiana en Lengua Mexicana y Castellana* of 1539, nor of a previous work, either by Pablos or a possible predecessor, the existence of which might be inferred from the reading of this title. Happily, the single fragment of Pablos's next production, the *Manual de Adultos* of 1540, includes the colophon and affords indisputable evidence of the facts regarding its printing. Until 1559, twelve years after Pablos had become sole proprietor of his shop, his monopoly remained unbroken. In that year Antonio de Espinosa, who in 1550 had come from Spain in his employ, secured permission to open a rival press. Between 1563 and the end of the century, seven other presses were operated in Mexico. One of these, for a brief period, was managed by a woman — Doña Maria de Figueroa, the widow of Pedro Ocharte and presumably the daughter of America's first known printer, since, in 1563, Ocharte had taken over Pablos's establishment after marrying his daughter. Doña Maria de Figueroa attempted to issue in 1594 the *De Institutione Grammatica* by Father Alvarez. After issuing the first of its three books, the work was turned over to Pedro Balli, a prolific printer whose press was active from 1574 to the end of the century. Next to Pablos himself, Espinosa, Ocharte, and Balli were the most important of the early Mexican printers.

Gerson's *Tripartito*, of 1544, the first American book to contain wood engravings, was issued in the first period of Pablos's press, during the time when the original imprint 'en casa de Juan Cromberger' was in use. Its colophon bears the interesting statement ' El qual se imprimio en la grã ciudad d'Tenuchtiltlan Mexico desta nueua España en casa de Juã Crõberger.' Pablos, among his numerous productions, was responsible for the printing of Mendoza's *Ordenãças* of 1548, America's first volume of laws; for the handsome presswork in the *Constituciones del Arçobispado* produced in 1556; as well as for the first mathematical book of the New World, and Veracruz's *Phisica Specvlatio*, described in another chapter. Espinosa, the Spanish printer who was also a type-founder, produced Gilberti's *Grammatica* in 1559, the first year of his proprietorship, and in 1565 Molina's *Confessionario breue* and *Confessionario mayor* in the Mexican and Spanish languages. In the latter year, Ocharte, whose career was destined to be interrupted by the Inquisition, produced Anunciacion's *Doctrina Xp̄iana breue . . . en Lēgua Castellana y Mexicana*, a work presumably supplemented in 1575 by Pedro Balli's edition of that author's *Doctrina Christiana muy cvmplida*. The profusion of cuts inserted in Ocharte's edition, 1571, of the *Doctrina Christiana en la lengua Guasteca* by Fray Juan de la Cruz is presumably due, to a considerable extent at least, to the known presence in Ocharte's establishment of a journeyman skilled in wood engraving. All together, the Mexican printers are credited with over two hundred sixteenth century imprints. Espinosa surpassed them all in the strength and beauty of his workmanship. His *Missale Romanum* of 1561, rich in its balanced arrangements of types, in red and black, and in its masterly woodcuts, is still said to rank as ' the handsomest book ever produced in America.'

Antonio Ricardo of Turin, who printed in Mexico from 1577 to 1579, moved to Lima in 1580. Because of his foreign birth, the necessary license was for a time withheld. In 1584, apparently with considerable trepidation on the part of the Peruvian officials, he was permitted to set up copy for a *Doctrina Christiana* in the Quichua and Aymara languages. Work upon this, as it neared completion, was interrupted by an order to issue the official proclamation of a change in the calendar. The *Pragmatica* produced in midsummer 1584, therefore, ranks as the first Peruvian imprint, and, in fact, as the first work printed in South America. In 1593, printing was introduced into the Philippines, which region, however, is not customarily included within the scope of Americana. In 1594, a news-sheet was issued in Lima announcing the capture off the coast of Peru of Richard Hawkins and his roving ship *The Dainty*, thus affording a sixteenth century prototype of the news-sheets that were to develop into the newspapers of succeeding centuries.

The introduction and progress of printing in Mexico in 1539 called forth, in comparatively recent years, two important and comprehensive bibliographical works — Garcia Icazbalceta's *Bibliografía Mexicana del siglo XVI* and Medina's *La imprenta en Mexico, 1539–1821*. An analytical index to the *Bibliografía* was compiled (in English) by Catharine A. Janvier in 1890; and Medina's work in its introductory volume gives biographical accounts of Mexico's printers. Wagner's *Sixteenth-Century Mexican Imprints*, which appeared in the 'Eames volume' in 1924, gives the present location of two hundred and four Mexican titles. The circumstances relative to the opening of the first press in South America and the issuing of the *Pragmatica* are told in Winship's *Printing Press in South America*, in Medina's brochure on *La primera muestra tipografica . . . de la America del Sur*, and more fully in McMurtrie's *First Printing in South America*. The last two of these monographs include facsimiles of the only recorded copy (that at the John Carter Brown Library) of the King of Spain's *Pragmatica* conveying the Papal decree on the adoption of the Gregorian calendar. The great work on early Peruvian printing is Medina's *Imprenta en Lima* which lists a total of 3,948 titles issued between 1584 and the close of the colonial era.

Since Antonio Ricardo, the first printer of Peru, had previously had a press in Mexico, it is very probable that the contemplated transliteration of the so-called 'Harkness manuscripts,' now in the New York Public Library, will bring forth new information regarding the beginning of American book-making. In the words of Dr. Rosenbach:[1] "No other such valuable collection for the study of the beginnings of American printing exists. For that matter, it is probably the most complete record that has come down to us of the first printing on any continent. It covers a period of more than thirty years, from the first established press in Lima, 1584, until the death of the second printer in 1618. . . . Most valuable of all, it places the beginning of type-founding in the Americas as before 1604. . . . Here we have the earliest pressmen and the book binders contracting to work for Antonio Ricardo . . . at the very start of his business in 1584. The four letters of these artisans give details of the utmost interest about the first press, such as . . . methods of work, relation of master to man, remuneration, etc. The papers are all signed by Antonio Ricardo as well as by the contracting workmen. Next comes the long record of Ricardo's successor, the ill-fated Francisco del Canto. The long-drawn-out and highly involved law-suits into which he was plunged, from 1590 until his death in 1618, cause the records concerning him to be unusually full. . . . Indeed, his head workman set up shop just outside the municipal prison so that he might have the benefit of his master's guidance." It is naturally with a feeling of keen interest, that bookmen await the publication of these records.

Throughout the colonial period, Mexico was the largest center of printing in Spanish America. Medina's total of 3,948 titles in his *Imprenta en Lima* stands next in number to the 12,412 recorded in his *Imprenta en Mexico*. The convenience incident to a local printing press was not limited to these metropolitan towns. Medina's *Imprenta en Lima* includes the record of the works printed, from 1610 to 1613, at Juli in the province of La Paz. Medina's *Imprenta en la Puebla de los Angeles, 1640–1821* and his *Imprenta en Guatemala, 1660–1821* record the works issued by two other presses established in Spanish America during the seventeenth century. The second edition of Andrade's *Ensayo bibliografico Mexicano del siglo XVII* appeared in 1899.

---

[1] Quoted by the kind permission of Mr. H. M. Lydenberg.

The following century was to see the diffusion of the art throughout various regions of South America, the islands, and the Viceroyalty of Mexico. Beginning with the first press in Paraguay — at
the Jesuit mission in Loreto, operated by native Indians who, in
1703, are known to have cut type preliminary to their adventures
in typography — presses were established in relatively quick succession. Dr. Schuller and Sr. Medina have written of early printing
in Paraguay; and the latter has issued bibliographies recording the
introduction of printing into Havana, 1707 and Oaxaca, 1720. The
existence of a single copy of a *Jamaica Almanack* for 1734 [pre-
sumably printed in the autumn of 1733] is noted in Mr. Frank
Cundall's *Press and Printers of Jamaica prior to 1820,* in which he
refers to the possibility of a newspaper having been printed as early
as 1722 in Great Britain's base, close to the territory of Spain's rival
colonies. Posada's *Bibliografía Bogotana* gives a facsimile of the
title-page of Ricaurte y Terreros's *Septenario* printed in Santa Fé
de Bogotá 'en la Imprenta de la Compañia de Jesvs' in 1738. This
places printing at Bogotá one year earlier than was known to Sr.
Medina when he issued his *Imprenta en Bogotá* in 1904. The best
general survey (in English) of printing in Spanish America is Mr.
Winship's brief but highly condensed account which appeared in the
'Peddie volume' in 1927; and, as he has said, "Señor José Toribio
Medina's monumental bibliographies provide material for a comparison of the output of the Spanish-American press before the year
1820, unmatched elsewhere." Winship's record of *Early South
American Newspapers* was published by the Club of Odd Volumes
in 1908. Sr. Medina's monographs on the later presses cover the
introduction of printing into Quito in 1760, Córdoba in 1766, Buenos
Aires in 1780, Guadalajara in 1793, and Veracruz in 1794. A monograph on *Un Incunable Chileno,* by Ramon A. Laval, places the
introduction of printing into Santiago de Chile as early as 1776.
Other works of Medina carry the record beyond 1800 to the end of
the colonial period during which brief interval, under pressure
of the needs of the time, printing was introduced into eighteen or
more towns. Medina's *Notas bibliográficas referentes á las primeras
producciones de la imprenta en algunas ciudades de la América Española, 1754–1823,* records the first imprints of Ambato, 1754;

Nueva Valencia, 1764; Nueva Orleans, 1769 [now known to have had a French press in 1764]; Puerto España, 1786, and Santiago de Cuba, 1796. Dr. Nicolas León's *Bibliográfia Mexicana*, published from 1902 to 1908, relates to Mexicana of the eighteenth century.

Although Dr. Richard Garnett contributed a note on 'Paraguayan and Argentine Bibliography' to *Bibliographica* in 1895, in which a slight reference is made to Pernambuco, accounts of the beginning of bookmaking in the Portuguese colony of Brazil have been strangely elusive. Finally, a note of introduction to the President of the Instituto Historico e Geographico Brasileiro of Rio de Janeiro, courteously provided by Dr. Rodolfo R. Schuller of Vienna, brought the following quotation from a book now out of print, the *Paginas de historia* by Dr. Max Fleiuss. And this quotation, through the further courtesy of Mr. A. de Oliveira Aguas, Portuguese Consul at the Port of Providence, is here rendered into English: "At the beginning of the eighteenth century, someone whose name tradition does not specify established a small printing press for the exclusive purpose of printing exchange-drafts and religious prayers at Recife in the State of Pernambuco, Brazil. The Governor of the State of Pernambuco, at that time Castro Moraes, made no objection to this establishment, but the Crown's order dated July 8, 1706 [the Crown having learned of the case], decreed the sequestration of the whole plant and printing accessories and notified the owner thereof, as well as the employees, to print no more books or sundry pieces (p. 471). In the year 1747, by the Crown's decree of July 6 — to the Governor of Pernambuco, D. Marcos de Noronha — the sequestration was ordered of a certain quantity of printing type landed at Pernambuco, as well as the arrest of those persons implicated in the matter. (Pereira da Costa: *The Establishment and Development of the Press in Pernambuco, i.e., Estabelecimento e desenvolvimento da imprensa em Pernambuco*) (p. 472)."

"It is to be assumed that similar printing material was clandestinely shipped to Brazil, and consigned to the first printing plant established by Antonio Izidoro da Fonseca in that year [1747] in the City of Rio de Janeiro — during the term of office of Sergeant-Major of Battles, Captain-General of Rio de Janeiro, São Paulo and

Minas, Gomes Freire de Andrade, Count of Bobadella, under the initiative and liberal patronage of the latter. As a matter of fact, since 1736, [and] with the foundation of the 'Academy of the Happy and Select,' in 1752, the literary movement favored by Count Bobadella broke forth with the support of the first and second printing plant of Izidoro. The undermentioned works, which are extremely rare, were printed in the first plant which functioned in this Capital [Rio de Janeiro] and the second in the whole of Brazil: *Relação da entrada do Bispo D. Antonio do Desterro*, 1747 [by Doutor Rousado da Cunha], 4°, 20 pages; *Romance historico* (in praise of the same Bishop), f°; *Collectanea de 11 epigrammas, em Latim, e um Soneto, em vernaculo* (applauding the same Bishop) ; *Exame de bombeiros* (Examination of Firemen). [The work last named is] a very interesting production, written by the Lieutenant-Field-Master, General José Fernandes Pinto Alpoim, dedicated to Bobadella. Even though the cover attributes its origin to a printing plant at Martinezabad, Madrid, in the year 1748, this volume is reported as clandestinely printed by Izidoro, at Rio, a volume of 444 pages, 4° size, with eighteen engravings and the picture of Gomes Freire de Andrade made by the engraver José Francisco Chaves (p. 472)." A brief essay by Dr. Brandenburger (*Gutenberg Festschrift*, 1925), which came to my attention just as this data went to press, records another Rio de Janeiro imprint of 1747, a thesis presented and still preserved at the local Jesuit college; and entitled '*Hoc est Conclusiones Metaphysicae de Ente Reali* . . . Ex secunda typographia Antonii Isidori da Fonseca. Anno Domini MDCCXLVII.' Printing was revived in Brazil with the establishment of the 'Impressão Regia' at Rio de Janeiro in 1808.

The aesthetic quality of the sixteenth century imprints did not prevail throughout succeeding centuries. As one surveys the works of the colonial period as a whole, inferior presswork gradually becomes the order of the day. The following table of 'firsts' may serve to picture the diffusion of printing throughout colonial Mexico and South America — bearing in mind, of course, that certain points may alter from time to time, especially upon the full deciphering and publication of the 'Harkness manuscripts.'

A Tentative Table of The Introduction of Printing into Hispanic America

Place	First Printer Known	Establishment of Press	First Imprints (credited and extant)
Mexico City	Juan Pablos Financed by Juan Cromberger, whose imprint appears up to 1545 For an account of a possible attempt to establish an earlier press in Mexico, see Medina, *Imprenta en Mexico*, v.I, p. XLVII	1539 In 1547, taken over by Pablos from Cromberger's heirs	Breve y más compendiosa Doctrina Christiana en Lengua Mexicana y Castellana. Mexico, 1539 At the cost of Bishop Zumárraga No copy known Manual de Adultos. Mexico: En casa d'Juã Cromberger, 1540 Fragment in Biblioteca Nacional, *Madrid* Facsimile in Garcia Icazbalceta
Lima, Peru	Antonio Ricardo	1584	Pragmatica sobre los diez Dias del Año. Ciudad de los Reyes [Lima], 1584 One copy known: John Carter Brown Library, *Providence*
Juli, Peru	Jesuit Mission *i.e.*, Francisco del Canto, en la Casa de la Compañia de Iesvs	1610	Bertonio, P. Ludovico. Vocabvlaria de la Lengva Aymara. Iuli: En la casa de la Compañia . . . por Francisco del Canto, 1612 Two copies known: José Toribio Medina, *Santiago de Chile;* John Carter Brown Library, *Providence*
Puebla de los Angeles, Mexico	[?Francisco Robledo]	1640	Salcedo, P. Mateo. Arco triunfal. Puebla de los Angeles [printer of the *Arco triunfal*], 1640 Palafox y Mendoza, Juan de. Historia real. Ciudad de los Angeles: Por Francisco Robledo, 1643 Two copies known: Biblioteca de la Universidad, *Granada;* José Toribio Medina, *Santiago de Chile*

A TENTATIVE TABLE OF THE INTRODUCTION OF PRINTING
INTO HISPANIC AMERICA — *Continued*

Place	First Printer Known	Establishment of Press	First Imprints (credited and extant)
Guatemala, Guatemala	Joseph de Pineda Ybarra	1660	Quiñones y Escobedo, Francisco de. Sermon predicado en el Muy Religioso Convento de Nvestro Seraphico. Guatemala: Por Ioseph de Pineda Ybarra, 1660 One copy known: D. Antonio Graiño, *Madrid*
Loreto, Paraguay	Jesuit Mission, with native operatives	1705	Nieremberg, Ivan Eusebio. De la Diferencia entre lo temporal y eterno Crisol de Desengaños. Impresso en las Doctrinas, 1705 Trelles copy cited by Medina Garriga, P. Antonio. Instrvccion practica para Ordenar Santamente la vidã; En Loreto, en la Imprenta de la Compañia, 1713 One copy known: John Carter Brown Library, *Providence*
Pernambuco, Brazil	Unknown	Before July 8, 1706, at which date the press was closed by order of the King of Portugal	Unknown
Havana, Cuba	Unknown Carlos Habré	1707	Gonzalez del Alamo, Francisco. Disertacion médica. Habana [printer of the *Disertacion Médica*], 1707 Menendez, Francisco. Rubricas generales del Breviario Romano. Havana: Impresso en la Imp. de Carlos Habrí, 1727 One copy known: José Toribio Medina, *Santiago de Chile*

A Tentative Table of The Introduction of Printing
into Hispanic America — *Continued*

Place	First Printer Known	Establishment of Press	First Imprints (credited and extant)
Oaxaca, Mexico	Doña Francisca Flores	1720	Santander, Sebastian de. Sermon fvnebre qve en las honrras de ... Iacinta Maria Anna de S. Antonio. Oaxaca: Por Doña Francisca Flores, 1720 One copy known: José Toribio Medina, *Santiago de Chile*
Bogotá, Colombia	Jesuit Order	1738	Ricaurte y Terreros, Juan. Septenario al Corazon Doloroso de Maria Santissima. Santa Fe de Bogotá: En la Imprenta de la Compañia de Jesvs, 1738
Rio de Janeiro, Brazil	Antonio Izidoro da Fonseca	1747	Rousado da Cunha. Relação da entrada que fez ... d. Fr. Antonio do Desterro Malheyro, Bispo ... Rio de Janeiro, na segunda officina de Antonio Isidoro da Fonseca, 1747*
Ambato (near Quito) Ecuador	Jesuit Order	1754 Equipment subsequently transferred to Quito	Catalogus personarum ... Provinciæ Quitensis Societatis Jesu. Confectus anno 1754. Ambato: Typis eiusdem Societatis [1754]
Quito, Ecuador [Transferred from Ambato]	[Jesuit Order]	1760 Although a license was granted for printing in 1741, no evidence is known of printing at that early date	Aguirre, P. Juan Bautista de. Oracion funebre ... á la feliz Memoria del Ilmo. Señor Doctor D. Juan Nieto Polo del Aguila, Obispo de la ciudad de Quito. Quito, 1760†
Nueva Valencia, [Venezuela]	Unknown	1764	Cisneros, Joseph Luis de. Descripcion exacta de ... Benezuela. Valencia, 1764 Two copies known: British Museum, *London;* John Carter Brown Library, *Providence*

* For reference to another imprint of 1747, a 'Thesis' known in one copy, at the Jesuit College in Rio de Janeiro, see p. 146.   † The first imprint checked for location in Medina's *Quito* is his copy of the *Breve Relacion* of 1766.

A Tentative Table of The Introduction of Printing into Hispanic America — *Continued*

Place	First Printer Known	Establishment of Press	First Imprints (credited and extant)
Nueva Orleans, Mexico [*i.e.*, Louisiana]	Denis Braud A French printer who was granted a license by the French government just before Louisiana passed under the control of Spain	1764	Extrait de la Lettre du Roi, a M. Dabbadie, Directeur Général . . . a la Louisianne. [New Orleans] Denis Braud [1764] One copy known: Edward A. Parsons, *New Orleans* O'Reilly, Alejandro. Don Alexandro O Reilly, Comendador . . . Nueva Orleans [Denis Braud], 1769 The first known imprint in Spanish, said to be in the type of Denis Braud. One copy known: Howard Memorial Library, *New Orleans*.
Córdoba del Tucumán, Argentina	Jesuit Order	1765 Equipment subsequently transferred to Buenos Aires	Clarissimi viri D. D. Ignatii Duartii et Quirosii. Cordubæ Tucumanorum: Typis Collegii R. Monsserratensis, 1766 One copy known: José Toribio Medina, *Santiago de Chile*
Santiago, Chile	Unknown	1776	Modo de Ganar el Jubileo Santo . . . En Santiago de Chile, 1776 One copy known: Biblioteca Nacional, *Santiago de Chile*
Buenos Aires, Argentina	Local Orphanage ("La Imprenta de los Niños Expositos")	1780 With equipment from Córdoba	Don Iuan Iosef de Vertiz y Salcedo, Comendador . . . A broadside in facsimile in Medina's *Imprenta en Buenos Aires;* signed and dated in manuscript 'en Buenos Ayres á diez y seis de mayo de mil setecientos y ochenta.'
Puerto España, Trinidad	Don Juan Cassan	1786	Chacon, José Maria. Ordenanza publicada en el Puerto de Espana, el 11 de Agosto de 1786. De la Imprenta de Don Juan Cassan [1786] Archives of the Indies

A Tentative Table of The Introduction of Printing into Hispanic America — *Continued*

Place	First Printer Known	Establishment of Press	First Imprints (credited and extant)
Guadalajara, Mexico	Don Mariano Valdés Tellez Giron	1793	Elogios fúnebres . . . la buena Memoria de su Prelado el Illmô. y Rmô. Señor Mtrô. D. Fr. Antonio Alcade. Guadalaxara: En la Imprenta de Don Mariano Valdés Tellez Giron, 1793 Two copies known: British Museum, *London;* José Toribio Medina, *Santiago de Chile* Novena de la milagrosa Imágen de Nuestra Señora de Aranzazú. Reimpressa en Guadalaxara en la Imprenta de D. Mariano Valdés Tellez Giron, 1793 One copy known: José Toribio Medina, *Santiago de Chile*
Veracruz, Mexico	D. Manuel López Bueno	1794 With the possibility, based upon blank clearance papers dated Vera Cruz 1745, that printing began at that early date	Alabanzas al Nombre Santisimo del gloriosisimo patriarca Sr. S. Joseph. Reimpreso en Veracruz por D. Manuel López Bueno, 1794 Two copies known: John Carter Brown Library, *Providence;* José Toribio Medina, *Santiago de Chile*
Santiago, Cuba	Unknown	1796	[Gazeta de Santiago de Cuba. 1796]
	D. Mathias Alqueza	With the possibility that printing was introduced by the publication of Hechavarria's *Carta á todos los Médicos,* in 1771, although this title has now been attributed to Havana.	Oses de Alzua, Joaquin. Exhortacion A todos los Fieles de la Diocesis de Cuba . . . publicado en la Gazeta de 19 de Junio de 1798. Impresa en el Colegio Seminario de Cuba, por D. Mathias Alqueza [1799] One copy known: José Toribio Medina,* *Santiago de Chile*

* Various bibliographical works by Sr. Medina record the introduction of printing into Montevideo (by the British, in 1807); Caracas (1808); Puerto Rico (1808); Cartagena (1809); Guayaquil (1810); Mérida de Yucatán (1813); Curazao (1814); Tunja (1814); Popayán (1816); Santa Marta (1816); Angostura (1819); Arequipa (1821); Querétaro (1821); Santo Domingo (1821); El Cuzco (1822); Maracaibo (1822); Panamá (1822); and Trujillo (1823); and the publications of the opposing armies in *La imprenta del Ejército Libertador,* 1820–1825 and in *La imprentoa del Ejército Realista,* 1821–1825.

North America, 1639–1800

Exactly a hundred years after the first press in North America had been established in Mexico,[2] and very nearly a hundred and fifty years after Columbus and his 'ocean fleet' set sail for the New World, a printing office was opened in the British American colonies. This first press was set up close to Harvard College, possibly in the home of President Dunster, and operated by Stephen Daye, the latter being sometimes credited with having introduced printing into the territory now within the United States. Daye, however, started for America in the employ of the Reverend Josse Glover, a sponsor for Harvard College; but Glover died in the summer of 1638 while he and Daye, whom he had secured to run the press for their mutual support, were crossing the Atlantic. From the beginning made at Cambridge in 1639, printing gradually spread throughout the British colonies. By the outbreak of the Revolutionary War, it had become well established in each of the thirteen colonies that were destined to form the United States. By 1776, according to the count in Evans's *American Bibliography,* 14,638 imprints had been issued and these, the surviving titles from that early period, represent only a portion, probably little more than a third, of the total number of works which were printed.

The history of printing in America is, in a sense, a step aside from the study of Americana. That is, in the study of Americana of the sixteenth and the later centuries, printing no longer occupies the position of individual importance that it held in European history during the fifteenth century. By 1539, and still more by 1639, the art of printing had become an established economic factor in the progress of civilization and the opening of a provincial printing press promised merely an opportunity for local self-expression. Thus the coming of a printer to a new field has a place of importance in the history of that region; whereas, once the press had become established, and it and its subsequent rivals a matter of course in that locality, the imprint on a book — the name of the place, printer, and date of its printing — becomes a means of identifying the place and

---

[2] For an account of early printing in Mexico, see the preceding section on Hispanic America.

period of the work issued, rather than a thing in itself. In other words, the emphasis changes from the career of the printer as a man, to the subject of the books which he produced and to their part in the development and thought of the community. The printer himself is looked upon as a business man. He is no longer the apostle of a new order in the means of transmitting thought. It is for this reason that emphasis is here placed upon the introduction of printing into each colony, rather than upon its subsequent growth, although a more detailed survey, on the same basis, might be made to include the introduction of printing into each town. With the printing shop an accepted part of everyday life, the books produced within each community, great or small, become properly a part of its literary history. The Press Restriction Acts which sought to restrict printing in England to London, York, and the universities, happily were not enforced to the exclusion of printing in America, with the result that, in its early days in the colonies, the diffusion of printing was relatively more general than in the mother country.

Whoever would write of early American presses must have recourse ultimately to the *History of Printing in America* by Isaiah Thomas of Worcester, printer and antiquarian. Thomas's span of life, running from 1749 to 1831, gave him personal knowledge of a period in which the printing press played a particularly important rôle in the history of our country, and the innate interests which led him to found the American Antiquarian Society caused him to unearth and to record many a tale of colonial bookmaking of earlier days. His style is simple and free. There is nothing perfunctory in his bio-bibliographical history of American printers and presses. He treats of his craft as a master would speak of a violin which he loves, and he brings to his task a wealth of antiquarian lore. It is the second edition, 1874, which the student should read, since that posthumous reprint follows the annotations made by Isaiah Thomas during his latter years. Yet, in the course of the reading, it should not be forgotten that information regarding various important points has been greatly increased through later research. For this reason, Thomas's *History*, even in its revised edition of 1874, should be read for its antiquarian and human interest; and precise questions of date and precedence should be gathered from later sources.

A condensed but comprehensive account of the introductory period of typography in the British colonies and in Canada is given in Mr. Lawrence C. Wroth's essay in Peddie's *Printing, a Short History of the Art,* 1927. Evans's *American Bibliography,* in the course of its first ten volumes lists the known imprints of the region now comprised in the United States, year by year, from 1639 to 1796. Mr. Updike devotes a chapter of his *Printing Types* to a discussion of types used in the American colonies from the time of the first Cambridge press.

The most recent treatise is Mr. Wroth's volume on *The Colonial Printer,*[3] the result of an intensive study of the colonial press in New England, the middle, and southern colonies; of the equipment of the colonial printing house and the colonial printing press; of type faces, paper and printing ink in colonial days; of such allied topics as the general conditions of the trade, journeymen and apprentices, and bookbinding; and of the general character of the books themselves. Its period runs from the establishment of the first press to 1780, with especial emphasis upon the typographical history of the colonies between the first press of 1639 and that licensed to James Johnston in 1762 in Savannah, Georgia, the last of the English colonies to acquire a press; and with careful explanations and the weighing of evidence in questions of dates and precedence. In the intervening century and a quarter, writes Mr. Wroth, more than one hundred master printers had been at work in twenty-five towns, and in the year that Johnston set up his printing house in the thirteenth colony about forty presses were in active operation throughout the country. The press had become in this epoch a mobile vehicle for the conveyance of ideas, and the story of its beginnings in the American communities has interest of peculiar quality for those who love to keep in memory the spiritual struggle of that pioneer people, dwelling far from its intellectual sources, keenly though unconsciously set on the business of evolving a culture of its own that even yet has not become the distinctive thing to which it is tending. It is because the formation of this American culture has been carried on independently in distinct, geographically defined groups that in the outline of printing beginnings now to be

---

[3] Now in press.

The Influence of England, France, and Mexico upon The Colonial Press

BRITISH ISLES

Cambridge, Mass.
(*Stephen Daye*, 1639)

Boston, Mass.
(*Marmaduke Johnson*, 1674)
(*John Foster*, 1675)

Philadelphia, Pa.
(*William Bradford*, 1685)

* Burlington, N. J.
(*Samuel Keimer and Benjamin Franklin*, 1728)

New York, N. Y.
(*William Bradford*, 1693)

* Perth Amboy, N. J.
(*William Bradford*, 1723)

Woodbridge, N. J.
(*James Parker*, 1754)

Charleston, S. C.
(*Thomas Whitemarsh*, 1731)
(*Lewis Timothy*, 1733)

Wilmington, Del.
(*James Adams*, 1761)

Baltimore, Md.
(*Nicholas Hasselbach*, 1765)

Jamestown, Va.
(*William Nuthead*, 1682)

St. Mary's City, Md.
(*William Nuthead*, 1686)

Annapolis, Md.
(*Dinah Nuthead*, 1696)

Williamsburgh, Va.
(*William Parks*, 1730)

Newbern, N. C.
(*James Davis*, 1749)

New London, Conn.
(*Thomas Short*, 1709)

Newport, R. I.
(*James Franklin*, 1727)

Portsmouth, N. H.
(*Daniel Fowle*, 1756)

Charleston, S. C.
(*Eleazer Phillips, Jr.*, 1731)

Savannah, G..
(*James Johnston*, 1762)

Dresden, Vt., now Hanover, N. H.
(*Alden and Judah Padock Spooner*, 1778)

Westminster, Vt.
(*Judah Padock Spooner and Timothy Green*, 1780)

FRANCE

New Orleans, La.
(*Denis Braud*, 1764)

MEXICO

Monterey, Cal.
(*Unknown printer*, 1833)
(*Agustin Vicente Zamorano*, 1834)

MEXICO?

Santa Fé, New Mexico
(*Imprenta de Ramon Abreu á Cargo de Jesus Maria Baca*, 1834)

* Of temporary duration only.

presented the sectional relationships have been emphasized rather than the chronological order of the first establishment in the several colonies. In the foregoing table, which shows the influence of England, France, and Mexico upon the colonial press, and which is here reproduced through the courtesy of Mr. Wroth and of Mr. Frederick Coykendall, Chairman of the Publications Committee of the Grolier Club of New York, "chronology has given place to lines of influence, genealogically presented, and cold priority has yielded to spiritual affinity":

Nevertheless, cold priority becomes a matter of interest as one studies the gradual introduction of printing into colonial life and the influence which the printing press was destined to exert in the days of pre-Revolutionary discussion. The basis for this is the skeleton outline of the introduction of printing into each colony. Strangely in keeping with the ethos of America, the first issue from the first press was [*The Freeman's Oath*] on record as having been printed in the winter of 1638–39. This was shortly followed by the publication of William Peirce's [*Almanack*] said by Thomas to have run from March 1639 through the following February, as was the custom in 'old style' calendars.[4] The third production of the Cambridge press, a more pretentious affair, was the metrical version of the *Whole Booke of Psalmes*. This issue of 1640, which is the first 'American' imprint now known to be extant, has been reproduced in facsimile by Mr. Eames and described in his *List of Editions of the " Bay Psalm Book,"* as it is commonly called. In 1648, the Cambridge press passed into the hands of Samuel Green, the subsequent head of a family of colonial printers, whose personal claim to glory rests largely upon his production of various translations for the instruction of the natives. In 1661, in company with Marmaduke Johnson, Green brought out the Reverend John Eliot's remarkable translation of the New Testament into the local Indian dialect. In 1663, a stupendous work, the complete " Eliot Indian Bible " was issued by these temporary partners, both the Old and the New Testaments be-

---

[4] A custom which prevailed until 1752, when the Gregorian calendar was finally adopted by England. Prior to 1752, England's legal and ecclesiastical year began on March 25; and events occurring in January, February or before March 25 of a given year are rated, in ' new style ' reckoning, as in the following year. Thus, the date of the Revolution of February 1688, may be transliterated either as February 1689 ' new style,' or as February 168$\frac{8}{9}$.

ing printed in the local Indian dialect. The history of the first half century of the press is recorded in Roden's *Cambridge Press, 1638–1692;* and *The Early Massachusetts Press, 1638–1711,* is discussed in the work of that title written by G. E. Littlefield for the Club of Odd Volumes in 1907. Marmaduke Johnson, who had been sent to America to assist Samuel Green in issuing the Indian Bible, subsequently ran an independent press in Cambridge for nearly a decade. Just before his death in 1674, and after considerable effort, he succeeded in securing a license to print in Boston. In 1675 by right of purchase from the estate of Johnson, John Foster, the first engraver in the British colonies, opened the first Boston printing office. His bibliography, beginning with *An Almanack* and two sermons by Increase Mather issued in 1675, is given in S. A. Green's *John Foster, the Earliest American Engraver and the First Boston Printer.*

The next colony to have a press was presumably the Quaker settlement in Pennsylvania, although — as described in Lawrence C. Wroth's *History of Printing in Colonial Maryland, 1686–1776 —* an attempt to establish a press in Jamestown, Virginia, and its prohibition by the King's order in 1683 had caused Virginia's deposed printer to set up his press in St. Mary's City, Maryland, either before or during 1686. The first Maryland imprint, from the press of William Nuthead in St. Mary's City, as recorded in Mr. Wroth's *Colonial Printer,* is the [*Declaration of Reasons and Motives for the Present Appearing in Arms of their Majesties Protestant Subjects in the Province of Maryland*], known only through its London reprint of November or December, 1689. Nuthead's press is known to have been carried on by his widow, who later moved to the new capital, Annapolis. Although none of her imprints are on record, several exist from the press of Thomas Reading, the second printer.

The first Pennsylvania imprint was the *Kalendarium Pennsilvaniense* printed by William Bradford in Philadelphia in 1685. With this as a beginning, Hildeburn's *Century of Printing* records between four and five thousand titles issued in Pennsylvania between 1685 and 1784, during which time "the Bradfords, Franklin, Bell, the Sowers, the German Pietists at Ephrata, the Dunlaps, Goddard, the Halls, and other active printers in and near Philadelphia expressed in type the active intelligence of their community." Several years after the opening of Pennsylvania's first press, William Bradford was arrested and brought to trial because of his publication of George Keith's controversial tracts, one of which was claimed to be seditious. The story is that one of the jury, in attempting to decipher the type in the printing form which had been produced in court, dropped the chase thus dislocating the type and destroying the evidence of its anonymous printing. Perhaps it was the ill-feeling caused by the trial (or was it the honorarium "of fourty pounds Current money of Newyorke per annum for his sallary & have the benefite of his printing besides what serves the publick ") that caused William Bradford's acceptance of New York's solicitation for a printer.

Bradford removed to New York in 1693 and during that year eased his mind by publishing (presumably in New York) *New England's Spirit of Persecution transmitted to Pennsilvania* and *A Paraphrastical Exposition on A Letter from a Gentleman in Philadelphia*, the latter known in a single copy only. His main activity, however, was in printing official papers, since it was "for the printing of our Acts of Assembly & publick papers " that a local printer had been desired. The first of these to bear a New York imprint, and an imprint date, was *An Act for raising six Thousand Pound for the payment of three Hundred Volunteers . . . to be imployed . . . at Albany*, which appeared in two issues in 1693 and was probably preceded on the press by three known Acts of earlier origin.

In 1928, the bibliographical details of *The First Year of Printing in New-York, 1693–1694*, were set forth in a monograph by Mr. Eames, together with an authoritative account of Bradford's affairs, quite as interesting as the quaint story of the loss of the printing form. The publication of Mr. Eames's researches illustrates the fact that bibliographical works should be consulted with due regard to their own date of imprint. Mr. Eames's monograph of 1928, for instance, brings forth information unrecorded in Hildeburn's *List of the Issues of the Press in New York, 1693–1752* or in his *Sketches of Printers and Printing in Colonial New York;* and even Mr. Wroth's paragraph on New York in the 'Peddie volume' of 1927 was published without the benefit of Mr. Eames's critical study of the introductory period. In order to understand the history of the colonial press in New York, therefore, the student must build his data upon a comparative study of all these sources, their evaluation and verification; and the results of such a study will be found in the pages of Mr. Wroth's *Colonial Printer*. In such a study, it is generally advisable to read the most modern bibliographical work first, and from that point to work backward into the history of the case.

Two events of importance in the first century of 'American' printing occurred at the beginning of the last decade of the seventeenth century. A paper mill, destined to be the forerunner of a thriving industry, was established near Philadelphia, at Germantown, in 1690. In the same year, the first newspaper within the territory of the United States — the *Publick Occurrences, both Forreign and Domestick* — was issued in Boston in a single number, September 25, 1690, and immediately suppressed. In 1704, the history of the American newspaper made a second and permanent start with the issuing of *The Boston News-Letter* of April 24. Although numerous monographs have been published on the bibliographical aspects of colonial newspapers, the definitive work on this subject, which is of amazing volume, is Mr. Clarence S. Brigham's *Bibliography of American Newspapers, 1690–1820*.

The first colony to open a press in the eighteenth century was Connecticut. In 1709, Thomas Short, moving from Boston to New London, took over the printing of papers of the Connecticut Assembly which, up to this time, had been published in Cambridge or Boston. The activities of Connecticut's first printer, which have been described in a monograph by W. De L. Love and in Trumbull's *List,* include a broadside proclamation for a fast in Connecticut printed by Thomas Short in June 1709. This is sometimes ranked as Connecticut's first imprint, but it usually gives place to *An Act for Making and Emitting Bills of Publick Credit,* on the ground that the Act itself was passed prior to the order for the fast.

In Rhode Island, printing was started in Newport in 1727 by James Franklin (brother of Benjamin Franklin), who became involved in political difficulties in Boston and in that year issued, in Newport, *John Hammett's Vindication and Relation* giving an account of his separating from the Baptists, and joining the Quakers; and, (presumably toward the end of the year) *The Rhode*

Island Almanack, For . . . 1728. By Poor Robin. The latter work, known in one copy only, was issued in facsimile in 1911. Mr. C. E. Hammett's *Contribution to the Bibliography and Literature of Newport* was issued in 1887, and the subject has been more recently treated in a compilation of titles made by Miss Rebecca P. Steere and others, entitled *Rhode Island Imprints. A List of Books, Pamphlets, Newspapers and Broadsides Printed at Newport, Providence, Warren . . . between 1727 and 1800.* Mr. Howard M. Chapin's essay in the ' Eames volume ' relates to *Ann Franklin of Newport, printer, 1736–1763.*

Virginia, whose effort to open a printing office in Jamestown had been forestalled by Royal edict nearly fifty years before this time, somewhat redeemed herself, typographically speaking, by the fact that in 1730 William Parks (a Maryland printer, who in that year established a branch office at Williamsburg, Virginia) printed John Markland's *Typographia, an Ode on Printing.* The publication in 1926 of Lawrence C. Wroth's monograph on *William Parks, Printer and Journalist of England and Colonial America. With . . . a Facsimile of the Earliest Virginia Imprint Known to Be in Existence* (the *Charge to the Grand Jury* of the Hon. William Gooch, 1730) has had the desirable result of bringing new matter to light regarding Virginia's first successful press. A list of *Additions* to the William Parks imprints was published by Mr. Wroth in The New York Herald Tribune's section on *Books,* Sunday, September 11, 1927. In his table of first certain imprints included in his *Colonial Printer,* the first Williamsburg imprint is listed as [*The New Virginia Tobacco-Law*] 1730, of which no copy is known. As indicated in the table by the use of brackets, Governor Gooch's *Charge* is undisputed in its rank, as the " earliest Virginia imprint known to be in existence." Clayton-Torrence's *Trial Bibliography of Colonial Virginia,* which relates to the period from 1608 to 1776, includes works about Virginia as well as those printed within the state.

Two presses, started in South Carolina in the last months of 1731, were brought to a close by the deaths of their owners. Although it is believed that a newspaper was started by Eleazer Phillips, Jr., the first of the short-lived printers, only the name of it exists, but copies are known of *The South Carolina Gazette* which was published by his rival, Thomas Whitemarsh, up to the time of his death. This was later revived by Lewis Timothy who established the first permanent printing office in the colony in Charleston, in 1733, under the auspices of Benjamin Franklin. A bibliographical account of *The First Presses of South Carolina*, from 1731 through the Revolutionary War, was written by A. S. Salley, Jr. for the second volume of *Proceedings and Papers* of the Bibliographical Society of America.

In 1749, sixteen years after Lewis Timothy established his shop in Charleston, a press was opened by James Davis of Virginia in Newbern in the colony of North Carolina. Davis continued as public printer until 1777, and without a rival until 1764. Although Weeks's monograph on *The Press of North Carolina in the Eighteenth Century* cites *A Collection of All the Public Acts of Assembly*, 1751, as the first dated work of North Carolina, the *Journals of the House of Burgesses* of 1749, of which no copy is on record, is believed to have been Davis's first imprint.

The colony of New Hampshire, as in the case of New York and Rhode Island, owed the opening of its first press to a printer's persecution in another colony. As in the preceding century, this was an age in which men had the temerity to think. They expressed their convictions unhesitatingly (and anonymously) in print, in matters both religious and political; and in the harrassing consequences the printers often shared. In 1756, Daniel Fowle, who had been jailed and fined for a work criticising the Massachusetts Assembly and attributed to his press, removed to Portsmouth. According to a surviving copy of Ames's *Almanack*, printed by Fowle in 1757, "The first Printing Press set up in Portsmouth, New Hampshire, was on August 1756; the Gazette publish'd the 7th of October; and this Almanack November following." Evidently the *New Hampshire Gazette* of October 7, 1756 — New Hampshire's first newspaper, and presumably its first imprint, save for its Prospectus — was issued beneath a fixed star. It stands today as "the oldest newspaper in the United States."

During the preceding year, James Parker, a newspaper printer of wide repute of New York and New Haven, returned to his native town of Woodbridge, New Jersey, and opened the first permanent

New Jersey press. Two earlier imprints, however, exist: the New Jersey *Acts* of 1723 which, according to its title-page, was printed by William Bradford in Perth Amboy in 1723; and the *Acts* of 1727–1728 " printed and sold " in Burlington by Samuel Keimer in 1728. These debatable imprints are ably accounted for by Mr. Wroth, in his essay in the ' Peddie volume.' The issuing of paper money during each of these years, it seems, might well have occasioned the temporary activity of a printing press in New Jersey, since Franklin and Keimer are known during the winter of 1727–1728 to have been in Burlington for the purpose of issuing currency. The earliest imprint, so far as known, from Parker's Woodbridge press was *The Votes and Proceedings of the General Assembly of the Province of New Jersey . . . April 17, 1754 . . . June 21, 1754*. Nelson's *Check-List*, according to its title-page, includes the ' issues of the press of New Jersey, 1723, 1728, 1754–1800 '; and an essay by him on *Some New Jersey Printers and Printing in the Eighteenth Century* was issued by the American Antiquarian Society in 1911. The immediate publication is expected of a bibliography of New Jersey imprints, based upon a recent survey.[5]

Two other colonies, Delaware and Georgia, acquired local printing offices before the Revolution. No bibliography is as yet devoted to early Delaware imprints, although a monograph on the subject is known to be well under way.[5] Several pieces are listed in Hildeburn's *Century of Printing. Issues of the Press in Pennsylvania* as having been printed by James Adams in Wilmington, Delaware, in 1761. The only extant issue among these is Thomas Fox's *Wilmington Almanack* for 1762.

The first Georgia press dates from its first known imprints, the *Georgia Gazette* of April 7, 1763, and *An Act to prevent stealing of Horses and neat Cattle* of 1763, although an Act for the encouragement of its printer James Johnston ' lately arrived in this province from Great Britain ' was passed by the Georgia Assembly in March 1762. The circumstances relating to the installment of *James John-*

---

[5] Several bibliographies are in process of compilation, as theses for the degree of Master of Arts in the School of Library Service in Columbia University. Among these, the bibliographies of Miss Constance Humphrey on New Jersey imprints, of Miss Dorothy L. Hawkins on Delaware imprints, and of Mr. R. Webb Noyes on Maine imprints are expected to appear in the near future.

ston, first Printer in the Royal Colony of Georgia were recorded by
Mr. Douglas C. McMurtrie in *The Library* of June, 1929.

In the course of the eighteenth century, three events occurred
which had a bearing upon the approaching Revolution. The results of the trial of a prominent New York printer in 1735 (described in Rutherfurd's *John Peter Zenger. His Press, his Trial and
a Bibliography of Zenger Imprints*) introduced into the colonies
the principle of the liberty of the press — thus, in the words of
Gouverneur Morris, inculcating ' the germ of American freedom.'
Thanks to the experiments in type-cutting made by Abel Buell as
early as 1769 and by Fox and Bey (in Germantown) after 1770,
the establishment of the ' American ' type-founding industry made
the colonists in that respect economically free of England by the
time of the Revolution. Mr. Wroth's essay on *The First Work with
American Types*, in the ' Eames volume '; his discussion of the
origins of type-founding in North and South America, in the April,
1926 issue of *Ars Typographica;* and his monograph on *Abel Buell
of Connecticut*, recount the beginnings of type-founding in the colonies, between 1769 and the end of the century. Simultaneous with
this beginning and likewise under pressure of the needs of the times,
the press built in 1769 by Isaac Doolittle of New Haven, for William
Goddard of Philadelphia, marks the beginning of the ' American '
printing-press industry. The first ' all-American ' book — as to
paper, types, and ink — the now unknown *Impenetrable Secret,* was
advertised by a Philadelphia press in 1775.

In the days of pre-Revolutionary discussion, the printers made
their decisions one by one and ranged themselves on the side of the
radicals or of the Tories, according to their political sympathies and
convictions. The extent of their industry during this period is made
evident by the imprints, nearly five thousand in number, which are
listed in Evans's *American Bibliography* between 1765 and 1776.
The fate of James Rivington, Tory printer of New York, has been
made the subject of an essay by Mr. George H. Sargent, in *The
Americana Collector* of June, 1926. The conditions in New York's
newspaper world during the Revolution have been discussed by Mr.
I. N. Phelps Stokes in the first volume of his *Iconography of Manhattan Island.* A bibliography of the newspapers and the separately

printed works of Philip Freneau, the 'poet of the American Revolution,' has been compiled by Mr. Victor H. Paltsits. Paul Leicester Ford's two volumes, entitled *Journals of Hugh Gaine Printer*, record the issues from Gaine's New York press from 1752 to 1800; and a survey of Mr. Brigham's *Bibliography of American Newspapers* would indicate the variety of newspapers in circulation in the thirteen revolting colonies during the years from 1765 to 1784. The *Gazette françoise*, a newspaper printed on the French fleet anchored in Newport harbor, has been reproduced and described by Mr. Howard M. Chapin in a Grolier Club monograph.

Throughout the twenty-year span of the Revolution and its prewar discussions, the two hundred or more presses operating during that period were busily engaged in setting type not only for newspapers but for political tracts, the official papers of the Continental Congress, proclamations, the laws of the respective colonies, town ordinances, tracts on the controversy over an American Episcopate, sermons on the anniversary of the Boston Massacre or on the burning political questions of the day, and for the usual run of almanacks, primers, textbooks, and juvenile literature — a total in all, according to Mr. Evans, of 8,761 pieces. In general, the bibliographies and monographs covering this period, such as those listed below in the section of Selected Bibliographies, treat of these imprints by subjects rather than by printers. The bibliographical material relative to the period of reconstruction is likewise customarily treated by subjects. During these later years, American presses concerned themselves with public documents, Fourth of July sermons, the political and economic writings of the great leaders of the times — Hamilton, Franklin, Jefferson, Madison — travels, histories, and at the end of the century with reviews of Washington's patriotic career, in the flood of funeral orations and eulogies, which followed his death in December 1799.

During the troublous days of the Revolution, the Vermont press came into existence. In 1778, Alden Spooner set up a press in the border town of Dresden which, during the following year, passed under the jurisdiction of New Hampshire. The products of Alden Spooner's first year of work, and of his possibly occasional partner Judah Padock Spooner, are recorded in the bill for services rendered to the state. The first entry in the bill, which is still extant, is for blank commissions printed for the State of Vermont. The second is a dual entry for printing a Thanksgiving proclamation, now known in one copy, and an election sermon. Each of these entries was made while Dresden was politically a part of Vermont. Nevertheless, the question exists in the minds of some bibliographers as to whether or not they should be ranked as Vermont pieces. Fortunately for the history of Vermont typography, the press licensed to Judah Padock Spooner and Timothy Green in 1779 or 1780 was set up in Westminster, Vermont, on non-debatable ground. Gilman's *Bibliography of Vermont* relates largely to works about Vermont, rather than to the imprints of the State. Mr. H. G. Rugg's paper on *The Dresden Press* lists the first dated imprint as 1779.

After the Revolution, the printing press no longer clung to the coastwise states. In the words of Mr. Wroth's note on the subsequent diffusion of printing: " The successful close of the Revolution saw an immediate movement of emigrants to the free lands beyond the mountains. From Philadelphia, through Lancaster over the Laurel Hills to Pittsburgh and the Ohio country; from Maryland and Virginia, through Cumberland to Pittsburgh over the trail made for the passage of Braddock's slaughtered army; from Virginia and the Carolinas, through the Cumberland Gap to Kentucky; from New England and New York to Buffalo and the Lake Country — these were the lines the people followed in that sudden piercing of the Appalachian barrier, and wherever the pioneer ventured, the printer quickly followed."

Thwaites' *Ohio Valley Press Before the War of 1812–15* describes the opening in 1786 of the first press west of the Alleghanies, in the frontier town of Pittsburgh. In the following year, the first Kentucky imprint (likewise a *Gazette*) was issued at Lexington, by John and Fielding Bradford, on August 11, 1787. Wiley's essay on *Eighteenth Century Presses in Tennessee* begins its typographical record with the issue, on November 9, 1791, of *The Knoxville Gazette;* and the Thwaites monograph just referred to records the issuing of *The Centinel of the North-Western Territory* two years later at Cincinnati, Ohio. A further account of these journals will be found in the interesting chapter on " Newspapers and Maga-

zines," and in the appended bibliographies, in R. L. Rusk's *Literature of the Middle Western Frontier, 1925.* These first imprints
afford indisputable proof of the important part which the publication of the news had come to assume in the lives of the people, since
the suppressed issue a hundred years before of the first newspaper
in the British colonies. According to the list of 'Printers and
Publishers' in Evans' *American Bibliography*, printing was 'instituted in District of Maine, 1785, A. D.' in the town of Falmouth.
A bibliography of Maine imprints, it is said, will soon be off the
press.[6]

The printing of music, which as noted in Metcalf's *American
Writers and Compilers of Sacred Music* was introduced into the
colonies in 1698, is further described in Metcalf's *American
Psalmody*, a checklist of books containing tunes and printed in
America from 1721 to 1820. Howe's directory of *Music Publishers
in New York City before 1850*, published in Volume XXI of the New
York Public Library *Bulletin*, contains several entries prior to 1800.
Sonneck's *Bibliography of Early Secular American Music* relates
largely to eighteenth century material. *The Music of the Ephrata
Cloister*, which is the title of a monograph by J. F. Sachse, contains
facsimile reproductions of portions of various Ephrata imprints
dating from the *Gebethe*, 1745 or before. The *First Century* of
German Printing in America, 1728–1830, an important factor in
Pennsylvania's typographical history described by Seidensticker,
was published in 1893 by the German Pionier-Verein of Philadelphia. French newspapers in the United States before 1800
provide the general topic for a series of contributions by G. P. Winship and others, in the 1920 volume of the *Papers* of the Bibliographical Society of America. In the 'Eames volume' of 1924,
Mr. Henry W. Kent contributed a paper on a French Philadelphian
press, entitled *Chez Moreau de Saint-Méry, Philadelphie*, with a
list of twenty-four imprints between 1795 and 1797 developed with
the coöperation of Mr. Winship. Mr. Charles Evans's *American
Bibliography*, with its lists of printing towns and presses at the end
of each volume, has now nearly reached the year 1800. And
Monsieur Faÿ, in a Grolier Club publication of 1927, has contributed

[6] See note on p. 162.

to the history of printing a volume of *Notes on the American Press at the End of the Eighteenth Century.*

In the territories adjoining the thirteen original colonies, and their western reaches, four provincial presses were established between 1751 and 1776. Had it not been for the death of Bartholomew Green, Junior, soon after he transferred his Boston press to Halifax, the earliest of these would have been a direct typographical descendant of Massachusetts's second printing house. As it was, the project of opening a press in Nova Scotia passed into the hands of John Bushell of Boston. The latter, in January 1752, issued the *Halifax Gazette,* the first known Canadian imprint. The circumstances attending the introduction of printing into this northern province are described in Isaiah Thomas's *History of Printing in America* and in the note on Canada in Mr. Wroth's contribution to the ' Peddie volume '; while the career of the *Halifax Gazette* during the enforcement of the Stamp Act has been recounted by Thomas.

Quebec is credited with a private press within the middle decade of the century. According to the arguments advanced by Monsieur Philéas Gagnon in his *Essai de bibliographie canadienne,* a mandate issued by the Bishop of Quebec may have been printed in Quebec in 1759 and another in Montreal during the autumn of the same year. Printing, however, is definitely known to have been in process directly after Canada was added to the British Dominions in 1763. Two printers from the British colonies immediately moved to Quebec and established the firm of Brown and Gilmore. The first number of their *Gazette de Québec* was issued June 21, 1764. The account book of the firm seems to indicate the *Presentment of the Grand Juries* as their first separate piece other than a newspaper, and Languet's *Le Catéchisme du diocèse de Sens* of 1765 as the first separate piece published solely for their French-speaking clientèle. Monsieur N. E. Dionne, in the *Inventaire chronologique des livres,* published by the Royal Society of Canada, groups the French and English imprints of the province in independent volumes, the bibliographies in each instance extending from 1764 to the date of publication. Close to a hundred titles were issued in Quebec between 1764 and the end of the century. Wright's *Early Prayer Books of America* describes the Indian Prayer Book printed at Quebec in 1767 and other Indian works printed in Quebec and Montreal; and the *Charlemagne Tower Collection of American Colonial Laws* includes laws printed in Halifax in 1767 and in Quebec during 1767 and later years.

One of the last acts of the French government, before the southern colony of Louisiana was ceded to Spain, was the granting of a printers' monopoly to Denis Braud of New Orleans. By a curious anomaly of Fate, the first issue from the press was the *Extrait de la Lettre du Roi a Monsieur Dabbadie, Directeur Général, commandant pour sa Majesté, a La Louisianne* conveying, to the distress of the French inhabitants of Louisiana, the news of their separation from the mother country. The career of Denis Braud, and the subsequent relations of this French press to the Spanish officials of the province, have been described by Mr. Wroth and Mr. McMurtrie, the latter in a monograph entitled *Early Printing in New Orleans, 1764–1810. With a Bibliography of the Louisiana Press.*

Fleury Mesplet was the first commercial printer of Montreal — for the good Bishop, Henri-Marie Dubreil de Pontbriand, providing he printed or caused to be printed a broadside in Montreal in 1759, can hardly be counted under that head. In 1776, Mesplet who, under the encouragement of Benjamin Franklin, had been endeavoring to carry on French printing in Philadelphia, was sent to Montreal by the Continental Congress, to aid in securing support from its French inhabitants. After various vicissitudes — one of the most trying of which was no doubt the period of uncertainty following the withdrawal of the American army of occupation — the Montreal press was established. Its first issue was the *Réglement de la Confrerie de l'Adoration perpétuelle du S. Sacrement,* 1776, a 'nouvelle edition,' since the work had been previously printed by Mesplet in Philadelphia. The story of the hardships encountered by *Fleury Mesplet, the First Printer at Montreal,* and of the financial support rendered by Charles Berger, has been told by Mr. Mc-Lachlan in the *Transactions* of the Royal Society of Canada in 1906. The *Transactions* of 1920 contain Mr. McLachlan's notes on *Some Unpublished Documents relating to Fleury Mesplet;* and an account of the Mohawk-English primer issued on Mesplet's press in 1781, while Mesplet himself was in prison, has been given by Mr. McLachlan in the *Canadian Antiquarian and Numismatic Journal* of April 1908. In 1791, Canada was officially divided into the two provinces of Upper and Lower Canada; and each province was granted the privilege of a legislature composed of a popular assembly and a legislative council, the latter being nominated by the British Crown which also retained the right of veto.

Less than three hundred and fifty years after Gutenberg began his experiments in making metal types, printing presses were in operation in the New World, from Quebec to Buenos Aires. And less than three centuries and a half after Columbus, in private audience with Ferdinand and Isabella, had explained his project of sailing westward overseas, a New World had been repeopled by colonists from the Old; and, with the exception of Canada and certain minor colonies in South America, the colonists of two continents had freed themselves from European control and embarked upon a new political adventure of their own, stimulative in its principles, even yet problematical in its world-wide results.

REFERENCE SECTIONS

REFERENCE SECTION I

NOTES AND DEFINITIONS

CONTENTS

I. Bibliographical Points [1]

---

[1] Bibliographical terms such as *colophon, explicit, format, chain-lines, gathering, incipit,* etc., which are discussed in the main text of this volume, are not defined here since the sections relating to them may be found through the index, under: Bibliographical Methods, Terms and Usage (Incunabula).

NOTES AND DEFINITIONS

1. Bibliographical Points

Americana. — In general, *Americana* is a progressive term which, beginning with the discovery of America, may cover a variable period according to circumstance, relating to the Western Hemisphere or to its development, whether in whole or in part. For instance, *colonial Americana* (a sense in which the term *Americana* is frequently used) is generally accepted to mean the period from 1492 to the close of the colonial era within each American province. The final date for Americana relating to the British colonies is thus set after the Revolutionary War, frequently at the year 1800; the final date for Spanish Americana varies from 1810 to 1824; whereas interest in a section of hitherto undeveloped territory may occasion the placing or extending of its period of Americana later than that of an established community, as in the case of California and of various sections of the West.

In its usual application, *Americana* may be said to comprise all that has been printed *about* the Americas, printed *in* the Americas, or written *by* Americans, with a frequent restriction of period to that of the formative stage in the history of the two continents or their constituent parts. The term as technically used in a bibliographical sense does not apply to manuscripts, although manuscript source material comprises an equally important basis of American history. Only the study of printed source material belongs to the realm of bibliography. Since this work treats only of bibliography, neither its text nor its reference sections relate to manuscript sources or to their study through deciphering, transcription, or calendaring.

In general, *Americana* may be said to comprise all that has been printed *about* the Americas, printed *in* the Americas, or written *by* Americans, with a frequent restriction of period to that of the formative stage in the history of the two continents or their constituent parts.

Blank leaf. — A blank leaf is the unprinted unit of one of the folded sheets comprised within a quire or gathering. Such a leaf sometimes occurs because the printer allowed a leaf at the beginning of the book, as a protection to the text; in other instances, if the text failed to cover all of the final quire of paper, a blank leaf would be left at the end; in still others, if two or more presses were working simultaneously in printing sections of the book, one printer might end with an unused leaf at the close of his allotment of text, thus occasioning a blank leaf midway in the book. Sometimes, in early books, such a leaf is preceded by a printed Latin phrase stating that no portion of the text is lacking.

The value of the blank leaf consists not in its blankness — as the emphasis in some sales catalogues might lead us to think — but in its presence. Provided that it is an *original* (that is, that it is an integral part of the original sewed fold or signature) its presence proves that a *printed leaf* is not lacking. Had it been torn out, the gathering in its imperfect state would have left one in doubt as to whether or not some portion of the text were missing.

The first step to be taken in dealing with a blank leaf is to see, from the count of the leaves, if it may legitimately be a part of the signature. If that is the case, then one must seek to determine if the blank leaf is actually a part of the signature (*i.e.,* not an insertion). Bookbinders in their laudable desire to insert end-papers harmonious with the paper of the book, and certain bookdealers, in their un-laudable desire to dispose of a copy that is seemingly perfect, may have inserted a leaf closely similar to the original. The blank leaf must therefore be studied with especial care before its presence as an original may be claimed.

It is under such circumstances that one sees a bookman open his volume and, holding it horizontally on a level with his eyes, pull gently and alternately upon each of the conjugate (or conjoined) leaves in the gathering or sewed fold. Does one pull seem to answer the other? That is, are the two leaves — the blank leaf and its conjugate in the gathering — part of the same piece of paper? Or, if the entire signature, or gathering, will pull up ever so little at the base of the binding, can he see that its first and last leaves are one continuous sheet? If so, he knows that the blank leaf is genuine and his query is answered. If not — if the binding is so tight that the leaves will not respond to his gentle pull, and so tight that, in examining the gathering of paper at the base of the binding, he cannot follow out the sheets and their conjugates — then the matter must remain open until evidence is forthcoming.

The comparative thickness and flexibility of the paper may tell him something. By holding various leaves against the light, he may measure the distance between a given number of chain-lines in each, and compare this measurement with the distance between the same number in the blank leaf; or he may find a watermark at intervals throughout the book. If by good fortune, the blank leaf bears a watermark, it may be found to correspond to others in the book; or, better still, if part of the water-mark is on the blank leaf and part on its conjugate, then the case is proved.   Unless there is the unquestionable proof of the continuous sheet, or of the duplicated or continuous watermark, the blank leaf should not be counted as original.   Unless the proof is certain, then such a phrase as *124 ff.* (*last leaf blank*) cannot be employed; the case should be stated *124 ff.* (*last leaf blank, probably wanting*) if there is any ele-ment of uncertainty; or, *124 ff.* (*last leaf blank, wanting*) if evidence shows it is not an original, the use of the two latter phrases of course presupposing that, in the collation of the book, with the entries in vari-ous authoritative bibliographies, the fact has been established that a perfect copy should have a blank leaf in its make-up.   (The fact that the text may come to an end on the next to the last leaf of the signature is not, in itself, sufficient to prove that a blank leaf should follow, for an index, a table, or some supplementary matter might well have been printed on the original last leaf of the signature.)

Blockbooks. — Although contemporary with incunabula, the so-called blockbooks are of an entirely different genus.   Incunabula com-prise the books issued during the fifteenth century whose texts have been set up and printed *with movable metal types.*   Blockbooks, although produced during the same period, are those printed *a full page at a time,* each page being printed from a wooden block which had first been carved with the illustrations and text for the entire page.   Such books are some-times called 'xylographic books,' or 'xylographica,' meaning that they are wood-engraved throughout.

Condition. — A copy of a book is said to be *unique* when no other copy of that edition, or issue, is on record; *perfect* when collation shows its quires to be complete, and its text to be complete or its total number of leaves to correspond to the total in authoritative bibliographies; *im-perfect* when some portion is found to be lacking; *uncut* when the width and proportions of the margins and the edges of the leaves, from their roughness, indicate them to be of the original size (in which considera-tion the presence of an original binding often adds weight;) *cropped* when the margins have been cut so closely that the text has been dam-aged; *unopened* when the folds at the side or top of the quires have not been slit, a circumstance which rarely occurs in incunabula but is not un-common in Americana; *untouched,* when not rubricated nor illuminated.

With the exception of *unique, perfect,* and *unopened,* these terms are more or less relative. They may be qualified respectively, according to circumstance, by such adverbs as *slightly, presumably, somewhat, badly,* etc.

Copy. — The term *copy* is used, in bibliographical lore, in the sense of *specimen.* To say that one has *two copies* of the same book is another way of saying that one has *two specimens* of the same issue or edition. To say that a book is *the only known copy of the first edition* of a work means that it is *the only specimen of the first edition which is known to be in existence.* (The term is *not* used to indicate that one book has been copied from another: for the terms which are used to indicate re-production, see below under *Facsimile and reprint.*)

Edition. — A book may be said to be of *another edition* when it is of an *entirely different setting* of type, that is, when the book has been en-tirely reset by the same or another printer.

The terms *first* and *second edition* should not be assigned unless there is a valid, chronological reason for giving one edition precedence over the other. Unless the precise chronology is known, some descrip-tive phrases should be employed which will differentiate between them, as *the 27-line edition,* and *the 28-line edition.* If each edition is thus described by an outstanding feature, there can be no confusion.

(After a minute examination of two copies of a work has proved them to be of the same typesetting, and therefore of the same edition, it not infrequently happens that the page-for-page and line-for-line col-lation (and, if necessary, a minute comparison of the relative position of given words in various lines) will show slight differences, as the omission or reversal of letters, minor alterations in type or possibly in typesetting, etc., these variations being either of an *accidental* or *inconsequential* nature. Since a slight chronological difference would be implied by calling one of these editions a variant of the other, it is better to select a salient feature for description, as *the 37-line edition, with running-titles in black letter,* and *the 37-line edition, with running-titles in italics;* or *the 38-line edition, with ' ordiation' on p. 6, l. 2* and *the 38-line edition, with ' ordination' on p. 6, l. 2.*)

The number of an edition, as stated on the title-page of a book, cannot always be taken literally, as the number is sometimes erroneously given. Evidence has been known to prove that the statement of edition was used as a means of concealing a pirated edition, or an unauthorized reprint. In other instances, a duplication of numbering may have resulted if two printing offices were at work simultaneously in reprinting an earlier edition. If there is sound evidence to prove that the edition is not as stated on the title-page, the latter should be transcribed exactly as in the original, and it should then be stated in a note that the book is of *the so-called ' 5th edition,'* with a brief explanation of its real status and some indication of the reason for the assignment.

(See also below, under Issue.)

Facsimile. — A facsimile is a lithographic or a photomechanical reproduction of an original, or of some portion of it, made for the purpose of presenting an accurate picture of the original. The term is thus defined in order to include the facsimiles which (in earlier days) reproduced, by the lithographic process, tracings that had been made by hand; and which (in modern times) are made by one or another of the mechanical processes that are based, fundamentally, upon some form of photographic reproduction.

In general, a reproduction may be called a facsimile when it is a process, or photomechanical, reproduction of a selected original as against the *reprint* which may serve to suggest the picture of an original, by means of a setting of type. The terms *facsimile reproduction* and *facsimile reprint* are also used to indicate photomechanical reproduction, although the latter term introduces an unfortunate ambiguity.

Facsimiles are of two kinds, those which can be printed on the same page with type, from *line-blocks* or from *half-tone* plates; and those which have to be separately printed by processes called *photogravure, heliogravure, heliotype,* or *artotype.* The facsimiles made by these latter processes are the more exact, since they reproduce every characteristic of the original so minutely that even the texture of the paper, and the blemishes upon it, are clearly brought out.

(See also below, under Reprint.)

Folio. — When the word *folio* is abbreviated as *F.* or *ff.* the reference, in the first instance, is to a leaf within the book; and, in the second, to the total number of leaves comprising the book — *i.e., F.* 124 refers to leaf 124; whereas 124 *ff.* means that the book has a foliation, or total, of 124 leaves.

When the word *folio* is abbreviated as *f., f °.,* or *fol.,* it designates the size or format of the volume. For a discussion of the make-up of a folio volume, see Chapter II, above, Incunabula: Identification and

Collation. If the gatherings, within a folio volume, each comprise two folded sheets, the gathering itself is sometimes called a *duernus* [plural, *duernions*]; when they comprise three folded sheets, a *ternus* [*ternions*]; or, if made up of four folded sheets, a *quarternus* [*quarternions*]. If a larger number of folded sheets is included within the gathering, as an aid to the binder in sewing the quires together, the whole may be spoken of as a *folio in 8s* or a *folio in 10s*.

Imprint. — An imprint is the statement at the bottom of a title-page which gives the place of printing; the name of the printer, or publisher, or both; and the date of printing. Although the term refers technically to the statement of the facts regarding the issuing of a book, it is sometimes used to designate the book itself; as, an imprint from an early American press. Since title-pages are not common to incunabula, the term is usually applied to books of later date — although, since the term *imprint* is derived from the root of the word *Imprimatur,* the official authorization ' Let it be printed,' which is sometimes found in early books — its use in a generic sense is not inapplicable to a book of any period.

Incunabula. — This is a bibliographical term applied to books *printed with movable metal types* during the latter half of the fifteenth century. It is thus a specialized application of the classical word meaning *swaddling clothes,* a *birthplace,* or a *beginning,* not inappropriately applied to the origin and infancy of printing, as the time ' when the printing art lay in the cradle.' The German term *Wiegendruck* (cradle printing) embodies the same quaint idea of infancy.

The period of so-called incunabula (which is also sometimes called the period of Early Printed Books) extends from about 1450 to the year 1500. That is, it covers slightly over fifty years; for, several brief ephemeral pieces are known to have been printed during the decade prior to 1450. It has been stated with some justice that, if the period of infancy were to be limited to the introduction of new features, it might be closed at the year 1476; or, if it were to be extended until the passing of the old school of printers, it might reach to about 1520. The year 1500, however, is universally accepted as the end of the period. This fixed date is not so arbitrary as it might seem. As noted in Chapter I, certain principles of book-building, introduced into the books printed before 1500, have not altered materially in succeeding years. At the time of the incoming century, the experiments and innovations attempted by various fifteenth century printers had either been dropped as impractical or adopted permanently; the essential principles of book-building had become established; and printing had won for itself a place among the enduring enterprises of the day. Hence, the year 1500 is not an inappropriate date for the end of the period.

A disquisition on the term 'incunabulum' by Dr. E. von Rath is included in Dr. Haebler's catalogue of the von Klemperer collection, *Frühdrucke aus der Bucherei Victor von Klemperer.* Dresden, 1927.

Issue. — If the term 'edition' is reserved for a complete new setting of type, a book in which an important *portion* of its contents has been deliberately altered, reset, or enlarged, takes its place logically as *another issue.*

If two issues bear different dates, or if there is valid reason for chronological sequence (as in the case of the 1671 edition of Ogilby, in the second issue of which an engraving is omitted and four pages are reset in large type to cover the deficiency) the latter may justly be termed a *re-issue.* Otherwise (since the term 're-issue' implies chronological sequence) descriptive phrases may be used to better advantage, as *the issue with 3 paragraphs on p. 39,* and *the issue with 4 paragraphs on p. 39; the issue with the 11-line title-page,* and *the issue with 12-line title-page; the issue with 'To the Reader' on p. 5,* and *the issue with p. 5 blank;* or, in the case of a joint production by two printers, *the issue with imprint: Mexici excudebat Antonius Espiñosa, 1576,* and *the issue with imprint: Mexici excudebat Petrus Ocharte, 1576; the issue with imprint: Paris: Chez Louis Billaine, MDCLXXII,* and *the issue with imprint: Paris: Chez Claude Barbin, MDCLXXII.*

No hard and fast rule can be laid down in distinguishing between an edition with accidental variations and an issue with deliberate alterations. It is a matter of judgment. In many cases, one bibliographer may legitimately differ from another in such an opinion. It is for this reason that a qualifying phrase, giving a salient feature of the variation, is essential.

(See also above, under Edition.)

Portolan Charts and Portolans. — The term *Portolan charts* is used to designate the detailed and often very accurate maps used by mariners in coastwise sailing. Since they date from an early period, the majority of the portolan charts are in manuscript, often exquisite in their tracery.

The *portolan* itself is the book of sailing directions, so-called from the *Portolano* of the early Italian mariners. The first printed portolan is the *Portolano Rizo,* the anonymous *Questa e une opera necessaria a tutti li nauigāti,* printed by Bernardino Rizo at Venice in 1490 (reprinted in Kretschmer's *Die italienischen Portolane,* Berlin, 1909).

Press. — Many of the early printers worked in several towns in the course of their careers; others combined and re-combined with a varying group of partners, or alternately worked alone and in partnership with others. For the sake of clarity in identifying types, etc., a change of location is counted as a new press; a change in the make-up of a firm is counted as a new press if a considerable interval elapsed before the recurrence of activity. Changes in personnel, without interruption in the activity of the press, may be counted as (1), (2), and (3) in the history of that press. In the field of incunabula, each group of books which clusters about a title-book is tentatively counted as a press (as in the case of the group of anonymously printed books assigned to the 'Printer of the *Speculum Humanae Saluationis*' at Utrecht).

Printer's device. — By this is meant the device adopted by a given printer as an emblem for his press. Such a device, called also the printer's mark, is often found in incunabula as a decorative wood-engraving just below the colophon. In later books, it is found normally on the title-page above the imprint, in which case it is necessary to discriminate between a printer's device and an ornamental device which may sometimes occupy the same position. The printer's mark frequently bears his name or initials, or a symbolical reference to himself or to his craft.

For a list of monographs relating to printer's marks (many of which works, containing data later than the year 1500, are applicable also to Americana) see below, Section V, Incunabula, Selected Bibliographies and Bibliographical Monographs, section B. III, under *Printer's Marks.*

Registrum. — This is the register or list given at the end of Italian, French, or Spanish incunabula as an aid to the binder in arranging the gatherings. Such a registrum frequently comprises a list of the signatures, by the first letter or symbol of each (hence the word registration for signaturing); but it may comprise a list of the catchwords, or of the last words of each gathering.

In early German books, however, the registrum is ordinarily the index.

Reprint. — A reprint is a subsequent printing of a work, not as a new edition but as a re-rendering of text. For purposes of differentiation, reprints may be divided into two classes: (1) Literary reprints, which may be either a re-rendering of the text of a selected original, or an inter-collation of various copies or editions combined into a per-fected reading; (2) typographical reprints, which present a selected original in a new setting of type, frequently attempting, through the type-designs, arrangement, spelling, punctuation, etc., to suggest, as far as it is possible, the appearance of the selected original. It is only, of course, with the terms employed in describing typographical reprints that bibliography is concerned.

A *type-facsimile* is a reprint influenced typographically by the origi-nal, being as close a reproduction of the original as the resources of the modern printing press permit. It is not a facsimile, for it is not a photo-mechanical or process reproduction. It is rather a typographical re-construction, representing the original as closely as circumstances allow. It has sometimes been called a *line-for-line and page-for-page reprint,* which term, although cumbersome, has the advantage of describing its status unmistakably, being usable in a note although hardly appropriate to a title-page. It is also variously called a *type-facsimile reprint* and a *'facsimile' reprint,* the quotation-marks in the latter instance being used to convey the fact that, within its limits, the reprint endeavors to fulfill the functions of facsimile, without being an actual facsimile reproduction.

Frequently when a reproduction is not in facsimile throughout, it comprises a *facsimile* of the original title-page and a *reprint* of the re-mainder of the book. Care must be exercised, therefore, to use the terms *facsimile* and *reprint* with precision, not only in notes describing the book but in the collation as well.

(See also above, under Facsimile; and see *The Library*, March, 1926.)

2. COLLATION: TABULATED RECORD

The following suggestions for bibliographical analysis, according to the principles indicated in Chapter II, are applicable in general to books printed up to the end of the *sixteenth century.* Those points in the out-line which relate in particular to *fifteenth century* books are designated as for incunabula. For books of the *seventeenth* and *eighteenth* cen-turies, a consideration of points 1, 2, 3, 6, and 7 is presumably sufficient. (Grouping by centuries, in this way, is merely a convenient means of indicating the varying changes in treatment from earlier to later periods. The analysis of each book must be further determined by the character of the book itself, for no hard and fast rule can be laid down for the collation or analysis of any early book, whatever its period.)

A. Collation in which the tabulated record should comprise:

1. The *size* of the book according to make-up. (See Index, under *Format.*)

2. The analysis of the book by *signatures.* (See Index, under *Signaturing.*)

3. The total number of *leaves,* or of *pages.* (See Index, under *Foliation,* and under *Pagination.*)
   (In some bibliographies, the order of nos. 2 and 3 will be found reversed in the collation, an arrangement which is purely a matter of personal taste or convenience.)

4. The number of *columns* to the page, if the text is so printed. (In incunabula, the number of *lines* to the average page, as well as the number of *columns;* and, if desired, the number of lines on a *definite page,* with the size in millimeters of the type page of that page.
   (See Index under *Columns,* and[1] also under *Lines,* and *Type page.*)

5. The identification of the *type* — in early books as *Gothic* or *Roman;* in later books, only when *Black Letter* is used throughout, or for a major portion of the book. (See Index, under *Type, Identification of.*)

6. The presence of a *printer's device,* also of *illustrations, maps, diagrams,* etc., with their number if desirable. (In incunabula, the presence of *woodcut initials, printed marginal notes,* etc., should also be noted.) (See Index, under *Printer's device; Woodcuts,* etc.; *Cartography.*)

7. Following these factors of collation there should come a block of brief *notes,* comprising the following paragraphs:

   (a) The bibliographical *reference numbers* with which the collation of the copy has been found to agree; (see Chapter II above, Incunabula: Indentification and Collation; and Chapter III, Bibliographical Material; or Americana: Chapter I, Preliminary Survey.) (See also the various reference titles in the two lists of Selected Bibliographies and Bibliographical Monographs, at the end of the volume.)

   (b) A statement of *edition,* or *issue,* if such a statement is necessary;

---

[1] (In incunabula, the type measurement should also be given, according to the number of millimeters covered by twenty lines, on the page whose line-count is quoted above, under 4. See Index, under *Type measurement.*)

(See notes on Edition and Issue, above, under Notes and Definitions: Bibliographical Points.)

(c) *Imperfections* in the copy. (See Index, under Bibliographical Methods, Terms and Usage (Americana), (Incunabula).)

(d) A note on the *binding*, if it is of importance — *i.e.,* if it has been signed by a binder of repute; or if it is known to be a contemporary binding. (See Notes and Definitions: Early Bookbindings.)

(e) A statement of *provenance,* so far as previous owners of the copy are definitely known. (It frequently happens that (*d*) and (*e*) may be combined — as *Wodhull copy. Bound by Roger Payne,* the latter statement signifying that it is a signed binding.)

(Of the five concise paragraphs which may on occasion comprise the notes, two relate to the work as such, and three to the circumstances of the copy in hand. The distinction must be kept clearly in mind between variations in printing or in make-up, which constitute another issue, and the so-called accidents of condition which affect merely the given copy. See above, notes on Edition and Issue.)

In instances where no bibliographical descriptions of a book are to be found, the book should be re-collated by another person, or by the same person after an interval of a day or more. In either case, it is well to start with a fresh record-sheet and to build up the collation anew, comparing the two records afterward, point by point, in the interests of accuracy and of the proper evaluation of the bibliographical factors involved.

Fifteenth and Early Sixteenth Century Books. — When the analysis has been completed, and its factors verified as far as possible with all available bibliographies, a typewritten record of the analysis, such as is indicated above, should be dated and signed by the collator, marked with the press-mark of the book and filed for future reference. Meanwhile, the catalogue card should be made. Because of the fullness of the tabulated record, the catalogue card need be only very brief in its statements, in which case, of course, the fact that a complete analysis has been made, and the press-mark or location of the record, should be noted on the card. (See the following section on Cataloguing: Card Entries.)

Late Sixteenth Century, Seventeenth, and Eighteenth Century Books. — Although it may occasionally be desirable to file a tabulated record of analysis, in general, as time goes on, the bibliographical points which need be considered are so brief in their substance that the full analysis may be given on the catalogue card, and the device of the filed, typewritten analysis may be abandoned.   (See the following section on Cataloguing: Card Entries.)

3. CATALOGUING: CARD ENTRIES

It stands as an axiom that the entries on a catalogue card should be expressed as concisely as possible.   Brevity is quite easily attainable in the case of early works, whose collation has already been tabulated in detail, as suggested in the preceding section on Collation.   In the case of later imprints, each book must be considered separately, and treated according to its need.

In any case, on a catalogue card the author-entry will of course be followed by a brief title, and by the statement of place of printing, printer, and date.   Size should be given by format, even though it may sometimes be desirable to give exact measurements in parentheses.   Such points of collation should be given, and such notes briefly expressed, as will enable a person who consults the card to recognize at once the book he is seeking; or to determine, through its title-entry and its subject classification, whether the book is likely to serve his purpose.   Whenever possible, at least two reference numbers from authoritative bibliographies should be given in the notes, as such numbers often afford the most ready means of identification.   A duplicate card for important books is requested by the Library of Congress.

Incunabula and Earliest Americana. — Although Dr. Arnold C. Klebs in his *Desiderata in the Cataloguing of Incunabula* [2] presents a strong case for the ideal in the matter of author-entries, it must be remembered that, unless one has meantime mastered the *Gesamtkatalog* system, author-entries for these early books will be in a transitional stage until the completion of the *Gesamtkatalog* shall have made uniform entries, with dates of birth, etc., easily available.   The interval may be bridged by assigning the form which proves to be most commonly found and then cross-referencing from other author-entry forms if variant forms make it desirable.   (Whenever the *Gesamtkatalog* entries are used, it must be noted that although its Latin and other entries may be followed, care must be exercised not to include inadvertently a German phrase which, for our use, should be in English.)   If a more elaborate card is desired for incunabula, the ' Rules for Cataloguing Incunabula, Simplified Form,'

---

[2] Bibliographical Society of America.   Papers, X:3.   July, 1916.

drawn up by a committee of the American Library Association (*Papers and Proceedings, 1925*) may be used to advantage. Facts regarding the place of printing, printer, or date, which are not definitely stated in the colophon or on the title-page, may be supplied, in brackets. Whenever it is possible, subject-entries should be assigned to incunabula just as to other books. Although in shelving incunabula it is often desirable to arrange them chronologically by countries, and of course to keep them safely locked or in a treasure room, nevertheless their subject-content should be classified and recorded whenever circumstances permit. A discussion of this matter will be found in the section entitled The Ultimate Goal in Incunabula, Chapter II above.

In general, such an entry as this will suffice:

IC 55

Bible.   *Latin.*

[Biblia Latina.]
[Mainz: Printer of the 42-line Bible, 1450–1455?, *i.e.,* before August 1456.] 2 v. fol.

> *Gesamtkatalog der Wiegendrucke* 4201. Hain *3031. British Museum: *Cat.* 1:17. IC 55. Seymour de Ricci: *Cat.* (Mayence) 34 (2). ***Census*** p. 43 & 230.
> The so-called ' Gutenberg Bible.'
> Paper copy; with leaves from the first and second impressions, in the reset sections.
> King George III's copy.
>
> 1. Bible. *Latin.* Mainz, Gutenberg, c. 1450–1455? (42 lines)—Bibliography. 2. Bibliography—*Early Printed Books—15th century.* 1. Gutenberg, Johann, 1397?–1468.

This brief card serves to identify the British Museum's paper copy of the ' Gutenberg Bible.' The information and the bibliographical reference works cited in M. Seymour de Ricci's *Catalogue raisonné des premières impressions de Mayence,* and in the volume (just issued) of the *Gesamtkatalog* will lead one on into a general bibliographical study of the first printed Bible. Hain takes its part in the bibliographical history of the work. The *Census* lists the copies owned in America prior to 1918. And, in addition to its usual function as a bibliographical reference work, the detailed description of King George III's copy in the British Museum's *Catalogue of books printed in the XVth century* may be used in this instance, for purposes of illustration, to represent the typewritten record of collation which normally would be filed away, if one were describing an individual copy.

In the same way, the detailed study of various editions of the *Fasciculus temporum,* made some years ago as the present writer's contribution to the 'Eames volume,' may be allowed to stand for the cataloguer's filed record of collation; and a copy of the *Fasciculus* may be entered in card form in this simple fashion:

Inc.
R643F

[Rolewinck, Werner,]   1426–1502.
    Fasciculus temporum.   Cologne: Heinrich Quentell, 1479. fol.

Hain *6923. *Census* p. 93. Stillwell: *Fasc. temp.* (table B.)
A reprint of the text of the Winters edition of 1476, and of the index of the Götz edition of [1478]; with signature marks, a cut of the Adoration of the Magi, and some additional matter.
Imperfect copy.

1. Chronology. 2. Europe—*History, to 1474.* I. Title.

Later Americana. — Since the phrasing of Americana title-pages is frequently long and involved, the title-entry on a catalogue card must necessarily be given in a condensed form. In general a title-entry need comprise only the opening phrase on the title-page, provided it forms a *complete title-phrase* in its wording, and is indicative of the *subject matter,* or character, of the book.   Or, the title-entry may be a brief condensation of the title-page, in which case it should *begin with the words of the title,* and should follow the *exact wording of the title,* meanwhile being so dotted, to indicate omissions, as to give an adequate synopsis, and at the same time to remain in itself a *complete sentence or title-phrase.*   As may be imagined, the triple task is not always an easy one, of making the title tell its own story with due regard both to brevity and to precision in quoting its phrases.

If the make-up of a book is simple, a typewritten record of its analysis is not needed. The full collation may be put upon the catalogue card:

                                                    Am
                                                    T6g

  Smith, John,   1580–1631.

    The true travels, adventvres, and observations of Captaine Iohn Smith, in Europe, Asia, Affrica, and America, from...1593. to 1629...Together with a continuation of his generall history of Virginia, Summer-Iles, New England...since 1624. to...1629; as also of the...river of the Amazons, the iles...in the West Indies... London: Printed by J. H. for Thomas Slater, 1630. 6 p.l.,60 p. folded pl. sm.fol.

    Sabin 82851.
    The first issue, but with signatures F and G of the corrected impres-

                (Continued on next card)

                                                    Am
                                                    T6g

  Smith, John,   1580–1631.

    The true travels, adventvres, and observations of Captaine Iohn Smith, in Europe, Asia, Affrica, and America, from . . . 1593. to 1629 . . .   (Card 2)

    sion. With engraved coat-of-arms on verso of title-page, and the folded plate in its second state.
      Bound with this is his: The generall history of Virginia . . . London, 1627. King Charles I's copy. With the royal arms upon the binding.

    1. Voyages and travels.

In the card cited, the title-page has been greatly condensed. The full title will be found in Sabin 82851. In condensing the title for the card, the wording of the original has been followed exactly and, at the same time, the effort has been made to give the gist of the contents of the book as set forth in its title. The bibliographical features of the book have been brought out in the notes, after a collation of this — the John Carter Brown Library — copy with the points of variation described in the Sabin entry. The card may serve, therefore, as an example of an instance in which all the salient points are present. (If no variation of issue were on record, *i.e.*, if all copies presumably had the coat-of-arms on the verso of the title-page and no variations either in the text or on the folded plate, there would have been no object in recording these points upon the printed card. In other words, only such informa- tion is needed upon the card, as will enable historians and bibliographers to identify the book, or its issue — and if too many bibliographical fac- tors are involved to appear upon a card, they may be recorded on a typewritten record, separately filed.)

A simple work, in which no variations of issue are known, may be entered with the full collation on the card. Even the signaturing may be given if it seems desirable; but, whether given or not, the signatures should of course be collated in the process of cataloguing and their total used to balance the foliation, or doubled to balance the pagination, as the case may be.

                                                                   Am
                                                                   R2f

Chauncy, Charles,   1705–1787.

    A discourse occasioned by the death of the Reverned [*sic*] Jonathan Mayhew, D.D. late pastor of the West- Church in Boston. . .   Boston: Printed by R. and S. Draper, Edes and Gill, and T. and J. Fleet, MDCCLXVI. 40 p. 8°.

    Evans 10254. Ford: *Bibliotheca Chaunciana*, no. 39.

    1. Mayhew, Jonathan, 1720–1766.

In the four examples cited in this note, the first involved an elaborate bibliographical study preliminary to the making of the record of collation, a study so minute that, in the end, the copy could be differentiated by a phrase of a dozen words. In the second, after an equally detailed study of the work, the status of the edition could be summarized in a single sentence. In the third, so few bibliographical factors were involved that the full statement could appear upon the card. In the fourth, nothing was told because there was nothing to tell, beyond the fact that the work had been identified in two bibliographical works — in this instance, happily, both in a general work on Americana and in a monograph devoted to the works of the author. Regardless of the time which may be put into the collating and identifying of a work, it is only the barest essentials that are needed upon a card. It is the preliminary work, the supporting data, and the details of the collation-record which vary in length, rather than the card catalogue entry. That is purposefully reduced to simplest terms. Excepting in its condensation of involved titles, in giving size by format [which may be given also in linear measurement if desired], and in the quoting of reference numbers in the notes, the card catalogue entries for Americana prior to 1824 differ very little from the rules of general cataloguing. (For questions relative to collation, see the tabulated outline of Collation which precedes this section, and for a discussion of the points involved, see, Americana, chapter I, Preliminary Survey.)

4. EARLY BOOKBINDINGS

The study of early bindings, like Dr. Haebler's *Inkunabelkunde,* is an ' independent discipline.' It has no relation to the study of incunabula or early Americana except that, as an early book is not infrequently found in its original covers, one may become consumed with a desire to identify its binding — and the conscientious cataloguer to write some annotation in its honor.

A safe thing for an amateur to do is merely to call attention to the binding by some such phrase as this: *In an early stamped binding, brown leather over wooden boards, with metal clasps, corners, and bosses.* Thus, without attempting to assign the binding to locality or to date, one may convey some idea of its character by the simple use of descriptive terms. In other words, unless the collector or cataloguer is sure of himself, and with reason, it is well to avoid an attempt at assignment, devoting himself instead to a brief description which is so worded as to give a clue to the evidence which the binding may be expected to yield. Mr. G. D. Hobson suggests that cataloguers should be asked to give the subject, if the binding is decorated with a large panel stamp; and should be invited to learn certain phrases commonly used in describing early bindings, as:

Stamps used, five. — Round (dragon); square (monster); rectangular (foliage); circular (Tudor rose); free (fleur de lys).

Design. — Stamps massed in closely set rows; *or* Stamps set singly in lozenge shaped compartments; *or* Field of the boards divided by a St. Andrew's cross [*i.e.*, the main expanse of each cover divided off by a saltire or transverse cross — a cross like an X].

Thus, in becoming familiar with such phrases as these and the terms appended to this note, the amateur will gradually build up a scaffold of knowledge — that presently he may join the new critical school which has come into being within the last few years. In the titles listed toward the end of this section on bindings, certain of the older books relating to this subject are conspicuous by their absence, thus throwing emphasis upon the works of the newer and more constructive school of research. The critical study of early bindings is an alluring subject. One cannot but feel its charm in reading Mr. E. Ph. Goldschmidt's book on *Gothic and Renaissance Bookbindings,* London 1928, of which the following compilation of excerpts (quoted through the courtesy of Mr. Goldschmidt and of his publishers, Messrs. Ernest Benn, Limited, London) may serve as a brief summary.

History. — With the exception of the stamped bindings of the latter half of the twelfth century, "not until the beginning of the fifteenth century . . . do we find any general practice of book decoration in universal use in civilized Europe, for not before then did the annual production of new books attain such proportions that a recognized style and craftsmanship for this special work could be developed." — Page 3.

" The same sudden increase of book writing and book reading that led to the general adoption of this simple and easy fashion of decoration [stamped bindings], was also one of the determining factors which prepared the ground for that more momentous development: the invention of printing. . . . The fourteenth century witnessed the lowest degradation into which the Christian Church has ever fallen; the Great Schism brought about a total dilapidation of the churches, the abbeys, the schools and of clerical discipline. . . . This extremity of decay was followed by its natural reaction: a general yearning for thorough reform. . . . While the Church Militant deliberated in state at the

Councils, there was among the monks a quiet rallying round some few enthusiasts for ascetic discipline and the regular life of poverty, obedience, prayer and devout study." — Page 6. " So their later brethren of the reformed abbeys of the fifteenth century, by resuming the godly work of reading and writing as a religious duty, created with their own hands at first, and later with the aid of the printing press, the great libraries of Europe, which were the storehouse of all traditional knowledge and the mine in which the Renaissance scholars made their discoveries." — Page 7. " What the Brothers of the Common Life did for the propagation of the comparatively cheap books of devotion and other practical books for school use, for the laity or for the parish priests, was done for the great libraries and collegiate churches by the scholars and scribes of Windesheim . . . who gathered round Gerard Groot at Deventer." — Page 10. " The extant bindings from their libraries [Windesheim] are sufficient to convince us that every one of their houses had its own bindery." — Page 11.

Characteristics. — " Fifteenth-century bookbindings, whether from monastic or other binderies, are generally of strong leather (calf or pigskin) on wooden boards and are decorated with a framework of blind lines dividing the cover into compartments; these compartments are then ornamented with stamps produced by engraved metal dies. These binding stamps offer an infinite variety of subjects — animals, monsters, flowers, leaves and purely ornamental designs." — Page 16.

" There are, however, certain familiar types of bindings which, to the expert, immediately betray their origin at first glance, and we observe that the typical characteristics of fifteenth-century bindings belong to certain *regional groups.*" — Page 17. [For projections of the Augsburg, Erfurt, Vienna, Nuremberg, Paris and English types of binding, see Goldschmidt, pages 18–23. And for his discussion of regional types, significant stamps, and marks of monastic binderies, see pages 17–28.]

Identification. — " The chief source of error which vitiates the vast majority of publications on old bindings is the almost ineradicable tendency to attribute the binding to the town where the book is printed and approximately to the date of its publication." — Page 116. " If on such principles we were to estimate the lifetime of Mr. Henry Rivière, who has bound many Caxtons and Shakespeare Folios, as well as First Editions of Rudyard Kipling, we would have to conclude that he easily beats Methuselah's record." — Page 117.

" Books were invariably issued by their publishers in rough sheets, and . . . the organization of the book trade was such that the printers, wherever they were working, found no difficulty in marketing their goods in all parts of Europe." — Page 39. " Books travelled unbound in sheets all over Europe in all directions, and . . . at the great Book Fairs at Frankfurt and at Lyons the new publications of practically all countries were exposed for sale very soon after they left the press." — Page 43.

" The most . . . prolific presses were in Venice, Augsburg, Nürnberg, Antwerp, Lyons, London, great trading centres with well-organized communications with all parts of Europe, but not with any considerable proportion of potential book buyers among their residents. . . . But when we come to consider the geographical distribution of the *centres of bookbinding,* when we analyze the domiciles of those bookbinders about whom some data are available, we find them, very naturally, residing where their clients were most numerous: in the university towns. A very striking illustration of this fact is the town of Erfurt in the centre of Germany. The university of Erfurt, founded in 1379, was one of the most frequented in Germany in the fifteenth century, but printing at Erfurt remained very insignificant. . . . On the other hand we have, so far at least, twelve bookbinders who signed their bindings in full, and who have been traced in the Erfurt archives and university registers." — Pages 44, 45.

Internal evidence. — " If there is no early ownership entry at all discoverable in the book, the next thing to observe in trying to localize the binding, are the materials used by the binders. By this I do not mean the leather, about which we know little. . . . The accessory materials used by the binder, such as the paper lining of the covers, the manuscript vellum fragments on which the back is sewn, the constituent sheets of which the pasteboards are made up, are susceptible of reasoned description and often afford the best available clue to the binder's domicile." — Page 119.

" Vellum, being much stronger than any paper, was very much sought after by the bookbinders . . . and they seem to have bought up eagerly any scraps that they could get hold of. Such fragments are always worth deciphering." — Page 121. " Any casual bit of scribbling in the covers or on the fly-leaves of a binding may be of considerable value to us in determining the origin of a binding. . . . Almost any scrap of handwriting may lead to interesting conclusions about the history of the book before us, and is well worth examining and certainly worth preserving." — Page 122.

"I cannot earnestly enough pray all collectors, librarians, or any owners and custodians of old books, not to interfere with any scraps of paper or vellum found in their covers, and not to remove anything either written or printed from their bindings, whether on the ground that it is interesting or on the ground that it appears uninteresting! . . . There is no such thing as restoring an old binding without obliterating its entire history. Even if the restorer promises to leave 'everything as it was,' he cannot preserve such characteristic details as the attachment of the original bands to the boards, details that further research may well prove to be of decisive significance for determining the provenance of a book. If an old binding is nearly or completely falling to pieces, it should be preserved such as it is in a flannel-lined case, but it should never be patched, relined, rebacked, or otherwise barbarously treated. . . . Every book that has through the kindness of fate come down to us in its original binding through the centuries is a precious relic, bearing in a hundred hidden ways the whole tale of its history, and the hand that dares to 'renew it' destroys all that is significant, leaving nothing but an empty mask. As for the well-meaning people who deliberately remove the written or printed linings from old book covers 'because they are interesting,' the curse of Ernulphus on their vandalism!" — Page 123.

A Selection of Bookbinding Terms

Blind tooling. — The designs made by the impressing of the binder's tools upon the leather, without the use of gold. (See also below, Stamped Bindings.)

Board covers. — The foundation of each cover of a fifteenth century binding is almost invariably a wooden slab, sometimes half an inch in thickness. The boards are held to the book by the heavy cords to which the folded paper of the book is sewn and which are then frayed out, glued to the wooden covers, pounded hard and allowed to dry before the leather is stretched across the whole. Since modern usage applies the term 'board covers' to the cardboard foundations used in modern books, it is customary to describe early bindings as — in white [or brown] leather over *wooden boards*.

Bosses. — The small metal stubs or knobs sometimes part of the metal corners of a fifteenth century binding and which, when the book is placed upon its side, raise it slightly from the desk.

Cameo bindings. — Renaissance bindings bearing the reproduction of classic heads or designs from antique coins. (See Goldschmidt, p. 70–73.)

Catch. — The small metal base fastening the clasp to the side of the covers.

Clasp. — The metal buckle attached to the edges of the covers, thus holding the book tightly together to the exclusion of dust and book-worms. Leather ties are sometimes found attached, for the same purpose; and leather straps frequently join the clasp to the catch.

Compartments. — The square, lozenge-shaped, or triangular sections made by the intersection of fillets or ornamental bands.

Cuir-ciselé. — Freehand designs made by the skilful use of a pointed tool, a sharp knife, and a round punch for stippling the background; wrought directly on the binding, without the use of stamps or any mechanical device. Each book so bound is thus a piece of original craftsmanship. (See Goldschmidt, p. 75–82; Loubier, p. 69, etc.)

Diaper pattern. — An all-over design made by the repetition of one or more tools, sometimes close together in a panel, and sometimes placed at regular intervals in square or lozenge-shaped compartments.

Fillets. — The long lines tooled upon a binding to frame a panel, or to divide the cover into compartments.

Frame. — A rectangle made up of fillets, or of closely spaced compartments, and large enough to enclose a panel of appreciable size.

Free tooling. — An ornament not confined in a compartment of any sort. According to Mr. Goldschmidt, ' any tool the design of which is not enclosed within some geometrical form, such as a circle, rectangle, or lozenge.'

Gauffered edges. — The designs, usually in gilt, wrought upon the compressed edges of the leaves of the book.

Leather. — The study of fifteenth century leather must also be a special ' discipline,' since even those who, by the constant handling of old books, have learned to differentiate between the various kinds find it difficult to describe the identifying points in words. In general, it may be said that, in the early bindings, vellum, sheep and goat skin were quite commonly used in Italy; calf and doeskin in France, calf in The Netherlands, and England; pigskin in Germany, vellum in Spain and Italy. Rough soft doeskin, which does not admit of any tooling, was used now and then everywhere during the fifteenth century.

Vellum may perhaps be recognized by the facts that it often presents a hard glazed surface; and that, as it grows taut with age, its stamped designs have a tendency to flatten out. Unless one has developed a ' feeling' for leather — a quite slow-growing attainment — it is no doubt wise to cling to the non-committal statement — brown leather [or white] over wooden boards.

Lederschnitt. — The German equivalent of Cuir-ciselé [*q.v.*].

Loop. — The metal ring sometimes found attached to one edge of the back cover of a book, thus forming the first link in the metal chain which bound the book to some ancient reading desk.

Lozenge. — A diamond-shaped compartment.

Palmette. — A conventional leaf-shaped ornament.

Panel-stamp. — A labor-saving device developed at the end of the fifteenth century, by means of which the entire surface of a cover (or a large part of it) might be stamped by one tool, in a single operation.

Raised bands. — The heavy horizontal bands at the back of a binding, made by the cords upon which the folded sheets, or gatherings within the book, were sewn.

Roll. — A revolving metal disc with a series of decorative ornaments engraved upon its outer edge — a labor-saving device, adopted at the end of the fifteenth century, by means of which a repetition of certain motifs could be impressed in a continuous operation, instead of each being tooled in a separate impression.

Rosette. — A circular medallion containing a formal design, frequently some version of the Tudor rose.

Rubbing. — A pencilled reproduction, made by transferring the plastic impression of the cover-design upon thin paper.

Scroll. — A pennant-like shape, for the inclusion of a motto or of a binder's name.

Stamped bindings. — A term synonymous with blind-tooling and signifying the designs made by impressing the binder's tools upon the leather without the use of gold as an outline. The word ' stamp' is sometimes loosely used for the binder's tool, as well as for the impression made by that tool. The tool itself should properly be called the die.

Reference Works

The literature relating to the subject of bookbinding is of vast proportions; the books, however, which are really useful according to the
standards of the present time are not very numerous. A selection of the
more important of these is as follows:

GOLDSCHMIDT, E. P.   Gothic & Renaissance bookbindings.   London,
Ernest Benn, Ltd., 1928.   2 vols.

> A purposeful discussion and analysis of bookbindings. With an introduction
> giving the historical background of the subject and including: six imaginative
> drawings representing the 'typical' characteristics of the bindings of Augs-
> burg, Erfurt, Vienna, Nuremberg, Paris, and England; an account of the intro-
> duction of gold-tooling into Naples about 1480 and, under Neapolitan in-
> fluence, at the Court of Matthias Corvinus at Buda; a careful analysis of
> 268 bindings in the author's representative collection; special indexes giving
> binders' and booksellers' names; monastic binderies; ciphers and initials, sub-
> jects of panels, stamps, and rolls; and ninety-eight plates showing reproduc-
> tions of bindings. Fifty additional photographs are included in the limited
> Edition de Luxe. (For excerpts from Mr. Goldschmidt's introduction, quoted
> with the kind permission of the author and of Messrs. Ernest Benn, Ltd.,
> see above, at the beginning of this section on bookbindings.)

GOTTLIEB, T.   Bucheinbände.   Auswahl von technisch und geschicht-
lich bemerkenswerten Stücken.   Wien, 1911.

> A work of outstanding importance, containing 100 plates. Its introduction
> is a historical study of bookbinding based on serious critical research.
> A tribute to Dr. Gottlieb, with some account of his works, is given by E. P.
> Goldschmidt in *The Library*. Dec. 1929. Ser. 4, vol. X, no. 3, p. 274–281.

HULSHOF, A. AND J. SCHRETLEN.   De Kunst der oude Boekbinders.
Utrecht, 1921.

> An account of the early bindings in the University Library, Utrecht. Illus-
> trated with rubbings of early stamps and panels.

HUSUNG, M. J.   Bucheinbände aus der Preussischen Staatsbibliothek
zu Berlin.   Leipzig, 1925.

> A sumptuous volume, with reproductions of fifteenth century bindings among
> its one hundred plates, and authoritative text.

——   Aus der Frühzeit des Bucheinbandstempels.   (Pages 28–33 in
Zs. für Bücherfreunde.   N. F. 19, 1927.)

LOUBIER, H.   Der Bucheinband von seinem Anfängen bis zum Endes des 18. Jahrhunderts. 2te Auflage. Leipzig, 1926.

According to its critics this work is of rather uneven value; although not of the newer analytical school, hence uncritical in its estimates, it is handy, compact, and very systematically arranged. German bindings are said to be treated more fully and with much greater knowledge than those of other countries, and its chapter on cut leather bindings is said to be excellent.

WEALE, W. H. J.   Bookbindings and rubbings of bindings in the National Art Library, South Kensington. London, 1894–98.

This presupposes a considerable knowledge of the subject of bookbindings and is not illustrated.

WEALE, W. H. J. AND L. TAYLOR.   Early stamped bookbindings in the British Museum. London, 1922.

Contains a large number of drawings of binding stamps, and its descriptions are as admirable as in 'Weale.'

English Bindings and Binders

GIBSON, S.   Early Oxford bindings. London, 1903. (Bibliographical Society. Illustrated Monographs. X.)

This contains a chronological list of Oxford binders, c. 1180–1640; and a list of bindings, c. 1460–1647.

GRAY, G. J.   The earlier Cambridge stationers and bookbinders . . . London, 1904. (Bibliographical Society. Illustrated Monographs. XIII.)

HOBSON, G. D.   English binding before 1500. Cambridge, 1929 (Sandars Lecture at Cambridge University, 1927.)

—— Bindings in Cambridge libraries. Cambridge, 1929.

Mr. Hobson's two books together constitute the first attempt to deal comprehensively with the early English bindings decorated with small stamps, and are an important contribution to the study and the history of bookbinding.

German Bindings

HERBST, H.   Erfurter Buchbinder des 15. Jahrhunderts. (In: Archiv für Buchbinderei. Halle, 1926).

—— Nürnberger Lederschnittbände (In: Die Leipziger Stadtbibliothek und ihre Kleinodien. Leipzig, 1927).

JAHRBUCH DER EINBANDKUNST.   Herausgegeben von Hans Loubier und Erhard Klette. Leipzig, 1927–

> An annual of the bookbinding art, comprising to date: Erster Teil. Die alte Einbandkunst. Zweiter Teil. Die neue Einbandkunst.

LOUBIER: FESTSCHRIFT. Buch und Bucheinband. Aufsätze und graphische Blätter zum 60. Geburtstage von Hans Loubier. Leipzig, 1923. Edited by Dr. M. J. Husung.

RHEIN, A. Zur Geschichte der Stempeldruckeinbände. (Jahrbuch für Einbandkunst. Leipzig, 1927.)

> An account of Erfurt bindings, 1430–1530.

SCHWENKE, P. Die Buchbinder mit dem Lautenspieler und dem Knoten (In: Wiegendrucke und Handschriften. Festgabe für Konrad Haebler. Leipzig, 1919).

> An account of the lute-player and rope-knot designs used at Erfurt during the 15th century, by John Fogel and his successors.

Scandinavian Bindings

RUDBECK, BARON. Svenske Bokband. I. Stockholm, 1912.

Early Signed Bindings

GLAUNING, O. Ein Beitrag zur Kenntnis der Einbände Johann Richenbachs. (In: Die Leipziger Bibliothek und ihre Kleinodien. Leipzig, 1927.)

> (For a reproduction of a signed Richenbach binding, see also the frontispiece in: The John Carter Brown Library. *A list of books printed in the fifteenth century.* Oxford, 1910. This American-owned example of his work brings the total to 24 known bindings, signed and dated by Richenbach, between 1467–1475.)

HUSUNG, M. J. Das Porträtsignet des Johann von Paderborn als Bucheinbandstempel. (Sonderabzug aus dem Gutenberg-Jahrbuch, 1927.)

According to Mr. G. D. Hobson, to whose kindness I am indebted for various notes, there were more stamped bindings produced in Germany during the fifteenth century than anywhere else in Europe, and more has been written about them ' than in all the rest of the world.' Mr. Hobson's summary of German literature on early bindings and on the subject in general is as follows: There is much that has " to be laboriously discovered. Articles on bindings of every kind stalk majestically through *Zeitschriften* and *Archiven* and *Festgaben,* lurk unexpectedly in *Jahrbücher* and *Sonderhefte* and *Veröffentlichungen.* The *Archiv für Buchbinderei* (Halle, W. Knapp), a periodical devoted chiefly to modern binding, publishes nearly every month an article on the history of the art, usually of considerable interest. Much still remains to be done; but the lines, along which the art of decorating bookbindings developed, are gradually becoming clear. In another half a century, it should be possible to fill in with the details."

FOREIGN BIBLIOGRAPHICAL TERMS

ENGLISH	FRENCH	GERMAN
1. Author-entry	Fiche auteur Nom de l'auteur	Name des Verfassers
2. Blank (i.e., unprinted)	Blanc	Leer Unbedruckt
3. Blank leaf	Feuillet blanc	Leeres Blatt Unbedrucktes Blatt
4. Border	Bordure	Randleiste
5. Brackets [ ]	Crochets	Eckige Klammern
6. Broadside	Feuille volante In-plano Placard	Einblattdruck
7. Capital letter (upper-case letter)	Majuscule	Grosser Buchstabe Majuskel Versalie
8. Catchwords	Réclames	Kustoden
9. Collation	Collation	Kollation
10. Colophon	Achevé d'imprimer Colophon	Schlussschrift Kolophon
11. Color printing	Impression en couleurs	Farbendruck
12. Column	Colonne	Spalte
13. Column heading	Titre courant	Kolumnentitel Spaltenüberschrift
14. Copy	Exemplaire	Exemplar
15. Date	Date	Datum

ITALIAN	SPANISH	INDEX*
ome dell' autore	Entrada de autor	Abdruck, 53
	Ficha del autor	Abweichende Ausgabe, 68
	Nombre del autor	Achevé d'imprimer, 10
		Altezza, 27
anco	En blanco	Altura, 27
		Anchura, 72
		Anno, 65, 73
arta bianca	Hoja blanca	Anno di stampa, 16
		Año, 73
		Antiqua, Antiqua-Schrift, 54
egio [if ornamental]	Orla	Anverso, 52
argine [of margins only]		Assemblage, 25
		Ausgabe, 17
arentesi quadra	Corchetes	Bianco, 2
		Blanc, 2
oglio di carta stampato	Hoja impressa	Blanco, en, 2
solamente da una parte	por un lado	Blanco entre las líneas, 33
	Hoja suelta	Blatt, 34
		Blattzählung, 22
a majuscole	Mayúscula	Bogen, 56
		Bordure, 4
		Breite, 72
		Cahier, 51
ichiami	Reclamos	Caja de impresión, 63
		Capo-linea, 13
ollazione	Colación	Caractère bas de casse, 36
		Caractères, 64
ote tipografiche	Colofón	Caractères gothiques, 26
		Caracteres góticos, 26
		Caractères italiques, 32
tampa a colori	Impreso en color	Caractères romains, 54
		Caracteres romanos, 54
		Caractères typographiques, 64
olonna (*sing.*)	Columna	Caratteri, 64
(a due colonne, *plu.*		Caratteri corsivi, 32
a tre colonne, *etc.*)		Caratteri gotici, 26
		Caratteri italici, 32
apo-linea	Título del folio	Caratteri romani, 54
		Caratteri tondi, 54
		Carta, 34
semplare	Ejemplar	Carta aggiunta, 59
		Carta bianca, 3
Data	Fecha	Carta geografica, 37

* The numbers in the Index refer to those in the first column of this Table.

ENGLISH	FRENCH	GERMAN
16. Date of printing	Date d'impression	Druckdatum
17. Edition	Édition	Ausgabe
18. Editor (who has revised or edited the text)	Éditeur*	Herausgeber
19. Engraved on copper Engraving on copper	Gravé sur cuivre Gravure sur cuivre	In Kupfer gestochen Kupferstich
20. Exponent	Exposant	Exponent
21. Facsimile	Fac-similé	Faksimile Faksimile-Ausgabe
22. Foliation	Foliotage	Blattzählung
23. Folio (fo.; 2º)	In-folio (2º)	Folio (2º)
24. Format (size)	Format	Format
25. Gathering (folded sheets)	Assemblage	Lage
26. Gothic type	Caractères gothiques	Gotisch Gotische Schrift
27. Height	Hauteur	Höhe
28. Imprint (the book printed with movable metal types)	L'Imprimé	Druck
29. Incunabula	Incunables	Inkunabeln Wiegendrucke
30. Initial	Initiale	Initial Initiale

* In French *éditeur* may mean editor, but it more often means publisher.

ITALIAN	SPANISH	INDEX*
ıno di stampa	Fecha de impresión	Carte, 37
		Carte numerate, 40
lizione	Edición	Carticino, 59
		Carton, 59
Titore	Editor	Chiffré, non, 66
	Editor literario	Colación, 9
		Collazione, 9
		Colofón, 10
ciso in rame	Grabado en cobre	Colonna, 12
cisione in rame ·	Lamina grabada en cobre	Colonne, 12
		Colophon, 10
ponente	Exponente	Columna, 12
		Composizione tipografica, 63
csimile	Facsímil	Corchetes, 5
		Crochets, 5
		Cuadernillo, 51
umerazione delle carte (*leaves*)	Foliación	Cuarto, 50
		Data, 15
aginazione (*pages*)		Date d'impression, 16
		Datum, 15
		Druck, 28
folio (2º)	En folio	Druckdatum, 16
		Drucker, 46
ormato	Formato	Druckermarke, 47
		Druckername, 73
egatura	Reunion de pliegos	Druckerzeichen, 47
		Druckort, 45
		Durchschuss, 33
aratteri gotici	Letra gótica	Edición, 17
	Caracteres góticos	Éditeur, 18, 48
		Édition, 17
tezza	Altura	Editor, 18, 48
		Editore, 18, 48, 49
		Editor literario, 18
tampa	Impreso	Edizione, 17
tampato		Einblattdruck, 6
		Ejemplar, 14
		Entrada de autor, 1
ncunabuli	Incunables	Entrada de título, 62
		Esemplare, 14
		Esponente, 20
ettera iniziale	Inicial	Estampación, 60
	Letra inicial	Exemplaire, 14

* The numbers in the Index refer to those in the first column of this Table.

ENGLISH	FRENCH	GERMAN
31. Interlinear comments	Gloses interlinéaires	Interlinearglosse
32. Italic type	Caractères italiques	Kursiv Kursive Kursivschrift
33. Leading (between lines)	Interligne Ligne de blanc	Durchschuss
34. Leaf	Feuillet Folio	Blatt
35. Line	Ligne	Zeile
36. Lower-case or small letter	Caractère bas de casse Minuscule	Gemeine (*plu.*) Kleiner Buchstabe Minuskel
37. Map	Carte	Karte
38. Marginal notes	Manchettes	Marginalien
39. Musical notation	Notation musicale	Notendruck
40. Numbered leaves	Feuillets chiffrés	Gezählte Blätter
41. Octavo (8º)	In-octavo (8º)	Oktav (8º)
42. Page	Page	Seite
43. Parchment	Parchemin	Pergament
44. Parentheses ( )	Parenthèses	Runde Klammern
45. Place of printing	Lieu d'impression	Druckort
46. Printer Typographer	Imprimeur Typographe	Drucker Typograph
47. Printer's mark (or device)	Marque de l'imprimeur Marque typographique	Druckermarke Druckerzeichen

* For *issue*, see No. 68 *Varian tissue*.

ITALIAN	SPANISH	INDEX*
Glossa interlineare	Glosas interlineáles	Exemplar, 14
		Exponente, 20
Caratteri corsivi	Letra cursiva	Exposant, 20
Caratteri italici		Facsímil, 21
		Fac-similé, 21
		Faksimile, 21
Interlineazione	Blanco entre las líneas	Faksimile-Ausgabe, 21
	Regletas interlíneas	Farbendruck, 11
		Fecha, 15
Carta	{ Hoja	Fecha de impresión, 16
		Feuille, 56
		Feuillet, 34
Riga (*sing.*)	Línea	Feuillet blanc, 3
Righe (*plu.*)		Feuillets chiffrés, 40
		Feuille volante, 6
Minuscole	Minúscula	Ficha, 62
		Ficha de autor, 1
		Fiche auteur, 1
		Fiche matières, 62
Carta geografica	Mapa	Filigrana, 71
		Filigrane, 71
Note in margine	Notas marginales	Foglio, 56
		Foglio di carta stampato sola-
Note musicali	Notación musical	mente da una parte, 6
		Foliación, 22
Carte numerate	Hojas numeradas	Folio, 34
		Folio, in-, 23
n ottavo (8°)	En octavo (8°)	Foliotage, 22
		Formato, 24
Pagina	Página	Fregio, 4
		Gemeine, 36
Pergamena	Pergamino	Gezählte Blätter, 40
		Glosas interlineáles, 31
Parentesi	Paréntesis	Gloses interlinéaires, 31
		Glossa interlineare, 31
Luogo di stampa	Lugar de impresión	Gotisch, 26
		Gotische Schrift, 26
Stampatore	Impresor	Grabado en cobre, 19
Tipografo		Grabado en madera, 74
		Gravé sur cuivre, 19
Marca tipografica	Marca del impresor	Gravure sur bois, 74
(Impresa tipografica)		Gravure sur cuivre, 19
(Insegna tipografica)		Grosser Buchstabe, 7

* The numbers in the Index refer to those in the first column of this Table.

ENGLISH	FRENCH	GERMAN
48. Publisher (*i.e.*, pro- duced at the cost of)	Éditeur	Verleger
49. Publisher's mark (or device)	Marque de libraire	Verlegermarke Verlegerzeichen
50. Quarto (4°)	In-quarto (4°)	Quart (4°)
51. Quire	Cahier	Lage
52. Recto (upper side of a leaf)	Recto	Vorderseite
53. Reprint	Réimpression	Abdruck Wiederabdruck
54. Roman type	Caractères romains	Antiqua Antiqua-Schrift Lateinische Schrift
55. Rubrication	Rubriques, Les	Rubriken
56. Sheet (*i.e.*, before be- ing folded)	Feuille	Bogen
57. Signature marks	Signatures	Signaturen
58. Signature mark, added	Repère	Norm
59. Slip (supplementary, *or* cancel)	Carton	Karton Schaltblatt
60. Stamped impression (not printed with type)	Impression à froid Impression timbré	Stempelaufdruck
61. Text	Text	Text
62. Title-entry	Fiche matières	Sachtitel Titel

ITALIAN	SPANISH	INDEX*
ditore	Editor	Hauteur, 27
ibraio		Herausgeber, 18
		Höhe, 27
nsegna del libraio	Marca del editor	Hoja, 34
(or editore)		Hoja blanca, 3
		Hoja de papel, 59
n quarto (4°)	En cuarto (4°)	Hoja encartada, 59
		Hoja impresa, 6
uaderno	Cuadernillo	Hoja suelta, 6
		Hojas numeradas, 40
ecto	Anverso	Holzschnitt, 74
	Recto	Impresa tipografica, 47
		Impreso, 28
istampa	Reimpresión	Impreso en color, 11
		Impresor, 46
		Impression à froid, 60
aratteri romani	Caracteres romanos	Impressione, 60
aratteri tondi	Letra redonda	Impression en couleurs, 11
	Letra romana	Impression timbré, 60
		Imprimé, 28
ubriche	Rúbricas	Imprimeur, 46
ubricazione		Incisione in legno, 74
		Incisione in rame, 19
oglio	Pliego	Inciso in rame, 19
		Incunables, 29
		Incunabuli, 29
egistro	Signatures	In-folio, etc. cf. Folio, etc.
egnature		Inicial, 30
		Initiale, 30
egno		Inkunabeln, 29
egnale		Insegna del libraio, 49
		Insegna tipografica, 47
arta aggiunta	Hoja de papel	Intaglio in legno, 74
articino (if small)	Hoja encartada (cancel)	Interligne, 33
		Interlinearglosse, 31
mpressione	Estampación	Interlineazione, 33
		Issue, 68
		Jahr, 73
		Justification, 63
esto	Texto	Karte, 37
		Karton, 59
itolo	Entrada de título	Klammern, eckige, 5
	Ficha	Klammern, runde, 44

* The numbers in the Index refer to those in the first column of this Table.

ENGLISH	FRENCH	GERMAN
63. Type-page	Justification (of breadth only)	Satzspiegel
64. Types	Caractères Caractères typographiques	Typen
65. Undated (s.a., *sine anno*)	s.d. (sans date)	o.J.(ohne Jahr) Undatiert
66. Unnumbered	Non chiffré	Nicht numeriert Ungezählt
67. Variable (number of lines)	Variable	Wechselnd
68. Variant issue	Tirage avec différences	Abweichende Ausgabe
69. Vellum	Vélin	Velin
70. Verso (under side of a leaf)	Verso	Rückseite
71. Watermark	Filigrane	Wasserzeichen
72. Width	Largeur	Breite
73. Without name of place, printer, or year	Sans indices typographiques S.l.n.d. (Sans lieu ni date)	Ohne Ort, Drucker, und Jahr
74. Wood engraving	Gravure sur bois	Holzschnitt
75. Work, The	Œuvre Ouvrage	Werk

ITALIAN	SPANISH	INDEX*
omposizione tipografica	Caja de impresión	Kleiner Buchstabe, 36
		Kollation, 9
		Kolophon, 10
aratteri	Letras	Kolumnentitel, 13
ipi	Tipos	Kupfer gestochen, in, 19
		Kupferstich, 19
nza data	Sin fecha	Kursiv, Kursive, Kursiv-schrift, 32
		Kustoden, 8
on numerata (one leaf)	Sin foliación	Lage, 25, 51
on numerate (if more than one)	Sin foliar	Lamina grabada en cobre, 19
		Largeur, 72
ariabile	Variable	Larghezza, 72
on uniforme	Vario	Lateinische Schrift, 54
		Leer, 2
ariante	Variante de la tiraje	Leeres Blatt, 3
		Letra cursiva, 32
ergamena	Vitela	Letra gótica, 26
		Letra inicial, 30
erso	Reverso	Letra redonda, 54
	Verso	Letra romana, 54
		Letras, 64
iligrana	Filigrana	Lettera iniziale, 30
	Marca de agua	Libraio, 48
		Lieu d'impression, 45
arghezza	Anchura	Ligne, 35
		Ligne de blanc, 33
enza luogo, nome di ti-pografo, e anno	Sin indicaciones tipográfi-cas	Línea, 35
		Lugar de impresión, 45, 73
	Sin lugar de impresión, nombre de impresor, ó año	Luogo di stampa, 45
		Majuscole, 7
		Majuscule, 7
		Majuskel, 7
ncisione in legno	Grabado en madera	Manchettes, 38
ntaglio in legno		Mapa, 37
		Marca de agua, 71
)pera	Obra	Marca del editor, 49
		Marca del impresor, 47

* The numbers in the Index refer to those in the first column of this Table.

* The numbers in the Index refer to those in the first column of this Table.

LATIN CONTRACTIONS AND ABBREVIATIONS

CONTENTS

LATIN CONTRACTIONS AND ABBREVIATIONS

I. LATIN CONTRACTIONS AND ABBREVIATIONS IN
FIFTEENTH CENTURY PRINTED BOOKS

I. A selection of abbreviations found in colophons
and incipits of fifteenth century printed books
(in which it should be noted that the
long ſ is frequently used for s, u for v,
and j for i; and that variations in
type-design should be allowed for, in
recognizing the following contraction signs)

∼ or ‾ over a vowel frequently indicates the omission of n or m, as: Amẽ (Amen);
iṗressa (impressa); millesimoquadringētesi-
mo (millesimoquadringentesimo); nõ (non);
finitū et cōpletū est hoc opusculū (finitum
et completum est hoc opusculum); cũ
diligentia emẽdate (cum diligentia emen-
date)

∼ or ‾ over a consonant indicates in general the
omission of two or more letters, as:
p̃dicata (predicata); q̃ (quae); anno a
natiuitate dñi (anno a natiuitate domini);
in oppido Rostockceñ (in oppido Rostock-
censi); imṗssum (impressum);
speculaꝑ (speculatur); Deo G̃ras
(Deo Gratias)

∼ or ‾ occasionally indicates that a word is much

condensed, as : Pōti (Pontificatus) ; in domo fratrū clericoᴋ coīs vite (in domo fratrum clericorum communis vitꞏꞇaꞇe)

~ through þ may indicate the omission of ro, as : þfessores (professores); þlogus incipit (prologus incipit) ; þpter (propter) ; þvidētia (providentia)

~ through q is frequently an abbreviation for quam , as: ꝙ

~ through þ may indicate the omission of er or ar, as: impresse in Ulm þ Conradū Dinckmut (impresse in Ulm per Conradum Dinckmut) ; editū þ fratrē Hermannum de Schilditz (editum per fratrem Hermannum de Schilditz); a þtu virginis salutifero (a partu virginis salutifero)

– through q is often an abbreviation for qui

ʒ frequently stands for e with attendant letters as; qʒ (que) ; atqʒ (atque); eiusqʒ (eiusque); sʒ (sed) ; scʒ (scilicet)

ʒ occasionally stands for m, as: etiaʒ or eciaʒ (etiam) ; or for us, as: omnibʒ (omnibus)

ɔ at the beginning of a word may stand for com, con, or cum, as: ɔpositus (compositus) ; þ cuius ɔpletione laudetur deus (pro cuius completione laudetur deus) ; ɔfeſſore (confessore); ɔqʒ (cumque)

ɔ at the end of a word may denote that us

or is has been omitted, as: frater Jacobꝫ de Voragine (frater Jacobus de Voragine); mẽſꝫ (mensis)

ꝯ at the beginning of a word may stand for con, as: in Eltuil est ꝯſũmatũ (in Eltvil est consummatum); a phrase which in other colophons may be found to read: in Eltuil est ꝯſũmatũ

ꝰ at the end of a word indicates the omission of us or of cum, as: in artibꝰ magistrum (in artibus magistrum); Boeciꝰ ī de cōsolatōe phie (Boethius in De consolatione philosophicae); pater om̃ipotens eterne deꝰ (pater omnipotens eterne deus); vocatꝰ (vocatus); cirꝰ (circum); qꝰꝫ (quicumque)

ꝺ represents d or, occasionally, de: qꝺ (quid) s̃c̃ꝺa (secunda); ꝑ discretum Conradum fyner ꝺ gerhuſzen (per discretum Conradum Fyner de Gerhuszen)

KL stands for Kalendas, as: viii KL. decẽbr̃ (viii Kalendas decembris)

~ or " over q denotes the omission of a with attendant letters, as: q̃ (quam); anno dñi Millesimoq̈drin gẽtesimo (anno domini Millesimoquadringentesimo)

~ a symbol easily confused with ~, denotes qui when over q, as: q̃

° with h may mean hoc, as: h°opus (hoc opus) Sometimes ° merely functions as a

period ; but when with M in a date it
may be taken as an abbreviation
for Millesimo, as : M°q̈dringētesimo

ꝗ with q is an abbreviation for quia, as: qꝗ.
Frequently this symbol is crossed, as :

ꝝ standing for rum, as : In imperiali nunc
vrbe Auguste vindelicoꝝ (In imperiali
nunc urbe Augustꝛaꝛe vindelicorum); retributionem bonoꝝ : et maloꝝ dāna-
tionem iudex faciet (retributionem
bonorum : et malorum damnationem
iudex faciet) ; eoꝝ (eorum)

ꞇ, ꝉ, or &, when used independently, stand
for et

ꞇc̄ or ꞇc̈ may stand for etc. or may be used
to indicate the omission of a word or
phrase, as: anno ꞇc̈ lxxj (anno Millesimoquadringentesimo lxxi) ; whereas, if
the symbol follows the date, the printer
often seems to imply a phrase such
as : Sit laus Deo ; Deo Gratias; Finit
feliciter ; or Amen.

(Contraction signs, arranged for the most part by
letters and including later usage in English
abbreviations, will be found on pages 319-324
of R. B. McKerrow's Introduction to Biblio
graphy for Literary Students, 1927. A record
of the contractions common to mediaeval

manuscripts, many of which found their way into early printed books, is given in Adriano Cappelli's <u>Dizionario di Abbreviature latine et italiane</u>. 2da ed. Milano, Hoepli, 1912 [also, Leipzig, 1928].)

(An essay on <u>Die Abkürzungszeichen in den Wiegendrucken</u> by Dr. Ernst Crous appeared in <u>Gutenberg-Festscrift</u>, 1925, from which the following facsimile has been reproduced.)

Efecerūt scrutan
tes scrutimo · ait
pš · Scrutantes
aliorꝫ pctā sunt
cōfessores · Scru
timū aūt ē ínꝙsitio facta ín ofes
sione · Jn qūo ꝗ multū confesso
res defiaūt non bīnea suffiaēẑ
ter se bn̄tes i audiētia confessi
omis : oseꝗnt' defiaūt eaā ín se a
gratia dei multū offēdentes Ne
ergo defiaant · ꝙᵈ essz ad sui a
alioꝛū pmaē · diligēter osideret
a obseruēt ꝙᵈ ait Aug⁹ī dcrco
de pe · di · vi · c · i · videlicꝫ · Caueat
spūalis íudex vt ficut nō cōmí
fit aímē neꝗaíe : ita non careat
mūnē faē · Judíaaria emī ptās
boc exposcit : vt ꝙᵈ bēat íudica
re : discernat · Diligēs igiˀ ínꝙsi
toꝛ a subtílis iuestígatoꝛ sapīē
ter a ꝗsi astute ínterroget a pe
mítēte : ꝗ forte prewreaudia wl
let occultare · Hec ille Vbi tria
ínsinuat pfat⁹ dꝛctoꝛ · ꝗ reꝗrū
tur i ydoneo ofessoꝛe · Primū ē
vt bēat auctoritatē fiue ptatez
absoluēdi opetētem · Secūdū
vt bēat sāam ad bmōi suffiaēẑ
tem · Terciūvt faaat ínterroga
cōez de peccatis diligētem ·

Original.

[ᵃ]Efecerūt scrutan||tes scrutinio · ait || pš ·
Scrutantes || alioꝛ pctā sunt || cōfessores
Scru||tiniū aūt ē inꝙsitio facta in ofes||
sione · Jn quo ꝗ multi confesso||res defi
ciūt non bene ꝫ sufficiēẑ||ter se bn̄tes l audiētia
confessi||onis : oseꝗnt' deficiūt eciā in se a ||
gratia dei multū offēdentes Ne || ergo de
ficiant · ꝙᵈ essz ad sui ꝫ || aliorū pnicie · dili
gēter osideret || ꝫ obseruēt ꝙᵈ ait Aug⁹ l ||
decre. || de pe · di · vi · c · i · videlicꝫ · Caueat ||
spūalis iudex vt sicut nō cōmi-||sit crime
neꝗcie : ita non careat || munē scie · Judi||
ciaria eni ptās || hoc exposcit : vt ꝙᵈ bēat
iudica||re : discernat · Diligēs igiˀ inꝙsi||toꝛ ꝫ
subtilis suestigatoꝛ sapiē||ter ꝫ ꝗsi astute in
terroget a pe||nitēte : ꝗ forte pre verecūdia vel||
let occultare · Hec ille Vbi tria || insinuat
pfat⁹ doctoꝛ · ꝗ reꝗrū-||tur l ydoneo ofessoꝛe ·
Primū ē || vt bēat auctoritatē siue ptatez ||
absoluēdi opetētem · Secūdū || vt bēat sciam
ad bmōi sufficiē-||tem · Terciūvt [/] faciat in
terroga||cōez de peccatis diligētem ·

Gesamtkatalog der Wiegendrucke (I. Band).

Defecerunt scrutantes scrutinio, ait psalmus. Scrutantes aliorum peccata sunt confessores. Scrutinium autem est inquisitio
facta in confessione. In quo quia multi confessores deficiunt, non bene et sufficienter
se habentes in audientia confessionis, consequenter deficiunt etiam in se a gratia dei
multum offendentes. Ne ergo deficiant, quod
esset ad sui et aliorum perniciem, diligenter
considerent et observent, quod ait Augustinus
in Decreto magistri Gratiani, De poenitentia,
Distinctione VI., capitulo 1., videlicet : Caveat
spiritualis iudex, ut, sicut non commisit
crimen nequitiae, ita non careat munere
scientiae. Iudiciaria enim potestas hoc exposcit : ut quid habeat iudicare discernat.
Diligens igitur inquisitor et subtilis investigator sapienter et quasi astute interroget a
poenitente quae forte prae verecundia vellet
occultare. Haec ille. Ubi tria insinuat praefatus doctor, quae requiruntur in idoneo
confessore. Primum est, ut habeat auctoritatem sive potestatem absolvendi competentem. Secundum, ut habeat scientiam ad
huius modi (officium?) sufficientem. Tertium,
ut faciat interrogationem de peccatis diligentem.

Moderner Abdruck.

Antonius Florentinus: Confessionale (Defecerunt), Köln, Ulrich Zell, um 1473 (Hain 1171b), Bl 4 a α.

A facsimile showing a paragraph from a fifteenth century edition of the *Confessionale* of Antonius Florentir
transliterated according to the usage of the *Gesamtkatalog der Wiegendrucke*, and expanded into modern Latin; fro
an essay on abbreviation signs in incunabula, by Dr. Ernst Crous in *Gutenberg-Festschrift* (1925), reproduced wi
the kind permission of the Gutenberg-Gesellschaft and of Dr. Crous.

3. LATIN ABBREVIATIONS EMPLOYED IN HAIN'S

REPERTORIUM BIBLIOGRAPHICUM

The bibliographical descriptions, which accompany the titles quoted in Hain's *Repertorium*, comprise a series of Latin phrases, each of which is generally composed of two or more Latin terms given in abbreviated form. Since no punctuation marks are used to separate the phrases, the abbreviations for the entire collation often follow one another without pause. For this reason, it is well to familiarize oneself with the phrase-groups, especially since, in some instances, the meaning of the abbreviations may vary according to the phrase in which they are employed. For instance, *c.* may stand for *cum, circa,* or *custodibus;* or *n.* may mean *nomine, numeris,* or *numerati.* The following selection is from the abbreviated phrases more commonly employed by Hain in his *Repertorium Bibliographicum:*

c. 1490   (circa 1490)
   About 1490

c. figg. astronom.   (cum figuris astronomicis)
   With astronomical drawings

c. figg. xyl.   (cum figuris xylographicis)
   With woodcut illustrations

c. ff. n.; c. fol. num.   (cum foliorum numeris)
   With foliation, or numbered leaves

c. litt. initial.   (cum litteris initialibus)
   With initial letters

c. marginal.   (cum [notis] marginalibus)
   With marginal notes

c. f. c. et pp. n.   (cum signatoribus, custodibus et paginarum numeris)
   With signatures, catchwords and page numbers

c. s. et cust.   (cum signatoribus et custodibus)
   With signatures and catchwords

c. f. et ff. n.   (cum signatoribus et foliis numeratis)
   With signatures and numbered leaves

c. f. a–k.   (cum signatoribus a–k)
   With signatures a–k

c. sign. A.   (cum signatore A)
  With signature A
col.   (columnae) Columns
Expl.: (Explicit:) Explicit:
f.   (folio) In-folio [of medium size]
f. maj.   (folio majore) Large folio
f. min.   (folio minore) Small folio
f. singulum.   (folium singulum)
  Broadside; or a single leaf
f. vacuum.   (folium vacuum)
  Blank leaf
ff.   (folia) Leaves
ff. male num.   (folia male numerata)
  Leaves incorrectly numbered
ff. n.; ff. num.   (folia numerata)
  Leaves numbered [with foliation]
ff. non num.; s. ff. n.   (folia non numerata; sine foliis numeratis)
  Leaves unnumbered [without foliation]
F.   (folium) A leaf [usually accompanied by its number and followed
  by a quotation from caption, incipit, or colophon — as, *F. 6:*]
F. 1. a.   (folio 1 recto)
  [On] leaf 1, the upper side
F. 1. a. vacat.   (folium 1 recto vacat)
  Recto of first leaf blank
F. 1. b.   (folio 1 verso)
  [On] leaf 1, the back
g. ch.   (goticis characteribus) In Gothic characters [type]
gr. ch, rubro et nigro.   (graecis characteribus rubris et nigris)
  [In] Greek characters, in red and black
Icon.   (icones) Diagrams
In fine: At the end [usually followed by a transcript of the colophon]
In fine hebr.: (in fine, hebraeis characteribus:)
  At the end, in Hebrew:
Insign. typogr.   (insigne typographici)
  With the printer's device, or the printer's mark

Insign. typogr. rubra.   (insigne typographici rubra)
    With printer's mark in red

inverso: On the verso:

l. (lineae)
    Lines [as, 24 l., 24 lines to the page]

post a. — (post annum —)
    After the year — [i.e., printed later than —]

pp. n. [usually a part of the phrase — *c. f. c. et. pp. n.*]

r. ch. (Romanis characteribus) [In] Roman characters [type]

Registr. (registrum) Register

s. a. (sine anno) Without year [of printing]

s. fol. num. (sine foliorum numeris)
    Without foliation

s. l. a. et typ. n. (sine loco, anno et typographici nomine)
    Without place, year, and printer's name

s. f. (excepta sign. a) (sine signatoribus, excepta signatore a)
    Without signatures, excepting signature a

Scutum typogr. (scutum typographici)
    Printer's device, or shield

seq. f. vacuum (secutum folium vacuum)
    Following leaf blank

sic Thus [used to call attention to the fact that a misprint or error has
    been copied exactly as in the original; in some bibliographies the
    symbol (!) is used for the same purpose]

Tab. alphabetica (tabula alphabetica)
    Index

text. a glossa circumd. (textus a glossa circumdatus)
    Text surrounded by glosses

tit.: (titulus:) Title, or caption:

ult. s. num. (ultimum sine numero)
    Last [leaf] without a number

‖ [A sign indicating the line-ending of the original]

4. (quarto) In-quarto (4°.)

8. (octavo) In-octavo (8°.)

12. (duodecimo) In-twelvemo (12°.)

For abbreviations employed by Copinger, with their English equivalents, see p. xvi in
vol. I of Copinger's *Supplement,* London, 1895.

REFERENCE SECTION IV

PLACE-NAMES OF
FIFTEENTH CENTURY PRINTING TOWNS

PLACE–NAMES OF
FIFTEENTH CENTURY PRINTING TOWNS

The asterisk * in this table indicates a form of place-name found, during the compilation of the present table, in the *colophon* or *incipit* of a fifteenth century printed book. (Earlier forms and those taken from manuscripts will be found in [Deschamps]: *Dictionnaire de Géographie.* Paris, 1870. New edition, 1922.)

Brackets [ ] occurring in the British Museum or the *Gesamtkatalog* columns indicate that the form has not yet been determined upon; or that it has not yet been used in one or the other of the forthcoming catalogues of incunabula.

† The modern vernacular forms not found in the *Century Cyclopedia of Names* nor in Lippincott's *Gazetteer* are quoted from Deschamps (D), Fumagalli (F), or Haebler (H).

Allowing for the interchange of *u* for *v*, *j* for *i*, and *o* for *a*, it will be noticed that, in instances where several Latin forms have been seen for a given place-name, the stem almost invariably remains constant. The case endings are more or less variable, as *a; ae; e; em; eñ* or *ensi* or *n; i; ii* or *ij; ium; um* with a line over the final letter of an abbreviated word, if the case ending is to be understood. Here we have locative and adjectival forms, as *Argentine* and *Argentineñ.* In the latter case, the substantive has been omitted, and here, as in other instances where the adjectival form is given, the substantive should be understood, as [*in urbe*] *Argentineñ[si]* , [*in urbem*] *Augustensem,* [*in urbem*] *Toletanum;* as is also the case with the phrase [*in civitate*] *Nurembergensium,* in which the genitive plural is used to denote 'the city of the Nurembergers.'

For Hebrew place-names, see the end of this table.

Fifteenth Century form	Form used by the British Museum	Form used in the *Gesamtkatalog der Wiegendrucke*	The modern vernacular form †	Country or Province
*Abbeuille	Abbeville	Abbeville	Abbeville	France
Agrippineñ *See* Colonie				
Albani *See* Sancti Albani				
*Albie	Albi	Albi	Albi	France
*Aldenardi	Audenarde	Audenarde	Oudenaarde Oudenarde	Belgium
*Alosteñ	Alost	Alost	Alost	Belgium
*Altauilla *Eltuil	Eltvil	Eltville	Elfeld Eltville	Germany
*Andegaueñ	Angers	Angers	Angers	France
*Antwerpie	Antwerp	Antwerpen	Antwerpen Anvers	Belgium
*Aquila	Aquila	Aquila	Aquila Aquila degli Abruzzi	Italy

Fifteenth Century form	Form used by the British Museum	Form used in the *Gesamtkatalog der Wiegendrucke*	The modern vernacular form †	Country or Province
*Argentiñ *Argentine *Arguntineñ *Ciuitatis Argentiñ *Strospurg	Strassburg	Strassburg	Strasbourg Strassburg	Alsace-Lorraine
*Ascolo *Ascvli	[ ]	Ascoli	Ascoli Ascoli Piceno	Italy
*Augspurg *Augusta *Auguste *Augustensem *Augustensi *Augustae Vindelicorum	Augsburg	Augsburg	Augsburg	Germany
*Augusta Bracharēsi	[ ]	Braga	Braga	Portugal
*Auinione	Avignon	Avignon	Avignon	France
*Babenbergñ *Babenbergensem *Bamberge	Bamberg	Bamberg	Bamberg	Germany
*Barchinone *Barcynonia	Barcelona	Barcelona	Barcelona	Spain
*Barci [*See also* Hebrew list]	[ ]	Barco	Barco (F)	Italy
*Basilea *Basileæ *Basilee *Basilieñ *Basiliensi	Basel	Basel	Bâle Basel	Switzerland
*Bergomi	Bergamo	Bergamo	Bergamo	Italy
*Beronensi *Beronensis	Beromünster	Beromünster	Moutier Münster	Switzerland
*Bisuncii *Bisuntij	Besançon	Besançon	Besançon	France
*Blaubürren'	Blaubeuren	Blaubeuren	Blaubeuren	Germany

Fifteenth Century form	Form used by the British Museum	Form used in the *Gesamtkatalog der Wiegendrucke*	The modern vernacular form †	Country or Province
*Bologna *Bononiae *Bononiensis *Felsina [*See also* He- brew list]	Bologna	Bologna	Bologna	Italy
Bracharēsi *See* Augusta Bracharēsi				
*Brehant Lo- deac	[ ]	Bréhant- Loudéac	Bréhant- Loudéac (D)	France
*Brixia [*See also* He- brew list]	Brescia	Brescia	Brescia	Italy
*Bruges *Brugis	Bruges	Brügge	Bruges Brugge	Belgium
*Brünn *Brunna *Brunnae *Brunēsi	Brünn	Brünn	Brno	Bohemia
*Bruxellēsium	Brussels	Brüssel	Bruxelles	Belgium
*Budae *Bude	Buda-Pest	Budapest	Buda-Pesth	Hungary
*Burgdorf	Burgdorf	Bŭrgdorf	Berthoud Burgdorf	Switzerland
*Burgos	Burgos	Burgos	Burgos	Spain
*Buscoducis	[ ]	's Hertogen- bosch	Bois-le-Duc den Bosch 's Hertogen- bosch	Holland
*Cadomi	Caen	Caen	Caen	France
*Callar	[ ]	[ ]	Cagliari	Italy
*Callium	[ ]	Cagli	Cagli	Italy
Çamora *See* Zamora				
*Capue	Capua	Capua	Capua	Italy

Fifteenth Century form	Form used by the British Museum	Form used in the *Gesamtkatalog der Wiegendrucke*	The modern vernacular form †	Country or Province
*Caragoça *Cesaragusta	Saragossa	Zaragoza	Zaragoza	Spain
*Carnotēsis	[ ]	Chartres	Chartres	France
*Casale Maiori [*See also* Hebrew list]	[ ]	Casalmaggiore	Casalmaggiore	Italy
*Casalis sancti Evaxii	[ ]	Casale	Casale Casale Monferrato	Italy
*Casellarum Oppido *Casselis	[ ]	Caselle	Caselle Torinese (F)	Italy
*Cathalauni	[ ]	Châlons	Châlons-sur-Marne	France
	[ ]	[ ]	Cettinje [Although no signed book of the fifteenth century is known, a statement within the book incompletely recorded in Hain 5912 points to Cettinje as the place of printing rather than to Rieka, a suburb of Cettinje.]	Montenegro
Cesaragusta *See* Çaragoça				
Cexaro *See* S. Cexaro				
*Chableys *Chablis *Chabliys	Chablis	Chablis	Chablis	France
*Chamberry	Chambéry	Chambéry	Chambéry	France

Fifteenth Century form	Form used by the British Museum	Form used in the *Gesamtkatalog der Wiegendrucke*	The modern vernacular form †	Country or Province
*Ciuidad de Friuli *Ciuitate Austrie *Civitas Austriae	[ ]	Cividale	Cividale	Italy
Ciuitatis Argentiñ. *See* Argentiñ				
*Clavassii *Clavasium	Chivasso	Chivasso	Chivasso	Italy
*Cleinē Troya *Clein Troyga	Kirchheim in Elsass	Kirchheim	Kirchheim	Alsace-Lorraine
*Cluniaco	[Cluny]	Cluny	Cluny	France
*Colle	Colle	Colle	Colle	Italy
*Colonie *Colonie Agrippīe *Colonieñ *Coloniens *Agrippineñ Colonie	Cologne	Köln	Köln	Germany
*Comi	Como	Como	Como	Italy
*Compostellane	[ ]	Santiago	Santiago de Compostela	Spain
*Coria	[ ]	Coria	Coria	Spain
*Cracis *Cracouia *Cracoviensis	Cracow	Krakau	Kraków	Poland
*Cremonae *Cremone	Cremona	Cremona	Cremona	Italy
Cucufatum *See* Sanctū Cucufatum				
*Culenborch *Culenburch	[ ]	Kuilenbŭrg	Culenborg Kuilenburg	Holland
*Cusentiae	[Cosenza]	Cosenza	Cosenza	Italy

Fifteenth Century form	Form used by the British Museum	Form used in the *Gesamtkatalog der Wiegendrucke*	The modern vernacular form †	Country or Province
*Cutnach	Kuttenberg	Kŭttenberg	Kutna Hora	Bohemia
*Danczyk *in Gdano	Danzig	Danzig	Danzig	Germany
*Dauentriae *Dauentriensem *Dauetrie	Deventer	Deventer	Demter Deventer	Holland
*Delf *Delfensi *Delff	Delft	Delft	Delft	Holland
*Dertusie	[ ]	Tortosa	Tortosa	Spain
*Diuione	Dijon	Dijon	Dijon	France
*Dole	[ ]	Dôle	Dôle	France
*Ebreduneñ	[ ]	Embrun	Embrun	France
Eltuil See Altauilla				
*Engolisme	[ ]	Angoulême	Angoulême	France
*Erffordie *Erfordensi *Erifordēsi *Erphordie	Erfurt	Erfurt	Erfurt	Germany
*Esslingen	Esslingen	Esslingen	Esslingen	Germany
*Exii	Jesi	Jesi	Jesi	Italy
*Eystetñ *Eystettñ	Eichstätt	Eichstätt	Eichstätt Eischstädt	Germany
[See Hebrew list]	[ ]	Faro	Faro	Portugal
Felsina See Bologna				
*Ferrarie [See also Hebrew list]	Ferrara	Ferrara	Ferrara	Italy
*Firenza *Firenze *Florentia *Florentiae	Florence	Florenz	Firenze	Italy

Fifteenth Century form	Form used by the British Museum	Form used in the *Gesamtkatalog der Wiegendrucke*	The modern vernacular form †	Country or Province
*Fiuizani *Fivizani *Fivizano	Fivizzano	Fivizzano	Fivizzano (F)	Italy
*Forliuii	[ ]	Forli	Forli	Italy
*Freiberg	Freiberg	Freiberg	Freiberg	Germany
*Freisinge *Freisingen	Freising	Freising	Freising	Germany
*Friburgensi *Friburgi *Friburg in Brissgaw *Friburgo	Freiburg im Breisgau	Freiburg	Freiburg Freiburg-im-Breisgau	Germany
*Fulginei	Foligno	Foligno	Foligno Fuligno	Italy
*Gand *Gandaui *Ghend	Ghent	Gent	Gand Gend	Belgium
*Gayeta	[ ]	Gaeta	Gaeta	Italy
Gdano *See* Danczyk				
*Gebeneñ *Geneue *Geneve	Geneva	Genf	Genève	Switzerland
*Genue *Janue	Genoa	[ ]	Genova	Italy
Germano *See* Sancto Germano				
*Giennensi *See* Jahen				
*Girona	[ ]	Gerona	Gerona	Spain
*Gou *Goude	Gouda	Gouda	Gouda Ter-Gouw	Holland
*Goupilleres	[ ]	Goŭpillières	Goupillières	France

Fifteenth Century form	Form used by the British Museum	Form used in the *Gesamtkatalog der Wiegendrucke*	The modern vernacular form †	Country or Province
*Gracionopoli	Grenoble	Grenoble	Grenoble	France
*Granada *Grenada	Granada	Granada	Granada	Spain
[*See* Hebrew list]	[ ]	Gŭadalajara	Guadalajara	Spain
*Haerlem *Herlem	[ ]	Haarlem	Haarlem	Holland
*Hafnye *Kiobenhavn	Copenhagen	Kopenhagen	Kjöbenhavn	Denmark
*Haganaw *Hagenaw *Hagennaw *Hagenow *Hagenowe	Hagenau	Hagenau	Hagenau Haguenau	Germany
*Haidelberg *Heidelberg *Heidelberga *Heydelberge *Heydelbergensis	Heidelberg	Heidelberg	Heidelberg	Germany
*Hamborgensi	Hamburg	Hamburg	Hamburg	Germany
*Hasselt	[ ]	Hasselt	Hasselt in Overyssel	Holland
*Herbipolense *Herbipolensi *Herbipolñ *Herbñ	Würzburg	Würzburg	Würzburg	Germany
*Hispalis *Ispalis	Seville	Sevilla	Sevilla	Spain
*Holmensem *Holmis *Stockolmiae	Stockholm	Stockholm	Stockholm	Sweden
*Huepte	[ ]	Huete	Huete	Spain
*Illerde *Illerdensis	[ ]	Lérida	Lérida	Spain

Fifteenth Century form	Form used by the British Museum	Form used in the *Gesamtkatalog der Wiegendrucke*	The modern vernacular form †	Country or Province
*Ingoldstat *Ingolstat *Ingolstadensi *Jngoldstat	Ingolstadt	Ingolstadt	Ingolstadt	Germany
*Iscar *Ischar [*See also* Hebrew list]	[ ]	Hijar	Hijar Ixar	Spain
Ispalis *See* Hispalis				
*Jahen [From *incipit*] *Giennensi	[ ]	[ ]	Jaén [No signed book of the fifteenth century known.]	Spain
Janue *See* Genue				
Kiobenhavn *See* Hafnye				
*Lantenac	[ ]	Lantenac	Lantenac (D)	France
*Lantreguer [Treguier, as early as 1511]	[ ]	Tréguier	Tréguier	France
*Laugingen	Lauingen	Laŭingen	Lauingen	Germany
*Lausanne *Lausannemsem	Lausanne	Lausanne	Lausanne	Switzerland
*Leidensi *Leyden *Leydis	[ ]	Leiden	Leiden Leyden	Holland
*Leipczick *Lipczēsis *Lipczk *Lipsensi *Liptz *Lypktzensi	Leipzig	Leipzig	Leipzig	Germany
*Leiriae [*See also* Hebrew list]	Leiria	Leiria	Leiria	Portugal

Fifteenth Century form	Form used by the British Museum	Form used in the *Gesamtkatalog der Wiegendrucke*	The modern vernacular form †	Country or Province
*Lemouiceñ *Lemouicensis	[ ]	Limoges	Limoges	France
*Lisboa [Ulyssipone] *Vlyxbone [*See also* Hebrew list]	Lisbon	Lissabon	Lisboa	Portugal
*Lōdonias *London *Londoñ *Londoniarx	London	London	London	England
*Louaniēsi *Louanii	Louvain	Löwen	Leuven Loven	Belgium
*Lubeck *Lubek *Lubicana *Lubicensi *Lubicēsi	Lübeck	Lübeck	Lübeck	Germany
*Lucae	Lucca	Lucca	Lucca	Italy
*Lugdunensis *Lugduni *Lyon	Lyons	Lyon	Lyon	France
*Luneborch	Lüneburg	Lüneburg	Lüneburg	Germany
Lyon *See* Lugdunensis				
Lypktzensi *See* Leipczick				
*Maessana *Messanae	Messina	Messina	Messina	Italy
*Magdeborch *Magdeburgensi *Magdeburgēsi *Magdeburgk	Magdeburg	Magdeburg	Magdeburg	Germany
*Magūcia *Maguntina *Moguntina *Mogūtie *Mogūtine	Mainz	Mainz	Mainz [Mayence, in Fr.]	Germany

Fifteenth Century form	Form used by the British Museum	Form used in the *Gesamtkatalog der Wiegendrucke*	The modern vernacular form †	Country or Province
*Maiori de Balearibus *Val de Musse	[ ]	Mallorca	Majorca Mallorca	Spain
*Mantuae *Mantue [*See also* Hebrew list]	Mantua	Mantua	Mantova	Italy
	[ ]	Gripsholm	Mariefred [No signed book of the fifteenth century is known.]	Sweden
Marienborck	Marienburg	Marienbŭrg	Marienburg	Germany
Marsipoli *See* Merszborg				
*Matisconeñ	[ ]	Mâcon	Mâcon	France
*Mediolanēsis *Milano	Milan	Mailand	Milano	Italy
*Mēmingʒ *Memmingen	Memmingen	Memmingen	Memmingen	Germany
*Merszborg *Marsipoli	Merseburg	Merseburg	Merseburg	Germany
Mertensdyck *See* Tsente Mertensdyck				
*Meteñ *Metensi *Metzs	Metz	Metz	Metz	Alsace-Lorraine
*Mīchē *Minchen *Monaci	Munich	München	München	Germany
*Misnensis	Meissen	Meissen	Meissen	Germany
*Monasterij vuessalie *Monasterij westualie	Münster in Westfalen	Münster	Münster	Germany [Westfalen]

Fifteenth Century form	Form used by the British Museum	Form used in the *Gesamtkatalog der Wiegendrucke*	The modern vernacular form †	Country or Province
Monasterio Sorteñ *See* Sorteñ				
*Monte regali *Mõte r'gali	[ ]	Mondovi	Mondovi	Italy
*Monteserrato	Montserrat	Montserrat	Montserrat	Spain
*Monti Regio	[ ]	Monterey	Monterey (H)	Spain
*Murcia	[ ]	Murcia	Murcia	Spain
*Mutinae *Mutine	Modena	Modena	Modena	Italy
*Nantes	[ ]	Nantes	Nantes	France
*Narbone *Narbonesis	[ ]	Narbonne	Narbonne	France
*Neapoli *Neapolis *Neapolitano [*See also* Hebrew list]	Naples	Neapel	Napoli	Italy
*Nonatule	[ ]	Nonantola	Nonantola	Italy
*Noua Plzna *w nowen Plzni [at New Pilsen]	Pilsen	Pilsen	Plzen	Bohemia
*Nouimagēsi *Nouimagio	[ ]	Nimwegen	Nijmegen	Holland
*Nouis	[ ]	Novi	Novi Ligure	Italy
*Nozanum	Nozzano	Nozzano	Nozzano (F)	Italy
*Nuremberga *Nuremberge *Nurembergensem *Nurembergensis *Nurembergensium *Nurenbergk	Nuremberg	Nürnberg	Nürnberg	Germany
*Offenburg	Offenburg	Offenburg	Offenburg	Germany

Fifteenth Century form	Form used by the British Museum	Form used in the *Gesamtkatalog der Wiegendrucke*	The modern vernacular form †	Country or Province
*Olomuncensi *Olomuucz	Olmütz	Olmütz	Olmütz	Bohemia
*Orleans	[ ]	Orléans	Orléans	France
	[ ]	Orense	Orense [No signed book of the fifteenth century is known.]	Spain
*Ottonia	[ ]	Odense	Odense	Denmark
*Ouetū	[ ]	Oviedo	Oviedo	Spain
*Oxoñ *Oxonie *Oxoniis	Oxford	Oxford	Oxford	England
*Padua *Patauina *Patauus *Patavii *Patavini	Padua	Padua	Padova	Italy
*Pampilonensi *Pamplona *Pōplona	[ ]	Pamplona	Pamplona	Spain
*Panormi	Palermo	Palermo	Palermo	Italy
*Papiae *Papie	Pavia	Pavia	Pavia	Italy
*Parhisii *Paris *Parisiana *Parisiensis *Parisius *Parrhisiis	Paris	Paris	Paris	France
*Parmae	Parma	Parma	Parma	Italy
*Patauie *Patauiensi	Passau	Passau	Passau	Germany
*Perpiniani *Perpinya *Ƥpiniani	Perpignan	Perpignan	Perpignan	France [Very close to the present boundary of Spain]

Fifteenth Century form	Form used by the British Museum	Form used in the *Gesamtkatalog der Wiegendrucke*	The modern vernacular form †	Country or Province
*Perusia *Perusie	Perugia	Perugia	Perugia	Italy
*Petragorisensis	[ ]	Périgueux	Périgueux	France
*Pfortzheim *Phorce *Phorçheim	Pforzheim	Pforzheim	Pforzheim	Germany
*Pictauis	Poitiers	Poitiers	Poitiers	France
*Pinerolii	Pinerolo	Pinerolo	Pinerolo	Italy
*Pisa *Pisis *Pysana	Pisa	Pisa	Pisa	Italy
*Piscia *Piscie	Pescia	Pescia	Pescia	Italy
*Placentie *Placētie	Piacenza	Piacenza	Piacenza	Italy
[*See* Hebrew list]	[ ]	Piove di Sacco	Piove Piove di Sacco	Italy
Plzna *See* Noua Plzna				
*Polliano	[ ]	Pogliano	Pogliano (F)	Italy
*Portesii	Portesio	Portese	Portese (F)	Italy
*Porto	[ ]	Porto	o Porto	Portugal
*Prazskem [*i.e.*, w starem miestie Pražskem, a: the old town of Prague]	Prague	Prag	Praha	Bohemia
*Promentour	Promenthoux	Promenthoux	Promenthoux (D)	Switzerland
*Prouins	[ ]	Provins	Provins	France
*Ratispone *Ratisponensis	Ratisbon	Regensburg	Regensburg	Germany

Fifteenth Century form	Form used by the British Museum	Form used in the *Gesamtkatalog der Wiegendrucke*	The modern vernacular form †	Country or Province
*Regii *Regium	[ ]	Reggio nell' Emilia	Reggio nell' Emilia	Italy
[*See* Hebrew list]	[ ]	[ ]	Reggio di Calabria	Italy
*Rennes	Rennes	Rennes	Rennes	France
*Reuttlingē *Reuttlingñ *Rutlingen	Reutlingen	Reutlingen	Reutlingen	Germany
*Ro: *Roma *Romae *Romana *Rome *Romę [*See also* Hebrew list]	Rome	Rom	Roma	Italy
*Rostockceñ	Rostock	Rostock	Rostock	Germany
*Rothomagi *Rothomagēsi *Rouen	Rouen	Rouen	Rouen	France
*Rubeimōtis	Rougemont	Rougement	Rougement	Switzerland
*Rychensteyn [Although quite generally believed to have been a printing town, rather than a house in Cologne, the matter is still open to question.]	Reichenstein	[ ]	Reichenstein (D)	Germany
*Salinensi	[ ]	Salins	Salins	France
*Salmanticae *Salmantice *Salmanticensis	Salamanca	Salamanca	Salamanca	Spain
*Saluciēsiū *Salutiis	[ ]	Saluzzo	Saluzzo	Italy

Fifteenth Century form	Form used by the British Museum	Form used in the *Gesamtkatalog der Wiegendrucke*	The modern vernacular form †	Country or Province
*S. Cexaro	[ ]	San Cesario	San Cesario sul Panàro (F)	Italy
*Sancti Albani *Sanctum Albanium *Seynt Albons	St. Albans	St. Albans	St. Albans	England
*Sancto Germano	San Germano	San Germano	Cassino [Formerly San Germano]	Italy
*Sancto Vrsio	[ ]	Santorso	Sant'Orso (F)	Italy
*Sanctū Cucufatum	[ ]	San Cŭcŭfate	San Concufate (H)	Spain
Santiago Sant Juao *See* Compostellane				
*Saona	[ ]	Savona	Savona	Italy
	[ ]	Savigliano	Savigliano [The name Savigliano does not appear in any of the fifteenth century books believed to have been printed there.]	Italy
*Scādiani *Scandiano	[ ]	Scandiano	Scandiano (F)	Italy
*Schiedā *Schiedam	[ ]	Schiedam	Schiedam	Holland
*Scoenhouē *Scoenhouieñ	[ ]	Schoonhoven	Schoonhoven	Holland
*Senensis *Senis	Siena	Siena	Siena	Italy

Fifteenth Century form	Form used by the British Museum	Form used in the *Gesamtkatalog der Wiegendrucke*	The modern vernacular form †	Country or Province
*Seni [*i.e.*, početi i svišene v Seni, begun and finished at Zengg.]	[ ]	Zengg	Zengg Senga Sinj	Jugoslavia
*Sleswicensis *Sleswick	Schleswig	Schleswig	Schleswig [Slesvig]	Germany [In the possession of Denmark, until 1864]
[*See* Hebrew list]	[ ]	Soncino	Soncino	Italy
*Sorteñ *Monasterio Sorteñ	Schussenried	Schussenried	Schussenried	Germany
*Spire *Spireñ *Spirensi	Speier	Speyer	Speyer	Germany
*Stendael *Stendal	Stendal	Stendal	Stendal	Germany
Stockolmiae *See* Holmensem				
Strospurg *See* Argentiñ				
*Stutgartē	Stuttgart	Stuttgart	Stuttgart	Germany
*Sublacensi	Subiaco	Subiaco	Subiaco	Italy
*Surse im Ergow	Sursee	Sursee	Sursee	Switzerland
Swolle *See* Zwolle				
*Tarracone	Tarragona	Tarragona	Tarragona	Spain
*Tarvisanus *Taruisiae *Tarvisii *Taruixina *Triuiso	Treviso	Treviso	Treviso	Italy

Fifteenth Century form	Form used by the British Museum	Form used in the *Gesamtkatalog der Wiegendrucke*	The modern vernacular form †	Country or Province
*Taurini *Thaurini	Turin	Turin	Torino	Italy
*Tholosa *Tholose	Toulouse	Toulouse	Toulouse	France
*Thubingensis *Thuwingñ *Tubingñ *Tuwingñ	Tübingen	Tübingen	Tübingen	Germany
*Thuriceñ	Zürich	Zürich	Zürich	Switzerland
*Toledo *Toletanum *Toleti	Toledo	Toledo	Toledo	Spain
*Tore de bel Vesin	[ ]	Torrebelvicino	Torrebelvicino (F)	Italy
*Traiectñ *Traiecto inferiori *Tutrecht *Vtrecht	Utrecht	Utrecht	Utrecht	Holland
*Trecen *Trecis	[ ]	Troyes	Troyes	France
*Treueris	Trier	Trier	Trier [Trèves in Fr.]	Germany
*Treuio	[ ]	Trevi	Trevi	Italy
*Tridentinū *Tridento *Tridēti *Trient	Trent	Trient	Trento [It.] Trient [Gr.] Trent [Eng.]	In the Tyrol
*Troscolano *Tusculani	Toscolano	Toscolano	Toscolano	Italy
*Tsente Mertensdyck	[ ]	Sankt Maartensdijk	Maartensdijk (D)	Holland
*Turoneñ *Turonis	[ ]	Tours	Tours	France
Tusculani *See* Troscolano				

Fifteenth Century form	Form used by the British Museum	Form used in the *Gesamtkatalog der Wiegendrucke*	The modern vernacular form †	Country or Province
*Tzenna	Zinna	Zinna	Zinna	Germany
*Udine *Utini	Udine	[ ]	Udine	Italy
Ulm *See* Vlm				
Ulyssipone *See* Lisboa				
*Urach *Vrach	Urach	Urach	Urach	Germany
*Urbini	Urbino	Urbino	Urbino	Italy

Val de Musse
  See Maiori de
  Balearibus				

*Valencia *Valentia *Valentie *Valētia	Valencia	Valencia	Valencia	Spain
*Valentin[us]	[ ]	Valence	Valence [possibly a printing town]	France
*Valladolid	[ ]	Valladolid	Valladolid	Spain
Vallenchiennes	[ ]	Valenciennes	Valenciennes	France
*Vallis scē marie	Marienthal	Marienthal	Marienthal [im Rheingau]	Germany
*Venesia *Venetia *Venetiarum *Venetiis [or Uenetiis] *Venetijs *Venetum *Venexia	Venice	Venedig	Venezia	Italy
*Vercellis	Vercelli	Vercelli	Vercelli	Italy
*Veronae [or Uerona]	Verona	Verona	Verona	Italy
*Vicencie [or *Uicenza] *Vincentia *Vincentiae	Vicenza	Vicenza	Vicenza	Italy

Fifteenth Century form	Form used by the British Museum	Form used in the *Gesamtkatalog der Wiegendrucke*	The modern vernacular form †	Country or Province
*Viena *Vienne [or Uienne] *Wien *Wienne	Vienna	Wien	Wien	Austria
*Vienne	Vienne	Vienne	Vienne	France
*Viquerie	[ ]	Voghera	Voghera (D)	Italy
*Viterbii	Viterbo	Viterbo	Viterbo	Italy
*Vlm *Vlme *Vlmensi	Ulm	Ulm	Ulm	Germany
Vlyxbone *See* Lisboa				
Vtrecht *See* Traiectñ				
Watzsteñ	Vadstena	Vadstena	Vadstena	Sweden
*Westmestre *Westmonasterii *Westmynstre	Westminster	Westminster	Westminster	England
Wienne *See* Viena				
*Winderperg *Winterperg	Winterberg	Winterberg	Winterberg	Bohemia
*Wrat' *Wratislauieñ	Breslau	Breslau	Breslau [Wracislawa when part of Poland, or under Bohemia]	Germany

*Zamore
*Zamorensis
  *Çamora
  [*See also* Hebrew list]
	[ ]	Zamora	Zamora	Spain

*Zweinbruckē *Zweinbrugcken	Zweibrücken	Zweibrücken	Zweibrücken	Germany
*Zwolle *Zwollis *Swolle	Zwolle	Zwolle	Zwolle	Holland

HEBREW PLACE-NAMES OF
FIFTEENTH CENTURY PRINTING TOWNS

ITALY

Barco	ברק	*
Bologna	בולוניא	*
Brescia	ברישה	*
Casalmaggiore	קזאל מיורי	*
Ferrara	פיראררה	*
Mantua	מנטואה	*
Napoli	נאפולי	*
Pieve di Sacco	פייביא די שקו	*
Reggio di Calabria	ריגו בסוף קלבריאה	*
(Roma	רומא)	‡
Soncino	שונצין or שונצינו	*

PORTUGAL

Faro	פארא or פארה	*
Leiria	לייריאה	*
Lisbon	אשבונה	*§

SPAIN

Guadalajara	ואדי אל חיגארה	*§
Ixar	אישאר	*
Zamora	סאמורה	*

‡ Rome is not expressly mentioned in any of the Hebrew editions ascribed to it but, in one of them, three printers occur as of Rome.

§ Transliterated, respectively, Asbona and Vadi Al-Higara.

The asterisk * in this table indicates a form of place-name found, during the compilation of the present table, in the *colophon* or *incipit* of a fifteenth century printed book.

REFERENCE SECTION V

INCUNABULA

SELECTED BIBLIOGRAPHIES AND MONOGRAPHS

CONTENTS

INCUNABULA: SELECTED BIBLIOGRAPHIES AND
BIBLIOGRAPHICAL MONOGRAPHS

I. Works of General Reference

A. *Bibliographies*
(*Listed Chronologically*)

HAIN, L. [F. T.]   Repertorium bibliographicum, in quo libri omnes
ab arte typographica inventa usque ad annum MD. typis expressi.
Stuttgartiae, 1826–38.   2 v. in 4.   I

The items marked with an asterisk were seen by Hain in the Hof- und Staatsbibliothek, Munich. (*See also* Copinger; Burger; Reichling.) Issued in
photo-lithographic reprint, Stuttgart, 1920.
Zur Biographie Ludwig Hains. Von E. v. Rath. (*In* Bok- och Biblioteks-
historiska Studier tillägnade Isak Collijn. Upsala, 1925.)

COPINGER, W. A.   Supplement to Hain's *Repertorium bibliographicum.*   In two parts.   London, 1895, 1898, 1902.   2 v. in 3.   2

Contents: I. (Part 1.)   Nearly 7,000 corrections of and additions to the
collations of works described by Hain. (Part 2.) Nearly 6,000 volumes
not referred to by Hain: Abano-Ovidius.   II.   Pablo-Zutphania.   Addenda
to V. I, pts. 1 and 2. Burger's *Printers and publishers of the fifteenth century.* Reprinted at Berlin, 1926.

PELLECHET, M. L. C.   Catalogue général des incunables des bibliothèques publiques de France.   Paris, 1897–[to date].   [3 v. to
date].   3

Continued, after Mlle Pellechet's death, by M. Polain. Vols. I–III comprise Abano-Gregorius.

PROCTOR, R. [G. C.]   An Index to the early printed books in the
British Museum: from the invention of printing to the year 1500.
With notes of those in the Bodleian Library.   London, 1898–1903.
2 v.   4

Arranged chronologically by countries, and towns, in the order of the introduction of printing. Invaluable because of Proctor's assignment of place

and date to works issued anonymously. *Supplements, 1899–1902.* London, 1900–1903. *Registers to the four Supplements issued by Robert Proctor, 1899–1902.* By Konrad Burger. London, 1906.

BURGER, K.   The Printers and publishers of the fifteenth century with lists of their works.   (*In* Copinger, W. A.   Supplement to Hain's Repertorium. . . .   Vol. II.   London, 1902.)   5

Oftentimes invaluable in tracing a difficult title in Hain, Copinger, Proctor, or Pellechet.   Additional entries have been compiled and issued by T. de Marinis, under title: *Aggiunte e correzioni all' Index di K. Burger.* Firenze, 1904.   (Burger's "*Register: Die Drucker des XV. Jahrhunderts*" was issued at Leipzig in 1891; and his *Supplement zu Hain und Panzer* at Leipzig in 1908.)

REICHLING, D.   Appendices ad Hainii-Copingeri *Repertorium bibliographicum.* Additiones et emendationes.   Monachii, 1905–11, 1914. 8 v.   6

Vols. 1–6 consist of two sections each: I. Additiones. II. Emendationes. Vol. 7, Indices Fasciculorum, I–VI.   Vol. 8, Supplement: Index auctorum generalis, etc.

BRITISH MUSEUM (Department of Printed Books) Catalogue of books printed in the XVth century now in the British Museum.   London, 1908– [to date]. [5 v. to date.]   7

With important introductions by Mr. Pollard and Mr. Scholderer and notes on dates and types introducing, under the towns, the works of the various printers.   The volumes issued to date comprise Germany, German-speaking Switzerland, Austria-Hungary, and Italy in part — *i.e.,* Subiaco, Rome, and Venice.   Vol. VI, Italian imprints, is announced as in press.

ANNMARY BROWN MEMORIAL (Providence)   Catalogue of books. . . from the presses of the first printers showing the progress of printing with movable metal types through the second half of the fifteenth century.   Collected by Rush C. Hawkins, catalogued by Alfred W. Pollard, and deposited in the Annmary Brown Memorial at Providence, Rhode Island.   Oxford, 1910.   8

Because of Mr. Pollard's historical notes, which introduce the titles of each country, town, and printer, and the representative character of the collection, the catalogue affords a survey of fifteenth century printing.

PEDDIE, R. A.   Conspectus incunabulorum.   An index catalogue of fifteenth century books, with references to Hain's *Repertorium,* Copinger's *Supplement,* Proctor's *Index,* Pellechet's *Catalogue,* Campbell's *Annales* & other bibliographies.   London, 1910–14.   9

BIBLIOGRAPHICAL SOCIETY OF AMERICA   Census of fifteenth century books owned in America. New York, 1919.   10

First issued in the *Bulletin of the New York Public Library*, April-December, 1918. Vol. 22, nos. 4–12, and Aug. 1919. Edited by George Parker Winship. Compiled by a committee of the Society, comprising: G. P. Winship, G. W. Cole, V. H. Paltsits, and C. L. Nichols.

GESAMTKATALOG DER WIEGENDRUCKE, KOMMISSION FÜR DEN Gesamtkatalog der Wiegendrucke. Leipzig, 1925– [to date.] [3 v. to date.]   11

A bibliography of all the known editions of incunabula. Started in 1904 under the directorship of K. Haebler; directed since 1920 by E. von Rath. Vol. I edited by E. Crous and others; Vols. II, etc., edited by M. J. Husung and others.

Bericht über den Plan eines Gesamtkatalogs der Wiegendrucke. Von K. Haebler. (In *Zentralblatt für Bibliothekswesen.* XXII. Leipzig, 1905, p. 509–517.)

Nachträge zu Hain's Repertorium . . . Als Probe des Gesamtkatalogs der Wiegendrucke. Leipzig, 1910. (393 previously undescribed incunabula.)

Vorläufer des Gesamtkatalogs der Wiegendrucke. Von E. v. Rath. (In *Werden und Wirken. Hiersemannfestschrift.* Leipzig, 1924.)

For the *Catalogue* of the Pierpont Morgan Library, 1906–1907, see no. 631; and for lists of catalogues containing bibliographical data see below, under nos. 454–456.

B. *Gazetteers and Maps*
(Relative to Early Printing)

COTTON, H.   A typographical gazetteer. Oxford, 1831.   12

With appendix giving the Latin names of academies sometimes found on the title-pages of books; list of books on vellum in the Bodleian library (1459–1815); a chronological list [now out of date] of places at which printing is known to have been exercised, 1457–1829, etc. First issued at Oxford in 1825.

[DESCHAMPS, P. C. E.]   Dictionnaire de géographie ancienne et moderne à l'usage du libraire et de l'amateur de livres. Par un bibliophile. Paris, 1870. (Supplement to: [Brunet, M. J. C.] Manuel du libraire et de l'amateur de livres.)   13

Reprinted in 1922. A dictionary of place-names used during various centuries and therefore not always pertinent to fifteenth century usage. (For a list of Latin place-names taken from the colophons of incunabula, see Reference Section IV of the present volume, Place-names of Fifteenth Century Printing Towns.)

REICHHART, G.   Topographisch-chronologisch geordnetes Verzeichniss der Druckorte des 15. Jahrhunderts. (*In* Zentralblatt für Bibliothekswesen. Beiheft XIV. Beiträge zur Incunabelkunde. Leipzig, 1895, p. 159–447.) 14

Arranged alphabetically by places. The author's *Die Druckorte des XV. Jahrhunderts* was issued at Augsburg in 1853. Although still valuable in many respects, these gazetteers have now been more or less superseded by the individual researches of later scholars.

BRITISH MUSEUM (Department of Printed Books) Germania typographica. (British Museum. Catalogue of books printed in the XVth century. . . . London, 1908– [to date]. Vol. III, frontispiece.) 15

A map prepared by J. V. Scholderer.

TEICHL, R. Der Wiegendruck im Kartenbild. (Sonderabdruck aus der Festschrift der Nationalbibliothek in Wien.) Wien, 1926. 16

A very clever map, which, by means of colored dots, shows not only the towns in which printing was practiced during the fifteenth century, but also the decade or period when it was introduced. With two tables [already slightly out of date]: one listing the towns chronologically; the other, alphabetically, with dates showing the continuance of printing and the name of the first printer in each town.

C. *Handbooks* (*Bibliographical, etc.*)

HAEBLER, K. Handbuch der Inkunabelkunde. Leipzig, 1925. 17

A condensed survey of "Incunable-knowledge," to which enhanced value is given by the fact that, in the course of Dr. Haebler's discussion of the elements which characterize early printing, he cites the actual titles or the Hain numbers of various works in which these elements appear. The handbook comprises two parts, *The Science* and *The Book*.
Contents: I. *Die Wissenschaft*. 1. Begriff und Abgrenzung. 2. Geschichte und Literatur. 3. Geschichte des Buckdrucks. II. *Das Buch*. A. Vorbereitung und Anordnung. 1. Papier. 2. Format. 3. Registrum. 4. Signaturen. 5. Blattzählung. 6. Kustoden. B. Der Druck. 1. Typenguss. 2. Druckerpresse. 3. Punkturen. 4. Spalten. 5. Schriftgrade. 6. Formen. 7. Typen. 8. Initialen. 9. Holzschnitte. 10. Druckermarken. 11. Farbendruck. 12. Noten. 13. Titel. 14. Korrektoren. 15. Datierung. 16. Auflagen. 17. Vertrieb. 18. Preise. 19. Privilegien. 20. Nachdruck. 21. Zensur. 22. Verschollene Wiegendrucke. 23. Einbände. 24. Eintragungen. 25. Literaturgeschichte.

—— Typenrepertorium der Wiegendrucke. Halle, then Leipzig, 1905–1924. 5 pts. in 6 v. (Sammlung bibliothekswissenschaftlicher Arbeiten.) 18

Part I: Deutschland und seine Nachbarländer. Part II: Italien, Nederlande, Frankreich, Spanien, Portugal, England. Part III: Tabellen I, Antiqua

Typen. Part III: Tabellen II, Gotische Typen. Part IV: Ergänzungsband I. Part V. Ergänzungsband II.

See also the essay by E. Freys entitled *Joh. Baptist Bernharts "Gesammelte Schriften." Ein Vorläufer von Haeblers Typenrepertorium.* (*In* Wiegendrucke und Handschriften. Festgabe Konrad Haebler zum 60. Geburtstage. Leipzig, 1919, p. 145–174.)

McKERROW, R. B. An Introduction to bibliography for literary students. Oxford, 1927.   19

A discussion of the processes involved in the transition between the author's manuscript and the printed book, particularly with regard to the books of the sixteenth and seventeenth centuries. With detailed explanations of methods and terms.

The following pages have reference to incunabula or are especially relevant to the present volume: 22–23 (pinholes); 25–28 (definitions); 29–37 (imposition); 38–52 (press); 55–63 (single-page printing, etc.); 73–89 (signatures, foliation, etc.); 97–102 (paper); 109–121 (decoration, etc.); 130–131 (size of edition); 146–163 (bibliographical description, etc); 164–174 (chain-lines, wire-lines, water-marks, *illus.*, etc.); 175–183 (edition, impression, issue); 222–238 (cancels, insertions, fakes); 264–280 (early printing, etc.); 288–293 (types); 306 note (type measurement); 315 (comma); 319–322 (abbreviations and contractions in early printed books).

———— Notes on bibliographical evidence for literary students and editors of English works of the sixteenth and seventeenth centuries. (Reprinted from the *Transactions* of the Bibliographical Society, Vol. XII.) London, 1914.   20

Contains diagrams demonstrating the imposition of page blocks of type, and the folding of sheets of paper into folio, quarto, or octavo formats, etc.

PEDDIE, R. A. Fifteenth century books: A guide to their identification. . . . London, 1913.   21

Although superseded in some particulars, this is a useful guide in its lists of library catalogues, annotations, etc.

Po[LLARD] A. W. Bibliography and bibliology. (Encyclopædia Britannica. 11th ed. Cambridge, 1910–1911, Vol. 3, p. 908–911.)   22

An essay by Mr. Pollard entitled *The Objects and methods of bibliographical collations and descriptions* appeared in *The Library.* New series. 1907. Vol. VIII, p. 193–217.

WIEGENDRUCK-GESELLSCHAFT (Berlin) Der Buchdruck des 15. Jahrhunderts. Berlin, 1929–.   23

A valuable list of bibliographies and monographs contemplated by the Wiegendruck-Gesellschaft, of which two numbers — *Der Buchdruck Frankreichs*

und der Französischen Schweiz (ed. by E. v. Rath) and *Der Buchdruck
Spaniens und Portugals im fünfzehnten Jahrhundert* (ed. by K. Ohly) —
have been issued.

———

A handbook entitled *Some noteworthy firsts in Europe during the fifteenth
century* by Miss E. Miriam Lone is announced among the fall publications
of 1930, comprising a series of annotated titles of known ‘firsts,’ *i.e.,* countries
and their languages, types, technical points, illustrations, medicine, law,
arts, sciences, etc.

D. *Histories and Surveys*

PEDDIE, R. A., *ed.*   Printing: A short history of the art.   London,
1927.   24

Contents: Germany, by E. Crous; Italy, by G. Fumagalli; France, by
C. Mortet; Holland and Beligum, by M. Sabbe; Spain and Portugal, by J. P.
R. Lyell; Great Britain and Ireland, by H. R. Plomer; Scandinavia, by
L. Nielsen; Eastern Europe and Slavonic countries, by L. C. Wharton;
Spanish America, by G. P. Winship; North America (English-speaking), by
L. C. Wroth.   With an appendix relating to Asia, Africa, Australasia, and
an ‘Index of printers and places.’

POLLARD, A. W.   Fine Books.   New York, London, 1912.   25

The following chapters relate to fifteenth century printing, in whole or in
part: III. The invention of printing, Holland.   IV. The invention of printing, Mainz.   V. Other incunabula.   VI. The development of printing.   VII.
Early German and Dutch illustrated books.   VIII. Early Italian illustrated
books.   IX. Early French and Spanish illustrated books.   XII. Printing
in England (1476–1580).   XIV. English woodcut illustrations.   XV. Engraved illustrations.   Select bibliography, p. 311–316.

WINSHIP, G. P.   Gutenberg to Plantin.   An outline of the early history
of printing.   Cambridge, 1926.   26

Contents: The invention of typography, 1440–1456; the period of development, 1460–1480; the spread of printing throughout Germany; the establishing of printing as a business; the printers encounter the Renaissance; Venice
becomes the headquarters of the book trade; printing reaches the whole
European world; the first private presses; the use of pictures, etc.

———

Three surveys of a general nature contain brief sections on incunabula:
Schneider, G., *Handbuch der Bibliographie.* 3. unveränderte Aufl.   Leipzig,
1926; Bohatta, H., *Einfürhrung in die Buchkunde. Ein Handbuch für Biblio-
thekare, Bücherliebhaber und Antiquare.* Vienna, 1927; Van Hoesen, H. B.,
and F. K. Walter.   *Bibliography* . . . New York, 1928.

Dr. George Sarton’s *Introduction* to the history of science, the publication
of which was begun by the Carnegie Institution of Washington in 1927, will
be found of immense value, in its completed form, in tracing the develop-

ment of systematized positive knowledge, the transmission of knowledge through the ages, and the interrelation of the factors contributing to the advancement of science and the progress of mankind.

II. SPECIALIZED BIBLIOGRAPHIES AND MONOGRAPHS

A. *Countries* *

I. GERMANY

(*a*) IN GENERAL

CROUS, E. Germany. (*In* Peddie, R. A., *ed.,* Printing: A short history of the art. London, 1927, p. 1–13.) 27

A concise and valuable account of the experimental period at Mainz; with a survey of the diffusion of the printing art through Germany and Switzerland; and a chronological list of the towns into which the art was introduced.

HAEBLER, K. Die deutschen Buchdrucker des XV. Jahrhunderts im Auslande. München, 1924. 28

An account of the early German printers at work in foreign lands, with a *Personenregister,* an Introduction describing the beginnings of printing in Germany, and a chapter on the reaction of foreign countries upon German printing.

A list of 150 early German printers in Italy is given in the *Festschrift . . . zum 500 jährigen Geburtstage von Joh. Gutenberg,* Leipzig, 1900, *in* D. Marzi's *I Tipografi in Italia.*

POLLARD, A. W. [Early printing in Germany] Introduction. (*In* British Museum. Catalogue of books printed in the fifteenth century. London, 1908–1913. Vol. I–III.) 29

With a map (Vol. III) of early German printing towns and *Notes on the presses of Part III,* by J. V. Scholderer.

UPDIKE, D. B. Type and type-forms of the fifteenth century in Germany. (*In his* Printing types. Cambridge, 1922. Vol. I, p. 58–69.) 30

VOULLIÉME, E. Die deutschen Drucker des fünfzehnten Jahrhunderts. Zweite Auflage. Berlin, 1922. 31

A series of concise paragraphs giving a survey of early printing in Germany and German-speaking towns; arranged alphabetically by places, and illus-

---

* Arranged in the order of the introduction of printing, but with towns listed alphabetically under each country.

trated by facsimiles of types and colophons. With a type-table of M's (from Haebler's *Typenrepertorium der Wiegendrucke*) and a chronological list of printing towns. Issued as a supplement to Burger's *Monumenta Germaniae et italiae typographica*. First issued in 1916, without the revisions and facsimiles which appear in the second edition.

(*b*) By Towns

(1) AUGSBURG

PROCTOR, R. [G. C.]   Ulrich von Ellenbog and the press of S. Ulrich at Augsburg. (*In his* Bibliographical essays. London, 1905, p. 73–88.)   32

(2) BAMBERG

ZEDLER, G.   Die Bamberger Pfisterdrucke und die 36 zeilige Bibel. Mainz, 1911. (Gutenberg Gesellschaft. Veröffentlichungen. X, XI.)   33

Reviewed by Mr. Scholderer in *The Library*, 1912, p. 230–236.

(3) COLOGNE

PROCTOR, R. [G. C.]   The early printers of Köln. (*In his* Bibliographical essays. London, 1905, p. 120–219.)   34

VOULLIÉME, E.   Der Buchdruck Kölns bis zum Ende des fünfzehnten Jahrhunderts. Ein Beitrag zur Inkunabelbibliographie. Bonn, 1903. (Publikationen der Rhein. Gesellschaft für Geschichtskunde 24.)   35

Reviewed by Proctor in *The Library*. 1903, p. 392–402.

(4) ELTVIL

HARRISSE, H.   Les premiers incunables balois et leurs dérivés: Toulouse, Lyon, Vienne-en-Dauphine, Spire, Eltvil, etc., 1471–1484.   2. ed.   Paris, 1902.   36

(5) FRANKFURT

ZÜLCH AND MORI   Frankfurter Urkundenbuch zur Frühgeschichte des Buchdrucks. Frankfurt a. M., 1920.   37

(6) FREIBURG

PFAFF, F.   Der erste Freiburger Buchdruck 1493–1600. Freiburg, 1893.   38

(7) HAGENAU

HANAUER, A.   Les Imprimeurs de Hagenau. Strassburg, 1904.   39

(8) HAMBURG

COLLIJN, I. [G. A.]   Neuen Beiträgen zur Geschichte des ältesten
Buchdrucks in Hamburg. Hamburg, 1907. (Jahrbuch der Ham-
burgischen Wissenschaftlichen Ausfalten. VII.)   40

(9) HEIDELBERG

ROTH, F. W. E.   Geschichte und Bibliographie der Heidelberger Buchdruckereien, 1485–1510. Heidelberg, 1901.   41

(10) LEIPZIG

HAEBLER, K.   Der Capotius-Drucker: Martin Landsberg. Uppsala,
1907. (Gesellschaft für Typenkunde des XV. Jahrh. Beiträge zur
Inkunabelkunde. II.)   42

Relative to Tables 37 and 39 in the Society's *Veröffentlichungen,* Leipzig,
1907–.

(11) LÜBECK

COLLIJN, I. [G. A.]   Drei neu aufgefundene niederdeutsche Einblatt-
kalendar des 15. Jahrhunderts. Ein Beitrag zur Geschichte des
Lübecker Buchdrucks. Upsala, 1904.   43

———— Lübecker Frühdrucke. (*In* Zeitschrift des Vereins für Lü-
beckische Geschichte und Altertumskunde. Lübeck, 1908. Bd. 9,
Heft 2.)   44

CURTIUS, C.   Ein niederdeutscher Kalender aus Lübeck auf das Jahr
1491. Lübeck, 1906. (Beilage zu den " Vaterstädtischen Blättern,"
XXIII.)   45

(12) MAINZ

CROUS, E.   Gutenberg. (*In* Peddie, R. A., *ed.,* Printing: A short history of the art. London, 1927, p. 1–5.)   46

SEYMOUR DE RICCI.   Catalogue raisonné des premières impressions de
Mayence, 1445–1467. Mainz, 1911. (Gutenberg Gesellschaft.
Veröffentlichungen. VIII–IX.)   47

A bibliographical description of each title; with an account of the location
of copies, and bibliographical references under each entry.

ZEDLER, G.   Die 42 zeilige Bibeltype im Schöfferschen Missale Mogun-
tinum von 1493. Mainz, 1908. (Gutenberg Gesellschaft. Veröffentlichungen. VI.)   48

———— Das Mainzer Catholicon. Mainz, 1905. (Gutenberg Gesellschaft. Veröffentlichungen. IV.)   49

See also below, under: III. Origin and Invention of Movable Type, and
Printing Before 1457, nos. 487–503 and 539–564 respectively.

(13) MERSEBURG

HAEBLER, K.   Die Merseburger Druckerei von 1479 und ihr Meister.
Uppsala, 1912. (Gesellschaft für Typenkunde des XV. Jahrh.
Beiträge zur Inkunabelkunde. V.)   50

LANGE, H. O.   Eine Merseburger Buchdruckerei um das Jahr 1479.
Uppsala, 1907. (Gesellschaft für Typenkunde des XV. Jahrh.
Beiträge zur Inkunabelkunde. V.)   51

Relative to Tables 23 and 24 in the Society's *Veröffentlichungen*, Leipzig,
1907–.

METZ

See below, under: France.

(14) MUNICH

WEIL, E.   Die Wiegendrucke Münchens. Ein bibliographisches Verzeichnis mit neun Typentafeln. München, 1923.   52

A description of thirty-three books printed at Munich in the fifteenth century,
with facsimiles of types.

(15) MUNSTER

CROUS, E.   Münster in Westf. und der Wiegendruck. (*In* Wiegendrucke und Handschriften. Festgabe zu Konrad Haeblers 60.
Geburtstag. Leipzig, 1919.)   53

LANGE, H. O.   Der Drucker Johann Limburg in Münster. Uppsala,
1907. (Gesellschaft für Typenkunde des XV. Jahrh. Beiträge zur
Inkunabelkunde. III.)   54

Relative to Table 73 in the Society's *Veröffentlichungen*, Leipzig, 1907–.

(16) REGENSBURG

SCHOTTENLOHER, K.   Das Regensburger Buchgewerbe im 15. und 16.
Jahrhundert. Mainz, 1920. (Gutenberg-Gesellschaft. Veröffentlichungen. XIV–XIX.)   55

(17) SPEIER

HARRISSE, H. Les premiers incunables balois et leurs dérivés: Toulouse, Lyon, Vienne-en-Dauphine, Spire, Eltvil, etc., 1471–1484. 2. ed. Paris, 1902.
56

(18) STRASSBURG AND VICINITY

COLLIJN, I. [G. A.] Adolf Rusch i Strassburg, Tryckaren med det bisarra R. (*In his* Bokhistoriska Uppsater. Stockholm, 1905–.)
57

DZIATZKO, K. Kirchheim im Elsäss, eine bisher unbekannte Druckstätte des XV. Jahrhunderts. (*In his* Sammlung. 1895. Heft 8: 23, *etc.*)
58

PROCTOR, R. [G. C.] Marcus Reinhard and Johann Grüninger. (Bibliographical Society. Transactions. V. 1899.)
59
Reprinted in his *Bibliographical essays.* London, 1905, p. 19–38.
Regarding the relationship and careers of Marcus Reinhard of Lyon and Johann Grüninger [Johann Reinhard (?)] of Strassburg.

SCHMIDT, CH. Répertoire bibliographique Strasbourgeois jusque vers 1530. Strasbourg, 1893–1910.
60

———— Zur Geschichte der ältesten Bibliotheken und der ersten Buchdrucker zu Strassburg. Strassburg, 1882.
61

SCHORBACH, K. AND M. SPIRGATIS Heinrich Knoblochtzer in Strassburg (1477–1484). Strassburg, 1888. (Bibliographische Studien zur Buchdruckergeschichte Deutschlands. I.)
62
Nachträge in *Sammlung bibliothekswissenschaftlicher Arbeiten.* Heft 8. Leipzig, 1895.

VOULLIÉME, E. Zur ältesten Buchdruckergeschichte Strassburgs. (*In* Zentralblatt für Bibliothekswesen. XXXII. 1915, p. 309–321.) 63

(19) ULM

WEGENER, J. Die Zainer in Ulm. Strassburg, 1904.
64
Reviewed by Dr. Voulliéme in *Zentralblatt für Bibliothekswesen.* XXI. 1904, p. 517–520.

————

See also below, under: II. Books of Hours, etc.; Mathematics (Music); III. Advertisements; Color Printing; Greek Type; Origin and Invention of

Movable Type; Printers' Marks; Printing Before 1457; Type; Type Founding; and under the following section, Selected Bibliographies — Woodcuts, Metal Engravings, etc. For other monographs and specialized bibliographies relating to early printing in German towns, see the introductory sections in: British Museum. Department of printed books. *Catalogue of books printed in the XVth century.* London, 1908–1913; and Peddie, R. A., *Fifteenth-century books.* London, 1913, p. 65–70.

2. ITALY

A) IN GENERAL

FUMAGALLI, G.   Italy.   (*In* Peddie, R. A., *ed.*, Printing: A short history of the art. London, 1927, p. 38–52, 61–62.)   65

A brief discussion of the traditions and theories regarding early experimental work in Italy; a sweeping review of the introduction of printing into the Italian towns, of the work of the leading printers and of the 'Wanderdrucker' from Germany; with a brief list of bibliographies, etc.

——— Lexicon typographicum Italiae.   Dictionnaire géographique d'Italie pour servir à l'histoire de l'imprimerie dans ce pays. Florence, 1905.   66

Arranged alphabetically by towns; with accounts of printers and printing and, in each instance, a careful weighing of bibliographical data up to the time of publication.

HAEBLER, K.   Die italienischen Fragmente vom Leiden Christi.   Das älteste Druckwerk Italiens. München, 1927.   67

Advances the thesis that a fragment, recently found, of a 'History of Christ's Passion' may have been printed in Italy by a German printer, possibly a pupil of Gutenberg's, as early as 1462.

——— Subiaco-Rom, 1465–1471, etc.   (*In his* Die deutschen Buchdrucker des XV. Jahrhunderts im Auslande. München, 1924.) 68

A series of chapters on German printers: Subiaco-Rom, 1465–1471; Venedig, 1469–1471; Mailand, 1469–1500; Humanisten und Drucker, 1471–1474; Rom, 1472–1479; Rom, 1480–1500; Venedig, 1471–1480; Die hebräischen Drucker, 1475–1500; Das übrige Italien, 1471–1475; Mittel- und Ober-Italien, 1475–1500.

MARZI, D.   I tipografi tedeschi in Italia durante il secolo XV.   (*In* Festschrift . . . zum 500 jährigen Geburtstage von Joh. Gutenberg. Leipzig, 1900.)   69

Lists the names of more than 150 early German printers in Italy.

UPDIKE, D. B.   Type and type-forms of the fifteenth century in Italy. (*In his* Printing types. Cambridge, 1922. Vol. I, p. 70–81.) 70

b) By Towns or Provinces

(1) ABRUZZO

PANSA, G. La tipografia in Abruzzo dal secolo XV al secolo XVIII. Lanciano, 1891.   71

(2) AQUILA

VECCHIONI, G. L'arte della stampa in Aquila. Aquila, 1908.   72

See also under: Abruzzo.

(3) ASTI

BERLAN, F. La introduzione della stampa in Savigliano, Saluzzo ed Asti nel secolo XV. Torino, 1887.   73

BARCO *

(4) BOLOGNA *

MARINIS, T. DE Ouvrages imprimés à Bologna au XV. Siècle. Florence, 1914.   74

SIGHINOLFI, L. Francesco Puteolano e le origini della stampa in Bologna e Parma. (*In* La Bibliofilia. XV. 1913–14.)   75

——— I mappamondi di Taddeo Crivelli e la stampa Bolognese della cosmografia di Tolomeo. (*In* La Bibliofilia. X.)   76

SORBELLI, A. I primordi della stampa in Bologna. Bologna, 1908.   77

(5) BRESCIA *

CHRISTIE, R. C. An incunabulum of Brescia hitherto ascribed to Florence. (*In* Bibliographical Society. Transactions. London, 1898, p. 233–237.)   78

LECHI, L. Della tipografia bresciana nel secolo XV. Brescia, 1854.   79

PEDDIE, R. A. Printing at Brescia in the fifteenth century. London, 1905.   80

* A Hebrew printing town. See below, under: III, (10) Bibliographical and Historical Aspects, Hebrew printing, nos. 466–479.

(6) CAPODISTRIA

FUMAGALLI, G.   La questione di Pamfilo Castaldi.   Milan, 1891.   81
Refutes the arguments supporting early printing at Capodistria.

MOTTA, E.   Pamfilo Castaldi.   (*In* Rivista Storica Italiana, 1884.)   82

CASSALMAGGIORE *

(7) CREMONA

MOTTA, E.   Il tipografo Dionigi da Parravicino a Cremona, 1471.
Como, 1888.   83

FERRARA *

(8) FLORENCE

BOLOGNA, P.   La stamperia fiorentina del monasterio di S. Jacopo di
Ripoli e le sue edizioni.   Torino, 1893.   84

NESI, E.   Il diario della stamperia di Ripoli.   Florenz, 1903.   85

(9) MANTUA *

ARNAULLET, P.   Les associations d'imprimeurs à Mantoue.   (*In* Le
Bibliographe Moderne, 1898.)   86

(10) MILAN

BERLAN, F.   La introduzione della stampa in Milano.   Venezia, 1884.
                                                                    87

SCHOLDERER, [J.] V.   Printing at Milan.   (*In* The Library.   March,
1927.   Ser. IV, vol. VII, no. 4, p. 355–375.)   87 :a
With an important table, giving a subject analysis of Milanese incunabula.

(11) NAPLES *

FAVA, M. AND G. BRESCIANO   La stampa a Napoli nel XV secolo.
Leipzig, 1911–1912.   2 v.   (Sammlung Bibliothekswissenschaftlicher
Arbeiten.   Hefte 32–33.)   88

MARINIS, T. DE   Les Libraires allemands à Naples au XVe siècle.
Florence, 1904.   89

* A Hebrew printing town.   See below, under: III, (10) Bibliographical and
Historical Aspects, Hebrew printing, nos. 466–479.

(12) PARMA

SIGHINOLFI, L. Francesco Puteolano e le origini della stampa in Bologna e Parma. (*In* La Bibliofilia. XV. 1913–14.)   90

(13) PERUGIA

LANGE, H. O. Les plus anciens imprimeurs à Pérouse 1471–1482. (*In* Oversigt over des Kgl. Danske Videnskabs Selskabs Forhandlinger. VI. 1907.)   91

ROSSI, A. L'arte tipografica in Perugia durante il secolo XV. Perugia, 1868.   92

PIEVE DI SACCO *

REGGIO DI CALABRIA *

(14) ROME *

AUDIFFREDI, J. B. Catalogus historico-criticus Romanarum editionum saeculi 15. Romae, 1783.   93

Supplemented by Bresciano, G. *Ad catalogum hist.-crit. romanarum.* Paris, 1897.

DEGERING, H. Wer war der Drucker der Erstausgabe des Vitruv? Ein Beitrag zur Geschichte des römischen Buchdrucks. (*In* Wiegendrucke und Handschriften. Festgabe Konrad Haebler zum 60. Geburtstage. Leipzig, 1919, p. 175–202.)   94

POLLARD, A. W. [Subiaco and Rome] (*In* British Museum. Catalogue of books printed in the XVth Century. London, 1908– [to date]. Vol. IV.)   95

SCHOLDERER, [J.] V. The Petition of Sweynheim and Pannartz to Sixtus IV. (*In* The Library. London, 1915, p. 186–190.)   96

See also the notes by E. G. Duff and J. P. Edmond on *Sweynheim and Pannartz* in: Edinburgh Bibliographical Society. *Publications,* II.

(15) SALUZZO

BERLAN, F. La introduzione della stampa in Savigliano, Saluzzo ed Asti nel secolo XV. Torino, 1887.   97

---

* A Hebrew printing town. See below, under: III, (10) Bibliographical and Historical Aspects, Hebrew printing, nos. 466–479.

(16) SAVIGLIANO

BERLAN, F.   La introduzione della stampa in Savigliano, Saluzzo ed Asti nel secolo XV.   Torino, 1887.   98

(17) SICILY

OLIVA, G.   L'arte della stampa in Sicilia nei secoli XV & XVI.   Catania, 1911.   99

SONCINO *

(18) SUBIACO

DUFF, E. G. AND J. P. EDMOND   Sweynheim and Pannartz.   Notes and collations.   (*In* Edinburgh Bibliographical Society.   *Publications.* II.)   100

FUMAGALLI, C.   Dei primi libri a stampa in Italia e specialmente di un Codice Sublacense impresso avanti il Lattanzio e finora creduto posteriore.   Lugano, 1875.   101

POLLARD, A. W.   [Subiaco and Rome]   (*In* British Museum.   Catalogue of books printed in the XVth Century.   London, 1908– [to date].   Vol. IV.   101:a

(19) TRENT.   Listed by Proctor, etc., under Austria; see below under no. 251.

(20) TREVISO

SCHOLDERER, [J.] V.   A Fleming in Venetia: Gerardus de Lisa, printer, bookseller, schoolmaster, and musician.   (*In* The Library.   December 1929.   Series 4, Vol. X, no. 3, p. 252–273.)   102

With a subject analysis of Trevisan editions.

(21) TURIN

FICKER, O.   Der erster Druck Turins und sein Drucker.   (*In* Zeitschrift für Bucherfreunde.   Oct. 1900.)   103

MANZONI, G.   Annali tipografici torinesi del Secolo XV.   Torino, 1863.   104

(22) VENICE

BROWN, H. [R.] F.   The Venetian Printing Press.   London, 1891. 105

* A Hebrew printing town.   See below, under: III, (10) Bibliographical and Historical Aspects, Hebrew printing, nos. 466–479.

KARATAEV, I. P. Opisanie slaviano-russkikh knig. St. Petersburg, 1883. 106

Vol. I, 1491–1652, includes one fifteenth century book in Cyrillic type, assigned to the press of Andreas Torresanus in Venice; a work said by L. C. Wharton to be in Glagolitic type (see the latter's essay on *Jugoslavia,* in: Peddie, R. A., *ed., Printing: A short history of the art.* . . London, 1927, p. 276–277).

REDGRAVE, G. R. Erhard Ratdolt and his work at Venice. London, 1894. (Bibliographical Society. Illustrated Monographs. I.) 107

RENOUARD, A. A. Annales de l'imprimerie des Alde. 3e ed. Paris, 1834. 108

SCHOLDERER, [J.] V. [Early Printing at Venice] Introduction. (*In* British Museum. Catalogue of books printed in the XVth Century. Part V. London, 1924.) 109

——— Printing at Venice to the end of 1481. (*In* The Library, 4th Series, V. Oxford, 1925, p. 129–152.) 110

(24) VERONA

GIULIARI, G. B. Della tipografia veronese. Verona, 1871. 111

See also below, under: II. Books of Hours, etc.; Mathematics (Geometry, Music); Medicine and allied subjects; III. Greek Type; Hebrew Printing; Printers' Marks; Type; and under the following section, Selected Bibliographies — Woodcuts, Metal Engravings, etc.

For additional monographs relating to early printing in Italy see under towns, Fumagalli, G. *Lexicon typographicum Italiae.* Florence, 1905.

3. SWITZERLAND

A) IN GENERAL

BRITISH MUSEUM (Department of Printed Books) Catalogue of books printed in the XVth century now in the British Museum. Part III. . . . German-speaking Switzerland. . . London, 1913. 112

The section relating to Switzerland, p. 713–804, comprises imprints from Basel, Beromünster, Burgdorf, Zürich and unassigned titles; a brief account of early German-Swiss printing is given in Mr. Scholderer's *Notes on the presses of Part III.*

CROUS, E. Germany [and Switzerland.] II. The fifteenth century. (*In* Peddie, R. A., *ed., Printing: A short history of the art. London, 1927, p. 5–13.*) 113

A quick review of the diffusion of printing through Germany and Switzerland, with a chronological list of the towns into which the art was introduced.

VOULLIÉME, E.   Die deutschen Drucker des 15. Jahrhunderts. 2d
ed. Berlin, 1922.   114

> Relates to early printing in Germany and Switzerland, with biographical
> and bibliographical notes relating to each printer.

B) BY TOWNS

(1) BASEL

HARRISSE, H.   Les premiers incunables bâlois et leurs dérivés: Toulouse, Lyon, Vienne-en-Dauphiné, Spire, Eltvil, etc., 1471–1484.
2. ed. Paris, 1902.   115

HECKETHORN, C. W.   The printers of Basle in the XV. & XVI. centuries. Their biographies, printed books and devices. London, 1897.
                                                                     116

JOHNSON, A. F.   The first century of printing at Basle.   London,
1926. (Periods of typography.)   117

KOEGLER, H.   Einige Basler Kalender des XV. und der ersten Hälfte
des XVI. Jahrhu derts.   (In Anzeiger für schweizerische Altertumskunde. Band. ʻ1. 1909. Zurich, 1910.)   118

SCHOLDERER, [J.] V.   Michael Wenssler and his press at Basel.   (In
The Library, 1912, p. 283–321.)   119

STEHLIN, K.   Regester zur Geschichte des Buchdrucks bis zum Jahre
1501. Aus den Büchern des Basler Gerichtsarchivs. Leipzig, 1888–
89. (Archiv für Geschichte des deutschen Buchhandels. XI, XII.)
                                                                     120

> According to Mr. Scholderer in his account of this work (no. 119 above),
> it contains "1632 excerpts dealing with early printers and printing, from
> contemporary legal and other documents preserved at Basel."

(2) BEROMÜNSTER

AEBI, J. L.   Die Buchdruckerei zu Beromünster im fünfzehnten Jahrhundert. Einsiedeln, 1870.   121

(3) GENEVA

FAVRE, G.   Notice sur les livres imprimés à Genève dans le XVe siècle.
2. éd. Genf, 1855.   122

GAULLIEUR, E. H. A.   Études sur la typographie génevoise du XVe
au XIXe siècle et sur les origines de l'imprimerie en Suisse. Genève,
1855.   123

> Reprinted from the Bulletin de l'Institut national génevois, 1855. II, p. 33–
> 292.

(4) LAUSANNE

BERNUS, A.   L'Imprimerie à Lausanne . . . jusqu'à la fin du 16e siècle.
2 èd. Lausanne [1904].   124

First issued in *Gazette de Lausanne*, July 4–5, 1902, and separately printed.

See also below, under: III. Printers' Marks; and under the following section, Selected Bibliographies — Woodcuts, Metal Engravings, etc.

In *Der Buchdruck des 15. Jahrhunderts* (Wiegendruck-Gesellschaft. No. I,
ed. by E. v. Rath. Berlin, 1929) essays on early printing in Geneva are
noted as in the following publications: *Revue de la Suisse cath.* 16:1884/5;
Publ. de la Société Suisse de Bibliophiles, 2:3; and *Genèva* 2: 1924; 3: 1925.

4. FRANCE

a) IN GENERAL

BRITISH MUSEUM (Department of Printed Books)   Short-title catalogue of books printed in France and of French books printed in
other countries from 1470 to 1600 now in the British Museum. Oxford, 1924.   125

Prepared by Dr. Henry Thomas, assisted by A. F. Johnson and A. G. Macfarlane.

CLAUDIN, A.   Histoire de l'imprimerie en France au XVe et au XVIe
siècle. Paris, 1900, 1901, 1904, 1914.   126

L'imprimerie à Paris, Vols. 1–2; L'imprimerie à Lyon, Vols. 3–4. The
fourth volume, which was partially printed at the time of M. Claudin's
death, was completed by M. Lacombe in 1914 and released to the public
in 1920.

For a list of Claudin's writings see: Seymour de Ricci. *Documents sur la
typographie* . . . *en France.* Londres, 1926, p. 5–33.

————— Private printing in France during the fifteenth century. (*In*
Bibliographica. Part X, p. 344–370.)   127

Records the existence of eleven private presses.

Separately issued: [London, 1896.] Reissued under title: *Les Imprimeries
particulières en France au XVe siècle.* Paris, 1897.

DELALAIN, P.   Essai de bibliographie de l'histoire de l'imprimerie
typographique et de la librairie en France. Paris, 1903.   128

HAEBLER, K.   Paris 1470–1500, etc. (*In his* Die deutschen Buchdrucker des XV. Jahrhunderts in Auslande. München, 1924.)   129

A series of chapters on German printers in *Paris,* 1470–1500; *Lyon,* 1473–
1500: *Das übrige Frankreich,* 1476–1500.

LABANDE, L. H.   L'Imprimerie en France au XVe siècle.   (*In* Festschrift zum 500jähr. Geburtstage von Johann Gutenberg. Leipzig,
1900.)   130

LEPREUX, G.   Gallia typographica ou répertoire biographique et
chronologique de tous les imprimeurs de France. Paris, 1909, 1911.
                                                                    131
Reviewed by Dr. Voulliéme in *Zentralblatt für Bibliothekswesen.* XXVIII.
1911, p. 40–46; and XXIX.   1912, p. 282–85.

MORTET, C.   The fifteenth century.   (*In* Peddie, R. A., *ed.,* Printing,
A short history of the art. London, 1927, p. 63–75 and 110–111.)
                                                                    132
With brief sections relating to the first Paris press; later Parisian printers;
printing at Lyons; the characteristics of early French printing; innovations
in printing; the use of printers' devices; the influence of publishers; and a
list of selected sources. Translated from the French by André Paulian.

SEYMOUR DE RICCI, *ed.*   Documents sur la typographie et la gravure
en France, aux XVe et XVIe siècles, reunis par A. Claudin. Publiés
et commentés par Seymour de Ricci. Londres, 1926.   133
A list of Claudin's writings is given on p. 5–33 with the heading: *Bibliographie
des publications d'Anatole Claudin (1833–1906).*

THIERRY-POUX, O.   Premiers monuments de l'imprimerie en France
au XVe siècle. . .   Paris, 1890.   134
"Sur 167 volumes décrits par M. Thierry-Poux, 163 se trouvent à la
Réserve du Dépt. des imprimés de la Bibliothèque Nationale. Cet ouvrage
donne une liste raisonnée des premiers travaux imprimés dans 41 villes ou
bourgades de France au XVe siècle." — Vallée.

UPDIKE, D. B.   Type and type-forms of the fifteenth century in France.
(*In his* Printing types. Cambridge, 1922. Vol. 1, p. 82–92.)   135

B) BY TOWNS

    (1) ABBEVILLE

LEDIEU, A.   L'Imprimerie et la librairie à Abbeville avant 1700.
Abbeville, 1887.   136

    (2) ALBI

CLAUDIN, A.   Origines de l'imprimerie à Albi en Languedoc (1480–
1484) . . . Paris, 1880. (Antiquités typographiques de la France.
I.)   137

See also, under: Languedoc. An essay by Dr. Konrad Haebler on *Die Wiegendrucke von Albi* is said to be included in a forthcoming issue of the *Beiträge zur Forschung* published by J. Rosenthal, Munich.

(3) AVIGNON

LABANDE, L. H. Le premier livre imprimé à Avignon au XVe siècle. (Gutenberg-Festschrift. 1925.) 138

PANSIER, P. Histoire du livre et de l'imprimerie à Avignon du XIVe au XVIe siècle. Avignon, 1922. 139

(4) BORDEAUX

CLAUDIN, A. Les Origines et les débuts de l'imprimerie à Bordeaux. Paris, 1897. 140

(5) CAEN

DELISLE, L. Catalogue des livres imprimés ou publiés à Caen avant le milieu du XVIe siècle, suivi de recherches sur les imprimeurs et les libraires. Caen, 1903–1904. (Bulletin de la Société des Antiquaires de Normandie, tomes XXIII, XXIV.) 141

(6) CHÂLONS-SUR-MARNE

L'HOTE, A. Histoire de l'imprimerie à Châlons-sur-Marne, 1488–1894. Châlons-sur-Marne, 1894. 142

A list of printers, booksellers and binders of Châlons-sur-Marne was published by L'Hote during 1894.

(7) CHARTRES

DURAND, G. Les Imprimeurs typographes de Chartres depuis 1482. Chartres, 1900. 143

(8) CLUNY

DELISLE, L. Livres imprimés à Cluni au 15e siècle. Paris, 1897. 144

(9) DIJON

CLÉMENT-JANIN, M. H. Recherches sur les imprimeurs dijonnais et sur les imprimeurs de la Côte-d'Or. 2. éd. Dijon, 1883. 145

(10) GRENOBLE

PROCTOR, R. [G. C.] Incunabula at Grenoble. (*In his* Bibliographical essays. London, 1905, p. 39–44.) 146

(11) LANGUEDOC

PELLECHET, M.   Quelques hypothèses sur l'imprimerie en Languedoc au 15e siècle. [Paris, 1893.]   147

From *Journal Général de l'Imprimerie, Chronique*.   21 Janv. 1893.   See also, under: Albi.

(12) LIMOGES

CLAUDIN, A.   Les origines de l'imprimerie à Limoges.   Paris, 1896.
148

First issued in *Bibliophile limousin*, 1895–1896, X, XI.   To the issue of the following year, Claudin contributed *Notes pour servir à l'histoire de l'imprimerie à Limoges: l'atelier de Paul Berton*.

(13) LYON

BAUDRIER, H. L., AND J.   Bibliographie lyonnaise.   Lyon-Paris, 1895–1921.   12 v.   149

CLAUDIN, A.   Les Pérégrinations de J. Neumeister, compagnon de Gutenberg en Allemagne, en Italie et en France (1463–1484), son établissement définitif à Lyon (1485–1507), d'après les monuments typographiques et les documents originaux inédits.   Paris, 1880. (Antiquités typographiques de la France. I.)   150

For Claudin's great work on early printing at Lyon, Vols. 3–4 of his *Histoire de l'imprimerie*, see above, under: France. General Works. A review of Vol. 3, by F. W. Bourdillon, appeared in *The Library,* 1905, ser. II, no. 23, Vol. VI, p. 257–264.

HARRISSE, H.   Les premiers incunables bâlois et leurs dérivés: Toulouse, Lyon, Vienne-en-Dauphiné, Spire, Eltvil, etc., 1471–1484. 2. ed.   Paris, 1902.   151

RATH, E. VON   Die Drucker von Buyers Ausgabe der Werke des Bartolus von 1482.   Ein Beitrag zu Buchdruckergeschichte Lyons. Berlin, 1913.   (Beiträge zum Bibliotheks und Buchwesen.   Paul Schwenke . . . gewidmet.)   152

(14) METZ

SEYMOUR DE RICCI   Le premier livre imprimé à Metz.   (Bulletin du Bibliophile et du Bibliothécaire, 1925.)   153

(15) ORLÉANS

JARRY, L.   Les Débuts de l'imprimerie à Orléans.   Orléans, 1884.
154

(16) PARIS

CLAUDIN, A.   The first Paris press, an account of the books printed for G. Fichet and J. Heylin in the Sorbonne, 1470–1472. London, 1898. (Bibliographical Society. Illustrated Monographs. VI.)

155

The Fichet *Letter* of Jan. 1, 1472, containing reference to Gutenberg, has been reproduced under the editorship of L. Sieber, Basel, 1887; and of L. Delisle, Paris, 1889.

———— Liste chronologique des imprimeurs parisiens du quinzième siècle (1470–1500). Paris, 1901.   156

For Claudin's great work on early printing in Paris, Vols. 1–2 of his *Histoire de l'imprimerie,* see above, under: France. General Works.

RENOUARD, P.   Imprimeurs parisiens: libraires, fondeurs de caractères, et correcteurs d'imprimerie jusqu'à la fin du XVIe siècle. Paris, 1898.   157

The author's *Documents sur les imprimeurs, libraires . . . ayant exercé à Paris de 1450 à 1600* was issued at Paris in 1901.

(17) POITIERS

CLAUDIN, A.   Origines et débuts de l'imprimerie à Poitiers, bibliographie des premiers livres imprimés dans cette ville (1479–1515). Paris, 1897. (Antiquités typographiques de la France. II, III.) 158

Accompanied by his *Monuments de l'imprimerie à Poitiers, recueil de facsimiles des premiers livres,* Paris, 1897 (Antiquités. . . III.); and supplemented by his *Les Origines et les débuts de l'imprimerie à Poitiers, nouvelles recherches.* Paris, 1898, which appeared first in *Bulletin du bibliophile,* April, 1898.

(18) ROUEN

LE VERDIER, P.   L'Atelier de Guillaume Le Talleur, premier imprimeur rouennais. Rouen, 1916.   159

(19) SALINS

CLAUDIN, A.   Les Origines de l'imprimerie à Salins en Franche-Comté, 1484–1485. Paris, 1892.   160

STRASSBURG

Listed by Proctor, etc., under: Germany; see above, under nos. 57–63.

(20) TOULOUSE

CLAUDIN, A.   Les Enlumineurs, les relieurs, les libraires et les imprimeurs de Toulouse aux XVe et XVIe siècles (1480–1530).   Paris, 1893.   161

One hundred copies reprinted from *Bulletin du bibliophile,* 1892.

HARRISSE, H.   Les premiers incunables bâlois et leurs dérivés: Toulouse, Lyon, Vienne-en-Dauphiné, Spire, Eltvil, etc., 1471–1484. 2. ed.   Paris, 1902.   162

(21) TOURS

GIRAUDET, E.   Les Origines de l'imprimerie à Tours (1467–1550). Tours, 1881.   163

(22) TRÉGUIER

DELISLE, L.   Mandements épiscopaux imprimés à Tréguier au XVe siècle.   (Bibliothèque de l'École des chartes.   T. 61.   Paris, 1900.)   164

(23) TROYES

CORRARD DE BREBAN   Recherches sur l'établissement et l'exercice de l'imprimerie à Troyes.   Paris, 1873.   165

3d ed., revised by O. Thierry-Poux.

(24) UZÈS

CLAUDIN, A.   L'Imprimerie à Uzès au XVe siècle, description d'un bréviaire inconnu imprimé dans cette ville en 1493.   Besançon, 1899.   166

Reprinted from *Bibliographe moderne.*   III.   1899.

(25) VALENCIENNES

GIARD, R. AND H. LEMAITRE   Les Origines de l'imprimerie à Valenciennes.   Jehan de Liège.   (*In* Bulletin du Bibliophile.   1903.)   167

(26) VIENNE

HARRISSE, H.   Les premiers incunables bâlois et leurs dérivés: Toulouse, Lyon, Vienne-en-Dauphiné, Spire, Eltvil, etc., 1471–1484. 2. ed.   Paris, 1902.   168

[PROCTOR, R. G. C.]   A Note on Eberhard Frommolt, of Basel, printer. London, 1895. (Tracts on early printing. II.)   169

See also below, under: II. Books of Hours, etc.; Fiction, Farces, & Romance; III. Greek Type; Printers' Marks; Type; and under the following section, Fifteenth Century Woodcuts: Selected Monographs.

For a list of bibliographies and monographs, rich in entries from foreign periodicals, etc., see: [Rath, E. von.] *Der Buchdruck frankreichs und der französischen Schweiz im funfzehnten Jahrhundert*. Berlin, 1929. (Wiegendruck-Gesellschaft) which is arranged chronologically under the following headings: I. *Bibliographie*. II. *Allgemeine Schriften*. III. *Einzelne Städte, Départments und Provinzen:* Abbeville, Albi, Angoulême, Avignon, Bordeaux, Bréhan-Loudéac, Bretagne, Caen, Chablis, Châlons-sur-Marne, Champagne, Chartres, Cluny, Côte-d'Or und Dijon, Franche-Comté . . . Grenoble, Languedoc . . . Limoges, Lorraine, Lyon, Mâcon, Metz, Nantes, Narbonne, Normandie, Orléans, Paris (*a,* Allgemeines; *b,* Einzelne Drucker und Verleger), Périgueux, Perpignan, Poitiers, Provins, Rouen, Salins, Savoie, Toulouse, Tours, Tréguier, Troyes, Uzès, Valenciennes, Vienne.

See also the list of Claudin's writings in: Seymour de Ricci, *ed., Documents sur la typographie*. . . Londres, 1926, p. 5–33; and various early titles in Peddie, R. A., *Fifteenth century books: A guide to their identification*. . . London, 1913, p. 78–84.

5. HOLLAND

A) IN GENERAL

BRADSHAW, H.   A classified index of the fifteenth century books in the collection of the late M. J. De Meyer. London, 1870. (Memoranda. II.)   170

With notes on printing in the Low Countries.

The first printed instance of Bradshaw's 'Natural History' or chronological place-entry method of arranging titles. Included in his *Collected Papers,* Cambridge, 1889.

——— List of the founts of type and woodcut devices used by printers in Holland in the fifteenth century. London, 1871. (Memoranda. III.)   171

CAMPBELL, M. F. A. G.   Annales de la typographie néerlandaise au XVe siècle. La Haye, 1874.   172

1–[4]. *Supplément.* La Haye, 1878–90. 4 v. *Additions* to the *Annales* was published by Robert Proctor in 1897. (Tracts on early printing. III.)

HOLTROP, J. W. Monuments typographiques des Pays-Bas au quinzième siècle. La Haye, 1868. 173

A collection of facsimiles made from originals at the Royal Library at The Hague and elsewhere.

KRUITWAGEN, B. Die Ausprüche Hollands auf die Erfindung der Buchdruckerkunst. Mainz, 1925. (Gutenberg-Festschrift.) 174

———— De Uitvinding van de Boekdrukkunst en hare eerste Voortbrengselen. Leiden, 1918. 175

[PROCTOR, R. G. C.] . . . Additions to Campbell's *Annales de la typographie néerlandaise au 15e siècle*. London, 1897. (Tracts on early printing. III.) 176

Fifty copies printed. Reprinted, with an author register, in his *Bibliographical Essays*. London, 1905, and comprising imprints from Utrecht, Delft, Gouda, Deventer, Nijmegen, Zwolle, Leiden, 's Hertogenbosch, Schoonhoven, etc.

SABBE, M. Holland and Belgium. (*In* Peddie, R. A., *ed.*, Printing, A short history of the art. London, 1927, p. 113–118.) 177

With a bibliographical list on p. 141–143.

UPDIKE, D. B. Type and type-forms of the fifteenth century in the Netherlands — Holland and Belgium. (*In his* Printing types. Cambridge, 1922. Vol. I, p. 93–98.) 178

ZEDLER, G. Von Coster zu Gutenberg, der holländische Frühdruck und die Erfindung des Buchdruckerkunst. Mainz, 1921. 179

B) BY TOWNS

(1) HASSELT

BAMPS, C. Historische Opzoekingen over de oude Hasseltsche Drukkers. Hasselt, 1887. 180

(2) ST. MARTENSDYKE

EVEN, E. VAN Notice sur Pierre Werrecoren, imprimeur à St. Martensdyke en Zélande. Bruxelles, 1851. 181

See also below, under: II. Mathematics (Music); III. Printers' Marks; Type; Type Founding; and under the following section, Selected Bibliographies — Woodcuts, Metal Engravings, etc. (A selection of titles relating to Coster of Haarlem is given below, under: III. Origin and Invention of Movable Type.)

6. BELGIUM

A) IN GENERAL

BERGMANS, P.   Les Imprimeurs belges à l'étranger.   Liste géographique des imprimeurs . . . depuis les origines de l'imprimerie jusqu'à la fin du XVIII siècle.   Gand, 1897.   182

BRADSHAW, H.   A classified index of the 15th century books in the De Meyer collection sold at Ghent, November, 1869.   (*In his* Collected papers.   Cambridge, 1889.)   183

First printed in 1870 as *Memoranda*. II.

[PROCTOR, R. G. C.]   . . . List of the founts of type and woodcut devices used by the printers of the Southern Netherlands in the fifteenth century.   London, 1895.   (Tracts on early printing. I.)   184

Reprinted in his *Bibliographical essays*.   London, 1905.   184

SABBE, M.   Holland and Belgium.   (*In* Peddie, R. A., *ed.,* Printing: A short history of the art.   London, 1927, p. 118–121.)   185

With a bibliographical list on p. 141–143.

UPDIKE, D. B.   Type and type-forms of the fifteenth century in the Netherlands — Holland and Belgium.   (*In his* Printing types. Cambridge, 1922. Vol. I, p. 93–98.)   186

VANDERHAEGHEN, F.   Bibliotheca Belgica.   Ghent, 1880.   187

VINCENT, J. B.   Essai sur l'histoire de l'imprimerie en Belgique.   Brussels, 1867.   188

Reprinted in Brussels in 1920.

B) BY TOWNS

(1) ALOST

BERGMANS, P.   Notice biographique sur Thierry Martens le premier imprimeur belge.   Paris, 1895.   189

HOLTROP, J. W.   Thierry Martens d'Alost.   Étude bibliographique.   La Haye, 1867.   190

(2) ANTWERP

SABBE, M.   Antwerpsche Druckerye.   Brussels, 1927.   191

(3) AUDENARDE

MEERSCH, D. J. VAN DE.   Audenaerdsche Drukkers, 1479–1830.
Audenaerde, 1864.   192

(4) BRUGES

BERGMANS, P.   L'Imprimeur Jean Brito et les origines de l'imprimerie
en Belgique, d'après le livre recent de M. Gilliodts van Severen.
Gand, 1898.   193

BRADSHAW, H.   Printers at Bruges in the fifteenth century.   Cambridge, 1866.   (Memoranda.   I.)   194

GILLIODTS VAN SEVEREN, L.   L'Oeuvre de Jean Brito, prototypographe
brugeois; étude critique pour servir d'introduction à l'histoire de
l'ancienne corporation des librairiers et imprimeurs de Bruges.
Bruges, 1897.   195

MICHEL, H.   L'Imprimeur Colard Mansion et le Boccace de la Bibliothèque d'Amiens.   Paris, 1925.   196

(5) BRUSSELS

VINCENT, A.   Les Imprimeurs et les libraires à Bruxelles au XVe
siècle.   (Extrait de l'Annuaire de la Société des Bibliophiles et Icono-
philes de Belgique.   1916.)   197

(6) GHENT

VANDERHAEGHEN, F.   Bibliographie gantoise.   Recherches sur la vie
et les travaux des imprimeurs de Gand (1483–1850).   Gand, 1858.
7 v.   198

See also below, under: III. Printers' Marks; Type; and under the following section, Fifteenth Century Woodcuts, etc.: Selected Monographs.

7. HUNGARY *

A) IN GENERAL

RECSEY, V.   Incunabula et Hungarica antiqua in Bibliotheka S. Montis
Pannoniae.   Budapest, 1904.   199

SEBESTYÉN, G. VON   Die erste Buchdruckerei in Ungarn, 1473.   (*In*
Gutenberg Gesellschaft.   Gutenberg Festschrift.   Mainz, 1925, p.
29–32.)   199 :a

* Listed by Proctor, etc., under: Austria-Hungary.

WHARTON, L. C. Hungary. (*In* Peddie, R. A., *ed.*, Printing: A short history of the art. London, 1927, p. 245–6.) 200

The history of early printing in the countries of Central and South Eastern Europe seems more in need of accurate bibliographical study than that of any other section. As Mr. Wharton has remarked about sixteenth century presses in Turcograecia, "Taking the area as a whole there are more conundrums than is convenient." The same might be said of fifteenth century printing in Hungary, Poland, Bohemia, Moravia, and Montenegro. Proctor, under Buda-Pest, lists a reference to two books printed by Andreas Hess in: Szabó. *Régi Magyar Könyvtár*, Vol. 2, nos. 1, 2.

8. SPAIN

A) IN GENERAL

BRITISH MUSEUM (Department of Printed Books) Short-title catalogue of books printed in Spain and of Spanish books printed elsewhere in Europe before 1601 now in the British Museum. By Henry Thomas, D.Litt. [London] 1921. 201

BRUNER Y PRIETO, F. Los incunables ibéricos de la Bibliothèque Nationale de Paris. Palma, 1924. 202

CANIBELL Y MASBERNAT, E. Precedentes e introducción de la imprenta en España. (*In* Gutenberg-Festschrift. 1925, p. 241–247.) 203

GASELEE, S. The early Spanish printing press. London, 1924. 204

GENOVÉS Y OLMOS, E. Catalech descriptiu de les obres impreses en llengua Valenciana desde 1474 fins [1913]. Valencia, 1911–1914. 205

HAEBLER, K. Bibliografía ibérica del Siglo XV. La Haya, 1903–1917. 2 v. 206

A contribution by F. García Romero, entitled *Algunas correcciones y adiciones a la Bibliografía ibérica del siglo XV*, appeared in *Bibliofilia* (Olschki) 1920–1921. Haebler's *Nachträge zur Bibliografía ibérica*, entitled *Zur ältesten Geschichte des Buchdrucks in Spanien*, appeared in *Zentralblatt für Bibliothekswesen*. XXVI. 1909.

———The early printers of Spain and Portugal. London, 1897. (Bibliographical Society. Illustrated Monographs. IV.) 207

Although some of its statements have now been superseded by Dr. Haebler's subsequent research, much of interest will be found in this work.

HAEBLER, K. Geschichte des spanischen Frühdruckes in Stammbäumen. . . Mit 489 Abbildungen. Leipzig, 1923.   208

A genealogical study of type families and the succession of presses from a typographical point of view. Nine type-family groups, comprising all of the fifteenth century printers of Spain, are considered: J. Vizlant, P. Vizlant, M. Flander, Rosenbach, Botel, and schools of native Spaniards and of German, French, and Italian printers in Spain.

Dr. Haebler's theory regarding printing in Ixar receives further support from Dr. Marx, in his *Some notes on the use of Hebrew type in non-Hebrew books, 1475–1520,* in *Bibliographical Essays. A Tribute to Wilberforce Eames.* Cambridge, Mass., 1924, p. 383–384.

———— Spanien, 1474–1500. (*In his* Die deutschen Buchdrucker des XV. Jahrhunderts im Auslande. München, 1924.)   209

An account of early German printers in Spain, whose work has also been described in Haebler's *Deutsche Buchdrucker in Spanien und Portugal.* (*In Zentralblatt für Bibliothekswesen.* XI. 1894, p. 529–564); and in his *Deutsche Drucker in Spanien und Portugal.* (*In Festschrift von Johann Gutenberg.* Mainz, 1900, p. 393–405.)

———— Tipografía ibérica del siglo XV. Reproducción en facsímile de todos los caracteres tipográficos empleados an España y Portugal hasta el año de 1500. Leipzig, 1902 .   210

With text in Spanish and in French. Excellent for its facsimiles, although in some sections the dates assigned to printers and their works have been altered by the results of Dr. Haebler's later research.

LYELL, J. P. R. Spain and Portugal. The fifteenth century. (*In* Peddie, R. A., *ed.,* Printing: A short history of the art. London, 1927, p. 144–155, 167.)   211

A list on p. 169–171 gives various bibliographical references.

PALAU Y DULCET, A. Manual del librero Hispano-Americano. Barcelona, 1923–.   212

A bibliography of Spanish and Latin-American works, from the introduction of printing until the present day, arranged chronologically under authors.

SANPERE Y MIQUEL, S. . . . De la introducción y establecimiento de la imprenta en . . . Aragón y Castilla y de los impresores de los incunables catalanes. Barcelona, 1909.   213

SCHULTE, A. Die deutschen Kaufleute und die Anfänge des Buchdrucks in Spanien. Bonn & Leipzig, 1921. (Festgabe Friedrich von Bezold.)   214

THOMAS, H.   Bibliographical Notes.   New York, 1921.   3 pts. in 2 v. (Extrait de la *Revue Hispanique*.)   215

> Contains essays entitled " A new fifteenth-century *Leyes del Estilo* and some other early law books "; and " More about early Spanish law books."

UPDIKE, D. B.   Type and type-forms of the fifteenth century in Spain. (*In his* Printing types.   Cambridge, 1922.   Vol. I, p. 99–112.)   216

B)   BY TOWNS OR PROVINCES

(1) ARAGON

LAMBERT, A.   Notes sur divers incunables d'Aragon inédits ou peu connus.   (*In* Bulletin Hispanique.   January-March, 1910.   XII:37.)
                                                                        217

(2) BARCELONA

COMET, J.   Introduction de l'imprimerie à Barcelone.   (*In* Revue Catalane.   VIII. 1914, p. 202–203.)   218

GUADALAJARA *

IXAR *

(3) LÉRIDA

JIMENEZ CATALÁN, M.   Apuntes para una bibliografía Ilerdense de los siglos XV al XVIII.   Barcelona, 1912.   219

(4) MONTSERRAT

ALBAREDA, A. M.   La imprenta de Montserrat (segles XV.ᵉ–XVI.ᵉ). [Montserrat] 1919.   (Analecta Montserratensia.   Vol. II.)   220

PERPIGNAN.   See above, under France.

(5) SARAGOSSA

LAMBERT, A.   Les Origines de l'imprimerie à Saragosse, 1473–85. (*In* Revista de Archivos.   XXXIII.   1915.)   221

[SÁNCHEZ, J. M.]   Bibliografía zaragozana del siglo XV.   Madrid, 1908.   222

---

* A Hebrew printing town.   See below, under: III, Bibliographical and Historical Aspects, Hebrew printing, nos. 466–479.

SERRANO Y SANZ, M.   La imprenta de Zaragozá es la mas antigua de España, prueba documental. Zaragoza, 1915.   223

This hypothesis has been questioned by other writers.

THOMAS, H.   The Printer George Coci of Saragossa. (*In* Gutenberg-Festschrift. 1925, p. 276–278.)   224

(6) SEVILLE

HAZAÑAS Y LA RUA, I.   La imprenta en Sevilla. Sevilla, 1892.   225

TENORIO, N. _ Algunas noticias de Menardo Ungut y Lanzalao Polono. (*In* Revista de Archivos. 3 Ep. V. 1901.)   226

(7) TARRAGONA

ARCO Y MOLINERO, A. DEL   La imprenta en Tarragona. Tarragona, 1916.   227

(8) TOLEDO

PÉREZ PASTOR, C.   La imprenta en Toledo. Madrid, 1887.   228

(9) VALENCIA

GENOVÉS Y OLMOS, E.   Catalech descriptiu de les obres impreses en llengua valenciana desde 1474 fins [1913]. Valencia, 1911–1914.
229

HAEBLER, K.   Zur Druckergeschichte von Valencia. (*In* Zentralblatt für Bibliothekswesen. XXVIII. 1911, p. 253–259.)   230

SERRANO Y MORALES, J. E.   Reseña histórica en forma de diccionario de las imprentas que han existido en Valencia desde la introducción del arte tipografico . . . con noticias bio-bibliograficas de los principales impresores. Valencia, 1898–99.   231

(10) VALLADOLID

ALCOCER Y MARTINEZ, M.   Catálogo razonado de obras impresas en Valladolid 1481–1800. Valladolid, 1926.   232

ZAMORA *

See also below, under: II. Mathematics (Music); Miscellaneous Subjects (Bible); III. Hebrew Printing; Printers' Marks; Type; and under the

* A Hebrew printing town. See below, under: III, Bibliographical and Historical Aspects, Hebrew printing, nos. 466–479.

following section, Selected Bibliographies — Woodcuts, Metal Engravings, etc. For Spanish incunabula relating to Columbus, see below, under: Selected Bibliographies — Americana: Period of Discovery: Columbus, nos. 659–668.

For a list of reference works, rich in early bibliographical titles and in monographs found in foreign periodicals, see [Ohly, K.] *Der Buchdruck Spaniens und Portugals im fünfzehnten Jahrhundert*. Berlin, 1929. (Wiegendruck-Gesellschaft). This is arranged chronologically under the following topics: I. *Bibliographia*. II *Allgemeine Schriften*. III. *Einzelne Landschaften und Städte;* Barcelona, Burgos, Catalonien, Coria, Cuenca . . . Lérida . . . Mallorca, Montalban, Montserrat, Pamplona . . . Salamanca, Santiago de Compostela, Sevilla, Tarragona, Toledo, Valencia, Valladolid, Zamora, Zaragoza.

9. POLAND *

A) IN GENERAL

ESTREICHER, K. J. T. Bibliografia polska. XV–XVI stólecia. . . Kraków, 1875. 233

Seven thousand, two hundred titles chronologically and alphabetically arranged. Not part of his *Bibliografia polska*, 1870–.

JUCHHOFF, R. Drucker- und Verlegerzeichen des XV. Jahrhunderts in den Niederlanden, England, Spanien, Böhmen, Mähren und Polen. München, 1927. 234

LAM, S. Le Livre polonais au XV et XVI siècle. Warsaw [1923]. 235

WHARTON, L. C. Poland. (*In* Peddie, R. A., *ed.*, Printing: A short history of the art. London, 1927, p. 254–255.) 236

B) CRACOW

BANDTKIE, J. S. Historya drukarn krakowskich. . . Kraków, 1815. 237

BENTKOWSKI, F. O naydawnieyszych ksiazkach drukowanych w Polozcze a w szczegoluosci o tych, ktore Jan Haller w Krakowie wydal. . . Warsawie, 1812. 238

BRITISH MUSEUM (Department of Printed Books) Catalogue of books printed in the XVth century now in the British Museum. Part III. . . . Austria-Hungary. . . London, 1913. 239

Includes imprints from Cracow.

* Listed by Proctor, etc., under: Austria-Hungary.

COLLIJN, I.   Der Drucker des Turrecremata in Kraukau, Caspar Hochfeder. (*In* Zentralblatt für Bibliothekswesen. Bd. XXIX. 1912.)   240

ESTREICHER, K. J. T.   Günther Zainer i Swietopełk Fiol. Przez E. K. (Biblioteka Warzawska. 1867. III.)   241

GOLOVATZKII, J. F.   Sweipolt Fiol und seine kyrillische Buchdruckerei in Kraukau, von Jahre 1491. Wien, 1876.   242

KARATAEV, I. P.   Bibliograficheskiia zamietki. . . 1491–1730. (*In* Russia o staroslavgnskikh. St. Petersburg, 1872.)   243

———— Chronologičeskij rospis slavjanskich knig, napečatannych kiril- lovskimi bukvami, 1491–1730. St. Petersburg, 1861.   244

———— Opisanie slaviano-russkikh knig. St. Petersburg, 1883.   245
Vol. I, 1491–1652, relates to early Slavic-Russian books printed in Cyrillic type, etc., and includes five that are assigned to Cracow before 1501.

RÓŻYCKI, K. VON   Die Inkunabeln des Druckers des Turrecremata in Krakau. Eine bibliographische und typographische Untersuchung. . . München, 1911.   246
Advances the theory that the five incunabula described may have been printed in the Bernadine (Franciscan) monastery at Cracow.— L. C.

———— Über den Krakauer Druck von Turrecremata, Explanatio in psalterium. (*In* Zentralblatt für Bibliothekswesen, 1895, p. 507– 512.)   247

WISLOCKI, W.   Incunabula typographica bibliothecae Universitatis Jagellonicae Cracoviensis. Cracow, 1900.   248
Contains references to Cracow book trade during the fifteenth century.

10. AUSTRIA *

A) IN GENERAL

BRITISH MUSEUM (Department of Printed Books) Catalogue of books printed in the XVth century now in the British Museum. Part III. . . . Austria-Hungary. . . London, 1913.   249

* Listed by Proctor, etc., under Austria-Hungary, which Empire included the early printing countries Austria, Hungary, Poland, Bohemia, and Moravia, here listed individually.

Includes imprints from Trent (Austria, now Italy), Cracow (Poland), Prague (Bohemia, now Czechoslovakia), Vienna (Austria), Winterberg (Bohemia), Brünn (Moravia, now Czechoslovakia), Kuttenberg (Bohemia), and Olmütz (Moravia).

LANGER, E., *ed.* Bibliographie der österreichischen Drucke des XV. und XVI. Jahrhunderts. Wien, 1913–   250

Vol. 1 relates to printers at Trient, 1475–82; Wien, 1482–1519; Schrattenthal, 1501–. Compiled by Dr. W. Dolch; with introduction *Aus der ersten Zeit des Wiener Buchdrucks,* by Dr. I. Schwarz; and a table of type variations, *Verzeichnis der Typen Winterburgers.* (Reviewed in *The Library,* 1914, p. 103–108, by [J.] V. Scholderer.)

B) BY TOWNS

(1) TRENT

BAMPI, G. Della stampa e degli stampatori nel principato di Trento fino al 1564. (Archivio Trentino. II. 1883.)   251

(2) VIENNA

DENIS, [J.] M. [K. P.] Wiens Buchdruckergeschicht bis 1560. Wien, 1782.   252

Nachtrag, 1793.

MAYER, A. Wiens Buchdrucker-Geschichte, 1482–1882. Wien, 1882–87.   253

With bibliographical notes on presses from 1482 to 1682; and 401 titles of works issued from 1482 to 1560 that were not known to Denis. (See above.)

SCHWARZ, J. Aus der ersten Zeit des Wiener Buchdrucks (1482–85). Wien, 1913.   254

Issued as an introduction to the *Bibliographie der österreichischen Drucke des XV. and XVI. Jahrhunderts,* 1913, edited by E. Langer.

VIENNA. CENTRAL-COMITE ZUR FEIER DER IV. SÄCULARFEIER DER EINFÜHRUNG DER BUCHDRUCKERKUNST IN WIEN Katalog der historischen Ausstellung von Wiener Buchdruckerzeugnissen 1482–1882. Wien, 1882.   255

A chronological list of presses, containing 273 titles of works issued before 1600. Preface signed: Dr. Wilhelm Haas.

See also under the following section: Fifteenth Century Woodcuts: Selected Monographs.

11. BOHEMIA *

A) In General

British Museum (Department of Printed Books) Catalogue of books printed in the XVth century now in the British Museum. Part III. . . . Austria-Hungary. . . London, 1913.   256

Includes imprints from Prague, Kuttenberg, and Winterberg.

Juchhoff, R. Drucker- und Verlegerzeichen des XV. Jahrhunderts in den Niederlanden, England, Spanien, Böhmen, Mähren und Polen. München, 1927.   257

Tobolka, Z. Český slovník bibliografický. Prag, 1910.   258

Dil I. Prvotisky, do roku 1500.

———— Knihopis československých tisků od doby nejstarši až do knoce XVIII. stoleti. Praze, 1925.   259

Dil I. Az do roku 1500.

Volf, J. Geschichte des Buchdrucks in Böhmen und Mähren bis 1848. Weimar, 1928.   260

Contents: Der Buchdruck in Böhmen (Die Wiegendrucke. Die Prager Buchdruckereien nach dem Jahr 1500. Die Druckereien der böhmischen Provinzstädte nach 1500).

Wharton, L. C. Bohemia. (*In* Peddie, R. A., *ed.*, Printing: A short history of the art. London, 1927, p. 269–272, 274.)   261

Zahradník, I. [T.] Über neuere Bibliographie der Incunabeln, besonders der Böhmischen. Prag, 1902.   262

A criticism of Anton Schubert's *Die Wiegendrucker der K. K. Studienbibliothek zu Olmütz,* Leipzig, 1901; also of several articles by Schubert on Bohemian incunabula which appeared in *Zentralblatt für Bibliothekswesen,* 1897–1899.

See also below, under: II. Bible; III. Printers' Marks.

12. ENGLAND

A) In General

British Museum (Department of Printed Books) Catalogue of books in the library of the British Museum printed in England . . .

———
* Listed by Proctor, etc., under: Austria-Hungary.

and of books in English printed abroad, to the year 1640. London,
1884. 263

Compiled largely by G. W. Eccles.

CAMBRIDGE UNIVERSITY LIBRARY   Early English printed books, 1475–
1640. Cambridge, 1900–7. 264

Compiled by C. E. Sayle.

DUFF, E. G.   A Century of the English book trade . . . 1457–1557.
London, 1905. 265

——— Fifteenth century English books. A bibliography of books
and documents printed in England and of books for the English
market printed abroad. London, 1917. (Bibliographical Society.
Illustrated monographs. XVIII.) 266

In 1912, this author issued a volume on *The English provincial printers, stationers, and bookbinders to 1557.*

——— The Printers, stationers, and bookbinders of Westminster and
London from 1476 to 1535. Cambridge, 1906. (The Sandars lectures, 1899 and 1904.) 267

Reviewed in *The Library*, 1907, p. 102–107. The 1899 lectures were first
printed under title: *The printers, stationers and bookbinders of London and
Westminster in the fifteenth century.* [Aberdeen, 1899.]

HAEBLER, K.   England, 1476–1500. (*In his* Die deutschen Buchdrucker des XV. Jahrhunderts im Auslande. München, 1924.) 268

HENRY E. HUNTINGTON LIBRARY (San Marino)   Check-list or brief
catalogue of the library of Henry E. Huntington. [English literature to 1640.] New York, 1919. 269

Compiled under the direction of George Watson Cole.

PLOMER, H. R.   Abstracts from the wills of English printers and stationers, from 1492 to 1630. London, 1903. (Bibliographical Society. Publications. 1903.) 270

——— England. (*In* Peddie, R. A., *ed.,* Printing: A short history of
the art. London, 1927, p. 172–180, 199–200.) 271

——— A short history of English printing, 1476–1898. London, 1900.
(Second edition, London, 1915.) 272

POLLARD, A. W.   Printing in England (1476–1580). (*In his* Fine
books. New York & London, 1912, p. 204–224; 250–256.) 273

POLLARD, A. W., AND G. R. REDGRAVE   A short-title catalogue of books printed in England . . . and of English books printed abroad, 1475–1640.   London, 1926.   (Bibliographical Society.)   274

UPDIKE, D. B.   Type and type-forms of the fifteenth century in England.   (*In his* Printing types.   Cambridge, 1922.   Vol. I, p. 113–124.)   275

B) BY TOWNS

(1) OXFORD

MADAN, F.   A Chart of Oxford printing, ' 1468 '–1900.   Oxford, 1904.   (Bibliographical Society.   Illustrated monographs.   XII.)
                                                                        276

Second issue, in 425 copies, slightly altered and corrected.   First issue, 100 copies, 1903.   The first book printed at Oxford, the *Exposicio sancti Jeronimi*, bears the date 17 Dec. M.CCCC. lxviij which is generally believed to be a misprint for 1478, one " x " probably having been omitted when the type was set.

———— The early Oxford press.   A bibliography of printing and publishing at Oxford, ' 1468 '–1640.   Oxford, 1895.   277

(2) ST. ALBANS

BRADSHAW, H.   The printer of the *Historia S. Albani*.   (*In his* Collected papers.   Cambridge, 1889.)   278

First issued as *Memoranda*. I.   1868.   A facsimile of the only known copy of the first issue from the St. Albans press, in the library of the University of Cambridge, has been issued under the title: Dati, Agostino.   *Augustini Dacti scribe super Tullianis. . . Printed by the schoolmaster printer at St. Albans about the year 1479*.   Cambridge, 1905.

(3) WESTMINSTER

BLADES, W.   The Life and typography of William Caxton, England's first printer, with evidence of his typographical connection with Colard Mansion, the printer at Bruges.   London, 1861–1863.   2 v.   279

See also the article on *William Caxton's stay at Cologne,* in: Bibliographical Society.   Transactions.   New Series IV.

BRADSHAW, H.   Notice of a fragment of the fifteen Oes and other prayers printed at Westminster by W. Caxton about 1490–91.   London, 1877.   (Memoranda. V.)   280

PLOMER, H. R.   William Caxton (1424–1491.)   London [1925].
281

———— Wynkyn de Worde and his contemporaries, from the death of
Caxton to 1535. London, 1925.   282

SEYMOUR DE RICCI   A census of Caxtons. [Oxford] 1909. (Bibliographical Society. Illustrated monographs. XV.)   283

WINSHIP, G. P.   William Caxton. A paper read at a meeting of the
Club of Odd Volumes in Boston, Massachusetts, U.S.A., in January
MDCCCCVIII. [Hammersmith] 1909.   284

See also below, under: II. Mathematics (Music); III. Advertisements;
Printers' Marks; Type; and under the following section, Selected Bibliographies — Woodcuts, Metal Engravings, etc.

13. DENMARK

a) IN GENERAL

COLLIJN, I. [G. A.]   Bidrag till Danmarks äldsta Boktryckerhistoria.
(*In his* Bokhistoriska Uppsater. Stockholm, 1907. X.)   285

———— En nyfunnen dansk Inkunabel. (*In his* Bokhistoriska Uppsater.
Stockholm, 1905–. III.)   286

LANGE, H. O.   Analecta Bibliographica. Copenhagen, 1906.   287

NIELSEN, L. M.   Dansk Bibliografi, 1482–1550. Copenhagen, 1919.
288

Designed to supersede G. Brunn's *Den danske Literatur fra Bogtrykker-
kunstens Indførelse i Danmark til 1550.* Copenhagen, 1870–1875. Reviewed
in *The Library,* 1920, p. 179–182.

———— Denmark. (*In* Peddie, R. A., *ed.,* Printing: A short history of
the art. London, 1927, p. 210–211.)   289

With a bibliographical list on p. 220.

———— Fra Johan Snell til vore Dage. Skildringer af Bogtrykker-
kunstens Historia i Odense. Odense, 1908.   290

See also below, under: III. Proof and Proof reading.

14. SWEDEN

a) In General

Collijn, I. [G. A.] Det äldsta svenska trycket? Ett nyfunnet Remigius fragment. Stockholm, 1923.   291

────── Blad ur vår äldsta svenska Boktryckerihistoria. (Nordisk boktryckarekonst, I–VI. 1905–1920.)   292

────── Boktryckeri Konstens Uppfinning och Guldålder. (IV. Sverige. Boktrykeri Kalender, 1910.)   293

────── Oversikt av det svenska boktryckets Historia, 1483–1700. (In S. Dahls Bibliotekshandbok. I. 1924, p. 183–272.)   294

Klemming, G. A., and A. Andersson Sveriges Bibliografi, 1481–1600. Uppsala, 1889–1892. (Skrifter utgifna af Svenska Literatursällskapet. X.)   295
Vol. I, 1481–1501.

────── and F. G. Nordin Svensk Boktryckeri-Historia, 1483–1883. Stockholm [1883].   296

Lagerström, H. Svensk Bokkonst; Studier och Antekningar över särdragen i svensk Bokstaveform och svenskt Typtryck. Stockholm, 1920.   297

Nielsen, L. Sweden. (In Peddie, R. A., ed., Printing: A short history of the art. London, 1927, p. 221–222.)   298
With a list of bibliographies on p. 231–232.

Schröder, J. H. Incunabula artis typographicae in Svecia. Upsala, 1842.   299

Schück, H. Den svenska Förlagsbokhandelns Historia. Stockholm, 1923.   300

Pages 22–42 relate to the early Swedish printers Johann Snell, Bartholomaeus Ghotan, and Johannes Fabri; and discuss the early presses at Vadstena and Mariefred.

See also below, under: III. Proof and Proof Reading; and under the following section, Fifteenth Century Woodcuts: Selected Monographs.

15. MORAVIA *

A) In General

BRITISH MUSEUM (Department of Printed Books) Catalogue of books printed in the XVth century now in the British Museum. Part III. . . . Austria-Hungary. . . London, 1913.   301

Includes imprints from Brünn and Olmütz.

DUDIK, B. Geschichtliche Entwickelung des Buchdrucks im Mähren, vom Jahre 1486 bis 1621. Brünn, 1879.   302

JUCHHOFF, R. Drucker- und Verlegerzeichen des XV. Jahrhunderts in. . . Mähren. . . München, 1927.   303

SCHUBERT, A. Die Wiegendrucker der K. K. Studienbibliothek zu Olmütz. Leipzig, 1901.   304

VOLF, J. Geschichte des Buchdrucks in Böhmen und Mähren bis 1848. Weimar, 1928.   305

See also below, under: III. Printers' Marks.

16. PORTUGAL

A) In General

HAEBLER, K. Bibliografía Ibérica del siglo XV. Enumeración de todos los libros impresos en España y Portugal hasta el año de 1500 con notas críticas. La Haya, 1903–17. 2 v.   306

An essay by F. García Romero, entitled *Algunas correcciones y adiciones à la Bibliografía ibérica del siglo XV*, appeared in *Bibliofilia* (Olschki), 1920–1921.

———— Deutsche Buchdrucker in Spanien und Portugal. (*In* Zentralblatt für Bibliothekswesen. 1894. Vol. 11, p. 529–564.)   307

———— Deutsche Drucker in Spanien und Portugal. (*In* Festschrift . . . von Johann Gutenberg. Mainz, 1900, p. 393–405.)   308

———— The early printers of Spain and Portugal. London, 1897. (Bibliographical Society.)   309

Much of interest will be found in this volume, even though Dr. Haebler's subsequent works have superseded some of its statements. Issued in German in *Zentralblatt für Bibliothekswesen*. XV. 1898.

* Listed by Proctor, etc., under: Austria-Hungary.

HAEBLER, K. Spanische und portugiesische Bücherzeichen des 15 und 16 Jahrhunderts. Strassburg, 1898.   310

—————— Tipografía ibérica del siglo XV. Reproducción en facsímile de todos los caracteres tipográficos empleados en España y Portugal hasta el año de 1500. Leipzig, 1902.   311

With text in Spanish and in French. Excellent for its facsimiles, although in some sections the dates assigned to printers and their works have been altered by Dr. Haebler's later research.

LYELL, J. P. R. Spain and Portugal. The fifteenth century. (*In* Peddie, R. A., *ed.; Printing: A short history of the art. London, 1927, p. 144–155, 167.)   312

MANUEL, KING OF PORTUGAL Early Portuguese books (1489–1600) in the library of H. M. King Manuel of Portugal. London, 1929–. Vols. 1–.   313

A survey of Portuguese typography of the sixteenth century with characteristic examples of the fifteenth century. With full collations and bibliographical notes in English and Portuguese, by H. M. King Manuel of Portugal.

PROENCA, RAÚL E ANSELMO, A. Bibliografia dos incunábulos portugûeses. (Anais das Bibliotecas e Arquivos. 1920. Series II, Vol. I, p. 186–191.)   314

SANTOS, M. DOS Bibliografia geral ou descrição bibliográfica de livros tanto de autores portugueses como brasileiros . . . impressos desde o seculo XV até à actualidade. Lisboa, 1914–17.   315

THOMAS, H. Short-title catalogues of Portuguese books and of Spanish-American books printed before 1601 now in the British Museum. London, 1926.   316

Reprinted from the *Revue hispanique,* Vol. LXV.

For Faro, Lisbon and Leiria, Portugal's three Hebrew printing towns of the fifteenth century, see below, under: III. Hebrew Printing. See also below, under: III. Printers' Marks; Type; and under the following section, Fifteenth Century Woodcuts: Selected Monographs. (In addition to various general works containing references to early printing in Portugal, *Der Buchdruck Spaniens und Portugal in fünfzehnten Jahrhundert.* Berlin, 1929 (Wiegendruck-Gesellschaft. II. *Ed.* by K. Ohly) quotes the following titles under Faro, Lissabon and Porto respectively: Slijper, E., *Eine portugiesische Talmudausgabe vor 1500* (In *Zeitschrift für Bucherfreunde. Jahrg.* 12: 1908–9. 1:207, *etc.*); Faria de Ataide e Melo, A., *Valentim Fernandes 1495–1518.* (In *Livros.* 1925, p. 146–147); and Cortesão, J., *Um novo incunábulo português.* (In *Anais das Bibliotecas e Arquivos.* Ser. II. Vol. 1. 1920, p. 10–13.)

17. MONTENEGRO

A) IN GENERAL

JAGIĆ, V. VON Der erste Cetinjer Kirchendruck vom Jahre, 1494. Eine bibliographisch-lexicalische Studie. . . Wien, 1894. 317

Relates to the *Oktoechos,* printed in Cyrillic type [Cetinje, 1494].

KARATAEV, I. P. Opisanie salviano-russkikh knig. St. Petersburg, 1883. 318

Vol. 1, 1491–1652, includes three fifteenth century books in Cyrillic type assigned to Cetinje.

WHARTON, L. C. Jugoslavia. (*In* Peddie, R. A., *ed.,* Printing: A short history of the art. London, 1927, p. 275–277.) 319

In which the writer notes the distinction between Glagolitic and Cyrillic types.

B. *Subjects*

I. BOOKS OF HOURS (HORÆ), LITURGIES, MISSALS, ETC.

BEAUPRÉ, J. N. Notice bibliographique sur les livres de liturgie des diocèses de Toul et de Verdun, imprimés au XVe siècle et dans la première moitié du XVIe. Nancy, 1843. 320

BOHATTA, H. Bibliographie der Livres d'Heures (Horæ B. M. V.), Officia, Hortuli animae, Coronae B. M. V., Rosaria und Cursus B. M. V. des XV. und XVI. Jahrhunderts. Wien, 1924. 321

First printed in 1909.

——— Katalog der liturgischen Drucke des XV. und XVI. Jahrhunderts in der herzogl. Parma'schen Bibliothek in Schwarzau. Wien, 1910. 322

Describes 118 rare missals, breviaries, etc. of the fifteenth century.

——— Liturgische Bibliographie des XV. Jahrhunderts mit Ausnahme der Missale und Livres d'Heures. Wien, 1911. 323

Supplements Weale's *Bibliographia liturgica,* London, 1886; and the author's *Bibliographie der Livres d'Heures . . . des XV . . . Jahrhunderts.* Vienna, 1909.

——— Liturgische Drucke und liturgische Drucker. Regensburg, 1926. 324

BOHATTA, H.   Versuch einer Bibliographie der Livres d'Heures . . .
des XV. und XVI. Jahrhunderts, mit Ausnahme der für Salisbury und
York gedruckten.   Wien, 1907.   325

BRUNET, J.C.   Notice sur les différentes éditions des Heures gothiques,
ornées de gravures imprimées à Paris à la fin du quinzième siècle et du
commencement du seizième.   Paris, 1884.   326

DESBARREAUX-BERNARD   Notice sur le Missel d'Uzès, imprimé à
Lyon en 1495 par J. Numeister.   (In Bulletin du Bibliophile.   1874.)
                                                                  327

ESSLING, PRINCE D'   Les Missels imprimés à Venise de 1481 à 1600.
Paris, 1894.   328

FRÈRE, E.   Des livres de liturgie des églises d'Angleterre imprimés à
Rouen.   Rouen, 1867.   329

HAEBLER, K.   Johann Grüninger der Drucker des Missale mit dem
Kanon Peter Schöffers.   (Gesellschaft für Typenkunde des XV. Jahr-
hunderts.   Beiträge zur Inkunabelkunde.   IV.   Upsala, 1911.)   330
Relative to tables 270–273 in the Society's Veröffentlichungen, Leipzig, 1907–.

HEITZ, P., ed.   Christus am Kreuz.   Kanonbilder der in Deutschland
gedruckten Messbücher des fünfzehnten Jahrhunderts. . .   München
[1910].   331
With introduction by W. L. Schreiber.

LACOMBE, P.   Livres d'Heures imprimés au XVe et au XVI siècle,
conservés dans les bibliothèques publiques de Paris.   Paris, 1907.
                                                                  332

LAMBERT, A.   Notes sur divers incunables d'Aragon inédits ou peu
connus.   (In Bulletin Hispanique.   XII:37.)   333

LANGLOIS, M.   Le Missel de Chartres imprimé en 1482.   Chartres,
1904.   334

POLLARD, A. W.   The Illustrations in French Books of Hours, 1486–
1500.   (In Bibliographica.   Pt. XII, p. 430–473.)   335

SCHOTTENLOHER, K.   Die liturgischen Druckwerke Erhard Ratdolts
aus Augsburg, 1485–1522.   Mainz, 1922.   (Gutenberg-Gesellschaft.
Sonder Veröffentlichungen.   I.)   336

SEIDLITZ, W. VON   Die gedruckten illustrierten Gebetbücher des XV.
und XVI. Jahrhunderts. (*In* Jahrbuch der Preussischen Kunstsamm-
lungen. V. 1884.)   337

SOCARD, A., AND A. ASSIER   Livres liturgiques du diocèse de Troyes,
imprimés aux XVe et XVIe siècles. Paris, 1863.   338

TRONNIER, A.   Die Missaldrucke Peter Schöffers und seines Sohnes
Johann. Mainz, 1908. (Gutenberg-Gesellschaft. Veröffentlichungen. VII.)   339

WEALE, W. H. J.   Bibliographia liturgica. Catalogus missalium ritus
latini ab anno 1475 impressorum. London, 1886.   340

> See also below, under: II. Mathematics (Music), nos. 363–374; III. Printing
> Before 1457, nos. 539–564. For bibliographical works relating to early Mis-
> sals, etc., printed at Mainz, see under titles of originals in: Seymour de Ricci,
> *Catalogue raisonné des premières impressions de Mayence, 1445–1457.*
> Mainz, 1911.

2. MATHEMATICS (ACCOUNTANCY, ARITHMETIC, ASTROLOGY, ASTRONOMY, GEOMETRY, MUSIC, NUMERALS)

A) IN GENERAL

CANTOR, M.   Die Zeit von 1450–1500. (*In his* Vorlesungen über
Geschichte der Mathematik. Leipzig, 1892; 2nd ed. 1900. Vol.
II, ch. XII.)   341

> An account of the mathematicians of the fifteenth century with some refer-
> ence to contemporary works.

DOPPELMAYR, J. G.   Historische Nachricht von den Nürnbergischen
Mathematicis und Künstlern. . . Nürnberg, 1730.   342

> Copiously annotated and rich in early titles and bibliographical information.
> It includes " Wercke die zur Mathesi in genere gehören; Arithmetische und
> algebraische . . . ; Geometrische . . . ; Optische . . . ; Astronomische . . . ;
> Geographische . . . ; Chronologische . . . ; Astrologische . . . ; Gnomo-
> nische Wercke; Wercke von der architectura civili; Musicalische Wercke;
> Kunst-Wercke in Kupffer; . . . in Holz-Schnitten," etc.

LIBRI, G. (*Collection of*)   Catalogue of the mathematical, historical,
bibliographical and miscellaneous portion of the celebrated library of
M. Guglielmo Libri. . . An extraordinary collection of the rarest
treatises in existence respecting ancient arithmetic, algebra, astronomy, and geometry. [London] Sotheby and Wilkinson, auctioneers,
1861. 2 pts.   343

MURHARD, W. A.   Litteratur der mathematischen Wissenschaften
. . . Leipzig, 1797–1805.   5 v.   344

Chronologically arranged under subjects, and rich in fifteenth and sixteenth
century titles.   Vol. 1, 1797, enthaltend die Litteratur der Mathematik
uberhaupt, der Arithmetik und der Geometrie; Vol. 2, 1798, der Geometrie
und der Analysis; Vol. 3–5, 1803–1805, der mechanischen und optischen
Wissenschaften (navigation, mathematical physics, hydraulics, optics, etc.).

POGGENDORFF, J. C.   Biographisch-literarisches Handwörterbuch zur
Geschichte der exacten Wissenschaften. . .   Leipzig, 1863, 1898,
1904, 1925–1926.   5 v. in 8 pts.   345

Relates to mathematicians, astronomers, physicists, chemists, etc., with a list
of writings and publications following the biographical sketch of each scientist.
For the most part, the accounts of the earliest scientists are to be found in
the original issue, vols. 1–2, 1863.

RICCARDI, P.   Biblioteca matematica italiana dalla origine della stampa
al primi anni del secolo XIX. . .   Modena, 1893.   346

In part a reprint of the 1870 edition.   Arranged alphabetically by authors
but with appendix chronologically arranged under subjects.

VALENTIN, G.   [Allgemeine mathematische Bibliographie.]   347

A bibliography in manuscript, begun in 1885 and still in process of compilation.   It aims to include all mathematical works published from the introduction of printing up to 1900 and is said to approximate 150,000 titles.   On file,
in card-catalogue form, at the Staatsbibliothek, Berlin.   A description of this
work is given by Herr Valentin and another by Herr Eneström in *Bibliotheca
Mathematica,* 1911.   Vol. 11, p. 153–157 and 227–232, respectively.

B) BY SUBJECTS

(1) ACCOUNTANCY

GORDON, C.   Books on accountancy, 1494–1600.   (*In* Bibliographical
Society.   Transactions.   XIII, p. 145–170.)   348

A facsimile of Paciolo's *De Computis,* Venice, 1494, the first printed treatise
on bookkeeping, is given on p. 110 in Richard Brown's *History of Accounting
and Accountants,* Edinburgh, 1905; Paciolo's work is discussed on p. 108–122.

(2) ARITHMETIC

FAVARO, A.   Intorno alla vita ed alle opere di Prosdocimo de' Beldo-
mandi matematico Padovano del secolo XV.   (*In* Boncompagni, B.,
Bullettino di bibliografia e di storia delle scienze matematiche e fisiche.
Roma, 1879.   Vol. XII.)   349

Contains some reference to Prosdocimo's work published in 1483.

SMITH, D. E. Rara arithmetica; a catalogue of the arithmetics written
before the year MDCI, with a description of those in the library of
George Arthur Plimpton of New York. . . Boston and London,
1908. 2 pts. in 1 v. 350

Lists over 550 works, in nearly 1,200 editions, issued during "the formative
period in the history of printed arithmetics." Of these about 25 are fifteenth
century imprints and the remainder are of the sixteenth century. Works on
algebra and geometry are included only when they treat also of arithmetic
or are of value in the study of the history of arithmetic. Well illustrated and
annotated, with a view to the needs of the bibliographer. Arranged chronologically by first editions, with a subject and place index at the end. Part 2,
p. 433–494, relates to manuscripts.

(3) ASTROLOGY

HELLMANN, G. Entwicklungsgeschichte des meteorologischen Lehrbuches. (*In* Beitrag zur Geschichte der Meteorologie, Berlin, 1917.
Nr. 6, t. II, p. 3–133.) 351

A critical bibliography divided into two parts: (I) Aristotle's meteorology,
a critical list of printed editions, translations and commentaries from 1474 to
1901, including 37 incunabula and 98 sixteenth century items. (II) A critical list of meteorological textbooks from 1500 to 1914. It mentions one
incunabulum and 56 sixteenth century items. — G. S[arton] in *Isis,* IV (I),
191.

SUDHOFF, K. [F. J.] Iatromathematiker, vornehmlich im 15. und 16.
Jahrhundert. (Abhandlungen zur Geschichte der Medicin. Hrsg.
von . . . H. Magnus . . . M. Neuburger und . . . K. Sudhoff.
II. Breslau, 1902.) 352

(4) ASTRONOMY

COLLIJN, I. Drei neu aufgefundene niederdeutsche Einblattkalender
des 15. Jahrhundert. Leipzig [1904]. 353

HAEBLER, K. Hundert Kalender-Inkunabeln. Herausgegeben von
Paul Heitz. Strassburg, 1905. 354

HELLMANN, G. Die Wettervorhersage im ausgehanden Mittelalter
(XII bis XV Jahrhundert). (*In* Beiträge zur Geschichte der Meteorologie, Berlin, 1917. Nr. 8, t. II, p. 169–299.) 355

"Divided into 3 parts: (1) Introductions to weather-forecasting by Western
writers. (2) Sources of these introductions. (3) The practice of weather-
forecasting. Check-list of incunabula 'Prognostics,' 264 in all, by 64 authors
(32 Italians, 23 Germans and Austrians, 3 Dutchmen). The oldest is by

Franciscus de Guascono of Venise, 1470, (earliest copy extant, 1474)."—
G. S[arton] in *Isis*, 1921, Vol. IV (1).

Thirty-seven incunabula relative to Aristotle's meteorology are listed in
the same volume, p. 3–133, under *Entwicklungsgeschichte des meteorologischen Lehrbuches.*

HOUZEAU, J. C., AND A. LANCASTER   Bibliographie générale de l'as-
tronomie. . . Bruxelles, 1882–1889. 3 v. in 4 pts.   356

> Vol. I in 2 pts. — Ouvrages imprimés et manuscrits. Arranged for the most
> part chronologically under astronomical subjects and treating of fifteenth
> and sixteenth century titles under such subjects as "Collections d'ouvrages
> historiques," "Astronomes de le renaissance," "Ouvrages d'astrologie
> générale postérieurs à l'usage de l'imprimerie," "Traités astrologiques des
> conjonctions, des éclipses et des comètes," "Astrologie médicale," etc. (pt. 1);
> "Calendriers postérieurs à l'emploi de l'imprimerie," "Ephémérides et
> Almanachs" (pt. 2.)
>
> Houzeau's *Vade-Mecum de l'Astronomie,* Bruxelles, 1882, lists an occasional
> fifteenth century title, which may be found through the *Table bibliographique,*
> p. 1039–1120.

LA LANDE, J. DE   Bibliographie astronomique . . . jusqu'à 1802. . .
Paris, 1803.   357

> In chronological arrangement throughout: p. 9–29, "Livres imprimés dans
> le XVe siècle"; p. 29–136, "Livres du XVIe siècle."

PULKOVO   Astronomicheskaiia observatoriia. Librorum in Bibliotheca Speculae Pulcovensis. . . Catalogus systematicus. . . Petro-
poli, 1860, 1880. 2 v.   358

> Arranged chronologically under the various astronomical subjects and re-
> cording various fifteenth and sixteenth century titles. Vol. 1, Otto Struve,
> *ed.;* v. 2, Eduardo Lindemanno elaborata. An ea.lier catalogue was edited
> by Struve in 1845, under the title *Librorum in Bibliotheca Speculae Pul-
> covensis contentorum catalogus systematicus.*

[SCHEIBEL, J. E.] Astronomische chronologische Bibliographie.
Fünfzehntes Jahrhundert. (*In his* Einleitung zur mathematischen
Bücherkenntnis. Bresslau, 1784. Vol. III, p. 1–53.)   359

> For other references to Calendars see below, under: III. Printing Before
> 1457.

(5) GEOMETRY

RICCARDI, P.   Saggio di una bibliografia Euclidea. . . Bologna, 1887–
1893.   360

> A chronological list of editions of Euclid from 1482 to date of publication.

THOMAS-STANFORD, C.   Early editions of Euclid's Elements. London,
1926. (Bibliographical Society. Illustrated monographs. XX.)
                                                                     361

VALENTIN, G. Die beiden Euclid-Ausgaben des Jahres 1482. (*In* Bibliotheca Mathematica. Gustaf Eneström, *ed.* Stockholm, 1893. No. 2, p. 33–38.)   362

(6) MUSIC

BARRIS MUÑOZ, R. El primer libro de música impresa en España (Sevilla, 1494). Cádiz, 1926.   363

CAZA, F. Tractato vulgare de canto figurato, Mailand, 1492, im Faksimile mit Übersetzung herausgegeben von Joh. Wolf. Berlin, 1922.   364

A facsimile of an important incunable, with a bibliography of other fifteenth century music books.

GOOVAERTS, A. Histoire et bibliographie de la typographie musicale dans les Pays-Bas. Antwerp, 1880.   365

LITTLETON, A. H. A Catalogue of one hundred works illustrating the history of music printing from the fifteenth to the end of the seventeenth century in the library of Alfred Henry Littleton. . . London, 1911.   366

MOLITOR, R. Deutsche Choral-Wiegendrucke. . . Regensburg, 1904.   367

Covers the period from 1457–1548.

RIEMANN, [C. W. J.] H. Notenschrift und Notendruck; bibliographisch-typographische Studie von Dr. Hugo Riemann. (*In* Roeder, *firm of, printers,* Leipzig. 1846–1896, Festschrift zur 50 jährigen Jubelfeier des Bestehens der Firma C. G. Roeder. . . Leipzig, 1896.)   368

Riemann's "Anhang" covers the period from 1473 to modern times, the early centuries being treated more fully.

SCHMID, A. Ottaviano dei Petrucci da Fossombrone, der erste Erfinder des Musiknotendruckes mit beweglichen Metalltypen und seine Nachfolger im sechzehnten Jahrhunderte. . . Wien, 1845.   369

Mit steter Rücksicht auf die vorzüglichsten Leistungen derselben und auf die Erstlinge des Musiknotendruckes. Eine nachträgliche, mit XXI Abbildungen ausgestattete Festgabe zur Jubelfeier der Erfindung der Buchdruckerkunst.

SPRINGER, H. Zur Musiktypographie in der Incunabelzeit. . . [Leipzig, 1903].   370

Sonderabdruck aus: Beiträge zur Bücherkunde und Philologie; August Wilmanns zum 25. März 1903 gewidmet.

SQUIRE, W. B.   Notes on early music printing.   (*In* Bibliographica.
IX, p. 99–122.)   371

STEELE, R.   Earliest English music printing; a description and bibliog-
raphy of English printed music to the close of the sixteenth century. . .
London, 1903.   (Bibliographical Society.   Illustrated Monographs.
XI.)   372

Covers the period from 1495–1600.   First published by R. Steele and R. A.
Peddie *in* Bibliographical Society.   Transactions.   Vol. 5, pt. 1, 1899, under
title *English printed music to 1600,* as the summary of a paper read before
the Society, Jan. 16, 1899.

VERNARECCI, A.   Ottaviano de' Petrucci da Fossombrone, inventore
dei tipi mobili metallici fusi della musica nel secolo XV. . .   2 ed.
Bologna, 1882.   373

WENDEL, C.   Aus der Wiegenzeit des Notendrucks.   (*In* Zentralblatt
für Bibliothekswesen.   1902.   XIX.)   374

(7) NUMERALS

HILL, G. F.   The Development of Arabic numerals in Europe, exhibited in sixty-four tables.   Oxford, 1915.   375

Tables XLI and LX reproduce Arabic numerals in printed books and engravings which were produced in Germany and in Italy during the years
1464–1508 and *c.* 1467–1509 respectively.

References to bibliographical works on mathematics, particularly to monographs and lists relating to the works published in various countries, will be
found in the Einleitung, *in* Wölffing, E., Mathematischer Bücherschatz.
Leipzig, 1903.

3. MEDICINE (ANATOMY, DRUGS, HERBALS, HYGIENE, PESTILENCE)

A) IN GENERAL

CARBONELLI, G.   Bibliographia medica typographica Pedemontana
saeculorum XV. et XVI.   Romae, 1914–[1919].   376

CHOULANT, L.   Graphische Incunabeln für Naturgeschichte und
Medicin.   Neudruck.   München, 1924.   377

Originally issued at Leipzig in 1858.

———— Handbuch der Bücherkunde für die ältere Medicin.   Leipzig,
1841.   2. ed.   378

First issued in 1828.   Relates mainly to the fifteenth and sixteenth centuries.

JOSEPHSON, A. G. S.   The Incunabula in the Senn collection at the John Crerar Library. Chicago, 1909.   379

Reprinted from the *Journal* of the American Medical Association, May 29, 1909, Vol. LII.

McCULLOCH, C. C.   A Checklist of medical incunabula in the Surgeon General's Library, Washington.   (*In* Annals of medical history. New York, 1917. Vol. I, no. 3, p. 301–315.)   380

Reprinted as a 'separate,' [New York, 1918]. Reviewed in *The Library,* 1919.

OSLER, W.   Bibliotheca Osleriana: a catalogue of books illustrating the history of medicine and science, collected, arranged, and annotated by Sir William Osler, Bt., and bequeathed to McGill University. Oxford, 1929.   381

Compiled by Dr. W. W. Francis, R. H. Hill, and Dr. A. Malloch. Reviewed in *The Library.* Fourth series, Vol. X, no. 3. Dec. 1929.

———— Incunabula Medica: A study of the earliest printed medical books, 1467–1480. Oxford, 1923. (Bibliographical Society. Illustrated Monographs. XIX.)   381:a

Edited by J. V. Scholderer. Comprises Sir William Osler's address before the Society, a conspectus of the medical books issued during the first period of incunabula; a tribute to him by Mr. Pollard; an appendix describing the medical dictionaries of the period; and a *Bibliographical List* of 217 editions of books wholly or in part of medical interest printed by the end of 1480.

SINGER, C.   The *Fasciculo di medicina, Venice 1493.* Florence, 1925. (Monumenta Medica. *Ed.* by H. E. Sigerist. II.)   382

SUDHOFF, K. [F. J.]   Deutsche medizinische Inkunabeln. Bibliographischliterarische Untersuchungen. Leipzig, 1908. (Studien zur Geschichte der Medizin, II–III.)   383

b) By Subjects

(1) ANATOMY

CHOULANT, L.   History and bibliography of anatomic illustration in its relation to anatomic science and the graphic arts. Translated and edited . . . by Mortimer Frank. Chicago, 1920.   384

Reviewed in *Isis,* 1922, IV, (2). First printed at Leipzig, 1852, under title *Geschichte und Bibliographie der anatomischen Abbildungen.*

GOLDSCHMID, E. Entwicklung und Bibliographie der Pathologisch-
Anatomischen Abbildung. Leipzig, 1925.   385

The object of this work, according to its announcement, is to provide a
bibliography of illustrated patho-medical works published from the fifteenth
to the twentieth century (1450–1925), and a history of the art of medical
illustrations.

HOLLÄNDER, E. Wunder, Wundergeburt und Wundergestalt in Ein-
blattdrucken des fünfzehnten bis achtzehnten Jahrhunderts. . .
Stuttgart, 1921.   386

A collection of prints dating from the fifteenth to the eighteenth century,
relating to anatomical monstrosities, etc., and containing about 5 incunabula
and 21 sixteenth century prints. Reviewed in *Isis,* 1922, IV, (3).

SINGER, C. A Study in early Renaissance anatomy. (*In his* Studies
in the history and method of science. Oxford, 1917, p. 79–164.)
            387

Illustrated by cuts from anatomical works published during the fifteenth
and sixteenth centuries.

(2) DRUGS

ZIMMERMANN, L. Saladini de Asculo. . . Compendium aromatorium.
Leipzig, 1919.   388

" Saladini's work on drugs was written between 1441 and 1463. Latin text
and translation is here given from a printed edition of 1572. It gives us a
good idea of the drug armamentarium of the Renaissance physician. It contains a contemporary list of the works needed, a catechism on the nature and
uses of drugs, a description of medical herbs, their habitats and the method
and time of gathering them, their doses, etc. It is under the Arabian influence and uses many Arabian terms." — G. S[arton], in *Isis* III. (Hain
lists the first printed edition as March 12, 1488.)

(3) HERBALS

ARBER, A. Herbals, their origin and evolution. A Chapter in the
history of botany, 1470–1670. Cambridge, 1912.   389

A chronological list of the prinicpal herbals published between these years.

KLEBS, A. C. Incunabula lists. I. Herbals. (*In* Bibliographical Society of America. Papers. Chicago [1917–18]. Vol XI, p. 75–93;
Vol. XII, p. 41–57.)   390

A descriptive and critical list of fifteenth century illustrated herbals located
in the United States, grouped under the entries: Macer Floridus, Apuleius
Barbarus, Grant Herbier, and the Hortus Sanitatis family, the latter comprising editions of *Herbarius latinus, Gart der Gesundheit* and the *Hortus
Sanitatis,* or 'larger Hortus.'

—————— Introduction (*In* L'Art ancien S. A. A Catalogue of early herbals mostly from the well-known library of Dr. Karl Becher, Karlsbad. Bulletin XII. Lugano, 1925.)   391

ROHDE, E. S.   The old English herbals. London, 1922.   392

With a chapter on 'Later manuscript herbals and the early printed herbals.'

SCHREIBER, W. L. . . . Die Kräuterbucher des XV. und XVI. Jahrhunderts. München, 1924.   393

(4) HYGIENE, PESTILENCE, ETC.

HEITZ, P.   Pestblätter des XV. Jahrhunderts. Strassburg, 1901.   394

KLEBS, A. C., AND K. SUDHOFF   Pestschriftes des XV. Jahrhunderts. München, 1926.   395

The definitive and enlarged edition of the work published by A. C. Klebs and E. Droz, under the title: *Remèdes contre le peste.* Paris, 1925. Also issued in English during 1925.

PROCTOR, R. [G. C.]   Ulrich von Ellenbog and the press of S. Ulrich at Augsburg. (*In his* Bibliographical Essays. London, 1905, p. 73–88.)   396

Ulrich von Ellenbog was a doctor of medicine, a writer and a collector; the annotations in the books collected by him range from 1476 to 1497.

SCHREIBER, W. L.   Pestblätter des XV. Jahrhunderts. Hrsg. von Paul Heitz. Strassburg, 1901.   397

SUDHOFF, K. [F. J.]   Aus der Frühgeschichte der Syphilis. Handscriften- und Inkunabelstudien, epidemiologische Untersuchung und kritische Gänge. Leipzig, 1912. (Studien zur Geschichte der Medizin. IX.)   398

—————— The earliest printed literature on syphilis. Florence, 1925. (Monumenta Medica. *Ed.* by H. E. Sigerist. III.)   399

Ten tractates from the years 1495–1498, in complete facsimile; with introduction by K. Sudhoff; adapted by C. Singer from the German edition: *Zehn Syphilis-drucke aus den Jahren 1495–1498.*

—————— Graphische und typographische Erstlinge der Syphilisliteratur aus den Jahren 1495 und 1496. München, 1912. (Alte Meister der Medizin und Naturkunde, IV.)   400

With reproductions of early anatomical and medical broadsides.

Medical incunabula, almost exclusively, are listed in the catalogues of Taeuber and Weil, booksellers, Munich.

The sections entitled *Bibliographie analytique* and *Critical Bibliography,* which are arranged by centuries in Isis, INTERNATIONAL REVIEW DEVOTED TO THE HISTORY OF SCIENCE AND CIVILIZATION (the quarterly organ of the History of Science Society, edited by George Sarton, D.Sc.) are frequently rich in titles relating to epidemics and hygienic conditions in the fifteenth century.

Just as this list goes to press, there comes the *Catalogue of medical incunabula contained in the William Norton Bullard loan collection deposited in the Boston Medical Library,* compiled by J. F. Ballard.

A bibliography of *Incunabula Opthalmica* by Dr. Casey A. Wood is promised in a forthcoming annotated translation of Benevenutus Grapheus' *De oculis eorum aegritudinibus.* [Ferrara, 1474.]

A catalogue of medical incunabula is being prepared by Dr. Arnold C. Klebs for the New York Academy of Medicine. This, it is understood, is to be developed into a comprehensive bibliographical treatise of medical and scientific incunabula.

4. MISCELLANEOUS SUBJECTS

A) IN GENERAL

BRUNET, G.   La France littéraire au XVe siècle.   Paris, 1865.   401

[HARASZTI, Z., *ed.*]   XVth-century books in the library.   (*In* The Boston Public Library. More books. Nov. 1929–.)   401:a

A valuable book-list with annotations on the literary content of the books described.

HARLESS, C. F.   Die Litteratur der ersten hundert Jahre nach der Erfindung der Typographie.   Leipzig, 1840.   402

POLLARD, A. W.   Introduction [A survey of the subject matter of German incunabula.]   (*In* British Museum. Catalogue of books printed in the XVth century. . . Part III. Germany. . . London, 1913, p. xiii–xxvii.)   403

STEELE, R.   What fifteenth century books are about.   (*In* The Library. Second Ser. 1903–1907.)   404

I. Scientific books, 1903, p. 337–354; II. divinity, 1904, p. 337–358; III. law, 1905, p. 137–155; IV. literature, 1907, p. 225–238. To the 9,681 incunabula examined in the course of his survey, Mr. Steele gives the following classification: science, 838; theology, 4,379; law, 930; literature, 3,534; in which proportion it should of course be remembered that it is not always the books most read that survive. Mr. Steele, for instance, believes that there was originally a much larger per cent of law books than a present-day count would indicate.

WINSHIP, G. P. (The Vollbehr incunabula)   [A commentary . . . on the Vollbehr collection of three thousand titles of incunabula displayed at the National Arts Club of New York. MCMXXVI. August twenty-third to September thirtieth. New York, August, 1926.]
                                                                            405
See also Section VI, Fifteenth Century Woodcuts, etc.: Selected Monographs.

B) BY SUBJECTS

(1) BIBLES

COPINGER, W. A.   Incunabula Biblica; or, The first half century of the Latin Bible; being a bibliographical account of the various editions of the Latin Bible between 1450 and 1500. With an appendix containing a chronological list of the editions of the sixteenth century. London, 1892.   406

A catalogue of the author's collection of Latin Bibles, with bibliographical particulars, was published in 1893.

HAEBLER, K.   The Valencian Bible of 1478. (*In* Revue Hispanique. XXI. 1909.)   407

SCHUBERT, A.   Die beiden ältesten vollständigen Biblia Bohemica-Inkunabeln. (*In* Zentralblatt für Bibliothekswesens. Leipzig, 1897, p. 104–9.)   408

Relates to the Prague Bible of 1488 and the Kuttenberg Bible of 1489, with reference to a Bohemian New Testament of 1475 and a Bohemian Psalter of 1487.
See also under: II. Germany; III. Printing Before 1457.

(2) BOCCACCIO

MICHEL, H.   L'Imprimeur Colard Mansion et le *Boccace* de la bibliothèque d'Amiens. Paris, 1925.   409

WILKINS, E. H.   The Genealogy of the editions of the *Genealogia Deorum*. (*In* Modern philology. Dec. 1919. Vol. XVII, no. 8.)
                                                                            410

Records five editions before 1500. By assembling bibliographical and literary evidence, the author establishes the parentage of the successive editions from 1472 to 1532.

CALENDARS.   See under: II, Specialized Bibliographies and Monographs, Mathematics (Astronomy), nos. 353–359. And under: III, Bibliographical and Historical Aspects, Printing Before 1457, nos. 539–564.

(3) CHRONICLES

COCKERELL, S. Some German woodcuts of the fifteenth century. Hammersmith, 1897.   411

Relates to the "Nuremberg Chronicle," etc.

MURRAY, A. G. W. The Edition of the *Fasciculus Temporum* printed by Arnold ther Hoernen in 1474. (*In* The Library, 1913, p. 57–71.)   412

STILLWELL, M. B. The *Fasciculus Temporum*. A genealogical survey of editions before 1480. (*In* Bibliographical essays. A tribute to Wilberforce Eames. [Cambridge, Mass.] June, 1924, p. 409–440.)
413

With a tabulated collation of Cologne editions, and a summary of the collations of the Louvain-Venice and Speier series. Twenty copies separately printed.

(4) CLASSICS

COPINGER, W. A. Incunabula Virgiliana. (*In* Bibliographical Society. Transactions. II. London, 1893–94, p. [123]–226.)   414

DUPLESSIS, G. Essai bibliographique sur les différentes éditions des oeuvres d'Ovide, ornées de planches, publiées aux XVe et XVIe siècles. Paris, 1889.   415

HALLE, J. (Bookseller) Incunabula typographica. Rare and valuable editions of the Greek and Latin classics printed in the fifteenth century mostly in their original bindings. Catalogue 66. Munich, 1928.   416

PALMER, H. R. List of English editions and translations of Greek and Latin classics printed before 1641. London, 1911.   417

With an introduction by [J.] V. Scholderer.

SANCHEZ, J. M. Note sur deux éditions espagnoles des économiques et politiques d' Aristote du XVe siècle. (*In* Revue des bibliothèques. XVIII. 1908, p. 379–384.)   418

See also below, under: III. Greek Type.

> COLUMBUS. See Americana: Selected Bibliographies and Bibliographical Monographs, period of early discovery: Columbus, nos. 659–668.

(5) DANTE

KOCH, T. W.   Catalogue of the Dante Collection presented by William Fiske to Cornell University Library.   Ithaca, 1898–1900.   419

VOLKMANN, L.   Iconografia dantesca: le rappresentazioni figurative della *Divina commedia,* edizione italiana a cura di G. Locella. Firenze, 1898.   420

(6) DREAMS

HELIN, M.   La Clef des songes.   Paris, 1925.   421

A bibliographical essay on fifteenth century editions of the *Somnia Danielis prophetae;* with a bibliography by E. Droz of fifteenth century books on the interpretation of dreams.

(7) FICTION, FARCES, AND ROMANCE

BOURDILLON, F. W.   The early editions of the *Roman de la rose.* London, 1906.   (Bibliographical Society.   Illustrated Monographs. XIV.)   422

With collations of 21 editions from *c.* 1481–1538.

GROLIER CLUB (New York)   A Catalogue of books in first editions selected to illustrate the history of English prose fiction from 1485 to 1870.   [New York, 1917.]   423

HEILAND, K., *ed.*   Der Pfaffe Amis von dem Stricker.   Munich, 1911. (Seltenheiten aus Süddeutschen Bibliotheken.   I.)   424

A facsimile of a medieval farce printed by J. Prüss at Strassburg in 1483. From one of the only two copies known, both being in the Bavarian State Library.

KRISTELLER, P., *ed.*   Ulrich Boner: Der Edelstein [In facsimile, with introduction.]   Berlin, 1908.   (Graphische Gesellschaft.   Ausserordentliche Veröffentlichung.   I.)   425

MARCHE, O., DE LA   Le Chevalier Délibéré.   London, 1898.   (Bibliographical Society.   Illustrated Monographs.   V.)   426

First printed at Gouda *c.* 1486; reissued at Schiedam in 1500.   With a preface by F. Lippmann.   (A note on "The printer of the Chevalier Délibéré" was published by Henry Bradshaw as his *Memoranda* XIII.)

See also Section VI, Fifteenth Century Woodcuts, etc.: Selected Monographs.

HEBREW WORKS.   See below, under: III, Bibliographical and Historical Aspects, Hebrew Printing, nos. 466–479.

(8) INDULGENCES

FOURNIER, P. F. Affiches d'indulgence manuscrites et imprimées des XIVe, XVe et XVIe siècles. (*In* Bibliothèque de l'Ecole des Chartes. LXXXIV. Paris, 1893.) 427

See also below, under: III. Printing Before 1457.

(9) LATIN GRAMMARS

DELISLE, L. Alexandre de Villedieu et Guillaume Le Moine, de Ville-dieu. (*In* Bibliothèque de l'École des Chartes. LV. Paris, 1894.) 428

KITTREDGE, G. L. Some landmarks in the history of Latin grammars. [Boston, 1903.] 429

A brochure containing several illustrations of fifteenth and sixteenth century grammars.

REICHLING, D. Das Doctrinale des Alexander de Villa-Dei. Berlin, 1893. (Monumenta Germaniae paedagogica. XII.) 430

This volume describes 162 fifteenth century editions. (See also the *Gesamtkatalog:* Alexander de Villa-Dei, for these and other titles.)
See also below, under: III. Printing before 1457.

MUSIC. In the fifteenth century a department of Mathematics. See above, under: II, Specialized Bibliographies and Monographs, Mathematics (Music), nos. 363–374.

PROCLAMATIONS. See below, under: III, Bibliographical and Historical Aspects, Broadsides, nos. 450–453.

PTOLEMY. See Americana: Selected Bibliographies and Bibliographical Monographs, Cartography and Geography, nos. 768–771.

(10) RAPPRESENTAZIONI (MIRACLE PLAYS)

DUDLEY, L. H., AND OTHERS Florentine woodcuts. (*In* Harvard Library. Notes. Cambridge, Nov. 1921. VI, p. 123–138.) 431

POLLARD, A. W. Florentine rappresentazioni and their pictures. (*In his* Old picture books. . . London, 1902.) 432

(11) RIFLE-MATCHES

FREYS, E., *ed.* Gedruckte Schützenbriefe des 15. Jahrhunderts. Munich, 1912. (Seltenheiten aus Süddeutschen Bibliotheken. II.) 433

A collection of facsimile reprints of fifteenth century broadsides relating to German rifle-matches.

(12) SAVONAROLA

AUDIN DE RIANS, S. L. G. E. [Bibliography of the writings of Savonarola.] (*In his* Trattato di frate Ieronimo Savonarola circa il reggimento e governo della citta di Firenze. 1847.) 434

DUDLEY, L. H., AND OTHERS Florentine woodcuts. (*In* Harvard Library. Notes. Cambridge, Nov. 1921. VI, p. 123–138.) 435

GRUYER, G. Les Illustrations des écrits de Jérome Savonarole publiés en Italie au XVe et au XVIe siècle. Paris, 1879. 436

OLSCHKI, L. S. Bibliotheca Savonaroliana. Les œuvres de Fra G. Savonarola . . . éditions, traductions. . . . Florence, 1898. 437

RATH, E. VON Einleitung (*In* Wiegendruck Gesellschaft. Girolamo Savonarola predica dell'arte del ben morire. Florenz: Bartolommeo de Libri um 1496. [*Facsimile*] Berlin, 1926.) 437:a

(13) SERMON-BOOKS

REDGRAVE, G. R. Some illustrated sermon-books. (*In* The Library, 1916, p. 44–52.) 438

Relates to the " Ship of Fools," Grüninger imprints, etc. See also Redgrave's *Illustrated books of Sebastian Brandt,* p. 47–60 in *Bibliographica.* V.

ZARNCKE, F., *ed.* Sebastian Brants Narrenschiff. Herausgegeben von Friedrich Zarncke. Leipzig, 1854. 439

" A critical edition of the German original with specimens of the various translations, a bibliography of early editions, and a critical estimate of later ones." — L.L.M.

A facsimile of the 1494 original edition in German was issued by the Gesellschaft der Bibliophilen, Weimar, 1913; and another, edited by Franz Schultz, the same year.

For further reference to the " Ship of Fools " see: Americana: Selected Bibliographies and Monographs. Period of Discovery, Columbus; and the facsimile edition (Basel, Feb. 11, 1494) issued by Dr. Hans Koegler for the Gesellschaft für Bibliophilen.

(14) THIRST

SIMON, A. L. Bibliotheca Bacchica. Bibliographie raisonnée des ouvrages imprimés avant 1800 et illustrant la soif humaine. . . London, 1927.   440

Vol. I. *Incunables,* with 60 illustrations.

(15) TRAVEL

DAVIES, H. W. Bernhard von Breydenbach and his journey to the Holy Land, 1483–4. London, 1911.   441

A bibliography of the first illustrated, printed book of travel.

HÜLSEN, C. Einleitung (*In* Wiegendruck Gesellschaft, *publ.* Mirabilia Romae, Rom, Stephen Planck, 20. November MCCCC-LXXXIX. Ein römisches Pilgerbuch des 15. Jahrhunderts in deutscher Sprache. Berlin, 1925.)   442

A facsimile, with a bibliographical survey of editions of the *Miribilia Romae,* p. 8–56 of the editor's Introduction.

For Illustrated Books relating to various subjects, see Section VI, Fifteenth Century Woodcuts, etc.: Selected Monographs.

III. BIBLIOGRAPHICAL AND HISTORICAL ASPECTS *

(1) ADVERTISEMENTS

BURGER, K. Buchhändleranzeigen des XV. Jahrhunderts. Leipzig, 1907.   443

MEYER, W. Bücheranzeigen des 15. Jahrhunderts. Separatabdruck aus dem Zentralblatt für Bibliothekswesen. Leipzig, 1885.   444

With an account of 22 early book-lists, 1469–1495, and a facsimile of the list issued by Peter Schoeffer at Mainz, 1469–70.

NICHOLSON, E. W. B. Caxton's advertisement. Photolithograph of the copy . . . in the Bodleian library, Oxford, being one of the only two copies known. London [1892].   445

VELKE, W. Zu den Bücheranzeigen Peter Schöffers. Mainz, 1908. (Gutenberg Gesellschaft. Veröffentlichungen.)   446

VOULLIÉME, E. Nachträge zu den Buchhändleranzeigen des 15. Jahrhunderts von K. Burger. (*In* Wiegendrucke und Handschriften. Festgabe für Konrad Haebler. Leipzig, 1919, p. 18–44.)   447

* Listed alphabetically.

(2) BOOK PRICES AND BOOKSELLING

HASE, O. VON   Die Koberger: Eine Darstellung des Buchhändlerischen Geschäftsbetriebs in der Zeit des Überganges vom Mittelalter zur Neuzeit. 2d ed., Leipzig, 1885.   448

> An exposition of business principles in the book trade, based upon the correspondence of Anton Koberger, 1493–1525. An account of Koberger's business correspondence and matters relating to bookselling will be found on p. 37–42 of Vol. I, of Goldschmidt's *Gothic & Renaissance bindings*, London, 1928. A list of 'Binders' and Booksellers' Names' appears on p. 331–343 of the same volume. (Another reference to Koberger occurs on p. 19–23 in Winship's *Gutenberg to Plantin*. Cambridge, 1926.)

PLOMER, H. R.   Two lawsuits of Richard Pynson. (*In* The Library, 1909, p. 115–133.)   449

> Said to contain more information on the size of editions and wholesale prices of fifteenth century books than anything previously written.
>
> See also *The Library*, 1918, p. 150–152. An interesting account of the practice of rating the price according to the quires of the book will be found on p. 36 of Vol. I, of Goldschmidt's *Gothic & Renaissance bookbindings*. London, 1928.
>
> Quotations on *modern* selling-prices of incunabula are given in a check list by Max Sandar, entitled *Prices of incunabula*. Milan, 1930.

(3) BROADSIDES

COLLIJN, I.   Ettbladstryck från femtonde Århundradet. Stockholm, 1905, 1912.   450

CROUS, E.   Das Religiös-Kirchliche Leben des ausgehenden Mittelalters im Spiegel der Einblattdrucke des 15. Jahrhunderts. Ludwigshafen a. Rh., 1925. (Gedenkschrift zum 400 jährigen Jubiläum der Mennoniten oder Taufgesinnten.)   451

GESAMTKATALOG DER WIEGENDRUCKE, KOMMISSION FÜR DEN Einblattdrucke des XV. Jahrhunderts. Ein bibliographisches Verzeichnis. Halle a. S. 1914. (Sammlung bibliothekswissenschaftlicher Arbeiten. H. 35–36.)   452

HEITZ, P.   Kolorierte und schwarze Einblattdrucke des 15. Jahrhunderts. I. Strassburg, 1899.   453

> See also under: II. Mathematics (Astronomy: Calendars); Medicine (Anatomy); Indulgences; Rifle-Matches; III. Printing Before 1457.

(4) CATALOGUES OF COLLECTIONS

GESAMTKATALOG DER WIEGENDRUCKE, KOMMISSION FÜR DEN Abkürzungen für Angeführte Quellen (*In* Gesamtkatalog der Wiegendrucke. Leipzig, 1925–. Bd. I, p. xxiii–xxxi.) 454

A list of 282 bibliographical reference titles including the catalogues of five
American collections, *i.e.*, of the Walters collection, 1906; of the Pierpont
Morgan Library, 1906–1907; of the Hoe collection, 1907; of the Plimpton
collection of arithmetics, 1908; and of the Annmary Brown Memorial, 1910.

PEDDIE, R. A. Catalogues of collections of incunabula. (*In his* Fifteenth century books: A guide to their identification. . . London,
1913, p. 53–62.) 455

A list of 105 catalogues arranged alphabetically by location and including
four American catalogues, *i.e.*, of the Walters collection, 1906; of the Pierpont Morgan Library, 1906–1907; of the Senn collection at the John Crerar
Library, 1909; and of the Annmary Brown Memorial, 1910.

SEYMOUR DE RICCI Catalogues et collections d'incunables. (*In* Revue
archeologique, 1915. I, p. 283–302.) 456

The *Census of fifteenth century books owned in America,* 1919, complied
by a committee of the Bibliographical Society of America, in its "List of
Contributors" records twenty-one catalogues of American collections of
incunabula, *i.e.*, Massachusetts Historical Society (Thomas Dowse collec-
tion), 1870; Free Library of Philadelphia, H. Josephine Widener Branch
(Copinger collection), 1895; The Grolier Club, 1895; Missouri Botanical
Garden (Sturtevant Prelinnean Library), 1896; Clark University, 1906;
Isabella Stewart Gardner collection, 1906; Henry Walters collection, 1906;
John Pierpont Morgan Library, 1906–1907; Levi Ziegler Leiter collection,
1907; John Crerar Library (Senn collection), 1907; New York State Library
(Duncan Campbell collection), 1908, destroyed by fire in 1911; Annmary
Brown Memorial, 1910; Brown University (John Carter Brown Library and
general libraries), 1910; David N. Carvalho collection, 1911; Yale University
(William Loring Andrews collection), 1913; Library of Congress (John Boyd
Thacher collection), 1915; Henry E. Huntington collection, 1917; Vassar
College Library, 1917; Lewis Stephen Pilcher collection, 1918; St. Bonaven-
ture's Seminary, 1918; U. S. Surgeon-General's Library, 1918.

To such a list should now be added the reports of the Chapin Library (Williams College) and of the Newberry Library; *Harvard Library notes;* the
current issues of the Boston Public Library's *More books* (with annotations
on subject matter); the recent catalogues of the William Norton Bullard loan
collection (Boston Medical Society) and of the *Bibliotheca Osleriana* (Mc-
Gill University); the forthcoming catalogue of the New York Academy of
Medicine; L. C. Harper's *Selection of Incunabula,* 1927–1930, compiled by
Miss E. Miriam Lone; *etc.* For catalogues and publications relating
to the Pierpont Morgan Library, the Hispanic Society of America, the
Thacher collection in the Library of Congress, the Henry E. Huntington
Library, the Lenox collection in the New York Public Library, the John
Carter Brown Library, *etc.*, see below, under nos. 1277–1284.

(5) CENSORSHIP

ZARETZKY, O.   Der erste Kölner Zensurprozess.   Köln, 1906.   457

A facsimile of the copy in the Stadtbibliothek, Cologne.

(6) COLOPHONS AND TITLE-PAGES

GARNETT, R.   On some colophons of the early printers.   (*In his* Essays in librarianship and bibliography.   New York, 1899.)   458

POLLARD, A. W.   An Essay on colophons, with specimens and translations.   Chicago, 1915.   459

With an introduction by R. Garnett.

———— Last words on the history of the title-page, with notes on some colophons and twenty-seven facsimiles of title-pages.   London, 1891.
460

(7) COLOR PRINTING

WALLAU, H.   Die zweifarbigen Initialen der Psalterdrucke von Joh. Fust und Peter Schöffer.   (*In* Festschrift zur Gutenbergfeier.   Mainz, 1900, p. 261–304; Leipzig, p. 325–378.)   461

WEALE, W. H. J.   Catalogue of the manuscripts and printed books exhibited at the historical music loan exhibition.   London, 1886.
462

With a discussion of the manner in which the colors were printed in the Psalter of 1457.

See also above, under: III. Broadsides.

(8) FACSIMILES

CROUS, E.   Faksimilia von Wiegendrucken.   (*In* Zeitschrift für Buchkunde.   I.   1924, p. 148–153.)   463

Lists nearly a hundred incunabula that have been completely reproduced in facsimile.

See also below, under: III. Type.

(9) GREEK TYPE

PROCTOR, R. [G. C.]   The Printing of Greek in the fifteenth century. Oxford, 1900.   (Bibliographical Society.   Illustrated Monographs. VIII.)   464

SCHOLDERER, [J.] V. Greek printing types 1465–1927. Facsimiles from an exhibition of books illustrating the development of Greek printing shown in the British Museum, 1927. With an historical introduction. London, 1927.   465

With 17 facsimiles from fifteenth century books.

(10) HEBREW PRINTING

AMRAM, D. W. The Makers of Hebrew books in Italy. Philadelphia, 1909.   466

This covers the period from 1475 to modern times; reference works on Hebrew printing are listed on p. 409–413.

AMZALAK, M. B. A Tipografia hebraica em Portugal no século XV. Coimbra, 1922.   467

FREIMANN, A. Die hebräischen Inkunabeln der Druckereien in Spanien und Portugal. (*In* Gutenberg-Festschrift. Mainz, 1925.)
                                                                             468

———— Thesaurus typographiae Hebraicae saeculi XV. Berlin, 1924–.
                                                                             469

———— Über hebräische Inkunabeln. Leipzig, 1902.   470

HAEBLER, K. Hebräische Drucke. (*In his* Geschichte des Spanisches Frühdruckes in Stammbäumen. Leipzig, 1923, p. 41–49.)   471

———— Die hebräischen Drucker, 1475–1500. (*In his* Die Deutschen Buchdruck des XV. Jahrhunderts im Auslande. München, 1924, p. 124–127.)   472

MANZONI, G. Annali tipografici del Soncini nel secolo 15 e nel secolo 16. Bologna, 1886.   472 :a

Beginning with the year 1483.

MARX, A. Some notes on the use of Hebrew type in non-Hebrew books, 1475–1520. (*In* Bibliographical essays. A tribute to Wilberforce Eames. [Cambridge, Mass.] June, 1924, p. 381–408.)
                                                                             473

SACCHI, F. I Tipografi ebrei di Soncino. Studii bibliografici. Cremona, 1877.   474

Relates to Hebrew printing from 1483–1547.

SCHOLDERER, [J.] V. Printing at Ferrera. (*In* Gutenberg Gesell-schaft. Gutenberg Festschrift. Mainz, 1925, p. 73–78.)   474 :a

SCHWAB, M. Les Incunables orientaux et les impressions orientales au commencement du 16e siècle. Paris, 1883.   475

This work deals with Hebrew incunabula, 1475–1540; and the introduction treats of the origin of printing in all Semitic languages. Bibliographical works are listed on p. 23–25.

SIMONSEN, D. Hebraisk Bogtryk i aeldre og nyere Tid. Kjøbenhavn, 1901.   476

Covers the inclusive dates, July 30, 1474–1894.

——— Über Frühdrucke spanischer und portugiesischer Juden. (*In* Zeitschrift für Bücherfreunde. Jahrg. I. 1897–98, Vol. 2.)   477

SOAVE, M. Dei Soncino celebri tipografi Italiani nel secolo XV et XVI. Venezia, 1878.   478

Relates to the period 1483–1547.

STEINSCHNEIDER, M. Catalogus librorum Hebraeorum in Bibliotheca Bodleiana. Berolini, 1852–60.   479

While primarily a catalogue of Hebrew and other Jewish books in the Bodleian Library, 1475–1851, this is at the same time an attempt to compile a complete bibliography of Hebrew books, 1475–1732. The books not in the Bodleian are given in brackets. An epoch-making book in the history of Hebrew bibliography.

———

A description and critique of bibliographical works on Hebrew incunabula will be found in Dr. Alexander Marx's *Literatur über Hebräische Inkunabeln.* Berlin [1926]. (Soncino-Gesellschaft der Freunde des Jüdischen Buches. Sonderdruck aus den Soncino-Blättern. 1:2. 1926.) See also the articles by J. Jacobs in the *Jewish Encyclopedia,* entitled *Incunabula; G. B. Rossi;* and *Soncino.* Just as this book goes to press, there comes a welcome book on Hebrew printing: Cowley, A. E., *A concise catalogue of the Hebrew printed books in the Bodleian Library.* Oxford, 1929.

ILLUSTRATED BOOKS. See the following section, Fifteenth Century Woodcuts, Metal Engravings, etc.: Selected Bib-liographies and Bibliographical Monographs, nos. 601–649.

(11) INDEX

SCHMIDT, A. Zeilenzählung in Druckwerken. Inhaltsverzeichnisse und alphabetische Register in Inkunabeln. (*In* Zentralblatt für Bibliothékswesen. Leipzig, 1896. Vol. XIII, p. 13–30.)   480

INITIALS.   See the following section, Fifteenth Century
Woodcuts, Metal Engravings, etc.: Selected Bibliographies
and Bibliographical Monographs, nos. 601–649.

(12) INK

CARVALHO, D. N.   Forty centuries of ink; or A chronological narrative concerning ink and its background.   New York, 1904.   481

DE VINNE, T. L.   Printing ink.   (*In his* Notable printers of Italy
during the fifteenth century.   New York, 1910, p. 159–162.)   482

See also below, under: III. Orient, Printing in.

(13) ORIENT, PRINTING IN

CARTER, T. F.   The Chinese origins of movable types.   (*In* Ars Typographica.   1925.   II.)   483

———— The great expansion of movable type printing in Korea.   (*In
his* The invention of printing in China. . .   New York, 1925, p. 169–
179.)   484

With translations of documents recording the establishment of a type foundry
in 1392 and a royal edict regarding the making of bronze type in 1403.

———— The invention of printing in China and its spread westward. . .
New York, 1925.   485

With chapters on paper-making in China; ink; block printing in China,
Egypt, and Europe; playing cards as a factor in the westward movement of
printing; the invention of movable type in China; the great expansion of
movable type printing in Korea; the pedigree of Gutenberg's invention.   The
chapter on movable type in China gives translations from a contemporary
account of early printing published before 1093, and a synopsis of the history of printing published in 1314.   An illustration from the "world's oldest
printed book — the Diamond Sutra of 868" — appears in the section on
blockbooks.

McKERROW, R. B.   An introduction to bibliography.   Oxford, 1927.
(See p. 265–267.)   486

(14) ORIGIN AND INVENTION OF MOVABLE TYPE.

CLAUDIN, A.   Un nouveau document sur Gutenberg, témoignage
d'Ulric Gering, le premier imprimeur parisien et de ses compagnons
en faveur de l'inventeur de l'imprimerie.   Paris [1883].   487

CROUS, E.   Gutenberg.   (*In* Peddie, R. A., *ed.,* Printing: A short
history of the art.   London, 1927, p. 1–5.)   488

ENSCHEDÉ, C. Laurens Jansz. Coster, de Uitvinder van de Boekdrukkunst. Haarlem, 1904. 489

FALK, F. Der Stempeldruck vor Gutenberg. (*In* Gutenberg-Festschrift. Leipzig, 1900.) 490

"The practice of stamping a legend, either a pious ejaculation or a note of
ownership, on the covers of a binding goes back to considerable antiquity
and a good deal beyond the origin of early printing in 1450. These lettered
bindings afford clear proof that the idea of printing words from single letters
was familiar long before Gutenberg and that the 'Invention of Printing'
did not consist in that discovery but in the solving of more complex technical
problems." Goldschmidt, Vol. I, p. 171.

HUSUNG, M. H. Neues Material zur Frage des Stempeldrucks vor
Gutenberg. (*In* Gutenberg-Festschrift z. Feier des 25 jährigen
Bestehens der Gutenberg-museums in Mainz. Mainz, 1925, p. 66–
72.) 491

JOSEPHSON, A. G. S. The invention of printing as recorded in notes
and colophons of fifteenth-century books. [Chicago, 1917.] 492

Reprinted from: Bibliographical Society of America. *Papers.* Vol. XI,
no. 1, 1917. For additional titles see: B. S. A. *Papers.* Vol. XII, 1918.

KRUITWAGEN, B. Die Ausprüche Hollands auf die Erfindung der
Buchdruckerkunst. (Gutenberg-Festschrift. Mainz, 1925.) 493

———— De Uitvinding van de Boekdrukkunst en hare eerste Voortbrengselen. Leiden, 1918. (Handelingen van de Maatschappij der
Nederlandsche Letterkunde.) 494

MORI, G. The Essence of Gutenberg's invention. (*In* Ars Typographica. New York, October, 1925. Vol. II, no. 2, p. 101–144.)
495

An essay which is based upon the results of actual laboratory experimentation in reproducing the earliest fifteenth century types, and which results in a
hypothesis as to the stages of development during the invention of movable
type — wooden models and sand-cast molds; engraved brass punches and
lead casts or matrices; and engraved steel punches and copper matrices.

———— Was hat Gutenberg erfunden? Ein Rückblick auf die Früh-
tecknik des Schriftgusses. Mainz, 1921. 496

MORTET, C. Les Origines et les débuts de l'imprimerie d'après les
recherches les plus recentes. Paris, 1922. 497

POLLARD, A. W.   The Invention of printing — Holland.   The invention of printing — Mainz.   (*In his* Fine books.   New York, 1912. Ch. III–IV.)   498

An essay by Mr. Pollard entitled *Gutenberg, Fust, Schoeffer, and the invention of printing* appeared in *The Library.*   New Series.   Vol. VIII.   1907, p. 69–99.

SCHORBACH, K.   Die urkundlichen Nachrichten über Johann Gutenberg mit Nachbildungen und Erläuterungen.   (*In* Mainzer Gutenbergfestschrift.   1900.)   499

SCHREIBER, W. L.   Darf der Holzschnitt als Vorläufer der Buchdruckerkunst betrachtet werden?   (*In* Zentralblatt für Bibliothekswesen, 1895.   XII, p. 201–266.)   500

WINSHIP, G. P.   The invention of typography.   1400–1456.   (*In his* Gutenberg to Plantin.   Cambridge, 1926, p. 3–8.)   501

ZEDLER, G.   . . . Die neuere Gutenbergforschung und die Lösung der Costerfrage.   Frankfurt, 1923.   502

——— Von Coster zu Gutenberg.   Der holländische Frühdruck und die Erfindung des Buchdrucks.   Leipzig, 1921.   503

On verso of title-page: Mit Unterstützung der Holländischen Gesellschaft der Wissenschaften zu Haarlem.   The author concludes that both Coster and Gutenberg must be regarded as the inventors of type-printing: Coster as having produced a rather imperfect fount of type, and Gutenberg as having perfected the invention and made it practicable.

See also under: III. Orient, Printing in; Printing Before 1457.

(15) PAPERMAKING

AITKEN, P. H.   Some notes on the history of paper.   (*In* Bibliographical Society.   Transactions.   XIII.)   504

HEAWOOD, E.   Sources of early English paper-supply.   (*In* The Library.   December 1929.   Series 4, Vol. X, no. 3, p. 282–307.)   504:a

HUNTER, D.   Fifteenth century papermaking.   (*In* Ars Typographica. July 1926.   Vol. III, no. 1, p. 37–51.)   505

——— Handmade paper and its water marks: A bibliography.   [New York, 1917.]   506

——— The Literature of papermaking, 1390–1800.   [Chillicothe, O.] 1925.   507

———— Old papermaking. [Chillicothe, O.] 1923.   508

Treats of the methods used by the old makers of papers and of water-marks. The reproductions of watermarks are dated according to the first instance of their use known to the author.

JENKINS, R.   Early attempts at paper-making in England, 1495–1586. (*In* Library Association Record, 1900. II, p. 479–488.)   509

MCKERROW, R. B.   An Introduction to bibliography. Oxford, 1927. (See p. 97–98.)   510

ZONGHI, A.   Le marche principali delle carte fabrianesi dal 1293 al 1599. Fabriano, 1881.   511

See also above, under: III. Orient, Printing in; and below, Watermarks.

(16) PRINTERS' MARKS

BERJEAU, J. P.   Early Dutch, German, and English printers' marks. London, 1866–[69].   512

BRADSHAW, H.   On the engraved device used by Nicolaus Götz of Sletzstadt, the Cologne printer, in 1474. (*In his* Collected papers. Cambridge, 1889.)   513

CROUS, E.   Französische Büchermarken des 15. Jahrhunderts. (Archiv für Schreib- und Buchwesen. Jahrg. 1 :4. 1927.)   514

FREIMANN, A.   Printers' marks (*In* Jewish Encyclopedia. X. New York, 1905, p. 200–204.)   515

HAEBLER, K. . . . Spanische und Portugiesische Bücherzeichen des XV. und XVI. Jahrhunderts. Strassburg, 1898. (Die Bücher-marken oder Buchdrucker und Verlegerzeichen. V.)   516

———— Verlegermarken des Jean Petit. Halle a. d. S., 1914.   517

HAVRE, G. VAN   Marques typographiques des imprimeurs et libraires Anversois. Antwerp, 1883–84. (Maatschappij der Antwerpsche bibliophilen. Nr. 13–14.)   518

HEITZ, P., *ed.*   Die Basler Büchermarken bis Anfang des 17. Jahr-hunderts. Strassburg, 1895. (Die Büchermarken oder Buchdrucker und Verlegerzeichen.)   519

With introduction by C. Bernoulli.

HEITZ, P. Elsässische Büchermarken bis Anfang des 18. Jahrhunderts. Strassburg, 1892. (Die Büchermarken oder Buchdrucker und Verlegerzeichen.)   520

With introduction by K. A. Barack.

———— Die Frankfurter Drucker- und Verlegerzeichen bis Anfang des 17. Jahrhunderts. Strassburg, 1896. (Die Büchermarken oder Buchdrucker und Verlegerzeichen.)   521

———— Genfer Buchdrucker, und Verlegerzeichen im XV. XVI. und XVII. Jahrhundert. Strassburg, 1908. (Die Büchmarken oder Buchdrucker und Verlegerzeichen.)   522

———— Die Zürcher Büchermarken bis zum Anfang des XVII. Jahrhunderts. Zurich, 1895.   523

HUSUNG, M. J. Chrysostomus Hanthaler als Fälscher eines Inkunabelsignets. (*In* Gutenberg-Jahrbuch. 1928, p. 115–117.)   524

———— Die Drucker- und Verlegerzeichen Italiens im XV. Jahrhundert. München, 1929. (Drucker- und Buchhändlermarken des XV. Jahrhunderts. IV.)   525

With an alphabetical list of printers and publishers, 242 reproductions arranged alphabetically by towns, and a concordance of references to Haebler and Kristeller.

JUCHHOFF, R. Die Drucker- und Verlegerzeichen des 15. Jahrhunderts in den Niederlanden, England, Spanien, Portugal, Böhmen, Mähren und Polen. München, 1927. (Drucker- und Buchhändlermarken des XV. Jahrhunderts, III.)   526

KRISTELLER, [J.] P. . . . Die italienischen Buchdrucker- und Verlegerzeichen bis 1525. Strassburg, 1893. (Die Büchermarken oder Buchdrucker und Verlegerzeichen.)   527

LECLERC, E. Marques des imprimeurs et libraires en France au 15e siècle. (*In* Papyrus. VIII. 1927.)   528

McKERROW, R. B. Printers' and publishers' devices in England. . . 1485–1640. London, 1913. (Bibliographical Society. Illustrated Monographs, XVI.)   529

MEYER, W. J. Die französischen Drucker- und Verlegerzeichen. München, 1926. (Drucker- und Buchhändlermarken des XV. Jahrhunderts, II.)   530

PLOMER, H. R.   English printers' ornaments.   London, 1924.   531

POLAIN, [M.] L. [F. A.]   Marques des imprimeurs et libraires en France au XVe siècle.   Paris, 1926.   (Documents typographiques du XVe siècle. I.)   532

Comprises 209 plates, with 'Table des devises,' p. 204–205.

POLLARD, A. W.   Printers' marks of the XVth and XVIth centuries. (*In* The Connoisseur. II. London, 1902, p. 262–.)   533

RENOUARD, P.   Les marques typographiques parisiennes du XVe et du XVIe siècles.   Paris, 1926–28.   534

ROBERTS, W.   Printers' marks; a chapter in the history of typography. London, 1893.   535

SCHRETLEN, M. J.   Printers' devices in Dutch incunabula.   (*In* Ars Typographica. New York. July 1926. Vol. III, no. 1, p. 53–64.)
                                                                 536

WEIL, E.   Die deutschen Drückerzeichen des XV. Jahrhunderts. München, 1924.   (Drucker- und Buchhändlermarken des XV. Jahrhunderts, I.)   537

With 102 facsimiles of German printers' marks, and an alphabetical "Druckerregister."

ZARETZKY, O.   Die Kölner Büchermarken bis Anfang des XVII. Jahrhunderts.   Strassburg, 1898.   (Die Büchermarken oder Buchdrucker und Verlegerzeichen.)   538

An account of fifteenth century printers' devices is given in F. I. Schechter's *Historical Foundations of the Law relating to Trade-Marks*, New York, 1925. (Columbia Legal Studies, Vol. I.)   This was printed also under the title *Early Printers' and Publishers' Devices*, in: Bibliographical Society of America. *Papers*. Chicago, 1925, Vol. 19, with a list of works relating to this subject on p. 23–28.   R. A. Peddie's list of works on *Printers' Marks* appears on p. 36–37 of his *Fifteenth-Century Books*. London, 1913.

(17) PRINTING BEFORE 1457

AUBERT, M.   Les anciens Donats de la Bibliothèque Nationale.   (*In* Le Bibliographe Moderne, 1909.)   539

CROUS, E.   Germany. I. Gutenberg.   (*In* Peddie, R. A., *ed.* Printing: A short history of the art. London, 1927, p. 1–5.)   540

With a brief bibliographical list.

DZIATZKO, K.   Satz und Druck der 42-zeiligen Bibel.   (*In his* Beiträge zur Kenntnis des Schrift-, Buch- und Bibliothekswesens, VII.   Sammlung Bibliothekswissenschaftlicher Arbeiten, Heft 15.)   541

HUPP, O.   Gutenbergs erste Drucke.   Ein weiterer Beitrag zur Geschichte der ältesten Druckwerke.   München-Regensburg, 1902.   542

———— Ein Missale speciale Vorläufer des Psalteriums von 1457. München, 1898.   543

———— Zum Streit um das Missale speciale Constantiense.   Strassburg, 1917.   544

INSEL-VERLAG (Leipzig)   [Gutenberg Bible, in complete facsimile] Leipzig, 1913–1914.   2 v.   545

Colophon, Vol. 2: " Diese Faksimile-Ausgabe des zweiten Bande der zweiundvierzigzeilen Gutenberg-Bibel erschien im Jahre 1914 im Insel-Verlag zu Leipzig.   Die Wiedergabe im mehrfarbigem Lichtdruck erfolgte durch die Hofkunstanstalt Albert Frisch in Berlin nach dem Pergament-Exemplar der königlichen Bibliothek in Berlin und dem der Ständischen Landesbibliothek in Fulda.   Gedruckt wurden 300 Exemplare, davon Nr. 1–3 auf Pergament, die übrigen auf van Gelder-Bütten.   Durch Professor Ansgar Schoppmeyer in Berlin wurden die Exemplare Nr. 1–3 mit der Hand ausgemalt und bei diesen, wie auch bei 10 Exemplaren auf Büttenpapier Nr. 4–13 das Gold mit der Hand aufgelegt.   Der Einband ist dem Fuldaer Exemplar nachgebildet." " Den Subskribenten auf die Gutenberg-Bibel beehren wir uns mitzuteilen, dass das von Herrn Geheimrat Dr. Paul Schwenke zu bearbeitende Supplementheft zur Gutenberg-Bibel im Herbst 1914 erscheinen und den Subskribenten unberechnet nachgeliefert werden wird." Prospectus.

JOACHIM, J.   *Die Mahnung der Christenheit wider die Turken* aus dem Ende von 1454.   (*In* Sammlung bibliothekswissenschaftlicher Arbeiten, XIV.   1901.)   546

MARTINEAU, R.   Notes on the Latin Bible of forty-two lines, 1455. (*In* Bibliographica.   Pt. VII, p. 333–.)   547

With a tabulated collation of variations.

NEUHAUS, J.   Das erste gedruckte Buch Gutenbergs in deutscher Sprache.   Kjøbenhavn, 1902.   548

Cover-title: *Die Mahnung.*   Mainz, 1454.

PALTSITS, V. H.   The 42-line Bible of Gutenberg.   (*In* The Publishers' Weekly.   Feb. 9, 1901.)   549

Also 75 copies separately printed.

———— Missale speciale; being a further examination of the pretensions urged in behalf of this early specimen of typography. New York, 1900.   550

Fifty copies reprinted from The Publishers' Weekly, March 31, 1900.

———— The newly-found edition of the Missale speciale. [New York, 1899.]   551

Twenty-five copies reprinted from The Publishers' Weekly, May 20, 1899.

PROCTOR, R. [G. C.]   The "Gutenberg" Bible.   (*In* The Library, II. 1901.)   552

RATH, E. VON   Aufgaben der Wiegendruck-Forschung.   Festvortag bei der Feier des 25 jährigen Jubiläums des Gutenberg-Museums am 27. Juni 1925 in Mainz. Mainz, 1925.   553

SCHRÖDER, E., AND OTHERS   Das Mainzer fragment vom Weltgericht, der älteste Druck mit der Donat-kalender-type Gutenbergs. Mainz, 1904–. (Gutenberg-Gesellschaft. Veröffentlichungen. III, V.) 554

SCHWENKE, P.   Die Donat- und Kalender-type. Mainz, 1903. (Gutenberg Gesellschaft. Veröffentlichungen. II.)   555

Continues and supplements Zedler's *Die älteste Gutenbergtype*. Mainz, 1902.

———— Neue Donatstucke in Gutenbergs Urtype.   (*In* Zentralblatt für Bibliothekswesen, XXV. 1908.)   556

————Untersuchungen zur Geschichte des ersten Buchdrucks. (Festschrift zur Gutenbergfeier. [Burg b. M., 1900].)   557

———— Zweiundvierzigzeilige Bibel. Ergänzungsband zur Faksimile Ausgabe herausgeg. von P. Schwencke. Leipzig, 1923.   558

SEYMOUR DE RICCI   Bible Latine dité de 42 lignes. (*In his* Catalogue raisonné. . . Mainz, 1911, p. 25–36.)   559

———— Catalogue raisonné des premières impressions de Mayence (1445–1467). Mainz, 1911. (Gutenberg-Gesellschaft. Veröffentlichungen. VIII–IX.)   560

With bibliographical references and a census of copies under each title.

WYSS, A.   Ein deutscher Cisianus für das Jahr 1444 gedruckt von Gutenberg. . . Strassburg, 1900. (Drucke und Holzschnitte des XV. und XVI. Jahrhunderts in getreuer Nachbildung. V.)   561

Wyss, A.   Der Turkenkalender für 1455, ein Werk Gutenbergs.   (Festschrift zur Gutenbergfeier.   [Burg b. M., 1900].)   562

Zedler, G.   Die älteste Gutenbergtype.   Mainz, 1902.   (Gutenberg-
Gesellschaft.   Veröffentlichungen.   I.)   563

Relates to " Ein neu entdeckter astronomischer Kalender für das Jahr 1448."
Supplemented in 1903 by Schwenke's *Die Donat- und Kalendertype.*

──────Die Mainzer Ablassbriefe der Jahre 1454 und 1455.   Mainz,
1913.   (Gutenberg-Gesellschaft.   Veröffentlichungen.   XII, XIII.)
                                                               564

With descriptions of the known varieties and copies of the Indulgences of
1454–1455.
See also above, under: III. Origin and Invention of Movable Type.
For tributes to the Melk copy of the 42-line Bible, now at Yale University,
see: Seymour de Ricci, *The Gutenberg Bible. The first printed book, the
Melk copy.*   New York, Anderson Galleries, 1926; and Keogh, A., *The
Gutenberg Bible as a typographical monument.*   (In *The Yale University
Library Gazette.*   New Haven, June, 1928.   Vol. I, no. 1) and in *Ars Typo-
graphica.*   New York.   July, 1926.   Vol. III, no. 1.)
A tribute to the vellum copy in the Vollbehr collection was issued by Mr.
E. Emerson under the title *Incunabulum Incunabulorum,* New York [1928],
in which the owners of twelve known vellum copies are listed as follows:
Dr. Vollbehr, Berlin; Huntington Library, San Marino; Vatican Library,
Rome; Morgan Library, New York; Buch Museum, Leipzig; British Mu-
seum, London; Universitäts-Bibliothek, Göttingen; Bibliothèque Nationale,
Paris; Staats Bibliothek, Berlin; Archiepiscopal Library, London; Landes-
Bibliothek, Fulda; Universitäts-Bibliothek, Leipzig; plus 16 fragments in as
many cities.   [The Vollbehr collection has recently been secured for the
Library of Congress.]
For a list of vellum and paper copies of the Gutenberg Bible see: Seymour
de Ricci, *Catalogue raisonné des premières impressions de Mayence, 1445–
1467.*   Mainz, 1911; which catalogue is also rich in the record of bibliographical material relating to early printing at Mainz.

(18) PRINTING PRESS

Enschedé, C.   Houden Handpersen in de Zestiende Eeuw.   (*In* Tijd-
schrift voor Boek-en Bibliothekwezen.   1906.   IV.)   565

Madan, F.   Early representations of the printing press.   (*In* Bibliographica.   Pt. II, p. 223–248.)   566

With a reproduction of the earliest known engraving of a printing-press, in
an edition of the *Dance of death* printed at Lyons on Feb. 18, '1499.'

(19) PROOF AND PROOF READING

Collijn, I.   Det äldsta danska Korrekturet.   Stockholm, 1917.   567

Facsimile of the earliest known Danish proof sheet, with the reader's corrections in red ink.

———— Bidrag till svensk Bokhistoria. [Uppsala] 1903.   568

Contains an article on a fifteenth century proof sheet.

REICHHART, G.   Alphabetisch geordnetes Verzeichniss der Correctoren der Buchdruckereien des 15. Jahrhunderts. (*In* Zentralblatt für Bibliothekswesen. Beiheft XIV. Beiträge zur Incunabelkunde. V. Leipzig, 1895, p. 1–158.)   569

(20) TYPE

BRITISH MUSEUM (Department of Printed Books)   Catalogue of books printed in the XVth century now in the British Museum.   Facsimiles.   London, 1908–.   570

The facsimiles of specimen types, which are grouped at the end of each volume of the official *Catalogue,* are accompanied in each instance by a " List of facsimiles with references to their sources."

———— Facsimiles from early printed books in the British Museum. [London] 1897.   571

Selected pages from representative specimens of the early printed books of Germany, Italy, France, Holland, and England.

BURGER, K., AND E. VOULLIÉME   Monumenta Germaniae et Italiae typographica.   Deutsche und italienische Inkunabeln in getreuen Nachbildungen.   Berlin, (1892)–1916.   572

For an accompanying volume of notes on printing in Germany and in German-speaking towns, see: Voulliéme, E. *Die deutschen Drucker.* . . Berlin, 1916. 2d ed., 1922.

DUFF, E. G.   Early English printing; a series of facsimiles of all the types used in England during the XVth century, with some of those used in the printing of English books abroad.   London, 1896.   573

DUNN, GEORGE, *ed.*   Photographs.   See Woolley Facsimiles.

GESELLSCHAFT FÜR TYPENKUNDE DES XV. JAHRHUNDERTS   Veröffentlichungen. Halle, 1907–. Vols. 1–.   574

With over 1,300 plates in facsimile, each type being shown not only by a specimen of an actual type-page, but also by a complete alphabet gathered from the original. With a separate type register by V. Madsen. Accompanied by *Mitteilungen der Gesellschaft* and *Beiträge zur Inkunabelkunde,* I–V: Lange, H. O., Eine Merseburger Buchdruckerei um das Jahr 1479; Haebler, K., Der Capotius-Drucker Martin Landsberg; Lange, H. O., Der Drucker Johann Limburg in Münster; Haebler, K., Johann Grüninger der Drucker des Missale mit dem Kanon Peter Schöffers; Haebler, K., Die Merseburger Druckerei von 1479 und ihr Meister.

HAEBLER, K.   Der deutsche Wiegendruck in Original-Typenbeispielen.
München, 1927.   575
With 115 examples.

———— Der italienische Wiegendruck in Original-Typenbeispielen.
München, 1928.   576

———— Typenrepertorium der Wiegendrucke.   Halle, then Leipzig,
1905–1924. 5 pts. in 6 v.   (Sammlung bibliothekswissenschaftlicher
Arbeiten.)   577
The standard work for type description and type identification. Comprises:
Part I. Deutschland und seine Nachbarländer; Part II. Italien, Nederlande,
Frankreich, Spanien, Portugal, England; Part III. Tabellen I, Antiqua
Typen, and Tabellen II, Gotische Typen; Part IV. Ergänzungsband I;
Part V. Ergänzungsband II.

———— West-European Incunabula.   60 original leaves from the
presses of the Netherlands, France, Iberia, and Great Britain.
Munich, 1928.   578
Describing the influence of various printers on one another, and 'cuts of
types' used in different presses. Translated from the German by André
Barbey.

HOLTROP, J. W.   Monuments typographiques des Pays-Bas au quin-
zième siècle. La Haye, 1868.   579
A collection of facsimiles made from originals at the Royal Library at The
Hague and elsewhere.

MORISON, S.   German incunabula in the British Museum. London,
1928.   580
A compilation of 152 facsimiles of books in Gothic letter from fifteenth century presses in Germany, German Switzerland and Austria, selected as
masterpieces of fine printing.

ONGANIA, F.   L'arte della stampa nel rinascimento italiano. Venezia,
1894.   580:a
Both this and Ongania's *Early Venetian printing* contain reference to the
early printing of music.

SCHOLDERER, [J.] V.   Greek printing types, 1465–1927.   Facsimiles
from an exhibition of books illustrating the development of Greek
printing shown in the British Museum, 1927.   With a historical
introduction. London, 1927.   581

THIERRY-POUX, O.   Premiers monuments de l'imprimerie en France
au XVe siècle. Paris, 1890.   582

With 167 facsimiles on 40 plates, and "une liste raisonée des premiers travaux imprimés dans 41 villes ou bourgades de France au XVe siècle."

TYPE FACSIMILE SOCIETY (London)   Publications of the society for the years 1900–1909.   Oxford [1900–1913].   583

Specimens of early printing types reproduced in collotype.   Edited by R. Proctor, with table and indexes by K. Burger.

UPDIKE, D. B.   Printing types: their history, forms, and use.   A study in survivals.   Cambridge, 1922.   2 v.   584

Comprises: I. The invention of printing: The cutting and casting of types in relation to their design.   II. A font of type and its case: The typographical point: Point-set and lining types.   III. The Latin alphabet and its development up to the invention of printing.   IV. Types of the fifteenth century in Germany.   V. . . . in Italy.   VI. . . . in France.   VII. . . . in the Netherlands.   VIII. . . . in Spain.   IX. . . . in England, etc.

VOULLIÉME, E.   Die deutschen Drucker des fünfzehnten Jahrhunderts. Kurzgefasste Einführung in die Monumenta Germaniae et Italiae typographica.   Berlin, 1916.   585

A volume of valuable notes intended to accompany the *Monumenta Germaniae et Italiae typographica*, edited by K. Burger and E. Voulliéme, [1892]–1916, *q.v.*   Second edition, illustrated with facsimiles of specimen types, Berlin, 1922.

WEGENER, J.   Die deutsche oberrheinische Type (M ^{44}) im 15. und 16. Jahrhundert.   Leipzig, 1909.   (Sammlung bibliothekswissenschaftlicher Arbeiten.   26 Heft.   II. serie, 9 Heft.)   586

The '(M ^{44})' refers to the table of M-forms in Haebler's *Typenrepertorium*.

(WOOLLEY FACSIMILES)   Photographs of fifteenth-century types, of the exact size of the originals, designed to supplement published examples, with references to Robert Proctor's *Index* of books in the British Museum and Bodleian Library.   Woolley [Hall, Maidenhead] 1899–[1905].   587

See also above, under: II. Poland; Montenegro; III. Greek Type; Hebrew Printing.

(21) TYPE DESIGNS

CROUS, E.   Die gotischen Schriftarten im Buchdruck.   (*In* Crous, E., and J. Kirchner.   Die gotischen Schriftarten.   Leipzig, 1928, p. 27–25.)   588

A classification of the Gothic handscripts of the Middle Ages, taken over by the early printers.   With seven facsimiles of gothic types in incunabula and the reproduction, on plate 59, of the 101 M-forms from Dr. Haebler's *Typenrepertorium der Wiegendrucke*.

Husung, M. J.   Aus der Zeit des Übergangs von der Handschrift zum Druck.   (*In* Mittelalterliche Handschriften. . . Festgabe zum 60. Geburtstage von Hermann Degering. Leipzig, 1926, p. 155–159.)

589

Johnson, A. F.   The Classification of Gothic types.   (*In* The Library. March 1929. Fourth series, vol. IX, no. 4, p. 357–380.)   590

Relates to foreign and English terms used in differentiating between the varied forms of Gothic types. With facsimiles illustrating the so-called Text Type, Fere-Humanistica, Schwabacher, Wittenberg, Letter, Early Fraktur, and Round Text Type.

Morison, S., *ed.*   Alphabetum.   Facsimile edition of the XVth century treatise on classic letter design printed at Parma by Damianus Moyllus about 1480. Paris, 1927.   591

"This treatise on the proportion of the Roman letters seems to be the earliest of its kind, for it was printed in 1480, and has only recently come to light by the discovery of a single copy at Florence. Moyllus treats of each letter of the alphabet in turn, giving its outline and mathematical proportion." E. P. Goldschmidt.

Olschki, L. S.   Incunables illustrés imitant les manuscrits.   Le passage du manuscrit au livre imprimé. Florence, 1914.   592

(22) TYPE FOUNDING

Consentius, E.   Die Typen der Inkunabelzeit.   Eine Betrachtung. Berlin and Leipzig, 1929.   593

According to its prospectus, this work stands in opposition to the theories of Proctor and Haebler, who have maintained that each early press produced its own types.

Enschedé, C.   Fonderies de caractères et leur matériel dans les Pays-Bas du XVe au XIXe siècle. Haarlem, 1908.   594

Haebler, K.   Handbuch der Inkunabelkunde. Leipzig, 1925. (See p. 61–64.)   595

An essay by Dr. Haebler on *Schriftguss und Schriftenhandel in der Frühdruckzeit* appeared in *Zentralblatt für Bibliothekswesen.* XLI:81.

———— Typefounding and commerce in type during the early years of printing. (*In* Ars Typographica. New York. July, 1926. Vol. III, no. 1, p. 1–35.)   596

From fifty contemporary, documentary sources Dr. Haebler shows that type founding existed as a sub-industry of the printing shop, but probably not as a separate industry before 1500.

KRUITWAGEN, B.   De Incunabeldrukker en Lettersteker Henric Pieters-
soen, die Lettersnider van Rotterdamme (*c.* 1470–1511).   (*In*
Rotterdamsch Jaarboekje 1919.)   597

MORI, G.   The Essence of Gutenberg's invention.   (*In* Ars Typographica.   New York, October, 1925.   Vol. II, no. 2, p. 101–144.)
                                                                  598

An essay which is based upon the results of actual laboratory experimentation in reproducing the earliest fifteenth century types, and which results in a
hypothesis as to the stages of development during the invention of movable
type: wooden models and sand-cast molds; engraved brass punches and
lead casts or matrices; and engraved steel punches and copper matrices.

See also above, under: III. Origin and Invention of Movable Type.

(23) WATERMARKS

BRIQUET, C. M.   . . . Les Filigranes.   Dictionnaire historique des
marques du papier des leur apparition vers 1282 jusqu'en 1600.
Genève, 1907.   4 v.   599

Reprinted at Leipzig in 1924.   With reproductions of 16,112 watermarks,
grouped under the headings: Aigle, Ancre, Armoiries, Balance, Bœuf, Cercle,
Chapeau, Clef, Cloche, Coupe, Couronne, Croissant, Croix, Crosse, Dauphin,
Etoile, Fleur, Fruit, Homme, Hutchet, Lettres, Licorne, Lion, Main, Monts,
Noms, Oiseau, Ours, Pot, Raisin, Roue, Serpent, Sphère, Té, Têtes, Tour;
and accompanied by explanatory texts and indexes.   In 1892, the author
issued an essay entitled: *De la valeur des filigranes du papier comme moyen
de déterminer l'âge et la provenence de documents non datés;* and, in 1910,
*Les filigranes, ont-ils un sens caché?   Une signification mystique ou sym-
bolique?*

HEITZ, P.   Les Filigranes des papiers contenus dans les incunables
strasbourgeois de le Bibliothèque Impériale de Strasbourg.   Strasbourg, 1903.   600

No. 2 in a series of three essays on watermarks, with the cross of Bâle.

See also above, under: III. Papermaking.

FIFTEENTH CENTURY WOODCUTS
SELECTED MONOGRAPHS

CONTENTS

FIFTEENTH CENTURY WOODCUTS, METAL ENGRAVINGS,
ETC.: SELECTED BIBLIOGRAPHIES AND
BIBLIOGRAPHICAL MONOGRAPHS

MONOGRAPHS RELATING TO BOOK ILLUSTRATIONS AND
FIFTEENTH CENTURY ENGRAVING *

BAER, L.   Die illustrierten Historienbücher der 15 Jahrhunderts.
Strassburg, 1903.   601

BLUM, A.   Les Origines du livre à gravures en France.   Paris-Bruxelles,
1928.   602

BUTSCH, A. F.   Die Bücherornamentik der Renaissance.   Eine Auswahl
stylvoller Titeleinfassungen, Initialen, Leisten, Vignetten und Druck-
erzeichen hervorragender italienischer, deutscher u. französischer
Officinen aus der Zeit der Frührenaissance.   Leipzig, 1878–81.   603

Vol. 2 has title: *Die Bücherornamentik der Hoch- und Spatrenaissance.* Re-
issued in 1921, in portfolio, with cover-title: *Bücher-ornamentik der Renaissance, historisch-kritisch.*

COLLIJN, I. [G. A.]   Iconographia Birgittina typographica.   Birgitta
& Katherina i medeltida Bildtryck, med Reproduktioner.   Upsala,
1915–.   604

CONWAY, W. M.   The Woodcutters of the Netherlands in the fifteenth
century.   Cambridge, 1884.   605

Part III lists the books containing woodcuts.

COURBOIN, FR.   La Gravure en France, des origines à 1900.   Paris,
1923.   606

DALBANNE, C., *publisher*   Livres à gravures, imprimés à Lyon au XVe
siècle.   Lyon [1925–26.]   607

I. *La légende dorée.* Matthieu Husz et Pierre Hongre 1483. II. *L'abuzé
en court* [Lyon, *c.* 1484]. *Le doctrinal du temps présent.* [Lyon, *c.* 1484].
(Ed. by E. Droz.) III. *Ponthus et la belle Sidoine.* Lyon, G. Le Roy;

* Listed alphabetically by authors.

Lyon, G. Ortuin. (Ed. by E. Droz.) IV. *Les subtiles fables d'Esope.* Lyon, Matthieu Husz 1486. (Ed. by J. Bastin.)

DUDLEY, L. H., AND OTHERS   Florentine woodcuts. (*In* Harvard Library. Notes. Cambridge, Nov. 1921. VI. p. 123–138.)   608

ESSLING, PRINCE D'   Études sur l'art de la gravure sur bois à Venise. Paris, Florence, 1894–1914.   609

The author's *Livres à figures vénitiens de la fin du XVe siècle et du commencement du XVIe,* in four volumes, was issued in Paris, 1907–1909.

GUSMAN, P.   La Gravure sur bois et d'épargne sur métal, du XIVe au XXe siècle. Paris, 1916.   610

A work entitled *La gravure française au XVIIIe siècle* was issued by this author in [1921].

HEITZ, P.   Der Initialschmuck in den elsässischen Drucken des 15. und 16. Jahrhunderts. Strassburg, 1897.   611

Zweite Reihe. *Zierinitialen in Drucken des Johann Grüninger.* (Strassburg, 1483–1531.)
A work entitled *Strassburger Holzschnitte zu Dietrich von Bern — Herzog Ernst — Der Hürnen Seyfrid — Marcolphus* was edited by Heitz in 1922. For a list of thirty-five books on early wood-engraving edited by Heitz between 1906 and 1920, see the *Abkürzungen* in: Weil, E., *Der Ulmer Holzschnitt im 15. Jahrhundert.* Berlin, 1923.

HIND, A. M.   Catalogue of early Italian engravings preserved in the department of prints and drawings in the British Museum. London, 1900–09.   612

The third edition of the author's *Short history* of engraving was issued at London in 1923, under title: *A History of engraving and etching from the 15th century to 1914.*

JENNINGS, O.   Early woodcut initials; containing over thirteen hundred reproductions of ornamental letters of the fifteenth and sixteenth centuries. London [1908].   613

A brief essay by this author entitled *Some old initial letters* appeared in *The Library,* 1901.

JOHN RYLANDS LIBRARY (Manchester) Woodcuts of the fifteenth century in the John Rylands Library. Manchester, 1915.   614

With introduction and notes by Campbell Dodgson. Contains a facsimile of the St. Christopher of 1423, the earliest woodcut of unquestioned date.

KRISTELLER, [J.] P.   Books with woodcuts printed at Pavia. (*In* Bibliographica. Pt. III. London, 1895, p. 347–372.)   615

———— Early Florentine woodcuts, with an annotated list of Florentine illustrated books. London, 1897. 616

———— Florentinische Zierstücke in Kupferstich aus dem XV. Jahrhundert. Berlin, 1909. 617

His *Florentine book-illustrations of the fifteenth and early sixteenth centuries* appeared in *Bibliographica,* p. 81–111, Part V, and p. 227–256, Part VI.

———— Kupferstich und Holzschnitt in vier Jahrhunderten. Berlin, 1905. 618

———— Die lombardische Graphik der Renaissance. Nebst einem Verzeichnis von Büchern mit Holzschnitten. Berlin, 1913. 619

———— [Preface. In a facsimile of:] Ulrich Boner. Der Edelstein. (Bamberg, 1461) [Berlin, 1908]. (Graphische Gesellschaft. Ausserordentliche Veröffentlichung. I.) 620

A reproduction of the first illustrated book printed with movable metal type. A complete facsimile of the Berlin copy of an undated edition, and six pages from the 1461 dated edition in the Wolfenbüttel library.

———— Die Strassburger Bücher-Illustration im XV. und im Anfange des XVI. Jahrhunderts. Leipzig, 1888. 621

"Verzeichnis der in Strassburg gedruckten illustrierten Bücher," p. 73–155.

LYELL, J. P. R. Early book illustration in Spain. London, 1926. 622

With an introduction by Dr. Haebler. An essay by Lyell, entitled *Notes on early book illustrations in Spain* appeared in *The Library,* 4th series, VI, Oxford, 1925.

MABBOTT, T. O. Seal-prints and a seal-paste-print of the fifteenth century. (Siegeldrucke & Siegelteigdruck) New York, 1928. 623

Reprinted from the *Bulletin of the New York Public Library* of August, 1928.

MACFARLANE, J. Antoine Vérard. London, 1900. (Bibliographical Society. Illustrated Monographs. VII.) 624

MARINIS, T. DE Catalogue d'une collection d'anciens livres à figures italiens, appartenant à T. de Marinis. Milano, [1925]. 625

With preface by Seymour de Ricci.

MONCEAUX, H. Les Le Rouge de Chablis, calligraphes et miniaturistes, graveurs et imprimeurs: étude sur les débuts de l'illustration du livre au XVe siècle. Paris, 1896. 2 v. 626

MORRIS, W.   On the artistic qualities of the woodcut books of Ulm and Augsburg in the fifteenth century.   (*In* Bibliographica.   Part IV, p. 437–454.)   627

Extracts from this appeared in the preface to S. C. Cockerell's essay on *Some German woodcuts of the fifteenth century.*   London, 1897.

MUTHER, R.   Die deutsche Bücherillustration der Gothik und Früh-renaissance (1460–1530).   München and Leipzig, 1884.   628

OLSCHKI, L. S.   Le Livre illustré au XVe siècle.   Florence, 1926.   629

Germany is represented by 73 incunabula (in 123 facsimiles); England by 10 (13); Spain, 10 (13); France, 33 (45); Italy, 87 (134); the Low Countries, 12 (16).

The author's *Incunables illustrés imitant les manuscrits; le passage du manuscrit au livre imprimé,* Florence, 1914, will be found of interest, and also various catalogues issued by the firm of Olschki, booksellers, Florence.

PERRINS, C. W. D. (Collection of)   Italian book-illustrations and early printing.   A catalogue of early Italian books in the library of C. W. Dyson Perrins.   Oxford, 1914.   630

Edited by A. W. Pollard.

PIERPONT MORGAN LIBRARY (New York)   Catalogue of manuscripts and early printed books from the libraries of William Morris, Richard Bennett, Bertram, Fourth Earl of Ashburnham, and other sources now forming a portion of the library of J. Pierpont Morgan.   London, 1906–07.   631

Four vols., of which three relate to early printing, the English incunabula being catalogued by E. Gordon Duff; Horæ by A. W. Pollard; French and Italian incunabula by A. W. Pollard and R. Proctor jointly; German illustrated books by R. Proctor; incunabula of Germany and the Low Countries by S. Aldrich; manuscripts by M. R. James.   General editor, A. W. Pollard. With illustrations which "show the character of the types and woodcuts used in all the chief printing centres of Europe, while the text recites the contents and describes the make-up of some of the chief masterpieces of the press."

POLLARD, A. W.   Early illustrated books.   A history of the decoration and illustration of books in the 15th and 16th centuries.   3d ed. New York, 1927.   632

First ed., 1893; 2d ed., revised and corrected, 1917.

——— Fine Books.   New York and London, 1912.   633

Early German and Dutch illustrated books, p. 100–122; Early Italian illustrated books, p. 123–142; Early French and Spanish illustrated books, p. 143–164; English woodcut illustrations, p. 250–256; Engraved illustrations, p. 268–273; Selected bibliography, p. 314–315.

———— Italian book illustrations, chiefly of the fifteenth century. London, 1894. (The Portfolio monographs on artistic subjects. XII.)
634

An essay on *The woodcut designs for illumination in Venetian books, 1469–73* by Mr. Pollard appeared in *Bibliographica*, p. 122–128 of Part IX.

———— Old picture books, with other essays on bookish subjects. London, 1902.
635

Contains: Old picture books; Florentine rappresentazioni and their pictures; The transference of woodcuts in the fifteenth and sixteenth centuries; Es tu scholaris?; Printers' marks of the fifteenth and sixteenth centuries; etc.

———— Some notes on English illustrated books. (*In* Bibliographical Society. Transactions, 1900. VI, p. 29–61.)
636

———— The transference of woodcuts in the fifteenth and sixteenth centuries. (*In* Bibliographica. Part VIII, p. 343–368.)
637

Also in his *Old picture books, with other essays on bookish subjects*. London, 1902.

RATH, E. VON   Die Kupferstichillustration im Wiegendruckzeitalter. (Archiv für Buchgewerbe. 1927.)
638

REDGRAVE, G. R.   Erhard Ratdolt and his work at Venice. London, 1899. (Bibliographical Society. Illustrated Monographs. I.) 639

The first issue, 1894, and its supplement of 1895 are included in this edition.

RENOUVIER, J.   Des gravures sur bois dans les livres de Simon Vostre. Paris, 1862.
640

RIBEIRO, A.   As primeiras gravuras em livros portuguêses. (*In* Anais das Bibliotecas e Arquivos. 1921. Series II, Vol. 2, p. 284–291.)
641

RONDOT, [C. F.] N.   Les Graveurs sur bois et les imprimeurs à Lyon au XVe siècle. (*In* Revue du Lyonnais. Lyons, 1895. Mai-déc. 1895. 5. sér., XIX.)
642

Separately issued, Lyon-Paris, 1896. An essay by this author entitled *La Gravure sur bois à Lyon au XVe siècle* was printed as p. 46–59, in *Bibliographica*, Part IX.

SAYLE, C.   Initial letters in early English printed books. (*In* Bibliographical Society. Transactions, 1905, p. 15–47.)
643

SCHRAMM, A.   Bilderschmuck der Frühdrucke. Leipzig, 1920–.   644

A pictorial encyclopedia of all the known book illustrations of the fifteenth century; to comprise twenty-eight volumes. According to its prospectus: The aim of the present publication is to provide the whole of fifteenth century book illustrations reproduced in black and white in the full size of the originals. The work when completed will consist of 28 large folio volumes, of which some 15 will embrace all the known book illustrations contained in German incunabula, while 5 further volumes will be devoted to the Italian fifteenth century book illustrations and as many may be required to represent those of the other European countries. The general arrangement thus being by countries, the single volumes will contain the presses of the several towns in chronological order of their coming into existence, beginning with the Bamberg press of Albrecht Pfister as being the first fifteenth century printer to use illustrations in his books. The whole series will be concluded by two index volumes of which one will register the entire fifteenth century book production from the iconographical point of view."

The ten volumes published prior to 1928 comprise reproductions of the book illustrations used by Albrecht Pfister, Bamberg (305 illustrations); Günther Zainer, Augsburg (754); Johann Bämler, Augsburg (781); Anton Sorg, Augsburg (3,096); Johann Zainer, Ulm (501); Konrad Dinckmut, Ulm (682); Lienhart Holle, Johannes Reger, Johann Schaeffler and Hans Hauser, Ulm (407); the Cologne press (956); the presses at Esslingen, Urach, Blaubeuren, Stuttgart, Reutlingen, and Tübingen; the printers of Lübeck (Pt. 1, the Brandis brothers.) With bibliographical footnotes.

SCHREIBER, W. L.   Un Catalogue des incunables à figures imprimés en Allemagne, en Suisse, en Autriche-Hongrie, et en Scandinavie, avec des notes critiques et bibliographiques. Leipzig, 1910–11. (*In his* Manuel de l'amateur de la gravure sur bois et sur métal au XVe siècle. V.)   645

———— Manuel de l'amateur de la gravure . . . XVe siècle. Berlin, 1891–1911. 8 v. in 9.   646

German edition, Leipzig, 1926–, under the title: *Handbuch der Holz- und Metallschnitte des XV. Jahrhunderts.* The contents of these invaluable volumes, which relate to woodcuts, block-books and illustrated incunabula, are listed on Library of Congress card no. 1-F-2363-Additions. Numerous important works have been issued by Dr. Schreiber on fifteenth century prints, engravings, block-books, etc.

SCHRETLEN, M. J.   Dutch and Flemish woodcuts of the fifteenth century. London, 1925.   647

According to its prospectus, all the block-books and all the Dutch and Flemish incunabula are here passed in review, and the pictures reproduced are carefully selected with a view to giving a complete idea of the work of every master. With a foreword by M. J. Friedlaender.

TRONNIER, [H. E.] A.   Die Lübecker Buchillustration des fünfzehnten Jahrhunderts. Strassburg, 1904.   648

WEIL, E.   Der Ulmer Holzschnitt im 15. Jahrhundert. Berlin, 1923.
                                                                    649

With well illustrated text and a supplementary section containing a *Katalog der Ulmer Holzschnittbücher des 15. Jahrhunderts; Zusammenstellung der Kalender-Drucke; Verzeichnis der anderen behandelten Druck*e (Kartenspiele, Einblattholzschnitte, Kupferstiche, Blockbücher, Inkunabeln); and *Abkürzengen,* a valuable record of books on wood engraving, many of which are not noted in the present list.

See also above, under Incunabula: II. Books of Hours, etc.; Medicine (Anatomy); Miscellaneous Subjects (Rappresentazioni, Sermon-Books, etc.); III. Color Printing; Printers' Marks.   Other titles relating to book illustration, single prints, etc., will be found in: Pollard, A. W., *Fine books.* London, 1913, on p. 314–315; in: Peddie, R. A., *Fifteenth-century books.* London, 1913, p. 28–34; and in: Weil, E., *Der Ulmer Holzschnitt.* Berlin, 1923, p. 144–146.   A general survey of the subject is given in: Weitenkampf, F., *Illustrated books of the past four centuries.* Bulletin of the New York Public Library, November, 1920.

Excepting for a brief note above, under Notes and Definitions, the subject of block-books is not treated in the present volume.   Lists of reference books, however, will be found on p. 311 and p. 27–28 of the two books noted above, by Pollard and Peddie, and an essay on block-books comprises Chapter II of *Fine books.*

For the *attributes* by which saints may be recognized, see: Drake, M. and W., *Saints and their emblems.*   London, 1916; Bles, A. de., *How to distinguish the saints in art by their costumes, symbols, and attributes.*   New York, 1925; and Vol. 7 of the forthcoming reprint of W. L. Schrieber's *Manuel,* under title: *Handbuch der Holz- und Metallschnitte des XV. Jahrhunderts.*

AMERICANA:

SELECTED BIBLIOGRAPHIES AND MONOGRAPH

CONTENTS

AMERICANA: SELECTED BIBLIOGRAPHIES
AND BIBLIOGRAPHICAL MONOGRAPHS †

I. GENERAL WORKS ‡

* SABIN, J. (Continued after 1881 by Wilberforce Eames) A Dictionary of books relating to America, from its discovery to the present time. New York, 1868–.   650

Vols. I–XX, parts I–CXX, in 1928. An alphabetical author list comprising 84,187 titles, A — Seba Smith, within its first twenty volumes, many of which, beginning with 'Pennsylvania,' have Mr. Eames's annotations. A statement in vol. XX, by Mr. H. M. Lydenberg, chairman of the present publication committee under the Bibliographical Society of America, tells of Mr. Eames's assumption of the work after Mr. Sabin's death, of the two periods when publication came to a standstill, and of the effort and encouragement given to its continuance since 1924.

* CHURCH, E. D. (*Collection of*) A Catalogue of books relating to the discovery and early history of North and South America. New York, 1907. 5 v.   651

Compiled and annotated by George Watson Cole; and listing 1,293 titles printed before 1801. In five volumes arranged chronologically, 1482–1884; with facsimile pages. The Church collection has now been assimilated by the Henry E. Huntington Library, San Marino, California.

JOHN CARTER BROWN LIBRARY (Providence) Bibliotheca Americana. Catalogue of the John Carter Brown Library in Brown University, Providence, Rhode Island. Providence, 1919–[to date]. [2 v.]
                                              652

The first two volumes, 1919 and 1922, arranged chronologically, carry the titles through the year 1658. A third volume is in process of compilation. The original catalogue of the Library, also entitled *Bibliotheca Americana,* was issued in two editions, 1865–1871 and 1875–1882 respectively.

---

† For works of a general nature in which occasional reference to Americana may be found, see the final section, nos. 1264–1276. For Evans' *American Bibliography* see: British Possessions, Colonial Publications, no. 975, and the United States, no. 1074.

‡ That is, relating to Americana in general.

The asterisk (*) indicates that, in the reference works thus checked, annotations will be found giving the location of copies of the original editions recorded therein.

II. Period of Discovery and Early Exploration

A. *In General*

* [Harrisse, H.]   Bibliotheca Americana Vetustissima.   A description of works relating to America, published between the years 1492 and 1551.   New York, 1866.   653

Comprises 304 titles arranged chronologically.

* —————— Bibliotheca Americana Vetustissima. . . Additions.   Paris, 1872.   654

"Not a continuation of the B. A. V. but a series of notes and additions intended to aid towards forming a complete list of works relating to the discovery, history and geography of America, printed previous to the year 1551." *Introduction.*

—————— The Discovery of North America, a critical, documentary, and historic investigation, with an essay on the early cartography of the New World. . . London, Paris, 1892.   655

To which are added a chronology of one hundred voyages westward, projected, attempted, or accomplished between 1431 and 1504, biographical accounts of the three hundred pilots who first crossed the Atlantic, etc.

B. *Pre-Columbian Period*

Lucas, F. W.   The Annals of the voyages of the brothers Nicolò and Antonio Zeno in the North Atlantic about the end of the fourteenth century, and the claim founded thereon to a Venetian discovery of America.   London, 1898.   656

Critically reviewed in *The Nation,* January 26, 1899.

Nordenskiöld, A. E.   Om bröderna Zenos resor och de äldsta kartor öfver norden.   Stockholm, 1883.   657

Stevens, H.   Historical and geographical notes on the earliest discoveries in America, 1453–1530.   New Haven, 1869.   658

See also below, under: Cartography and Geography.   Pre-Columbian Period, nos. 748–754.

The asterisk (*) indicates that, in the reference works thus checked, annotations will be found giving the location of copies of the original editions recorded therein.

C. *Period of Discovery*

(1) COLUMBUS

COLUMBUS, C. [Letter of Columbus. Barcelona, 1493. From the original in the New York Public Library.] (Massachusetts Historical Society. [Photostat facsimile,] no. 3, 1919.) 659

Facsimile of the unique copy of the first edition. Also reproduced in facsimile by J. Maisonneuve, Paris, 1889.

COMMISSIONE COLOMBIANA Raccolta di documenti e studi pubblicati dalla R. Commissione Colombiana pel quarto centenario dalla scoperta dell' America. Roma, 1892–94. 6 pts. in 14 v. 660

Parte VI, 1. Bibliografia degli scritti italiani o stampati in Italia sopra Cristoforo Colombo, la scoperta del Nuovo Mondo e i viaggi degli italiani in America. Compilata da G. Fumigalli con la collaborazione di P. Amat di S. Filippo.

* EAMES, W. Columbus' letter on the discovery of America (1493–1497). (*In* New York Public Library. Two important gifts to the New York Public Library by Mr. George F. Baker, Jr. New York, 1924, p. 4–8.) 661

With a list of the seventeen known editions.

———— The Letter of Columbus on the discovery of America. A facsimile of the pictorial edition, with a complete reprint of the oldest four editions in Latin. Printed by order of the Trustees of the Lenox Library. New York, 1892. 662

FUMAGALLI, G., AND P. AMAT DI S. FILIPPO Bibliografia degli scritti italiani o stampa in Italia sopra Cristoforo Colombo, la scoperta del nuovo mondo e i viaggi degli italiani in America. Rome, 1893. (*In* Commissione Colombiana. Raccolta di documenti e studi. Roma, 1893. Parte VI, Vol. I.) 663

The bibliography comprises sections relating to: Precursori di Colombo; Cristoforo Colombo (biographies, etc.); Testimonianze antichissime dell' opera di Colombo, 1493–1550; Edizioni posteriori al 1550.

HAEBLER, K. Sur quelques incunables espagnols relatifs à Christophe Colomb. (*In* Le Bibliographe moderne. III. 1899, p. 365–386.) 664

Separately issued at Besançon in 1900.

The asterisk (*) indicates that, in the reference works thus checked, annotations will be found giving the location of copies of the original editions recorded therein.

[HARRISSE, H.] . . . Christophe Colomb et les académiciens espagnols. Paris, 1894. 665

Contains a list of the editions of the Columbus letter, with the location of copies as known at the date of publication, and notes on the various facsimiles and reprints of each edition.

———— Qui a imprimé la première lettre de Christophe Colomb? Extrait du *Zentralblatt für Bibliothekswesen*. 1892. Leipzig, 1892. 666

*———— Un rarissime Americanum. Paris, 1897. 667

Relates to the *Sermon* of Bishop Carvajal, containing one of the first references to the New World. Reprinted from *Bulletin du bibliophile,* Feb. 15, 1897.

THACHER, J. B. Christopher Columbus. His life, his work, his remains, as revealed by original printed and manuscript records. Together with an essay on Peter Martyr of Anghera and Bartolomé de Las Casas, the first historians of America. New York and London, 1903–1904. (Collector's edition. 3 v. bound in 6 pts., with folder of facsimiles.) 668

Accompanied by facsimiles of *The Spanish Quarto Letter of Columbus* giving an account of the first voyage; *The Syllacius* giving the first published account of the second voyage; *The Libretto* giving the first published account of the third voyage; *The Lettera* giving the first published account of the fourth voyage.

An essay entitled *The Islands beyond the Ganges* by Z. Haraszti, with excerpts from the Haynes translation of Columbus' letter to Gabriel Sanchez, and a facsimile of the first page of the Columbus letter printed at Rome in May, 1493, appeared in: Boston Public Library. *More books.* May, 1929.

For editions of the *Narrenschiff* of Sebastian Brant, containing contemporary reference to the discovery of the New World, see: A. Blum, *La Nef des folles de Josse Bade* (In *Byblis.* V. 1926, p. 13–17); G. R. Redgrave, *Illustrated books of Sebastian Brandt* (In *Bibliographica.* V, p. 47–60) and *Some illustrated sermon-books* (In *The Library.* 1916, p. 44–52); P. Renouard, *Bibliographie des impressions de Jodocus Badius Ascensius.* Paris, 1909; and the critical survey in F. Zarncke's *Sebastian Brants Narrenschiff.* Leipzig, 1854. A facsimile of the 1494 edition in German was issued by the Gesellschaft der Bibliophilen, Weimar, 1913; and another edited by Franz Schultz during the same year. The English translation of Alexander Barclay was issued at Edinburgh and New York (Appleton), in 1874.

(2) LINE OF DEMARCATION

*GOTTSCHALK, P. The earliest diplomatic documents on America. The Papal Bulls of 1493 and the Treaty of Tordesillas reproduced and translated. Berlin, 1927. 669

The asterisk (*) indicates that, in the reference works thus checked, annotations will be found giving the location of copies of the original editions recorded therein.

With facsimiles of the three known copies of the edition of the Bull of May 4, 1493, believed to have been printed at Logrono at about the year 1512; of the only known copy of the other edition of the same Bull from an unidentified press of possibly the same date; and of the only known printed copy of the Bull of September 26, 1493, assigned to Toledo in 1530. Reviewed by L. C. Wroth under title *Early Papal Bulls on America,* in: The New York Herald Tribune. *Books* (Notes for bibliophiles), Sunday, June 24, 1928.

[HARRISSE, H.] The diplomatic history of America. Its first chapter, 1492–1493–1494. London, 1897. 670

THACHER, J. B. [The Papal Bulls.] The Vatican register. Text of the Treaty of Tordesillas. The line of Demarcation. (*In his* Christopher Columbus. His life, his work, his remains. New York and London, 1903–1904. Vol. II, p. 93–209.) 671

(3) VESPUCCIUS

FISCHER, J., AND F. VON WIESER The Cosmographiæ introductio of Martin Waldseemüller in facsimile. Followed by the four voyages of Amerigo Vespucci, with their translation into English; to which are added Waldseemüller's two world maps of 1507. With an introduction. New York, 1907. (United States Catholic Historical Society. Monograph IV.) 672

HUGUES, L. Amerigo Vespucci, Giovanni Verrazzano, Juan Bautista Genovese. Notizie sommarie. (*In* Commissione Colombiana. Raccolta di documenti e studi. Roma, 1892–94. Parte V, 2.) 673

[LIVINGSTON, L. S., *ed.*] The first four voyages of Americus Vespucius. A reprint in exact facsimile of the German edition printed at Strassburg, by John Grüninger in 1509. New York, 1902. 674

* PROCTOR, R. Jan van Doesborgh, printer at Antwerp. An essay in bibliography. London, 1894. (Bibliographical Society.) 675

Describes the unique copy, at the John Carter Brown Library, of the Dutch version of the letter of Vespuccius to Lorenzo de' Medici recounting and giving the date of his third voyage.

[QUARITCH, B., *ed.*] The first four voyages of Amerigo Vespucci. Reproduced in facsimile with translations. . . London, 1893. 676

With a facsimile of the Florentine edition assigned to 1505 or 1506.

SARNOW, E., AND K. TRÜBENBACH, *ed.* Mundus Novus. Ein Bericht Amerigo Vespucci's an Lorenzo de Medici über seine Reise nach

The asterisk (*) indicates that, in the reference works thus checked, annotations will be found giving the location of copies of the original editions recorded therein.

Brasilien in den Jahren 1501/02. Nach einem Exemplare der zu Rostock von Hermann Barckhusen gedruckten Folioausgabe, im Besitze der Stadtbibliothek zu Frankfurt a.M. In Faksimile. Strassburg, 1903. 677

VARNHAGEN, F. A. DE Amerígo Vespucci, son caractère, ses écrits (même les moins authentiques), sa vie et ses navigations, avec une carte indiquant les routes. Lima, 1865. 678

This study was followed by the publication of his: Ainda Amerigo Vespucci. Novos estudos . . . especialmente em favor da interpretaçao dada á sua 1ª viagem, em 1497–98, ás costas do Yucatan e Golfo Mexicano. Vienna, 1874.

VIGNAUD, [J.] H. Americ Vespuce, l'attribution de son nom au Nouveau Monde. . . [Paris] 1912. (Extrait du Journal de la Société des Americanistes de Paris. Nouv. ser. IX. 1912.) 679

WIESER, FR. V., ed. Die Cosmographiae Introductio des Martin Waldseemüller (Ilacomilus). In faksimiledruck. Strassburg, 1907. 680

See also below, under: Cartography. Waldseemüller, nos. 778–779.

(4) CABOT

BELLEMO, V. Giovanni Caboto. Note critiche. (*In* Commissione Colombiana. Raccolta di documenti e studi. Roma, 1892–94. Parte V., 2.) 681

HARRISSE, H. John Cabot the discoverer of North-America and Sebastian his son. A chapter of the maritime history of England under the Tudors 1496–1557. London, 1896. 682

With a list of 'Contemporary historians,' p. 461–469.

[————] Sébastien Cabot navigateur vénitien (1497–1557). Étude d'histoire critique et documentaire. Paris, 1895. 683

MEDINA, J. T. El veneciano Sebastián Caboto al servicio de España y especialmente de su proyectado viaje á las Molucas por el Estrecho de Magallanes y al reconocimiento de la costa del continente hasta la gobernación de Pedrarias Dávila. Santiago de Chile, 1908. 684

'Bibliografia Hispano-Cabotiana,' Vol. I, p. 551–574, comprises a list of works published between 1516 and 1763.

WINSHIP, G. P. Cabot bibliography. With an introductory essay on the careers of the Cabots based upon an independent examination of the sources of information. London, 1900. 685

———— Some facts about John and Sebastian Cabot. From the *Proceedings* of the American Antiquarian Society. . . . April 25, 1900. Worcester, 1900.   686

D. *Period of Early Exploration*

A) IN GENERAL

*ATKINSON, G.   La Littérature geographique française de la Renaissance.   Répertoire bibliographique.   (Avec 300 reproductions photographiques.)   Paris, 1927.   687

A list of 524 works printed in French before 1610, with a note under each title stating the countries visited during the voyage described.

FERNANDEZ DE NAVARRETE, M.   Coleccion de los viajes y descubrimientos.   Madrid, 1825–37.   5 v.   688

FUMAGALLI, G., AND P. AMAT DI S. FILIPPO   Bibliografia Italo-Americana della geografia di America.   (*In* Commissione Colombiana. Raccolta di documenti e studi.   Roma, 1892–93.   Parte VI, p. 113–217.)   689

Comprises Opere originali di autori italiani, e traduzioni italiane di opere straniere sulla geografia americana; Viaggiatori italiani in America; Bibliografia alfabetica dei singoli viaggiatori, etc.

HAKLUYT SOCIETY (London)   Works issued by the Hakluyt Society. London, 1847 [to date].   690

Series I. Vols. 1–100, 1847–1899. Extra series, Hakluyt's *Principal Navigations* and *Purchas his Pilgrimes*, 32 vols., 1903–1906. Series II. Vols. 1–[61], 1899–[1927]. The hundred and sixty odd volumes, so far issued, comprise reprints and works relating to Columbus, Raleigh, Drake, Hawkins, De Soto, Benzoni Champlain, Hudson, Cieza de Leon, Cortes, Garcilaso de la Vega, Xeres, Zeno, Magellan, Frobisher, Acosta, Schmidt, Cabot, Corte Real, etc. (For the contents of the first and second series, to 1923, see: Library of Congress, card no. 6–6987.) Valuable introductions and notes invariably accompany each reprint. An address by Sir Clements Markham on *Richard Hakluyt: his life and work. With a short account of the aims and achievements of the Hakluyt Society* was issued in London in 1896.

HARRISSE, H.   . . . Travaux nautiques des Portugais.   Paris, 1898.
                                                                      691

A review of Sousa Viterbo's *Trabalhos nauticos dos Portuguezes nos seculos XVI e XVII*. Parte I. Lisbôa, 1898.

The asterisk (*) indicates that, in the reference works thus checked, annotations will be found giving the location of copies of the original editions recorded therein.

LINSCHOTEN-VEREENIGING (The Hague) Werken uitgegeven door de Linschoten-Vereeniging. s' Gravenhage, 1909 [to date].   692

Relates for the most part to voyages of the sixteenth and seventeenth centuries. Each volume contains a list of the Society's publications up to the date of its printing, the volume for 1928 being no. 30.

SOUSA VITERBO, F., *Marques de* Trabalhos nauticos dos Portuguezes nos seculos XVI e XVII. Lisbôa, 1898–1900. 2 v. (Academia Real das Sciencias.)   693

Part I, reviewed by Henri Harrisse in *Travaux nautiques des Portugais.* Paris, 1898.

THOMAS, H. English translations of Portuguese books before 1640. (*In* The Library. Fourth Series. Vol. VII. No. 1. June 1926, p. 1–30.)   694

With references to Hakluyt, Eden, Purchas, etc.

TIELE, P. A. Mémoire bibliographique sur les journaux des navigateurs néerlandais réimprimés dans les collections de De Bry et de Hulsius et dans les collections hollandaises du XVIIe siècle. Amsterdam, 1867.   695

———— Nederlandsche bibliographie van land- en volkenkunde. Amsterdam, 1884.   696

WINSHIP, G. P. Sailors' narratives of voyages along the New England coast 1524–1624. Boston, 1905.   697

With a brief bibliographical note introducing each narrative.

B) EARLY VOYAGERS AND EXPLORERS

(1) CARTIER

BIGGAR, H. P., *ed.* The Voyages of Jacques Cartier published from the originals with translations, notes and appendices. Ottawa, 1924. (Canada. Public archives. Publications. II.)   698

(2) CHAMPLAIN

BIGGAR, H. P., *ed.,* The Works of Samuel de Champlain in six volumes. Reprinted, translated and annotated by six Canadian scholars. Toronto, 1922–. (The Champlain Society.)   699

Vol. I, 1599–1607, appeared in 1922 with a portfolio of plates and maps; Vol. II, 1608–1613, in 1925.

* Gagnon, P.   Notes bibliographiques sur les écrits de Champlain, manuscrits et imprimés.   (*In* Société de Géographie de Québec. Bulletin, juillet, 1908.   À Champlain 1608–1908.   [Québec, 1908,] p. 55–77.)   700

"L'oeuvre littéraire et historique de Champlain, se compose surtout de cinq relations de voyage, dont quatre concernant notre pays, furent imprimées en 1603, 1613, 1619 et 1632," p. 55.

(3) DRAKE

Wagner, H. R.   Sir Francis Drake's voyage around the world.   Its aims and achievements.   San Francisco, 1926.   701

Reviewed by L. C. Wroth in: The New York Herald Tribune.   *Books.* Sunday, Feb. 13 and 20, 1927.

(4) HUDSON

Murphy, H. C.   Bibliographical description of the various printed Dutch records concerning Hudson.   (*In his* Henry Hudson in Holland.   Reprinted . . . by Wouter Nijhoff.   The Hague, 1909, p. 77–100.)   702

Describes the various contemporary editions and maps published by Van Meteren Gerritsz, and De Laet.

Paltsits, V. H.   Hudson, 1609.   [Reference list.]   (*In* Stokes, I. N. Phelps, Iconography of Manhattan Island.   New York, 1915–1928. Vol. VI, p. 255–256.)   702 :a

(5) LAUDONNIÈRE

Gaffarel, P. L. J.   Histoire de la Floride française.   Paris, 1875.
                                                                                                          703

With bibliographical introduction and a partial reprint of Laudonnière's letters, following the edition of 1586.

(6) MAGELLAN

Da Mosto, A.   Il primo viaggio intorno al globo di Antonio Pigafetta. (*In* Commissione Colombiana.   Raccolta di documenti e studi.   Roma, 1892–94.   Parte V, 3.)   704

The asterisk (*) indicates that, in the reference works thus checked, annotations will be found giving the location of copies of the original editions recorded therein.

ROBERTSON, J. A.   Printed books.   (*In his* Magellan's voyage around the world by Antonio Pigafetta.   Cleveland, 1906.   Vol. II, p. 272–304.)   704 :a

(7) NUÑEZ DE BALBOA

GAFFAREL, P. L. J.   Nuñez de Balboa, la première traversée de *l'isthme* américain.   Paris, 1882.   705

Re-issued in 1895.

(8) PIZARRO

POGO, A.   The anonymous *La conquista del Peru* (Seville, April 1534) and the *Libro vltimo del Svmmario delle Indie Occidentali* (Venice, October 1534).   (*In* American Academy of Arts and Sciences.   Proceedings [July, 1930].)   706

An exhaustive study of the textual relation of the two works named in the title, together with an introduction and a bibliography of the works connected with them — chiefly by Oviedo, Xeres, and Estete, dating from 1526 to 1929.

A critical review by Dr. Pogo, of a reproduction of the first work named, appeared in *Isis,* May 1930, p. 244–250.

(9) RALEIGH

BRUSHFIELD, T. N.   A Bibliography of Sir Walter Ralegh, Knt.   2d ed.   Exeter, 1908.   707

[EAMES, W.]   A Bibliography of Sir Walter Raleigh.   New York, 1886.   707 :a

Thirty-four copies reprinted from Sabin's *Dictionary,* Vol. XVI.

(10) RIBAULT

GRAVIER, G.   Deuxième voyage du Dieppois Jean Ribaut à la Floride en 1565.   Relation de N. Le Challeux.   Précédeé d'une notice historique et bibliographique.   Rouen, 1872.   (Société Rouennaise de Bibliophiles.   IV.)   708

(11) SMITH

ARBER, E., *ed.*   Travels and works of Captain John Smith, President of Virginia, and Admiral of New England, 1580–1631. . . . A new edition, with a biographical and critical introduction, by A. G. Bradley.   Edinburgh, 1910.   2 v.   709

The asterisk (*) indicates that, in the reference works thus checked, annotations will be found giving the location of copies of the original editions recorded therein.

* EAMES, W. A Bibliography of Captain John Smith. New York, 1927. 710

Reprinted from Sabin's *Dictionary*, Vol. XX.

[LIVINGSTON, L. S.] Captain John Smith's circular or prospectus of his Generall Historie of Virginia, New-England, and the Summer Isles. Reproduced from the only known copy in the collection of the Society of Antiquaries, London. With notes. Cambridge, 1914. 711

Relates to the prospectus sent out late in 1623.

(12) SOTO

RYE, W. B., *ed.* The Discovery and conquest of terra Florida of Don Ferdinando De Soto and six hundred Spaniards, his followers, written by a gentleman of Elvas. . . Reprinted from the edition of 1611. Edited with notes and an introduction. (Hakluyt Society. Publications. London, 1851.) 712

With a map indicating Soto's route to the Mississippi River. A translation, following one by Buckingham Smith, 1866, was issued with introduction by T. H. Lewis, in: Jameson, J. F., *ed. Spanish explorers . . . 1528–1543.* New York, 1907.

(13) VERRAZZANO

BACCHIANI, A. Giovanni da Verrazzano and his discoveries in North America, 1524, according to the unpublished contemporaneous Cèllere Codex of Rome, Italy. English version and introduction by Edward Hagaman Hall. (*In* American Scenic and Historic Preservation Society. Fifteenth Annual Report. 1910, p. 135–226.) 713

With a summary of the long controversy over Verrazzano's claims, brought to an end in 1909 by the discovery of the Cèllere Codex which, in the words of Mr. V. H. Paltsits, "establishes beyond peradventure the genuineness of Verrazzano's letter and the certainty of his discovery of New York harbor in 1524." The Codex (now in the J. Pierpont Morgan Library) is given in facsimile, with an introduction, in Mr. I. N. Phelps Stokes's *Iconography of Manhattan Island,* Vol. 2.

HUGUES, L. Amerigo Vespucci, Giovanni Verrazzano, Juan Bautista Genovese. Notizie sommarie. (*In* Commissione Columbiana. Raccolta di documenti e studi. Roma, 1892–94. Parte V., 2.) 714

The asterisk (*) indicates that, in the reference works thus checked, annotations will be found giving the location of copies of the original editions recorded therein.

PALTSITS, V. H. Verrazzano, 1524. [Reference list.] (*In* Stokes, I. N. Phelps. Iconography of Manhattan Island. New York, 1915–1928. Vol. VI, p. 254.) 715

For Columbus, Vespuccius, and Cabot, see above, under: Period of Discovery, nos. 659–668, 672–686.

E. *Collected Narratives of Voyages*

(1) DE BRY

CAMUS, A. G. Mémoire sur la collection des grands et petits voyages, et sur la collection des voyages de Melchisedech Thévenot. Paris, 1802. 716

* [COLE, G. W.] De Bry's collection of "Great and Small Voyages." (*In* Church, E. D., Collection of. A catalogue of books relating to . . . America. New York, 1907. Vol. I, p. 316–478; Vol. II, p. 478a–580.) 717

CRAWFORD, J. L. L., *Twenty-sixth Earl of.* . . . Grands et petits voyages of De Bry. London, 1884. 718

(Bibliotheca Lindesiana. Collations and notes. No. 3.)

HUTH, H. A Description and collation of the series of "De Bry's Voyages" contained in the library of Mr. Henry Huth. [London] 1880. 719

STEVENS, H. N. The De Bry collector's painefull peregrination along the pleasant pathway to perfection. (*In* Bibliographical essays. A tribute to Wilberforce Eames. June, MCMXXIV. [Cambridge, Mass.] 1924, p. [269]–276.) 720

(2) EDEN

ARBER, E., *ed.* The first three English books on America [?1511]–1555 A.D., being chiefly translations, compilations, &c, by Richard Eden. Westminster, 1895. 721

First issued at Birmingham in 1885. Eden's three works comprise translations, etc., from the writings of Peter Martyr, Münster, and Sebastian Cabot, with extracts from the works of other Spanish, Italian and German writers of the time.

The asterisk (*) indicates that, in the reference works thus checked, annotations will be found giving the location of copies of the original editions recorded therein.

(3) FRACAN DA MONTALBODDO

JOHN CARTER BROWN LIBRARY (Providence) Fracan, 1507, 1508, etc. (*In* John Carter Brown Library. Bibliotheca Americana. Catalogue. . . Providence, 1919. Vol. I.) 722

Editions of Fracan's *Paesi Nouamente retrouati* are also listed in Harrisse's *Bibliotheca Americana Vetustissima* and in Sabin's *Dictionary,* under Montalboddo.

SHUMWAY, D. B. Ghetelens Nye unbekande Lande. (Separatabdruck aus dem Jahrbuch des Vereins für nieder-deutsche Sprachforschung. Jahrgang 1907. Leipzig. XXXIII, p. 53–72.) 723

Discusses the unique copy in the John Carter Brown Library of the translation into Low-German, 1508, of Fracan's *Paesi nouamente retrouati.*

(4) HAKLUYT

GOLDSMID, E., *ed.* The principal navigations, voyages, traffiques, and discoveries of the English nation. Collected by Richard Hakluyt, preacher, and edited by Edmund Goldsmid, F. R. H. S. Edinburgh, 1885–1890. 16 v. 724

Editor's *Preface:* "I have taken upon myself to alter the order of the different voyages. I have grouped together those voyages which relate to the same parts of the globe, instead of adopting the somewhat haphazard arrangement of the original edition."

PARKS, G. B. Richard Hakluyt and the English voyages. New York, 1928. (American Geographical Society. Special publication no. 10.) 725

With a list of Hakluyt's publications, p. 262–265; reprints of the *Voyages,* p. 265–267; and a list of English books on geography and travel to 1600, p. 269–277.

RALEIGH, W., *ed.* The English voyages of the sixteenth century. (*In* Hakluyt Society. The principal navigations, voyages, traffiques & discoveries of the English nation . . . by Richard Hakluyt. Glasgow, 1903–1905. 12 v. Extra series. Vol. XII, p. 1–120.) 726

Comprises three sections, entitled: The voyagers. Richard Hakluyt. Poetry and imagination.

The Hakluyt Society also issued a reprint of Hakluyt's *Divers voyages touching the discovery of America* with notes and an introduction by J. W. Jones, London, 1850. An address by Sir Clements Markham on *Richard Hakluyt: his life and work. With a short account of the aims and achievements of the Hakluyt Society* was issued in London in 1896.

(5) HULSIUS

ASHER, A. Bibliographical essay on the collection of voyages and travels, edited and published by Levinus Hulsius and his successors at Nuremberg and Francfort from anno 1598 to 1660. London and Berlin, 1839. 727

* [COLE, G. W.] Hulsius' collection of voyages. (*In* Church, E. D., Collection of. A catalogue of books relating to . . . America. New York, 1907. Vol. II, p. 601–745.) 728

[LENOX, J.] Voyages of Hulsius. New York, 1877. (Contributions to a catalogue of the Lenox Library. No. I.) 729

The list begins with the first issue of Hulsius' first edition, 1598.

LIBRETTO. See below, under: Martyr.

(6) MARTYR

MARIÉJOL, J. H. . . . Pierre Martyr d'Anghera. Sa vie et ses oeuvres. Paris, 1887. 730

PENNESI, G. Pietro Martire d'Anghiera e le sue relazioni sulle scoperte oceaniche. (*In* Commissione Colombiana. Raccolta di documenti e studi. Roma, 1892–94. Parte V, 2.) 731

SCHUMACHER, H. A. Petrus Martyr, der Geschichtsschreiber des Weltmeeres. Eine Studie. New York, 1879. 732

THACHER, J. B. Peter Martyr. (*In his* Christopher Columbus. His life, his work, his remains. New York and London, 1903–1904. Vol. I, p. 3–110.) 733

For an account of the *Libretto,* 1504, with facsimile reproduction and translation, see Vol. II, Pt. II, p. 439–514, of Thacher's *Columbus.*

(7) PURCHAS

PURCHAS, S. Hakluytus posthumus or Purchas his pilgrimes. . . (Hakluyt Society. Publications. Extra series. 20 v. Glasgow, 1905–1907.) 734

(8) RAMUSIO

* [EAMES, W.] Ramusio. (*In* Sabin, J., Dictionary of books relating to America. New York, 1868 [to date]. Vol. XVI, p. 303–316.) 735

See also under Pizarro, no. 706, for the *Svmmario* whose editorship is generally attributed to Ramusio.

The asterisk (*) indicates that, in the reference works thus checked, annotations will be found giving the location of copies of the original editions recorded therein.

(9) THÉVENOT

CAMUS, A. G.   Mémoire sur la collection des grands et petits voyages, et sur la collection des voyages de Melchisedech Thévenot.   Paris, 1802.   736

[LENOX, J.]   The Voyages of Thévenot.   New York, 1879.   (Contributions to a catalogue of the Lenox Library.   No. III.)   737

The list begins with the variant issues of Thévenot's *Relation des divers voyages curieux,* 1663–1696.

III. CARTOGRAPHY AND GEOGRAPHY

A. *In General*

[EAMES, W.]   List of maps of the world illustrating the progress of geographical knowledge from the earliest times to the end of the seventeenth century.   New York, 1904.   (New York Public Library.)
                                                                                                                                          738
Valuable also as a chronological checklist.

HARRISSE, H.   Cartographia Americana Vetustissima, 1461–1493–1536.   (*In his* Discovery of North America. . .   London, Paris, 1892, p. 363–648.)   739

———— Découverte et évolution cartographique de Terre-Neuve et des pays circonvoisins 1497–1501–1769.   Essais de géographie historique et documentaire.   London, Paris, 1900.   2 v.   740

NORDENSKIÖLD, A. E.   Facsimile-atlas to the early history of cartography with reproductions of the most important maps printed in the XV and XVI centuries.   Stockholm 1889.   741

Translated from the Swedish original by Johan Adolf Ekelöf and Clements R. Markham.

PHILLIPS, P. L.   List of geographical atlases in the Library of Congress with bibliographical notes. . .   Washington, 1909–1920.   4 v.
                                                                                                                                          742
" The reader should consult 3 indexes, in vol. II, III and IV.   Among the atlases analyzed in this work one will find 42 editions of Ptolemy, of which 32 are previous to 1600; 62 editions of Abraham Ortelius; 30 of Mercator; Corneille Wyttfleit's Descriptionis Ptolemaicae augumentum, Louvain, 1597; Christopher Saxton's Maps of England and Wales, London, 1574–1579; Antoine Lafrery's Geografia, Roma, 1575 (?) with copious bibliographical notes in vol. III, p. 81–92," etc.   — Reviewed by Dr. George Sarton in *Isis,* 1921.   Vol. IV (1).

PHILLIPS, P. L.   A List of maps of America in the Library of Congress, preceded by a list of works relating to cartography.   Washington, 1901.   743

SCHULLER, R. R.   . . . Primera contribución al estudió de la cartografía americana.   Montevideo, 1905.   744
'Bibliografía,' p. [49]–56.

URICOECHEA, E.   Mapoteca Colombiana.   Coleccion de los títulos de todos los mapas, planos, vistas etc. relativos á la America española, Brasil, é islas adyacentes.   Arreglada cronologicamente.   Lóndres, 1860.   745
With an introduction on American cartography, and sections relating to America in general, South America, California, Florida, Texas, Mexico, Antillas, Central America, Guiana, New Granada, Venezuela, Brazil, Peru, the 'Confederacion Arjentina, Uruguai, Paraguai,' Chile, Patagonia, the islands of the Pacific, etc.

WINSOR, J.   The Kohl collection of maps relating to America.   A reprint of Bibliographical contribution number 19 of the Library of Harvard University.   Washington, 1904.   746
Now in the Library of Congress.

WRIGHT, J. K.   Aids to geographical research.   Bibliographies and periodicals.   New York, 1923.   (American Geographical Society. Research series.   No. 10.)   747

B. *Pre-Columbian Period*

D'ALBERTIS, E. A.   Le costruzioni navali e l'arte della navigazione al tempo di Cristoforo Colombo.   (*In* Commissione Colombiana.   Raccolta di documenti e studi.   Roma, 1892–94.   Parte IV, 1.)   748

FISCHER, J.   The Discoveries of the Norsemen in America with special relation to their early cartographical representation. . .   Translated from the German by Basil H. Soulsby.   St. Louis, 1903.   749

KRETSCHMER, K.   Die italienischen Portolane des Mittelalters.   Ein Beitrag zur Geschichte der Kartographie und Nautik.   Berlin, 1909. (Universität Berlin.   Institut für Meereskunde und des Geographischen Instituts.   Veröffentlichungen.   Heft 13.   Feb. 1909.)   750

LELEWEL, J.   Géographie du moyen âge.   Bruxelles, 1852.   4 v. in 1.
                                                                      751

NORDENSKIÖLD, A. E. Periplus. An essay on the early history of charts and sailing-directions. Translated from the Swedish original by Francis A. Bather, with numerous reproductions of old charts and maps. Stockholm, 1897. 752

UZIELLI, G., AND P. AMAT DI S. FILIPPO Mappamondi, carte nautiche, portolani ed altri monumenti cartografici specialmente italiani dei secoli XIII–XVII. (*In their* Studi biografici e bibliografici sulla storia della geografia in Italia. Ed. 2. Roma, 1882. Società Geografica Italiana. Vol. 2.) 753

WROTH, L. C. A manuscript portolan atlas in the Boston Public Library. (*In* The New York Herald Tribune, Feb. 8, 1925. Section V, p. 15–16.) 754

Although the occasion for writing this essay was the purchase of a manuscript, it gives a brief survey of the subject of early atlases and includes considerable matter on the printed portolans of the fifteenth and sixteenth centuries.

See also above, under: Period of Discovery. Pre-Columbian Period, nos. 656–658; and below, under: Ptolemy, nos. 768–771.

C. *Earliest Engraved Maps of the New World*

[1505–1506] STEVENS, H. N. The first delineation of the New World and the first use of the name America on a printed map. London, 1928. 755

An analytical comparison of three maps: (1) the Stevens-John Carter Brown Library map, *c.* 1505–6; (2) Waldseemüller-Wolfegg map, 1507; (3) Contarini-British Museum map, 1506, with facsimiles of the Stevens-John Carter Brown map and of the *Orbis Typus* of 1513.

1506 [DE VILLIERS, J. A. J.] A Map of the world designed by Gio. Matteo Contarini, engraved by Fran. Roselli, 1506. London, 1924. 756

Printed by order of the Trustees of the British Museum. An analysis and facsimile of "the first printed map known in which the discoveries made in the New World by Columbus and his contemporaries are represented, being one year earlier than Martin Waldseemüller's map of 1507 and two years earlier than that by Joannes Ruysch included in the edition of Ptolemy's *Cosmographia* published in Rome in 1508. No other copy is known."

——— HEAWOOD, E. A hitherto unknown world map of A.D. 1506. (*In* The Geographical Journal. Oct., 1923. Vol. LXII, no. 4, p. 279–293.) 757

1507   FISCHER, J., AND F. VON WIESER   Waldseemüller's large world
map of 1507. (*In* The 'Cosmographiæ introductio' of Martin Waldseemüller in facsimile. New York, 1907. United States Catholic
Historical Society. Monograph IV, p. 15–22.)   758

———— ————— Die Weltkarten Waldseemüllers (Ilacomilus) 1507
& 1516. The world maps of Waldseemüller (Ilacomilus) 1507 &
1516. Innsbruck, 1903.   759

D. *Cartographers and Geographers*

(1) APIAN

* ORTROY, F. VAN   Bibliographie de l'oeuvre de Pierre Apian. Besançon, 1902.   760

Extrait de *Bibliographe Moderne,* mars-octobre, 1901.

WAGNER, H. [K. H.]   Die dritte Weltkarte Peter Apians v. J. 1530
und die pseudo-Apianische Weltkarte von 1551. [Göttingen, 1892.]
(Königliche Gesellschaft der Wissenschaften. Nachrichten. Dec.
28, 1892. No. 16.)   761

(2) BEHAIM

RAVENSTEIN, E. G.   Martin Behaim, his life and his globe. With a
facsimile of the globe printed in colours, eleven maps and seventeen
illustrations. London, 1908.   762

(3) BLAEU

STEVENSON, E. L.   Willem Janszoon Blaeu, 1571–1638. A sketch of
his life and work, with an especial reference to his large world map
of 1605. New York, 1914. (The Hispanic Society of America.
Publications, no. 85.)   763

With a facsimile of the unique copy of the world map belonging to the
Society, a reproduction of the printing press of Blaeu, his printer's marks, etc.

(4) GLAREANUS

HEAWOOD, E.   Glareanus: his geography and maps. (Reprinted from
The Geographical Journal. June, 1905.)   764

The asterisk (*) indicates that, in the reference works thus checked, annotations will be
found giving the location of copies of the original editions recorded therein.

(5) HONDIUS

STEVENSON, E. L., AND J. FISCHER, *ed.*   Map of the world by Jodocus
Hondius, 1611. . . . Issued under the joint auspices of The American
Geographical Society and The Hispanic Society of America.   New
York, 1907.   765

(6) MERCATOR

ORTROY, F. VAN Gérard Mercator.   Lettres — requêtes — documents divers.   Bruxelles, 1912.   766

(7) ORTELIUS

BAGROW, L.   A. Ortelii catalogus cartographorum.   Gotha, 1928–.
                                                                      767

The work " aims to present systematically the essential facts regarding the
. . . works of the 87 cartographers listed in the 1570 edition of the *Theatrum.*"
— *Isis,* no. 40, XIII(1).

HESSELS, J. H.   Editions of the *Theatrum* of Ortelius and maps in the
Theatrum.   (*In his* Ecclesiae Londino-Batavae Archivvm.   [Canat-
brigiae, 1887.]   Vol. I, p. xxiii–lxi.)   767:a

(8) PTOLEMY

* [EAMES, W.]   A List of editions of Ptolemy's geography 1475–
1730.   New York, 1886.   768
Fifty copies reprinted from Sabin's *Dictionary,* Vol. XVI.

RYLANDS, T. G.   The Geography of Ptolemy elucidated.   Dublin,
1893.   769

STEVENS, H. N.   Ptolemy's geography.   An account of the origin and
scope of the Henry Stevens collection of the various editions 1475–
1730, now the property of Edward E. Ayer of Chicago.   London,
1908.   770
More recently deposited at The Newberry Library, Chicago.

——— Ptolemy's geography, a brief account of all the printed editions down to 1730.   2 ed.   London, 1908.   771

The asterisk (*) indicates that, in the reference works thus checked, annotations will be
found giving the location of copies of the original editions recorded therein.

(9) REISCH

* [EAMES, W.] A List of editions of the *Margarita philosophica*, 1503–1599. New York, 1886.   772

Not over a dozen copies separately issued from Sabin's *Dictionary*, Vol. XVI. The world-map issued with Reisch's *Margarita*, although it attempts no delineation of the New World, bears a reference to it.

FERGUSON, J. The *Margarita Philosophica* of Gregorius Reisch. A bibliography. (*In* The Library. September, 1929. Fourth series, Vol. X, no. 2, p. 194–216.)   772 :a

(10) ROSELLI

NUNN, G. E. World map of Francesco Roselli, drawn on an oval projection and printed from a woodcut supplementing the fifteenth century maps in the second edition of the *Isolario* of Bartolomeo Dali Sonetti, printed in Italy anno domini MDXXXII. Philadelphia, 1928.   773

See also no. 756.

(11) STOBNICZA

JOHN CARTER BROWN LIBRARY (Providence) Report to the corporation of Brown University, July 1, 1929. Providence, 1929.   774

The Stobnicza map is described on p. 28–31, and reference is made to the Waldseemüller, Ramusio, Lok, Thorne, Wright-Molyneux, Fitch, Romans, and other maps.

(12) VERRAZZANO

[HARRISSE, H.] La Cartographie Verrazanienne. Extrait de la *Revue de Géographie*. Paris, Nov. 1896.   775

[———] Un nouveau globe Verrazanien. Extrait de la *Revue de Géographie*, Paris, 1895.   776

STOKES, I. N. PHELPS Discovery and earliest cartography of the vicinity of Manhattan Island, from Vespuccius to Hudson. (*In his* Iconography of Manhattan Island. New York, 1915–1928. Vol. II, p. 5–39.)   777

(13) WALDSEEMÜLLER

[AVEZAC-MACAYA, M. A. P. D'] Martin Hylacomylus. Waltzemüller. Ses ouvrages et ses collaborateurs. Par un géographe bibliophile. Paris, 1867.   778

Extrait: *Annales des voyages*. 1866.

The asterisk (*) indicates that, in the reference works thus checked, annotations will be found giving the location of copies of the original editions recorded therein.

STEVENSON, E. L.   Martin Waldseemüller and the early Lusitano-Germanic cartography of the New World.   (*In* American Geographical Society.   Bulletin.   1904.   Vol. XXXVI. no. 4, p. 193–215.)
779
See also above, under: Earliest Engraved Maps of the New World, nos. 755–759.

E. *Regional Maps*

I. SPANISH COLONIES

MEDINA, J. T.   Ensayo acerca de una mapoteca Chilena.   Santiago de Chile, 1889.   780
The bibliography opens with an edition of Ptolemy, printed at Basel in 1540.

* PHILLIPS, P. L.   Guiana and Venezuela cartography.   (*In* American Historical Association.   Annual report, 1897.   Washington, 1898, p. 681–776.)   781
Arranged chronologically, from the sixteenth through the eighteenth century.

———— *ed.*   The Lowery collection.   A descriptive list of maps of the Spanish possessions within the present limits of the United States 1502–1820.   Edited with notes by Philip Lee Phillips.   Washington, 1912.   (Library of Congress.)   782
The titles are checked for location in the Lowery Collection or in the collection of the Library of Congress:

———— . . . Notes on the life and works of Bernard Romans.   Deland, Fla., 1924.   2 v.   783
With reproductions of Bernard Romans' maps of Florida, 1774.

* ROTH, H. L.   Bibliography and cartography of Hispaniola.   (Royal Geographical Society.   Supplementary Papers.   London, 1887.   Vol. 2, pt. 1.)   784

WAGNER, H. R.   Quivira, a mythical California city.   (*In* California Historical Society.   Quarterly.   Vol. III.   No. 3.   San Francisco, Oct. 1924, p. 262–267.)   785
Relates to the maps of Ortelius and Mercator, and to various sixteenth century delineations of California.

The asterisk (*) indicates that, in the reference works thus checked, annotations will be found giving the location of copies of the original editions recorded therein.

2. FRENCH COLONIES

DIONNE, N. E.   . . . Cartes, plans, atlas relatifs à la Nouvelle-France et à la Province de Quebec, 1508–1908. Quebec, 1909. (Inventaire Chronologique. IV.)   786

HARRISSE, H.   Notes pour servir à l'histoire, à la bibliographie et à la cartographie de la Nouvelle-France et des pays adjacents, 1545–1700. Paris, 1872.   787

A supplement entitled *Cartographie de la Nouvelle France* was issued by G. A. Marcel in 1885.

MARCEL, G. [A.]   Cartographie de la Nouvelle France, supplément à l'ouvrage de M. Harrisse. Paris, 1885. (Extrait de la *Revue de Géographie.*)   788

3. DUTCH COLONIES

ASHER, G. M.   A List of the maps and charts of New-Netherland, and of the views of New-Amsterdam, by G. M. Asher. Being a supplement to his Bibliographical essay on New-Netherland. Amsterdam, New York, 1855.   789

Part II of his *Bibliographical and historical essay,* 1867.

STOKES, I. N. PHELPS   Cartography: An essay on the development of knowledge regarding the geography of the east coast of North America; Manhattan Island and its environs on early maps and charts. (*In his* Iconography of Manhattan Island. New York, 1915–1928. Vol. II.)   790

4. BRITISH COLONIES AND THE UNITED STATES

(1) CAROLINA

FORD, W. C.   Early maps of Carolina. New York [1926].   791

Reprinted from the *Geographical Review,* Vol. XVI., no. 2, April, 1926, p. 264–273. The earliest engraved map noted is that printed in 1666.

(2) MARYLAND

PHILLIPS, P. L.   The rare map of Virginia and Maryland by Augustine Herrman. . . Washington, 1911.   792

(3) MIDDLE COLONIES

STEVENS, H. N.   Lewis Evans. His map of the Middle British Colonies in America. A comparative account of eighteen different editions between 1755 and 1814. Third edition . . . with some additional notes on a second edition of the map of 1749. London, 1924.   793

The first and second editions were published in 1905 and 1920 respectively, the second edition with some account of the map of 1749.

(4) NEW ENGLAND

GREEN, S. A. Hubbard's map of New England, 1677. (*In his* Ten Fac-simile reproductions relating to old Boston and neighborhood. Boston, 1901, p. 5–12.)   794

Reproductions of " The Wine Hills " and " The White Hills " impressions are also given in his *John Foster, the earliest American engraver.* Boston, 1909.

(5) NEW YORK

STOKES, I. N. PHELPS Hudson's mapping of the vicinity of Manhattan Island. (*In his* Iconography of Manhattan Island. New York, 1915–1928. Vol. II, p. 41–61.)   795

Followed by a chapter on the first Dutch surveys of the vicinity of Manhattan Island, the figurative maps of Block and Hendricks, 1614–1616. See also, Asher; and Stokes, under: Regional Maps: Dutch Colonies.

(6) NORTHWEST AND MISSISSIPPI VALLEY

PHILLIPS, P. L. The first map and description of Ohio, 1787, by Manasseh Cutler. A bibliographical account. Washington, 1918.
                                                                                      796

* —— The first map of Kentucky, by John Filson. Washington, 1908.   796:a

A bibliographical account of the map made to accompany Filson's *Discovery, settlement and present state of Kentucke,* Wilmington, 1784. With a fac-simile reproduction from the copy in the Library of Congress.

—— The rare map of the Northwest. 1785. By John Fitch, inventor of the steamboat. A bibliographical account with facsimile reproduction. Washington, 1916.   797

Relates to the region of the Great Lakes, including part of Kentucky.

(7) VIRGINIA

FORD, W. C. Captain John Smith's map of Virginia, 1612. New York [1924].   798

Reprinted from the *Geographical Review,* Vol. XIV, no. 3, July, 1924, p. 433–443.

The asterisk (*) indicates that, in the reference works thus checked, annotations will be found giving the location of copies of the original editions recorded therein.

PHILLIPS, P. L.   The rare map of Virginia and Maryland by Augustine Herrman, first lord of Bohemia manor, Maryland., Washington, 1911.   799

A bibliographical account of a seventeenth century map, with a facsimile reproduction from the copy in the British Museum.

———. . . Virginia   cartography;   a   bibliographical   description. Washington, 1896. (Smithsonian miscellaneous collections. [XXX-VII. Art. IV.] Publication 1039.)   800

Begins with a discussion of the maps of Virginia and adjoining regions, prior to 1597 and to Capt. John Smith's map of 1608.

For regions now in the United States, see also above, under Spanish, French, and Dutch colonies.

IV. COLONIZATION AND COLONIAL GROWTH

A. *Spanish and South America*

ALLEGRI, M.   Girolamo Benzoni e la sua historia del Mondo Nuovo. (*In* Commissione Colombiana.   Raccolta di documenti e studi. Roma, 1892–94.   Parte V, 3.)   801

An account of Spanish America written by an Italian, resident in the New World for fifteen years.   A translation of Benzoni's work 'shewing his travels in America from 1541 to 1556' was issued by Rear-Admiral W. H. Smyth in the Hakluyt Society *Publications,* London, 1857.

AMADOR DE LOS RIOS, J., *ed.*   Historia general y natural de las Indias . . . por el Capitan Gonzalo Fernandez de Oviedo y Valdés. . . Madrid, 1851–55. 4 vols. (Real Academia de la Historia.)   802

With an introduction giving an account of the life of Oviedo and a critique of his works.

BACKER, AUGUSTIN DE, AND ALOYS DE   Bibliothèque des écrivains de la Compagnie de Jésus, ou Notices bibliographiques. . . Liège, 1853–61. 7 v.   803

Second ed. Brussels, 1869–1876. 3 v. See also, Sommervogel.

CARAYON, A.   Bibliographie historique de la Compagnie de Jésus. Paris, 1864.   804

Missions d'Amerique, Chap. IV, p. 176–202. The titles, which are arranged chronologically, relate to missions in New France and in various countries of South America.

* DE PUY, H. F.   . . . An early account of the establishment of Jesuit missions in America. Worcester, 1921.   805

Relates to the *Vida del P. Francisco de Borja . . . General de la Compania de Iesvs,* by P. de Ribadeneyra, Madrid, 1592, with reference to missions in the West Indies, Florida, Peru, Brazil; and to three titles on missions in Brazil, 1552, 1553, and 1555.

FUMAGALLI, G., AND P. AMAT DI S. FILIPPO   Linguistica. (*In* Commissione Colombiana. Raccolta di documenti e studi pubblicati . . . pel quarto centenario dalla scoperta dell'America. Parte VI, p. 143–148.)   806

GARCIA ICAZBALCETA, J.   Apuntes para un catálogo de escritores en lenguas indígenas de América. México, 1866.   807

* MEDINA, J. T.   Bibliotheca Hispano-Americana (1493–1810). Santiago de Chile, 1898–1907. 7 v.   808

———— Diccionario de anónimos y seudónimos Hispano-Americanos. Buenos Aires, 1925. 2 v.   809

———— La primitiva inquisición americana (1493–1569); estudio histórico. . . Santiago de Chile, 1914. 2 v.   810

MENDEZ BEJARANO, M.   Bio-bibliografía Hispálica de ultramar o papeletas bio-bibliográficas de escritores nacidos en la provincia de Sevilla. Madrid, 1915.   811

Contains biographical accounts of Las Casas, Cieza de Leon, Enriquez de Guzman, etc.

MOSES, B.   Spanish colonial literature in South America. London and New York, 1922. (The Hispanic Society of America. Hispanic notes & monographs.)   812

A critique of colonial literature from the beginning of the Spanish settlement of South America to the eve of the revolutionary period. With a *Catalogue,* under authors' names, of the early books mentioned in the text.

PALAU Y DULCET, A.   Manual del librero Hispano-Americano. Inventaire bibliográfico de la producción científica y literaria de España y de la América latina desde la invención de la imprenta hasta nuestros dias. Barcelona, 1923–1927. 7 v.   813

Vol. I, p. 21–39: *Diccionario geografico-tipografico,* comprising an alphabetical list of the towns of Spain and Latin America, with the dates of the introduction of printing.

The asterisk (*) indicates that, in the reference works thus checked, annotations will be found giving the location of copies of the original editions recorded therein.

ROHDE, E. S.   The old English herbals.   London, 1922.   814

With a chapter on herbals of the New World, referring to Frampton's translation in 1577 of Monardes' *Dos Libros* of 1569; the *Hortus Peruvianus Medicinalis* [London, 1715] etc.

* SABIN, J.   A List of the editions of the works of . . . Alonso [*i.e.,* Antonio] de Herrera.   Extracted from a *Dictionary of books relating to America* by Joseph Sabin.   New York, 1876.   815

In connection with Herrera's *Descripcion de las Indias Occidentales,* 1601, which relates to the history of America from its discovery to 1555, a note states that Herrera "had access to the most secret of the archives of Spain."

SCHULLER, R. R.   Lingüística Americana.   Notas bibliográficas.   De la *Revista de Archivos, Bibliotecas y Museos.*   Madrid, 1912.   816

——— Novus orbis.   ¿ De A. Montanus o de O. Dapper ?   [Santiago de Chile, 1906 ?]   817

Relates to the authorship of *De nieuwe en onbekende weereld . . . beschreeven door Arnoldus Montanus.*   Amsterdam, 1671.

SOMMERVOGEL, C.   Bibliothèque de la Compagnie de Jésus.   Bruxelles, 1890–1909.   10 v.   818

Première partie: *Bibliographie par les pères Augustin et Aloys de Backer.* Nouvelle édition.   A two-volume work entitled *Dictionnaire des ouvrages anonymes et pseudonymes publiés par des religieux de la Compagnie de Jésus* was issued by Sommervogel at Paris in 1884.

Four supplements to De Backer-Sommervogel were issued by E.-M. Rivière, under the title *Corrections and Additions,* 1911–1917.

VIÑAZA, [C. MUÑOZ Y MANZANO], *Conde de la*   Bibliografía española de lenguas indígenas de América.   Madrid, 1892.   819

Begins with the *Doctrina* of 1539; lists 96 titles of the sixteenth century, 148 of the seventeenth century, and 148 of the eighteenth century.

WAGNER, H. R.   Lopez de Gomara.   (*In his* Spanish Southwest, 1542–1794.   Berkeley, 1924, p. 17–42.)   820

B. *Mexico and Central America*

I. SUBJECT MONOGRAPHS

A) MEXICO

GARCIA ICAZBALCETA, J.   Don Fray Juan de Zumárraga, primer Obispo y Arzobispo de México.   Estudio biográfico y bibliográfico. México, 1881.   821

The asterisk (*) indicates that, in the reference works thus checked, annotations will be found giving the location of copies of the original editions recorded therein.

FERNÁNDEZ DEL CASTILLO, *ed.* Libros y libreros en el siglo XVI. Mexico, 1914. (Mexico. Secretaria de relaciones exteriores. Publicaciones del archivo general de la nación. VI.) 822

An account of the cases of various Mexican printers and booksellers in conflict with the Inquisition of the sixteenth century.

GONZALEZ OBREGON, L. El capitan Bernal Diaz del Castillo, conquistador y cronista de Nueva España. Noticias biográficas y bibliográficas. Mexico, 1894. 822:a

MEDINA, J. T. Bartolomé de Las Casas. (*In his* Biblioteca Hispano-Americana. Santiago de Chile, 1900. Vol. II, p. 469–479.) 823

MENA, R. Filigranas o Marcas transparentes en papeles de Nueva España del siglo XVI. Mexico, 1926. (Mexico. Secretaría de Relaciones Exteriores. Monografías Bibliográficas Mexicanas. V.) 824

NEW YORK PUBLIC LIBRARY (New York) List of works in the New York Public Library relating to Mexico. New York, 1909. (Excerpt: *Bulletin.* Oct.-Dec., 1909.) 825

PILLING, J. C. The Writings of Padre Andres de Olmos in the languages of Mexico. Washington, 1895. (Extract from the *American Anthropologist,* Vol. VIII, no. 1.) 826

The first work listed is the *Arte de la Mexicana* of about 1555.

SABIN, J. A List of the printed editions of the works of Fray Bartolomé de Las Casas, Bishop of Chiapa. Extracted from a *Dictionary of books relating to America* by Joseph Sabin. New York, 1870. 827

SALA, R. . . . Marcas de fuego de las antiguas bibliotecas mexicanas. Mexico, 1925. (Mexico. Secretaría de Relaciones Exteriores. Monografías bibliográficas mexicanas. II.) 828

Furnishes a means of identifying Mexican-owned books by the brands found on the edges of the books.

THACHER, J. B. Bartolomé de Las Casas. (*In his* Christopher Columbus. His life, his work, his remains. New York and London, 1903–1904. Vol. 1, p. 113–159.) 829

WAGNER, H. R. Lopez de Gomara. (*In his* Spanish Southwest, 1542–1794. Berkeley, 1924, p. 17–42.) 830

B) Central America: Darien †

Cundall, F. Bibliography. (*In his* The Darien venture. New York, 1926, p. 138–141. (The Hispanic Society of America. Hispanic notes & monographs.) 831

Cundall's *Bibliography of the West Indies,* Kingston, 1909, includes a section on Panama, with 43 titles relating to Wafer, or the Darien period, 1669–1779.

P[arlane], J[ames] Notes on the Scots' Darien expedition taken from books and contemporary pamphlets in my possession. . . Manchester, 1888. 832

*Scott, J. A Bibliography of printed documents and books relating to the Darien company. By John Scott, C. B. Revised by George P. Johnston. Edinburgh, 1904, 1906. 833

Twenty copies reprinted from the *Publications* of the Edinburgh Bibliographical Society. A volume of additions and corrections was issued by the editor, G. P. Johnston, in 1906.

Winship, G. P., *ed.* A new voyage and description of the Isthmus of America by Lionel Wafer. Reprinted from the original edition of 1699. Cleveland, 1903. 834

With a bibliographical introduction.

See also *A List of books printed in Scotland before 1700,* [Edinburgh] 1904, issued by H. G. Aldis (Edinburgh Bibliographical Society).

2. COLONIAL PUBLICATIONS ‡

A) Introduction of Printing and Type-Founding

Garcia Icazbalceta, J. Bibliografía mexicana del siglo XVI. Primera parte. Catálogo razonado de libros impresos en México de 1539 á 1600. . . Precedido de una noticia acerca de la introducción de la imprenta en México. México, 1886. 835

Three hundred and fifty copies, 12 on large paper. An *Index* to this work was compiled by Catharine A. Janvier, and published in New York, January, 1890.

Medina, J. T. Introduccion. (*In his* La imprenta en Mexico (1539–1821) Santiago de Chile, 1907–1912. Vol. I.) 836

† That is, Panama.
‡ Printed within the colonies.

The asterisk (*) indicates that, in the reference works thus checked, annotations will be found giving the location of copies of the original editions recorded therein.

WINSHIP, G. P.   Early Mexican printers: A letter.   Cambridge, 1899.
(The Club of Odd Volumes.)   837

———— Spanish America.   (*In* Peddie, R. A., *ed.*   Printing: A short history of the art.   London, 1927, p. 306–318.)   838

An account of the first presses in Mexico, Peru, Paraguay, Colombia, etc.
With a reference on p. 308 to Espinosa, a type-founder who joined Pablos
in Mexico in 1550, and to whose "skill is doubtless due the fonts of fresh
type which appear after 1553," thus indicating that the early Mexican
printers carried on the European tradition of casting new type as it was
needed.   For a further discussion of this point, see: McMurtrie, D. C., The
first type-founding in Mexico (*In* The Library.   4th Series.   Vol. VIII.
1928).

WROTH, L. C.   The Origins of typefounding in North and South
America.   (*In* Ars typographica.   April 1926.   Vol. II, no. 4,
p. 273–307.)   839

Relates to type casting in Paraguay in 1705 or thereabouts; to the first
work, printed in Mexico in 1770, which bears a statement that it was printed
with local types; and to the efforts at type casting in the British colonies just
before the outbreak of the Revolutionary War.   With facsimiles.

B) PUBLICATIONS (MEXICO AND CENTRAL AMERICA)

(1) MEXICO

ANDRADE, V. DE P.   Ensayo bibliográfico mexicano del siglo XVII.
Segunda edicion.   México, 1899–1909.   2 v.   840

The last volume contains a *Bibliografía de Puebla del siglo XVII*.

ENGELHARDT, Z.   The earliest books printed in the New World.
(United States Catholic Historical Society.   Monograph series,
Vol. X.   1918.)   841

GARCIA ICAZBALCETA, J.   Apuntes para un catálogo de escritores en
lenguas indígenas de América.   México, 1866.   842

———— Don Fray Juan de Zumárraga, primer Obispo y Arzobispo de
Mexico. Estudio biográfico y bibliográfica.   Mexico, 1881.   842:a

For Garcia Icazbalceta's great work on early printing in Mexico, the *Bibliografía mexicana del siglo XVI,* see above, under: Mexico.   Introduction of
Printing, no. 835.

LEÓN, N.   Bibliografia mexicana del siglo XVIII.   México, 1902–
1908.   5 v.   (Instituto Bibliografico Mexicano.   Boletin.   I.)   843

* Medina, J. T.   La Imprenta en México (1539–1821).   Santiago de Chile, 1907–1912.   8 v.   844

*——— La Imprenta en Oaxaca (1720–1820) Notas bibliográficas. Santiago de Chile, 1904.   845

*——— La Imprenta en la Puebla de los Angeles (1640–1821) Santiago de Chile, 1908.   846

See also above, under: Andrade.

*——— La Imprenta en Veracrux (1794–1821) Notas bibliograficas. Santiago de Chile, 1904.   847

Pilling, J. C.   The Writings of Padre Andres de Olmos in the languages of Mexico.   Washington, 1895.   (Extract from the *American Anthropologist,* Vol. VIII, no. 1.)   848

The first work listed is the *Arte de la Mexicana* of about 1555.

* Smith, D. E.   The *Sumario compendioso* of Brother Juan Diez. The earliest mathematical work of the New World.   Boston, 1921.
                                                                       849

With a list of Mexican imprints up to the publication of the *Sumario* in 1556, and a brief account of Mexico and its first press.   Reviewed in *School and Society,* Aug. 13, 1921, by L. C. Karpinski who discusses the authorship of the *Sumario,* quoting Bancroft to the effect that Juan Diez was killed and eaten over thirty years before this work was published.

* Wagner, H. R.   Sixteenth-century Mexican imprints.   (*In* Bibliographical essays.   A tribute to Wilberforce Eames.   June, MCMXXIV.   [Cambridge, 1924,] p. [249]–268.)   850

With a table checked for the location of 204 titles.

Wright, J.   Early Prayer Books of America; being a descriptive account of Prayer Books published in the United States, Mexico, and Canada.   St. Paul, 1896.   851

With facsimile title-pages of the 'Missale Romanum,' Mexico, 1561; the Indian Prayer Book printed at Quebec in 1767; the Mohawk Prayer Book printed by William Bradford at New York in 1715; the Manual of Catholic Prayers, Philadelphia, 1774; revised Prayer Book of the Protestant Episcopal Church, Philadelphia, 1786; etc.

See also above, under: Introduction of Printing, nos. 835–839.

(2) Central America

* Medina, J. T.   La Imprenta en Guatemala (1660–1821) Santiago de Chile, 1910.   852

————

The asterisk (*) indicates that, in the reference works thus checked, annotations will be found giving the location of copies of the original editions recorded therein.

C. *South America*

I. REGIONAL MONOGRAPHS

(1) BRAZIL

ASHER, G. M.   A bibliographical and historical essay on the Dutch books and pamphlets relating to New-Netherland and to the Dutch West-India Company and to its possessions in Brazil, Angola, etc. Amsterdam, 1854–67.   2 pts.   853

Covers the period from 1614 to 1666.

BARBOSA MACHADO, D.   Bibliotheca lusitana historica, critica, e crono-logica.   Lisbon, 1741–59.   4 v.   854

BIBLIOTECA NACIONAL (Rio de Janeiro)   Catalogo da exposicao de historia do Brazil.   Rio de Janeiro, 1881.   2 v.   854:a

Lists various early works in the National Library of Brazil under the headings *Do Brazil em geral, Viagens, Chartas, Linguistica brazilica,* etc.; with a brief list of bibliographies of Braziliana.

* DE PUY, H. F.   . . . An early account of the establishment of Jesuit missions in America.   Worcester, 1921.   855

Reprinted from the *Proceedings* of the American Antiquarian Society for April 1920.   An account of the life of Francisco de Borja, the third General of the Jesuits, by Father Pedro de Ribadeneyra, Madrid, 1592; with a bibliographical note on three earlier accounts of the Jesuits in Brazil, printed at Rome, 1552 and 1553, and at Lisbon, 1555.

GARCIA, R.   Bibliographia geographica brasileira.   (*In* Revista do Instituto Historico e Geographico brasileiro.   Rio de Janeiro, 1919. LXXXV:139, p. 5–100.)   856

The section entitled *Obras Geraes* records various early titles relating to Brazil.

GARRAUX, A. L.   Bibliographie brésilienne.   Catalogue des ouvrages français & latins relatifs au Brésil (1500–1898).   Paris, 1898.   857

PHILLIPS, P. L.   A List of books relating to Brazil in the Library of Congress.   Washington, 1901.   858

RODRIGUES, J. C.   Bibliotheca brasiliense.   Catalogo annotado dos libros sobre o Brasil.   Rio de Janeiro, 1907.   859

Parte I: *Descobrimento da America: Brasil colonial, 1492–1822.*

The asterisk (*) indicates that, in the reference works thus checked, annotations will be found giving the location of copies of the original editions recorded therein.

SANTOS, M. DOS   Bibliografia gerál ou Descrição bibliográfica de livros tanto de autores portugueses como brasileiros . . . impressos desde o seculo XV até à actualidade. Lisboa, 1914–17.   860

STETSON, J. B., JR.   Bibliography: XVI century works relating to Brazil. (*In* Cortes Society. The histories of Brazil by Pero de Magalhães . . . translated . . . by John B. Stetson, Jr. New York, 1922, p. 238–251. [Documents and Narratives concerning . . . Latin America. No. V, Vol. II.])   861

WINSOR, J.   Editorial note on the bibliography of Brazil. (*In his* Narrative and critical history of America. Boston, 1889. Vol. VIII, p. 349–358.)   861 :a

Excepting for its chapters on Vespuccius and the discovery of Brazil, which have been superseded by the results of more recent research, Southey's *History of Brazil*, London, 1810–1819, is here said to rank as the outstanding work in English on early Brazilian history.

The *Bibliotheca Braziliensis*, London, 1930 (Maggs Bros., Catalogue 546), lists nearly 300 works printed between 1493 and 1825.

(2) CHILE

* MEDINA, J. T.   Biblioteca hispano-chilena (1523–1817). Santiago de Chile, 1897–1899. 3 v.   862

A critique of early Chilean literature was issued by Sr. Medina in 1878 under title *Historia de la literatura colonial de Chile*.

——— *ed.*   Nueve sermones en lengua de Chile por el P. Luis de Valdivia de la Compaña de Jesús reimpresos á plana y renglón del unico ejemplar conocido y precedidos de una bibliografía de la misma lengua. Santiago de Chile [1897].   863

SCHULLER, R. R.   Discovery of a fragment of the printed copy of the work on the Millcayac language by Luis de Valdivia; with a bibliographical notice. Cambridge, 1913.   864

Relates to a work apparently printed in four parts at Lima in 1607 for the use of the Allentiac Indians and comprising in the present fragment two pages of Valdivia's *Doctrina christiana* and the title-page of his *Confessionario* with imprint: En Lima, por Francisco del Canto, ano 1607. — L.C.

——— El vocabulario Araucano de 1642–1643, con notas críticas i algunas adiciones a las bibliografías de la lengua Mapuche (o Araucana). Santiago de Chile, 1907.   864 :a

The asterisk (*) indicates that, in the reference works thus checked, annotations will be found giving the location of copies of the original editions recorded therein.

(3) DUTCH GUIANA

KNUTTEL, W. P. C.   Catalogus van de Pamfletten-Verzameling berustende in de Koninklijke Bibliotheek.   's Gravenhage, 1889–1916. 7 v. with index and supplement.   865

OPPENHEIM, S.   An early Jewish colony in Western Guiana 1658–1666: and its relation to the Jews in Surinam, Cayenne and Tobago. (*Reprinted from* American Jewish Historical Society. *Publications.* No. 16.   1907.)   865:a

With reference to various seventeenth and eighteenth century works.   A section of supplemental data was issued in 1908.

(4) FRENCH GUIANA

DE NOUVION, V.   Extraits des auteurs et voyageurs qui ont écrit sur la Guyane, suivis du catalogúe bibliographique de la Guyane.   Paris, 1844.   (Société d'Études pour la Colonisation de la Guyane française.   Publications.   IV.)   866

TERNAUX-COMPANS, H.   Bibliographie de la Guyane française.   (*In his* Notice historique sur la Guyane Française.   Paris, 1843, p. 169–190.)   867

* WROTH, L. C.   Some early French Guiana tracts.   Reprinted from the Proceedings of the American Antiquarian Society for April, 1925. Worcester, 1926.   868

An addition to the bibliography of El Dorado, beginning with the *Projet d'une compagnie pour l'Amerique, c.* 1651.

(5) PARAGUAY

MITRE, B., *ed.*   Ulrich Schmidel.   Viaje al Río de la Plata (1534–1554) Notas bibliográficas y biográficas.   Buenos Aires, 1903.   869

[SCHULLER, R. R.]   . . . One of the rarest American books.   [Washington, D. C., 1913.]   870

Reprinted from *The American Anthropologist*, v. 15, no. 1, Jan.-March, 1913. Relates to Garriga's *Instrvccion practica*, printed in 1713 by the Guarani Indians at the Jesuit mission Loreto, in Paraguay.   An account of the same work was issued by Dr. Schuller under title: *Um livro americano unico*. . . Pará, Brasil, 1910.

See also below, under: Introduction of Printing, no. 874.

The asterisk (*) indicates that, in the reference works thus checked, annotations will be found giving the location of copies of the original editions recorded therein.

2. COLONIAL PUBLICATIONS †

A) INTRODUCTION OF PRINTING AND TYPE-FOUNDING

McMurtrie, D. C.   The first printing in South America.   Facsimile
of the unique copy of the " Pragmatica sobre los diez dias del año,"
Lima, 1584, preserved in the John Carter Brown Library.   With a
note on Antonio Ricardo, the printer.   Providence, 1926.   871

Medina, J. T.   La primera muestra tipográfica salida de las prensas
de la América del Sur.   Reimpression foto-litográfica.   Santiago de
Chile, 1916.   872
Relates to the *Pragmatica* of 1584.

Winship, G. P.   The printing press in South America.   Providence,
1912.   873
Reprinted from *The Academy,* London, Nov. 25, 1911.

Wroth, L. C.   The Origins of typefounding in North and South
America.   (*In* Ars typographica.   Vol. II.   No. 4.   April 1926,
p. 273–307.)   874
Relates to the " first essay in type casting in Paraguay in 1705 or thereabouts "; to the first work, printed in Mexico in 1770, which bears a statement that it was printed with local types; and to the efforts at type casting
in the British colonies just before the outbreak of the Revolutionary War.
With facsimiles.

B) IN GENERAL

John Carter Brown Library (Providence)   Books printed in South
America elsewhere than at Lima before 1801.   [Boston, 1908.]   875

Winship, G. P.   Spanish America.   (*In* Peddie, R. A., *ed.*   Printing:
A short history of the art.   London, 1927, p. 306–318.)   876
A brief account of the first presses in Mexico, Peru, Paraguay, Colombia,
Ecuador, Venezuela, Chile, and Argentina.

c) BY LOCALITY

(1) ARGENTINA

Garnett, R.   Paraguayan and Argentine bibliography.   (*In* Bibliographica.   London, 1895.   Vol. I, pt. III, p. 262–273.)   877

† Printed within the colonies.

* Medina, J. T. . . . Historia y bibliografía de la imprenta en Buenos-Aires (1780–1810). La Plata [1892]. 2 v. (Museo de La Plata. Anales. III. La imprenta en la América Española.) 878

* ———. . . . Historia y bibliografía de la imprenta en Córdoba (1766). La Plata [1892]. (Museo de La Plata. Anales. III. La imprenta en la América Española.) 879

(2) BRAZIL

Brandenburger, C. Die ältesten brasilischen Drucke. (*In* Gutenberg Gesellschaft. Gutenberg Festschrift. Mainz, 1925, p. 58–61.) 880

Fleiuss, M. [The beginning of printing in Brazil.] (*In his* Paginas de historia, [Rio de Janeiro, 19—] p. 471–472.) 881

A brief account in Portuguese, a translation of which will be found above, in the note on early printing in America, V. (See: Index.)

Garnett, R. [A reference to the possibility of printing in Pernambuco as early as 1648.] (*In* Bibliographica. London, 1895. Vol. I, pt. III, p. 265.) 881:a

(3) CHILE

Laval, R. A. Un incunable chileno. Modo de ganar el jubileo santo año de 1776. Noticia bibliográfica. [Santiago de Chile] 1910. 882

* Medina, J. T. Bibliografía de la imprenta en Santiago de Chile desde sus origines hasta Febrero de 1817. Santiago de Chile, 1891. 883

The first imprint is assigned to the year 1780. See also Medina's *Bibliotheca hispano-chilena*, no. 862.

(4) COLOMBIA

* Medina, J. T. La imprenta en Bogotá (1739–1821). Notas bibliográficas. Santiago de Chile, 1904. 884

Posada, E. Bibliografía bogotana. Bogotá, 1917–25. 2 v. (Biblioteca de Historia Nacional. XVI, XXXVI.) 885

Vol. I. comprises 547 titles printed between 1738 and 1819.

The asterisk (*) indicates that, in the reference works thus checked, annotations will be found giving the location of copies of the original editions recorded therein.

(5) ECUADOR

* MEDINA, J. T.   La imprenta en Quito (1760–1818).   Notas bibliográficas.   Santiago de Chile, 1904.   886

(6) PARAGUAY

GARNETT, R.   Paraguayan and Argentine bibliography.   (*In* Bibliographica.   London, 1895.   Vol. I, pt. III, p. 262–273.)   887

* MEDINA, J. T.   . . . Historia y bibliografía de la imprenta en el Paraguay (1705–1727).   La Plata [1892].   (Museo de La Plata. Anales.   III. La imprenta en la América Española.)   888

[SCHULLER, R. R.]   . . . One of the rarest American books.   [Washington, D. C., 1913.]   889

Reprinted from *The American Anthropologist*, V. 15, no. 1, Jan.-March, 1913.   Relates to Garriga's *Instrvccion practica*, printed in 1713 by the Guarani Indians at the Jesuit mission Loreto, in Paraguay.   An account of the same work was issued by Dr. Schuller under title: *Um livro americano unico.* . . Pará, Brasil, 1910.

See also above, under: Introduction of Printing and Type-Founding, no. 874.

(7) PERU

JOHN CARTER BROWN LIBRARY (Providence)   Books printed in Lima, 1585–1800.   [Boston, 1908.]   890

——— A Facsimile of the first issue of the *Gazeta de Lima* with a description of a file for the years 1744–1763.   Boston [1908].   891

* MEDINA, J. T.   La imprenta en Lima (1584–1824) Santiago de Chile, 1904–1905.   4 v.   892

——— Un incunable limeño hasta ahora no descrito.   Reimpreso á plana y renglón.   Santiago de Chile, 1916.   893

Relates to the *Relacion de lo sucedido* of Balaguer de Salcedo, 1594.

* ——— Bibliografía de las lenguas Iuechua y Aymará.   New York, 1930.   (Museum of the American Indian, Heye Foundation.   Contributions.   Vol. VII, no. 7.)   894

Edited by Dr. R. R. Schuller, whose contributions to the bibliography of these languages is announced in its 'Foreword' as among the forthcoming publications of the Heye Foundation.

The asterisk (*) indicates that, in the reference works thus checked, annotations will be found giving the location of copies of the original editions recorded therein.

WINSHIP, G. P.   Early South American newspapers.   With a facsimile of the first issue of the 'Gazeta de Lima' January, 1744.
Worcester, 1908.   (Club of Odd Volumes. XIV.)   895

Reprinted from the *Proceedings* of the American Antiquarian Society, October,
1908.

See also above, under: Introduction of Printing, nos. 871–873.

D. *Island Colonies*

I. REGIONAL MONOGRAPHS

(1) BERMUDA

COLE, G. W.   Bermuda in periodical literature, with occasional references to other works.   A bibliography.   [Brookline,] 1907.   896

With facsimiles of various seventeenth and eighteenth century title-pages
relating to the 'Barmudas, now called Sommer Ilands.'

* ———. . . . Lewis Hughes the militant minister of the Bermudas and
his printed works.   Worcester, 1928.   896 :a

Reprinted from the *Proceedings* of the American Antiquarian Society for
October, 1927.   The bibliography of Hughes's printed works begins with 'A
letter sent into England from the Svmmer Ilands,' printed at London in 1615.

(2) CUBA

* PEREZ, L. M.   Apuntes de libros y folletos impresos en España y el
extranjero que tratan expresamente de Cuba desde principios del siglo
XVII hasta 1812 y de las disposiciones de gobierno impresas en La
Habana desde 1753 hasta 1800.   Habana, 1907.   897

TRELLES, C. M.   Ensayo de bibliografia cubana de los siglos XVII y
XVIII.   Matanzas, 1907.   897 :a

(3) JAMAICA

CUNDALL, F.   Bibliographia Jamaicensis.   A list of Jamaica books and
pamphlets . . . in the library of the Institute of Jamaica.   Kingston,
[1902].   898

A supplement was issued in 1908.

(4) PHILIPPINE ISLANDS

* MEDINA, J. T.   Bibliografía española de las Islas Filipinas (1523–
1810).   Santiago de Chile, 1898.   899

The asterisk (*) indicates that, in the reference works thus checked, annotations will be
found giving the location of copies of the original editions recorded therein.

RETANA [Y GAMBOA], W. E.   Aparato bibliográfico de la historia general de Filipinas deducido de la colección que posee en Barcelona la Compañia General de Tabacos de dichas islas.   Madrid, 1906. 3 v.   899:a

Vol. I: Anos 1524–1800.

ROBERTSON, J. A.   Bibliography of the Philippine Islands printed and manuscript.   Preceded by a descriptive account of the most important archives and collections containing Philippina.   Cleveland, 1908.
899:b

(5) WEST INDIES

CUNDALL, F.   Bibliography of the West Indies (excluding Jamaica). Kingston, 1909.   900

Comprises seventeenth and eighteenth century titles relating to Barbados, Martinique, Dominica, Guadeloupe, Montserrat, Antigua, St. Kitts-Nevis, Virgin Islands, St. Thomas and St. Croix, Porto Rico, St. Domingo, Bahamas, Cuba, Florida, Honduras, Panama, Colombia, Venezuela, Curacao and St. Eustatius, British Guiana, Dutch Guiana, French Guiana, Tobago, St. Vincent, St. Lucia, and general works on the West Indies.   With twelve sixteenth century titles relating to British Guiana and the West Indies in general.

DAMPIERRE, J. DE   Essai sur les sources de l'histoire des Antilles françaises (1492–1664) Paris, 1904.   (Société de l'Ecole des Chartes. Mémoires et documents. VI.)   900:a

* DE PUY, H. F.   . . . An early account of the establishment of Jesuit missions in America.   Worcester, 1921.   900:b

Relates to the 'Vida del P. Francisco de Borja. . . General de la Compania de Iesvs,' by P. de Ribadeneyra, Madrid, 1592, with reference to missions in the West Indies, Florida, Peru, Brazil; and to three titles on missions in Brazil, 1552, 1553, and 1555.

NEW YORK PUBLIC LIBRARY (New York)   List of works relating to the West Indies.   New York, 1912.   (Excerpt from the *Bulletin of the New York Public Library.*   Jan.-Aug., 1912.)   900:c

TOWER, CHARLEMAGNE (*Collection of*)   The Charlemagne Tower collection of American colonial laws.   [Philadelphia] 1890.   (Historical Society of Pennsylvania.)   900:d

Comprises a record of laws relative to Barbados, 1721–1764; Bermuda, 1719; Charibee Leeward Islands, 1734–1740; Jamaica, 1684–1756; Montserrat, 1740; Nevis, 1740; St. Christopher, 1739; etc., as well as to the territory of the United States.   Edited by C. S. R. Hildeburn.

The asterisk (*) indicates that, in the reference works thus checked, annotations will be found giving the location of copies of the original editions recorded therein.

2. COLONIAL PUBLICATIONS †

(1) IN GENERAL

* MEDINA, J. T.   Notas bibliográficas referentes á las primeras producciones de la imprenta en algunas ciudades de la América Española (Ambato, Angostura, Curazao, Guayaquil, Maracaibo, Nueva Orleans, Nueva Valencia, Panamá, Popayán, Puerto España, Puerto Rico, Querétaro, Santa Marta, Santiago de Cuba, Santo Domingo, Tunja y ortos lugares) (1754–1823.)   Santiago de Chile, 1904.   901

Records five almost unknown eighteenth century presses: Ambato, 1754; Nueva Valencia, 1764; Nueva Orleans, 1769; Puerto España, 1786; and Santiago de Cuba, 1796; the remaining presses being of the early nineteenth century.

(2) CUBA

* MEDINA, J. T.   La imprenta en la Habana (1707–1810).   Santiago de Chile, 1904.   902

(3) JAMAICA

* CUNDALL, F.   The Press and printers of Jamaica prior to 1820. Worcester, 1916.   903

Reprinted from the *Proceedings* of the American Antiquarian Society, October, 1916.   Comprises: I. History.   II. Bibliography (Newspapers, Sheet almanacs, Book almanacs, Magazines, Books printed in Jamaica).   III. The printers of Jamaica.   The bibliography begins with the *Weekly Jamaica Courant,* [Kingston,] 1722.

(4) PHILIPPINES

* MEDINA, J. T.   La imprenta en Manila desde sus origenes hasta 1810. Santiago de Chile, 1896, 1904.   904

The first work listed is a *Doctrina cristiana* of 1593.   A volume of *Adiciones y ampliaciones* was issued by Sr. Medina in 1904.   [See also the following works by Retana y Gamboa.]

RETANA [Y GAMBOA], W. E.   La imprenta en Filipinas (1593–1810) con una demostración gráfica de la originalidad de la primitiva.   Adiciones y observaciones á la Imprenta en Manila de D. J. T. Medina. Madrid, 1899.   904:a

—————— Tablas cronológica y alfabética de imprentas é impresores de Filipinas (1593–1898).   Madrid, 1908.   904:b

† Printed within the colonies.

The asterisk (*) indicates that, in the reference works thus checked, annotations will be found giving the location of copies of the original editions recorded therein.

E. *North America*

I. SPANISH POSSESSIONS

COWAN, R. E.   Bibliographical notes on early California.   (*In* American Historical Association.   Annual report.   1904, p. 269–278.)
905

A brief survey mentioning Cabrillo's discovery of the Bay of San Diego in 1542, his skirting of the coast, the visit of Sir Francis Drake in 1579, the use of the name 'California,' by Montalvo, in 1510, etc.

———— A Bibliography of the history of California and the Pacific West, 1510–1906.   San Francisco, 1914.
906

* DE PUY, H. F.   . . . An early account of the establishment of Jesuit missions in America.   Worcester, 1921.
907

Relates to the 'Vida del P. Francisco de Borja. . . General de la Compania de Iesvs,' by P. de Ribadeneyra, Madrid, 1592, with reference to missions in the West Indies, Florida, etc.

FERNANDEZ DE NAVARRETE, M.   Relacion del viage hecho por las goletas Sutil y Mexicana en el año de 1792.   Madrid, 1802.   908

With an introduction comprising a history of exploration along the western coast of America.

HODGE, F. W.   Bibliography of Fray Alonso de Benavides.   [New York, 1919.]   (Museum of the American Indian, Heye Foundation. Indian notes and monographs.   III, no. 1.)
908 :a

SMITH, BUCKINGHAM   Relation of Alvar Nuñez Cabeça de Vaca. Translated from the Spanish.   New York, 1871.   909

With a bibliographical introduction.

* WAGNER, H. R.   The Spanish Southwest, 1542–1794.   An annotated bibliography.   Berkeley, 1924.
910

With over a hundred reproductions of title-pages of books relating to the regions now comprised in Texas, New Mexico, California, etc.

WINSHIP, G. P.   A List of works useful to the student of the Coronado expedition.   (Reprinted in advance from the *Fourteenth annual report* of the Bureau of Ethnology.)   Washington, 1896.   911

The asterisk (*) indicates that, in the reference works thus checked, annotations will be found giving the location of copies of the original editions recorded therein.

2. DUTCH POSSESSIONS

ASHER, G. M.   A bibliographical and historical essay on the Dutch
books and pamphlets relating to New-Netherland and to the Dutch
West-India Company and to its possessions in Brazil, Angola, etc.
Amsterdam, 1854–67.   2 pts.   912

Covers the period from 1614 to 1666. With 'A list of the maps and charts
of New-Netherland . . . being a supplement to his *Bibliographical essay*. . .'
Amsterdam, New-York, 1855.

PALTSITS, V. H.   The Founding of New Amsterdam in 1626.   Reprinted from the *Proceedings* of the American Antiquarian Society
for April, 1924.   Worcester, 1925.   913

See also his invaluable *Bibliography* in Vol. VI of Stokes's *Iconography of
Manhattan Island*. New York, 1928.

STOKES, I. N. PHELPS   The Dutch period 1609–1664.   (*In his* Iconography of Manhattan Island, 1498–1909.   New York, 1915–1928.
Vol. I, p. 1–115.)   914

The cartography of the Dutch period is discussed in Vol. II, p. 41–120, etc;
the chronology of the period is given in Vol. IV, p. 28–244 and in the section
of 'Addenda'; and a list of reference works is given in V. H. Paltsits'
Bibliography in Vol. VI, p. 255 *et seq.*, a list of 'Contemporary publications
and accounts' being given on p. 258–264 of Paltsits' *Bibliography*.

3. SWEDISH POSSESSIONS

EBELING, C. D.   Erdbeschreibung und Geschichte von America. Hamburg, 1793–1816.   7 v.   915

With a list of sources. According to Mr. A. Johnson, one of the best of
the early accounts of New Sweden appears in Vol. III, p. 27, 558–569, 1796;
and Vol. V, p. 126, 1799.

JOHNSON, A.   The Swedish settlements on the Delaware, their history
and relation to the Indians, Dutch and English, 1638–1664.   New
York, 1911.   2 v.   916

With a bibliography, Vol. II, p. 767–812, listing contemporary source-
material, works of reference, etc.

KEEN, G. B.   New Sweden, or the Swedes on the Delaware.   (*In* Winsor, J., *ed.* Narrative and critical history of America. Boston and
New York [1886]. Vol. IV, p. 443–488.)   917

Followed by a *Critical essay on the sources of information*, p. 488–502.

TERNAUX-COMPANS, H. Underrättelse om den Fordna svenska
Kolonien i Norra Amerika. Stockholm, 1844.   918

A *Notice sur la colonie de la Nouvelle Suède* was issued by Ternaux-Compans
at Paris in 1843.

An essay on *Willem Usselinx,* founder of the Dutch and Swedish West
Indian companies, was issued by J. F. Jameson in 1887.

4. FRENCH POSSESSIONS †

A) IN GENERAL

BACKER, AUGUSTIN DE, AND ALOYS DE   Bibliothèque des écrivains de la
Compagnie de Jésus, ou Notices bibliographiques. . . Liège, 1853–
1861. 7 v.   919

Second ed. Brussels, 1869–1876. 3 v. See also, Sommervogel.

CARAYON, A. Bibliographie historique de la Compagnie de Jésus.
Paris, 1864.   920

Missions d'Amerique, Chap. IV, p. 176–202. The titles, which are arranged
chronologically, relate to missions in New France and in various countries
of South America.

CHAILLEY-BERT, J. Les Compagnies de colonization sous l'ancien
régime. Paris, 1898.   921

Pages 20–25 contain a chronological list of French colonization companies
from 1599 through 1789, beginning with the 'Compagnie du Canada et de
l'Acadie' (1599), 'Compagnie du Canada ou de la Nouvelle France, fondée
par des marchands de Dieppe, Rouen, La Rochelle' (1602), 'Compagnie du
Canada, 2e, fondée par Champlain' (1613), etc.

DIONNE, N. E. Québec et Nouvelle France. Bibliographie. Inventaire chronologique des ouvrages publiés à l'étranger en diverses langues sur Québec et la Nouvelle France . . . 1534–1906. Quebec,
1906. (Inventaire chronologique. II.)   922

The list of titles begins with an account of Cartier's voyage of 1535–1536,
published in 1545.

DOUGHTY, A., AND J. E. MIDDLETON   Bibliography of the siege of
Quebec. . . With a list of plans of Quebec by P. Lee Phillips.
Quebec, 1901.   923

FORD, W. C. French Royal edicts, *etc.,* on America. (*In* Massachusetts Historical Society. Proceedings. April 1927. Vol. LX,
p. 250–304.)   923:a

Relates to Canada, the West Indies, Guiana, and Louisiana. For additional
titles, see no. 938:a.

† Prior to 1764.

GAGNON, P. Essai de bibliographie canadienne. . . Avec des notes bibliographiques. Quebec, Montreal, 1895–1913. 2 v. 924

Arranged alphabetically by authors, containing a table of editions of Hennepin, 1683–1880, in French, English, German, Dutch, Italian, and Spanish, etc.

GOYENS, J. Le P. Louis Hennepin, O. F. M. . . Quelques jalons pour sa biographie. Quaracchi, 1925. 924 :a

Extrait de *L'Archivum Franciscanum Historicum,* XVIII, 1925.

GRANT, W. L., AND H. P. BIGGAR, *ed.* The History of New France by Marc Lescarbot. With an English translation, notes and appendices by W. L. Grant, M. A. (Oxon.). And an introduction by H. P. Biggar, B. Litt. (Oxon.) Toronto, 1907–1914. (The Champlain Society.) 3 v. 925

A list of Lescarbot's works, beginning with imprints of 1598, comprises the first appendix.

GRAVIER, G. Cavelier de La Salle de Rouen. Paris, 1871. 926

With a bibliography beginning with Hennepin's *Description de la Louisiane,* Paris, 1683.

———— *ed.* Relation du voyage des Dames religieuses Ursulines de Roüen à la Nouvelle-Orleans. Avec une introduction et des notes. Paris, 1872. 927

With an account of *Les Normands sur le Mississipi 1682–1727* and a reprint of the *Relation* of Mlle Hachard issued at Rouen in 1728.

GRIFFIN, A. P. C. Bibliography of the discovery and exploration of the Mississippi Valley. (*In* Knox College. The Library. An annotated catalogue of books belonging to the Finley collection. Galesburg, 1924, p. 47–67.) 928

Begins with the travels of Jean Nicolet recorded in the *Relation de ce qui s'est passé en la Nouvelle France,* Paris, 1641.

———— Discovery of the Mississippi. Bibliographical account of the travels of Nicolet, Alloüez, Marquette, Hennepin, and La Salle in the Mississippi Valley. (*In* Stiles, H. R., Joutel's journal of La Salle's last voyage 1684–7. With . . . the map of the original French edition, Paris, 1713, in facsimile. Albany, 1906, p. 221–239.) 929

HARRISSE, H. Notes pour servir à l'histoire, à la bibliographie et à la cartographie de la nouvelle-France et des pays adjacents, 1545–1700. Paris, 1872. 930

A supplement entitled *Cartographie de la Nouvelle France* was issued by G. A. Marcel in 1885.

THE JESUIT RELATIONS AND ALLIED DOCUMENTS   Travels and explorations of the Jesuit missionaries in New France, 1610–1791. The original French, Latin, and Italian texts, with English translations and notes; illustrated by portraits, maps, and facsimiles. Edited by Reuben Gold Thwaites. Cleveland, 1896–1901. 73 v.   931

Vols. 1–71 are arranged chronologically, beginning with Acadia, 1610–1616; and ending with Lower Canada, Illinois, 1759–1791. With bibliographical data at the end of each, edited by V. H. Paltsits. Vols. 72–73, index. For a complete list of contents, see: Library of Congress card no. 3–6351.

[LENOX, J.]   The Jesuit Relations, etc. New York, 1879. (Contributions to a catalogue of the Lenox Library. No. II.)   932

Relating for the most part to the *Jesuit Relations* of the seventeenth century, although recording various other works relating to New France.

* PALTSITS, V. H.   Bibliographical description of Denys' book. (*In* Ganong, W. F., *ed.* The description and natural history of the coasts of North America (Acadia) by Nicolas Denys. Toronto, 1908. The Champlain Society, II, p. 49–55.)   933
The bibliography begins with two issues of 1672.

* ——— Bibliographical description of the *Nouvelle Relation de la Gaspesie.* (*In* Ganong, W. F., *ed.* New relation of Gaspesia with the customs and religion of the Gaspesian Indians by Father Chrestien Le Clercq. Toronto, 1910, p. 42–46. [The Champlain Society. V.])
                934
The bibliographical data begins with the issue of 1691.

——— Bibliography of the works of Father Louis Hennepin. Chicago, 1903.   935

Twenty-five copies separately printed from pages xlv–lxiv of R. G. Thwaites's edition of Hennepin's *A New Discovery.* A survey and critical evaluation of earlier bibliographies of Hennepin, providing data on the editions of his works from 1683 through 1699 according to the standards of 'modern scientific bibliography.'

* ——— A Bibliography of the writings of Baron Lahontan. Chicago, 1905.   936

Twenty-five copies reprinted from R. G. Thwaites's edition of Lahontan's *New voyages to North-America,* and beginning with the so-called 'Angel issue' of the *Nouveaux voyages* printed at The Hague in 1703.

The asterisk (*) indicates that, in the reference works thus checked, annotations will be found giving the location of copies of the original editions recorded therein.

* PILLING, J. C.   Bibliography of the Iroquoian languages.   Washington, 1888.   (Smithsonian Institution.)   937

Relates to the general region of New France, etc.

SOMMERVOGEL, C.   Bibliothèque de la Compagnie de Jésus.   Bruxelles, 1890–1909.   10 v.   938

Première partie: Bibliographie par les pères Augustin et Aloys de Backer. Nouvelle édition.   A two-volume work entitled *Dictionnaire des ouvrages anonymes et pseudonymes publiés par des religieux de la Compagnie de Jésus* was issued by Sommervogel at Paris in 1884.

Four supplements to De Backer-Sommervogel were issued by E. M. Rivière, under title *Corrections et additions*, 1911–1917.

* WROTH, L. C., AND G. L. ANNAN   Acts of French Royal administration concerning Canada, Guiana, the West Indies and Louisiana, prior to 1791.   A list compiled . . . upon the basis of Worthington C. Ford's *French Royal edicts, etc., on America.*   (*In* New York Public Library.   Nov. 1929–[].   Vol. XXXIII, no. 11–[], p. 789–[].)

Issued as a 'separate' in 1930.   938 :a

See also under: Early Voyagers and Explorers, etc., nos. 687–715; Collected Narratives of Voyages, nos. 716–737; and Regional Maps, nos. 786–788. For Canada after 1763, see below, under: Period of Revolutions and Reconstruction, nos. 1203–1211.

B) COLONIAL PUBLICATIONS

McMURTRIE, D. C.   The first printing in the Province of Quebec. Chicago, 1928.   939

"Relates to two broadsides printed by Henri-Marie Dubreil de Pontbriand, Bishop of Quebec, in 1759, one at Quebec City and the other at Montreal." — *More Books.*

For facsimile, see Gagnon's *Essai de bibliographie canadienne* (under Pontbriand), 1895.

For other works on early printing in Canada, see below, under: Period of Revolutions and Reconstruction.   Canada (1763–1800).   For a note on early printing in Quebec, see: *Ars typographica*, Vol. II, no. 4, p. 339.   April 1926.

5. BRITISH POSSESSIONS †

A) IN GENERAL

* COLE, G. W.   Elizabethan Americana.   (*In* Bibliographical essays. A tribute to Wilberforce Eames.   June, MCMXXIV.   [Cambridge, 1924,] p. [161]–178.)   940

Relates to 22 rare books in English, printed between 1520 and 1641, with a table of the 59 copies known.

† Prior to 1764.

The asterisk (*) indicates that, in the reference works thus checked, annotations will be found giving the location of copies of the original editions recorded therein.

* DEXTER, H. M.   The Congregationalism of the last three hundred years, as seen in its literature . . . with a bibliographical appendix. New York, 1880.   941

FORD, P. L.   List of some briefs in appeal causes which relate to America, tried before the Lords Commissioners of Appeals of Prize Causes of His Majesty's Privy Council, 1736–1758.   Brooklyn, 1889.
                                                                              942
From the John Carter Brown Library copy which bears an annotation by Mr. Eames on the title-page, reading " now in the Lenox Branch of the New York Public Library."

GOOLD, W.   Early papermills of New-England   (*In* Historic and Gene-alogical Register.   April, 1875.)   943
Relates to the papermills built in Pennsylvania in 1690 and 1710, the making of paper in New England after 1728, etc.

HARRIS, R., AND S. K. JONES.   The Pilgrim press.   A bibliographical & historical memorial of the books printed at Leyden by the Pilgrim fathers.   Cambridge, 1922.   944

HENRY E. HUNTINGTON LIBRARY AND ART GALLERY (San Marino) Check-list or Brief catalogue of the Library of Henry E. Huntington (English literature tò 1640).   New York, 1919.   945
Compiled under the direction of George Watson Cole.   Lists the voyages of Capt. John Smith and other English books relating to America before 1640, comprised in the Huntington Library.
Many works relating to the British colonies are included in the *Catalogue* of the Church collection, now assimilated by the Henry E. Huntington Library.   See the beginning of the section of Americana, under: General Works.

ROHDE, E. S.   The old English herbals.   London, 1922.   946
With a chapter on herbals of the New World, referring to Frampton's trans-lation in 1577 of Monardes' *Dos Libros* of 1569; Josselyn's *New England's rarities,* London, 1672; Hughes's *American Physitian,* 1672; and the *Hortus Peruvianus Medicinalis* [London, 1715].

SMITH, JOSEPH   Bibliotheca anti-Quakeriana; or A catalogue of books adverse to the Society of Friends.   London, 1879.   947

————— A descriptive catalogue of Friends' books, or books written by members of the Society of Friends, commonly called Quakers.   Lon-don, 1867.   2 v.   948
See also under: Period of Discovery, nos. 681–686; Early Voyagers and Ex-plorers, nos. 698–715; Collected Narratives of Voyages, nos. 716–737; and

The asterisk (*) indicates that, in the reference works thus checked, annotations will be found giving the location of copies of the original editions recorded therein.

Regional Maps, nos. 791–800. For the British colonies after 1763, see below, under: Period of Revolutions and Reconstruction, nos. 1074–1202.

B) REGIONAL MONOGRAPHS †

(1) MAINE ‡

WILLIAMSON, J.   A Bibliography of the state of Maine from the earliest period to 1891. Portland, 1896. 2 v.   949

(2) MARYLAND

HARPER, L. C.   A Maryland tract of 1646. (*In* Bibliographical essays. A tribute to Wilberforce Eames. June, MCMXXIV. [Cambridge, 1924,] p. [143]–148.)   950

Relates to " A moderate and safe expedient to remove jealousies and feares, of any danger, or prejudice to this state, by the Roman Catholicks."

WROTH, L. C.   Introduction (*In* A Declaration of the Lord Baltemore's plantation in Mary-land. London, 1633. Baltimore, 1929.)
950:a

A facsimile of the only known copy of the first dated work relating to Maryland.

————— The Maryland colonization tracts, 1632–1646. (*In* Essays offered to Herbert Putnam. New Haven, 1929.)   950:b

(3) MASSACHUSETTS

HUNNEWELL, J. F.   Bibliography of Charlestown, Massachusetts, and Bunker Hill. Boston, 1880.   951

A chronological list of works dating from 1650 and 1659 to 1880, with a list of contemporary newspaper accounts of the Battle of Bunker Hill.

For Massachusetts imprints, see below, under: Colonial Publications.

(4) NEW ENGLAND

* [EAMES, W.]   Bibliographical note. (*In* The Humble request of his Majesties loyal subjects the governour and the company late gone for New England. . . New edition in facsimile of the rare original of 1630. Washington, 1905.)   952

† Listed alphabetically.
‡ Originally part of Massachusetts.

The asterisk (*) indicates that, in the reference works thus checked, annotations will be found giving the location of copies of the original editions recorded therein.

LIVINGSTON, L. S., *ed.*   A briefe and true relation of the discouerie of the north part of Virginia.   By John Brereton.   Reproduced in fac-simile from the first edition of 1602.   With an introductory note. New York, 1903.   953

Relates to the voyage made in 1602 by Capt. Gosnold, Capt. Gilbert, and others by permission of Sir Walter Raleigh.

WINSOR, J.   The earliest printed sources of New England history, 1602–1629.   Cambridge, 1894.   954

Reprinted from the *Proceedings* of the Massachusetts Historical Society, November, 1894.

(5) NEW YORK

* NEUMANN, F., *ed.*   A brief description of New York formerly called New Netherlands.   By Daniel Denton.   Reprinted from the original edition of 1670.   With a bibliographical introduction.   Cleveland, 1902.   955

* PALTSITS, V. H.   Daniel Denton's Description of New York in 1670. (*In* Two important gifts to the New York Public Library by Mr. George F. Baker, Jr.   New York, 1924, p. 9–14.)   956

An account of the first separate publication in English, relative to the province of New York.   With a location list and notes on the nineteen copies known.

For works relating to early New York, see also Mr. Paltsits' *Bibliography* in Vol. VI of Stokes's *Iconography of Manhattan Island*.   New York, 1928.

STOKES, I. N. PHELPS   The English period, 1664–1763.   (*In his* Inconography of Manhattan Island, 1498–1909.   New York, 1915–1928.   Vol. I, p. 159–201.)   957

The chronology of the English period is given in Vol. IV, p. 245–729; and reference works are listed in V. H. Paltsits' *Bibliography* Vol. VI, p. 245 *et seq.*

——— The Inconography of Manhattan Island, 1498–1909.   Compiled from original sources and illustrated by photo-intaglio reproductions of important maps, plans, views, and documents in public and private collections.   New York, 1915–1928.   6 v.   958

With chapters on the period of discovery (1524–1609), the Dutch period (1609–1664), the English period (1664–1763), the Revolutionary period (1763–1783), the period of adjustment and reconstruction (1783–1811); and, in Vol. VI, 1928, a bibliography compiled by Victor H. Paltsits.   For contents, in so far as the work relates to the subject of this book, see analytical entries.

The asterisk (*) indicates that, in the reference works thus checked, annotations will be found giving the location of copies of the original editions recorded therein.

(6) SOUTHERN COLONIES

BOYD, W. K.   Some eighteenth century tracts concerning North Carolina. Raleigh, 1927.   959

CRANE, V. W.   The promotion literature of Georgia.   (*In* Bibliographical essays.   A tribute to Wilberforce Eames.   June, MCM-XXIV.   [Cambridge, 1924] p. [281]–298.)   960

———— The southern frontier, 1670–1732. Durham, 1928.   960:a
A historical study based upon the pamphlets and original archival sources relating to southern expansion in the seventeenth century, the beginnings of British western policy, international rivalries in the "old Southwest," the philanthropists and the genesis of Georgia, etc.   The references given in Professor Crane's footnotes and elsewhere in the book cover comprehensively the printed sources relating to this period and section.

DE RENNE, WYMBERLEY JONES (*The Library of*)   Books relating to the history of Georgia. . . [Savannah] 1905.   961
Begins with Montgomery's *Discourse concerning the design'd establishment of a new colony to the south of Carolina in the most delightful country in the universe,* London, 1717.   An enlarged catalogue of the De Renne collection, compiled and annotated by Oscar Wegelin, was issued in 1911.

WHITNEY, E. L.   Bibliography of the colonial history of South Carolina.   (From the *Annual report* of the American Historical Association for 1894, p. 563–586.) Washington, 1896.   962
Relates largely to works of the eighteenth century with occasional sixteenth and seventeenth century titles.

(7) VERMONT †

GILMAN, M. D., *comp.*   The Bibliography of Vermont. Burlington, 1897.   963
With additional material by G. G. Benedict (*ed.*), and T. L. Wood.

(8) VIRGINIA

LIVINGSTON, L. S.   Introductory note.   (*In* Hariot, T. A briefe and true report of the new found land of Virginia. . . Reproduced in facsimile from the first edition of 1588. New York, 1903.)   964
"The earliest printed original book in the English language relating to the region now comprised within the limits of the United States."

† Originally part of New York and New Hampshire.

NEW YORK PUBLIC LIBRARY (New York)　Virginia.　History by periods. (*In* Bulletin of the New York Public Library. Feb.-April, 1907. [List of works in the New York Public Library relating to Virginia,] p. 20–37.)　　　　965

Covers the period from the Raleigh colony, 1589, and Capt. Bartholomew Gilbert's voyage in 1603, to the communications on the resolutions of the Legislature of Virginia in 1800.　See also below, under the works of W. Clayton-Torrence, nos. 1072–1072:a.

STEVENS, H. (of Vermont)　Thomas Hariot, the mathematician, the philosopher and the scholar developed chiefly from dormant materials, with notices of his associates including biographical and bibliographical disquisitions upon the materials of the history of ' Ould Virginia.' London, 1900.　　　　966

c) RELATIONS WITH THE INDIANS

* DE PUY, H. F.　A Bibliography of the English colonial treaties with the American Indians, including a synopsis of each treaty.　New York, 1917.　　　　967

With a table giving the date of each treaty, and the place and date of imprint — the first being the *Articles of peace between . . . Charles II . . . and several Indian Kings and Queens, &c. Concluded the 29th day of May, 1677,* London, 1677.

FIELD, T. W.　An Essay towards an Indian bibliography.　Being a catalogue of books, relating to the . . . American Indians, in the library of Thomas W. Field.　With bibliographical and historical notes.　New York, 1873.　　　　968

NEWBERRY LIBRARY, EDWARD E. AYER COLLECTION (Chicago)　Narratives of captivity among the Indians of North America.　A list of books and manuscripts.　Chicago, [1912].　　　　969

Comprises over three hundred titles of original editions and their reprints, relating for the most part to captivities of the eighteenth century with an occasional rare account of earlier date.

A pamphlet, entitled *Notes on the historical source material in the Ayer Collection on the North American Indian* was issued by the Newberry Library in 1927.

* PILLING, J. C.　Bibliography of the Algonquian languages.　Washington, 1891.　(Smithsonian Institution.)　　　　970

Relates to the works of John Eliot, Capt. John Smith, Roger Williams, etc. For works relative to the Eliot Bible and Eliot Indian tracts, see below, under: Colonial publications: Indian languages.

The asterisk (*) indicates that, in the reference works thus checked, annotations will be found giving the location of copies of the original editions recorded therein.

* —————— Bibliography of the Iroquoian languages. Washington, 1888. (Smithsonian Institution.)   971

Relates to the general region of New France, New Sweden, etc.

* —————— Bibliography of the Muskhogean languages. Washington, 1889. (Smithsonian Institution.)   972

Relates to the general region of Florida, Georgia, the Carolinas, etc.

* —————— Bibliography of the Wakashan languages. Washington, 1894. (Smithsonian Institution.)   973

Relates to the region explored by Captain Cook, 1776–1780, etc.

WINSOR, J. The New-England Indians: A bibliographical survey, 1630–1700. Cambridge, 1895.   974

Reprinted from the *Proceedings* of the Massachusetts Historical Society, November, 1895.

See also below, under: Indian Language, nos. 1000–1001.

D) COLONIAL PUBLICATIONS †

(1) IN GENERAL

* EVANS, C. American bibliography by Charles Evans. A chronological dictionary of all books, pamphlets and periodical publications printed in the United States of America from the genesis of printing in 1639 down to and including the year 1820, with bibliographical and biographical notes. Chicago, 1903–. [10 v.]   975

Vols. I–VIII, 1903–1914, cover the period from 1639 through 1792; Vol. IX, 1925, the years 1793–1794; Vol. X, 1929, the years 1795, partly through 1796. Arranged chronologically, with authors listed alphabetically under each year, and comprising in 1929 a total of 30,832 titles. With subject index in each volume.

GREEN, S. A. A List of early American imprints belonging to the library of the Massachusetts Historical Society. Cambridge, 1895. 976

Titles arranged chronologically, 1643–1700. A supplementary list appeared in 1898, a second in 1899, and a third in 1903.

PAINE, N. A List of early American imprints 1640–1700 belonging to the library of the American Antiquarian Society. Worcester, 1896. 977

Reprinted from the *Proceedings* of the American Antiquarian Society, Oct. 1895.

† Printed within the colonies.

The asterisk (*) indicates that, in the reference works thus checked, annotations will be found giving the location of copies of the original editions recorded therein.

PARRINGTON, V. L.   The colonial mind 1620–1800. New York, 1927.
                                                                    978
A discussion of colonial literature and thought, not bibliographical.

* ROSENBACH, A. S. W.   An American Jewish bibliography. Being a
list of books and pamphlets by Jews or relating to them printed in the
United States from the establishment of the press in the colonies until 1850. [Baltimore, 1926.]   979
   Arranged chronologically, beginning with the Bay Psalm Book of 1640, in
   which Hebrew type was first used on the western continent and which contains, in its perface, "the first dissertation on Hebrew poetry and language
   to be published in America."

TYLER, M. C.   A History of American literature, 1607–1765.   New
York, 1879. 2 v.   980

UPDIKE, D. B.   Types used in the American colonies, and some early
American specimens.   (In his Printing types: Their history, forms,
and use. Cambridge, 1922. Vol. II, p. 149–159.)   981
   Begins with the establishment of the Cambridge press in 1638.

WROTH, L. C.   The colonial printer. New York [In press, 1930].
(The Grolier Club.)   982
   Covers the period from 1639 until 1800.

——— North America. (English-speaking.)   (In Peddie, R. A., ed.
Printing: A short history of the art. London, 1927, p. 319–362.)
                                                                  982 :a
   For a note on Isaiah Thomas's History of printing in America see below,
   under no. 1259.

(2) ALMANACS

* BATES, A. C.   Check list of Connecticut almanacs 1709–1850.
Worcester, 1914.   983
   Reprinted from the Proceedings of the American Antiquarian Society for
   April, 1914.

* CHAPIN, H. M.   Check list of Rhode Island almanacs 1643–1850.
Worcester, 1915.   (American Antiquarian Society.)   984

* MORRISON, H. A.   Preliminary check list of American almanacs
1639–1800. Washington, 1907. (United States. Library of Congress.)   985

      The asterisk (*) indicates that, in the reference works thus checked, annotations will be
   found giving the location of copies of the original editions recorded therein.

* NICHOLS, C. L.   Notes on the almanacs of Massachusetts.   Worcester, 1912.   986

A chronological list of Massachusetts almanacs, 1639–1850. Reprinted from the *Proceedings* of the American Antiquarian Society for April 1912. His **Checklist of Maine, New Hampshire and Vermont almanacs* was issued by the Society in 1929.

* PAGE, A. B.   John Tulley's almanacks, 1687–1702.   (*In* Colonial Society of Massachusetts. Papers. Dec. 1910, p. 207–223.)   987

* PALTSITS, V. H.   The Almanacs of Roger Sherman 1750–1761. Worcester, 1907.   988

One hundred copies reprinted from the *Proceedings* of the American Antiquarian Society.

WINSHIP, G. P., *ed.*   The Rhode-Island almanack for the year, 1728. Being the first ever printed in that colony, carefully reproduced. . . [Providence] 1911.   989

A facsimile of the first Rhode Island almanac, printed at Newport by James Franklin in 1728; with a bibliographical note on the only known copy, that in the Library of Congress.

See also note under no. 1109.

(3) BIBLES

* [EAMES, W.]   Bibliographic notes on Eliot's Indian Bible. . .   Washington, 1890.   990

Two hundred and fifty copies reprinted from Pilling's *Algonquian languages.*

NICHOLS, C. L.   The Boston edition of the Baskett Bible. Worcester, 1927.   991

Reprinted from the *Proceedings* of the American Antiquarian Society, April 1927. A monograph on the thesis 'that Kneeland and Green did print a quarto Bible for the booksellers of Boston, between 1750 and 1752,' which, if found, may be called ' our first Bible in the English language printed in the British colonies.'

O'CALLAGHAN, E. B.   A List of editions of the Holy Scriptures and parts thereof, printed in America previous to 1860; with introduction and bibliographical notes. Albany, 1861.   992

WRIGHT, J.   Early Bibles of America. New York, 1892.   993

With chapters on the Eliot Bible, the Saur Bible, the Aitken Bible, the first Douay version, the Thomas Bible, the Collins Bible, the first Greek Bible in America, etc.

The asterisk (*) indicates that, in the reference works thus checked, annotations will be found giving the location of copies of the original editions recorded therein.

(4) BROADSIDES

* [FORD, W. C.]   Broadsides, ballads &c.   Printed in Massachusetts, 1639–1800.   [Boston] 1922.   (Massachusetts Historical Society.)
994

* LANE, W. C.   Early   Harvard   broadsides.   Worcester,   1914. (American Antiquarian Society.)   995

The list starts with the *Thesis* of 1642, of which no copy is now known, and continues through 1810.

PAINE, N.   A List of early American broadsides, 1680–1800, belonging to the library of the American Antiquarian Society.   Worcester, 1897.   996

(5) CURRENCY

* DAVIS, A. McF.   Colonial currency reprints, 1682–1751.   Boston, 1910–1911.   4 v.   (Prince Society.)   997

Vol. I, p. viii–x: Chronological list of pamphlets, checked for the location of copies.

(6) DRAMA

WEGELIN, O.   Early American plays, 1714–1830.   Second edition revised.   New York, 1905.   998

The first edition appeared in 1900.

(7) FRANKLIN

* FORD, P. L.   Franklin bibliography.   A list of books written by, or relating to Benjamin Franklin.   Brooklyn, 1889.   999

For various monographs relating to Franklin, see below, under: Period of Revolutions and Reconstruction: Leaders: Franklin, nos. 1081–1085.

(8) INDIAN LANGUAGES

* [EAMES, W.]   Bibliographic notes on Eliot's Indian Bible and his other translations and works in the Indian language of Massachusetts. Washington, 1890.   1000

Two hundred and fifty copies reprinted from Pilling's *Algonquian languages*. (For Pilling's bibliographies of works in various Indian languages see above, under: British Possessions: Relations with the Indians, nos. 970–973.)

The asterisk (*) indicates that, in the reference works thus checked, annotations will be found giving the location of copies of the original editions recorded therein.

WINSHIP, G. P.   The Eliot Indian tracts.   (*In* Bibliographical essays. A tribute to Wilberforce Eames.   June, MCMXXIV.   [Cambridge, 1924,] p. [179]–192.)   1001

Reprinted as a separate, with additions, in 1925.

An essay on *Eliot's Indian Bible* by Z. H[araszti], with a page in facsimile, appeared in: Boston Public Library.   *More books.*   June, 1929.

See also above, under: British Possessions.   Relations with the Indians, nos. 967–974.

(9) JUVENILE LITERATURE

* BATES, A. C.   The History of the Holy Jesus.   A list of editions of this once popular children's book.   Hartford, 1911.   1002

Begins with an unknown edition advertised in the *Boston News Letter* as ' just published ' January 31, 1745.

* EAMES, W.   Early New England catechisms.   A bibliographical account of some catechisms published before the year 1800, for use in New England.   Worcester, 1898.   1003

Two hundred copies reprinted from the *Proceedings* of the American Antiquarian Society.   New series.   XII.   Relates ' chiefly to some of the catechisms for children and older persons, which were used in New England in the seventeenth and eighteenth centuries.'

* FORD, P. L.   The New-England primer.   New York, 1897.   1004

Appendix VI contains: Bibliography of the New England primer (1727–1799).

FORD, W. C.   The New England primer.   (*In* Bibliographical essays. A tribute to Wilberforce Eames.   June, MCMXXIV.   [Cambridge, 1924,] p. [61]–65.)   1005

An account of late developments in the history of the New England primer.

* HEARTMAN, C. F.   The New England primer issued prior to 1830. A bibliographical checklist. . .   [New York] 1922.   (Heartman's Historical Series, no. 15.   Second issue.)   1006

Begins with the issue of 1727 and records 143 issues before 1800.   An enlargement of the edition of 1915.

* MERRITT, P.   The Royal primer.   (*In* Bibliographical essays.   A tribute to Wilberforce Eames.   June, MCMXXIV.   [Cambridge, 1924,] p. [35]–60.)   1007

With a check list of eight English editions, 1750–1818, and seven American editions, 1753–1796.

The asterisk (*) indicates that, in the reference works thus checked, annotations will be found giving the location of copies of the original editions recorded therein.

(10) LAWS, STATUTES, PUBLIC DOCUMENTS, ETC.

(a) In General

BELDEN, C. F. D., *ed.*   Hand-list of legislative sessions and session laws, statutory revisions, compilations, codes, etc., and constitutional conventions of the United States and its possessions and of the several states to May 1912. Boston, 1912. (Massachusetts. State Library.)
1008

With historical notes or chronology preceding each section.

HASSE, A. R.   Materials for a bibliography of the public archives of the thirteen original states covering the colonial period and the state period to 1789. Washington, 1908.   1009

Reprinted from the *Annual Report* of the American Historical Association for 1906. II, p. 239–572.

TOWER, CHARLEMAGNE (*Collection of*)   The Charlemagne Tower collection of American colonial laws. [Philadelphia] 1890. (Historical Society of Pennsylvania.)   1010

Comprises a record of laws relating to the British colonies and to the United States from 1641 to about 1800, with some titles relating to Canada, Barbados, Bermuda, etc. Edited by C. S. R. Hildeburn.

(b) Connecticut

* BATES, A. C.   Connecticut statute laws. A bibliographical list of editions of Connecticut laws from the earliest issues to 1836. [Hartford] 1900.   1011

Begins with imprints of 1673 and 1702.

(c) Massachusetts

FARRAND, M., *ed.*   The Laws and liberties of Massachusetts, reprinted from the copy of the 1648 edition in the Henry E. Huntington Library. Cambridge, 1929.   1012

* FORD, W. C., AND A. MATTHEWS.   A Bibliography of the laws of the Massachusetts Bay 1641–1776. Cambridge, 1907.   1013

Reprinted from the *Publications* of the Colonial Society of Massachusetts. No. IV.

The asterisk (*) indicates that, in the reference works thus checked, annotations will be found giving the location of copies of the original editions recorded therein.

(d) New York

*HASSE, A. R.   Some materials for a bibliography of the official publications of the General Assembly of the colony of New York, 1693–1775. New York, 1903. (New York Public Library. Bulletin. Feb.-Apr. 1903.)   1014

HILDEBURN, C. R.   Bibliographical note. (*In* New York. Facsimile of the laws and acts of the General Assembly for their Majesties Province of New-York, etc. Printed and sold by William Bradford . . . 1694. Together with an historical introduction. New York, The Grolier Club, 1894, p. cliii–clviii.)   1015

(e) Pennsylvania

ADAMS, R. G.   A variant title to William Penn's " Frame of government." (The Pennsylvania Magazine of History and Biography, April 1925. Supplement to Vol. XLIX, no. 194.)   1016

With facsimile of the variant title-pages of 1682.

[MONTGOMERY, T. L.]   Check list of the laws, minutes, journals and documents published by Pennsylvania, 1682–1901. (*In* Pennsylvania. Report of the State Librarian of Pennsylvania 1903. [Harrisburg,] 1904, p. 117–213.)   1016:a

(f) Rhode Island

BONGARTZ, J. H., *ed.*   Check list of Rhode Island laws. Providence, 1893.   1017

A brief list of the public laws, and acts and resolves, from early colonial times to the date of publication. Revised in 1921.

A series of facsimiles of *Rhode Island acts and resolves,* Oct. 1747-Oct. 1800, sometimes designated as the 'Bongartz facsimile reprints,' 20 v., was issued at Providence, 1908-1925.

(g) Virginia

SWEM, E. G.   The Acts and the journals of the General Assembly of the colony, 1619–1776. Richmond, 1919. (*In his* Bibliography of Virginia. Pt. III.)   1018

(11) MUSIC

*METCALF, F. J.   American psalmody or Titles of books, containing tunes printed in America from 1721 to 1820. New York, 1917. (Heartman's Historical Series. XXVII.)   1019

The asterisk (*) indicates that, in the reference works thus checked, annotations will be found giving the location of copies of the original editions recorded therein.

METCALF, F. J.   American writers and compilers of sacred music.   New
York, [*c.* 1925].   1019:a
> With a frontispiece reproducing the earliest music printed in America, in
> the ninth edition of the Bay Psalm Book, 1698.

SACHSE, J. F.   The Music of the Ephrata Cloister. . .   Amplified
with fac-simile reproductions of parts of the text and some original
Ephrata music of the *Weyrauchs Hügel,* 1739; *Rosen und Lilien,*
1745; *Turtel Taube,* 1747; *Choral Buch,* 1754, etc.   Lancaster, 1903.
                                                                          1020

* SONNECK, O. G.   Bibliography of early secular American music.
Washington, 1905.   1021
> Relates largely to eighteenth century material.

(12) NEWSPAPERS AND PERIODICALS

* BEER, W.   Checklist of American periodicals, 1741–1800.   Worcester, 1923.   1022
> Reprinted from the *Proceedings* of the American Antiquarian Society,
> October, 1922.   A list of ninety-eight periodicals.

* BRIGHAM, C. S.   Bibliography of American newspapers, 1690–1820.
(*In* American Antiquarian Society.   Proceedings.   Oct. 1913-April
1927.)   1023
> A list, approximating 1,900 titles, of all the newspapers published in this
> country previous to 1821.   The states from Alabama to Virginia are covered
> in eighteen installments published in the Society's *Proceedings.*   The *Bib-
> liography,* with additions and corrections, will be separately issued in two
> volumes, presumably in 1930.

* CRITTENDEN, C. C.   North Carolina newspapers before 1790.
Chapel Hill, N. C., 1928.   (University of North Carolina.   The
James Sprunt Historical Studies.   XX.)   1024
> Begins with an account of the publication of *The North Carolina Gazette*
> in 1751.

GRISWOLD, A. T.   Annotated catalogue of newspaper files in the library
of the State Historical Society of Wisconsin.   Madison, 1911.   1025
> Arranged chronologically under states.

NELSON, W.   Notes toward a history of the American newspaper.
New York, 1918.   (Heartman's Historical Series.   XXXI.)   1026
> Covers the period from 1690 onward.   With a reference in its introduction
> to 'A narrative of the newspapers printed in New England,' printed in the
> *Collections* of the Massachusetts Historical Society, 1798 and 1800.

The asterisk (*) indicates that, in the reference works thus checked, annotations will be
found giving the location of copies of the original editions recorded therein.

SLAUSON, A. B. A Checklist of American newspapers in the Library of Congress. Washington, 1901. (United States. Library of Congress.) 1027

A 'Want list' was issued by the Library of Congress in 1909.

* STOKES, I. N. PHELPS Early New York newspapers. Bibliographical data. Check-list of some early New York newspapers, 1725–1811. (*In his* Iconography of Manhattan Island. New York, 1915–1928. Vol. II, p. 409–452.) 1028

WINSHIP, G. P. Newport newspapers in the eighteenth century. (*In* Newport Historical Society. Bulletin. XIV. Oct., 1914.) 1029

YALE UNIVERSITY, LIBRARY (New Haven) A List of newspapers in the Yale University Library. New Haven, 1916. 1029 :a

(13) POETRY

HALL, H. J. Benjamin Tompson, 1642–1714, first native-born poet of America. . . With an introduction. Boston, 1924. 1030

HUNNEWELL, J. F. Early poetry of the provinces, now parts of the United States. (*In his* New-England's crisis by Benjamin Tompson. Boston, 1894, p. 9–28. [The Club of Odd Volumes.]) 1031

STEINER, B. C. Early Maryland poetry. The works of Ebenezer Cook, Gent: Laureat of Maryland. Baltimore, 1900. (Maryland Historical Society. Fund Publication, no. 36.) 1032

Relates to *The Sot-weed factor* printed in London, 1708, etc.

STOCKBRIDGE, J. C. . . . A Catalogue of the Harris collection of American poetry. Providence, 1886. 1033

A list of the books given to Brown University by the Hon. Henry B. Anthony.

WEGELIN, O. Early American poetry. A compilation of the titles of volumes of verse and broadsides, written by writers born or residing in North America, and issued during the seventeenth and eighteenth centuries. New York, 1903. 1034

Covers the period 1650–1799. For additional titles see Wegelin's *Early American poetry, 1800–1820. With an appendix containing the titles . . . which were omitted in the volume containing the years 1650-1799.* New York, 1907.

The asterisk (*) indicates that, in the reference works thus checked, annotations will be found giving the location of copies of the original editions recorded therein.

(14) PRAYER BOOKS

WRIGHT, J. Early Prayer Books of America; being a descriptive account of Prayer Books published in the United States, Mexico, and
Canada. St. Paul, 1896.   1035

> With facsimile title-pages of the Mohawk Prayer book printed by William
> Bradford at New York in 1715; the Manual of Catholic Prayers, Philadel-
> phia, 1774; revised Prayer Book of the Protestant Episcopal Church, Phila-
> delphia, 1786; etc.

(15) RELIGIOUS WORKS

* DEXTER, H. M. The Congregationalism of the last three hundred
years, as seen in its literature . . . with a bibliographical appendix.
New York, 1880.   1036

* HOLMES, T. J. Increase Mather, his works, being a short-title catalogue of the works that can be ascribed to him. Cleveland, 1930.
                                                              1036:a

PAINE, N. Works of the Mathers. (*In his* List of books received by
the American Antiquarian Society from the sale of the first part of the
Brinley library . . . Worcester, 1879, p. 13–57.)   1037

SIBLEY, J. L. Biographical sketches of graduates of Harvard University. 1642–1689. Cambridge, 1873–1885. 3 v.   1038

> Biographical sketches followed, in each instance, by a list of the published
> writings of Harvard graduates — the Mathers, Wigglesworth, Urian Oakes,
> etc.

SMITH, JOSEPH. Bibliotheca anti-Quakeriana; or a catalogue of books
adverse to the Society of Friends. London, 1873.   1039

> Comprises occasional titles printed in the colonies.

—————— A descriptive catalogue of Friends' books, or books written by
members of the Society of Friends, commonly called Quakers. London, 1867. 2 v.   1039:a

> Comprises titles printed in the colonies and elsewhere.

* TUTTLE, J. H. Writings of Rev. John Cotton. (*In* Bibliographical
essays. A tribute to Wilberforce Eames. June, MCMXXIV.
[Cambridge, 1924,] p. [363]–380.)   1040

> With a list of 77 titles printed between 1630 and 1663.

> See also above, under: Bibles, nos. 990–993; and Music, nos. 1019–1021.

The asterisk (*) indicates that, in the reference works thus checked, annotations will be
found giving the location of copies of the original editions recorded therein.

(16) TEXTBOOKS

[GREENWOOD, J. M., AND A. MARTIN] Notes on the history of American text-books on arithmetic. Washington, 1899. 1041

Excerpt: United States Bureau of Education. *Report,* for 1897–1898. Ch. XVII. The list of arithmetical works begins with the 'Arithmetick vulgar and decimal' attributed to Isaac Greenwood and printed in Boston in 1729. Reference is made, however, to Hodder's 'Arithmetic' reprinted in Boston in 1719 from the London edition of 1661.

* KARPINSKI, L. C. Colonial American arithmetics. (*In* Bibliographical essays. A tribute to Wilberforce Eames. June, MCMXXIV. [Cambridge, 1924,] p. [242]–248.) 1042

With a list of 29 arithmetics and arithmetical works published in America between 1539 and 1776.

LITTLEFIELD, G. E. Early schools and school-books of New England. Boston, 1904. (Club of Odd Volumes.) 1043

A bibliographical account of New England text-books of the seventeenth and eighteenth centuries: the catechism, hornbook, spellers, readers, arithmetics, self-instructors, mathematical books, grammars in various languages, English, Latin and Greek dictionaries, etc. With facsimile title-pages.

(17) WITCHCRAFT

HOLMES, T. J. The Mather literature. Cleveland, 1927. 1044

Comprises chapters on collections of Mather literature, Increase Mather's termination of the witchcraft trials at Salem, an account of Mr. William Gwinn Mather's plan for an adequate Mather bibliography, etc.

———— The surreptitious printing of one of Cotton Mather's manuscripts. (*In* Bibliographical essays. A tribute to Wilberforce Eames. June, MCMXXIV. [Cambridge, 1924,] p. [149]–160.) 1044:a

Relates to Mather's *Another brand pluckt out of the burning, or More wonders of the invisible world* relative to the case of Margaret Rule.

MOORE, G. H. Bibliographical notes on witchcraft in Massachusetts. Worcester, 1888. (American Antiquarian Society.) 1045

WINSOR, J. The Literature of witchcraft in New England. Worcester, 1896. 1046

Reprinted from the *Proceedings* of the American Antiquarian Society, October, 1895.

The asterisk (*) indicates that, in the reference works thus checked, annotations will be found giving the location of copies of the original editions recorded therein.

(18) INTRODUCTION OF PRINTING

* EAMES, W., *ed.*   The Bay Psalm Book.   Being a facsimile . . . of the first edition, printed by Stephen Daye at Cambridge, in New England in 1640.   With an introduction by Wilberforce Eames. New York, 1903.   1047

Re-issued in 1912 by the New England Society in the City of New York, without the name of the editor on the title-page.

* [————] A List of editions of the " Bay Psalm Book " or the New England version of the Psalms.   New York, 1885.   1047 :a

Twenty-five copies reprinted from Sabin's *Dictionary,* Vol. XVI.

* RODEN, R. F.   The Cambridge press, 1638–1692.   A history of the first printing press established in English America, together with a bibliographical list of the issues of the press.   New York, 1905.   1048

For the beginning of type-founding, see below under: Beginning of Type-Founding, nos. 1169–1170:a.

(19) REGIONAL MONOGRAPHS

(*a*) *Connecticut*

LOVE, W. DEL.   Thomas Short, the first printer of Connecticut. [Hartford,] 1901.   (The Acorn Club.)   1049

Issued to accompany a facsimile of a broadside proclamation for a fast in Connecticut, printed by Thomas Short at New London, in June, 1709.

PALTSITS, V. H.   John Holt — printer and postmaster.   Some facts and documents relating to his career.   (*In* New York Public Library. *Bulletin.*   Sept. 1920.   Vol. 24, no. 9, p. 483–499.)   1050

Relates to Holt's activities and interests in Connecticut, New York, and Virginia, 1755–1784.

TRUMBULL, J. H.   List of books printed in Connecticut, 1709–1800. [Hartford,] 1904.   1050 :a

(*b*) *Georgia*

McMURTRIE, D. C.   James Johnston, first printer in the royal colony of Georgia.   (*In* The Library.   Fourth ser.   June 1929.   Vol. X, no. 1, p. 73–83.)   1051

Relates to an act for the printing of the laws of the province, by the General Assembly of Georgia, 4 March 1762; the beginning of printing in 1763; etc.

The asterisk (*) indicates that, in the reference works thus checked, annotations will be found giving the location of copies of the original editions recorded therein.

(c) Maryland

McCREARY, G. W.   The first book printed in Baltimore-town.   Nicholas Hasselbach, printer.   Baltimore, 1903.   1052

With a reprint of *A detection of the conduct and proceedings of Messrs. Annan and Henderson, April 18th. Anno Domini 1764 . . . wherein is contained some remarks by John Redick-le-man.*   Baltimore-town [1765].

* WROTH, L. C.   A History of printing in colonial Maryland, 1686–1776.   Baltimore, 1922.   1053

(d) Massachusetts

GREEN, S. A.   John Foster, the earliest American engraver and the first Boston printer.   Boston, 1909.   1054

The bibliography of Foster's printed books begins with an almanack dated 1675.   With facsimiles of the portrait of Rev. Richard Mather, the 'Wine Hills' and 'White Hills' issues of Hubbard's map of New England, etc., attributed to Foster.

LITTLEFIELD, G. E.   The early Massachusetts press 1638–1711.   Boston, 1907.   2 v.   (Club of Odd Volumes.)   1055

A volume on *Early Boston booksellers, 1642–1711,* was issued by this author at Boston, in 1900.

PAINE, N.   Early American engravings and the Cambridge press imprints 1640–1692 in the library of the American Antiquarian Society.   Worcester, 1906.   1056

See also above, under: Introduction of Printing, nos. 1047–1048.

(e) New Jersey

NELSON, W.   Check-list of the issues of the press of New Jersey, 1723, 1728, 1754–1800.   Paterson, 1899.   1057

———— Some New Jersey printers and printing in the eighteenth century.   Worcester, 1911.   (American Antiquarian Society.)   1057:a

(f) New York

* EAMES, W.   The first year of printing in New-York, May, 1693 to April, 1694.   New York, 1928.   1058

Reprinted from the *Bulletin* of the New York Public Library for January 1928.

The asterisk (*) indicates that, in the reference works thus checked, annotations will be found giving the location of copies of the original editions recorded therein.

* FORD, P. L.   The Journals of Hugh Gaine, printer.   New York, 1902.   2 v.   1059

Bibliography of the issues of Hugh Gaine's press 1752–1800, Vol. I, p. 87–174.

HILDEBURN, C. R.   A List of the issues of the press in New York, 1693–1752.   Philadelphia, 1889.   1060

———— Sketches of printers and printing in colonial New York.   New York, 1895.   1061

MOORE, G. H.   . . . Historical notes on the introduction of printing into New York, 1693.   New York, 1888.   1062

* RUTHERFORD, L.   John Peter Zenger.   His press, his trial and a bibliography of Zenger imprints.   New York, 1904.   1063

With a bibliography of the issues of the Zenger press, 1725–1751; and an account of Zenger's trial (1734–35) as the result of which the British colonies gained the freedom of the press, in the words of Gouvernour Morris, " the germ of American freedom."

See also V. H. Paltsits' essay on John Holt, no. 1050.

(g) North Carolina

WEEKS, S. B.   The Press of North Carolina in the eighteenth century. With biographical sketches of printers, an account of the manufacture of paper, and a bibliography of the issues.   Brooklyn, 1891.
1064

The bibliography cites as the first dated work *A collection of all the Public Acts of Assembly*, Newbern, 1751; and the text quotes an advertisement, Nov. 14, 1777, of a paper-mill near Hillsboro, Orange county.

(h) Pennsylvania

* HILDEBURN, C. R.   A Century of printing.   The issues of the press in Pennsylvania, 1685–1784.   Philadelphia, 1885–86.   2 v.   1065

4,700 titles arranged chronologically.

* SACHSE, J. F., ed.   Falckner's *Curieuse Nachricht von Pensylvania*. The book that stimulated the great German emigration to Pennsylvania in the early years of the XVIII century.   A reprint of the edition of 1702, amplified with the text of the original manuscript in the Halle archives.   Philadelphia, 1905.   1066

The asterisk (*) indicates that, in the reference works thus checked, annotations will be found giving the location of copies of the original editions recorded therein.

SEIDENSTICKER, O.   The first century of German printing in America 1728–1830.   Philadelphia, 1893.   (The German Pionier-Verein of Philadelphia.)   1067

(i) Rhode Island

CHAPIN, H. M.   Ann Franklin of Newport, printer, 1736–1763.   (*In* Bibliographical essays.   A tribute to Wilberforce Eames.   June, MCMXXIV.   [Cambridge, 1924,] p. [337]–344.)   1068

———— James Franklin, Jr., Newport printer.   (*In* The American Collector.   Edited by Charles F. Heartman.   June 1926.   Vol. II, no. 3, p. 325–329.)   1068 :a

HAMMETT, C. E.   A Contribution to the bibliography and literature of Newport, R. I., comprising a list of books published or printed in Newport.   Newport, 1887.   1069

* [STEERE, R. P.] *comp.*, AND OTHERS   Rhode Island imprints.   A list of books, pamphlets, newspapers and broadsides printed at Newport, Providence, Warren . . . between 1727 and 1800.   Providence, 1914.   1070

(j) South Carolina

SALLEY, A. S.   The first presses of South Carolina.   (*In* Bibliographical Society of America.   Proceedings and papers.   New York, 1908.   Vol. II, p. 28–69.)   1071

The record begins with the year 1731, and continues through the Revolutionary War.

(k) Virginia

* CLAYTON-TORRENCE, W.   A trial bibliography of colonial Virginia.   Richmond, 1908.   (Virginia State Library.   Department of Bibliography.)   1072

Relates to the period from 1608 to 1754.

* ———— A trial bibliography of colonial Virginia, 1754–1776.   Richmond, 1910.   (Virginia State Library.   Department of Bibliography.)   1072 :a

The asterisk (*) indicates that, in the reference works thus checked, annotations will be found giving the location of copies of the original editions recorded therein.

WROTH, L. C.   William Parks, printer and journalist of England and
colonial America.   With a list of the issues of his several presses and
a facsimile of the earliest Virginia imprint known to be in existence.
Richmond, 1926.   (William Parks Club. Publications. III.)   1073

> With a facsimile of the earliest Virginia imprint known, *A charge to the
> Grand Jury,* by the Hon. William Gooch, Governor of Virginia, printed at
> Williamsburg in 1730.

> *Additions to the list of William Parks imprints* were published by Mr. Wroth
> in: The New York Herald Tribune. *Books.* Sunday, Sept. 11, 1927.

> See also V. H. Paltsits' essay on John Holt, no. 1050.

> Bibliographies of Delaware, New Hampshire and New Jersey have been
> announced for a forthcoming issue of the *Papers* of the Bibliographical So-
> ciety of America.

V. Period of Revolutions and Reconstruction

A. *The United States* (1763–1776, 1776–1789, 1789–1800)

I. IN GENERAL

* EVANS, C.   American bibliography by Charles Evans.   A chronological dictionary of all books . . . printed in the United States of
America from the genesis of printing in 1639 down to and including
the year 1820, with bibliographical and biographical notes.   Chicago,
1903–[to date].   [10 v. to date.]   1074

> Vol. X, 1929, carries the bibliography partly through the year 1796.

* FINOTTI, J. M.   Bibliographia Catholica Americana: A list of works
written by Catholic authors, and published in the United States.
New York, 1872.   1075

> Part I, from 1784 to 1820 inclusive.

PARRINGTON, V. L.   The colonial mind 1620–1800.   New York, 1927.
1076

> A discussion of American literature and thought; not bibliographical.

* ROSENBACH, A. S. W.   An American Jewish bibliography.   Being a
list of books and pamphlets by Jews or relating to them printed in the
United States from the establishment of the press in the colonies until
1850.   [Baltimore, 1926.]   1077

> The asterisk (*) indicates that, in the reference works thus checked, annotations will be
> found giving the location of copies of the original editions recorded therein.

TYLER, M. C.   The literary history of the American revolution, 1763–
1783. New York, 1897. 2 v.   1078

See also above, at the beginning of the section on Americana: General Works,
nos. 650–652.

For accounts of the activities and writings of members of the Loyalist party,
see: Sabine, L., Biographical sketches of Loyalists of the American Revolution. Boston, 1864. 2 v.

2. PUBLIC LEADERS, WRITERS, ETC.

(1) BRACKENRIDGE

* HEARTMAN, C. F.   A Bibliography of the writings of Hugh Henry
Brackenridge prior to 1825. New York, 1917. (Heartman's Historical Series. XXIX.)   1079

(2) DICKINSON

HALSEY, R. T. H.   Letters from A Farmer in Pennsylvania, to the inhabitants of the British colonies by John Dickinson. With an historical introduction. New York, 1903.   1080

With a reprint of the Boston edition of 1768.

(3) FRANKLIN

* ADAMS, R. G.   The Passports printed by Benjamin Franklin at his
Passy press. Ann Arbor, 1925.   1081

With facsimiles and notes on three broadsides not in Livingston's *Franklin
and his press at Passy*.

CURTIS PUBLISHING COMPANY (Philadelphia. Museum) The Collection of Franklin imprints in the museum of the Curtis Publishing
Company. With a short-title check list of all the books, pamphlets,
broadsides, &c., known to have been printed by Benjamin Franklin.
Compiled by William J. Campbell. Philadelphia, 1918.   1082

* FORD, P. L.   Franklin bibliography. A list of books written by, or
relating to Benjamin Franklin. Brooklyn, 1889.   1083

The titles are arranged chronologically according to the year in which they
were written, beginning with two ballads of 1719, and the *New England
Courant* of 1721. With a section on the 'State Papers and Treaties in the
formation of which Franklin aided,' 1775–1787, etc.

The asterisk (*) indicates that, in the reference works thus checked, annotations will be
found giving the location of copies of the original editions recorded therein.

LIVINGSTON, L. S.   Franklin and his press at Passy.   An account of the books, pamphlets, and leaflets printed there, including the long-lost 'Bagatelles.'   New York, 1914.   (The Grolier Club.)   1084

SWIFT, L.   Catalogue of works relating to Benjamin Franklin, in the Boston Public Library.   Boston, 1883.   (Boston Public Library. Bibliographies of special subjects.   I.)   1085

(4) FRENEAU

* PALTSITS, V. H.   A Bibliography of the separate and collected works of Philip Freneau together with an account of his newspapers.   New York, 1903.   1086

The bibliography of the works of the 'Poet of the American Revolution' begins with his *American Village,* New York, 1772.

(5) HAMILTON

* FORD, P. L.   Bibliotheca Hamiltoniana.   A list of books written by, or relating to Alexander Hamilton.   New York, 1886.   1087

* ——— A List of editions of " The Federalist."   Brooklyn, 1886.
                                                                                    1087 :a

FORD, W. C.   Hamilton's " Publius."   Washington, 1886.   1088

A brief statement as to the authorship of " Publius " and Hamilton's reason for issuing a scathing rebuke to a member of the Continental Congress. Twenty-five copies reprinted from the *New York Evening Post.*

(6) JEFFERSON

* TOMPKINS, H. B.   Bibliotheca Jeffersoniana.   A list of books written by or relating to Thomas Jefferson.   New York, 1887.   1089

(7) TUCKER

FORD, P. L.   Josiah Tucker and his writings, an eighteenth century pamphleteer on America.   Chicago [1894].   1090

Reprinted from the *Journal of Political Economy.*   I.

(8) WASHINGTON

BAKER, W. S.   Bibliotheca Washingtoniana.   A descriptive list of the biographies and biographical sketches of George Washington.   Philadelphia, 1889.   1091

The asterisk (*) indicates that, in the reference works thus checked, annotations will be found giving the location of copies of the original editions recorded therein.

GRIFFIN, A. P. C. A Catalogue of the Washington collection in the Boston Athenaeum. [Boston], 1897. 1092

Appendix: The inventory of Washington's books . . . with notes in regard to the full titles of the several books, and the later history and present ownership of those not in the Athenaeum collection, by William Coolidge Lane.

HOUGH, F. B. Washingtoniana: or, Memorials of the death of George Washington. Roxbury, 1865. 2 v. 1093

* SKEEL, E. E. F., *ed.* Mason Locke Weems — His works and ways. In three volumes. . . New York, 1929. 1094

Vol. I: A bibliography left unfinished by Paul Leicester Ford (beginning with 'The life and memorable actions of George Washington, General and Commander of the Armies of America. Printed by and for George Keatinge' and accredited to Weems, in 1800). Vols. II and III: Letters, 1784–1825. Completed and edited by Emily Ellsworth Ford Skeel.

* STILLWELL, M. B. Washington eulogies. A checklist of eulogies and funeral orations on the death of George Washington, December 1799-February 1800. New York, 1916. (New York Public Library.) 1095

3. FRENCH RELATIONS

* CHAPIN, H. M. *Calendrier français pour l'année 1781* and the printing press of the French fleet in American waters during the Revolutionary War. Providence, 1914. (Contributions to Rhode Island Bibliography. II.) 1096

* —— *ed. Gazette françoise.* A facsimile reprint of a newspaper printed at Newport on the printing press of the French fleet in American waters during the Revolutionary War. With an introduction. . . New York, 1926. (The Grolier Club.) 1096:a

FAŸ, B. . . . Bibliographie critique des ouvrages français relatifs aux États-unis (1770–1800). Paris, 1925. 1097

Arranged chronologically, with critical notes on the works listed.

GRIFFIN, A. P. C. List of works relating to the French alliance in the American Revolution. Washington, 1907. (U. S. Library of Congress.) 1098

Comprises a few contemporary titles.

The asterisk (*) indicates that, in the reference works thus checked, annotations will be found giving the location of copies of the original editions recorded therein.

* Invitation serieuse aux habitants des Illinois *by* un habitant des Kaskaskias. Reprinted in facsimile from the original edition published at Philadelphia in 1772, with an introduction by Clarence Walworth Alvord and Clarence Edwin Carter. Providence, 1908. (Club for Colonial Reprints. IV.)   1099

With bibliographical data; and a historical introduction discussing the relations of the French and British colonists from 1763 to 1774, and of the desire on the part of the French colonists for a release from British military rule.

4. GOVERNMENT AND LOCAL PUBLICATIONS

A) Public Documents (United States)

(1) CONTINENTAL CONGRESS

* Ford, P. L.   Some materials for a bibliography of the official publications of the Continental Congress 1774–89. Boston, 1890. (Boston Public Library. Bibliographies of special subjects. VI.)   1100

* Ford, W. C., *comp.*   Bibliographical notes on the issues of the Continental Congress, 1774–[1779]. Washington, 1904–[1908]. 6 pts. (U. S. Library of Congress.)   1101

A series of separate publications, comprising: 1774 (1904); 1775 (1904); 1776 (1905); 1777 (1906); 1778 (1907); 1779 (1908). The journals for 1780 and 1781 were recorded in similar publications by Mr. Gaillard Hunt: 1780 (1910); 1781 (1914).

Friedenwald, H. . . . The Journals and papers of the Continental Congress. Washington, 1897.   1102

From the *Annual report* of the American Historical Association for 1896, Vol. 1, p. 83–135. With bibliographical appendix.

* Hunt, G.   Bibliographical notes on the issues of the Continental Congress, 1780–[1781]. Washington, 1910–[1914]. 2 pts. (U. S. Library of Congress.)   1103

A continuation of the series started by Mr. Worthington C. Ford in 1904.

(2) GOVERNMENT DOCUMENTS

* Ford, P. L.   A List of Treasury reports and circulars issued by Alexander Hamilton 1789–1795. Brooklyn, 1886.   1104

The asterisk (*) indicates that, in the reference works thus checked, annotations will be found giving the location of copies of the original editions recorded therein.

* GREELY, A. W.   Public documents of the first fourteen congresses, 1789–1817.   Papers relating to early congressional documents. Washington, 1900.   (56th Congress.   1st session.   Document 428.)
1105

Unless otherwise stated, the originals are in the Boston Athenaeum, the New York Public Library and the Library of the U. S. War Department, Washington.

B) SUBJECT MONOGRAPHS

(1) ALMANACS

* BATES, A. C.   Check list of Connecticut almanacs 1709–1850. Worcester, 1914.   1106

Reprinted from the *Proceedings* of the American Antiquarian Society for April, 1914.

* CHAPIN, H. M.   *Calendrier français pour l'année 1781* and the printing press of the French fleet in American waters during the Revolutionary War.   Providence, 1914.   (Contributions to Rhode Island Bibliography.   II.)   1107

* ———— Check list of Rhode Island almanacs 1643–1850.   Worcester, 1915.   (American Antiquarian Society.)   1107 :a

* MORRISON, H. A.   Preliminary check list of American almanacs 1639–1800.   Washington, 1907.   (U. S. Library of Congress.)
1108

* NICHOLS, C. L.   Notes on the almanacs of Massachusetts.   Worcester, 1912.   1109

A chronological list of Massachusetts almanacs, 1639–1850.   Reprinted from the *Proceedings* of the American Antiquarian Society for April, 1912.

See also note under no. 986.   A *Preliminary checklist* of New Jersey almanacs was issued by C. F. Heartman in 1929.

(2) ARCHITECTURE

* WALL, A. J.   Books on architecture printed in America, 1775–1830. (*In* Bibliographical essays.   A tribute to Wilberforce Eames.   June, MCMXXIV, [Cambridge, 1924], p. [299]–311.)   1110

Contains the titles, and location of copies, of ten architectural works printed before 1801.

The asterisk (*) indicates that, in the reference works thus checked, annotations will be found giving the location of copies of the original editions recorded therein.

(3) BIBLES

O'CALLAGHAN, E. B.   A List of editions of the Holy Scriptures and
parts thereof, printed in America previous to 1860; with introduction
and bibliographical notes.   Albany, 1861.   1111

WRIGHT, J.   Early Bibles of America.   New York, 1892.   1112
With chapters on the Eliot Bible, the Saur Bible, the Aitken Bible, the first
Douay version, the Thomas Bible, the Collins Bible, the first American edi-
tion in Greek (1800), etc.

(4) BROADSIDES

* [FORD, W. C.]   Broadsides, ballads, &c. printed in Massachusetts,
1639–1800.   [Boston] 1922.   (Massachusetts Historical Society.)
                                                                  1113

* LANE, W. C.   Early Harvard broadsides.   Worcester, 1914.
(American Antiquarian Society.)   1114
The list starts with the *Thesis* of 1642, of which no copy is now known, and
continues through 1810.

PAINE, N.   A List of early American broadsides, 1680–1800, belonging to the library of the American Antiquarian Society.   Worcester,
1897.   1115

WINSHIP, G. P.   Brown University broadsides.   Providence, 1913.
                                                                  1116
A note on a file of *Theses* ranging from 1769 through 1811.

(5) CONSTITUTION

* FORD, P. L.   Pamphlets on the constitution of the United States,
published during its discussion by the people 1787–1788.   Edited
with notes and a bibliography.   Brooklyn, 1888.   1117

(6) DENOMINATIONAL PUBLICATIONS, ETC.

BENSON, L. F.   The American revisions of Watts's Psalms.   Philadelphia, 1903.   1118
Reprinted from the *Journal* of the Presbyterian Historical Society.   The
bibliographical list begins with the Mycall Revision, printed in Newburyport
in 1781.

The asterisk (*) indicates that, in the reference works thus checked, annotations will be
found giving the location of copies of the original editions recorded therein.

GIBSON, F.   The standard editions of the American Book of Common Prayer.   (*In* McGarvey, W., Liturgiæ Americanæ or the Book of Common Prayer as used in the United States.   Philadelphia, 1895, p. lv–lxxiii.)   1119

Lists American editions from 1790 to 1808.

NELSON, W.   The Controversy over the proposition for an American Episcopate, 1767–1774.   A bibliography of the subject.   Paterson, 1909.   1120

TRINITY COLLEGE (Hartford)   A List of the early editions and reprints of the General Convention Journals, 1785–1814, in the library of Trinity College.   [Hartford], April, 1908.   (Bulletin.   New Series, Vol. V, No. II.)   1121

WRIGHT, J.   Early Prayer Books of America: being a descriptive account of Prayer Books published in the United States, Mexico, and Canada.   St. Paul, 1896.   1122

With facsimile title-pages of the Manual of Catholic Prayers, Philadelphia, 1774; revised Prayer Book of the Protestant Episcopal Church, Philadelphia, 1786; etc.

See also nos. 1075, 1077, 1164 and 1165.

(7) DRAMA

WEGELIN, O.   Early American plays, 1714–1830.   Second edition revised.   New York, 1905.   1123

The first edition appeared in 1900.

(8) FICTION

WEGELIN, O.   Early American fiction 1774–1830.   New York, 1913.
                                                                                                         1124

A third edition, corrected and enlarged, has been recently issued in New York, by Peter Smith.

(9) JUVENILE LITERATURE

* EAMES, W.   Early New England catechisms.   A bibliographical account of some catechisms published before the year 1800, for use in New England.   Worcester, 1898.   1125

Two hundred copies reprinted from the *Proceedings* of the American Antiquarian Society.   New series.   XII.   Relates 'chiefly to some of the catechisms for children and older persons, which were used in New England in the seventeenth and eighteenth centuries.'

The asterisk (*) indicates that, in the reference works thus checked, annotations will be found giving the location of copies of the original editions recorded therein.

* FORD, P. L.   The New-England primer.   New York, 1897.   1126

Appendix VI contains: Bibliography of the New England primer (1727–1799).

HALSEY, R. V.   Forgotten books of the American nursery.   A history of the development of the American story-book.   Boston, 1911.   1127

* HEARTMAN, C. F.   The New England primer issued prior to 1830. A bibliographical checklist. . . [New York] 1922.   (Heartman's Historical Series, no. 15.   Second issue.)   1128

Begins with the issue of 1727 and records 143 issues before 1800.   An enlargement of the edition of 1914.

* MERRITT, P.   The Royal primer.   (*In* Bibliographical essays.   A tribute to Wilberforce Eames.   June, MCMXXIV, [Cambridge, 1924] p. [35]–60.)   1129

With a check-list of eight English editions, 1750–1818, and seven American editions, 1753–1796.

WHITMORE, W. H., *ed.*   The original Mother Goose's melody, as first issued by John Newbery, of London, about A.D., 1760.   Reproduced in fac-simile from the edition as reprinted by Isaiah Thomas, of Worcester, Mass., about A.D., 1785.   Albany, 1889.   1130

(10) LAWS, STATUTES, PUBLIC DOCUMENTS, ETC.

(*a*) *In General*

BELDEN, C. F. D., *ed.*   Hand-list of legislative sessions and session laws, statutory revisions, compilations, codes, etc., and constitutional conventions of the United States and its possessions and of the several states to May 1912.   Boston, 1912.   (Massachusetts.   State Library.)   1131

With historical notes or chronology preceding each section.

HASSE, A. R.   Materials for a bibliography of the public archives of the thirteen original states covering the colonial period and the state period to 1789.   Washington, 1908.   1132

Reprinted from the *Annual Report* of the American Historical Association for 1906.   II. p. 239–572.

TOWER, CHARLEMAGNE (*Collection of*)   The Charlemagne Tower collection of American colonial laws.   [Philadelphia] 1890.   (Historical Society of Pennsylvania.)   1133

The asterisk (*) indicates that, in the reference works thus checked, annotations will be found giving the location of copies of the original editions recorded therein.

Comprises a record of laws relating to the British colonies and to the United States from 1641 to about 1800, with some titles relating to Canada, Barbados, Bermuda, etc. Edited by C. S. R. Hildeburn.

(b) Connecticut

* BATES, A. C.   Connecticut statute laws.   A bibliographical list of editions of Connecticut laws from the earliest issues to 1836.   Hartford, 1900.   1134

[———] A List of official publications of Connecticut 1774–1788 as shown by the bills for printing.   [Hartford] 1917.   (Acorn Club Publications.   XIV.)   1135

(c) Massachusetts

* FORD, W. C., AND A. MATTHEWS   A Bibliography of the laws of the Massachusetts Bay 1641–1776.   Cambridge, 1907.   1136

Reprinted from the *Publications* of the Colonial Society of Massachusetts. No. IV.

(d) New York

* HASSE, A. R.   Some materials for a bibliography of the official publications of the General Assembly of the colony of New York, 1693–1775.   New York, 1903.   (*In* Bulletin of the New York Public Library.   Feb.-Apr. 1903.)   1137

(e) New York City

STOKES, I. N. PHELPS   Period of adjustment and reconstruction.   New York as the State and Federal Capital, 1783–1811.   (*In his* Iconography of Manhattan Island, 1498–1909.   Vol. I, p. 367-408.)

1138

With some reference to the controversy involving Citizen Genet, local ordinances for the development of the city, etc.   The chronology of the period is given in Vol. V, p. 1179-1546.

(f) Northwest

* BUCK, S. J.   Territorial and state laws, 1788–1913.   (*In his* Travel and description, 1765–1865.   Springfield, 1914, p. 389–430.   Illinois State Historical Library.   Collections.   Bibliographical series.   II.)

1139

Includes 'Laws passed in the Territory of the United States, North-west of the River Ohio' and printed between 1792 and 1800.

The asterisk (*) indicates that, in the reference works thus checked, annotations will be found giving the location of copies of the original editions recorded therein.

(g) *Pennsylvania*

[MONTGOMERY, T. L.]   Check list of the laws, minutes, journals and documents published by Pennsylvania, 1682–1901.   (*In* Pennsylvania. Report of the State Librarian of Pennsylvania 1903.   [Harrisburg.] 1904, p. 117–213.)   1140

(h) *Rhode Island*

BONGARTZ, J. H., *ed.*   Check list of Rhode Island laws.   Providence, 1893.   1141

A brief list of the public laws, and acts and resolves, from early colonial times to the date of publication.   Revised in 1921.   (A series of facsimiles of *Rhode Island acts and resolves,* Oct. 1747-Oct. 1800, sometimes designated as the ' Bongartz facsimile reprints,' 20 vols., was issued at Providence, 1908–1925.)

(i) *Vermont*

WILBUR, J. B.   A Note on the laws of the republic of Vermont.   (*In* Bibliographical essays.   A tribute to Wilberforce Eames.   June, MCMXXIV, [Cambridge, 1924] p. [277]–280.)   1142

With a list of 32 Vermont laws printed between 1779 and 1791.

(j) *Virginia*

NEW YORK PUBLIC LIBRARY (New York)   Virginia.   History by periods.   (*In* Bulletin of the New York Public Library.   Feb.-April, 1907, [List of works in the New York Public Library relating to Virginia] p. 64–83, 99–125, 143–168.)   1143

Covers the period from the Raleigh colony, 1589, and Capt. Bartholomew Gilbert's voyage in 1603, to the communications on the resolutions of the Legislature of Virginia in 1800.

SWEM, E. G.   The Acts and the journals of the General Assembly of the colony 1619–1776.   Richmond, 1919.   (*In his* Bibliography of Virginia.   Pt. III.)   1144

(11) MUSIC

HOWE, M. A.   Music publishers in New York city before 1850.   (*In* New York Public Library.   Bulletin.   1917.   Vol. 21, no. 9, p. 589–604.)   1145

A directory containing several entries before 1800.

* METCALF, F. J.   American psalmody or Titles of books, containing tunes printed in America from 1721 to 1820.   New York, 1917. (Heartman's Historical Series.   XXVII.)   1146

———— American writers and compilers of sacred music.   New York, [1925].   1146:a

* SONNECK, O. G.   Bibliography of early secular American music. Washington, 1905.   1147

(12) NEWSPAPERS AND PERIODICALS

* BEER, W.   Checklist of American periodicals, 1741–1800.   Worcester, 1923.   1148

Reprinted from the *Proceedings* of the American Antiquarian Society, October, 1922.   A list of ninety-eight periodicals.

BRIGHAM, C. S.   Bibliography of American newspapers, 1690–1820. (*In* American Antiquarian Society.   Proceedings.   Oct. 1913-April 1927.)   1149

A list, approximating 1,900 titles, of all the newspapers published in this country previous to 1821.   The states from Alabama to Virginia are covered in eighteen installments published in the Society's *Proceedings*.   The bibliography, with additions and corrections, will be separately issued in two volumes, presumably in 1930.

* CHAPIN, H. M., *ed.   Gazette françoise.*   A facsimile reprint of a newspaper printed at Newport on the printing press of the French fleet in American waters during the Revolutionary War.   With an introduction. . . New York, 1926.   (The Grolier Club.)   1150

* CRITTENDEN, C. C.   North Carolina newspapers before 1790. Chapel Hill, N. C., 1928.   (University of North Carolina.   The James Sprunt Historical Studies.   XX.)   1151

GRISWOLD, A. T.   Annotated catalogue of newspaper files in the library of the State Historical Society of Wisconsin.   Madison, 1911.   1152

Arranged chronologically under states.

NELSON, W.   Notes toward a history of the American newspaper. New York, 1918.   (Heartman's Historical Series.   XXXI.)   1153

Covers the period from 1690 onward.   With a reference in its introduction to 'A narrative of the newspapers printed in New England,' printed in the Collections of the Massachusetts Historical Society, 1798 and 1800.

The asterisk (*) indicates that, in the reference works thus checked, annotations will be found giving the location of copies of the original editions recorded therein.

* PALTSITS, V. H.   Freneau and journalism.   (*In his* Bibliography of the separate and collected works of Philip Freneau together with an account of his newspapers. New York, 1903, p. 1–16.)   1154

RUSK, R. L.   The Literature of the middle western frontier.   New York, 1925.   2 v.   1154:a

Contains chapters on travel and observation, newspapers and magazines, controversial writings, etc.; with a list of works published before 1841 either by citizens of the Middle West or by travellers who visited that region.

SLAUSON, A. B.   A check list of American newspapers in the Library of Congress. Washington, 1901.   (U. S. Library of Congress.)   1155

A *Check list of American eighteenth century newspapers* was compiled by J. v. N. Ingram in 1912.

* STOKES, I. N. PHELPS   Early New York newspapers.   Bibliographical data.   Check-list of some early New York newspapers, 1725–1811.   (*In his* Iconography of Manhattan Island. New York, 1915–1928. Vol. II, p. 413–452.)   1156

An account of the fate of New York newspapers during the Revolutionary War is given in Vol. I, in the section relating to 'The Revolutionary Period, 1763–1783,' p. 299–334.

WINSHIP, G. P., *ed.*   . . . French newspapers in the United States before 1800. (Bibliographical Society of America. Papers. Vol. XIV, pt. II.   1920. Chicago [1923].)   1157

With essays on *Le Courier de l'Amérique*, Philadelphia, 1784, by A. H. Shearer; *Two or three Boston papers* and *French newspapers in the United States from 1790 to 1800* by G. P. Winship; *Moniteur de la Louisiane*, New Orleans, 1794, by W. Beer, etc.

——— Newport newspapers in the eighteenth century. (*In* Newport Historical Society. Bulletin. XIV. Oct., 1914.)   1157:a

See also, no. 1029:a.

(13) POETRY

FRENEAU, P.   The American village.   A poem by Philip Freneau. Reprinted in facsimile from the original edition published at New York in 1772, with an introduction by Harry Lyman Koopman and bibliographical data by Victor Hugo Paltsits. Providence, 1906. (Club for Colonial Reprints. III.)   1158

The asterisk (*) indicates that, in the reference works thus checked, annotations will be found giving the location of copies of the original editions recorded therein.

* HEARTMAN, C. F.   Phillis Wheatley (Phillis Peters).   A critical attempt and a bibliography of her writings.   New York, 1915. (Heartman's Historical Series. VII.)   1159

The first work published by Phillis Wheatley was an elegiac poem on the death of the Rev. George Whitefield printed in Boston in 1770, and reprinted in Boston, New York, Philadelphia, and London.

* PALTSITS, V. H.   A bibliography of the separate and collected works of Philip Freneau together with an account of his newspapers.   New York, 1903.   1160

The bibliography of the works of the ' Poet of the American Revolution ' begins with his *American Village,* New York, 1772.

STOCKBRIDGE, J. C.   . . . A Catalogue of the Harris collection of American poetry.   Providence, 1886.   1161

A list of the books given to Brown University by the Hon. Henry B. Anthony.

WEGELIN, O.   Early American poetry, 1800–1820.   With an appendix containing the titles of volumes and broadsides issued during the seventeenth and eighteenth centuries, which were omitted in the volume containing the years 1650–1799.   New York, 1907.   1162

An earlier volume, covering the period 1650–1799, was issued under a similar title in 1903.

(14) PRIVATEERING

HARBECK, C. T.   A Contribution to the bibliography of the history of the United States navy.   Cambridge, 1906.   1163

Contains a few eighteenth century imprints of the Revolutionary period, relative to American privateering, etc.

(15) RELIGIOUS WORKS

* DEXTER, H. M.   The Congregationalism of the last three hundred years, as seen in its literature . . . with a bibliographical appendix. New York, 1880.   1164

Comprises titles printed in America and abroad.

SMITH, JOSEPH   A descriptive catalogue of Friends' books, or Books written by members of the Society of Friends, commonly called Quakers.   London, 1867.   2 v.   1165

Comprises occasional titles printed in America.

See also nos. 1075, 1077, and 1118–1122.

The asterisk (*) indicates that, in the reference works thus checked, annotations will be found giving the location of copies of the original editions recorded therein.

(16) TEXTBOOKS

* KARPINSKI, L. C.   Colonial American arithmetics.   (*In* Bibliographical essays.   A tribute to Wilberforce Eames.   June, MCMXXIV, [Cambridge, 1924] p. [242]–248.)   1166

With a list of 29 arithmetics and arithmetical works published in America between 1539 and 1776.

(17) TRAVEL

* BUCK, S. J.   Travel and description, 1765–1865, together with . . . a list of territorial and state laws.   Springfield, 1914.   (Illinois State Historical Library.   Collections.   Bibliographical series.   II.)   1167

A chronological list giving 33 titles of books printed before 1800, relating to the territory northwest of the Ohio.

LEE, J. T.   A Bibliography of Carver's travels.   Madison, 1910.
1168

From the *Proceedings* of the State Historical Society of Wisconsin for 1909, p. 143–183.

———— Captain Jonathan Carver: Additional data.   Madison, 1913.
1168 :a

From the *Proceedings* of the State Historical Society of Wisconsin for 1912, p. 87–123.

See also R. L. Rusk's *Literature of the middle western frontier.*   New York, 1925.   2 v., no. 1154:a and R. G. Thwaites' *Early western travels,* Cleveland, 1904–1907.   32 v., no. 1251.

c) BEGINNING OF TYPE-FOUNDING

WROTH, L. C.   Abel Buell of Connecticut, silversmith, type founder, & engraver.   [New Haven] 1926.   (The Acorn Club.   XV.)   1169

———— The first work with American types.   Cambridge, 1925.   1170

Relates to various efforts in letter founding in English America, 1769–1775. Reprinted from: Bibliographical essays.   A tribute to Wilberforce Eames. [Cambridge] 1924.

———— The Origins of typefounding in North and South America.   (*In* Ars Typographica.   Vol. II.   No. 4.   April 1926, p. 273–307.)
1170 :a

Relates to the "first essay in type casting in Paraguay in 1705 or thereabouts," to the first work, printed in Mexico in 1770, which bears a state-

The asterisk (*) indicates that, in the reference works thus checked, annotations will be found giving the location of copies of the original editions recorded therein.

ment that it was printed with local types; and to the efforts at type casting in the British colonies just before the outbreak of the Revolutionary War. With facsimiles.

D) REGIONAL MONOGRAPHS

(1) IN GENERAL

EVANS, C. American bibliography . . . Chicago, 1903–[to date]. [10 v. to date.] 1171

See no. 1074.

FAŸ, B. Notes on the American press at the end of the eighteenth century. New York, 1927. (The Grolier Club.) 1172

WROTH, L. C. North America. (English-speaking.) (*In* Peddie, R. A., *ed*. Printing: A short history of the art. London, 1927, p. 319–373.) 1173

With sections on 'The diffusion of printing after the Revolution,' and on Canada.

For a note on Isaiah Thomas's *History of printing in America,* see below, under no. 1259.

(2) BY LOCALITY

(*a*) *Connecticut*

* BATES, A. C. The Work of Hartford's first printer. (*In* Bibliographical essays. A tribute to Wilberforce Eames. June, MCMXXIV. [Cambridge] 1924 p. [345]–361.) 1174

With a list of 51 titles printed at Hartford by Thomas Green between 1764 and 1768.

TRUMBULL, J. H. List of books printed in Connecticut, 1709–1800. [Hartford] 1904. 1174:a

(*b*) *Georgia*

McMURTRIE, D. C. James Johnston, first printer in the royal colony of Georgia. (*In* The Library. Fourth ser. vol. X, no. 1. June, 1929, p. 73–83.) 1175

Relates to an act for the printing of the laws of the province, by the General Assembly of Georgia, 4 March 1762; the beginning of printing in 1763; etc.

The asterisk (*) indicates that, in the reference works thus checked, annotations will be found giving the location of copies of the original editions recorded therein.

(c) Louisiana

McMURTRIE, D. C.   Early printing in New Orleans, 1764–1810. With a bibliography of the Louisiana press.   New Orleans, 1929.
1176

(d) Maine †

BOARDMAN, S. L.   Peter Edes, pioneer printer in Maine.   A biography. His diary while a prisoner by the British at Boston in 1775. . .   Bangor, 1901.   1177

An account of Edes in Boston, 1785; Newport, 1787; Augusta, 1795; and Bangor, 1815; with a chapter on the Edes press and its work.

WILLIAMSON, J.   A Bibliography of the state of Maine from the earliest period to 1891.   Portland, 1896.   2 v.   1178

A bibliography of Maine imprints, by R. W. Noyes, is in process of publication.

(e) Maryland

McCREARY, G. W.   The first book printed in Baltimore-town.   Nicholas Hasselbach, printer.   Baltimore, 1903.   1179

With a reprint of *A detection of the conduct and proceedings of Messrs. Annan and Henderson, April 18th . . . 1764 . . . wherein is contained some remarks by John Redick-le-man.*   Baltimore-town [1765].

* WROTH, L. C.   A History of printing in colonial Maryland, 1686–1776.   Baltimore, 1922.   1180

(f) Massachusetts

NICHOLS, C. L.   Bibliography of Worcester.   A list of books, pamphlets, newspapers and broadsides, printed in the town of Worcester, Massachusetts, from 1775 to 1848.   2d ed.   Worcester, 1908.   1181

First published in 1899.

————— Isaiah Thomas, printer, writer & collector. . .   With a bibliography of the books printed by Isaiah Thomas.   Boston, 1912. (The Club of Odd Volumes.)   1182

————— Three old Worcester books — volumes, typical of the work of Isaiah Thomas, the greatest printer of his times, possessing an ar-

† Originally part of Massachusetts.

The asterisk (*) indicates that, in the reference works thus checked, annotations will be found giving the location of copies of the original editions recorded therein.

tistic value rarely encountered today. (*In* The Worcester Magazine. Oct. 1910, p. 269–275.) 1183

For a note on Isaiah Thomas's *History of printing in America,* see below, under no. 1259.

TAPLEY, H. S. Salem imprints, 1768–1825. A history of the first fifty years of printing in Salem, Massachusetts. Salem, 1927. 1184

With a chronological list of the books and broadsides issued at Salem during these years.

(g) New Hampshire

It has been announced that the Bibliographical Society of America is soon to publish in its *Papers* a list of early New Hampshire imprints. See also below, under no. 1200.

(h) New Jersey

* HILL, F. P., AND V. L. COLLINS Books, pamphlets and newspapers printed at Newark, New Jersey, 1776–1900. [Newark], 1902. 1185

NELSON, W. Check-list of the issues of the press of New Jersey, 1723, 1728, 1754–1800. Paterson, 1899. 1186

A monograph by this author, entitled *Some New Jersey printers and printing in the eighteenth century,* was issued by the American Antiquarian Society in 1911.

(i) New York

* FORD, P. L. The Journals of Hugh Gaine printer. New York, 1902. 2 v. 1187

Bibliography of the issues of Hugh Gaine's press, 1752–1800, Vol. I., p. 87–174.

OPPENHEIM, S. The Chapters of Isaac the Scribe: a bibliographical rarity, New York, 1772 [n.p., 1914]. 1188

Reprinted from *Publications* of the American Jewish Historical Society, no. 22, 1914. With supplemental note. Isaac Pinto is suggested as a possible author.

SARGENT, G. H. James Rivington, the Tory printer. A study of the Loyalist pamphlets of the Revolution. (*In* The American Collector. Edited by Charles F. Heartman. June, 1926. Vol. II, no. 3, p. 336–341.) 1189

The asterisk (*) indicates that, in the reference works thus checked, annotations will be found giving the location of copies of the original editions recorded therein.

* WEGELIN, O.   The Brooklyn, New York, press.   1799–1820.   Reprinted from the Bulletin of the Bibliographical Society of America, July-Oct. 1912 [n. p., 1912].   1189 :a

See also V. H. Paltsits' essay on John Holt, no. 1050.

(j) North Carolina

WEEKS, S. B.   The Press of North Carolina in the eighteenth century. With . . . a bibliography of the issues.   Brooklyn, 1891.   1190

(k) Ohio Valley

RUSK, R. L.   The Literature of the middle western frontier.   New York, 1925.   2 v.   1191

Contains chapters on travel and observation, newspapers and magazines, controversial writings, etc.; with a list of works published before 1841 either by citizens of the Middle West or by travellers who visited that region.

THWAITES, R. G.   The Ohio Valley press before the War of 1812–15. Worcester, 1909.   (American Antiquarian Society.)   1191 :a

Comprises sections relating to Western Pennsylvania, 1786; Kentucky, 1787; and Ohio, 1793.

(l) Pennsylvania

* HILDEBURN, C. R.   A Century of printing.   The issues of the press in Pennsylvania, 1685–1784.   Philadelphia, 1885–86.   2 v.   1192

Four thousand, seven hundred titles listed chronologically.

KENT, H. W.   Chez Moreau de Saint-Méry, Philadelphie.   With a list of imprints enlarged by George Parker Winship.   (In Bibliographical essays.   A tribute to Wilberforce Eames.   June, MCM-XXIV.   [Cambridge] 1924, p. [66]–78.)   1193

The list comprises 24 titles, 1795–1797.

SEIDENSTICKER, O.   The first century of German printing in America 1728–1830.   Philadelphia, 1893.   (The German Pionier-Verein of Philadelphia.)   1194

(m) Rhode Island

HAMMETT, C. E.   A Contribution to the bibliography and literature of Newport, R. I. comprising a list of books published or printed in Newport.   Newport, 1887.   1195

* [STEERE, R. P., AND OTHERS]   Rhode Island imprints.   A list of books, pamphlets, newspapers and broadsides printed at Newport,

---

The asterisk (*) indicates that, in the reference works thus checked, annotations will be found giving the location of copies of the original editions recorded therein.

Providence, Warren . . . between 1727 and 1800. Providence,
1914. 1196

(n) South Carolina

SALLEY, A. S. The first presses of South Carolina. (*In* Bibliographical Society of America. Proceedings and papers. New York, 1908.
Vol. II, p. 28–69.) 1197

The record begins with the year 1731, and continues through the Revolutionary War.

(o) Tennessee

WILEY, E. Eighteenth century presses in Tennessee. (*In* Bibliographical Society of America. Proceedings and papers. New York, 1908.
Vol. II, p. 70–83.) 1198

The record begins with the issuing of *The Knoxville Gazette,* Nov. 5, 1791.
See also, no. 1191.

(p) Vermont

GILMAN, M. D., *comp.* The Bibliography of Vermont. Burlington,
1897. 1199

With additional material by G. G. Benedict, *ed.,* and T. L. Wood.

RUGG, H. G. The Dresden press. A paper read before the Ticknor
Club of Dartmouth College, May 1, 1918 [n.p., 1918]. 1200

Lists the first dated imprint as 1779, although undated works are assigned
to 1778. (The border town of Dresden subsequently became Hanover, N. H.)

* SPARGO, J. Anthony Haswell, printer, patriot, ballader. A biographical study with a selection of his ballads and an annotated
bibliographical list of his imprints. Rutland, 1925. 1201

The bibliography begins with the New England Almanack for 1781, and gives
Haswell's first Bennington imprint as 1783.

(q) Virginia

* CLAYTON-TORRENCE, W. A trial bibliography of colonial Virginia,
1754–1776. Richmond, 1910. (Virginia State Library. Department of Bibliography.) 1202

See also V. H. Paltsits' essay on John Holt, no. 1050.

Bibliographies of Delaware and New Jersey imprints have been announced
for a forthcoming issue of the *Papers* of the Bibliographical Society of
America.

The asterisk (*) indicates that, in the reference works thus checked, annotations will be
found giving the location of copies of the original editions recorded therein.

B. *Canada* (1763–1800)

DIONNE, N. E. Inventaire chronologique des livres . . . publiés en langue française dans la province de Quebec . . . 1764–1905. Quebec, 1905.   1203

The series, the *Inventaire chronologique,* was issued by the Royal Society of Canada in four volumes, 1905–1909, with a supplement, 1912. This list begins, with the first French book published in Canada, the *Catéchisme du diocèse de Sens.* Quebec, 1765. [For broadsides believed to have been printed in Quebec as early as 1759, see above, under: Colonization and Colonial Growth. North America: French Possessions (prior to 1764), no. 939.]

———— . . . Livres, brochures . . . publiés en langue anglaise dans la province de Québec . . . 1764–1906. Quebec, 1907. (Inventaire chronologique. III.)   1204

———— Québec et Nouvelle France. Bibliographie. Inventaire chronologique des ouvrages publiés à l'étranger en diverses langues sur Québec et la Nouvelle France . . . 1534–1906. Quebec, 1906. (Inventaire chronologique. II.)   1205

THE JESUIT RELATIONS and allied documents. Travels and explorations of the Jesuit missionaries in New France, 1610–1791. . . Edited by Reuben Gold Thwaites. Cleveland, 1896–1901. 73 v.
                                                             1206

With bibliographical data by V. H. Paltsits. Vol. 71 relates to Lower Canada, Illinois, 1759–1791.

MCLACHLAN, R. W. The first Mohawk primer. (*In* the Canadian Antiquarian and Numismatic Journal. April, 1908, p. 51–66.) 1207

Relates to the Mohawk-English primer issued by Fleury Mesplet at Montreal in 1781, and to various books printed in Indian languages between 1707 and 1781.

———— FLEURY MESPLET The first printer at Montreal. Toronto, 1906. (Royal Society of Canada. Transactions. 2d ser., XII: 2.)
                                                             1208

Lists the first imprint of Montreal as 1776. [For a broadside assigned to the early date of 1759, see above, under: Colonization and Colonial Growth. North America: French Possessions (prior to 1764), no. 939.]

Notes on Montreal's first printer, under title *Some unpublished documents relating to Fleury Mesplet,* were issued by Mr. McLachlan, p. 85–95 of the *Transactions,* section II, 1920.

TOWER, CHARLEMAGNE (*Collection of*) The Charlemagne Tower collection of American colonial laws. Philadelphia 1890. (Historical Society of Pennsylvania.) 1209

Comprises a record of laws relative to Nova Scotia, 1767, Quebec, 1767–1780, etc., as well as to the territory of the United States. Edited by C. S. R. Hildeburn.

WRIGHT, J. Early Prayer Books of America; being a descriptive account of Prayer Books published in the United States, Mexico, and Canada. St. Paul, 1896. 1210

With facsimile title-pages of the Indian Prayer Book printed at Quebec in 1767; the Mohawk Prayer Book printed by William Bradford at New York in 1715; etc.

WROTH, L. C. Canada. (*In* Peddie, R. A., *ed.* Printing. A short history of the art. London, 1927, p. 369–373.) 1211

C. *Hispanic-America* (1780–1824)

I. IN GENERAL

COESTER, A. The literary history of Spanish America. New York, 1916. 1212

With chapters on the colonial and revolutionary periods, p. 39–78 relating to the revolutionary literature of South America and p. 79–103 to that of Mexico.

A Bibliography of Spanish-American literature was issued by this author in the *Romanic Review*, Vol. III, no. 1, p. 68–101.

KENISTON, H. List of works for the study of Hispanic-American history. New York, 1920. (The Hispanic Society of America. Hispanic notes & monographs.) 1213

With a general section on *Revolution* comprising contemporary imprints p. 115–128; and specialized lists at the end of each of the sections devoted to Argentina, Bolivia, Brazil, Chile, Colombia, Ecuador, Paraguay, Peru, Uruguay, Venezuela, and Mexico.

MOSES, B. The intellectual background of the revolution in South America, 1810–1824. New York, 1926. (The Hispanic Society of America. Hispanic notes & monographs.) 1214

* WAGNER, H. R. The Spanish Southwest, 1542–1794. An annotated bibliography. Berkeley, 1924. 1215

With over a hundred reproductions of title-pages of books relating to the regions now comprised in Louisiana, Texas, New Mexico, California, etc.

The asterisk (*) indicates that, in the reference works thus checked, annotations will be found giving the location of copies of the original editions recorded therein.

2. REGIONAL MONOGRAPHS

A) MEXICO

* MEDINA, J. T.   La Imprenta en Guadalajara de México (1793–1821). Notas bibliográficas. Santiago de Chile, 1904.   1216

* ———— La Imprenta en Mérida de Yucatán (1813–1821). Notas bibliográficas. Santiago de Chile, 1904.   1217

* ———— La Imprenta en Mexico (1539–1821). Santiago de Chile, 1907–1912. 8 v.   1218

* ———— La Imprenta en Oaxaca (1720–1820). Notas bibliográficas. Santiago de Chile, 1904.   1219

* ———— La Imprenta en la Puebla de los Angeles (1640–1821). Santiago de Chile, 1908.   1220

* ———— La Imprenta en Veracruz (1794–1821). Notas bibliográficas. Santiago de Chile, 1904.   1221

B). CENTRAL AMERICA

* MEDINA, J. T.   La Imprenta en Guatemala (1660–1821). Santiago de Chile, 1910.   1222

* ———— Notas bibliográficas referentes á las primeras producciones de la imprenta en algunas ciudades de la América Española . . . (1764–1822). Santiago de Chile, 1904.   1223

Records the opening of a press in Panama in 1822.

C) SOUTH AMERICAN COUNTRIES

(1) ARGENTINA

GARNETT, R.   Paraguayan and Argentine bibliography. (*In* Bibliographica. London, 1895. Vol. I, pt. III, p. 262–273.)   1224

* MEDINA, J. T.   . . . Historia y bibliografía de la imprenta en Buenos-Aires (1780–1810). La Plata [1892]. 2 v. (Museo de La Plata. Anales. III. La imprenta en la América Española.)   1225

The asterisk (*) indicates that, in the reference works thus checked, annotations will be found giving the location of copies of the original editions recorded therein.

(2) BRAZIL

GARRAUX, A. L. Bibliographie Brésilienne. Catalogue des ouvrages français & latins relatifs au Brésil (1500–1898). Paris, 1898. 1226

RODRIGUES, J. C. Bibliotheca Brasiliense. Catalogo annotado dos libros sobre o Brasil. Rio de Janeiro, 1907. 1227

Parte I. Descobrimento da America: Brasil colonial, 1492–1822.

SANTOS, M. DOS Bibliografia gerál ou Descrição bibliográfica de livros tanto de autores portugueses como brasileiros . . . impressos desde o seculo XV até à actualidade. Lisboa, 1914–1917. 1228

(3) CHILE

* MEDINA, J. T. Bibliografia de la imprenta en Santiago de Chile desde sus origines hasta Febrero de 1817. Santiago de Chile, 1891. 1229

The first Chilean imprint now known is 1776 (see no. 882).

*———— Biblioteca Hispano-Chilena (1523–1817). Santiago de Chile, 1897–1899. 3 v. 1230

A list of 42 works printed between 1606 and 1815 is included in Sr. Medina's *Nueve sermones en lengua de Chile por el P. Luis de Valdivia de la Compaña de Jésus . . . precedidos de una bibliografía de la misma lengua.* Santiago de Chile, 1897.

(4) COLOMBIA

* MEDINA, J. T. La Imprenta en Bogotá (1739–1821). Notas bibliográficas. Santiago de Chile, 1904. 1231

*———— La Imprenta en Cartagena de las Indias (1809–1820). Notas bibliográficas. Santiago de Chile, 1904. 1232

POSADA, E. Bibliografía bogotana. Bogotá, 1917–1925. 2 v. (Biblioteca de Historia Nacional. XVI, XXXVI.) 1233

Vol. I. comprises 547 titles printed between 1738 and 1819.

(5) ECUADOR

* MEDINA, J. T. La Imprenta en Quito (1760–1818). Notas bibliográficas. Santiago de Chile, 1904. 1234

The asterisk (*) indicates that, in the reference works thus checked, annotations will be found giving the location of copies of the original editions recorded therein.

(6) PERU

JOHN CARTER BROWN LIBRARY (Providence)   Books printed in Lima
and elsewhere in South America after 1800. [Boston, 1908.]   1235

* MEDINA, J. T.   La Imprenta en Arequipa, El Cuzco, Trujillo y otros
pueblos del Perú durante las campañas de la independencia (1820–
1825). Notas bibliográficas. Santiago de Chile, 1904.   1236

* ———— La Imprenta en Lima (1584–1824). Santiago de Chile,
1904–1905. 4 v.   1237

(7) URUGUAY

* MEDINA, J. T.   Historia y bibliografía de la imprenta en Montevideo
(1807–1810). La Plata [1892]. (Museo de La Plata. Anales.
III. La imprenta en la América Española.)   1238

(8) VENEZUELA

* MEDINA, J. T.   La Imprenta en Caracas (1808–1821). Notas bibliográficas. Santiago de Chile, 1904.   1239

SANCHEZ, M. S.   Bibliografía Venezolanista. Contribucion al conocimiento de los libros estranjeros relativos a Venezuela . . . pub-
licados o reimpresos desde el siglo XIX. Caracas, 1914.   1240

The Sanchez collection of books relating to Venezuela was dispersed in 1913,
and divided among the Harvard University Library, the John Crerar Library, and Northwestern University Library.

VI. WORKS OF GENERAL REFERENCE, INCLUDING AMERICANA

A. *Facsimile and Reprint Series*

CHAMPLAIN SOCIETY (Toronto)   Publications. Toronto, 1907–[to
date].   1241

I. Lescarbot, V. 1, 1907. II. Denys, 1908. III. Seigniorial Tenure, 1908.
IV. The logs of the conquest of Canada, 1909. V. LeClercq, 1910. VI.
Hearne, 1911. VII. Lescarbot, V. 2, 1911. VIII. Knox, V. 1, 1914. IX.
Knox, V. 2, 1914. X. Knox, V. 3, 1916. XI. Lescarbot, V. 3, 1914. XII.
Thompson, 1916. XIII. Select British documents of the Canadian war of
1812, 1920. XIV. (ditto) V. 2, 1923. XV. (ditto) V. 3, pt. 1, 1926. [XVI.]
LaVérendrye, 1927. XVII. Select British documents . . . Vol. 3, pt. 2,
1928.

The *Publications* also include: The works of Samuel de Champlain. In six

The asterisk (*) indicates that, in the reference works thus checked, annotations will be
found giving the location of copies of the original editions recorded therein.

volumes. Reprinted, translated and annotated by six Canadian scholars under the general editorship of H. P. Biggar. Toronto, 1922, 1925–[ ]. [2 v.,
with portfolio.]

CLUB FOR COLONIAL REPRINTS (Providence) Publications. Providence, 1903–1916. 6 v. 1242

I. The fourth paper presented by Major Butler, with other papers edited
and published by Roger Williams in London, 1652. With an introduction and
notes by C. S. Brigham (1903). II. Boston in 1682 and 1699. A trip to
New-England by Edward Ward . . . with an introduction and notes by
G. P. Winship (1905). III. The American village. A poem by Philip Freneau
. . . with an introduction by H. L. Koopman and bibliographical data by
V. H. Paltsits, 1772 (1906). IV. Invitation sérieuse aux habitants des
Illinois . . . with an introduction by C. W. Alvord and C. E. Carter, 1772
(1908). V.—A scheme for a paper currency together with two petitions
written in Boston gaol in 1739–1740 by Richard Fry. With an introduction
by A. McF. Davis (1908). VI. Hypocrisie unmasked. . . By Edward Winslow, Governor of the Plymouth Colony . . . with an introduction by H. M.
Chapin. (1916.)

CORTES SOCIETY (New York) Documents and narratives concerning
the discovery and conquest of Latin America. New York, 1917–[ ],
nos. I–[ ]. 1243

I. [Anon.] Narrative of some things of New Spain . . . written by the
anonymous conqueror, a companion of Hernan Cortes. Translated . . . by
M. H. Saville. II. Sancho, Pedro. An account of the conquest of Peru.
Translated by P. A. Means. III. Alvarado, Pedro de. An account of the
conquest of Guatemala in 1524. Edited by S. J. Mackie, with a facsimile
of the Spanish original, 1525. IV. Pizarro, Pedro. Relation of the discovery . . . of the kingdoms of Peru. Translated by P. A. Means. V.
Magalhães, Pero de. The histories of Brazil . . . translated . . . by
J. B. Stetson, Jr., with a facsimile of the Portuguese original, 1576.

GORGES SOCIETY (Portland) [Publications. Portland, Me., 1884–.]
1244

Between 1884 and 1893, five volumes were issued reprinting or publishing:
I. Gardiner, H. New England's vindication, 1660. II. Baxter, J. P. George
Cleeve of Casco Bay, 1630–1667. III. Rosier, J. Rosier's Relation of Way-
mouth's voyage to the coast of Maine, 1605. IV. Thayer, H. O. The
Sagadahoc colony [i.e. — the 'Popham colony']. V. Baxter, J. P. Christo-
pher Levett of York, the pioneer colonist in Casco Bay.

HAKLUYT SOCIETY (London) Works issued by the Hakluyt Society.
London, 1847–(to date). 1245

Series I. Vols. 1–100, 1847–1899. Extra series, Hakluyt's *Principal Navigations* and *Purchas his Pilgrimes*, 32 v., 1903–1906. Series II, Vols. 1–[61],
1899–[1927].

The hundred and sixty odd volumes, so far issued, comprise reprints and
works relating to Columbus, Raleigh, Drake, Hawkins, Soto, Benzoni,

Champlain, Hudson, Cieza de Leon, Cortes, Garcilaso de la Vega, Xeres, Zeno, Magellan, Frobisher, Acosta, Schmidt, Cabot, Corte Real, etc. For the contents of the 1st and 2d series, up to 1923, see: Library of Congress, card no. 6–6987. Valuable introductions and notes invariably accompany each reprint. (See also above, under no. 726.)

THE JESUIT RELATIONS and allied documents. Travels and explorations of the Jesuit missionaries in New France, 1610–1791. . . Edited by Reuben Gold Thwaites. Cleveland, 1896–1901. 73 v.
1246

With bibliographical data at the end of each volume, edited by V. H. Paltsits. Vols. 72–73, index. (For a complete list of contents, see: Library of Congress, card no. 3–6351.) See also below, under: Thwaites, no. 1251.

LINSCHOTEN-VEREENIGING (The Hague) Werken uitgegeven door de Linschoten-Vereeniging. 's Gravenhage, 1909–[to date]. 1247

Comprise reprints of the voyages of the sixteenth and seventeenth centuries. Each volume contains a list of the Society's publications up to the date of its printing, the volume for 1928 being no. 30.

MASSACHUSETTS HISTORICAL SOCIETY (Boston) [Photostat reproductions of unique and rare Americana.] [Boston, 1919–to date.] [230 v. to date.]
1248

A series of separate photostat reproductions made from rare specimens of Americana wherever they may be; bound and distributed by the Massachusetts Historical Society to the following subscribing libraries: The New York Public Library, John Carter Brown Library, Massachusetts Historical Society, William L. Clements Library, Henry E. Huntington Library, American Antiquarian Society, The Newberry Library, The State Historical Society of Wisconsin, Library of Congress, Yale University Library, and New York Historical Society.

ORIGINAL NARRATIVES of early American history, reproduced under the auspices of the American Historical Association; general editor, J. Franklin Jameson. New York, 1906–[]. 1249

Comprise: Spanish explorers in the southern United States, 1528–1543: [i.e., The narrative of Alvar Nuñez Cabeça de Vaca, ed. by F. W. Hodge; The narrative of the expedition of Hernando de Soto by the Gentleman of Elvas, ed. by T. H. Lewis; The narrative of the expedition of Coronado, by Pedro de Castañeda, ed. by F. W. Hodge. With maps and a facsimile t.-p. of Cabeça de Vaca's *Relacion*, 1542]. Early narratives of the Northwest, 1634–1699, ed. by L. P. Kellogg, etc.

PRINCE SOCIETY (Boston) The Publications of the Prince Society. Boston, 1865–. 1250

Comprise: the Hutchinson Papers, a reprint of Wood's *New-England prospect*, Dunton's *Letters written from New-England*, 1688, the Andros tracts,

Morton's *New English Canaan,* voyages of Samuel de Champlain, voyages of the Northmen to America, Sir Walter Ralegh and his colony, Capt. John Mason the founder of New Hampshire, Sir Ferdinando Gorges and his province of Maine, Antinomianism in the colony of Massachusetts Bay, John Checkley or the evolution of religious toleration in Massachusetts, Sir Humphrey Gylberte and his enterprise, Colonial currency reprints, the New England company of 1649 and John Eliot, etc.

THWAITES, R. G., *ed.*   Early western travels, 1748–1846; a series of annotated reprints of some of the best and rarest contemporary volumes of travel, descriptive of the aborigines and social and economic conditions in the middle and far west, during the period of early American settlement.   Cleveland, 1904–1907.   32 v.   1251

A detailed list of contents is given on Library of Congress card, no. 4–6902 Additions.   For other works frequently spoken of under the generic title of 'The Thwaites reprints' see above, under: Jesuit relations.   See also Thwaites' editions of Hennepin, Lahontan — not here listed.

For various other reprints, see the *Tracts* compiled by Peter Force, *Reprints of rare Americana* edited by J. Christian Bay, the Sabin reprints, Old South leaflets, the publications of the Narragansett Club, the Filson Club, the Quivira Society, the Hudson Bay Company, etc.

See also the numerous facsimiles and reprints issued by the Hispanic Society of America, and the publications of various institutions noted below, under nos. 1277–1284.

B. *Historical Monographs and Surveys of Americana*

ADAMS, R. G.   The Gateway to American History.   Boston, 1927.
                                                                    1252

The purpose of this work and of the author's *Pilgrims, Indians and Patriots* is the reproduction of early pictures illustrating American history.

BOLTON, H. E.   The Spanish borderlands.   A chronicle of old Florida and the Southwest.   New Haven, 1921.   (The chronicles of America.)
                                                                    1252:a

[CLEMENTS, W. L.]   The William L. Clements Library of Americana at the University of Michigan.   Ann Arbor, 1923.   1252:b

A bibliographical survey of early source material.

GOLDER, F. A.   Bering's voyages: an account of the efforts of the Russians to determine the relation of Asia and America.   New York, 1925.   2 v.   (The American Geographical Society.)   1253

* GREENE, E. B., AND R. R. MORRIS   A Guide to the principal sources for early American history (1600–1800) in the City of New York. New York, 1929.   1253:a

In two parts relating to contemporary printed sources, manuscript collections, and later reference material relative to this early period. Classified in various ways and including public records; church histories; charters, statutes, and treaties; American periodicals; accounts of inter-colonial wars, etc.

HOWARD, C.   English travellers of the Renaissance. London, 1914.

1254

MOSES, B.   The intellectual background of the revolution in South America, 1810–1824. New York, 1926. (The Hispanic Society of America. Hispanic notes & monographs.)   1255

An account of the growth of the revolutionary movement based upon a survey of the writings of the time.

———— Spain overseas. New York, 1929. (The Hispanic Society of America. Hispanic notes & monographs.)   1256

"The following chapters are in effect marginal comments on some sections of the general history of Spanish America." *Preface*.

———— Spanish colonial literature in South America. London, New York, 1922. (The Hispanic Society of America. Hispanic notes & monographs.)   1257

A critique of colonial literature from the Spanish settlement of South America to the eve of the revolutionary period; with a *Catalogue,* under authors' names, of the books mentioned in the text.

PRIESTLEY, H. I.   The Coming of the white man, 1492–1848. New York, 1929. (A History of American life. I.)   1258

STEVENS, H., AND H. N. STEVENS, *booksellers, London*   Historical nuggets: Bibliotheca Americana. London, 1862, etc.   1258:a

THOMAS, I.   The History of printing in America, with a biography of printers and an account of newspapers. Worcester, 1810. 2 v. 1259

Re-issued at Albany in 1874. With important additions from annotations in the author's copy, and by the committee of publication.

A work still useful, especially in its later edition. Although its list of imprints is far from complete and occasionally the status of the first work from

The asterisk (*) indicates that, in the reference works thus checked, annotations will be found giving the location of copies of the original editions recorded therein.

a press known to Thomas has been changed through later research, the work as a whole should be consulted by anyone undertaking the study of the history of American typography.

WALDMAN, M.   Americana: The literature of American history.   New York, 1925.   1260

WILLIAMS, S. C.   Early travels in the Tennessee country, 1540–1800. Johnson City, Tenn., 1928.   1261

WINSOR, J., *ed.* . . . Narrative and critical history of America. [Boston, Re-issued 1923.] 8 v.   1262

First issued during 1884–1889. A series of historical essays based upon original sources, with bibliographical references, by the leading authorities of its time. Contents: I. Aboriginal America. II. Spanish exploration and settlements in America from the fifteenth to the seventeenth century. III. English exploration and settlements in North America, 1497–1689. IV. French exploration and settlements in North America, and those of the Portuguese, Dutch and Swedes, 1500–1700. V. The English and French in North America, 1689–1763. VI–VII. The United States of North America. VIII. The later history of British, Spanish and Portuguese America. Appendix: Manuscript sources of the history of the United States. . . Printed authorities. . . Chronological conspectus of American history.

A complete and detailed statement of the essays comprised within this compilation will be found on Library of Congress card, no. 2–3986/10 Revised.

WRIGHT, J. K.   The geographical lore of the time of the crusades. New York. (The American Geographical Society. Research series, no. 15.)   1263

See also: (1) Various works edited by R. G. Thwaites (in addition to those noted above, under nos. 1246 and 1251); *The American Nation* series edited by A. B. Hart; *The Chronicles of America* edited by A. Johnson; C. W. Alvord's *Illinois Country, 1673–1818,* and his various works on the Middle West; B. F. French's *Historical collections,* three series (1846–53, 1869, and 1875) relative to Louisiana and Florida; H. R. Wagner's *California voyages, 1539–1541,* and works relative to Drake and the Spanish Southwest; G. Chinard's *L'Exotisme américain dans la littérature française au XVIe siècle;* E. P. Cheyney's *European background of American history, 1300–1600;* (2) J. D. G. Shea's *History of Catholic missions among the Indians of the United States, 1529–1854,* and works on the Mississippi Valley; the works of H. H. Bancroft on the native races of the Pacific coast and Mexico; the publications of the Smithsonian Institution, the Bureau of American Ethnology, and of the Museum of the American Indian, Heye Foundation; the works of R. R. Schuller, F. W. Hodge, D. G. Brinton and Z. Nuttall on Indian linguistics and customs; (3) the publications of the American Historical Association, the Catholic Society of America, the United States Catholic Historical Society, the Société de la Propagation de la Foi (Montreal series, Quebec series, etc.), Essex Institute, various state historical societies; (4) The *Guides* to material about American history issued by the Carnegie Institution of Washington, and C. K. Jones's *Bibliography of Hispanic-American bibliographies.* For bibliographical monographs on special divisions of Americana, see above, under the various specialized sections.

C. *Catalogues and General Works*

BIBLIOTHÈQUE NATIONALE (Paris) Catalogue général des livres imprimés de la Bibliothèque Nationale. Paris, 1897–[1927]. [90] v. (France. Ministère de l'Instruction publique et des Beaux-Arts.)
1264

BOSTON. PUBLIC LIBRARY (*Ticknor collection*) Catalogue of the Spanish library and of the Portuguese books bequeathed by George Ticknor to the Boston Public Library. . . By James Lyman Whitney. Boston, 1879.
1265

BRINLEY, G. Catalogue of the American library of the late Mr. George Brinley. . . Hartford, 1878–1893. 5 v.
1266

Compiled by J. H. Trumbull. With biographical sketch and *Index* by W. I. Fletcher.

BRITISH MUSEUM. DEPARTMENT OF PRINTED BOOKS Catalogue of printed books in the library of the British Museum. . . London, 1881–1900. 393 pts.
1267

A supplement of 44 parts was issued between 1900 and 1905.

See also the *Short-title catalogue of books printed in Spain and of Spanish books printed elsewhere in Europe before 1601 now in the British Museum,* by Henry Thomas. [London] 1921; the *Short-title catalogue of books printed in France . . . from 1470 to 1600 now in the British Museum.* Oxford, 1924; and the *Short-title catalogue of Portuguese books and of Spanish-American books printed before 1601 now in the British Museum.* London, 1926.

A *Catalogue of the American books in the library of the British Museum at Christmas MDCCCLVI* was issued by Henry Stevens of Vermont, London, 1866.

CALIFORNIA, UNIVERSITY OF, LIBRARY Spain and Spanish America in the libraries of the University of California. A catalogue of books. . . Berkeley, 1928–.
1268

Compiled by Alice I. Lyser.

FERNANDEZ DE NAVARRETE, M. Coleccion de los viajes y descubrimientos. Madrid, 1825–1837. 5 v.
1269

Relates to Columbus, Vespuccius, Davila, Magellan, etc., and contains texts hitherto unpublished.

A series of bio-bibliographical notes on Spanish authors, explorers, soldiers, etc., was compiled by this author, and issued under title: *Biblioteca marítima española, obra póstuma.* Madrid, 1851. 2 v.

FORD, P. L.   Check list of bibliographies, catalogues, reference-lists, and lists of authorities of American books and subjects. Brooklyn, 1889. 1270

*GREENE, E. B., AND R. R. MORRIS   A Guide to the principal sources for early American history (1600–1800) in the City of New York. New York, 1929. 1270:a

In two parts relating to contemporary printed sources, manuscript collections, and later reference material relative to this early period. Classified in various ways and including public records; church histories; charters, statutes, and treaties; American periodicals; accounts of inter-colonial wars, *etc.*

LONDON. STATIONERS' COMPANY   A Transcript of the registers of the Company of Stationers of London, 1554–1640. London, 1875–77, Birmingham, 1894. 5 v. 1271

Edited by Edward Arber. For detailed contents, see Library of Congress card, no. 3–25361 Revised.

A Transcript of the registers of the Worshipful Company of Stationers: from 1640–1708 was edited by G. E. Briscoe Eyre, London, 1913–14. 3 v. Another issue printed on large paper for the Roxburghe Club.

See also P. L. Phillips' *List of books relating to America in the register of the London Company of Stationers, from 1562 to 1638,* Washington, 1897; or in: American Historical Association. *Annual report,* 1896, p. 1249–1261.

MACDONALD, W., *ed.*   Documentary source book of American history, 1606–1926. Third edition, revised and enlarged. New York, 1926. 1272

First issued in 1908; re-issued in 1916. Valuable not only for the texts of the important acts, treaties, etc., relating to the United States and its early colonial history but for annotations stating the occasion, purpose, etc., of these documents.

A volume of *Select charters and other documents illustrative of American history, 1606–1775,* was issued by this author in 1910.

MCKERROW, R. B., *ed.*   A Dictionary of printers and booksellers in England, Scotland and Ireland, and of foreign printers of English books 1557–1640. London, 1910. 1273

One of a series of works issued by The Bibliographical Society; preceded by E. G. Duff's *Century of the English book trade 1457–1557,* London, 1905;

The asterisk (*) indicates that, in the reference works thus checked, annotations will be found giving the location of copies of the original editions recorded therein.

and followed by H. R. Plomer's *Dictionary of the booksellers and printers who were at work in England, Scotland and Ireland from 1641 to 1667,* London, 1907, and his *Dictionary of the printers . . . at work . . . from 1668 to 1725,* Oxford, 1922.

NORTON'S LITERARY LETTER, comprising . . . a catalogue of rare and valuable books relative to America. New York, 1857–1860. 1273:a

Includes bibliographies of Maine by William Willis, New Hampshire by Samuel C. Eastman, and Vermont by Benjamin H. Hall. No more published.

* POLLARD, A. W., *comp.*   A short-title catalogue of books printed in England, Scotland, & Ireland, and of English books printed abroad 1475–1640. London, 1926. (The Bibliographical Society.)   1274

With " abridged entries of all 'English' books . . . copies of which exist at the British Museum, the Bodleian, the Cambridge University library, and the Henry E. Huntington library, California, supplemented by additions from nearly one hundred and fifty other collections."

G. R. Redgrave, *jt. comp.*

RICH, O.   Bibliotheca Americana Nova; or, A catalogue of books in various languages relating to America, printed since the year 1700. New York, 1835–1846.   1275

VINDEL, F.   Manual gráfico-descriptivo del bibliófilo hispano-americano, 1475–1850. [Vol. I announced for February, 1930.]   1276

See also various catalogues issued by the John Rylands Library, Manchester; the Christie-Miller *Catalogue of . . . early works relating to America from the renowned library at Britwell Court, Burnham, Bucks* [London, 1916] purchased before its public sale by The Henry E. Huntington Library; various specialized catalogues issued by London bookdealers, Quaritch, Stevens, Goldschmidt, Maggs, etc.; the *Bibliografía Madrileña* of Perez Pastor, Madrid, 1891–1907; Leclerc's *Bibliotheca Americana,* Paris, 1878; etc.

For general works devoted to Americana, see also above, under nos. 650–652.

The asterisk (*) indicates that, in the reference works thus checked, annotations will be found giving the location of copies of the original editions recorded therein.

MISCELLANEA
SELECTED MONOGRAPHS

CONTENTS

Section VIII

MISCELLANEA: SELECTED MONOGRAPHS

I. Eight Rare-Book Libraries (Incunabula and Americana)

American Antiquarian Society, *Worcester* A Survey of the library of the American Antiquarian Society, founded 1812. Worcester, 1928. 1277

A brief account of a reference library of half a million books relating to North and South America, and comprising among its special collections the largest collection of early newspapers in the country, early periodicals, general and local history, bibliography, biography and genealogy, New England primers, catechisms, almanacs, etc.

Annmary Brown Memorial, *Providence* The Annmary Brown Memorial. A descriptive essay by Margaret Bingham Stillwell. Providence, 1925. 1278

A brief account of the collection of incunabula started by the late Brigadier General Rush C. Hawkins in 1855, and deposited, July 2, 1907, in the Memorial erected to his wife.

A bio-bibliographical sketch of the founder was issued in 1923 under the title *General Hawkins as he revealed himself to his Librarian.*

The *Catalogue* of the collection, prepared by Alfred W. Pollard, was issued in 1910. See above, under no. 8.

Henry E. Huntington Library and Art Gallery, *San Marino* The Huntington Library and Art Gallery. The new plan of research, by George Ellery Hale. (*In* Scribner's Magazine. July 1927. LXXXII: no. 1, p. 31–43.) 1279

The Henry E. Huntington collection, begun officially in 1911, was brought together by the purchase in whole or in part of numerous world-famous collections of rare books. In 1919 the collection was transferred to a Board of Trustees. This was vested with increased powers in 1926 for 'the advancement of learning, the arts and sciences,' and the trust defined as 'a free public research library, art gallery, museum, and botanical garden.'

The essay noted above comprises an account of the origin and contents of the Huntington Library, written by one of the Board of Trustees, and describes briefly its superb collections of incunabula, Americana, Shakesperiana, English literature, manuscripts, etc., with some reference to the collections from which they came. For catalogues, see nos. 651 and 945.

The first annual report, entitled *Henry E. Huntington Library and Art Gallery. First Annual Report. July 1, 1927-June 30, 1928,* appeared in 1929.

HISPANIC SOCIETY OF AMERICA, *New York*   The Hispanic Society of America, founded 1904. New York, 1910.   1280

Its collections comprise Spanish literature from the time of the introduction of printing to the year 1700, thus making the Society's library one of the centers of both Spanish incunabula and Spanish Americana. Its numerous facsimile reproductions of rare books frequently relate to one field or the other. The purpose of the Society, its library, museum, etc., is for research and " the advancement of the study of the Spanish and Portuguese languages, and of the literature and history of the countries wherein Spanish and Portuguese are spoken."

A volume of *General information* and catalogue of publications was issued by the Society in 1917. Among its varied publications are the *Bibliographie hispanique,* 1905–1917, an annual catalogue of books and articles of importance in the Hispanic field; a *List of works for the study of Hispanic-American history,* by H. Keniston, 1920; a valuable series entitled *Hispanic notes & monographs, etc.*

A *List of books printed before 1601 in the library of the Hispanic Society of America,* by Clara L. Penney, was issued in 1929.

JOHN CARTER BROWN LIBRARY (BROWN UNIVERSITY), *Providence* The John Carter Brown Library. A history by George Parker Winship. Providence, 1914.   1281

The earliest known invoice of Mr. John Carter Brown's purchases in Americana is dated 1846, but he had been collecting in this field for at least five years. The present building, erected in accordance with the will of the late John Nicholas Brown, as a memorial to his father, was dedicated on May 17, 1904. A dedication volume was published in 1905.

Annual reports have been issued by the Library since 1911, and numerous monographs relating to Americana have been printed from time to time. The catalogue, entitled *Bibliotheca Americana* — which was issued in two editions (1865–1871, 1875–1882) by J. R. Bartlett — is now being re-edited. Two volumes prepared by W. C. Ford appeared in 1919 and 1922; the third volume, edited by L. C. Wroth, is in process of compilation.

LENOX LIBRARY (now a part of the New York Public Library), *New York*   Recollections of Mr. James Lenox of New York and the formation of his library. By Henry Stevens of Vermont. London, 1886.   1282

The Lenox collection of Bibles, Americana, etc., started by Mr. James Lenox in or before 1845, was incorporated as the Lenox Library on January 20, 1870, organized January 28, 1871, and subsequently housed in a special building. On May 23, 1895, however, it became a part of the New York Public Library, Astor, Lenox, and Tilden Foundations, and its treasures were moved to the main library building on Fifth Avenue, at Forty Second street.

A further account of the rare books in the latter library, of which the Lenox collection forms the nucleus, will be found in the *History of the New York Public Library, Astor, Lenox, and Tilden Foundations* by H. M. Lydenberg, assistant director, published by the Library in 1924. Reprints and bibliographical lists were issued by the Lenox Library, and in later years other lists have appeared in the *Bulletin* of the New York Public Library.

PIERPONT MORGAN LIBRARY, *New York.* The Pierpont Morgan Library: a review of the growth, development and activities of the library during the period between its establishment as an educational institution in February 1924 and the close of the year 1929. New York, 1930. 1283

An illustrated account of the library with a selected list of some of its treasures appeared in *The New York Times*, Sunday, February 17, 1924. With caption-heading: *J. P. Morgan gives library to the public for reference and literary research, with fund of $1,500,000. to maintain it.*

A *Catalogue* of manuscripts and early printed books from the Library of J. Pierpont Morgan, senior, was published in London, 1906–1907, in which the English incunabula were catalogued by E. Gordon Duff; Horæ by A. W. Pollard; French and Italian incunabula by A. W. Pollard and R. Proctor jointly; German illustrated books by R. Proctor; incunabula of Germany and the Low Countries by S. Aldrich; manuscripts by M. R. James. General editor, A. W. Pollard.

WILLIAM L. CLEMENTS LIBRARY (University of Michigan), *Ann Arbor.* The William L. Clements Library of Americana at the University of Michigan. Ann Arbor, 1923. 1284

A synopsis of source material based upon Mr. Clements' collection of Americana. The present building and its contents were presented to the University of Michigan on June 15, 1923, and a dedication volume was published during that year. A brochure on *The Whys and wherefores of the William L. Clements Library* was issued by R. G. Adams in 1925.

The preceding notes, relating to eight American libraries devoted to rare books, within the range of interest of the present volume, are based upon a rather inadequate series of descriptive monographs and brochures. The specialized libraries of the United States seem extraordinarily modest in recording their contents and purpose. It is only in two or three instances that they are adequately described in monographs or catalogues. Several, however, have reported that such publications are in preparation or under contemplation. The present list should be taken, therefore, as a tentative record including neither all of the special libraries nor all that should be available regarding most of those noted above.

Collections of Americana or incunabula in general reference libraries are not included, only those being noted (so far as titles are available) that are, or have been, separate institutions. Cognizance should be taken, however, of the rare books to be found in Harvard College Library; in the Grolier Club, New York; in the Ayer collection of Americana and the Wing collection of incunabula and bibliography at the Newberry Library, Chicago; the Thacher collection and other incunabula, and the Americana, at the Library of Congress; the medical incunabula in the John Crerar Library, Chicago, the U. S. Surgeon General's Library, the Boston Medical Society, and the New York Academy of Medicine; Spanish Americana at the University of California and the Boston Public Library; early Americana in the Massachusetts Historical Society, in numerous local historical societies; rare books in the Chapin Library in Williamstown, in the Boston Athenæum, etc.

The *Catalogue of the John Boyd Thacher collection of incunabula,* compiled by Frederick W. Ashley in 1915, describes a collection separately housed in the Library of Congress — apart from the Library's main collection of incunabula, which has been recently augmented by the acquisition of the Vollbehr books. A brief history of the Library of Congress, given at the hearing relative to the purchase of the Vollbehr collection of incunabula, appeared in the *Congressional Record* (71st Congress, H. of R., Feb. 7, 1930); and an account of the purchase of the Vollbehr collection was given in the 'Book Section' of the *Boston Evening Transcript,* July 26, 1930.

II. Tributes to Bibliographers

A. *European Bibliographers* †

1899. BRADSHAW   Collected papers of Henry Bradshaw . . . comprising 1. 'Memoranda'; 2. 'Communications' read before the Cambridge Antiquarian Society; together with an article contributed to the 'Bibliographer' and two papers not previously published. Edited for the Syndics of the University Press. Cambridge, 1889.
1285

Preface signed: F. J. [*i.e.,* Francis John Henry Jenkinson.]   The following essays and lists relate to incunabula or early engraving: VI. On the earliest English engravings of the indulgence known as the 'Image of Pity'; Note on an English block-printed broadside. VIII. The printer of the *Historia S. Albani.* XI. A classified index of fifteenth century books in the De Meyer collection. XII. On the engraved device used by Nicolaus Gotz of Sletzstat, the Cologne printer, in 1474. XIII. On two engravings on copper, by G. M., a wandering Flemish artist of the XV–XVI century. XIV. List of the founts of type and woodcut devices used by printers in Holland in the fifteenth century. XIX. Notice of a fragment of the fifteen Oes and other prayers printed at Westminster by W. Caxton about 1490–1491, preserved in the library of the Baptist College, Bristol. (The remaining titles relate to manuscripts or to topics of a later period.)

A Memoir of Henry Bradshaw, by G. W. Prothero, was issued in London in 1888.

1905. PROCTOR   Bibliographical essays, by Robert Proctor. London, 1905.   1286

† In chronological sequence.

A memorial volume, comprising a memoir by and a reprint of all of Proctor's bibliographical essays and papers. Printed for the donors and subscribers to The Proctor Memorial Fund, in an edition of 200 copies. Edited by A. W. Pollard.

Contents: Robert Proctor. Report of Proctor Memorial Fund. The Accipies woodcut. On two plates in Sotheby's 'Principia Typographica.' Marcus Reinhard and Johann Grüninger. Incunabula at Grenoble. The 'Gutenberg' Bible. A short view of Berthelet's editions of the statutes of Henry VIII. On two Lyonnese editions of the 'Ars Moriendi.' Ulrich von Ellenbog and the press of S. Ulrich at Augsburg. The French royal Greek types and the Eton Chrysostom. The early printers of Köln. Tracts on early printing: i. List of the founts of type . . . used by the printers of the Southern Netherlands in the fifteenth century. ii. A note on Eberhard Frommolt of Basel, printer. iii. Additions to Campbell's 'Annales de la typographie Néerlandaise au 15e siècle.' Table of Supplements to Campbell. Additions to Campbell's Annales. Author register.

1912. HARRISSE Henry Harrisse. Étude biographique et morale avec la bibliographie critique de ses écrits. Par H. Vignaud. Paris, 1912.   1287

Lists 94 titles of printed works, manuscripts, etc., relating to the discovery of America, Columbus, Cabot, Vespuccius, Cortereal, Portuguese navigators, New France, Verrazzano, etc.
A eulogy of Harrisse by H. Cordier, entitled *Henry Harrisse, 1830–1910,* listing 82 of his works, appeared in the *Bulletin du Bibliophile,* Chartres, [1910] and was separately printed.

1919. HAEBLER Wiegendrucke und Handschriften. Festgabe Konrad Haebler zum 60. Geburtstage. Leipzig, 1919.   1288

Die Schriften Konrad Haeblers, p. 1–17, by E. von Rath, the editor. With nine essays from other hands. Reviewed in *The Library,* 1920, p. 52–56.
See also *Konrad Haebler zum 70. Geburtstag nebst ein Verzeichnis seiner Schriften von 1918–1927.* Von E. v. Rath. (*In* Frühdrucke aus der Bücherei V. v. Klemperer. Dresden, 1927, p. 21–29).

1922. VOULLIÉME Ernst Voulliéme als Inkunabelforscher. Ein Verzeichnis seiner Arbeiten zu seinem sechzigsten Geburtstag. Bonn, 1922.   1289

Edited by E. von Rath.

1925. COLLIJN Bok- och bibliotheks-historiska studier tillägnade Isak Collijn på hans 50-årsdag. Upsala, 1925.   1290

With a bibliography of Dr. Collijn's writings, contributions from Scandinavian bibliographers, and also from Haebler, Polain, Voulliéme, von Rath, Loubier, etc. Edited by Axel Nelson.

B. *American Bibliographers*

1907–24. MEDINA Homenaje que la Sociedad de Historia y Geografía tributa a su socio honorario Don José Toribio Medina con ocasión de enterar cincuenta años de labor histórica y literaria. Santiago de Chile, 1924.   1291

Contents in part: Acuerdos del consejo universitario, etc.; La prensa de Chile en el dia de la fiesta. La fiesta universitaria; en la Argentina; en Lima. Chiappa: La obra de Medina, notas biográficas. Discurso de Don Domingo Amunátegui. Vaisse: Medina y sus obras. Medina y Harrisse. Chiappa: Catálogo de las publicaciones de Don José Toribio Medina, 1873–1914 (titles no. 1–226). Cruz: Continuación de la bibliografía de D. Victor M. Chiappa (titles no. 227–307). Cruz: Bio-bibliografia.

In 1907 Don Chiappa issued *Noticias acerca de la vida y obras de Don José Toribio Medina* (*Biblioteca Medina*) and *Noticia de los trabajos intelectuales de Don José Toribio Medina* (*Biblioteca Medina II*), the latter listing 96 titles.

1924. EAMES Bibliographical essays. A tribute to Wilberforce Eames. June, MCMXXIV. [Cambridge, 1924.]   1292

A collection of thirty-one bibliographical essays contributed by friends of Wilberforce Eames — seventeen relating to Americana before 1800 and two to incunabula. Edited by George Parker Winship and Lawrence Counselman Wroth.

With a biographical sketch of Mr. Eames and a list of his works by Victor Hugo Paltsits; and bibliographical essays or other contributions by: H. L. Koopman, L. L. Nichols, A. H. Lerch, P. Merritt, W. C. Ford, H. W. Kent, J. T. Medina, C. L. Nichols, G. L. Kittredge, L. C. Wroth, L. C. Harper, T. J. Holmes, G. W. Cole, G. P. Winship, R. S. Granniss, C. S. Brigham, C. B. Clapp, O. Wegelin, R. G. Adams, L. C. Karpinski, H. R. Wagner, H. N. Stevens, J. B. Wilbur, V. W. Crane, A. J. Wall, H. G. Rugg, C. M. Cate, H. M. Chapin, A. C. Bates, J. H. Tuttle, A. Marx, and M. B. Stillwell.

INDEX

INDEX

Numerals in italics refer to numbered titles in Reference Sections V–VIII. Technical and specialized entries, subdivided for incunabula and Americana, will be found below under the headings: Bibliographical Methods, Terms and Usage; Engraving; Maps; Prnting: History, Diffusion. Page numbers are in Roman type.

Jennings, O., *no. 613*
Jenson, Nicolas, 6
Jerome, St., *no. 276*
Jesuit Order, 84, 130, 132, 144, 147–
150; *see also* Religious orders and missions
Jesuit Relations, 84, 97, 98, *nos. 803–805, 818, 919, 920, 931, 932, 938*
Jimenez Catalán, M., *no. 219*
Joachim, J., *no. 546*
Johann von Paderborn, 198
John Carter Brown Library, *Providence*, 16, 70, 82, 91, 96, 120, 142, 190, 200, *nos. 652, 675, 722, 755, 774, 871–873, 875, 890, 891, 1235, 1248, 1281*
John Crerar Library, *Chicago*, 16, 139, *nos. 379, 1240*
John of Westfalia, *see* Johann von Paderborn
John Rylands Library, *Manchester*, 15, 32, 57, *no. 614*
Johnson, A. F., *nos. 117, 125, 590*
Johnson, Allen, *no. 1263*
Johnson, Amandus, 99, *no. 916*
Johnson, Edward, 96
Johnson, Marmaduke, *155–157*
Johnston, G. P., *no. 833*
Johnston, James, 154, 155, 162, *nos. 1051, 1175*
Joliet, Louis, 105
Jones, C. K., *no. 1263*
Jones, S. K., *no. 944*
Josephson, A. G. S., *nos. 379, 492*
Josselyn, John, *no. 946*
Joutel, Henri, 105, 106, 122
Juan y Santacilia, Jorge, 132, 133
Juchhoff, R., xvi, *nos. 234, 257, 303, 526*
Juet, R., 93
Juvenile literature (British colonies) 112, *nos. 1002–1007*; (United States) *nos. 1125–1130*

Kalendarium Pennsilvaniense, 157
Karataev, I. P., *nos. 106, 243–245, 318*
Karpinski, L. P., *nos. 849, 1042, 1166*
Keen, G. B., *no. 917*
Keimer, S., 155, 162

Keith, G., 158
Kellogg, L. P., *no. 1249*
Keniston, H., 139, *no. 1213*
Kent, H. W., *166, no. 1193*
Kentucke Gazette, 165
Kentucky, 165, *nos. 796–797, 1191, 1191:a*
Keogh, A., *no. 564*
Kino, Eusebio Francisco, 130
Kittredge, G. L., *no. 429*
Klebs, Arnold C., 40, 56, 186, *nos. 390, 395*
Klemming, G. E., *nos. 295, 296*
Klemperer, V. von, *Collection*, 181
Klette, E., 200
Kneeland and Green, *firm, no. 991*
Knoblochtzer, Heinrich, *no. 62*
Knoxville Gazette, 165, *no. 1198*
Knuttel, W. P. C., 89, *no. 865*
Koberger, Anton, *no. 448*
Koch, T. W., *no. 419*
Koegler, H., *no. 118*
Koelhoff, Johann, the Elder, 13
Koopman, H. L., *nos. 1158, 1242*
Korte Verhael, 100
Kretschmer, K., 182, *no. 750*
Kristeller, [J.] P., 56, *nos. 425, 525, 527, 615–621*
Kruitwagen, B., *nos. 174, 175, 493, 494, 597*
Kunne, Albrecht, 37

Labande, L. H., *nos. 130, 138*
Lacombe, P., *nos. 126, 332*
La Condamine, Charles Marie de, 132
Lactantius, 9, 12
Laet, Joannes de, 93, 99, *no. 702*
Lagerström, H., *no. 297*
Lahontan, L. A. L. d'Arce, *Baron* de, 110, *no. 936*
La Lande, J. de, *no. 357*
Lam, S., *no. 235*
Lambert, A., *nos. 217, 221, 333*
Lancaster, *no. 356*
Landsberg, M., *no. 42*
Lane, W. C., *nos. 995, 1114*
Lange, H. O., *nos. 51, 54, 91, 287*

DISCIPLINED
CREATIVITY
For Engineers

by

Robert L. Bailey

Associate Professor
Department of Electrical Engineering
University of Florida, Gainesville

ANN ARBOR SCIENCE
PUBLISHERS INC
P.O. BOX 1425 • ANN ARBOR, MICH. 48106

It is said that creativity can't be taught . . . that it usually can't be taught . . . that you must be born creative and hence you either have it or you don't.

Professor Bailey says it *can* be taught . . . that he has been enhancing creativity for years—ever since participating in the pioneering General Electric program some years back. His book is in fact the result of having successfully taught creative problem solving for 17 years at the University of Florida.

Bailey gives you a complete and highly usable How-to-Text/Reference book combined, describing the necessary steps in this "mysterious" process, and showing you when and how to take each one. A big book delivered in small easy-to-take doses, showing many living engineering examples of "how it was and is done." Illustrated with photographs, drawings, sketches, tables, charts. Quotations by many successful people on creativity help inspire you.

CREATIVITY HAS MANY SUBTLE FACETS: Judgment ● emotions ● renewal ● rewards ● models ● intuition ● choices ● values ● motivation ● problem-solving approach ● creativity stimulators ● vision ● programming ● inhibitors ● environment ● ethics ● relationships ● attitude ● communication ● groups ● information ● checking ● experiment ● patents ● records ● practice. Proper balance of these and other facets through judgment are needed by the disciplined creative engineer. This book shows you how to get that balance.

This book seeks to enhance the creativity of the individual engineer at the personal level and to **structure this know-how** in practical ways meaningful to both working engineer and student. A central thread throughout is a clear revealing, for the first time, of the total structure of the methodology for real-world creative problem solving, especially applied to the engineering creation of new products, processes, methods, techniques, and innovations. Many power-related exercises and examples are included, especially in the advanced energy conversion areas, thereby exposing the reader to some current frontiers in energy technology.

Fills the need for a long sought teachable college text for senior level *Creative Problem Solving* courses in addition to being useful to the practicing engineer and inventor.

We are presently seeing a gradual return to some of the original meaning of engineer—the artful contriver—**as design, engineering technology and other creative educational programs evolve within engineering education.**

The conclusion is inescapable that the engineer of the future **will need knowledge and ability to apply creativity to a broad spectrum** of problems. He will need to be highly creative to survive and successfully contribute practical solutions demanded by society. This is your new book to **demonstrate how creativity can be enhanced through Professor Bailey's orderly, logical and proven six-step method.**

For engineers of all disciplines, it's valuable in solving everyday as well as unusual problems. For those innovative engineering schools that have long wanted to teach creativity. With this book, you remove the mystery from this so-called mysterious subject.

A valuable book to engineers of all disciplines, students, inventors, college professors, managers of Research and Design, and others interested in practical ways of enhancing creative output.

You will use this book, read it, refer to it, teach from it— frequently. A book that captures, organizes, and clearly lays out what engineering is about—a creative, proven Profession.

CONTENTS

DEDICATED TO

the memory of:

Gladys Harlow Bailey

Who encouraged and inspired me as a youth

and

Francis Leo Bailey

Who taught me the meaning of discipline.

FOREWORD

Government officials often talk about the need for perspective. Historians point to the interrelatedness of events and trends. Economists take "macro views" and engineers talk about "a systems approach" to problems such as inflation, energy and environmental trade-offs, health care delivery, communication versus transportation trade-offs, population distribution among rural and urban areas, and the dependence of world food supply on energy availability.

Traditionally, the educational system has reacted to complex problems of this kind by specialization—creating smaller and smaller subfields for engineers and others to specialize in. This worked fine as long as the subfields were disjointed enough to be analyzed without too much consideration of other subfields, but today the engineering student can no longer expect to apply "cookbook" formulas or analytical techniques out of a manual of his specialty. What will be needed in the future will be the ability to synthesize as well as analyze. Synthesis, as this book uses it, does not mean just putting together a machine or building a new system, but rather the putting together of ideas from different disciplines or fields which heretofore have not been related. Professor Bailey has created in this book a laboratory for experimenting with synthesis, much as an engineering fundamentals workshop is a laboratory for analysis.

Many educators will argue that creativity cannot be taught. On one level this is obvious because creativity often requires leaps of insight which cannot be explained by purely analytical means. The practice of technology assessment poses a parallel problem. The mandate of Congress' new information arm, the Office of Technology Assessment, is to look at the indirect and long-term economic, social, and environmental impacts of new technologies. There are no straightforward analytical techniques for accomplishing this task, for technology assessment is essentially an art. However, there are a number of techniques and methods which are useful in creating the kind of environment in which this art can flourish.

What has been learned about technology assessment may be helpful in teaching creativity. This book and the course which goes with it will try to do that. This will not be an easy task because the great bulk of scientific and engineering education is aimed towards analysis instead of synthesis. But creative problem solving is infectious and self-reinforcing. It grows with use and the more one applies it, the greater one's capacity for applying it in the future becomes.

Craig Decker
Washington, D.C.

PREFACE

> ". . . there are advantages to be gained in a course having as
> the *primary purpose* the development of a method of approach,
> and in which the situations to be analyzed are not restricted
> to a single subject, but involve several fields."[1]

This book seeks to enhance your innate creative ability. It is principally
intended as a textbook for senior engineering students of all disciplines interested in creativity in engineering. Experience indicates that seniors have
acquired enough technical background to successfully engage in the excitement
of creative synthesizing activity. It may also be of value to practicing
engineers and managers interested in increasing their effectiveness. Those
in the advanced technical areas will be quite at home with the materials of
the book. All may find creativity as laid out in the logical "postage stamp"
flow charts and tables herein useful in real-world creative problem solving.

We aim toward helping you perceive and develop an integrated problem
solving approach. Integral with it must be developed vital personal attitudes
and philosophy for successfully solving, on a repetitive basis, engineering
problems requiring substantial originality. To convey such an approach, organization and teachability of the materials herein have been given considerable thought.

It is likely you will acquire from this text insight into an entirely
different more *personal* view of creativity and engineering. This view takes
you into the *thoughts* of the engineer struggling to create a *new* concept or
product. Positive principles and guidelines for engendering probable success
in creative work are advanced, but the possibility of failure is not ignored.
Shea,[2] with the wisdom of 20-20 hindsight, says:

> "It is easy to see in retrospect that textbooks have culled
> out the evidences of the struggle to find out what works and
> what does not."

We deal with that struggle here, sometimes on a personal basis since creativity
is so intensely personal. The personal approach may at first bother those
locked to the idea that all engineering textbooks must be written impersonally!

---

[1] Hammond, H. P. *et al.*, "Report of Committee on Engineering Education After
the War," *Journal of Engineering Education*, May, 1944, pp. 589-614.

[2] Shea, T. E., "An Industrial Point of View On Creative Engineering," *Creative
Engineering*, American Society of Mechanical Engineers, pamphlet, circa 1956,
p. 28.

The work is predicated on the theses that:

1. There is a major need to enhance the creative abilities of engineering students.

> "The development of creative ability is largely neglected as an explicit objective of engineering education. We believe it should have a recognized place in the undergraduate curriculum."[1]

DeSimone's[2] elegant book makes a similar more recent forceful case.

2. It *is* possible, by suitable teaching means, to enhance a student's innate creative abilities. The late Professor Arnold expressed the same feeling:

> ". . . the creative potential can be realized through training and exercises, just as the development of our full capabilities along analytical lines can be obtained."[3]

3. The individual and not a group is the basic source of creativity. John Gardner, on a macroscopic scale, expressed a similar concept:

> "The capacity of society for continuous renewal depends ultimately upon the individual."[4]

4. Creative ability is a vital important characteristic *essential* to the engineer engaged in research, development, design, manufacture, and operations.

> This thesis is at variance with the popular but incorrect view that only research and development engineers need be creative. The need for creative ability threads *throughout* the spectrum of engineering activity! Indeed, I would argue that creativity is one of the grand unifying fundamentals to all of engineering.

The title choice, "DISCIPLINED CREATIVITY For Engineers," should be defended, especially in light of the view held by many that the creative process is chaotic and unstructured. We now know enough about the creative process to see that some *order* does exist and that tentative steps can be taken toward 'hardening' this area for repetitive applicational use. Finding this order and disciplining ourselves to use it appears more apt to enable engineers to deal with *new* future problems than if we take the wholly unrestrained chaotic view. We basically are orderly thinkers and can proceed best when some loose orderly thought structure is manifest. Professor Morse has so clearly stated this case:

---

[1]Hammond, H. P., *op cit.*, p. 601.

[2]DeSimone, Daniel V., *Education for Innovation*, (London, Pergamon Press Ltd., 1968).

[3]Arnold, John E. "The Creative Engineer," *Creative Engineering*, American Society of Mechanical Engineers, pamphlet circa 1956, p. 20.

[4]Gardner, John W., *Self Renewal: The Individual And The Innovative Society*, (New York, N. Y.: Harper and Row Publishers, 1963, 1964), p. 54.

"What is needed is the development of a discipline in this
field; our knowledge must have structure to be truly useful."[1]

So discipline carries with it here the notions of orderliness and structure.
Further implications of 'discipline' connote the ideas of being in control of
ourselves and the problem, teaching, instructing, molding, training, and
strengthening. Discipline, in this book, does *not* carry with it the concepts
of punishment and chastisement! Further, discipline requires judgment, perhaps deferred, but present frequently in the creative thought process.
Professor Dean cogently states:

"The key problem is a proper balance between discipline and
imagination."[2]

Finally, I like the title!

The book is built around the major parts:

1. An Engineer's Preview of Disciplined Creativity

   • The engineer's need for creativity and a summary of what is
     known about it.

2. Morphology of Disciplined Creativity

   • An integrated problem solving approach. This is the heart of
     the book.

3. Personal Aspects of Disciplined Creativity

   • Explores a wide range of personal topics, each directly re-
     lated to successful creative engineering work.

4. Other Facets of Disciplined Creativity

   • Discusses other topics needed by the maturing creative engineer.

5. Appendices

   • Selected creative writings and references.

Overall, it covers the classical subjects usually associated with creativity as
well as much new material.

One can hardly write a textbook without reflecting on textbook modeling.
I have chosen the format of Text material, Examples, Discussion Topics, Exercises, and Creative Problems. The tenor throughout is deliberately catalytic,
open-ended, and not dogmatic. The text is intended to stimulate you to
thoughtful creative action. This approach will *irritate* lazy thinkers who
want to be told precisely what to think and do!

In the margins I have planted a few "flowers of interest"—quotations—
relevant to and reinforcing the nearest text subject. You may want to read
the text body first and the quotations later. If these inform, stimulate,
inspire, or bring some small pleasure to you, including them will have not

---

[1]Morse, Richard S., "Preparing Inventors and Entrepreneurs" in DeSimone, *op.
cit.*, p. 150.

[2]Dean, Robert C., Jr., "Trade-Offs and Constraints" in DeSimone, *op. cit.*,
p. 150.

been in vain. You are also encouraged to unshackle yourself from the notion that your textbook is not to be marked! Make prolific notes in the unused margin space as you study the text and questions arise!

The structure of the text is amenable to syllabus planning in a number of flexible ways, thus giving a Professor the maximum opportunity to plan a comfortable course sequence. Syllabus planning and other matters of interest to teachers are in the *Instructor's Workbook for Disciplined Creativity* available to bona fide teachers for a small fee by writing the author directly.

The concepts and materials herein have been class tested in EE 491 Creative Problem Solving at the University of Florida for sixteen years.[1,2] Over 2,000 electrical engineering students have, in various evolving forms, been exposed to this material. Additionally, I have used most of the text ideas in extensive actual creative engineering practice. That experience combined with a lifelong interest in and observation of many creative engineers and their methodologies has led to this text. It is one man's view of a complex important subject. Other views, perhaps clearer, will undoubtedly be created by those who follow. The ideas and principles espoused, based on the test of sustained experience of many creative people, appear to fit large classes of problems for engineers who honestly *try* them. They are the result of a substantial distillation process. The difficulty of codifying such advice has been concisely stated by Smith:

> "To give practical advice in regard to inventive and creative thinking is peculiarly difficult because such thinking is so individual and intuitive as to be utterly incompatible with any precise order or routine."[3]

Finally, no claim is made that this text covers *all* facets of this limitless subject. We only touch on the *principal* topics believed to be significant to future engineers. The original plan was for a two-volume comprehensive work. It was shortened for practical reasons. Reluctantly, chapters on cost, ethics, group creativity, modeling, when to stop creative work, and others were omitted in this abbreviated version. Also the important Part III—originally ten chapters—was compressed to one.

You will soon sense that there is *much* more in the References beyond these mere pages! The subject is an awesome one to we who have been lifetime students of it.

There is the possibility that "this attempt to reduce creativity to a ritual may be a colossal piece of impertinence."[4] Experience, both others and mine, appears otherwise, however. Some may even be irked to see the creative process demystified into a body of logic.

I would be remiss in failing to point out that, in general, the subject of creativity seems to either "turn one on" or "turn him off" and that the subject therefore has been controversial from time to time both in industry and academia.

---

[1]Mathews, B. E. and R. L. Bailey, "A Course in Creative Problem Solving," *IEEE Transactions On Education*, Vol. E-8, No. 4, December, 1965, pp. 85-90.

[2]Bailey, Robert L., "Disciplined Creativity—One *Key* To The Future," *PROCEEDINGS*, 1974 IEEE Southeastcon, Orlando, Fla., April 29-May 1, 1974, pp. 2-5.

[3]Smith, Elliott Dunlap, Introductory comments in pamphlet, *Creative Thinking and How to Develop It*, The American Society of Mechanical Engineers, August, 1946.

[4]King, Blake, "Object: Creativity," *Mechanical Engineering*, November 1963, pp. 38-41.

If you sense that this text is 'different' and experience some of the joyful-pain of *forward-looking* creative thinking, then the pleasure-pain of writing it will have been worthwhile. Hopefully, you will grasp some of the sense of inspiration and excitement inherent in significant creative engineering.

Materials for this work have come from so many sources as to make complete acknowledgments difficult. I am first indebted to the General Electric Company for providing stimulating growth opportunities for a poor, small-town youth with a latent creative talent. Those associated with GE's Creative Engineering Program in the early 1950's had a most decisive and long-range effect on my life and work. The late Dr. M. J. Larsen's vision and encouragement permitted establishing the first Creative Problem Solving Course at the University of Florida in 1961. I shall always be grateful for the interest, encouragement, and contributions of my former colleague, Dr. Bruce E. Mathews, in helping to initiate, defend, and teach the creative course at UF during its early years. The initial fuel of encouragement for this work was provided by my colleague, Dr. Olle I. Elgerd. Dr. R. A. Ramey has been a pillar of strength in warm personal encouragement during dark times, in interest and belief in this work, and in being a most helpful critic. Dr. P. S. Callahan's encouragement to complete the work was most helpful. Helpful suggestions, comments, and criticisms of the manuscript were generously given by Professors E. S. Priem, T. Kundel, W. F. Kaiser, Dr. T. Wade, Dr. F. Hiatt, Dr. E. A. Farber, and Dr. R. M. Abrams. Dr. John O'Malley's review of Chaps. 15 and 18 on Recording and Patents was particularly helpful as was Dr. Leon W. Couch's review of Chap. 12 on Technical Communicating. Dr. J. K. Watson contributed in a singular important way through constant encouragement during the period of seeking a publisher. The contributions of practicing engineers, George Marks, W. J. Kessler and M. C. Bartlett, to this work are also acknowledged. The early accumulation of some of the resource material by my former student, Mr. Joseph L. Voyer, was extremely helpful. To Dr. W. H. Chen, and Dr. E. R. Chenette, past Chairmen, Electrical Engineering Department, and Dr. D. G. Childers, present acting Chairman, I owe debts of gratitude for structuring an environment where this work could be created. The vision of Florida Power Corp., Tampa Electric Co., Florida Power and Light Co., and Gulf Power Corp. in making this work possible through their early partial sponsorship has helped make a dream of some years a reality. My thanks are extended to the legions of UF undergraduates, who with enthusiasm, perception, and uninhibited minds have served as a proving ground for the book materials.

My wife, Betty, was most helpful with the preliminary drafts. The manuscript typing was entirely by Miss Edwina Huggins without whom the book would not have materialized during its nine years of preparation. I am also indebted to Mrs. Margie L. Summers who did the drawings. Truly she made this part of the task a joy.

My thanks are due the authors and publishers, cited throughout, for permission to quote from published works relating to the general subject. Their important words of inspiration have made the various quotations possible.

Finally, my deepest appreciation is expressed to Mr. Edward E. Lewis, President, Ann Arbor Science Publishers, Inc., who made it possible to bring this book to publication. He saw beyond the in situ market situation and risked publishing it. Truly he understands the nature of a *creative* venture!

Opinions expressed in this work are mine for which I alone accept full responsibility.

Robert L. Bailey
Gainesville, Florida

ROBERT L. BAILEY has been enhancing creativity for years--ever since participating in General Electric's pioneering Creative Engineering Program.

An Associate Professor of Electrical Engineering at the University of Florida, the author in 1961 introduced the first course in Creative Problem Solving at UF. He and his colleagues have since taught the course to about 2,000 undergraduate engineering students during the past 17 years. He enjoys creating and teaching.

He is a member of the EE Department's Electric Energy Engineering group.

The author has worked in a wide range of engineering and management activity. His 11 years with industry and 18 years at UF have included many creations in research, development, design and manufacturing. Some are described herein. He was a consultant to the NSF/NASA Solar Energy Panel in 1972 which formulated the first coherent solar energy R&D program for the United States for 1972-2020. It is now being implemented by the U.S. Department of Energy, other agencies and companies.

Professor Bailey received his BEE from Auburn University and MSE from the University of Florida where he also did additional graduate work. He is a member of the Institute of Electrical and Electronic Engineers, International Solar Energy Society, American Society of Engineering Education, and several honor societies. He also received GE's Management Award for teaching excellence. He has authored many R&D reports and publications--all reflecting his creative spirit and talent for creating useful practical products.

IT COULDN'T BE DONE

Somebody said that it couldn't be done,
　　But he with a chuckle replied
That "maybe it couldn't," but he would be one
　　Who wouldn't say so til he'd tried.
So he buckled right in with the trace of a grin
　　On his face. If he worried he hid it.
He started to sing as he tackled the thing
　　That couldn't be done, and he did it.

Somebody scoffed: "Oh, you'll never do that;
　　At least no one ever has done it";
But he took off his coat and he took off his hat,
　　And the first thing we knew he'd begun it.
With a lift of his chin and a bit of a grin,
　　Without any doubting or quiddit.
He started to sing as he tackled the thing
　　That couldn't be done, and he did it.

There are thousands to tell you it cannot be done,
　　There are thousands to prophesy failure;
There are thousands to point out to you, one by one,
　　The dangers that wait to assail you.
But just buckle in with a bit of a grin,
　　Just take off your coat and go to it;
Just start to sing as you tackle the thing
　　That "cannot be done," and you'll do it.

　　　　　　　Edgar A. Guest[1]

[1]From *The Path To Home*, by Edgar A. Guest, [Chicago, Illinois: Contemporary Books, Inc., Circa 1936]. Used by permission.

PART I

AN ENGINEER'S

PREVIEW OF

DISCIPLINED CREATIVITY

CHAPTER 1

PERSPECTIVES - THE ENGINEER'S NEED FOR CREATIVITY

"We are reading the first verse of the first chapter of a book whose pages are infinite - - - " [175, p189]
Author Unknown

● Society needs creative engineers.

● Science and engineering distinguished.

● Forward looking industrial leaders and engineering educators say engineers need creativity.

1-1 Society And The Creative Engineer

THE PROBLEMS OF SOCIETY **are** of immense importance to the engineer [153]. We can't fail to be aware of society's significant major problems:

Population is growing. There is serious concern of the effects.

Poverty is a reality for most peoples of the earth.

Food Production faces a wide range of problems.

Ecology balance in nature is being upset as man accelerates his subduing of the earth, polluting rivers, streams, and air.

Urbanization of peoples creates numerous serious problems.

Housing for present and future people is a major problem in all countries.

Health Facilities in quantity and quality seem never enough regardless of affluence.

Deaths, both physical and of the spirit, pose serious losses to society of undeveloped potential.

"We cannot effectively talk about the needs of engineering until we have reflected on the needs of society."
J. Herbert Holloman [153]

---

[175] See Appendix II for References.

*"Basically, we seem
to be retrograding
rather than evolving.
We have only to look
about us to verify
this fact: to see
megalopolizing cities,
the breakdown of
nature, the pollution
of air, water and
earth; to see crime,
vice, and dissatisfac-
tion webbing like a
cancer across the
surface of the world.
Does this mark an end
or a beginning? The
answer, of course,
depends on our per-
ception and the action
we take."
Charles Lindbergh
[193, p61]*

Transportation problems, both mass and individual, proliferate at astonishing speed.

Natural Resources are being depleted at alarming rates.

Energy Sources and conversion means in all countries are hardly adequate.

Weather Control eludes man's best abilities.

Education at all levels has multiple problems.

Recreation and use of leisure time, both for individuals and masses, faces major problems.

Communication and improved relations between the peoples of the world cry for solution.

Space Exploration challenges man's creative technology and spirit. It faces significant problems.

Increasing Defense Burdens among all countries pose complex problems.

Society's major problems are of vital interest to the engineering profession. When engineers are sensitive to the macroscopic problems of society the probability of contributing our technical expertise toward helping create a better future world is high.

*"We should all be
concerned about
the future because
that is where we
will spend the
remainder of our
lives."
Charles F.
Kettering
[175, p190]*

One hallmark of the creative engineer is his *future* orientation. While he is aware of the present problems, he does not allow them to drown his vision of the future. He desires to contribute to the future by creating the *new* ideas and products needed by society.

GLIMPSES OF THE FUTURE may be seen in technical activities underway throughout the world. An example is a Rand Corporation report [124] by experts in six

major areas of human activity who envision:

"The World of 2000

The population size will be up to about
5.1 billion (65% more than 1963).

New food sources will have been opened up
through large scale ocean farming and the fabrication of synthetic protein.

*"We need a new kind
of engineer, one who
can build bridges to
society as well as
bridges across
rivers."
William H. Pickering
[251, p7]*

Controlled thermonuclear power will be a
source of new energy. New mineral raw materials
will be derived from the oceans. Regional
weather control will be past the experimental
stage.

General immunization against bacterial and
viral diseases will be available. Primitive
forms of artificial life will have been generated
in the laboratory. The correction of hereditary
defects through molecular engineering will be
possible.

Effective anti-ICBM defense in the form of
air-launched missiles and directed energy beams
will have been developed."

*" - - the modern
engineer's primary
concern should be
that of designing
and creating the
things that society
needs, and the
spark of genius
must be nurtured and
developed to the
maximum extent. - -"
Eric A. Walker
[363]*

The above and uncreated new technological ideas

of the future await us. What magnificent opportunities

lie before us to *use* our precious creative engineering

abilities! "Society's needs in the decades ahead will

call for engineering talent on a scale never before

seen in the United States or elsewhere." [365, p7]

Solving society's future *new* problems will involve

change.

CHANGE in the perceived needs of societies

and individuals is accelerating. The time increment

between conception and commercial implementation of

new product creations is historically shrinking.

The tempo of change *directly* affects you, the future engineer. Most firms employing engineers want to shrink the time from conception to production. Society's need, cost minimization, competition, or security urgency are motivations.

A firm may   build a production facility in toto, for example, *before* the product development and design engineering are completed. I was an engineering manager in one such exciting adventure in which a new electronics plant was built in Florida. Previously such a practice was unthinkable because of the large capital risk involved. Change has occurred.

On an individual level, we are not satisfied with the things our parents wanted out of life. Our children will not be satisfied with the things we want. Change is occurring.

In more specific engineering senses solid state devices are replacing vacuum tubes, the radio of yesterday has changed to radar, television, and then global and deep-space communications. The electric power industry has changed to a sophisticated highly complex technical system almost undreamed of 20 years ago. We design bridges by computer aided methods in contrast to older methods. The transportation industry is entering a whole era of changes as engineers focus on *new* methods, as the linear induction motor

" - - this type of engineer is the leaven that leavens the whole of the country. If a country has plenty of creative engineers doing real creative work, it moves forward with the times. If it does not, it falls behind, however good all its other people are."
  M. W. Thring [341]

"We are witnessing changes so profound and far-reaching that the mind can hardly grasp all the implications."
  John W. Gardner [116, p28]

"Doing engineering is practicing the art of the organized forcing of technological change."
  Gordon S. Brown [47, p53]

and air cushion vehicles. The engineering curriculum

through which you are struggling toward a degree

changed substantially in the past 10 years.

We live in and are immersed in change. Change

is the mood of our times, as Fabun has so interestingly

shown [96]. Finally, change has always been with

us. Our ability to perceive its occurrence is a

function of the time increment, Δt, over which we look.

There are some subtle implications of change.

One of these is its certainty. It is certain engineering

of tomorrow will not be what it is today. It is

certain that unless we are willing to up-date ourselves

continuously and creatively so we can cope with the

new difficult engineering problems of the future we

shall, after a few years, experience the 'half-life

of usefulness' phenomenon personally.

Change may imply an inadequacy of prior methods,

however satisfactory they may have previously been.

Society and individuals may feel threatened and

resist change even when objectively change is for their

betterment.

"No longer can an engineer expect to work in a given specialty for most of his life. With-in five years a problem area of broad interest can be completely mined out partly because of the number of miners, and partly because of the sophistication of their equipment."
James Vollmer
[358]

"This explains why technological innovation in an industry often stems from outside sources. Edwin Land, not Eastman Kodak, introduced the picture-in-a-minute camera. Monsanto, a chemical company and not a giant of the soap industry, pioneered the low-suds detergent. Sylvania, not General Electric spurred the introduction of the fluorescent lamp. Nylon came from DuPont, not the textile industry. And, as the classic of them all, Western Union was the logical candidate to introduce telephony and wireless communications, but did not" [74, p9].

"Technological invention and innovation are the business of engineering. They are embodied in engineering change."
Daniel V. DeSimone
[75, p4]

We shall explore resistance to change in

Chap. 9.

Two classes of engineering change are:

● <u>Minimally</u> <u>perceptible</u> <u>change</u>

<u>Example 1-1</u>

A mechanical engineer by carefully studying power losses in a coal-fired bulk electric power generation plant is able to increase the kwh/lb of coal by 0.1%. Result: annual fuel savings of kilo-dollars.

● <u>Step-function</u> <u>change</u>

<u>Example 1-2</u>

An engineer, examining the losses in a bulk power plant, conceives the idea of using direct energy converters as a 'topping cycle' to the plant to *use* the waste heat, thus increasing the overall plant efficiency 10%. Result: annual fuel savings of mega-dollars.

"Many of the major changes in history have come about through successive small innovations, most of them anonymous."
  John W. Gardner
  [116]

"The job of the inventors is to provide the lead for a lagging system."
  Jacob Rabinow
  [266, p75]

Society benefits from both classes of changes but substantially more from the step-function class. Further, it is clear that significant *new* departures from prior means of 'solving' the problems are essential for the step-function class.

It is largely the purpose of this book to fuel you for effecting creative step-function changes on a repetitive orderly basis. We must acquire many new tools in later chapters before reaching that goal.

" - - - the job of the engineer is to change the world."
  Robert C. Dean, Jr.
  [72]

WHERE PROBLEMS ARISE frequently puzzles the beginning engineer who usually *assumes* the problem on which he will work has been defined correctly.

Think about this:

> ● Problems arise from the perceived needs
> of a community of individuals.

"The characteristics of a productive facility and the signals from a social system furnish very specific facts which must become every bit as much a part of an engineering idea as any technology or scientific principle."
Francis K. McCune [206]

The proposition is especially clear to Roberts

and Lowen who have investigated the needs of the

developing countries. They say:

> " - - - the problems grow out of a
> real cultural setting and require a systems
> orientation which takes the total setting,
> including a variety of social factors, into
> account. Also significant is the fact that
> the solutions frequently require extreme
> ingenuity and inventiveness ." [277, p816]

Note their last statement. The same can be

said for engineering in more advanced countries.

" - - creativity, the source of technological advance, is of great importance not only for national progress, but perhaps for survival itself."
C. Stark Draper [82, p32]

Indeed, many thousands of scientists and engineers

who preceded you are now engaged in technical work

around the world seeking problem solutions and making

use of "extreme ingenuity and inventiveness"! They

are actively exercising Disciplined Creativity,

a term we shall define in Chap. 2.

" - - - the engineering profession clearly cannot isolate itself from this complex of men and functions as a well-defined caste, - - -"
H. P. Hammon, et al [139]

WHO SOLVES SOCIETY'S PROBLEMS of the future

is a very complex question. It is not within the

scope of the engineering profession to solve all of

society's problems. Engineers have in the past and

will continue in the future to bring a special

expertise to the solution of many of society's problems.

The engineer can be a dynamic forcing-function for

ushering orderly needed creative changes in himself,

things, systems, and others to the benefit of society.
The importance of the *individual* engineer educated to
cope creatively in a disciplined way with the *new*
problems of the future is inescapable.

DOES SOCIETY REALLY NEED CREATIVE ENGINEERS?

This question has been much discussed. Two schools

of thought exist:

"The lack of ideas and inventions in one generation can easily mean the loss of freedom in the next." Charles F. Kettering [173, p35]

● <u>No</u>, the status quo seekers would like **us** engineers to be "just like we've always been"--the reliable, predict-able, human component concept decried by Leonard [189].   This school would have engineers be conformists, solving all problems with *prior* existing techniques. How **we** are to face *new* situations where the prior art is inadequate to solve *new* problems is a mute question.

"Every era opens with its challenges, and they cannot be met successfully by elaborating methods of the past." Charles Lindbergh [193, p61]

● <u>Yes</u>, society needs and can use indi-viduals with as much creativity as they can muster, for it is from their ranks the saviors of society rise. These saviors are the engineers, inventors, innovators, entrepreneurs, and other creators who bring into existence *new* things for the future benefit of man. This school highly values nonconformity, uniqueness, originality and other aesthetic characteristics. What society is to *do* with such an individual in the flesh may be a **moot** question, espe-cially when he offers his creation to society and it involves making significant beneficial *changes*.

"We may learn some-thing about the renewal of societies if we look at the kind of men who contribute most to that outcome - the innovators." John W. Gardner [116, p28]

You can expect to encounter proponents of both schools

during your professional career. Should you choose

the latter, you may be in an important minority.

We should be aware from the beginning that the

creative innovating minority   places dilemmas on

society.

THE DILEMMA OF INNOVATING SOCIETIES **is** discussed

by Professor Fredrickson in a significant paper [110].

He sees

> " - - the basic dilemma of all innovating
> societies: On the one hand, their
> institutions and ways of doing things
> are founded alike on a belief in the
> efficacy of unfettered technological
> innovation for social progress and a
> fear that without such innovation, they
> will stagnate and decay."

He also raises some significant questions about

*"Creative imagi-
nation, calm
thought, artistic
production, the
gentle things of
life, the things
of the heart and
the soul have been
strangled in this
race to achieve and
produce more and
more, and humanity
has no idea what to
do with all its
material wealth
and all the pro-
ducts of its
activity."
Paul Tournier
[345, p73]*

> "the existence and propagation of what
> might be called the Creed of Technology.
> This is the widely held belief men-
> tioned previously that innovation
> *per se* is good and that technology is
> always progressive. - - Associated
> with the Creed of Technology is the
> Cult of the Product. If the former
> teaches that innovation of itself is a
> positive good, the latter is the logical
> consequence of belief in that teaching.
> - - - A third factor, with roots
> perhaps deeper in human nature than
> any other, is the Gospel of Growth."

He closes his minority view with the admonition

> "It is absolutely necessary - - -
> that innovating societies think about
> *why* they innovate and what the conse-
> quences of innovation are."

Why not treat yourself to one of the thrills of

a real education by going *beyond* your textbook,

search out his paper in your library, and read it

in full!

Discussion Topics

1. Explore ways the mature engineers in your engineering discipline become aware of significant engineering problems of society.

2. We identified a few of society's problems. Since it is not possible for you as an individual to solve *all* these problems, discuss "choice" and "focus" as they affect *your* engineering career.

3. Cite examples of where society has appeared to reject both the creator of new ideas and the idea he created. Does industry *really* want creative engineers?

4. "Why all this flap about 'change'? The past is good enough for me." Discuss.

5. Are new product changes always for the better?

6. What part, if any, does "competition" play in stimulating changes in products engineers conceive?

7. Cite examples of where product changes have obsoleted established businesses through introduction of new concepts or ideas.

8. Are there more or less opportunities for creative engineering work now than in Edison's day?

9. Explore whether engineers are creators of societal wealth.

Exercises

1-E1. Prepare a written outline of *your* honest feelings (*not* how you are "supposed to feel") about future vs. past orientation in your present engineering course sequence.

1-E2. Imaginatively list as many potential areas of application as you can for a low cost robot machine which would move heavy objects from one place to another repetitively.

1-E3.   An area of concern to the engineer is
        means of weather modification for the
        benefit of indigenous peoples. Suggest
        possible creative ideas for modifying
        the weather.

1-E4.   Suppose that a smog-free personal vehicle
        to replace the internal-combustion engine
        type has been invented. Identify and list
        all the implications on society of such a
        creation. Particularly, restrict your
        thinking to the "change-over" transient
        period.

Creative Problem

1-CP1. Consider a classical electric power
        generator driven by a rotary shaft,
        usually turbine driven. Explore
        creatively the possibilities of design-
        ing a reciprocating dynamo along these
        lines: "But the question is, why go to
        rotation? As I say, this is because
        the mechanical engineer has always
        handed over to the electrical engineer
        at the rotational point. If, however,
        you have somebody who is both a mechani-
        cal engineer and an electrical engineer,
        he immediately says, 'Why not design
        a reciprocating dynamo?' In that case,
        you can get a very nice system with two
        double-acting two-stroke cylinders
        pushing a rigid connecting rod backwards
        and forwards, working as a four-cyclinder
        two-cycle engine and pushing an aluminum
        loop backwards and forwards in a magnetic
        field and generating alternating current
        with the frequency of reciprocation.
        This is perfectly straightforward. It
        does not break any of the laws and it
        produces a very nice engine, because you
        have no sideways forces on the piston;
        you have no load-carrying bearings and
        no crankshaft. You can make a system
        weighing about half as much and which has
        a higher efficiency because of reduced
        frictional losses. This, again, therefore,
        is fairly obviously something which will
        come in the next ten years. The reason
        why it has not come in the past is because
        of this dichotomy between the mechanical
        and the electrical engineer." [341]

1-2 Science and Engineering Distinguished

SCIENCE AND ENGINEERING. One of the
perspectives we must clearly understand
early in our quest for creativity enhancement is the distinction between these two
very important areas. Both areas demand disciplined
creative effort, and much said herein may be applicable to both. Since our principal thrust is enhancing the engineer's creativity, we mostly avoid
the domain of creativity in science. We start with:

*"And God blessed
them, and said to
them, Be fruitful,
multiply, and fill
the earth and subdue
it (with all its
vast resources.)"
  Genesis 1:28 [5]*

*" -- at the very core
of engineering there
is just one thing --
an act of creative
thought, or in other
words the process of
having an idea."
  Francis K. McCune
  [206]*

⬤ Definition of Science

"Science is a quest for broad
generalizations that accord with verifiable facts. Its proximate goal is
truth." [364]

⬤ Definition of Engineering

"Engineering is the profession in
which a knowledge of the mathematical
and natural sciences gained by study,
experience and practice is applied with
judgment to develop ways to utilize,
economically, the materials and forces
of nature for the benefit of mankind."
                    (Engineer's Council for Pro-
                    fessional Development)
(For an interesting summary of some
other definitions of engineering, see
[306].)

Adherents have written much about each area. Most
contain the ideas in the definitions above, though
language differs.

Further insight into the nature of science

reveals:

> "Science does not merely discover the
> truth, but, through its invention of hypo-
> theses and establishment of concepts, it is
> a maker of truth, as the etymology of the term
> *scientific*, knowledge-making, implies.
>
> Science is a ceaseless striving for more
> understanding, the results of the prodding
> of curiosity that is so firmly implanted in
> the human mind. "The eye is not satisfied
> with seeing." Men must know the why of it
> all. What is the cause, and the cause behind
> that? What is the true essence of the unity
> of causes that seems to support, to control,
> and, as it were, to animate every corner of
> the knowable world? The *motivation* of the
> scientist is not, perhaps, basically different
> from that of a philosopher." [364, p11]

*"The scientist merely
explores that which
exists, while the
engineer creates
what has never
existed before."
Theodore Von
Karman [361]*

The reader interested in exploring some of the

beauty, rationale and methods of physical science will

find an entree in reference [46]. Be forewarned,

however, that *science is not engineering*! What *is*

engineering then?

*"Engineering's prime
mission is the cre-
ation of technical
things and services
useful to man."
Francis K. McCune
[206]*

> "The engineer is concerned with
> CREATING material objectives to serve
> human needs. The engineer USES the
> knowledge and understanding developed
> by the scientists." [4, p2]

I have deliberately emphasized two words above.

> "Engineering -- is more pragmatic
> and less -- relatively less -- speculative;
> it is production, operation, and manage-
> ment, as well as research, analysis, planning
> and design. Its goal is usually a clearly
> specified utility such as public health,
> communication, power, transportation, or
> housing, rather than the attainment of
> abstract truth." [250]

Zener sees engineers as "those people who use precise scientific principles in working toward their goals." [402] He elaborates:

> "Engineers have traditionally been people who work toward the attainment of practical goals. If a particular task requires the use of some particular physical phenomenon, then the more he understands this particular phenomenon the better able he will be to reach his goal. However, as an engineer he could not care less about his understanding per se. In contrast, scientists have traditionally been people whose sole drive was to understand the world around them. They could not care less what use was made of this understanding." [402]

Suits recognizes the importance of the gap between science and society filled by the engineer:

> "But science does not extend these gifts directly or automatically. For example, a fission experiment does not of itself generate useful atomic power. In this case, as in most others, there is a vast gap between new scientific knowledge and its usefulness to society." [322]

If you are interested in comparing scientists and engineers at the personal level, Peake's paper is an entree [243]. If you wish to explore some of the "legitimate concern over the philosophy and direction of engineering education," study DeSimone's elegant and revealing book [75].

ORIGIN OF TERM 'ENGINEER' We have distinguished the engineer from the scientist, intimated he is a professional, a possessor of scientific knowledge

"His head is in the clouds, but his feet are bedded in the solid rock of Fact and Reason."
Wilfred A. Peterson
[247]

"Nor are schools that teach the application of science to the art of killing men fitted to teach scientific methods of feeding, clothing, and housing men."
J. B. Turner
[198, p10]

"He is a man with a mission to minister to the welfare of the society in which he lives."
Vannevar Bush
[53, p9]

and engineering application skill, and a contributor
toward meeting society's needs. But there is another
important facet of engineering not mentioned. To
find it we must go back and see what 'engineer'
originally meant! We first explore some early
(circa 400 B.C.) connotations of 'technology.'

In antiquity there were those performing the
work of engineers [352]. They were aligned with
'technology' in various ways long before they were
generally called 'engineers,' though Plato (circa 380
B.C.) does use the term engineer in one of his
writings. [180, p19]

"He is a man who - - strives to add to the sum total of human intellectual accomplishments." Vannevar Bush [53, p9]

"Technology is *Machination*, an
artful method, the word derived from
the Greek 'mechanaomai' 'I contrive a de-
ception.' Thus what was at stake in
mechanical technology was to outwit
Nature by solving the apparent contradictions, and overcoming the difficulties." [180, p25]

Parsons' fascinating book [239] indicates
engineers were well known in the Renaissance.

Watkins, investigating the origin of the
title 'Engineer', says:

"The earliest use of the term
"Engineer" that I have found is in
Shakespeare, where Hamlet (III, 4)
speaks of the engineer hoist with
his own petard. - - - From the reports
of John Smeaton, F. R. S. (1797), we
learn that civil engineering became a
profession in England about 1760. It
is said of Smeaton, who was the first
expert witness called before English
courts in matters relating to his profession, that he was the first to use
the title 'Civil Engineer' when he signed
his name as such to testimony that he
gave in an important case." [371]

The exact origin of the term 'engineer' is

uncertain. Watkins, in a footnote, reveals:

> "We are told in Rees's Cyclopaedia,
> Vol. 13 (published about 1810), that
> "Engineer" or engineering in its general
> sense is applied to a contriver or maker
> of any kind of useful engine or machine."

Note the word 'contriver'! More recently, we

find [95] the terms engine, engineer, engineering

springing from the Latin ingenium (natural

capacity, invention) and gignere (to produce).

It now becomes clear that the *original*

meaning of 'engineer' carried with it connotations

of an artful contriver, one who was clever in

overcoming the difficulties of nature, one who

produces ingenious designs or invents. The above

ideas are today, in a loose sense, implied in the

term 'Creative Engineer.'

> "Among the characteristics of a
> creative engineer, he (Charles Stark
> Draper) lists the ability to recognize
> key problems, bring relevant knowledge
> to bear upon them, conceive effective
> solutions, and carry these through the
> innovative process." [75, p9]

How much of *the above* kinds of intellectual

activity have you been exposed to in your engineering

curriculum? Note that the degree granted upon your

graduation carries the word engineer' in it with all

the connotations above! Are you prepared to help

create, design or invent the *new* engineered products

of tomorrow resulting from the needs of society - - -

the kind of changes indicated in Sec. 1-1? If this

*"A man of inventive mind.
It marks the greatest genius,
- - - "*
  Baltasar Gracian
  circa 1601-1658
  [127]

"Engineering is a profession, an art of action and synthesis and not simply a body of knowledge. Its highest calling is to invent and innovate."
  Daniel V. DeSimone
  [75, pl]

"There are deeply held feelings that engineering education has become too science-based and has become removed to some degree from the creative act that the engineer or inventor has to perform to bring the results of science and technology to the benefit of society."
  J. Herbert
  Holloman [153, p23]

question leaves you slightly discomforted, cheer

up. You are not alone! DeSimone has capsulized

the situation:

*"I began to become
an outspoken critic
of typical engi-
neering programs,
trying to buck the
trend to make the
engineering school
the same as the
science school."*
  Simon Ramo [139]

" – – the art of creative engineering
has been orphaned in the engineering schools.
There are exceptions, of course, but we are
concerned here with the educational system
in general. In the years since the second
World War, there has developed in the engineering educational system -- not only in the
undergraduate, but in the graduate schools --
a regrettable and unnecessary schism between
the realms of science and engineering. Para-
doxically, in the schools of engineering, the
art of engineering has been largely neglected.
The stress has been on analysis rather than
synthesis, on the abstract rather than the
messy alternatives of the real world. As we
have noted, the subjects typically chosen as
graduate engineering theses generally have
little to do with the use of technology to
solve real social and industrial problems. – – –
One finds, instead, "dreary dissertations"
(Professor Arrowsmith's description) isolated
from contemporary realities. In the *engineering* schools why should not the art of engineering
be given at least equal status with science?
If not in the engineering schools, then where?"
[75, p12]

*"In fact, as far
as I can sense,
most faculty
members have
little interest
in creativity,
and know even less
about it."*
  *A. D. Moore
  [217, p27]*

AN INTEGRATING PERSPECTIVE of this brief

treatment of science and engineering is in Fig. 1-1

created by Thring, a Professor of Mechanical Engi-

neering. In his words:

*"Throughout the
whole fabric of
engineering educa-
tion, therefore,
there must be inter-
woven with instruction
in scientific princi-
ples – – – the en-
couragement of creative
talent – – –."*
  *H. P. Hammond,
et al. [140, p599]*

"The roots of the tree are pure
science – – –, and a peculiar thing coming
in here, called asthetics, about which the
architects and some other people are very
concerned. The trunk of the tree is called
human understanding and, in particular,
applied mathematics. The branches of the
tree are engineering and the extreme twigs
are the growing new fields of engineering
in which things are really happening. – – –
pure science is the roots which feed the tree

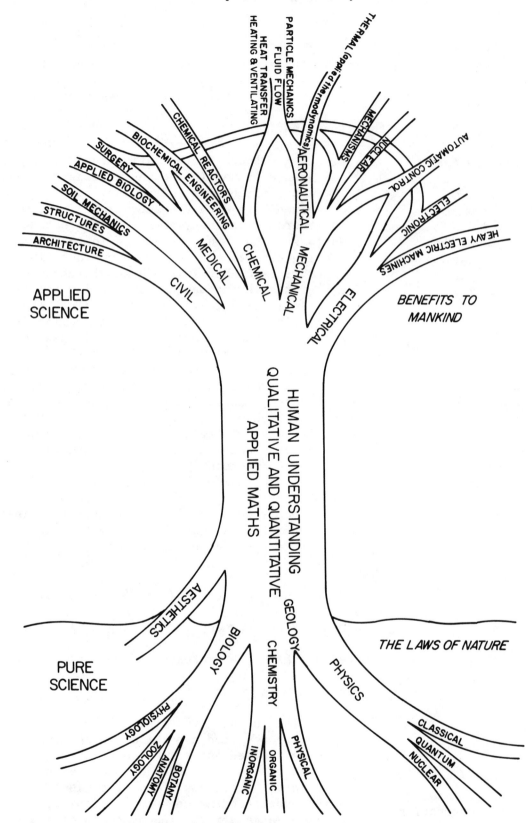

FIG 1-1   Thring's tree of useful knowledge [341]

but the actual growth of new life
comes on the twigs of extremely
specialized engineering. Some sort
of scheme of knowledge like this
is important." [341]

It is clear that the creative engineer's place

is in the branches of applied science working for

the benefits of mankind, forcing *new* twig growth --

to continue Thring's analogy.

Discussion Topics

1. An engineer conceives and analyzes a new
    drift-free DC amplifier for use in a
    system of human blood pressure measurement.
    He constructs and tests it in a laboratory.
    It works as he envisioned. Is he engaging
    in 'science' or 'engineering?'

2. The 'loss of signal' phenomenon for a
    space vehicle re-entering the earth's atmos-
    phere is well known. It is caused by an
    enclosure of the vehicle in hot ionized
    gases. A NASA man studies the thickness,
    distribution, charge density, type charges
    present, effects of atmospheric density, and
    other parameters on the plasma sheath. Is
    he engaging in 'science' or 'engineering?'

3. In the industrial world, where you will
    probably practice your engineering profession,
    will your work be clearly within the stated
    definition of engineering or will you have
    to occasionally move down the trunk of Thring's
    'tree of useful knowledge' toward science?

4. Briefly share with us a specific engineering
    course in your curriculum and a specific tech-
    nical problem on which you have worked which
    required you to recognize a real problem and
    invent a *new* solution to it.

5. Has 'the art of creative engineering been
    orphaned' in *your* engineering school? If so,
    explore *why*.

6. Can the engineer 'apply science'
    without 'knowing science?'

Exercises

1-E5. Suggest, by means of a list, educational
       ideas through which engineers can be made
       more sensitive to and aware of worthwhile
       problems 'for the benefit of mankind.'

1-E6. Suggest a list of possible educational
       ideas for effectively engaging students
       in your engineering discipline in 'creating
       material objects to serve human needs.'

1-E7. List the genuinely *clever* engineering
       creations to which you have been exposed
       in the past week. Can you trace the
       creation (not the analysis *of* the creation)
       of one of these back to 'an artful contriver?'
       Was he practicing 'engineering' or 'science'
       when he created it?

1-3 Engineering Practice, Education, and Creativity
       CREATIVITY NEEDED IN ENGINEERING PRACTICE
       You may assume that since you have been

largely steeped in analytics these are the only

tools needed by the engineer. Every mature engineer

who has practiced his profession knows otherwise. We

sense this in Colclaser's words:

*"It is usually
a shock to stu-
dents entering
practice to dis-
cover what a
small percentage
of the decisions
made by a de-
signer are made
on the basis of
the kind of cal-
culation he has
spent so much
time learning in
school."*
  *E. S. Taylor,
  et. al [332, p650]*

      "In many segments of industry, the
young man is looked upon first as an
engineer and second as an *electrical*
engineer with specific knowledge. Industrial problems do not divide themselves
neatly into the areas of electrical,
mechanical, chemical, or civil engineering;
rather, they are considered as general problems requiring a solution which the young
engineer is expected to provide. In the
majority of cases he must produce a physical
device which will accomplish a desired
result. This is not a "textbook" solution
but an original, creative effort." [64, p812]

It is clear that disciplined creativity (we'll
define it in Chap. 2) is required of the engineer
in *all* known work classifications, as shown in
Fig. 1-2, and not just in research and development
as is popularly supposed.

Typically you, the future engineer, will
either find yourself involved in or responsible for
a 'project' -- including *all* its aspects of which
analytics may be a small but important part. Thus
you will have to deal with the *whole* problem including all its sub-problems, some of which may be
out of your specialty.

Example 1-3

Early in my career as an
electrical engineer, working under
the direction of a very fine senior
mechanical engineer, I was asked to
"see what you can do about putting
the first color wheel in our General
Electric television camera." It was
to be my 'project.' The CBS color
television system with its red-green-
blue color wheels for both transmitter
and receiver was being seriously considered as a national TV system. The
job involved synchronous motors, belt-
ing, patent research, materials, heat
transfer, power generation systems,
circuitry, components, vendor relations,
mechanical engineering, and others,
most of which I initially knew little
if anything about -- but I learned!
Substantial amounts of creativity and
interdisciplinary work were required
to get it to the test stage.

"Creativity is in-
volved in research,
discovery of new
knowledge, in its
application, in
development engi-
neering, in the
manufacture of
the hardware, in
marketing and
sales, in the
raising of capital,
and in the supply-
ing of services."
   Jack A. Morton
   [75, p105]

"Book learning
alone does not
suffice, but must
be supplemented by
a study of things.
The former produces
'laborious thinkers,'
while industry needs
'thinking laborers.'
   J. B. Turner
   [198, p10]

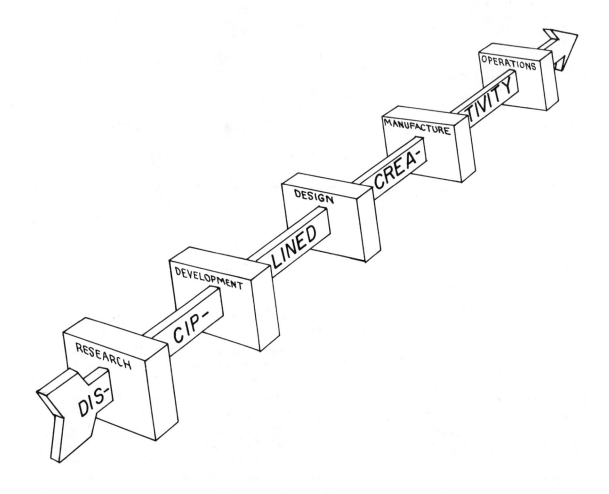

FIG. 1-2 Disciplined Creativity, *in addition to* analytical
ability, is needed by the engineer in *all* known
engineering functional work areas.

Increasingly, engineering appears to be moving toward an interdisciplinary approach as the sophistication of devices, processes, and systems grows. Though many contemporary engineers, managers, and others think the interdisciplinary concept is new, actually it is very old. One need only examine autobiographies of the 'creative greats' to learn of their mastery of *everything* pertaining to solving the problem they chose. One classic example is Leonardo da Vinci. [180, p128]

Forward looking engineering managers, regardless of company, are aware of the importance of creativity to engineering practice. This awareness is reflected in the periodic 'rating sheets' of engineers which specifically require evaluation of 'creativity', 'originality', or 'resourcefulness'. Management *knows* that the engineer's creativity is the life blood which insures the future viability of the company in the market place! Gilmer stimulatingly cited industry's need when he said:

> "Give us then, from the colleges and universities:
>
> ● Men who have been taught - even forced if necessary - to think for themselves;
>
> ● Men who distrust the obvious;
>
> ● Men who doubt the methods of the past;

Businesses fail because of their inability to recognize and solve problems.
Author unknown

" -- less than 3% of all patents issued today go to engineers, and the balance to individuals in other occupations."
Richard Paulson
[242]

●   Men who are able to conceptualize
the future;

●   Men who have the boldness and
imaginativeness to pioneer in the
development of new business
systems and new businesses;

●   Men who have the ingenuity and
drive to develop and reimprove
new devices and techniques.

*" - - - we recognize
that technological
innovation is in-
creasingly a way of
industrial life,
and that we must
reckon it as a
major factor in
our future busi-
ness plans."*
  Guy Suits
   [322, p33]

We need men who have been schooled in the
principles of creativity and who dare to
court the ridicule of the masses for the
sake of improving the lot of mankind." [118, p7]

Many other arguments could be advanced about the

practicing engineer's need for creativity.

The conclusion seems inescapable that

industry's managers, sensitively aware of the

future needs of society, are saying "We need dis-

ciplined creative engineers to help us initiate the

complex *new* changes of the future."

CREATIVITY NEEDED IN ENGINEERING EDUCATION

*"For the task of
preventing the new
generation from
changing in any
deep or significant
way is precisely
what most societies
require of their
educators."*
  *George B.
Leonard [189, p7]*

deserves our thoughtful consideration. The topic

is much beyond the scope of this book to cover in

any detail. We first examine the *origins* of the

term 'school'.

"The Greek word for leisure is
skole. Since the Greeks spent some
of their leisure in school, and since
without leisure there could be no school,
the word skole gradually took on a new
meaning. The Latins took it over as
scola. If you are interested in the kinds
of schools they had, read the dialogues of
Plato. They sought through discussion to
arrive at the truth, and did not confine

themselves to books. The world was
for them a book. Life was a book. The
universe was a book. And from such books
these ancients sought to discover the
truth, in order to enlarge and enrich
life." [43, p3]

*"All too often we
are giving our young
people cut flowers
when we should be
teaching them to
grow their own
plants. We are
stuffing their
heads with the
products of
earlier innovation
rather than teach-
ing them to inno-
vate."*
  John W. Gardner
  [116, p21]

Interesting! Do you look on your school as a place

to spend leisure? Many students see school as a

place of *work* where one can acquire the minimal

specific engineering knowledge of the *past* in order

to graduate. What a change! Is this prevalent

student attitude desirable? Has it originated with

students or faculty? Will this viewpoint produce

the necessary truly *great* engineers required by the

future? Does minimal knowledge acquisition equip

you to deal effectively with future *new* engineering

problems? Has engineering education dominantly been

aimed at equipping you for effectively handling

change? Isn't development of your creative engi-

neering abilities *essential* for managing change?

Has engineering education majored on analysis and

lost sight of the idea synthesizer -- the ingenious

one? These are important questions. Think about them

in your own situation. Discuss them. Discover some

of the excitement of creative thinking starting where

you are *now!*

*"The principal
goal of education
is to create men
who are capable
of doing new
things, not simply
repeating what
other generations
have done--men
who are creative,
inventive and
discoverers."*
  Jean Piaget
  [250, p58]

EXAMINATIONS OF ENGINEERING EDUCATION have been

both numerous and frequent. The situation in the mid

1960's has been ably summarized in DeSimone's book [75]

by Teare et al at a significant National Conference
On Creative Engineering Education.

"What the educational
experience almost
completely excludes
is the exercise and
development of the
students' creativity --
even though creativity
is probably the single
most important characte-
ristic demanded of a
modern, practicing
engineer.
  Ray E. Bolz and Robert
  C. Dean, Jr. [40, p128]

"In the last decade or so there has
been an increasing emphasis on applied
science and mathematics in both undergraduate and graduate engineering work.
Courses that might develop creativeness
have been squeezed out of curricula in
favor of others which cover new subject
matter. New recruits to the teaching
profession have been found among graduates
who have just received their doctorates.
Raised in a scientific and theoretical
atmosphere, nurtured on contracts and grants
from government agencies whose interests
are different from those of the civilian
market place, and mostly without industrial
experience of their own, they cannot be
expected to teach in a way that represents
the whole spectrum of engineering.

Although present engineering graduates can do some things much better than
the graduates of earlier generations, they
have had little contact with the real world
of engineering. They are better able to
analyze problems that have been given them
than create new things; better able to work
under direction than to give leadership in
meeting the needs of society; hesitant to
jump into uncharted areas; and relatively
uninterested in the part of engineering
that involves anticipating human needs or
optimizing designs that involve costs, reliability, product life, manufacturability,
salability and acceptability.

"Recent engineering
graduates were criti-
cized for unwilling-
ness and inability to
consider a complete
problem such as a
design problem. - - -
engineers with an
advanced degree are
even more prone to
avoid a complete
problem."
  E. S. Taylor
  [332, p649]

It is true that some of the best
graduates rise above their education or
supplement it on their own initiative and
do become good creative engineers. However,
many remain what their training has made them,
differential-equation technicians. With a
differently conceived education that gave
them breadth beyond engineering science, that
helped them learn how to deal with the whole
range of their professional work, and that
puts greater emphasis on creativity, more of
them would become engineering leaders. More
of them would contribute importantly to technology and, finally, more would help make technology contribute significantly to society." [334]

"Engineering is far
from static, for it
is essentially a
creative profession."
  L. E. Grinter [130]

Another important facet, not touched on above,

impinges on the real engineering world of "hardware"

-- the end result of much of the engineer's creativity.

Do the words of Teller, writing for Chemical Engineers,

strike a challenging ring?

> "As an attack and a weapon against
> any subject occupying space in the
> curriculum to the exclusion of 'funda-
> mental knowledge', the word 'hardware'
> is used in a derogatory manner. This
> mode of attack is dangerous, not only
> to the effectiveness of our curricula,
> but also to the practice of our pro-
> fession and the attitude of our young
> practitioners.

> It must be re-emphasized that our
> profession's objective is the creation
> and improvement of processes. It is
> agreed that the more effective our
> fundamental foundation, the more effec-
> tive our practice. But *our practice* is
> not to be deprecated. Fundamentals acts
> as a desirable fulcrum, but creativity
> is our objective." [335]

"Many engineering educators are therefore seeking ways of increasing thoroughness and breadth of instruction in fundamental matters and of stimulating among students initiative, resourcefulness, and originality.
H. P. Hammond [139]

The above problem areas of engineering educa-

tion and many more have been extensively examined

in major surveys of engineering education [362, 198, 377,

139, 140, 130, 51, 364, 365]. There is a thread in all

these from the earliest times advocating the desira-

bility of engaging the student in a creative college

learning experience.[1] Quotations from the most recent

are relevant:

---

[1]One of the earliest suggestions for creativity training of engineers
was made in 1906 by Prindle [259].   A similar plea was made by
Olken [228]   in 1933 who pressed for establishing graduate courses in
inventing.

"The Goals study recommends that
- - - analysis, synthesis, and design
should be given emphasis in engineering
curricula at all levels. - - - New kinds
of learning experience and high level
creative activity are needed at all
levels to prepare the student for leadership roles - - - " [364, p1]

" - - the importance of creative
design in both the undergraduate and
graduate programs deserves the immediate
attention of engineering educators. They
must develop greatly improved programs
which will stress creative design and
development, give the student an appreciation
of the importance of costs and an opportunity for experiencing the thrills of
invention -- the excitement of original
and imaginative thought in his chosen
field." [364, p24]

*"Finally, they
(accreditation cri-
teria) are intended
to encourage and
stimulate but never
to restrain the
creative and
imaginative."*
   *Engineers Council
   for Professional
   Development [1]*

"In the last year of his basic
engineering program the student might
undertake a fairly sophisticated engineering system design project as a
capstone of the program. This pedagog-
ical capstone should integrate the learning
experiences of the entire curriculum and
bring to bear the knowledge and tools the
student has acquired. Creativity, innovation and judgment should be encouraged.
The student should gain experience in the
use of optimization techniques and decision
theory which require consideration of performance, scheduling, reliability and cost." [365, p66]

*"Should the Univer-
sities turn out
students to fit
the world? With
all due respect to
my academic friends,
I say the answer is,
No. Their job is to
change the world by
encouraging their
students to become
world changers. It
is a tragedy just to
try to fit them to
the world, because
the world is not
right the way it is."*
   *Jacob Rabinow
   [263, p168]*

The tenor of these studies is that forward-

looking engineering educators consider it important

to future engineering success to develop your creative

ability. You may have already encountered a few pro-

fessors whose outlook is toward the creative and are

able to "wind you up for life." If so, consider

yourself fortunate!

Discussion Topics

1.   Select one of the marginal "flowers of
     interest." Discuss the extent, or lack
     of same, of its applicability to what
     you have seen so far of your engineering
     discipline.

2.   Explore, through discussion, the questions
     raised under *CREATIVITY NEEDED IN ENGINEERING
     EDUCATION*.

3.   Cite a *specific* course and a *specific*
     problem therein in your course of study
     to date in which you were expected to
     create a *new* combination of engineering
     ideas resulting in a possible *new* solu-
     tion to the problem.

4.   Assess the approximate percentage of
     your engineering education to date
     which you would judge as dominantly
     creative.

5.   Are you generally satisfied with your
     engineering education to date? Discuss
     the relationship, if any, between 'satis-
     faction' and likelihood of creating a *new*
     engineering idea.

6.   Our peers have indicated a need to develop
     our creative ability. Discuss whether this
     alone is sufficient justification for
     committing to attempt to develop *your*
     creativity.

7.   Consider Gilmer's quote. Discuss the
     extent to which your total engineering
     education to this point has equipped *you*
     with the needed attributes he cites.

     Does industry really need such men or is
     this all just 'high-sounding talk'?

8.   The text said that engineering is moving
     toward interdisciplinary problems. Discuss
     the extent to which your education to date
     has equipped you for this kind of activity.

Exercises

1-E8.   Identify textbooks for at least three engi-
        neering courses you have taken which, in
        retrospect, you wish had been written in a
        manner to elicit *your* creative ability
        more. Write out briefly why you think such
        texts are needed and why you think more such
        texts are not written.

1-E9.   Identify and list the reasons you can for
        why you probably have not had a dominantly
        creative course before now even though
        engineering educators have recognized the
        desirability of teaching creativity at
        least as far back as 1918, if not before.

1-E10. Applied to my engineering discipline,

   a.   Here is my conception of the work of an
        engineer in each functional area of
        Fig. 1-4.

   b.   Here is *why* I think the engineer does,
        or does not, need 'disciplined creativity'
        in each of these.

   c.   Here is *why* I have previously had the
        impression that only the R & D engineer
        needs creativity.

Chapter Summary

● Changing society has many problems.

● Creative engineers are vital to the future material
  progress of society, though in a short run outlook
  their 'output' may place dilemmas on society.

● Science is not engineering. Engineering's
  original meaning as an ingenious artful contriver
  is embodied in 'Creative Engineer'.

● A realistic look at present and projected practice
  reveals the engineer's need for creativity.

● Engineering education has a major need of more
  actively enhancing student creativity.

CHAPTER 2

NATURE OF CREATIVITY

" - - almost every phase of creative thinking calls for
intense mental effort."
William H. Easton [87, p1]

● Review of analytics.

● The nature of creativity.

● Definitions, particularly 'disciplined creativity.'

● Disciplined creativity acquirable.

● Personal rewards of its acqu'sition.

Chapter 1 established our need for being creative
but did not define it. In this Chap. we seek workable
definitions and some understanding of the nature of creativity. We start with familiar territory -- analytics.

2-1 The Analytic and Creative

*"Science, in
fact, works
only by analysis,
by dividing ad
infinitum the
object of study."
Paul Tournier
[345, p54]*

THE NATURE OF ANALYTICS **is** so well known that we

only make a few general observations:

● Analysis implies a separation process
-- a breaking down of a problem into
manageable component parts which can be
examined both separately and in relation
to the whole problem.

*"One normally tends
to catalog engi-
neers either as
analyzers or as
synthesizers --
the analyzers are
the appraisers and
evaluators; the
synthesizers are
those who are
creative and in-
genious in devising
new ways of doing things.
(cont.)*

● The beautiful, orderly, powerful methods
of mathematics probably are uppermost in
our minds when we think of "analytics."

● Your engineering education to this point
has probably been over 90 per cent 'analytic-
ly' oriented. You may therefore have the
erroneous idea that the engineer is mostly
an analyzer of problems given to him.

"This sharp division is somewhat fallacious, however, because there is considerable overlapping."
      J. Kenneth Salisbury
      [280, p17]

● In its broadest sense analytics extends beyond mathematics to also include verbal analysis for the large set of problems which cannot easily be symbolized -- at least we don't know *how* to do so now.

● Mentally, the practice of using analytics on a given problem is not easy. Considerable personal discipline is required to obtain results.

● Probably because of the existence of such a large number of textbook type engineering problems solvable by known analytical methods, no one has told you that someone somewhere had to first *create* the idea, system, component, or process which you are analyzing and that without the initial acts of creation no problem would have existed to be analyzed! Considerable clairvoyance is required, for example, to create the correct model to be analyzed.

"It is necessary to have a concept before it can be analyzed."
      E. S. Taylor, et. al
      [332, p649]

"The analytical part of an engineering education now seems to be considered the most difficult, most challenging part, while the remainder of engineering is considered to be an exercise of a lower order, conducted in a physical region located nearer the seat of the pants than the brain."
      E. S. Taylor, et al [332, p655]

● "The study of engineering analysis is being expanded at the expense of subjects entitled 'design' and involving synthesis."
[332, p645]

● Some engineering students appear gifted in analytical ability, while others are gifted in creative ability.

We shall later see that our analytical skill can be a valuable tool to the disciplined creative engineer.

THE NATURE OF CREATIVITY is probably less familiar than 'analytics.' We now treat this subject preliminarily.

Some gross observations about 'creativity' include:

● Practiced by individuals. A way of thinking, acting, and living peculiar to the person.

"The 'loving' of creativity should begin in the classroom."
  Daniel V. DeSimone
  [75, p10]

"What is a creative problem? It seems to me that all the problems that confront man may be classed in either one of two categories: They either have one right answer or they have a multiplicity of right or acceptable answers. The first group I call 'analytical,' the second group, which is by far the larger, I call 'creative.' Please note that the two groups are not antitheses."
  John E. Arnold
  [8, p19]

- **Difficult to practice.** Using creativity calls forth imagination, courage, motivation, inspiration, confidence, and other finer qualities within us to the near limit of our capacity. To practice creativity is to significantly stretch our *full* mental capacities!

- **Its uniqueness.** One of the many divine endowments to man -- probably the highest -- setting him above the animals and enabling him to cope with life situations. Creativity is not limited to engineering work. It can be observed in all areas of human activity, though engineers probably make more use of 'creativity' than many other disciplines.

- **Problem oriented.** Creativeness is manifest most clearly when a difficult-to-solve, *specific* new problem is faced by the individual engineer. Particularly needed when prior art means for solving the problem have 'run dry.' A workable problem-solving approach (Chaps. 3-9) is a key element to creativity.

- **Its forward look.** To create a new product or a new idea is to usher in the future. The subtle implication may be that "this thing isn't good enough now" and hence "here is my proposal for solving this problem better in the future." Thus creativity is related to invention.

- **Its elusiveness.** Creativity appears more akin to things spiritual than the neat, orderly, regimented familiar world of analytics. We have difficulty in even defining what it is. There are no universally accepted definitions. Yet we are able to recognize patterns and products of creative engineering activity. It is a difficult area to

research, though much research
has been conducted -- principally
by psychologists. We now dimly see
some of the principles emerging, as
the morphology treated in Part II.

● Its elegance. The beauty of a skillful
creative engineer *practicing* the
art of his profession surpasses
simple words! He envisions, conceives, calculates, observes, tests,
makes errors, courageously proposes
significant changes, supervises,
defends, travels, writes, and uses
a wide spectrum of abilities of
which the strict analyst may be
only vaguely aware.

● Its rewards. Almost all who have
engaged in creative work have
reported rich personal, deeply
satisfying, stimulating feelings
that motivate toward further creative
work. It is *exciting* to engage in
creative work! To engage in it is
to experience richer dimensions of
life and its meaning.

Creativity may be studied from two major points

of view:

● Creative process - an examination
of the mental, environmental,
and relationship processes and
how these influence the idea
being created. Psychologists
and a few engineers have principally taken this route.

● Creative product - an examination of
how one goes about creating a
new product. Focus is on the
product. Engineers typically
have taken this "case" route.

Actual creative problem solving is a mixture of both

'process' and 'product' -- the view woven through this

text.

Insight into the nature of creativity can be
gleaned from Field who asks:

*"To me it is that
mental process by
which man combines
and recombines his
past experience,
possibly with some
distortion, in such
a way that he arrives
at new patterns, new
configurations, and
arrangements that
better solve some
need of mankind."*
    John E. Arnold
      [8, p19]

"What is mechanical invention? Is it
engineering? No! But it utilizes engineering.
Is it mathematics? No! But it needs mathematics.
Is it science? No! Science is the cruel step-
mother -- willing to help feed and nourish the
child at times; she is more frequently ready to
prove by tradition, and her so-called 'accepted-
facts' convention, that the child is a sport
and should not survive - - - - " [103]

"Is it invention to develop a new theory
of design? A new method of stress analysis?
A new compilation of widespread data, to organize
it and present it for the use of engineers? Is
it invention to lead our profession by editorial
foresight and guidance, or by evolving a system
of pedagogy that trains and inspires engineers?
Is it invention to devise an organization or a
method of operation of factories or of equipments?

Surprisingly enough, the answer to all
of these questions is, no! Yet, each is a
creation, each involves visualization, and each
uses engineering principles. Nevertheless, it
is not invention as defined in the law. If it
be not invention, then, what is it?

*"Creativity -- is
the capability for
generating novel
and effective means
to achieve a de-
sirable result in
dealing with a
situation of
importance to
society."*
    C. Stark Draper
      [82, p32]

Each example given certainly involves
the use of constructive imagination. Each is
practiced by a sufficiently large group to have
evolved a recognizable technique; each is therefore, a form of art. [104, p13]

All have two attributes in common: their
practitioners must be creative, and they must
use engineering. The term creative engineering
is, therefore, a correct definition of their
activities and a proper and fitting name for
their art."

Freund gives us further insight by asking, "What
is creativity?"

" - - - creativity
may be defined
generally as the
ability to bring
new knowledge and
ideas into exist-
ence."
    Robert Q. Wilson
    [380]

"For one thing, engineering creativity is much more like inventiveness than like research. The creative engineer is a cousin to Edison and Marconi; he is no relation at all to Einstein or Enrico Fermi.

A creative engineering device is original; it's an innovation, like Henry Ford's Model T, which he designed for the common man. Before Ford's time, automobiles were the toys of the wealthy.

A creative engineering device is a unique, often startling, combination of engineering principles and other engineering data which are already known. A good example is computerized stabilizing fins on ships.

"Utility is in my
opinion the only
test of value in
matters of in-
vention."
    Benjamin
    Franklin [173, p73]

A creative device is useful and beneficial, a device, whereby the engineer "ministers to the people," to quote Vannevar Bush.

A creative engineering device causes widespread changes in industries, or in the mode of life of the people, or in both. The airplane is an example of such an influence.

Finally, the creative engineering device is very likely to be dramatic, spectacular, and newsworthy, like the first nuclear-powered submarine, or a space vehicle.

Engineering or technical creativity, then, is the ability to come up with engineering devices which are innovations, combinations of known engineering principles or data, useful and beneficial, which cause widespread changes in the industries or in the mode of life of the people, and very often dramatic and spectacular." [111]

Hopefully, our conceptions of 'what creativity is like' will mature as we progress through this textbook. We begin to appreciate the difficulty of hardened definitions in this field! Yet for progress we must agree on some broad definitions in our creativity quest, recognizing the limitations of definitions.

Definitions And A Viewpoint

*"All of the prev-
alent definitions
of creativity in-
clude the concepts
of something which
is new, rather
unexpected, and
nontrivial."*
    Myron A. Coler
    [65, p73]

- Creativity: The totality of highly
  personal knowledge and art required
  to create.

- Creation: A *new* association of existing
  elements which is new to the creator
  himself. [360, Ch. 1]

  (An interesting discussion will be
  found in the reference.) Note the
  ideas of newness, the previous existence
  of parts of the new creation, the concept of a resulting tangible combination,
  and the recognition that the combination
  was not previously known to the creator.

- Invention: "Act of inventing, or discovering through study, experiment, etc.;
  a devising or contriving, esp[ecially]
  of that which has not before existed." [373]

  This term is widely used in connection
  with patents where, interestingly, it
  has never been defined positively by
  Congress or the courts. They have
  defined it negatively, i.e. by statements of what is *not* invention!

- Innovation: The complex process of introducing new and novel ideas into use or
  practice.

  May or may not include invention. Includes the element of entrepreneurship.

*"Original thinking
is required when
problems are en-
countered for the
first time, or
when different
or unusual solutions
are wanted."*
    Morris O. Edwards
    (Quoted in [152])

- Discover: "To obtain for the first time
  sight or knowledge of, as of a thing
  existing already, but not perceived or
  known; to find out; to ascertain; - - -
  one discovers what existed before, but
  had remained unknown; one invents by
  forming combinations which are either
  entirely new, or which attain their
  end by means unknown before." [373]

- Research: Systematic investigation to
  discover unknown facts or *new* principles.

"The capacity to design includes more than mere technical competence. It involves a willingness to attack a situation never seen or studied before and for which data are often incomplete; it also includes an acceptance of full responsibility for solving the problem, on a professional basis."
   L. E. Grinter
   [129, p15]

● <u>Design</u>: " - - the process of applying the various techniques and scientific principles for the purpose of defining a device, a process, or a system in sufficient detail to permit its physical realization." [332, p647]

Note that one creating may or may not be engaging in inventing, which depends on a *legal* judgment of the creation, whereas to invent necessarily implies the exercise of creativity. We will probe invention further in Chap. 18 in connection with patents.

An analogical way of seeing the important facets of disciplined creativity is shown in Fig. 2-1. We shall explore these in the remainder of the text.

By way of further perspective, do be forewarned that there is a strong tendency in creativity literature for an author to 'lock-on' to *one* facet of creativity, become enamored with it, and imply it is the most important, if not the only part of creativity. Actually, creativity is a very complex process, and there are many facets and couplings between the facets.

"Indiscipline is closely akin to laziness and disorder."
   Paul Tournier
   [345, p123]

Undisciplined Creativity. There are some individuals, many of them inventors, who feel that creativity is basically an unordered, chaotic, entropy-generating process. Nothing we can do influences it. 'Inventors are born not made.' It has been studied

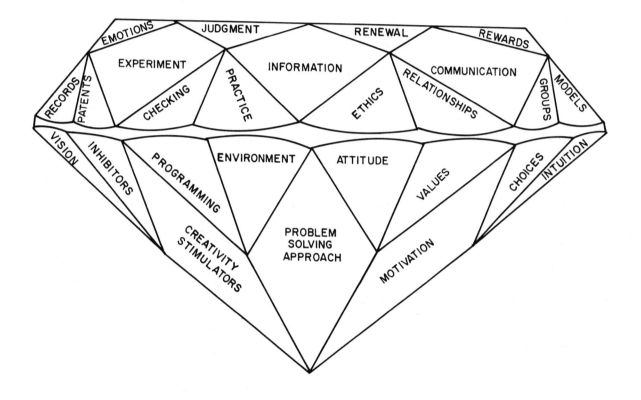

FIG. 2-1   The Gem of Creativity. Creativity has
many facets, not all of which are visible.
Proper balance of the facets through judgment
is needed by the disciplined creative
engineer.

for a long time by many people, and no coherent
orderly body of knowledge has emerged. Obtaining
a new idea is basically a chance proposition, and
nothing we can do will change that. Creativity
needs absolute and unrestrained freedom of all
kinds to produce anything. Don't tie the creative
engineer down to even a broad product range. He must
be free to create whatever comes to his mind, regardless of whether his or any company is now in that
business or remotely ever will be! The capstone of
the above school is 'give me *more* chaos if you expect me to create.'

The above attitudes reflect 'undisciplined
creativity.' They collectively signify a lack of
knowledge, maturity, and perspective. They also
minimize the important role of judgment in the creative process.

DISCIPLINED CREATIVITY is defined:

> ● <u>Disciplined</u> <u>Creativity</u>: The totality
> of highly personal knowledge and
> art chosen to orderly and consistently
> create useful things for the benefit
> of mankind.

Observe that the elements of order, judgment, and
choice enter into the definition. We shall find
in Chap. 3 that mature creative engineers who can
consistently solve *new* problems in a creative way
make use -- perhaps unconsciously -- of 'a problem

*"But whatever you
do you would be
well advised to
practice stern
discipline and
vigorous, un-
remitting effort.
For high quali-
ties and great
achievements are
not merely matters
of chance or
birth. They are
the products of
long and disciplined
toil."*
John F. Kennedy
[169]

solving approach.' No matter what the problem is, the step sequence in the approach seems ever present. This sequence is the 'order', structure, or morphology of creative work which if executed correctly by competent persons will have a high probability of resulting in a useful *new* thing of value.

The judgment implication is that a person skilled in disciplined creativity will clearly and cleanly exercise the necessary judgment at appropriate places throughout the total creative process.

"If you will succeed in life's business, do what you ought to do when you ought to do it, whether you want to or not."

[384, p21]

The choice implications are that we can *choose* to create; we *choose* to recognize a human need as 'a problem' worthy of creative effort; we *choose* to acquire the knowledge and art necessary; we *choose* to use judgment when it will most help solve the problem; we *choose* to temporarily discard judgment when essential to acquire new ideas; we *choose* to attempt maximization of the usefulness of the thing being created; and we *choose* to attempt improvement of the lot of man through offering our well thought-out new creation for society's consideration and use. Finally, we *choose* to be in control of ourself at all times throughout the process of creating and to be taught, instructed, molded, trained, and strengthened as a person by the creative work undertaken.

In summary, the disciplined creative engineer has perspective for the *total* problem on which he chooses to work, he has a higher than average probability of successfully solving his chosen problem, and he attempts the difficult matter of experiencing and controlling himself, his feelings, and his aspirations within desired bounds which he chooses to set.

Discussion Topics

1. Are creative problems really more complex than analytic problems, as Starkey indicates?

2. Defend or refute (*honestly*, the way you feel): a. "The EE *only* needs strong ability to analyze electrical circuits. He neither cares for nor realistically needs to know *anything* about creativity or idea synthesis." b. "The whole nebulous subject of creativity is both unteachable and useless to the EE's future." (Use your particular engineering discipline.)

3. Is there any prejudice against creativity?

4. Engineer A has had fun creating a new geometrical arrangement for making a microwave quarter wave impedance matching transformer. He builds a model, tests it, and finds it works as he visualized. Two days later he picks up a technical journal and finds there described essentially the same idea which engineer B with a competing company has also developed and published. Was A "creative?" Justify your position.

5. You have been talking to someone about this course. He has commented that he sees no purpose for creating new ideas unless they are good ones. How would you react to his comment?

6. Are *you* 'creative?' Cite a *specific*
    example of something you have created.
    How did the total process leave you
    feeling? Explore the extent to which
    all learning is creative.

7. What *specifically* have you done or thought
    today which you consider creative? Recheck
    the text definition of creativity. Ditto
    for the past week.

8. The text indicated creativity was 'problem
    oriented'. So is analytics! How then is
    creativity different?

9. Cite one of the 'creative giants' in your
    engineering discipline. Discuss *why* you
    think he was or was not creative.

10. Using the same engineer of (9), what evi-
    dences can you find for his having used
    'disciplined creativity' as defined in the
    text, even though he may have denied any
    discipline.

11. The text definition for disciplined creativity
    seems to mean that I can, by my choice, be
    creative. Is this really so or is creativity
    reserved for the 'one-in-a-million' born creative?

12. Discuss how 'disciplined creativity' differs
    from 'creativity'. Think in terms of a
    specific problem of contemporary interest
    in your engineering discipline.

Exercises

2-E1. Here is *my* improvement over the text definition
      of creativity. (Write out clearly.)

2-E2. The text did not define a creative act. Write
      a carefully thought-out definition.

2-E3. Consider the gem of creativity in Fig. 2-1.
      Prepare a list of specific qualities you consider
      a gem has. Does creativity seem to possess these
      same qualities? Explore item-by-item.

2-E4. Matches are laid out as VII = I. You are asked to
      move one match and make this a true equality.

2-E5.　Explore the literature cited in this section.
Write out alternate definitions of creativity
as seen by others.

2-2 Disciplined Creativity Acquirable

*"'Only a select
few are able to
invent'. This
belief, with us
for many years,
now has been
shown up for
just what it is
-- a myth."
Eugene Raudsepp
[268]*

UNIVERSALITY OF CREATIVITY.　Students sometimes
initially fear creativity *cannot* be acquired.　The
purpose of this Sec. is to allay such fears.

A perceptive look at the man-made part of the
world reveals unnumbered creations in all fields of
human effort.　It is clear that there are many individuals in society who actually *are* creating.　Within
your engineering discipline exciting creative work
is in process!　Are the individual engineers doing
this creative work possessors of some unacquirable
body of knowledge, technique, or methodology?　Or
is creativity a characteristic of all engineers and
therefore enhanceable? Can *I* enhance my creativity?
Now?　These and similar questions rush to our minds.

To find answers, we turn to Gitter who says:

"From this research, which has been
in process almost uninterruptedly since
1944, two conclusions have emerged:

1. The commodity called
   "creativity" is much more
   universally distributed among
   the population than is usually
   supposed.

2. The creative habit can be re-
   awakened in people who seem to

have lost it, and strengthened
in people who regularly display
it." [119, p93]

> "Creativity is not
> the exclusive
> property of a
> gifted few.
> Factory workers,
> clerks, janitors,
> and gardeners can
> be creative as
> well as executives,
> scientists, artists
> or technicians.
> The necessary in-
> gredient is the
> willingness to
> try."
> Don Fabun
> [97, p38]

DeSimone, reporting on the 1965 Wood's Hole

National Conference on Creative Engineering Education

attended by 86 experts in creativity from industry,

government, and education, says:

> "At Wood's Hole there was general
> agreement that the creative requisites
> of invention and innovation, including
> entrepreneurship, can be developed."
> [75, p14]

A number of forward-looking corporations

and educational institutions have long taught

educational programs for developing creative ability.

General Electric Company was one of the earliest

to pioneer such a program in 1937 for teaching

selected engineers from many disciplines the basic

elements of 'design' in a 2 year Creative Engineering

Program [401]. Westinghouse in 1960 developed and

initiated a 'Creativity in Manufacturing' course for

professional and management personnel [274]. Western

Electric has a course called 'Problem Solving' for

graduate engineers [374]. The State University of

New York at Buffalo has a variety of programs, summer

meetings, and courses in creativity, initiated by

Osborn and Parnes, for a wide spectrum of people. [237].

Finally, the University of Florida has had a 'Creative

Problem Solving ' course since 1961 [22, 205]. Others

could be cited.

CREATIVITY ACQUISITION STATEMENTS may now

be made:

●   Creativity enhancement is
        acquirable.

●   All engineers have some undeveloped
        creative potential.

●   Creative ability varies *widely*
        from person to person before and
        after formal creativity training.

●   Through proper discipline one's
        creativity may be enhanced *if* the
        person so chooses.

●   Creativity enhancement can be
        acquired via various means i.e.
        there is no *one* best method.

The above are some of the hypotheses on which this text is based. They may now seem surprisingly obvious. These matters have been extensively discussed in and out of the literature. Discussion will undoubtedly continue. You will encounter many with views opposite to those above and who can't understand why they never create anything new, novel, or exciting!

PERSONAL CHOICE NECESSARY. The importance of your making an honest choice about your need and desire for enhancing your creativity in a disciplined way cannot be underestimated. In choosing you realize the *personalness* of disciplined creativity -- a theme we shall repeatedly see ahead. It could be one of the

" - - - the average man develops so small a portion of his inherited abilities -- including creative abilities -- that the odds are in favor of any reasonable teaching environment which seeks to encourage creativity."
    Myron A. Coler
    [65, p76]

"Creative contributions are preponderantly if not exclusively made by self-motivated people."
    Myron A. Coler
    [65, p76]

most *important* choices of your professional engi-

neering career, vitally influencing your life work

and the effectiveness of your engineering contribution!

But, "what are the rewards," you ask, "for

acquiring disciplined creativity?"

PERSONAL REWARDS to the engineer exercising

disciplined creativity are:

*"But in many ways
ideas are more
important than
people -- they
are much more
permanent."*
    *Charles F.
    Kettering
    [173, p9]*

*" - - the correct idea
was at length developed
and I was filled with un-
utterable joy."*
    *Hern Rudolf Diesel
    [76, p343]*

- **Contributing** in significant tangible permanent ways for the benefit of mankind. Creates wealth.

- **Joy** of accomplishment and satisfaction as we solve significant *new* problems. We find creative engineering work exciting, fun, and deeply satisfying as we give of our expertise to mankind!

- **Adventure** is ever with and before us when we engage in disciplined creativity. We *make* new things happen rather than being spectators of the new. We need adventure to keep life from going sour.

- **Interesting** and **challenging** activity as we create the *new* things of tomorrow's world.

- **Work** is a necessity for us human beings. Our work renews and lifts us to new achievement heights.

- **Understanding** of ourselves as persons. A valuable by-product of solving sig-nificant creative engineering problems.

- **Financial** rewards, perhaps not immediate, may come to the disciplined engineer creating new solutions to problems.

- **Recognition** and **honors** are sometimes accorded to creative engineers in this life.

*"Perspective is the
quality that per-
mits an engineer
to assign correct
relative import-
ance to all things
within his scope.
- - - An engineer
without perspective
is a ship without a
rudder."*
    J. Kenneth
    Salisbury [280]

While the above positive rewards, all of a deeply satisfying personal nature, may be experienced by the practitioner of disciplined creativity, our perspective would be incomplete without mentioning 'negative rewards' may also exist. These include: risk taking (the creative engineer operates in a higher risk-taking mode than his more conventional colleagues); loneliness ("Nobody seems to understand my new ideas."); alienation ("He surely has some un-conventional ideas!"); ridicule; rejection; frequent failures; trouble; delayed recognition--sometimes following death; and many others.

Discussion Topics

1. Re-examine Gitter's first conclusion. Discuss how you might measure creativity of *an* engineer in your discipline.

2. "Why don't 'they' (whoever that is!) get up a really *good* creativity test for engineers that will tell me whether I do or don't have creative ability?" Discuss.

3. *Why* have various industrial firms found it necessary to generate courses for the engineer's creativity enhancement?

4. The statements on creativity acquisition make it appear that the choice is *yours* as to whether to exercise disciplined creativity in your engineering career. Discuss whether this is true or whether "the system" of employment in which you will work forces you to be creative. Can creativity be 'forced' from engineers?

5. Some people feel that the majority of engineers are not creative. Do you think this means we do

not have creative ability, we do not employ
our ability, we don't have the drive for
accomplishment, we don't have ideas, or that
we fail to exercise the required discipline?
Or is the whole statement wrong?

Exercises

2-E6. Re-examine the Chap. title. Make a list of
specific reasons why you think *you* will or will
not need disciplined creativity in your later
engineering practice.

2-E7. Search out the most creative faculty man in your
department of engineering. Talk with him personally.
Seek his answers to the personal rewards of engaging in disciplined creative engineering work.
Identify the criteria you or others used for determining that he was the *most* creative locally. Would
these criteria be applicable to all engineers? Are
his 'rewards' extrapolatable to you?

2-E8. Re-examine the contents and presentation order of
this entire chapter. Identify topics you think
it should have covered but did not, as the psychology
of creativity, mind models, childhood background
and others. Propose, in outline form, a *better*
structure which is consistent with the Chap. name.

Chapter Summary

● Some gross observations about creativity were
made. Creative 'process' and 'product' viewpoints are the main divisions for study purposes.

● Creativity was defined as the totality of
personal knowledge and art required to create.
Related definitions were cited.

● Undisciplined and disciplined creativity concepts
were advanced. The latter is of most use to the
future engineer, and it was carefully defined.

● Disciplined creativity is acquirable if we
choose to enhance our creative ability.

● The personal rewards of involvement in disciplined
creativity were briefly tabulated.

PART II

MORPHOLOGY
OF DISCIPLINED
CREATIVITY

CHAPTER 3

CENTRALITY OF A PROBLEM SOLVING APPROACH
TO DISCIPLINED CREATIVITY

" - the most distinctive thing about innovation today is
 that we are beginning to pursue it systematically."
                                    John W. Gardner [116, p75]

●   'Engineering efficiency' is briefly examined.
    One key ingredient is seen to be 'an approach'
    for solving engineering problems.

●   Our previous 'approach' is reflected to be
    the 'one-problem-one-solution' type.

●   The need is presented for 'an approach'
    for systematically dealing with the large
    set of engineering problems of a creative
    nature typically having a *multiplicity* of
    solutions.

●   A brief exposure is made to some 'approaches'
    used by earlier creative people.

●   The 'six-step approach' for solving engineer-
    ing problems of a creative nature and which
    is *the principal approach advocated in this
    text* is succinctly presented.

In Chap. 1 we saw the engineer's urgent

need for mastering the elements of disciplined crea-

tivity in order to deal with and help create in an

orderly way the world of tomorrow. We have, in

Chap. 2, explored all too briefly something of the

nature of creativity. We are now prepared to see that

an orderly means for solving problems - 'an approach' -

lies at the heart of the creative process and that

such an approach can be identified, learned, and

become an integral part of the mature disciplined

creative engineer. Such an approach or process

"*Morphology*
The Science of
structure or
form; - - "
[373]

we refer to as the morphology of the creative

process.

3-1 The Engineer's Efficiency

It is axiomatic that engineers deal with prob-

lems and that one who practices engineering is strongly

oriented toward problem solving. Though we shall

focus on "the problem" in depth in Chaps. 4 and

5, for present purposes we use Powell's definition

of:

●   A Problem: Any recognized situation requiring
      directed thought before action can be
      taken. [258]

Many other definitions exist as do ways of classifying

problems, e.g. creative, analytical, technical,

non-technical, subject area, etc. These details need

not concern us at this point except to recognize

the enormity in number of the set known as 'creative

problems'--those requiring a *new*, unique, creative

solution which are our principal concern.

Since technical problem solving is the work of

the engineer, we are led to consider the possibility

of optimizing, in a broad way, our personal problem

solving efficiency. Though there are many ways of

examining this general area (engineering managements

constantly study "engineering effectiveness"!), we

choose the following quasi-mathematical view and

*"Proper analysis
of facts produces
knowledge orga-
nized in a disci-
pline. This
discipline of
knowledge will
give merely
competent
persons effec-
tiveness and
will give
talented persons
extraordinary
effectiveness."*
 Peter F. Drucker
 [83, p9]

define:

(Eq. 1)

$\bullet \; \eta$ = An Engineer's Overall Efficiency = $\dfrac{\text{Our Output}}{\text{Total Input}}$

$\bullet \; \eta = \dfrac{\text{Our Contribution(s)}}{\text{Corporate (or other) resources plus personal inputs}}$

"Efficiency causes one to economize on his time, to plan his work well, and to exercise extreme self-discipline."
J. Kenneth Salisbury
[280, p19]

Clearly a highly effective engineer is one who is *contributing*, usually by means of solving significant engineering problems. Further Eq. 1 implies our efficiency is highest if we are able to solve problems with:

▲ Highest contribution - - (Maximum numerator)

▲ Lowest effort - - - - - (Personal input low)

▲ Lowest cost - - - - - - (Lowest personal and corporate inputs)

▲ Lowest losses - - - - - (Contribution = inputs-losses)

▲ Wisest use of total resources - - - - - - (Minimizing the denominator)

Finally our probability of having our contributions accepted may be higher *because* our overall efficiency is high.

From another viewpoint we can think of our individual overall efficiency as the product of several factors.

(Eq. 2)

$\bullet \; \eta$ = (Aptitude) (Intelligence) (Knowledge) (Problem Approach)$^{\alpha}$ (Motivation)$^{\beta}$ (Personal Factors)$^{\delta}$

It is clear that if α, β, and δ are constants and real numbers, not necessarily equal but greater than 1,

*"A full store-
house of know-
ledge is a
necessary but
not a sufficient
condition for
invention. To
this, one must
add an organized
method of attack."
W. H. Middendorf
G. T. Brown, Jr.
[215, p867]*

then the implication of Eq. 2 is that in maximizing
η we should seriously *first* address ourselves to the
last three factors. Doing so does not mean that
the first three are unimportant, for clearly if any
one of them is zero, $\eta = 0$, resulting in no contribution. The first three factors are probably fixed
by our heredity and prior education. Less
educational emphasis has probably been placed on our
problem solving approach, motivation, and personal
factors. Most serious investigators of the creative
process have recognized the importance of the factors
in Eq. 2, though semantics differ about how
to express and combine the factors. The
reader interested in exploring this area further will
find Shockley's paper [291] stimulating. He concludes,
for an eight factor productivity equation, that:

> " -- if one man exceeds another by
> 50 percent in each of the eight factors,
> his productivity will be larger by a
> factor of 25. On the basis of this
> reasoning we see that relatively small
> variation of specific attributes can
> again produce the large variation in
> productivity."

The α, β, and δ factors in Eq. 2 would tend to further
amplify differences between individual problem
solvers beyond that observed by Shockley.

While such "equations" as (1) and (2) should not
be pressed literally too far, they give us clues as
to what factors are important and merit our most

serious attention if we expect to, over our

*"If we do any-
thing at all
in life that
is worthwhile,
sooner or later
we find ourselves
in an in-fighting
spot in which we
seem to be put-
ting out so much
energy and getting
so little done.
Under these cir-
cumstances it is
wise to recog-
nize that our
mental health is
not so good."*
  *William Menninger
  [213, p17]*

professional lifetime, make *significant* creative

contributions. The important 'motivation' and

'personal factors' are so complex and so important

to the disciplined creative engineer that the

entirety of Part III of this book is devoted to

maximizing them.

It is clear from Eq. (2) that the most

important remaining factor is 'problem approach'

with which we now briefly deal. We shall

devote the remainder of Part II to it.

Discussion Topics

1. *Why* are there differences in efficiency between
    individual engineers in solving problems creatively?
    Are these differences small or large in your
    observations?

2. Discuss Eqs. (1) and (2). Uncover their strengths
    and weaknesses.

3. Discuss, *beyond* the text treatment, what factors
    determine an individual engineer's problem
    solving efficiency.

3-2 Our Previous Approach: One-Problem - One-Solution

Reflection and generalization of the kinds of

engineering 'textbook probems' with which you have

dealt up to now will most probably reveal that:

● The problem to be solved was *clearly*
  stated with virtually all the information you needed for a solution
  either in the problem or nearby. Neither
  excess nor too little information was
  given.

● The problem's location at the end of a given chapter gave you strong clues as to where to look for 'the solution.'

● The steps between problem and solution were fairly stereotyped.

● The solution was already known -- to *someone*, perhaps not you.

● Only one answer was 'right'.

Now, it could be argued on very strong grounds that it is *essential to master such a procedure during the early process of learning*. But about now in our engineering educational development we should expect to advance to a *higher* level in our problem solving methodology -- a more creative level! Let us briefly explore the matter.

"The creative individual may be the only person who appreciates that a problem even exists."
Harper Brown Keeler
[166, p26]

"The young engineer, for example, soon finds that a problem is not always clear or easily defined and that the solution does not involve merely substituting known values into a standard formula."
H. F. Barr
[24]

Did anyone ever discuss with you how problems arise and how one determines whether the problem is even *worth* solving? Did anyone ever tell you that being able to *recognize* the problem clearly enough to be able to write it down is frequently extremely difficult? Did anyone discuss with you how, in the first place, one sets up the model for the 'textbook problem' to be analyzed? Was it made clear to you that the model may not be precisely correct and that other models *also* may exist, perhaps incorporating different assumptions? Was it really driven home to you that *alternate* means of solving the problem exist -- perhaps requiring less engineering effort or cost -- leading to perhaps equally valid answers? Was it made clear to you that someone else, in reality, had already done most of the exciting creative thinking about the problem, leaving the more mechanistic parts for you to do? Was the concept of a

generalized 'approach' suitable
for solving a large set of engineering
problems of a creative nature even
broached?

Of course the answers are individualistic and
vary with locale; but after examining the above more
creative view, reasons for the popularity in engineering education of the one-problem-one-answer
approach are not hard to find.

Taylor et al [332, p651] have examined the
effect of the single-answer problem on engineering
attitudes and found:

" - - an engineer
is supposed to
be more than a
mobile re-
pository of know-
ledge who is
adept at attack-
ing single-answer
problems."
Daniel V. DeSimone
[75, p13]

"1.   Incomplete or contradictory data
      have little place in single-answer
      problems.

2.   Engineering judgment is not re-
      quired of either the student or
      the instructor, hardly a situation
      to encourage its development.

3.   The very existence of an objective
      standard puts the instructor in
      an almost impregnable position,
      which only a few of the bright
      students will dare to challenge.
      Skepticism and the questioning
      attitude are not encouraged by
      this situation. Neither the
      data, the applicability of the
      method, nor the result are open
      to question.

"Education is the
process of im-
parting knowledge,
nurturing habits
of thought, and
developing
capabilities for
action that supple-
ment and extend
natural human
capability."
C. Stark Draper
[82, p33]

4.   The single-answer problem usually
      suggests the infallibility of
      logic rather than the ultimate
      word of experiment. The early
      history of science bears witness
      to the paralyzing effect of this
      attitude.

It seems clear that the single-answer
question has a rather strong negative
effect on attitudes we hope to teach
our students."

Exercises

3-E1.   State **all** the reasons you can for *why* the
        'One-Problem-One-Solution' approach to problem
        solving may be suboptimal for creatively
        solving a realistic engineering problem of
        substance.

3-E2.   Reflect on the totality of textbook problems
        you have solved. List sequentially the *actual*
        steps you used in your 'approach.'

3-E3.   List ways the 'one-problem-one-solution' approach
        may have inhibited your creativity.

3-3   The <u>Engineer's</u> <u>Need</u> <u>For</u> 'An <u>Approach</u>' <u>For</u> <u>Multiple</u>
      <u>Solution</u> <u>Problems</u>

" - - *Innovative
activity starts
with a problem
to be solved."
John W. Gardner
[116, p27]*

        In view of the above discussion and our prior

education we intuitively sense that the 'one-problem-

one-solution approach' may be suboptimal for the

engineer desiring to make significant *creative*

contributions. To generate tomorrow's dynamic

solutions to the world's pressing problems of today,

some of which were glimpsed in Chap. 1, will re-

quire that we engineers be facile with *creating*

multiple solutions to a problem and that we be

able to make a clear determination of the best

solution after carefully weighing *all factors*.

We no longer will be able to take the easy way out

by saying 'this kind of problem has this kind of

answer.' Tomorrow that approach may be invalidated

when the problem is changed to one for which *no*

solution is known and genuine creative effort is

required to generate the best solution -- or even

one solution!

" - - when an
engineer goes
to work, he is
no longer just
an analyzer of
problems but
a synthesizer."
  Eric A. Walker
   [366, p89]

In our practice of engineering when we first realistically face a truly *new* problem for which *none* of the old answers 'fit,' it is then one keenly realizes the need for 'an approach' of some kind -- some generalized way of proceeding so that progress toward creating the best solution - or even *a* solution - can be made.

The principal advantages of acquiring a disciplined generalized approach to solving engineering problems are:

- **Improves problem solving efficiency** significantly when properly applied.

- **Working on the right problem** probability is increased.

- **Achieving a successful solution**--hopefully new, unique, useful, and creative-- can have a high probability since a multiplicity of solution alternatives has been created from which the apparent best solution has been chosen.

- **Implementation of the solution created** may be more likely.

- **Enhances tangible progress toward a solution** and minimizes confusion, getting lost in the problem, despondency and other creative inhibitors.

- **Facilitates crossing functional and discipline** boundaries when required to achieve a solution.

- **Increases confidence**, after a few successes, in the engineer's ability to both solve problems and create new solutions where required.

- **Minimizes mistakes**, possibly very major, which could easily be made.

"The greatest invention of all -
one that we
seldom hear
much about - is
the invention
of the method
of invention."
  Paul J. Stuber
   [321, p4930]

Fortunately, advanced-thinking creative people in a wide variety of fields of human endeavor have thought about the problem of 'an approach' for solving *new* problems. It is only comparatively recently that these approaches have been disseminated. Even today, because of the many unknowns about the functioning of the creative mind, agreement is by no means universal on the steps in the complex creative process, i.e. the steps in 'an approach' leading to a creative solution of the problem. In spite of that situation the seeking engineer is able to ferret out the threads of problem solving approaches which have worked for successful problem solvers and led to new, unique, creative, and useful solutions. We examine some of these in the next section.

"The romantic theory that an invention will appear in full bloom without conscious effort on the part of the gifted inventor has been deprecated."
W. H. Middendorf
G. T. Brown, Jr.
[215, p861]

" - - Many have found that there is enjoyment in bringing order out of chaos."
Phil Simpson
[295, p17]

Discussion Topics

1. Do most individuals have mature well-thought-out 'problem solving approaches'? Explore the connection between 'problem solving approach' and an individual engineer's probability of making an invention.

2. Reexamine the Chap. title. Why is 'an approach' for solving engineering problems so central? Why not just treat every engineering problem confronting us in 'the obvious manner?'

Exercises

3-E4. Try to identify a single product in use today that came into being in 'a brilliant flash' and required little else afterwards for the product or idea to be successful. Justify your position factually and historically by specific references.

3-E5. Write a brief essay on what 'successful' means for a truly *new* engineering idea or concept.

3-E6. An engineer approaches *new* problems haphazardly. List the potential personal consequences.

3-4 Some Problem Solving Approaches

"The first concept of an idea is one thing -- the working model is another, and as every inventor knows, popular acceptance -- still another."
  Charles F. Kettering
    [173, p28]

"In talking to many successful inventors I have found no two follow exactly the same rules. Each has developed his own preferred approach to finding and selecting problems. Still, it would be highly instructive to a student to learn about some of these successful techniques so that he can select those which particularly appeal to him and thus assemble his own bag of tricks."
  William Bollay
    [39, p64]

A sampling of some of the published problem solving approaches advocated by various individuals is shown in Table 3-1. Those chosen are of particular interest to engineers. The interested reader is necessarily referred to the references for additional exposition on any one. Only the barest skeleton of each is here included because of space limitations. Additional interesting problem solving approaches will be found in references [34, 69, 78, 82, 85, 101, 123, 130, 149, 152, 166, 182, 215, 217, 256, 342, 347, 364, 375, 381, 400, 68, 70, 155, and 261].

It is instructive to compare in some detail the steps in the various approaches shown in Table 3-1. The steps have been arranged in horizontal rows to facilitate the rough comparison which you should make. We note in passing that approaches range from the beautifully simple three-step approach of yesteryear by Diesel to the more sophisticated modern approaches by Asimow and Von Fange involving six steps.

By searching out what is actually done in each step and by overlooking the semantics difficulties, which are considerable, we note that there are many

TABLE 3-1   A Summarized Comparison of Some 'Approaches' for Solving Problems of a Creative Nature

THOUGHT FORMATION Wallace [369]	SCIENTIFIC METHOD [286]	RESEARCH Walkup [367]	DISCOVERY, INVENTION Zwicky [403, p107]	INVENTION Diesel [76, p346]	INVENTION Rossman [279]	DESIGN & MANUFACTURE Asimow [12, p42]	DESIGN & MANUFACTURE Von Fange [360]	MANAGEMENT (Army) [385]
Preparation	Observation and Experiment	Problem Formulation Fact Finding Analysis	Problem Concisely Formulated		Observation of A Need or Difficulty Analysis of Need Survey Available Information	Analysis of Problem Situation	Investigate Direction	Prob. Identification Prob. Research Prob. Definition
			Localize/Analyze Important Parameters				Establish Measures	
Incubation Illumination	Analysis and Synthesis Hypothesis	Incubation Decision	Construct 'Morphological Box' Containing All Potential Solutions. Evaluate Solns.	Idea Conception	Formation of All Objective Solns. Analysis of Solns. Birth of New Idea	Synthesis of Solutions Evaluation and Decision	Develop Methods	Idea Hopper Idea Filter
			Optimum Solns. Selected and Applied			Optimization	Optimize Solution	
Verification	Inference	Action		Carrying Out	Experimentation, Test, Selection, Perfection of Final Embodiment	Revision	Complete Solution	Idea Tester
	Comparison and Analogy			Introduction	NOTE: This process based on surveying 500 Patent Attorneys, 300 Research Directors, 700 Active Inventors	Implementation	Convince Others	Formulate Plan for Change Coordinate Action

common threads between the approaches used in

research, discovery, invention, design, manufacture,

and management. Thus if the problem solving approach

is the 'ordered' part of discipline, we now glimpse

added evidence of the validity of Fig. 1-3 in

Chap. 1 showing disciplined creativity permeating

research to operations.

" - - how much higher a thing to discover that by means of which all things else shall be discovered with ease."
Francis Bacon
[15, p174]

Exercise

3-E7.   Study Table 3-1 carefully and critically.
        Particularly focus on the 'holes' in some of
        the approaches. Identify them. Cite specific
        reasons *why* you believe 'holes' exist. What
        consequences might an engineer encounter if
        he literally applied any approach without
        being aware of its shortcomings?

3-5 The Six-Step Approach Central To Disciplined Creativity

" - - the concept that a general- ized engineering method can and should be for- malized for students has been gaining increased acceptance among engineering educators."
Stephen Yerazunis
Arthur A. Burr
[400, 835]

From the previous section the strong suggestion

emerges that some kind of problem solving

approach structure appears common to the entire

functional span of engineering activity. A knowledge

of *it* and the ability to apply it repetitively

to problems would indeed be a powerful tool in the

hands of a disciplined creative engineer seeking to

create *new* solutions. An overview of such an approach

is now to be presented. *It forms the important*

structure around which disciplined creativity

concepts are wrapped.

A mature disciplined 'six-step approach' guide

to problem solving advocated in this text is laid

out in Fig. 3-1.

It is the approach we shall learn about and apply

in future Chaps. as we deal with it in detail.

For our present purposes, however, a non-detailed

overview of it is adequate. It represents an

integration of the approaches in Table 3-1 in the

senses that it attempts to include the best features

of any one and that it may be applicable to research,

invention, development, design, manufacture, or

operations when properly applied. Thus we can

become proficient in a *single* problem solving

approach rather than six (or more)!

The best way to understand Fig. 3-1 is by

means of a brief sketchy pseudo-example. Follow

the figure closely through it.

Example 3-1

Assume you are an engineer with a private
consulting engineering firm majoring in large
scale 'systems' type problems. A representative
of a major airlines company has approached your
firm about the possibility of 'doing something
about these aircraft hijackings' being experienced by his company. The problem is assigned
to you by your manager, the senior member in
the firm, with the request 'make me a report with
some engineering recommendations in it as
soon as possible.'

You initiate the 'problem inquiry' stage
not being sure whether the problem is to pass
new laws regulating air piracy, to initiate
Sunday School classes, to train air crews in
Judo techniques, or to create a new metallic
detector for firearms on boarding passengers.
The facts on how many hijackings have occurred

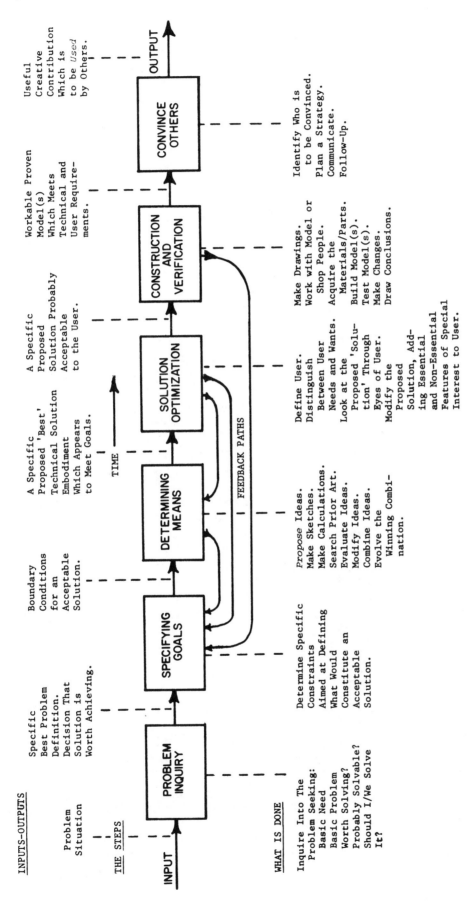

FIG. 3-1 The six-step system approach to solving in a mature disciplined
          manner an engineering problem requiring a creative solution.
          The figure gives an overview of the approach.

in the past 5 years are accumulated after considerable trouble retrieving the information. The facts on total costs of hijacking to the airline industry and the clients firm are found, thus giving a firm financial incentive to solve the problem. The problem is found to be definitely worth solving to both client and the airline industry in general.

"Every product sold today started somewhere as an idea."
  Philip R. Marvin
  [201, p56]

You decide the real problem is: create a means of detecting that a boarding passenger is carrying a firearm or dangerous weapon. Such apparatus, which would have to be created, would be inconspicuously installed in airline terminals throughout the client's service territory. A report is written coherently integrating the results of the problem inquiry phase and recommending detection apparatus be created. After considerable discussion, meetings, phone calls, and other interactions you and your manager are finally able to secure a decision by your client company to proceed with creating such a new apparatus. Estimated funding and time goals are worked out mutually as are the detail goals of the detector. It is decided it must detect an iron object the size of a pocket knife or larger on a person and that the apparatus must instantly visually alert the airlines agent boarding passengers whose job it would be to legally search suspicious passengers. Other specific goals are formulated and agreed upon with the client company. Boundary conditions for an acceptable detector solution are now known and are in writing.

"His (Edison's) method of attacking an inventive prob- lem of major importance was always the same. He would attempt nothing until he had a clear comprehension of the existing state of the art - - -"
  [339, p113]

The 'determining means' phase is entered. The similarity of the problem to submarine detection is recognized early. You kick around ideas for 'how would you detect an iron object' with creative colleagues. Eighty-eight ideas are proposed. Of these the most promising solution appears to lie in a magnetometer-like system as the winning combination. You make an in-depth engineering study of magnetometer art, early discovering important parts are 'classified' and are not available to you. You therefore find it necessary to create something new. You propose several electrical systems which might solve the problem. Calculations are made to check the sensitivity of detection of the proposed systems. One is found capable

"I couldn't stand anyone claiming there was only one way to do things."
William P. Lear
[187, p26]

of detecting shoe nails -- too sensitive -- but it is chosen anyway and a 'sensitivity control' incorporated. The proposed system embodiment is checked against the 'specified goals' and appears acceptable.

'Solution optimization' is now attempted. The proposed apparatus is looked at carefully through the eyes of the airline employees who would use it as well as the potential hijacker. You observe that if electric power were off temporarily on the ground, it would be possible for a potential hijacker to board undetected. Since the proposed apparatus would be all solid state circuits with low power drain, the proposed system is modified to include an emergency battery operated supply. Various battery types and characteristics are investigated now so as to be sure the proposed circuit will perform. A specific proposed schematic emerges along with a proposed packaging embodiment scheme which will permit installation in a narrow aisle through which passengers thread.

Parts and materials are accumulated, and under your direction several technicians and model shop people assemble a working model for you. You discover they require constant attention. Finally the model is through construction. The first laboratory tests are only mildly successful. It will only detect objects the size of small anvils! The sensitivity is increased after considerable 'fiddling' with the circuitry. It is now capable of detecting pocket knives but not smaller objects. You decide the basic system and circuitry embodiment is sound and would detect knives and firearms on the person of a potential hijacker. Arrangements are made for a trial at the ramp of your client's airline. After 3 months testing the statistics are convincing to you.

The 'convince others' phase is now entered. Your manager, the client's representative, and the manager of engineering for the airline firm are recognized as the key people. A strategy is conceived for a meeting to be attended by them at the terminal where the trial detector is installed. The apparatus is

seen in action. Results of tests are reviewed.
Questions are answered. Opposition to the
proposed larger-scale replication is met and
overcome by you. The airline representatives
decide to instal similar systems company wide.

Your professional 'output' from applying
disciplined creativity has yielded a *new*
detection system. You have the unspeakable
joy of having your new creation accepted
and used! You have contributed significantly.
Subsequently other airline companies adopt
your system with minor modifications. You are
asked to present technical papers highlighting
the newly created system. You later go on
to solving engineering problems in other areas
of human need.

(Note: To convey an overview of the six-
step approach the above example has largely
omitted the difficulties. Realistic
creative engineering problem solving is seldom
so kind. We shall treat these matters more
realistically in future chapters.)

*"In order to be
effective over
a span of
time you must
either be
effective in
all steps of
the innovative
process, or
you must
get yourself
tied in with
an outfit
which is
strong in all
steps."*
*Jack A. Morton
[220, p105]*

Though the previous example used the six-step

disciplined creative approach on an electrical

systems problem, proper application of it to

problems in mechanical, civil, chemical and other

engineering areas can also produce new creative

solutions. The approach, after practice (the

endless important subject of creative engineering

'practice' is beyond our scope here), can also

be used in engineering research to operations areas

for solving problems from the naive to the extremely

complex. After practice a creative individual

applies it, or some near equivalent, reflexively.

Many students and engineers have used it to create

new engineering products which afterwards even

they were amazed they could have created! It

has withstood the test of time by many who have

mastered its use in solving engineering problems

bordering on the rim of present knowledge. It

is the quintessence of disciplined creativity.

Because of its crucial importance, we shall

devote Chaps. 4-9 to the approach shown in Fig. 3-1

with one chapter per step explaining that step or

phase in detail. Chapter 4 deals with the first

step.

Discussion Topics

1. Are there any missing or unneeded steps in the
   principal approach?

2. Discuss the possibility of *an* engineer omitting
   some of the steps in the principal approach,
   e.g. for situations where someone else, perhaps
   in another organization, has already done the
   first two steps.

3. Explore the possibility that you may be more
   effective as an individual in some of the phases
   than others. What can be done about those on
   which you are weak? Now reexamine Morton's quote.

4. If disciplined creative problem solving is a
   sequence of orderly steps as shown in Fig. 3-1,
   where does the 'flash of inspiration' commonly
   associated with the birth of a new idea fit
   into this morphology?

5. If the six-step disciplined problem solving
   approach advocated is of such great importance
   to the creative engineer, *why* hasn't such an
   approach been made plain and generally
   taught in other engineering courses before
   arriving at your present educational level?

6. It often seems that engineers wait for a new idea to occur, see if there is any need for it, and finally define or specify it. Explain *why* this situation might exist. Contrast the efficiency of that approach with the principal disciplined approach advocated in the text.

7. Discuss differences, if any, between the engineer being creative in general vs being creative in *specific* senses in meeting human needs. Can the principal approach be helpful in the specific sense?

8. Discuss how, ideally, within a modern engineering based corporation creative proposals by *individual* engineers might be brought to the awareness level of management.

9. How is personal experience and practice with the six-step approach related to maximizing our η?

Exercises

3-E8. a. List the steps in the 'six-step approach' advocated in the text.

        b. Write out your own brief description of what is done in each step.

3-E9. Study Olken's paper, "Creativity Training for Engineers – Its Past, Present, and Future," in Appendix I. Compare in a summarized written form his "two main phases" of the creative process with the principal approach advocated in this text.

3-E10. Think about your needs for practice in applying the **six**-step approach. In writing:
        a. Identify your weakest steps needing practice.
        b. How are the feedback paths in Fig. 3-1 related to engineering judgment and prior experience in applying the approach?
        c. Explore how your future problem solving failure--in one or several steps--may be related to your presently practicing the approach.
        d. Inventors strongly emphasize 'persistence.' How are persistence and practice abilities related to Fig. 3-1? To our η?

3-E11. List all the topics you think a universal creative problem solving approach should encompass.

3-E12. List specific topics relevant to the chapter title which were not discussed but which you feel should have been included.

Chapter Summary

● Engineering efficiency 'equations' were shown in which 'problem solving approach' was a principal factor.

● Our previous approach, a 'one-problem-one-solution' type applicable to textbook problems, was seen to be suboptimal for a lifetime of making *significant* creative contributions to engineering.

● The engineer's need for progressing to a more advanced stage involving multiple approaches to *new* problems requiring creativity was laid bare.

● Several significant approaches to problem solving were summarized and compared.

● The 'six-step disciplined creative approach' advocated in this text was revealed in a perspective sense. Future chapters will treat each step individually.

CHAPTER 4

DISCIPLINE OF PROBLEM INQUIRY

" -- the creating of the problem is as big an invention
as the solving of the problem--sometimes, a much greater
invention."

Jacob Rabinow [266, p84]

● The need for a 'problem inquiry' major phase.

● A morphological model for systematically
guiding thought during 'problem inquiry.'

● Some guides.

● Common failures.

In Chap. 3 we saw the engineer's need for an

ordered problem solving methodology. The 'six-step

disciplined approach' advocated in this text was

presented in an overall simplified form. Having

seen the overall process, we now closely examine

the first major phase, 'Problem Inquiry.'

Chapters 5-9 will treat each remaining phase

similarly.

*"I often think we
have so many facili-
ties that we lose
track of the prob-
lem. Problems, as
you know, are solved
in the mind of some
intensely interested
person."
Charles F.
Kettering
[173, p57]*

Throughout our study of this and subsequent major

phases we shall be examining 'behind the scenes' com-

plex and *highly personal* processes for what the engineer

may think, feel, and do in order to creatively solve

his engineering problem(s). The viewpoint is markedly

different from 'how it looks when published'. Thus

we shall look beneath the facade to get at the basic

creative thought process. Frequent reference to the

creative problem solver's personal attitudes and

characteristics necessarily must enter our discussion
along the way.

For our initial learning purposes, we attempt to
clearly separate the impersonal problem solving process steps from the more personal thoughts of the
creative problem solver. After later acquiring skill
in practicing creative engineering work, you
will see that such a division is artificial with

*" - - a problem in
the stage of being
'recognized' is a
highly emotional
subject."
John R. M. Alger
Carl V. Hays
[4, p13]*

lines of distinction actually being more diffuse.
Thus *the mature creative problem solver tends to become
deeply involved PERSONALLY with the steps in the
problem solving process.* Personal involvement is
desirable, necessary, and unavoidable because of the
nature of creative work.

4-1 <u>Need</u> <u>and</u> <u>Purposes</u> <u>for</u> 'Problem Inquiry' Phase

*"To be aware that
a problem exists
is the prerequi-
site for any
attempt to solve
the problem."
A. G. Fredrickson
[110, p148]*

An engineer confronted with a significant situation of a non-textbook type problem requiring truly
new creative thought may, by prior education, vaguely
sense that the first thing to do in assaulting the
situation is to 'determine what the problem is'. *How*
he is to go about defining the problem ("Where do
I start?") is even more vague, especially if the
situation is complex, bristling with conflicts, nothing
seems well defined, or interdisciplinary work appears
involved.

From a different view, astute observation of your

"Much effort is wasted in the attempt to do something which does not need to be done."
John H. Barr
[25, p105]

" - - they are few who look into the depths."
Baltasar Gracian
[127, p95]

contemporary engineering scene may reveal 'solutions' which have been created, at great expense, which perhaps should never have been created had a *thorough* initial inquiry been made into the basic need the 'solution' was *supposed* to have fulfilled but doesn't. The 'solution' was created because the problem solver felt compelled to create a solution--any solution-- omitting the important difficult initial steps and questions involved in a thorough in-depth inquiry into *the problem.*

From yet another viewpoint, the thinking pro- fessional engineer has to personally deal with the questions, "Can I honestly afford to risk my or my employer's effort, time, resources, and reputation creating a 'solution' for 'the problem' without being *sure* I am working on the right problem? Suppose I create 'a solution' after x years/months/weeks at a net cost of y mega/kilo/dollars only to *then* discover I was working on the *wrong* problem? What net contribution have I made to humanity *then*? Can I possibly justify *not* being sure I am working on the *right* problem by not executing a thorough examination of all plausible definitions of the problem?"

We quickly sense the subsequent waste, inefficiency, and failure possibilities for the engineer when a careful deliberate initial inquiry into THE PROBLEM is omitted. The necessity for a 'problem inquiry' initial major phase is based on study, reflection, and

generalization of the problem solving experiences

of many creative engineers and inventors.

Its principal purpose is:

> ● Purpose of 'Problem Inquiry' Phase:
>
> To determine and validate the best problem definition for the given initial situation.

A systems view of this initial phase is shown

in Fig. 4-1.

Its relationship to the other major phases of

disciplined creativity was seen in Fig. 3-1. Obser-

vations about this phase:

"I try to get a picture of the situation that an invention applies to - -"
G. E. Howard
[156, p71]

● Input to the phase is a 'situation', defined as "one's position with regard to conditions and circumstances." [360, p121]. In the most general sense *the problem solver always enters the phase with 'a situation' from which he must find 'the problem'*. Only for relatively simple problems (of a typical 'textbook' type) does one initiate the problem solving process with the input being a known clearly defined problem. By far the majority of engineering problems of a *significant* nature requiring creative solutions are begun with 'a situation' rather than 'the problem'. We have already acquired a preliminary feeling for 'the situation' in Example 3-1.

"To deal with the future, we must perceive the un-perceived - - -"
George B. Leonard
[189, p52]

● The 'Problem Inquiry' phase itself has, as its name suggests, the principal emphasis on *the problem*. Here the problem solver is concerned with finding what, in his judgment, the true problem appears to be when extracted from the complex situation. He initially seeks to identify and understand the basic need which a later solution to 'the problem' is to fulfill.

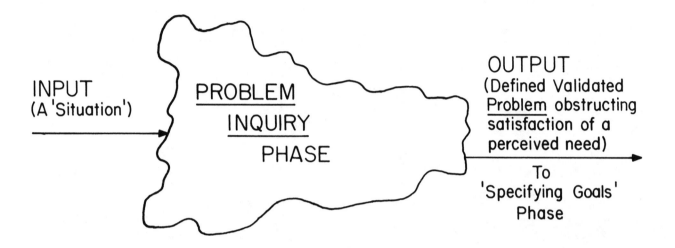

FIG. 4-1 Systems view of the first phase of
          the six-step disciplined problem
          solving approach of Fig. 3-1. The
          problem solver's emphasis in this
          phase is on *the problem* rather than
          'the solution.'

"In inventing, the
first step is to
ascertain what type
of invention is
needed to fill a
certain need."
  R. S. Bassett
  [32]

"His (Kettering's)
principal point is
that if one is to
have a productive
career in science,
one must have some
well-defined ob-
jective, whether
this be the develop-
ment of a better
engine, the split-
ting of the atom,
or the discovery of
a better means for
the control of
cancer."
  C. P. Rhoads
  [276, p185]

He examines THE PROBLEM from many viewpoints. Typically he finds that what he or others initially thought was 'the problem' is not really the problem after all. He soon learns that achieving problem understanding is not the same as achieving solution understanding.

The irregular outline of the phase shown in Fig. 4-1 symbolizes the abstractness, lack of form, roughness, and uncertainty in the initial situation. The fact that the problem definition becomes clearer toward the end of the phase is symbolized by a converging tendency with considerably less uncertainty than existed when we began it.

● The output consists principally of the clearly defined problem, which has been written, analyzed, and validated. Additionally, the basic need has been identified and verified which could be met were the problem solved. Other important facts about the problem are also known here, as we shall see in Sec. 4-2.

We need to clearly understand that the output of the 'problem inquiry' phase is not 'the solution' to the problem, though we should have a conception of a broad area within which we later expect to create a solution.

Hopefully a workable understanding of this important initial major phase of problem solving will accrue as we examine details in Sec. 4-2.

Discussion Topics

1. Will all engineers confronted with an identical 'situation' formulate the same problem?

2. Distinguish 'the situation' and 'the problem'.

3. If your engineering manager hands you a 'problem' to be solved, is it really best to plunge in solving it without inquiring into why it is a problem in the first place?

4. "That is management's job to 'inquire into the problem'. They know what the best definitions are! The engineer's function is to just create solutions for problems given to him by his management." Discuss.

5. "It is always clear what 'the problem' is, so
    it is a waste to spend time boring into it."
    Discuss.

6. Cite a specific example of a product created by
    engineers which was supposed to fill a need but
    failed to do so. Was creative effort wasted?
    Could a careful 'problem inquiry' have avoided
    it?

7. The 'purpose' statement in the text seems to
    imply that the definition of an engineering
    problem may change if the initial 'situation'
    later changes. Discuss.

Exercises

*"To jog the under-
standing is a
greater feat than
to jog the
memory; - - "
Baltasar Gracian
[127, p71]*

4-E1. Select the textbook of an engineering subject
       you took which interested you. Determine the
       percentage of problems or exercises therein
       which pose 'a situation' from which *you* are
       to determine what the real *problem* is. (*Not*
       the 'solution'!) How do you account for *why*
       emphasis has principally been on 'the solution'
       rather than 'the problem'?

4-E2. Focus on the situation of teaching laboratories
       in your engineering discipline at your institution.
       Clearly define in writing at least three significant
       'problems' needing creative thought. Justify
       each problem.

4-E3. Inquire within your engineering discipline *how*
       the need is recognized for writing a new
       textbook in (a) a well established course (b)
       an emerging new technical area for which no
       textbooks exist.

4-2 **What the Problem Solver Does in the 'Problem Inquiry'
Phase**

PHASE MORPHOLOGY The previous Sec. conveyed

functional understanding of the 'problem inquiry'

major phase. Such understanding is necessary but not

sufficient. We now treat in limited detail the

structure, concepts, and some things the problem

solver might think, feel, or do while thinking-through

this phase. Such details are needed to successfully

apply the morphology to a specific real-life

engineering situation.

Figure 4-2 shows a morphological guide for the

'problem inquiry' phase. *IT IS THE HEART OF THE*

SUBJECT. The word *guide* is emphasized.

The model is intended to be used as a guide

("What do I do next?") in the sense of conveying

'here is an ordered method for how I *might* proceed

during the phase'. We do not intend to imply that

it is the *only* way the phase could be structured;

but the particular structure shown has the merit of

lending a plausible articulated order to a major

"There is apparently a great inertia or resistance in the average person to initiate the innovating process."
Joseph Rossman
[279, p98]

part of problem solving which at best is difficult

and at its worst tends toward hopeless chaos if some

structured means of proceeding is not adopted. It

further contains all the important steps and issues

which are relevant to this major phase--steps and

issues with which I must deal when seriously inquiring

into a particular 'problem' of significance. Finally,

following the order indicated in the chart may be

helpful in insuring that I don't accidentally fail

to deal with an important problem facet which I might

overlook without some guide.

We shall frequently refer to this important

figure. Volumes could be written about parts of it.

They in fact have been, e.g. the fields of technical
marketing and patents to name only two. We shall deal
with the figure only in enough detail to convey a
working knowledge for application to your specific
engineering problem(s). You may later creatively
explore its full implications.

The 'problem inquiry' phase attempts to
sequentially answer the important questions:

"Your questions
can control the
solution of a
problem."
Edward Hodnett
[151, p35]

● What is the basic need?

● What is the basic problem?

● Is it worth solving?

● Is it probably solvable?

● Should I/we solve it?

The flow chart sub-divides each question into
tractable steps. A column beneath each step lists
a number of actions we might take. These
are in the approximate sequence for dealing
with each item. The sequence is not rigid.
The items in the columns and the steps in
the flow chart are thus tentative in nature as we
flexibly and creatively deal with our specific
engineering 'problem'.

We shall now briefly explain each principal step
in Fig. 4-2, citing specific engineering examples
as we proceed.

Problem Awareness is the beginning of the entire

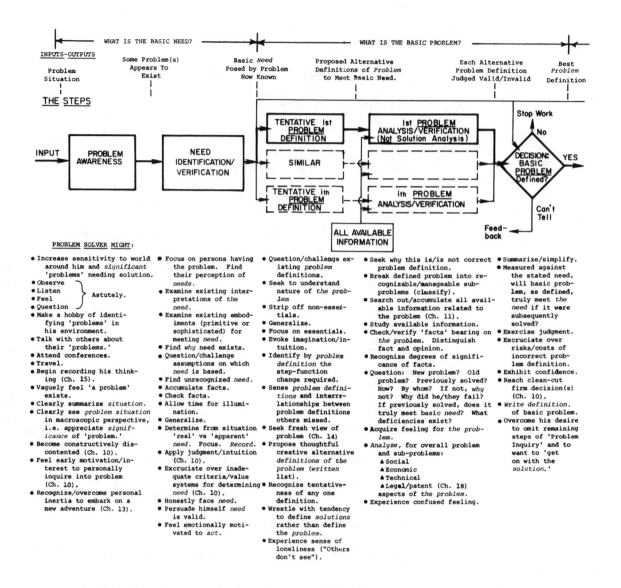

FIG. 4-2   Morphological model guide for the 'Problem Inquiry' phase. This is
an exploded view of FIG. 4-1 and of the first major phase of the
six-step disciplined creative approach shown in FIG. 3-1. The
principal emphasis for the problem solver is on *the problem*
rather than 'the solution.'

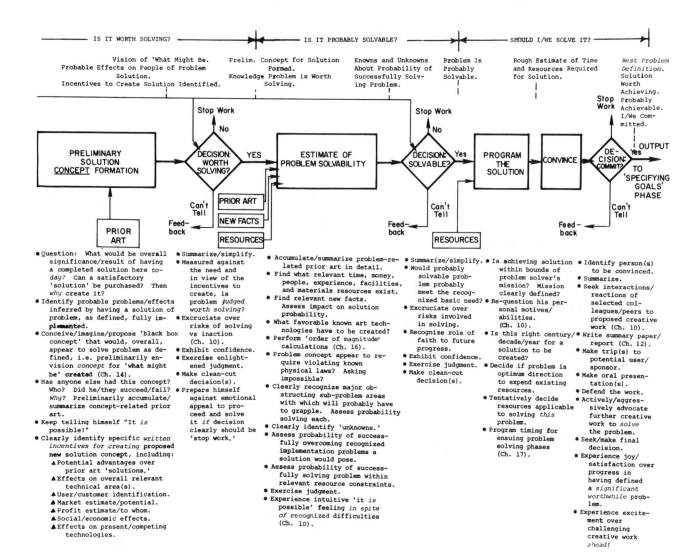

Vision of 'What Might Be.
Probable Effects on People of Problem
Solution.
Incentives to Create Solution Identified.

Prelim. Concept for Solution
Formed.
Knowledge Problem is Worth
Solving.

Knowns and Unknowns
About Probability of
Successfully Solv-
ing Problem.

Problem Is
Probably
Solvable.

Rough Estimate of Time
and Resources Required
for Solution.

*Best Problem
Definition.*
Solution
Worth
Achieving.
Probably
Achievable.
I/We Com-
mitted.

PRELIMINARY SOLUTION CONCEPT FORMATION → **DECISION: WORTH SOLVING?** — YES → **ESTIMATE OF PROBLEM SOLVABILITY** → **DECISION: SOLVABLE?** — Yes → **PROGRAM THE SOLUTION** → **CONVINCE** → **DECISION: COMMIT?** — Yes → OUTPUT TO 'SPECIFYING GOALS' PHASE

Stop Work — No (for each decision)

PRIOR ART

Can't Tell / Feed-back

PRIOR ART / NEW FACTS / RESOURCES

RESOURCES

- Question: What would be overall significance/result of having a completed solution here *to-day*? Can a satisfactory 'solution' be purchased? Then *why* create it?
- Identify probable problems/effects inferred by having a solution of problem, as defined, fully im-plemented.
- Conceive/imagine/propose 'black box concept' that would, overall, appear to solve problem as de-fined, i.e. preliminarily en-vision *concept* for 'what might be' created (Ch. 14).
- Has anyone else had this concept? Who? Did he/they succeed/fail? Why? Preliminarily accumulate/ summarize concept-related prior art.
- Keep telling himself "It *is* possible!"
- Clearly identify specific *written incentives* for creating **proposed new solution concept**, including:
  ▲ Potential advantages over prior art 'solutions.'
  ▲ Effects on overall relevant technical area(s).
  ▲ User/customer identification.
  ▲ Market estimate/potential.
  ▲ Profit estimate/to whom.
  ▲ Social/economic effects.
  ▲ Effects on present/competing technologies.

- Summarize/simplify.
- Measured against the need and in view of the incentives to create, is problem *judged worth solving*?
- Excruciate over risks of solving vs inaction (Ch. 10).
- Exhibit confidence.
- Exercise enlight-ened judgment.
- Make clean-cut decision(s).
- Prepare himself against emotional appeal to pro-ceed and solve it *if* decision clearly should be 'stop work.'

- Accumulate/summarize problem-re-lated prior art in detail.
- Find what relevant time, money, people, experience, facilities, and materials resources exist.
- Find relevant new facts. Assess impact on solution probability.
- What favorable known art tech-nologies have to be created?
- Perform 'order of magnitude' calculations (Ch. 16).
- Problem concept appear to re-quire violating known physical laws? Asking impossible?
- Clearly recognize major ob-structing sub-problem areas with which will probably have to grapple. Assess probability solving each.
- Clearly identify 'unknowns.'
- Assess probability of success-fully overcoming recognized implementation problems a solution would pose.
- Assess probability of success-fully solving problem within relevant resource constraints.
- Exercise judgment.
- Experience intuitive 'it *is* possible' feeling *in spite of* recognized difficulties (Ch. 10).

- Summarize/simplify.
- Would probably solvable prob-lem probably meet the recog-nized basic need?
- Excruciate over risks involved in solving.
- Recognize role of faith to future progress.
- Exhibit confidence.
- Exercise judgment.
- Make clean-cut decision(s).

- Is achieving solution within bounds of problem solver's mission? Mission clearly defined?
- Re-question his per-sonal motives/ abilities. (Ch. 10).
- Is this right century/ decade/year for a solution to be created?
- Decide if problem is optimum direction to expend existing resources.
- Tentatively decide resources applicable to solving *this* problem.
- Program timing for ensuing problem solving phases (Ch. 17).

- Identify person(s) to be convinced.
- Summarize.
- Seek interactions/ reactions of selected col-leagues/peers to proposed creative work (Ch. 10).
- Write summary paper/ report (Ch. 12).
- Make trip(s) to potential user/ sponsor.
- Make oral presen-tation(s).
- Defend the work.
- Actively/aggres-sively advocate further creative work to *solve* the problem.
- Seek/make final decision.
- Experience joy/ satisfaction over progress in having defined a *significant worthwhile* prob-lem.
- Experience excite-ment over challenging creative work *ahead!*

creative thought process. The implication here is that I, in the total 'situation' and environment in which I find myself, become sensitive to the situation to the extent that *I become aware of the SIGNIFICANT engineering problems* ('Problem' was defined in Sec. 3-1. It is also sometimes defined as 'a perplexity' or a 'state of disorder'.) which literally surround me and cry out for creative solutions. To say 'significant' implies a recognition and selection process has occurred in my mind. A highly creative engineer is typically sensitively aware of his total situation, of events in his immediate world, of events in the macroscopic sense, and of his personal reactions to the situation, and is able to classify, sort, and order these so as to be conscious of the *significant* problems.

It is *here* at the very beginning that *the engineer may become very discontented with the perceived situation. His discontent motivates him to action in a CONSTRUCTIVE way* to deal with the situation. We call this observable phenomenon *constructive discontent.*

Example 4-1

If I am truly *satisfied* with the 38 percent coal-to-electricity conversion efficiency of an electrical generation plant, it is unlikely I will ever create a higher efficiency non-polluting plant, perhaps based on new principles.

"There is no question but that 'problem sensitivity' is a prime requisite of the creative person, and that it must be closely tied up with the development of a 'questioning attitude'."
  John E. Arnold
  [11, p252]

" - - even in the fields most successfully exploited, the ground has only been broken."
  Nikola Tesla
  [338]

"He is unhappy with things as they are and wants to change them. He is a non-conformist. He is dissatisfied with what he finds and wants to improve things."
 Joseph Rossman
 [279, p49]

It is thus clear that an important early ingredient of *successful* creative problem solving is personal *discontent* of a CONSTRUCTIVE nature. It is frequently surprising how many people in the engineer's environment fail to understand and appreciate the absolute *necessity* for the creative engineer to become thoroughly and genuinely discontented with the situation he perceives as a necessary prelude to *constructive* thought and action.

Experience indicates that the engineer's problem awareness ability can be enhanced with practice by deliberately engaging in activities of the kind indicated in the column under 'Problem Awareness', Fig. 4-2.

"Necessity is the cause of many inventions but the best ones are born of desire."
 G. Marconi
 [199]

At the output of 'problem awareness' one or more 'problems' appear to exist. We do not yet know *what* the problem is or indeed what the significant *need* is which 'the problem', which is only here vaguely coming into focus, is intended to alleviate.

Example 4-2

A manufacturing engineer suddenly becomes aware of a problem. His production people are having difficulty assembling the new compact electronic power supply released by engineering for a pilot run.

Discussion Topics

1. How can engineers be stimulated to aggressively become aware of product improvement possibilities rather than passively accept the problems forced upon them by field complaints, manufacturing difficulties, or competition?

2. What is the probability of your creating a
    truly *new* concept without being first discon-
    tented with the perceived situation?

Exercises

4-E4. List specific new improvements to a
       screwdriver.

4-E5. Select an area of specialization in your engineering
       discipline which *interests* you. Find one *original*
       research paper or report on that specialty. Study
       it. Write out, in 3 sentences or less:

       a. What technological advance does this
           paper present?

       b. What *new* invention problem does this
           paper suggest to you?

       c. Do many authors fail to clearly expose
           new problems suitable for creative
           attack?

4-E6. Arrange to 'spend the day' with one of your
       professors. Prepare a list of the significant
       new problems of which you became aware.

*"I invent by first
finding out a need
or demand . ."*
Jerome Alexander
[3, p108]

NEED IDENTIFICATION/VERIFICATION is the next step
in Fig. 4-2. From the totality of 'the situation'
the creative engineer deliberately seeks to determine
the basic NEED posed by 'the situation', to bring that
need into a state of consciousness, and to verify that
the need is genuine and significant. My need for
penetratingly questioning, generalizing, finding the
'real' vs 'apparent' need, and applying good engineering
judgment particularly stand out here. It is also
clear that *different engineers may identify differing*
needs.

*"I didn't hang
around much with
other inventors or
the executive
fellows. I lived
with the sales
gang. They had
some real notion
of what people
wanted."*
Charles F. Kettering
[174, p53]

It may seem trite to emphasize the importance
of this early step in the creative problem solving

process, 'need identification/verification'. Yet,

an historical case could be made for how individual

and corporate fortunes have been unnecessarily

wasted because of failure to carefully, thoroughly,

and penetratingly perform this step. Rossman's careful

pioneering study [279] of 710 active inventors

repeatedly indicates the individual inventor's need

for clearly initially identifying 'the need' before

involvement in the detailed problem solving process.

Subsequent extended experience and observation of

creative engineers in modern corporate environments

also underscores the step's importance.

"The importance of establishing the need can hardly be overstated. Too often an organization will plunge into a project and develop a technical success while achieving a financial failure because the assumed need was ephemeral and disappeared in the light of reality."
 Morris Asimow
 [12, p18]

Example 4-3

A creative engineer in 'the situation' of
being employed with a Utility Co. in the planning
department identifies the need a city will have
in x years for energy. He verifies the need
by a careful study of per capita, per household,
and total system energy needs in past years and
judiciously extrapolates his curves to predict
probable future energy requirements.

It is very easy for the problem solver to slip

into fuzzy, unstructured thinking at this point and

confuse 'the need' with 'the problem definition' or

'the solution' or other factors. In Example 4-3 the

utility engineer possibly would identify the

city's energy need as synonymous with

electric energy and building another power

plant ('solution' oriented). A more creative

engineer would question the validity of the

"What is required, rather, is a sense of proportion and priorities geared to the real needs of man and to the hard facts of his existence on this planet."
 A. G. Fredrickson
 [110, p125]

electric assumption and back up in his thinking
to recognize "the human *need* is total energy--of *all*
kinds." He would then examine *total* energy in the
forms of electric, gas, petroleum, solar, human,
biological and others. He would also want to know *why*
the energy is needed, what is to be done with it,
and whether it will be efficiently utilized and by
what sectors of society. His sense of the
significance of the problem situation and the need
posed by it will therefore be considerably broader
and in more depth than the first engineer. Further,
by thus generalizing the problem, he may open many
more creative possibilities for later meeting the
future energy needs of the city than if he restricted
the need identification to 'electric energy only'.
Also generalizing assists him to *understand the*
larger 'problem' posed by 'the need'.

The step terminates with a written statement
of the TRUE need posed by 'the situation', as perceived
by the problem solver. A summary of the factual bases
and arguments which appear to verify the correctness
of the need may also be included.

Example 4-4

"There is a basic macroscopic human need in
the forseeable future for converting the radiant
energy of the sun into electricity. Approximately
1 kw/m^2 impinges normally on the earth's surface
on a cloudless day. The energy is wasted as heat.
The total known supply of fossil fuels is estimated

" - - putting it on
paper for a cold
appraisal of the
implications of
each phase can
show how little
we really know
about what is
wanted."
  Eugene K. Von
  Fange
  [360, p139]

to be exhausted in x years, leaving the sun's radiant energy as a major energy source for supplying the world's estimated population of y billions by z date."

Discussion Topics

1. Discuss how a creative engineer with a firm might assign priorities and choose a 'need' on which to focus for 'problem inquiry'.

2. Identify some of the personal difficulties the engineer may encounter in recognizing and verifying 'the need'.

3. Both the text and Fig. 4-2 advocate the engineer's need for 'generalizing'. What is a 'generalization'? When should the engineer use it in his work? Are there dangers involved in 'generalizing'? Identify.

4. Can the engineering problem solver overdo the questioning approach? Identify probable consequences of doing so on his relations with others in the problem environment.

TENTATIVE PROBLEM DEFINITIONS are now proposed in view of the stated need as the next step in Fig. 4-2.

"You have to identify the real problem, and you have to identify the total problem."
Edward Hodnett
[151, p12]

" - - how strong the temptation is to seize mentally on some concept of hardware that seems to provide a feasible solution before the real problem is understood, - -"
Morris Asimow
[12, p20]

To propose discerning alternate tentative definitions of the problem can be a considerable chore. *It usually requires hard creative thinking* to strip off non-essentials, to generalize the problem in its full scope--itself an act of divergent thinking--, to work my imagination to the point where I can *identify the desired step-function change by the tentative problem definition*, and finally to experience beauty and a sense of loneliness by glimpsing the possibilities latent in a truly new definition of the problem--a definition perhaps not perceived by those preceding me.

Example 4-5

Assume I am a creative engineer with a forward looking utility company in the situation of inquiring into the future electric energy demands which will likely be required. I have previously carefully defined the need as:

'More energy must be made available to customers'.

Guided by Fig. 4-2, I might now tentatively define my 'problem' in several ways:

"It is dangerous to particularize a problem too soon, because this kind of early definition may mean that the broad scope inherent in the situation will never be liberated. Premature particularization is very often a symptom of an individual's concern with being impractical."
William J. J. Gordon [125, p140]

"His (the inventor's) versatility suggests new roads to travel which would not occur to the average person."
Joseph Rossman [279, p49]

1st Problem Definition: Generate more energy from present equipment.

2nd Problem Definition: Provide additional power generation capacity of conventional type.

3rd Problem Definition: Tie existing system in with interconnected area power network.

4th Problem Definition: Create a significantly higher overall conversion efficiency generation plant.

5th Problem Definition: Create a new means for converting the present 60 percent waste thermal heat into electricity.

6th Problem Definition: Create a nuclear power plant.

7th Problem Definition: Create on-site independent multiple power generators.

8th Problem Definition: Create a new type non-polluting generation means based on converting solar energy to electricity.

From Example 4-5 we observe insights into 'problem definition':

● <u>Generalizing</u> in broad terms may be involved. Such generalizing is both desirable and necessary.

● <u>Multiple definitions</u> of the problem usually exist. The creative problem solver's task is to bring them *all* into consciousness. To do so is an act of creative synthesis. 'Formula-type thinking' is inappropriate here. The problem solver who thinks only in terms of one or two alternative definitions may be seriously handicapping himself, his firm, and society in a long term sense.

● There <u>are *WIDE* differences</u> between the problem definitions. If the desired step-function change is decided to be the 8th definition and this is later pursued, I most certainly will *not* create improvements to the present equipment as in definition 1!

● The <u>language</u> used in the problem definition statement becomes important. Much excrueiation may be required for me to say precisely what I *mean*.

● The <u>engineer</u> does <u>not</u> have to 'close his eyes' to alternative problem definitions, focus on one, commit to it hastily, spend x megadollars, and *then* discover, "There were *other* definitions of the problem which I should have explored earlier before committing to this wrong approach."

● The <u>'means'</u> suggested by the language of defining the problem are *not* being 'designed' or 'created'. That may or may not come later. Rather, here it is more like "Let us 'play' with this *new definition* of the problem and inquire if it may lead us to a new, unique, and useful creation for meeting the perceived need."

" - - there are many cases on record where the problem statement was ambiguous or ill conceived, and after thousands of dollars had been spent, the solution was abandoned because it didn't solve the real problem. So, time spent in the problem statement to be sure what the problem is could turn out to be the most important step of all."
  Chester M. Sinnett
  [298, p4]

"Problem solving is dealing in futures."
  Edward Hodnett
  [151, p39]

<u>Discussion Topics</u>

1. Figure 4-2 suggests 'strip off non-essentials'. Is there danger in *over*simplifying the definition of an engineering problem? *How* can one tell if he is oversimplifying?

2. 'Problem inquiry', among other things, is aimed at achieving problem understanding. Discuss differences, if any, between *problem* understanding and *solution* understanding.

3. Discuss the role imagination plays in 'defining the problem'.

"The importance of first gathering and studying the data necessary to focus our efforts cannot be over-emphasized."
  Eugene K. Von Fange [360, p150]

PROBLEM ANALYSIS/VERIFICATION follows the creative act of posing alternative problem definitions in Fig. 4-2. *Each proposed definition is carefully and critically examined.*

Example 4-6

As a circuit development engineer in the early phase of the 6AJ4/6AM4 Ultra High Frequency amplifier tube development, the need for creating tube test equipment* for manufacturing had been recognized. The power gain of every tube made was to be measured. I defined the alternative problem definitions as:

a. Make no measurements of tube power gain at 900Mhz.

b. Replicate an existing laboratory apparatus.

c. Create new gain test apparatus based on totally new principles.

Briefly the problem analysis/verification thinking went respectively:

a. Following this course implies measuring μ, r_p and g_m is enough to certify each tube will predictably amplify at 900 Mhz. Did we know enough about the tube-circuit equivalent circuit to reliably predict 900 Mhz gain from low frequency measurements? No, we didn't!

"It is important that the analysis be quantitative as well as qualitative."
  Joseph Rossman [279, p53]

b. The apparatus, though accurate, was very tricky to operate. It appeared only I could operate it. At best I could only measure 20 tubes/day--far too slow and costly for 100 percent testing in a factory producing hundreds/day.

---

*The 'test equipment' subject occurs frequently in engineering.

c. This approach would demand scrapping our prior-art laboratory gain test apparatus and procedures and creating new apparatus based on fresh different principles. It would take time and cost money to create-- if it could even be done.

You have to ask a precise question to get a precise answer."
    Edward Hodnett
    [151, p37]

Why even measure power gain at all? Because it was known to be a significant engineering parameter for a radio frequency amplifier. Is some other parameter *also* significant? Yes, the noise figure. Could noise figure and gain measurement apparatus be combined? No, we would probably have to create a separate test set for noise figure. (A colleague did so.)

I spent a few days examining available microwave books and journals seeking to find if anyone else had previously encountered a similar power gain measurement problem. Not much of value resulted.

What kind of people would probably have to operate the to-be-created test set? A chat with the engineer responsible for factory testing turned up the answer--relatively inexperienced young girls.

"Progress in the practical and scientific fields is a slow correction of wrong assumptions."
    Edward Hodnett
    [151, p52]

Why is the laboratory gain test so slow? Because of the necessity of using slotted lines, tuning, impedance matching each tube, carefully setting the bandwidth to 10 Mhz and other complications. Is the experiential assumption that the gain measurement *has* to be slow and tedious valid? Probably not. Is there any hope of significantly simplifying the laboratory apparatus so it could be operated by an 18 year old girl? No, not even by pushing my creative ability to the limit. A fresh approach appeared required.

Pursuing definition (c) further, I decided to break the power gain test set problem into the sub-problems:

a. Amplifier circuit

b. Power flow detector

c. Auxiliary apparatus

Clearly all three would have to be created.

Why had no one previously created such a power gain test set? UHF mass produced amplifier tubes had not existed until our development engineering group created them!

The technical aspects posed by problem definition (c) above would be formidable. There appeared to be no known proven means for achieving such a test set, and few people appeared to have creatively addressed the power gain measurement problem.

" - - much trouble
comes from the
difficulty of
putting the right
meaning on the
facts you do have."
Edward Hodnett
[151, p43]

It was clear creating a 900 Mhz power gain test set would have a significant favorable effect on the later manufacture and sales of tubes for the UHF television market if *it* were to blossom. Without a power gain test set we could not be reasonably certain of product quality.

" - - frequently the
most fruitful areas
for the scholar
are in those inde-
finable locations
somewhere along
the diffuse
boundaries of
more clearly
recognized
sciences."
Joseph H. Simons
[294]

I begin to experience a confused feeling which I analyzed to be caused by entering a problem area where facts and knowledge were *not* clearly ordered. I also recognized that the general line of thinking and inquiry was on, near, or beyond the boundaries of the then present art. Additionally, there was uncertainty in my mind about "What is ahead in this area where few appear to have thought? (I later had the immense satisfaction of successfully creating the 900 Mhz power gain test set and seeing it extensively used.)

In Problem Analysis/Verification:

● A questing attitude permeates the thinking.

● Information about 'the problem' *and* existing solutions may be found intermixed as 'all available information' is collected and sifted. The information usually is not exhaustively and meticulously complete here (Is it *ever*?).

● The principal emphasis is on *the problem* and understanding *it* rather than focusing on and analyzing the known solutions, if any exist.

● Focus is on the broader problem obstructing realizing a solution.

- It _may_ _be_ _necessary_ _to_ '_feed_ _back_' and restate the ith problem definition in the form of a more specific basic problem. _That_ problem may be the one to which I should apply my creative energies--assuming that the revised definition later successfully competes in my mind with the _other_ analyzed/verified definitions of 'the problem'. Several restatements may be made as problem understanding grows.

- The '_problem_ _definition_' is _not_ stated in terms of an implied solution. Thus our creative abilities can be given full range in the later major step, 'determining means'.

- _My_ _personal_ _attitudes_ _and_ _characteristics_ markedly influence the analysis/verification step. If I fail to have imagination here, I can easily invent excuses for _not_ pursuing the ith problem definition further. If I am lazy, I may fail to avail myself of _all_ available information and therefore decide to kill a problem definition pregnant with creative possibilities. Different creative engineers will analyze/verify the ith problem in different ways and depths.

DECISION ON DEFINING THE PROBLEM, Fig. 4-2, is essential to further progress. At this decisive step in 'problem inquiry' I generally have facing me i alternative problem definitions each of which has been analyzed and verified. From these _I must now decide WHICH appears to be the 'best' definition_ in view of the 'need' and the existing 'situation'.

"_We believe that the use of decision methods encourages creative endeavors._" _Martin Kenneth Starr_ [_313, Preface_]

'Decisions' are important to the creative engineer and repeatedly occur throughout the entire disciplined creative problem solving approach. Our situation tomorrow is determined partly by the decisions of today. We briefly identify the essential elements.

*"It is difficult
to say when you
are dealing with
a fact."
Edward Hodnett
[151, p46]*

A Decision is:

● Not possible without 'alternatives'. It
is generally desirable for the alternatives
to be based on facts.

● A private act by a person. Though the
problem solver may be influenced by others,
in the end he privately makes it in his
own personal way.

● Influenced by the total prior history of
the individual--his private thoughts,
values, feelings, intuitions, hopes,
aspirations, difficulties, environ-
ment--the total person (Chap. 10).

● Bound up with freedom concepts. To have
no alternatives or to have alternatives
tyrannically imposed for 'decisions' is not
freedom. (Freedom is treated in Chap. 10.)

● Accompanied by feelings of conflict. Only
rarely are conflicting elements absent in
engineering decision.

● Occasioned by personal excruciation over
weighing and trading off on conflicting
elements.

● Involved with the judgment capability of
the person, i.e. his ability to wisely
sum up and choose between alternatives.

● Occasioned by time passage. It may be
microseconds or years, but the time element
is always present and an essential ingredient.

● Accompanied by risk taking. The possibility of
'failure' is ever near. One seeks to *minimize*
risks by disciplined preparatory work before
reaching a decision. Risks are hardly ever
zero.

● May involve consequences for ourselves and
others. We should know them.

● A vital part of the creative process. Without
crisp correct decisions at critical points
progress of the creative work may be seriously
impeded, perhaps to zero.

*"A design decision
is therefore a very
complex problem."
Martin Kenneth
Starr [313, p2]*

*"To pursue an
ill-omened, un-
promising project
is to 'continue
forcing vitamins
and medicines
into a dead horse'."*
Thomas T. Woodson
[383, p57]

*"It is wise to
assemble and
compare several
good ideas before
selecting a par-
ticular new-pro-
duct possibility
for development."*
Gustav E. Larson
[186, p4]

Returning to the first decision step in Fig. 4-2,

I carefully summarize and simplify everything that I

have done and thought about for *each* alternative

definition of the problem. Having done so, *I now*

compare each definition individually against my earlier

basic 'need statement' in order to be SURE my problem

definition would alleviate the basic need if the problem,

as defined, were to be solved. Here it is not

unusual to discard some of the *i* problem definitions

which appear to *not* alleviate the basic need. Of the

definitions remaining, I now compare them against

each other. My goal is to decide which appears to be

the *best* definition--'appears' because we can never

truly *know* until much later when the problem is

solved and the creation is introduced to the market-

place. Even then we may not 'know'. The tentative-

ness of my actions is again underscored as I personally

struggle with trying to decide on the 'best' problem

definition.

Decision on the 'best' problem definition is

crucial, for the character of *all* the creative

engineering work to follow may be set here. A

creation may never come into being unless the problem

solving engineer *decides* to correctly define the

problem.

Clearly if there is no satisfactory problem defini-

tion, I must stop work. If I 'can't tell', I may

want to 'feedback' through one or more previous steps

and rethink them until I *am* able to make a satisfactory

decision with which I can personally live.

"Confidence in
one's analysis
of the facts is
perhaps the
secret to success-
ful action."
Phil Simpson
[295, p21]

Example 4-7

Today *I tentatively DECIDED*, after weighing
future world energy need considerations along
with other possible definitions, that my best
problem definition is:

> "Create a new type solar-electricity
> collection/conversion means poten-
> tially capable of supplying bulk power."

I now have some modest confidence that it
is the *correct* problem definition because of the
disciplined preparatory thinking about *the*
problem.

Discussion Topics

1. Figure 4-2 showed four major decisions are required
   in 'problem inquiry'. Discuss the nature of a
   'decision' and a 'conclusion'.

2. Discuss the probability of the engineer creating a
   truly new product/system if a clear decision of
   the problem definition has not been made. Consider
   President Kennedy's decision to send men to the
   moon as a discussion starter.

3. History clearly shows that many *finished* inventions
   are held up to initial ridicule and criticism. In
   view of that fact discuss the advisability of the
   creative engineer exposing his best problem
   definition. What effects on his problem solving
   ability will adverse criticism have here? Should
   he be modest or openly arrogant?

4. Consider an engineer in environments:

   a. Pressing for short term 'fixes'. He
      values not departing very far from
      'what we're doing now'.

   b. Pressing for long term permanent solutions.
      He values uniqueness, new creations,
      challenge of venturing into relatively
      uncharted areas, and has vision and
      imagination.

" ' - - is it worth
doing?' is the first
question he (Edison)
asks when faced with
a new problem."
  Joseph Rossman
  [279, p30]

Discuss how his 'environment' and his 'values'
influence the problem definition decision.

PRELIMINARY SOLUTION CONCEPT FORMATION is the

first step in Fig. 4-2 toward answering the important

question "Is it worth solving?" We are thinking in

a broad sense of "*Is the problem intrinsically worth*

solving?" We are asking, "If the problem, as defined,

were to be later solved would it constitute a net

contribution to humanity?" In general, it is difficult

to answer the larger question without first generating

a clearer conception of 'what might be' created in

response to the best problem definition decision of

the preceding step.

One guide for proceeding is indicated in the

column under Concept Formation in Fig. 4-2.

"He who is truly
creative can
distinguish
between those
matters worthy
of change and
those that are
not worth the
effort."
  Robert Q. Wilson
  [380, p12]

Example 4-8

In the early fifties it was my privilege to
contribute several years as an engineer in a
Receiving Tube Development engineering organization. A handful of we tube and circuit engineers
cooperating with an even smaller number of research engineers did the development engineering
work which eventually led to the creation and
commercial introduction of the 6BY4, 7077 and
similar vacuum tube types, all of which were
significant step-function contributions to both
tube and communication system arts.

"It is folly for any
inventor to spend
much time or money
on a new idea before
making an investiga-
tion of the technical
literature in order
to determine what has
been done before him."
  Joseph Rossman
  [279, p179]

The Federal Communications Commission (FCC)
had just opened the 470-890 Mhz spectrum for
Ultra High Frequency (UHF) television (TV) use.
There was an urgent need for commercially available
low cost tubes for use in millions of television
receivers. The tubes must work satisfactorily
as radio frequency (RF) amplifiers, mixers, and
local oscillators at UHF--all triode vacuum tubes.
The present example, however, concerns only RF
amplifier tubes for UHF.

We had expended considerable engineering effort creating and commercially introducing 6AJ4 and 6AM4 RF amplifier tubes of 9 pin miniature glass type. In spite of our having pushed that state-of-the-art to the limit, these suffered certain performance and technical problems inherent to the miniature type tube geometry.

It was recognized something new was required. The best problem definition appeared to be:

> "Create a new RF amplifier triode suitable for use at UHF."

"Inventors are unconscious social changers." Joseph Rossman [279, p6]

The significance of having a completed problem solution was clearly recognized as making it possible to significantly extend the service area of every UHF TV station. The reason was that most of the 'snow' on a TV picture is caused by noise originating within the set and specifically at the RF amplifier or mixer stages. Creation of a low noise RF amplifier tube would potentially permit many millions of people in fringe areas to receive acceptable TV pictures. Without it the signal/noise ratio was so poor the picture was useless. The critical component which would make the larger system possible was clearly recognized to be a low noise receiving tube.

It was known that high frequency tubes could be purchased. They were 'lighthouse tubes' developed in World War II for radar use. We studied these carefully. They were large, very costly, and unsuitable for use in TV receivers. Several companies, including mine, manufactured such tubes for the military market.

Creative thinking about the 'ideal RF amplifier tube' led to the new concept, among others, of creating a ceramic triode tube for use at UHF with:

"Systematic or projected inventions are the outstanding feature of our age." Joseph Rossman [279, p15]

1. A physical size approximating a pea
2. Low noise figure
3. High power gain
4. Extreme ruggedness (for possible later industrial/military market)
5. Mechanically significantly simpler and easier to manufacture than the then existing glass tubes.

The concept was a significant departure from the then existing TV glass tube technology, especially in the use of ceramic materials. Pioneering work on ceramics had been initiated by a few of our research engineers who had built a substantial body of knowledge therein.

Some incentives for creating the new concept were:

" - - recognize that existing facilities-- and equipment cannot be sacrificed for something different merely because it is different."
Joseph Rossman
[279, p176]

1. Its small size would remove technically troublesome resonances in prior art glass tubes to frequencies higher than the UHF TV band.

2. Ceramic materials would potentially permit the tube to operate at envelope temperatures significantly higher than prior art glass, opening up the possibility of a whole new high temperature electronics technology.

3. If made cheaply enough, the UHF TV receiver market alone would number in the millions. Each receiver tuner would use at least one and possibly more such tubes. Industrial and military market potentialities were also clearly recognized. (Quantitative estimates of all were made).

4. If the noise figure were low enough, it could provide UHF TV reception to millions of citizens in fringe areas.

5. The entire tube industry appeared in need of introduction of a significant *new* concept.

6. Such a new product would be strong competition for the then blossoming transistor technology, both for low and high frequency applications.

"It is difficult to say what is impossible, for the dream of yesterday is the hope of today and the reality of tomorrow."
Robert Hutchings Goddard
[121]

(We later successfully created and commercially introduced the ceramic tube. It was the genesis of many new product offsprings which have been manufactured for many years, finding applications in satellites, military radars, aircraft transponders, radio astronomy, and other areas. It is interesting to note that though it was initially created for the mass UHF TV market, because of cost its principal contribution eventually was to industrial, government, and military markets. Thus creative engineers may create a new product for *one* sector of society and have it eventually accepted and widely used by *another* sector!)

There is an indefinable air of excitement for
the engineer in the 'Concept Formation' step, as in
many other parts of disciplined creative work!

*"Everything worth-
while which has been
achieved by an
individual, a group,
or humanity as a
whole was done by
striving toward
a definite, clearly
defined--although
sometimes un-
attainable--goal."
Erich A. Farber
[99, p784]*

One exits it with a reasonably clear (but not
precise!) *vision of 'What Might Be' created to solve
the defined problem, the probable effects on others
of creating it, and a list of clearly identified incentives for creating it.* He must next make a
decision.

Discussion Topic

Is it better for the engineer to first write down
his own 'concept' thoughts or to first do an exhaustive prior art search and be influenced by
it?

Exercises

4-E7. Propose new and unique concepts for significantly
improving the teaching laboratories in your engineering discipline. Ideas may include hardware,
an organized program, or improved procedures.

4-E8. It is conceivable that future automobile travel
will be on highways with automatic steering and
control facilities. When this occurs, a vast
market for accessories occupants can enjoy or
employ while safely travelling will open up.
Identify and list these.

4-E9. Suggest new concepts which might make use of
the RC time constant property of a resistor-
capacitor network.

4-E10. An engineer has decided that his best problem
definition is 'create a *new* useful product
using Joule heating'. Propose such a concept
and carry it through the remaining 'problem
inquiry' steps.

4-E11. Assume you are going to write a technical book on
your engineering specialty. Make an estimate of
the market potential for your book (a) In your
country (b) Worldwide. Justify your estimate.

DECISION ON WORTH SOLVING, Fig. 4-2, must now be made. All the factors regarding 'decisions' discussed earlier again enter. *I weigh the preliminary solution concept(s) and all the incentives for creating a solution against the earlier written need.* I may decide that the concept is *not* worth creating based on the total evidence available at that time in which case the 'problem inquiry' phase for that concept terminates. If I can't tell whether it is worth solving, I reiterate one or more of the previous thought process stages until I can reach a decision.

"But in picking that problem be sure to analyze it carefully to see that it is worth the effort. It takes just as much effort to solve a useless problem as a useful one."
  Charles F. Kettering
  [173, p11]

"The point is simply that if a technological innovation has a good side (as it almost always does), it will more than likely have a bad side as well."
  A. G. Fredrickson
  [110, p144]

Example 4-9

Today I *decided* the problem of creating a new significantly improved high voltage pulse transformer for the specialized electronic product manufactured in our plant is worth solving. The critical transformer winding would be created around the concept of a porous insulation material impregnated with thermosetting epoxy resin. The concept is believed superior to our present transformer winding using high grade plastic sheet insulation. Production experience has clearly shown extremely low yields of satisfactory transformers of that design. A new fresh approach is urgently needed and would alleviate the need for an economically manufacturable transformer.

(Such a transformer design was subsequently successfully created, after many failures, by a handful of us engineers and technicians. Transformers based around the preliminary concept pushed the state-of-the-art for minimum size, high voltage, temperature, and mechanical shock. They were successfully manufactured for many years.)

If the decision is "yes, the defined problem *is* worth solving," we proceed to the next step.

Discussion Topic

Should Fredrickson's 'bad side' of a proposed
new engineering creation influence the 'worth
solving' decision? Should ecological considerations enter?

*"Being able to pre-
dict which problems
you are not likely
to solve is good for
your peace of mind."
Edward Hodnett
[151, p6]*

ESTIMATE OF PROBLEM SOLVABILITY is the next

step in Fig. 4-2. We recognize initially the *difficulty*

of assessing the probability of solving a problem

which, to this point, has been clearly defined but

only a very *rough* concept exists for its solution on

which we are asked to base our entire answer. A

voice within the engineer cries out "Give me more

details before I answer the question!" But when we

get those, we want more! Carried far enough, we would

thus have the *solution*, and an estimate of solvability

would not be required. But a solution will require

time, energy, money, and other resources, and *it is*

essential to have some estimate of the likelihood of

success before committing our precious resources!

One of the first things I might do is to

list *what time, money, people, experience,*

facilities, and materials RESOURCES exist which might

enhance problem solvability.

*"When you learn
how to mobilize
your data and
bring them to
bear on your
problems, you
are no longer
a rank amateur."
Edward Hodnett
[151, p42]*

Example 4-10

See Exercise 4-E12.

Making the list may reveal that I have more

resources available for solving the problem than a

cursory examination shows. Don't forget to

include important matters-of-the-spirit of yourself on the list! If you by now have a strong feeling that 'this thing has just *got* to be solvable', that attitude, history shows, may be the biggest plus in your favor--far more perhaps than physical resources.

Note that in making a resource assessment list we are *not* necessarily saying that any or all these resources *are* going to be committed to solving the problem. We are simply appraising ourselves of the *full* potential; for if I/we appear to have a small probability of solving the problem with our *full* resources, it is certain the probability will be less with partial resources!

I now decide to bore into the relevant prior art in detail, if any exists. It usually does. Knowledge of the related prior art may substantially aid in assessing solution probability. My earlier work has probably uncovered technical papers bearing on some aspect(s) of the problem. I may search out the reference in these, eventually tracing any threads of my present problem back to its origins. It may require substantial scholarliness, time, patience, energy, and liberal use of the Xerox process to accumulate and study such prior art. ('Information' is treated in Chap. 11).

"The necessity for getting facts straight leads the professional problem solver to take what seems to the layman fantastic pains in checking even small details."
Edward Hodnett
[151, p48]

An important source of prior art is Patents (Chap. 18), copies of which are available at modest prices provided the patent number is known. Alternatively a patent attorney may be engaged to run a full fledged 'patent search' which usually turns up many new facts. The creative problem solver is alert to patents and their potential applicability.

I may next attempt to focus on the proposed solution concept from the angle of attempting to see what, if any, new technologies will probably have to be created to probably solve the problem.

Example 4-11

"The inability to obtain materials necessary for making an invention are often very serious obstacles." Joseph Rossman [279, p165]

Assume an engineer has decided an electric auto is worth creating. After appraising himself of the related prior art, he concludes that a new energy storage technology must be created before a mass produced, mass accepted auto will result. It is clear that stored energy/kg and stored energy/M^3 must be several orders of magnitude above existing battery technology.

I may now make some very rough orders of magnitude calculations[1]--"back of the envelope" kind of thing-- so as to help satisfy myself I am not attempting to solve an impossible problem or violate a known law. I may even here perform a few SIMPLE experiments. It is recognized that later this 'beginning of modeling' step will probably be much refined and sophisticated.

"- - we here emphasize the necessity for extreme care in the prediction of project success during the feasibility inquiry." Thomas T. Woodson [383, p57]

Example 4-12 (continued from Example 7)

Assume I have decided the problem of converting solar energy directly to electricity is worth solving. Clearly order of magnitude know-

---

[1]See Chap. 16 for details.

ledge of sunlight intensity and collector/converter area are important things to know in assessing "Is it probably solvable." Normally incident sunlight intensity is ~ 1 kw/m^2. If a proposed converter could be made 50 percent efficient, a simple calculation shows that ~ 4 m^2 collector/converter area will be required to deliver 2 kW electrical power output to supply a home. The collector area required appears reasonable for ordinary homes.

Will its efficiency be Carnot limited? No, not as long as it avoids heat engine cycles. (Recall the Carnot efficiency limitation applies only to heat engines!) Some kind of new direct conversion process appears indicated.

We continue to proceed in the manner indicated by the previous line of thought through the remaining issues in the 'Problem Solvability' column in Fig. 4-2. Notice that we are *not* seeking to create alternative solutions but to *assess the probability of solving the problem WITHIN the envisioned concept.*

"He often bubbles over with enthusiasm because he visualizes his inventions and seldom doubts that he will not achieve his aim."
Joseph Rossman
[279, p53]

Because of the many unknowns, we may not be able to conclude this step with a solution probability $p = x_1$ percent hardened statement. Rather *we may conclude it with a strong FEELING.* Perhaps when more is known about the creative process this stage could be mathematically modeled and such a probability predicted.

Exercises

4-E12. Generation of a 'resource list' was advocated as an aid in estimating problem solvability. Here is my example of such a generalized list:

4-E13. If you were the project development engineer responsible for creating a worldwide satellite communications system, identify and list the sub-problems (*not* solutions!) you or your company would probably have to solve before the concept is probably realized.

4-E14. An electronic design engineer has decided that it is worth creating a fresh new line of power supplies for commercial marketing. Identify and list all the sub-problems he can reasonably expect to encounter before probably creating its design.

4-E15. A research engineer has been asked to 'look into the possibility of our firm creating (and later marketing) a completely noise free RF amplifier suitable for television and radar receivers in fringe areas'. Clearly identify the problems he should recognize before estimating solvability.

4-E16. Assume your manager has decided to call an international conference in his technical specialty. He asks you to prepare a list of the problems which will probably have to be solved.

4-E17. Assume you felt motivated to write a *new* technical text in an area interesting you. Identify and clearly list the problems on which an estimate of solvability must be made.

DECISION ON SOLVABILITY is now required in Fig. 4-2.

It is a two-part decision. *"Would the probably solvable problem probably meet the recognized basic need if the problem is later successfully solved within the proposed concept?"* If the answer is no, work stops, and the problem inquiry phase is aborted. If we can't tell, we reiterate as previously. If the answer is 'yes', from the previous step we summarize the facts, opinions, beliefs, knowns, and unknowns and make clear decisions of 'yes', 'no', or 'can't tell' for problem solvability. Faith, confidence, courage, and judgment may be required in large amounts.

"Failure to ask a key question is often the only reason for not solving a problem."
  Edward Hodnett
  [151, p36]

Discussion Topic

Identify specific engineers or inventors in the past who decided to solve 'impossible' problems and succeeded. Conjecture the effect on society had he/they *not* decided it was probably solvable.

PROGRAM THE SOLUTION is the first part of the important final question "Should I/we solve it?" in Fig. 4-2. During this latter part of 'Problem Inquiry' we are basically dealing with the subject of commitment. Commitment is the prelude to action by an individual or firm aimed at, hopefully, later successfully solving the defined problem. *Without commitment by someone no action will occur*, and our potential creative contribution may be nulled.

Notice the first questions in this step, "Is achieving solution within bounds of problem solver's mission? Mission clearly defined?" Again, the problem solver's values and his environment impinge.

If we decide the problem *is* within our individual or organizational mission to solve it, we now may want to reflect on what our true personal motives are in solving it. If our motives are not thought out, we may want to do so before committing. *Without strong personal motives the successful outcome of the later solution is endangered.*

Next *it is wise to think deliberately about the timing of the proposed creation by asking, "Is this the right century/decade/year for a solution to be created?"*

"The work to be done, the goal you seek, will be achieved only when you get off dead center and make a start."
  Wilfred A. Peterson
  [248, p59]

"Make no little plans; they have no magic to stir men's blood and probably in themselves will not be realized. Make big plans. - - Let your watchword be order."
  Daniel Burnham
  [52, p62]

"This is the penalty of being an inventor. If you invent something when everybody wants it, it is too late; it's been thought of by everybody else. If you invent too early, nobody wants it because it is too early. If you invent very late, after the need has passed, then it is just a mental exercise. I assure you that it is very hard to invent just at the right time."
Jacob Rabinow
[265, p75]

Failure to ask this difficult question has gotten engineers, inventors, and corporations into deep trouble which perhaps could have been avoided if some *thinking* creative person had earlier asked and answered it. If my problem definition and proposed solution concept appear to be *much* ahead of the times I may be called derogatorily 'an impractical visionary'. If my timing is too late in posing the problem, the competition will already have started to create a solution and be much ahead of us. There are no pat answers here, but a careful study of engineering case histories can be helpful, as well as biographies of successful engineers and inventors.

In a previous step we had identified our resources *potentially* applicable to solving the problem. We now take a closer look at these, perhaps along with other competing demands for our resources, and *decide if expending our resources on the problem defined and validated to date is that on which we wish to expend these resources. Deciding WHICH resources we want to apply to solving the specific proposed problem is then addressed.* Typically, such programming means proposing people, money, time, and facilities in a practical articulated 'action plan'. *The embodiment of the 'action plan' entails a proposed schedule of some kind*, a topic treated in Chap. 17. It is likely

that a strong commitment to solve the problem has not
been made until one gets down to the *details* of working
out such a plan and expresses these in the form of a
chart or tabulation.

*"He who knows much
may take a chance,
and let his imagi-
nation roam; but
he who knows little,
and take chances,
voluntarily tries
suicide; - - "
Baltasar Gracian
[127, p249]*

Having made the basic decision to commit to
solving the problem as embodied in a proposed program
or plan we are now ready to enter perhaps the most
difficult part of 'problem-inquiry'--the final part.

Discussion Topics

1. The text advocated laying definite plans with
   tentative time commitments for realizing the
   proposed new engineering creation. Some engineers
   and inventors maintain that it is impossible to
   schedule a new invention or creation. Discuss.

2. Is there a difference between personal motives for
   solving a problem and 'incentives for creating a
   solution'?

3. Suppose the problem is judged probably solvable
   but solving it is not within my or my organization's
   mission. Discuss what positive action the problem
   solver can take.

*" - - for many
engineers treat
all new things
pessimistically."
A. Y. Dodge
[79, p220]*

CONVINCING OTHERS, Fig. 4-2, of our total thinking
about the need, the problem, validness and all the other
factors we have examined is generally essential if the
proposed concept is to be successfully created in the
remaining 5 major steps.

First we may *think about who* SPECIFICALLY *has to
be convinced* to insure positive progress toward solution. Knowing that ahead of time can be helpful in
structuring and writing our engineering report or
presentation summarizing the 'problem-inquiry' major

phase. Typical other actions are shown in the Convince/

Decision column in Fig. 4-2.

It may take appreciable time for the creative

engineer to successfully traverse the convince/decision

steps. Only rarely, it appears, does the engineer find

himself in the environment where his report or presen-

tations are so thorough, complete, and clear that his

management of outstanding vision and decisiveness

quickly reaches the decision to proceed to the next

major phase. You are forewarned to *expect many*

difficulties here, both with yourself and others before

the commit decision is firmly made by yourself,

appropriate engineering management, or sponsor. Once

the firm decision is made to proceed, the problem

solver may experience a deep abiding sense of joy and

satisfaction which those of lesser persistence may

not know.

*"The inventors
of our most useful
inventions spent
many years con-
vincing the public
of the usefulness
and utility of
their devices.
They met with
apathy, indiffe-
rance and preju-
dice everywhere."
Joseph Rossman
[279, p166]*

Discussion Topics

1. Of what use in the 'convince' step is the 'action
   plan' created in the previous step?

2. Discuss the likelihood of an engineer being
   given management authorization to proceed for
   the cases:

   a. He has an exceptionally creative
      concept but has no specific action
      plan, resorting to 'hand waving'.

   b. He has a mildly creative concept,
      a specific written program proposal,
      clearly thought out justifications,
      and enthusiasm for proceeding.

Exercise

4-E18. Select a pet engineering idea on which you
would like to do further creative work. Assume
you have a friend in a government agency who
knows of your 'problem inquiry' work, is impressed by its potential for advancing the
state-of-the-art, and that he has arranged a
meeting between you, himself, and a top technical
advisor to the government agency's headquarters.
The advisor recommends projects on which the agency
should put its money. You have 30 minutes *only*
of these busy men's time. They have agreed to
meet in your hotel room. *Outline* your presentation aimed at a successful contract award for
developing your idea.

4-3 Some 'Problem Inquiry' Phase Guides

As our ability to use Fig. 4-2 grows through

experience we typically encounter the need for

additional guides. A few are tabulated

in Table 4-1.

These, as many other facets of disciplined creativity,

are the distillate of wisdom and experience from a

broad spectrum of engineers and kinds of engineering

activity. With the expectation you will want to do

some exploring and adding to the list in your own

personal way, we forego an exposition of these here,

simply stating them in a concise form.

"Many failures invariably precede success." H. E. Warren [370, p75]

4-4 Some Common Failures

We have tacitly touched on the creative engineer's

possibility of 'failing'. Failure is used in the

sense of blocking progress toward ultimately creating

GUIDES DIRECTLY RELATED TO SPECIFIC SUB-STEPS IN FIG. 4-2

● Significance of Problem: Its macroscopic sense is sought
      with written reasons for *why* it is significant.

● Recording of Thought and actions in a notebook is a necessity.

● Problem Definition occurs only when it is *written*.

● Incentives to Create: Generate a specific written list.

● Written Document: Summarizing the phase is helpful and necessary.

GUIDES APPLICABLE TO ALL SUB-STEPS IN FIG. 4-2

● Time is required to retreat and thoroughly think-through a
      'problem-inquiry' phase.

● Deliberateness: Each sub-step can be deliberately creatively
      focussed on and probably successfully completed.

● Tentativeness: All process sub-steps and actions are tentative,
      flexible, and subject to possible later modification by the
      problem solver.

● Motivation: A major personal essential for viable phase progress.

● Thinking, sometimes questioningly and excruciatingly, permeates all
      sub-steps.

● Questing Attitude characterizes the phase.

● Generalizing, seeing broad patterns, and stripping to essentials
      penetrates the phase.

● Vision/Judgment/Confidence constitute major personal 'inputs'.

● Anticipate Opposition by yourself or others by generating
      solid sensible reasons for actions throughout phase.

● Omission of Sub-steps may be done with discretion on some
      specific problems.

● Risk of 'Failure' is ever present at each sub-step.

TABLE 4-1

Tabulation of some further guides applicable to the 'Problem Inquiry'
major phase of disciplined creative problem solving.

that which we envision.

Failure is so common in actual 'problem inquiry' creative work as to merit briefly identifying some of the most common ones.

"Some fail to strike, when the iron is hot, because they fail to see the opportunity."
Baltasar Gracian
[127, p71]

Table 4-2 tabulates a few common failures. The sequence approximates that in Fig. 4-2. We understand that this tabulation is a generalization based on observation in a wide spectrum of engineering activity and experiences of many. The table is only suggestive, as *other failures can and usually do crop up on a specific engineering problem.* They are not listed in order of importance. Many important lessons for enhancing 'success' could be learned from a careful scholarly study of failure. The subject is beyond the scope of the present work.

Discussion Topics

1. *Why* is the subject of 'engineering failures' a relatively mute topic? Or is it from your viewpoint?

2. Think back over your total engineering education and estimate the percentage of total class time spent dealing with the subject of 'failure' in the technical sense. Will this same percentage exist for your future professional engineering work?

3. What, if anything, do the quotes in Table 4-2 have to do with the failure statements?

4. Ask your Professor to share some of his 'failures' in 'problem inquiry' made during his prior creative engineering work.

'NEED DETERMINATION' FAILURES	'COMMITMENT' (continued)

'NEED DETERMINATION' FAILURES

Failure To Perceive Significance of problem.
"No one should pick a problem, or make a resolution, unless he realizes that the ultimate value of it will offset the inevitable discomfort and trouble that always goes along with the accomplishment of anything worth while. So let us not waste our time and effort on some trivial thing."
Charles F. Kettering [173, p59]

Failure To Identify A Need that is bona fide.
"The first step is to conceive a need or use--."
Elihu Thomson [340, p73]

Failure To Recognize Need/Problem soon enough.
"Often problems not solved earlier have not been posed earlier."
A. W. Frazier [109]

Failure To Get Correct Facts.
"Much of the difficulty of problem solving comes from the impossibility of getting all the facts together before making a decision."
Edward Hodnett [151, p43]

Failure To Make Correct Assumptions.
"He possesses the capacity of seeing non-obvious things."
Joseph Rossman [279, p48]

'BASIC PROBLEM?' FAILURES

Failure By Defining Problem in terms of a solution.
"The way a problem is stated can block its diagnosis."
Edward Hodnett [151, p22]

Failure By Wrong Problem definition.
"The most difficult problem in new product development is not the solution of scientific or technical difficulties, but the original determination of what product is wanted in the first place."
D. Henry Edel, Jr. [89, p153]

Failure To Be 'Open' to all alternative problem definitions.
"An unstated problem cannot be solved. Many problems go unsolved for centuries for lack of adequate statement."
Edward Hodnett [151, p19]

Failure To 'Focus' caused by indecisiveness.
"Yet, when in desperation they finally clutch at any straw and focus their attention upon it, they rapidly uncover more than enough material."
Eugene K. Von Fange [360, p151]

Failure To Analyze non-technical problem aspects.
"A design project, abandoned after it has progressed far toward completion because the customer does not now want what he claimed he wanted originally, is just as hurtful as one abandoned for technical reasons."
Morris Asimow [12, p53]

'WORTH SOLVING?' FAILURES

Failure To Conceive A Solution Concept for 'what might be' created.
"I like the dreams of the future better than the history of the past."
Thomas Jefferson [162, p14]

Failure To Purchase An Existing Solution, reinventing it.
"--how much creative talent is wasted every year by people trying to 're-invent the wheel' within every professional pursuit."
Eugene K. Von Fange [360, p147]

Failure To Recognize 'The Impossible.'
"--the hopelessness of attempting the impossible such as perpetual motion."
Joseph Rossman [279, p174]

Failure To Identify A Market.
"Experience suggests that innovative operations fail, first of all, because of misjudgment of markets."
Richard S. Morse [218, p98]

Failure To Check Prior Art.
"--we began looking for books pertaining to flight--we found little."
Orville Wright [386, p3]

Failure To Generate Incentives to create solution.
"Why should a corporation spend its earnings and deprive its stockholders of dividends to develop something that will upset its own market or junk all its present equipment?"
W. M. Grosvenor [131, p33]

'PROBABLY SOLVABLE?' FAILURES

Failure To Assess Probability of solving problem.
"One seldom perfects an idea without many failures."
Joseph Rossman [279, p45]

Failure To Assess Resources potentially applicable to solution.
"With careful planning, taking into consideration the resources available,---the chances for successful introduction will be greatly enhanced."
Benjamin W. Roberts and Walter Lowen [277, p817]

'COMMITMENT' FAILURES

Failure To Convince self/others of need to create solution.
"Nearly all the inventors stress that it is highly important not only to perceive the need but also to have a clear idea of the object in view."
Joseph Rossman [279, p58]

'COMMITMENT' (continued)

Failure To Allocate Time for realistically creating solution.
"--all available time was needed for the development of what was really new to the art."
Eugene K. Von Fange [760, p145]

Failure To Allocate Resources to successfully solve problem.
"--it is much easier to get into something than to get out of something, well."
Baltasar Gracian [127, p53]

Failure To Time Solution creation correctly.
"I assure you that it is very hard to invent just at the right time."
Jacob Rabinow [265, p75]

Failure To Recognize Pessimism of well-intentioned but ill informed 'others' about a truly new creation.
"If you are going into new work, I can tell you--that the biggest job you will have is to strong-arm the opposition of well-meaning people."
Charles F. Kettering [174, p164]

MODUS OPERANDI FAILURES

Failure To Think through a structured 'Problem Inquiry' phase in whole or in part.
"--discipline provides an intermediate intellectual structure or strategy which molds and guides the attack on categories of problems."
Morris Asimow [12, p3]

Failure By Creating Wrong Solution before problem is defined.
"One of the most expensive ways to do research is to arrive at some difficult technical goal, and then find that you don't really want to be there."
Guy Suits [323, p5]

Failure To Examine All Facets of 'the problem,' becoming enamored with one facet only as the market.
"Look beneath. For ordinarily things are far other than they seem; --The false is forever the lead in everything, continually dragging along the fools: the truth brings up the rear, is late, and limps along upon the arm of time,--."
Baltasar Gracian [127, p138]

Failure To Remember Basic Need at critical decisions.
"Then comes a study of the whole problem, as to the wisdom of such an improvement."
F. F. Forshee [107, p76]

Failure Because In Too Great A Hurry.
"The time element appears to be a highly important factor because the inventor must allow many neural patterns to form."
Joseph Rossman [279, p99]

Failure To Record thoughts.
"It is my contention from experience that development can be accomplished in mind and on paper at a great saving in both time and money."
W. H. Carrier [54, p76]

PERSONAL FAILURES

Failure To Be Motivated by situation/need/problem.
"No problem is so big or so complicated that it can't be run away from."
Linus [195]

Failure To Question at all sub-phases.
"This is wrong. We must rather, if we wish our ultimate result to be worthwhile, seriously question that which is given."
Eugene K. Von Fange [360, p142]

Failure In Honestly facing needed step function changes.
"The inventor must be honest to himself and be ready to be his own most severe critic."
Joseph Rossman [279, p53]

Failure Of Courage to focus/persist to end of phase.
"Genius for invention is merely the capacity for concentration and for work."
Emile Berliner [36, p42]

Failure/Unwillingness To Risk venturing into the truly new.
"--man drives into the future with his eyes fixed firmly on the rearview mirror."
George B. Leonard [189, p93]

Failure To Maintain 'It Is Possible' Attitude.
"Most inventors of course, strongly believe in their ability and powers."
Joseph Rossman [279, p36]

Failure To Recognize Emotions and their effects on defining the problem.
"--unquestionably in all creative effort there is a decided emotional tone."
Joseph Rossman [279, p86]

Failure By Oversimplifying/Overcomplicating parts of problem.
"--the inventor and the creative engineer spend too much time in concentrating upon the technical problem in hand, and do not look outside their work to watch sufficiently social and market trends that have a most important influence on their ultimate success."
Crosby Field [104, p14]

Failure To Generalize/Summarize/Simplify complex parts of problem.
"Thinking and discussing in generalities are required."
Eugene K. Von Fange [360, p148]

Failure To Achieve Problem Understanding.
"There is a great difference between knowing a thing and understanding it."
Charles F. Kettering [174, p21]

Failure To Apply Good Judgment at appropriate point/time.
"--it is even more important to reject unsound ideas than it is to perceive good ones."
W. H. Carrier [54, p75]

TABLE 4-2 Tabulation of some common failures in the 'Problem Inquiry' phase. Many others exist. The possibility of failure is ever near to the truly creative problem solving engineer. *Actual* failure is far more frequent than is 'success'!

Exercise

4-E19. Select a technical engineering course in which
        you were truly interested. Examine a textbook
        thoroughly for any evidences of dealing with
        engineering 'failure'. Write a brief summary
        of your findings.

4-5 In Retrospect

We see there was substantial *difficult* thinking

involved in recognizing the basic need, defining the

problem correctly, and obtaining a personal and organi-

zational commitment to proceed to the next major phase,

'Specifying Goals', the subject of Chap. 5. Unavoidably

the details of 'problem inquiry' were seen to be

complex from both process and personal viewpoints.

While some inventors claim to be able to quickly

take great intuitive leaps through this phase, or

its equivalent, those of us with lesser creative

abilities may perhaps achieve comparable results on

a *repetitive* basis by executing a more disciplined

approach as elucidated in this chapter.

Discussion Topics

1. This chapter appears to indicate that every
    product created is potentially significantly im-
    provable. Identify a product *not* capable of
    improvement. Justify *why*.

2. What relationships, if any, do Chaps. 10, 13, and
    14 have to 'problem inquiry'?

Exercise

4-E20. Write your version of the purpose, input, and
        output of the 'problem inquiry' major phase of
        creative problem solving. List what you might
        do in it when confronted with an engineering
        situation demanding creativity.

Creative Problems

4-CP1.   Inquire into a to-be-created new product idea
         useful in the home using this chapter as a guide.

4-CP2.   Starting with the need of 'service to the public',
         consider the television system created by engineers.
         Using this chapter as a guide, inquire into the
         possibility of a fresh new concept of this system--
         what it should be, what it should do, what services
         should be offered, etc.

4-CP3.   Consider your hometown. Inquire into the problem
         of creating a *new* product or service which would
         lead to formation of a small company which would
         manufacture and market it.

4-CP4.   Starting from 'the situation' of classroom
         teaching, inquire into the problem of significantly
         improving the teaching-learning process in
         engineering education. Seek to advance a bold
         new concept.

4-CP5.   Inquire into the situation faced by blind persons.
         Propose a new creative concept for aiding such
         persons.

4-CP6.   Assume that an engineer had decided that his
         basic problem is 'create improved new means of
         vibration isolation for a mass'. He has recognized
         the problem repeatedly occurs in a wide spectrum
         of engineering applications. Propose a new
         concept and carry it through the remaining
         'problem inquiry' steps of this chapter.

4-CP7.   An electrical engineer working in the Aeronautical
         Division of a large company is asked to 'look
         into the possibilities of our creating a low
         cost VHF 360 channel aircraft transceiver and make
         me a recommendation.' Using this chapter as a
         guide, perform a 'problem inquiry'.

4-CP8.   Inquire into the problem of significantly improving
         air traffic control in a nation with large numbers
         of civil and military aircraft flying at all times.

4-CP9.   Starting from 'the situation' of significant
         problems in your engineering discipline, select
         one for 'problem inquiry' under the guidance
         of your professor. Using Fig. 4-2 as a guide,
         'inquire' into your chosen problem.

4-CP10. Others of a more detailed nature as assigned by
         your Professor.

Chapter Summary

● The first major phase of creative problem solving, 'problem inquiry', was sequentially structured around the important questions:

▲ What is the basic need?
▲ What is the basic problem?
▲ Is it worth solving?
▲ Is it probably solvable?
▲ Should I/we solve it?

● The process and action details were seen to be complex but amenable to structured thought and hence *repetitively applicable* to an arbitrary problem of our choosing.

● The 'Problem Inquiry' morphology was compressed into Fig. 4-2.

● A few guides helpful in this phase were exposed in Table 4-1.

● Some 'failure' possibilities were identified in Table 4-2.

CHAPTER 5

DISCIPLINE OF SPECIFYING GOALS

"I often say that when you can measure what you are
speaking about and express it in numbers you know
something about it; but when you cannot measure it
in numbers, your knowledge is of a meagre and unsatisfactory kind: - - - "

Lord Kelvin [167, p80]

● Need and purpose for a 'Specifying
Goals' major step in creative problem
solving.

● 'Goal' is defined.

● Principles for 'Specifying Goals.'

● Examples are given.

5-1 Need and Purposes for 'Specifying Goals'

*"To be an in-
ventor one
first must
know what is
needed."
James M.
Lafferty
[184, p94]*

We have seen in the previous Chap. that

the net result of the problem inquiry phase is

a valid specific problem resulting from a per-

ceived need. Further I, the problem solver,

at this point in the approach am honestly *con-*

vinced of the *need* for achieving a satisfactory

solution so that as I progress toward a solution

and deal with difficulties ahead I do not have

to *also* worry excessively about working on the

wrong problem! I have by choice *focused* on a

specific major problem to the exclusion of all

others. I now know, or have reasonable assurance,

that the problem has not been solved in the prior-art

to my satisfaction and that creative engineering effort appears needed to effect a satisfactory solution.

We may have an inclination here to 'get on with the solution.' But the application of disciplined creativity tenet would say, "Wait! What constitutes a 'satisfactory' solution? Shouldn't we know that *before* we plunge into the details of creating a 'satisfactory solution' only to discover after many months and dollars that all along we had been working toward the *wrong* engineering criteria?" For example, we may have decided to focus on the need for 'improved batteries.' Specifically what constitutes an 'improvement' over the present-art devices? For what specific goals should we aim in order to both solve the problem and insure maximizing our creative contribution?

Reflection and generalization of the problem solving experiences of many creative engineers indicates the wisdom of including in a universal problem solving approach a discrete step for 'Specifying Goals' whose principal purpose for the engineer is:

"Once a problem is recognized clearly and all parties concerned have agreed on its nature, the development of detailed specifications becomes vital."
John R. M. Alger and Carl V. Hays [4, p15]

● <u>Purpose</u> <u>of</u> '<u>Specifying Goals</u>' Phase:

> To define the constraints (the limits of acceptability) requisite for *successfully* solving the problem.

A systems view of this phase is shown in Fig. 5-1.

The purposeful input is the result of the pre-

vious problem inquiry phase. The desired out-

puts reflect what the system to be created is

to do or provide in response to the eliciting

need input. They are more precise than that

of the need input and are deduced by the problem

solver from the probable need of the system user

or the nature of the problem. It seems almost

inevitable that undesired outputs accompany the

production of those desired.

> *"We must try to set up some defi- nite goals that have the benefit of all mankind as their objective."*
> A. G. Fredrickson
> [110, p148]

> *"Just having an idea or a vague awareness of a need is not sufficient. To be productive one must define the limits of the problem as soon as possible - - -"*
> Terrence W. Fenner
> [102, p26]

Example 5-1 A communication system permits transmission of the video picture information but contains noise resulting in a 'snowy' picture.

Example 5-2 A nuclear power plant, built to eliminate air pollution, ejects heat re- sulting in thermal pollution of the cooling water, possibly damaging the ecology.

The idea of boundedness or constraints

clearly applies to inputs, the system to be

created, and the outputs. It is largely the

job of the creative engineer in this phase to

infer the probable limits of acceptability in

an integrated manner such that the resulting

creation will achieve the intended function.

The execution of this phase can do several

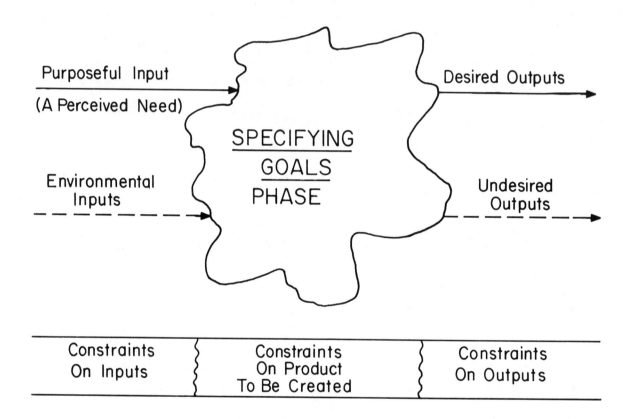

FIG. 5-1 Systems view of the 'Specifying Goals' phase
          for the system, device, process, or engineer-
          ing material to be created. (Adapted from
          Morris Asimow, *Introduction To Design*,
          Prentice-Hall, 1962. Used by permission.)

things for us while solving a complex engineering

problem.

*A problem well
defined is half
solved.*

*'Specifying Goals' Helps the Creative Problem
Solver by:*

- Forcing us to think *in detail* about the requirements for an acceptable solution. (*Not how* the solution is to be achieved!)

- Stimulates interest. Provides accomplishment feeling.

- Helps remove nebulousness and doubt often found in initial phases of problem solving.

- Serving as reference standards against which later work is measured, i.e. when our solution later meets the goals, the problem is solved. We know engineering work should then stop.

- Avoiding possible personal or company embarrassment when others ask, "What are you trying to achieve?"

*"Only by setting
up defined goals
will it be possible
to develop prior-
ities and insti-
tutions that can
guide the innovative
genius of men onto
paths that will be
truly, as opposed
to superficially,
beneficial."*
  *A. G. Fredrickson
  [110, p148]*

- Legally defining, in contractual situations, what is to be created. The engineer's output from this phase then is 'The Specifications.'

- Helping to maximize the probability of making a significant contribution ('step-function change') to the state-of-the-art surrounding the problem.

Discussion Topics

1. If an engineer is unable to formulate specific goals *before* detailed solving of the problem begins discuss the probability of his being able to later recognize 'the solution.'

2. Explore possible dangers to the engineer who wants to 'get on with the problem *solution*' and omit the 'specifying goals' phase entirely.

3. What can be done in a situation where an engineer's manager says he does not know what he wants until he sees a proposed 'solution' to the problem?

4. Consider Fig. 5-1. Select from one of your engineering courses a specific problem of the analytical type which you have solved. Explore whether a 'specifying goals' phase was there, perhaps unconsciously. Can you generalize the result to all analytical problems?

Exercises

5-E1. Review Chap. 3, clarifying in your mind where the 'Specifying Goals' phase fits into the overall problem solving approach taught in this text.

5-E2. In your own words, write out the principal purpose of the 'specifying goals' phase of disciplined creative problem solving.

5-E3. Write out clearly your specific goals in taking this course (other than 'to graduate!').

5-2 What is a Specified Goal?

A DEFINITION is helpful in clarifying the

intent of this phase of the morphology of dis-

ciplined creativity.

"Specify: To mention or name in a specific or explicit manner; to tell or state precisely or in detail." [373]

"Goal: The end to which a design tends; aim; purpose. Syn. Destination, end, object." [373]

● Specified Goal: The specific detailed statement defining the aim, purpose, end result, or constraint which the problem solver believes the created problem solution must meet.

Example 5-3

'The communication system to be created shall for a composite video input signal of 1.0 volt p-p have a signal-to-noise ratio in excess of 45db at the output terminals, measured in accordance with test drawing xxxx.'

Example 5-4

'The high speed train to be created shall be capable of sustained operating speeds of at least 350 MPH.'

Example 5-5

'The vehicle to be created shall be capable
of infinitely variable speeds between 0-5
MPH when operating on flat areas while in
the lunar surface environment.'

Most creative engineering problems require multiple
goals.

CLASSES OF SPECIFIED GOALS ARE:

● Primary Goals: Those which the problem solver,
    through exercise of his disciplined judg-
    ment, considers most fundamental.

    If the solution to be created fails to
    meet one or all of these, the intended
    step-function contribution either will
    not be achieved or its effect will be
    substantially blunted.

    Example 5-6 The 350 MPH speed in the train
    example above would be a primary goal.
    If the problem solver aimed for 125
    MPH speed, then, when the work is finished,
    he would have simply built another
    train without contributing to the state-
    of-the-art, as such trains exist in
    Japan and England.

● Secondary Goals: Those which the problem solver,
    through exercise of his disciplined judgment,
    considers of lesser importance than Primary
    Goals.

    Example 5-7 'The vehicle shall be so struc-
    tured as to permit passenger egress in 10
    seconds or less from any place within
    the vehicle.'

Each of the above classes may be sub-classed

as technical and non-technical goals, though in

actuality the boundary between these sub-classes

is not always distinct.

For each of the above major classes of goals

we creative problem solvers typically find

ourselves faced with the choices of:

● Idealistic Goals: Those goals which we be-
     lieve to be the absolute upper limit of
     performance achievable, typically under
     simplified idealistic conditions. Such
     goals are seldom achievable in actuality.

● Realistic Goals: More modest goals which
     take into account total problem under-
     standing and have, as judged by the
     problem solver, a high probability
     of being actually achieved.

We begin to sense beneath the above structure

that the creative problem solver's vision in his

choice of parameters and numbers largely determine

whether his goals are 'idealistic' or 'realistic.'

We further sense that, in general, goals are not

time invariant. For example, in 1950 to creative

aircraft engineers a speed goal of 1800 MPH for

a passenger-carrying plane would have been

'idealistic.' In 1970 such a goal was considered

'realistic.'

CHARACTER OF GOALS IN ENGINEERING FUNCTIONAL

AREAS is of concern to the disciplined creative

engineer of vision. Even though the same general

problem is being worked on in each area, the

character of the engineering goals and the emphasis

thereon shifts as we examine 'specifying goals'

in research, development, design, and operations

functional areas. In 'research' problem solving

emphasis might be heavily centered on the 'primary goals', perhaps to the total exclusion of the 'secondary goals.' For example, the research engineer might have his hands so full of problems trying to create a new constant voltage solid-state device that he pays absolutely no attention to specifying goals for how the resulting creation is to be physically 'packaged' or structured. To him if the fundamental goal of achieving constant voltage characteristics is not achieved, there will be *no* need for focussing on the secondary goal of 'packaging.' In contrast, a creative design engineer taking the improved device from development engineering might establish forward-looking creative goals for six new commercial product families of devices. His goals would, in general, be more numerous, detailed, and specific than that of the original research engineer. Both sets of goals might exhibit substantial vision and creativeness, though their character is different.

SATISFACTORY AND UNSATISFACTORY SPECIFICATION OF GOALS merits the problem solver's considered attention during this phase. One of the objects in formulating goals is to be both specific and quantitative. An example best illustrates the point.

"Performance specifications can also be used for transactions involving novel systems and unique equipment, as in research and development programs. The contract is let to the producer who proves, by his proposal, that he has the competence and know-how to meet the specified goals."
Walter L. Fleischmann
[105]

"Defining the word 'satis- factorily' may be an extremely complex exercise in semantics."
John R. M. Alger and Carl H. Hays [4, p15]

Example 5-8a: Unsatisfactory Specified Goal

'The telemetry package shall perform satisfactorily at cold temperature.'

Such a goal raises important questions for the problem solver. *What* telemetry package? The first hand-made model? Production Units? Shouldn't it say it is not yet in existence but must be created? What does 'satisfactorily' mean? Shouldn't thought be given to defining what we *mean* by 'satisfactorily?' How cold? Shouldn't numbers be used? Degrees centi- grade or Fahrenheit? Any special constraints on $T(t)$ in arriving at 'cold' temperature? Does dT/dt matter at all? And others? Clearly such a 'goal' is nearly *useless* to the problem solver!

Example 5-8b: Satisfactory Specified Goal

'The developmental prototype telemetry package to be created shall at a temperature of $+25^{\circ}C$ meet the test requirements of drawing xxxx immediately before thermal test. After placing it in an environmental chamber, the temperature shall be lowered at a rate less than $10^{\circ}C/hr.$ until $-20^{\circ}C$ is reached at which temperature the package shall be thermally stabilized for at least 10 hrs. following which it shall meet the require- ments of drawing xxx while at $-20^{\circ}C.$'

THE SEMANTICS PROBLEM will surely be faced by every creative problem solver attempting to formulate clear unambiguous goals. Both the above examples point up a few of the difficulties. The semantics problem is never truly 'solved.' Compromises of language and symbols are simply made so as to most accurately communicate what we, the creative problem solvers, *mean*. The implication is that we *know* what we mean when we formulate a goal and that *thinking* has

preceded the formulation! The occasional less-
than-optimum goals sometimes formulated by
engineers can reflect unfavorably on our profession as well as the creative problem solver
personally. These unsavory situations can
usually be avoided by exercising discipline and
diligence during this phase so as to choose
language, symbols, and expression forms which
minimize the semantics difficulty to others who
may use our specified goals.

Discussion Topics

1. For a given engineering problem, will only
    one or several goals be required? How will
    the problem solver know how many are necessary?

2. Is 'specifying goals' more or less con-
    ceptually demanding than actually 'solving
    the problem?'

3. Many forward-looking people are concerned about
    the increasing air pollution as population
    continues to increase exponentially. Focus
    on 'air pollution.' Assume you are an
    engineer desiring to 'change the world' toward
    less air pollution. Explore, by discussion,
    difficulties anticipated in 'specifying
    goals' for clean air.

4. Of a given set of specified goals for an
    engineering problem, can they be classified
    into the four neatly defined categories
    of the text? What mental attribute is
    strongly required here?

Exercises

5-E4. If you were the engineer trying to create
       an artificial human heart, what primary goals
       would you specify? (List.)

5-E5. A high speed, compact, light weight DC motor is to be developed to propel a canoe. Here are the specified primary and secondary goals I propose for this creation: (List).

5-E6. An electrical engineer has determined that a need and market exist for a solid-state microphone-earphone system for use by private pilots and passengers. It would mount entirely on the head, including energy sources, and have no external connecting wires. Everyone in the cabin would wear one of these devices. The presence of microphone sound would activate the transmitter, permitting all others inside the cabin to hear above the noise level.

     a. An 'idealistic' set of goals would be: (List)

     b. A 'realistic' set of goals would be: (List)

5-E7. Here are 'idealistic' specified goals I propose for a greatly improved 60 Hz household electrical outlet: (List. Try *hard* to not be biased by present-art designs!)

5-E8. In the early 1970's there was a widespread movement to aesthetically 'clean-up' electric utility high voltage transmission lines, towers, and distribution poles. Consider the goal 'the tower design shall be both functional and aesthetically pleasing.'

     a. Prepare a written criticism of the stated goal.

     b. Here is my proposal for an improved goal.

5-E9. Consider a large jet air terminal. Assume a valid need exists for creating a step-function improvement in baggage handling.

     a. Here are the specific goals I would establish for the system to be created: (List).

     b. Here are the above goals arranged by primary, secondary, idealistic, and realistic classes.

5-E10. A switch manufacturer has determined that
        a need and market exist for a new cam-
        actuated microminiature switch for use in
        an unmanned space vehicle. Here are the
        primary goals I would specify: (List).

5-E11. Prepare a list of specific personal goals
        to which, as a contributing engineer, you
        might aspire at the 10 year post-graduation
        point.

5-E12. Select a new engineering idea of your choice.
        Suppose this idea was to be 'researched.'
        Cite the specific research goals. Ditto
        for development, design, and manufacture.

5-3 Where Goals Originate

The genesis of 'goals' is with the *individual*

creative engineer attempting to solve the prob-

lem (Group creativity, unfortunately, is beyond the

scope of the present work). "But," you ask, "how will

I know what is the 'right' goal to establish?"

The answer is that 'right' is relative to

time, you the individual problem-solver, and

the situation in which the problem is cast.

What is 'right' will be determined by your under-

standing of the problem, your knowledge, vision,

judgment, experience, and expertise in the art

of applying disciplined creativity.

Thoughtful reflection will reveal that

the foundation of goals rests on the 'values'

of the individual problem solver--a topic we

shall touch in Chap. 10. Because I value

time, one of my specified goals might include

*"Life has mean-
ing only if it
remains a per-
petual becoming,
a definite goal
in front of one
and not behind."
Bernard Shaw
[344, p140]*

a time statement goal about roughly when the problem may be solved. Similarly I might pose a cost goal which is founded on my sense of value for the completed solution.

Certain attributes of the problem solver are required to successfully originate goals. The salient ones are:

"He (Charles F. Kettering) tried to fill his mind not with figures but with understanding."
T. A. Boyd
[42, p41]

- **Problem Understanding** – It is difficult to originate goals for creating a new 'step-function change' in the electrical x-y recorder art, for example, without understanding the strengths and weaknesses of existing recorders.

- **Discipline** – The orderly, deliberate, conscious determination of what the goals should be.

- **Vision** – The capacity to recognize what "might be" if we select the appropriate goals.

- **Judgment** – The capacity to intelligently and logically weigh alternative goals.

- **Decisiveness** – Appropriate number choices must be made, usually with inadequate engineering information available.

- **Questing Attitude** – The attitude that seeks out the best goals, questions *why* these are best, reformulates better goals in the light of new information. May require challenging accepted conventions, facts, and methods. Suggests the need for courage.

- **Determination** – To overcome difficulties, especially of the unknowns.

- **Intuition** – The inner voice which tells me a certain goal is necessary in spite of all 'logical' evidence and data to the contrary.

We begin to, perhaps, appreciate the problem
solver's need for the highly personal topics
discussed in Part III, for these collectively
directly influence our ability to 'specify goals.'

Some helpful guides for *how* we go about
specifying goals are in Sec. 5-4.

Discussion Topics

1. Discuss: "It is the role of management to
    set goals. The engineer has nothing to do
    with them once they are set."

2. Examine again the given list of qualities.
    Honestly discuss the extent with which you
    are satisfied with yourself on each of these.
    Does this suggest your *personal* need for
    new professional goals?

3. Explore goals as published when the problem
    is finally solved vs goals established
    initially while actually solving the problem.

4. Your manager, recognizing the need for
    significant improvements in the 'state-of-
    the-art' of relays for missile system use,
    hands you a set of rigid specifications for
    such a relay and asks you to 'invent one.'
    Would you accept these specifications without
    question? *Why*?

5. An engineer is given the problem of creating
    an improved solid state video amplifier to
    be used in an airborne radar. Given specifi-
    cations require 100 db gain, flat response
    to 8 Mhz, maximum weight of 6 ozs, and
    operate satisfactorily between $-100^{\circ}F$ and
    $+200^{\circ}F$. Should the engineer question the
    validity of these specified goals before
    proceeding to create a solution? *Why*?

Exercises

5-E13.   Most faculty and students would agree on
         the desirability of improving the effectiveness
         of the educational engineering laboratories.
         While this is a complex area, perhaps part
         of the *in*effectiveness of laboratories may
         be caused by a lack of specific goals which
         the laboratory experience is expected to
         achieve in your engineering education.
         Select a laboratory. List as many specific
         educational goals as you can think of for
         it.

5-E14.   An engineer has felt the need for a step-
         function change in television receiver
         displays. He wants to create a 'picture-
         on-the-wall' type display means. Some
         primary goals might be: (List).

5-E15.   An electrical engineer seeks to create a
         new ultra-ultra stable low voltage dc
         supply to furnish a few milliamperes
         to a dc amplifier. His specific goals might
         be: (List).

5-E16.   Make a list of 'idealistic' proposed goals
         for a burglar-proof lock to be created for
         a household door.

5-E17.   If you were a mechanical engineer creating
         the urban vehicle for personal use 10 years
         from now, (a) prepare a list of the specific
         goals toward which you would aim such a
         creation, (b) show item-by-item how, if at
         all, these are related to your 'values,'
         and (c) by each goal identify the mental
         qualities you exercised in arriving at your
         proposed set of goals.

5-4 Some Principles For Specifying Goals

In this section some guides are proposed

for specifying goals. Their formulation is in-

tended to loosely structure our thinking during

this phase. They are *not* intended to be slavishly

followed but to be thought stimulants to the

particular creative problem the engineer is trying

to solve. These principles for success in the

specifying goals phase are distilled from a wide

spectrum of engineering and engineers and re-

present some of the lessons learned from pro-

fessional engineering experience--some disciplined

and some undisciplined. No 'equation' exists

for proving or disproving their validity. Don't

waste your precious creative energy attempting

to find one! Their validity rests on the testing

ground of experience of the many creative

engineers who have preceded you and on whose

shoulders you are favored to stand at this

point in time. With experience you will be able

to add to these principles.

●Written Goals: Write your goals down.

> Frequently the origin of our troubles in
> solving the engineering problem may be
> traced back to failure to write out what
> our goals were.

> Example 5-9 'I seek to create a new im-
> proved means for converting solar energy
> to electricity subject to the constraints:
> (list)' might appear in my written re-
> cords. (The whole matter of record-
> ing creative work is discussed in
> Chap. 15.)

●Tentativeness of Goals: Your goals are time
varying.

> Once we have written them down we are apt
> to think, "That's a *good* goal. That is

*"A good engi-
neer is adroit
in negotiating
changes in
specifications
or trade-offs."
John R. M. Alger
and Carl V. Hays
[4, p16]*

what I am after! It is a fundamental--
unchanging." Experience, especially
during the earliest creative work,
indicates the problem solver proposes
tentative goals which he works toward
and later *modifies* as new understanding
is acquired.

Example 5-10 It was my privilege to be a
circuit engineer on the team of
development engineers which created
the new low noise capability high
temperature 6BY4 ceramic receiving
tube and subsequent product offsprings. Our initial goal was to
make a low noise radio frequency
amplifier tube for use in the then
forthcoming Ultra High Frequency
television receiver market. Subsequent
experience indicated the necessity of
modifying our goal toward the military,
space, and industrial market with
somewhat different goals.

> ● Function Statement: Excruciate much over the
> *function* the creation is to perform.
> Arrive at a written statement.

A corollary is 'solution avoidance,'
i.e. the *function* statement, insofar
as is judged possible, should *not* have
implicit in it a preconceived, perhaps
prejudiced, 'solution.' To do so will
severely adversely constrict my creativity in the 'Determining Means' phase
later.

"Spend more time than you think necessary in deciding what functional and other criteria the design must meet."
Blake King [176]

Example 5-10a - Satisfactory Goal 'The instrument to be created shall accept a
DC input signal E and exhibit a DC
output signal

$$E_o = E_1 \ln E$$

where E_1 is to be some known constant.'

Example 5-10b - Weak Goal 'The instrument
shall take the log of the input signal
by means of a circuit of multiple
biased vacuum tubes.' Notice the implied solution! Further creative
engineering may reveal 'the solution'

entirely unsatisfactory, which it
actually was for this problem.

● Number To Be Created: Clearly state the number
    of devices, systems, or apparatus to
    be created.

This simple, obvious, principle can save
the creative engineer much later grief
and embarrassment.

    Example 5-11 'A single spacecraft prototype
    is to be created.'

● Correct Parameters Identified: Assure yourself
    that both technical and non-technical
    parameters are the correct ones on which
    numerical goals are to be established.

Much valuable creative engineering effort
has been lost by engineers quibbling over
'correct' numbers to use on a parameter
which perhaps should not have been included at all, i.e. is unnecessary or
irrelevant.

    Example 5-12 "Consider the ice industry.
    The refrigerating engineer of 20 years
    ago evaluated all ice-making processes
    using only one standard-kilowatt hours
    consumed per ton of ice produced. The
    literature was weighted heavily with
    the result of huge amounts of so-called
    'research' on how to reduce costs KW
    by KW! Yet the engineers of that time
    reported to code authorities of the
    National Recovery Administration that
    the early machines for making small
    ice at the place it is consumed should
    be prohibited. They claimed that such
    machines and the new ice product they
    made had no advantages whatsoever over
    the then standard large blocks of ice
    weighing 300 lb. each. Today, machines
    freezing ice in the form of small arched
    wafers are everywhere, even in small
    stores, and no one cares much about the
    KWH, per ton - their justification lies
    in other factors of cost saving and
    convenience." [104, p15]

The problem solver should be alert to
recognizing the possible need for
engineering sub-studies, either theoretical or experimental, before correct
parameters can be proposed. For example,
an extensive bio-engineering sub-study
might be judged essential before establishing the minimum safe cabin pressure
in a man-orbiting space laboratory.

● Need For Parameter Numbers: Where judged
possible, strive toward numerical goals
for all engineering parameters.

---

*"With char-
acteristic
daring, he
(Kettering,
Circa 1918)
told a gather-
ing of paint
suppliers
that it ought
to be possible
to finish an
automobile
body in an
hour instead
of two weeks."*
T. A. Boyd
[42, p125]

Such goals should be as quantitative and
specific as knowledge and circumstances
permit.

The problem solver should be alert
to the possible need for making 'orders
of magnitude' estimates on some goals.
This subject is treated in Chap. 16.

Example 5-13 'The engine to be created shall
exhibit a minimum thrust of 10,000,000
lbs. at air mass zero condition.'

A corollary to this principle is to, where

possible, clearly state tolerances. It should

be unnecessary for a contractor to *build* the

engine and *then* discover that the engineer

originally specifying the goal really meant 'a

minimum thrust' but failed to say so with the

result that the contractor interpreted the goal

in his favor. Establishing meaningful tolerances

may require much discipline by the problem solver.

Details of this subject are many and much

beyond the scope of this book.

In attempting to apply the principle the

problem solver typically encounters the problems

below.

Fuzziness may exist because of either
our own ignorance at this phase of
the problem or a deliberate desire to
not be quantitative for some reason.
If you were the engineer creating a
new lunar surface landing vehicle for
the *first* time, how long would you
specify the vehicle legs to be in the
face of alleged 'authoritative' scientific evidence that the lunar surface
is covered with dust to an unknown
great depth? Our knowledge may be
more than fuzzy! So what does the
engineer propose as a goal in order
to 'make progress' on the problem?
He, after weighing all advice, finally
decides to "make the legs x inches
long," and simply proceeds on faith
that his numerical choice of "x"
will subsequently prove correct.
If it isn't, he establishes a new
numerical goal in light of later
knowledge and experience. He doesn't
'do nothing' until *all* knowledge is
available! (Will all 'necessary' facts
ever be available?)

Overspecifying is well known in creative work. To specify a goal that
is too nearly 'idealistic' may
result in either perceived impossibility
of obtaining a solution or require
resources beyond our bounds.

Sometimes the problem solver may
deliberately numerically overspecify,
i.e. 'aim high,' in order to effect
a step-function change contribution to
the state-of-the-art.

Example 5-14 Representatives of a
government agency once approached my
company to create a development
model of an important device for a
weapon system. Physical size was
'no problem.' After months of engineering work the first model shown

"*Impossible re-
quirements in
specifications
sometimes creates
bad feelings.
If used the ven-
dor may spend
much money
attempting to
meet the re-
quirements.
When he finally
gives up and
requests a re-
laxation of the
specification,
the purchaser
wants con-
sideration
for it.*"
*Walter L.
Fleischmann
[105]*

them was about desk size. Their
engineers said, "That's too big!
Cut it in half and we will buy it."
After more months of creative engineering work an operable unit half-
desk size was successfully demonstrated. They then pulled the same
trick *again*! After several such
challenges, the device was successfully reduced to quite small size
with the result that the state-of-
the-art had been significantly ad-
vanced--all as a direct result of
the challenge imposed by "impossible,
overspecified goals." That technology might still be only *slightly*
smaller than desk size had not such
'impossible' goals been specified!"

● <u>Physical Goals</u>: Specify the detailed physical
        goals.

The parameters and prodding question in
Table 5-1 may be of frequent help in implementing this principle.

● <u>Initial Performance</u>: Specify the *initial*
        performance goals.

Some helps to this end are shown in
Table 5-2.

● <u>Useful-life</u>: Specify the useful-life goals.

For those creative engineering problems
where useful-life is important the
suggestions in Table 5-3 may be starters.

● <u>Other Factors</u>: Determine what other factors,
        if any, should be considered.

Some possibilities are identified in
Table 5-4.

"He (Kettering
Circa 1918)
wanted to
make the elec-
tric refrig-
erator a por-
table apparatus
that needed
only be plugged
into a socket."
  T. A. Boyd
  [42, p124]

● Size
    Is it important?
Maximum? Minimum?
Why must it be the
proposed size?

● Weight
    Is it a factor
in a 'successful'
solution? What
happens if it weighs
too much? Too little?
Should it weigh 1/10
of proposed weight?
Ten times? Why must
it be the proposed
weight?

● Portability
    Is it an impor-
tant factor in a
successful creation?
What does 'portable'
mean?

● Appearance
    Is it important
to the user? What
impression must it
leave? Who will
decide acceptability?

● Marking
    Should the device be
identified? What is to
be communicated? Why?

● Energy Source
    Is one needed? Can
it be eliminated? Re-
duced? Enlarged? Why
must it be driven by this
source?

● Adjustments
    Will user adjustment
be required? Why
Can it be eliminated?
Will user know how to
adjust it?

● User Failure Modes
    Can it be misused?
How? Is corrective
goal action required?

TABLE 5-1 Detailed physical goals--thought
           prodders.

" - - if your
conclusion is
that the ope-
rator should
be able to
make daily
adjustments
on your in-
vention by
hitting it
with a rock,
say so."
  Blake King
  [176, p41]

● Function Check
    How will you tell
that a created solution
initially achieves the
intended function?
Who will judge?

● Tests
    Will any be required?
What? Is test sequence
important? What happens
if the testing order is
inverted? Will test
apparatus be required?
Its nature? Special?
Standard? Are tests
to be recorded? How?
By whom? Confirmation
required?

● Environmental
    What thought has
been given to the total
environment the device
will see? Should it be
specified? Can it be?
Will it see hot, cold,
vibration, vacuum,
magnetic field, shock,
or other environments?
What new information is
required?

TABLE 5-2 Initial-performance goals--thought
           prodders.

"Specifications must be clear."
Walter L. Fleischmann [105]

● <u>End-of-life</u>
  Does it need defining? Can it be defined? *Why* is this the 'end-of-life'?

● <u>Accelerated</u> <u>Tests</u>
  Will they be required? *Why*? Can they be defined? Will there be a correlation problem with normal end-of-life tests?

● <u>Reliability</u>[1]
  Is it important that the item to be created not fail during normal life? What are the consequences to the device? To other systems? Will there be a 'half-failure?' What? Consequences?

● <u>Quality</u> <u>Assurance</u>[1]
  What goals are necessary to insure a quality-built product? *Why*? Will it be necessary to control the process of construction?

TABLE 5-3 Useful-life goals--thought prodders.

---

1. Useful information on these specialized fields of engineering will be found in the *IEEE Transactions On Reliability*.

*"The measure of
individual
achievement lies
in the timing
- -"*
  *Abbott Payson
  Usher [352, p79]*

*" - - the tech-
nical documents
have to be
written so that
they can be
interpreted in
only one way
by the reader."*
  *Walter L.
  Fleischmann
  [105]*

● Time
   What time goal is
to be set? Can it be
shortened? *Why* does
it have to be so short?

● Cost
   What is the created
device to cost? To
whom? Manufacturer?
Retailer? Government?
Is the proposed price
'right?'

● General Requirements
   Are there to be any?
If so, why? If not,
why? Is shoddy work-
manship acceptable?
How will it be con-
trolled? Who is re-
sponsible for what?
What about my creation
in another's operations?
How are revisions to
goals to be handled
as work progresses?

● Reference Documents
   Are they needed?
Why? Do they clarify
or confuse? Are MIL
specifications appro-
priate? ASTM standards?
Industry standards?
Are applicable parts
clearly cited?

● Social
   Is a market survey
of desired features
needed? Will the
statistics mean any-
thing for a *new*
creation? What human
factors need considera-
tion in the intended
use? Convenience
factors? What goals
are known desired and
what are anticipatory
requirements?

● Clarity and Ambiguity
   Are my goals clearly
written? Are they am-
biguous? If *I* were a
contractor reading them
alone, would I clearly
know what is to be
created?

● Trouble Anticipation
   Do my goals clearly
say *who* is to be con-
tacted when trouble
arises in execution?
Do they say *what* is
to be done if some or
all goals are not met?
Do they say *where*
the work is to be done?

● Justification
   Do I have terse, clear-
cut statements justi-
fying each goal? Should
these be included in
the formal goal state-
ment document?

TABLE 5-4 Other factors--thought prodders.

> ● <u>Revealing</u> <u>vs</u> <u>Concealing</u> <u>Goals</u>: Make a decision
> with which you are comfortable as to
> whether to conceal or reveal your goals
> to others.

Some problem solvers let their associates
and management know their goals for
acceptability of the problem solution while
others elect to conceal their goals until
the problem is solved. Concealment may
be dangerous if a large project is involved and everyone has varying interpretations of what is wanted. Further,
there is an ethical problem in concealment.
Concealment may be advantageous in environments of ridicule where such ridicule
would adversely affect me, the problem
solver, and possibly prevent my creating
an acceptable solution to the problems.
Revealing goals can be useful to the problem solver if he seeks their review by
more experienced creative engineers.
Possible errors, blind spots, and incom-
pleteness can be identified and corrected
provided it is done in an atmosphere of
helpfulness and positive outlook and not
in a 'you will never be able to do that'
attitude.

Each case is different. Exercise your
judgment carefully in applying this
principle.

> ● <u>Stopping</u> <u>Goals</u> Phase: After goals are estab-
> lished which are reasonably satisfactory
> to you, make the clean-cut decision to
> *stop* this phase.

*"We find that
in research a
certain amount
of intelligent
ignorance is
essential to
progress; for,
if you know too
much, you won't
try the thing."
Charles F.
Kettering
[42, p106]*

Such a decision is crucial to making
progress toward solving the problem.
Without it we flounder in the swamp of
doubts and unknowns raised in this phase
and rationalize ourselves to perpetually
stay until *all* questions are answered.

<u>Discussion</u> <u>Topics</u>

1. One principle stated the problem solver's
    goals should be written. Discuss some of the
    forms the writing might take, as hasty notes,
    formal reports, and drawings.

2. The principles of this Sec., in toto,
    appear to be aimed at foreseeing and fore-
    stalling every conceivable condition and
    constraint on 'the solution.' Discuss
    the engineer's conflict between risk-taking
    and stopping work on the goals phase.

3. What role can our highly developed analytical
    skills play in helping us 'specify goals'
    for a device or system to be created?

4. *Why* is the 'need for numbers' principle
    necessary when seeking to solve complex
    creative engineering problems of the
    type you will encounter in professional
    practice? Are all goals reducible to
    numbers?

5. Discuss some of the subtle ways, perhaps
    unaware to the problem solver, 'goal
    specifying' may be so *restrictive* as to
    presuppose 'a solution' to the problem.

Exercises

5-E18. Specify the goals for an 'ideal textbook'
        in the technical area which most *interests*
        you.

5-E19. Many Colleges of Engineering have an
        Engineers' Fair. 'Specify the goals'
        for an ideal technical exhibit therein.

5-E20. Assume that a problem inquiry phase has
        turned up the need for creating a new ideal
        socially acceptable drink. Simply identify
        the parameters for 'specifying goals' for
        such a drink.

5-E21. From a problem inquiry phase an engineer has
        determined there is a need and a market for
        an ultra compact, miniaturized, lightweight
        VHF (118-136 Mhz) communications transceiver
        for aircraft use. His specified goals
        might be: (List).

5-E22. An existing 108-136 Mhz aircraft transceiver
        for navigation and communications is to be
        redesigned using integrated circuits techniques.
        Here are the goals I would specify for this
        project: (List).

5-E23.   With the aid of your girl friend or wife,
         specify the goals for your ideal home using
         principles of this section.

5-E24.   If you were an engineer with a strong streak
         of entrepreneurship and wanted to create
         a step-function change in the home building
         industry by creating a mass-produced ultra low-
         cost home for ghetto peoples, propose a set
         of specific goals for the home.

5-E25.   One major problem of affluent societies
         is garbage disposal. Assume a problem inquiry
         phase has shown the need for a household
         garbage disposer for solids. Here is my
         proposal for the specific goals for this
         product to be created: (List).

5-5 Example Problems-'Specifying Goals Phase'

Example 5-15 A historically interesting document
exemplifying many of the principles embodied
in this phase is shown in Fig. 5-2. It is
worthy of your careful study.

Discussion Topics

For Fig. 5-2:

1. Find the 'function statement.' Does it
    exist? Is it clear?

2. How many flying machines, according to the
    document , are to be created?

3. Have all the correct parameters been identified?
    Is the test to be run at tree-top level or
    10,000 feet?

4. How many feet/min. is the machine to ascend?

5. What parts of this specification are 'fuzzy?'

6. For 1907 was this goal statement 'over-
    specified?'

GENERAL REQUIREMENTS

The general dimensions of the flying machine will be determined by the manufacturer, subject to the following conditions:

1. Bidders must submit with their proposals the following:
    (a) Drawings to scale showing the general dimensions and shape of the flying machine which they propose to build under this specification.
    (b) Statement of the speed for which it is designed.
    (c) Statement of the total surface area of the supporting planes.
    (d) Statement of the total weight.
    (e) Description of the engine which will be used for motive power.
    (f) The material of which the frame, planes, and propellers will be constructed. Plane received will not be shown to other bidders.

2. It is desirable that the flying machine should be designed so that it may be quickly and easily assembled and taken apart and packed for transportation in army wagons. It should be capable of being assembled and put in operating condition in about one hour.

3. The flying machine must be designed to carry two persons having a combined weight of about 350 pounds, also, sufficient fuel for a flight of 125 miles.

4. The flying machine should be designed to have a speed of at least forty miles per hour in still air, but bidders must submit quotations in their proposals for cost depending upon the speed attained during the trial flight, according to the following costs:

    40 miles per hour, 100 per cent
    39 miles per hour, 90 per cent
    38 miles per hour, 80 per cent
    37 miles per hour, 70 per cent
    36 miles per hour, 60 per cent
    Less than 36 miles per hour rejected
    41 miles per hour, 110 per cent
    42 miles per hour, 120 per cent
    43 miles per hour, 130 per cent
    44 miles per hour, 140 per cent

5. The speed accomplished during the trial flight will be determined by taking an average of the time over a measured course of more than five miles, against and with the wind. The time will be taken by a flying start, passing the starting point at full speed at both ends of the course. This test subject to such additional details as the Chief Signal Officer of the Army may prescribe at the time.

6. Before acceptance, a trial endurance flight will be required of at least one hour during which time the flying machine must remain continuously in the air without landing. It shall return to the starting point and land without any damage that would prevent it immediately starting upon another flight. During this trial flight of one hour, it must be steered in all directions without difficulty and at all times under perfect control and equilibrium.

7. Three trials will be allowed for speed as provided for in Paragraphs 4 and 5. Three trials for endurance as provided for in Paragraph 6, and both tests must be completed within a period of thirty days from the date of delivery. The expense of the tests to be borne by the manufacturer. The place of delivery to the Government and trial flights will be at Fort Myer, Virginia.

8. It should be so designed as to ascend in any country which may be encountered in field service. The starting device must be simple and transportable. It should also land in a field without requiring a specially prepared spot and without damaging its structure.

9. It should be provided with some device to permit of a safe descent in case of an accident to the propelling machinery.

10. It should be sufficiently simple in its construction and operation to permit an intelligent man to become proficient in its use within a reasonable length of time.

11. Bidders must furnish evidence that the Government of the United States has the lawful right to use all patented devices or appurtenances which may be a part of the flying machine, and that the manufacturers of the flying machine are authorized to convey the same to the Government. This refers to the unrestricted right to use the flying machine sold to the Government, but does not contemplate the exclusive purchase of patent rights for duplicating the flying machine.

12. Bidders will be required to furnish with their proposal a certified check amounting to ten per cent of the price stated for the 40-mile speed. Upon making the award for this flying machine, these certified checks will be returned to the bidders, and the successful bidder will be required to furnish a bond, according to Army Regulations, of the amount equal to the price stated for the 40-mile speed.

13. The price quoted in proposals must be understood to include the instruction of two men in the handling and operation of this flying machine. No extra charge for this service will be allowed.

14. Bidders must state the time which will be required for delivery after receipt of order.

FIG. 5-2   A U. S. Signal Corps. "Advertisement and Specifications for a Heavier-Than-Air Flying Machine," dated December 23, 1907. Note the role of 'vision' in item 9 which still is not available on aircraft. [56]   (*Courtesy Air Force Museum.*)

7. How long was the machine to last?

Creative Problems
5-CP1. As assigned by your Professor.

5-6 Omitting the Step of Specifying Goals

It may sometimes be possible for the problem

solver to omit this phase when:

● The problem is relatively simple.

● Goals already exist with which the
   engineer is in agreement and there
   is no need for new goals to be
   written.

● The creative engineer working on
   the problem intuitively knows what
   is needed because of intimate
   familiarity with the problem.

It is largely a matter of engineering

judgment as to whether to omit it or execute it.

Before deciding to omit it on a given problem

the possible consequences of omission should be

faced of:

*"Often the dis-
cussions become
highly emotional
- -"*

*John R. M. Alger
and Carl V. Hays
[4, p15]*

● Embarassment: To you, your management and your company when and
   if it is later revealed, possibly
   after expending great sums,
   that 'the engineer didn't
   know what constituted an acceptable solution.'

● Wasted Effort: Possibly working
   toward solutions manifesting
   wholly unacceptable performance
   characteristics.

● Loss of Goodwill: Especially between
   your company and a sub-contractor
   when disagreements arise over

> testing the thing to be created.
> Arguments may ensue and adversely
> affect the problem, yourself,
> and both companies with the re-
> sults spreading like a cancer
> in both.
>
> ● <u>Inability</u> <u>to</u> <u>Stop</u> <u>Work</u>: The problem
>   solution work may go on and on,
>   and no one appears to know when
>   the problem is 'solved' and
>   work should stop.

It is a sad spectacle to see a major engineering project flounder, be severely criticized,
and die because either no, or incomplete, goals
have been specified because of an undisciplined
problem solving approach by the engineer(s)
attempting solution.

For engineering problems of substance requiring much time, effort, and resources for a
solution to be created it may be wise to execute
this phase *thoroughly* before proceeding to the
next phase of 'determining means.'

Chapter Summary

● *'Specifying goals' is an important major step
  in a mature disciplined problem solving approach.*

● Goals originate with the disciplined creative
  problem solver and may require his full
  spectrum of talents to propose them.

● Principles for specifying goals were advanced.

● Examples were given for this phase.

● Possible omission of this phase and the consequences were briefly broached.

CHAPTER 6

DISCIPLINE OF DETERMINING MEANS

"But goals are achieved by some *means*, and sooner or
later even the most impulsive man of action will discover that some ways of achieving the goal are more
effective than others."
                                    John W. Gardner [116, p47]

●   **Need** and purposes for a 'Determining
     Means' major step in creative problem
     solving.

●   A model structure for the problem solver's
     thinking and action.

●   Some principles for 'Determining Means.'

●   Engineering examples.

6-1 <u>Need</u> <u>and</u> <u>Purposes</u> <u>for</u> '<u>Determining</u> <u>Means</u>' <u>Phase</u>

"*Mean: That
through which, or
by the help of
which, an end is
attained; some-
thing tending to
an object de-
sired.*" *[373]*

In the previous chapter we saw that the

problem solver establishes a set of specific goals

defining what constitutes, to him, acceptable solution

constraints on the problem to be solved. The important

issues of whether it should be solved and the en-

visioned value of an acceptable solution have long

since been faced. By now the need serves

as a background motivational spur toward achieving

an acceptable solution. In toto the previous two

phases have resulted in a clear *definition* of the

problem.

We must now 'determine a means,' i.e. create

a proposed solution.

All of us have seen in the professional
journals and magazines of our respective engineering
disciplines clever finished solutions described for
some engineering problem. Such works are
so numerous that we may have the feeling we can never
'catch up' with the activity in our engineering area!
But have you thoughtfully paused to think and
inquire *how* such a clever solution was created?
What did the engineering problem solver think and do
behind-the-scenes which he did *not* reveal in the
finished smooth-reading published paper that enabled him to arrive at the revealed creative solution?
What alternatives were considered and discarded?
How, if at all, did the problem solver's feelings
affect the solution? Was the solution found in a
'flash of insight' or was it the result of sustained disciplined striving? Is it possible that
knowing the methodology and approach used in
actually achieving a solution is *the* fundamental
thing worth learning to enable me to solve future
problems I shall face, especially those requiring
new solutions not to be found in texts or prior-art
literature? Oh! Did the author describing that
clever solution in fact reveal his actual methods?
Didn't he focus on the *solution* description?

This chapter deals with the uncommon 'inside
story' of a skeletal structure for what the

*" - - thinking is
much tougher than
working or **talk-**
ing."*
  William Shockley
  [292, p169]

disciplined creative engineer might feel, think,
and do during the 'determining means' phase.
It is *here* we are to focus on the apparent
best way of *solving* the problem, particularly
in a new or unique fashion. Clearly up
to now we have, in effect, merely defined
clearly the problem to be solved without yet
proposing *how* it is to be solved. We are thus
led to define:

> ● <u>Purpose</u> <u>of</u> '<u>Determining</u> <u>Means</u>' <u>Phase</u>:
>
>   To define to the satisfaction
>   of the problem solver the
>   tentatively best 'means' to a
>   solution of the problem being
>   solved.

An overview of this phase is shown in

Fig. 6-1.

Observe the following about this phase:

  ● <u>Input</u> to the phase is the totality of
     specified goals which the solution must
     meet. Without the goals no solution
     output would be forthcoming. It is
     generally essential in a mature
     creative problem solving approach to
     have goals clearly identified *before*
     expending the problem solver's precious
     resources to create a new solution.

*"We at once set to
work to devise a
more efficient means
of maintaining the
equilibrium."*
  Orville Wright
  [388, p8]

  ● <u>The</u> <u>Step</u> involves creating a proposal[1]
     for a new system, device, process,
     or other physical thing. The irregular
     outline symbolizes the initial abstractness
     of that which is to be created, i.e.
     its solution form is hardly clear during
     the early part of this phase. As we progress

[1]An attitude of "Here is my *proposed* solution" dominates the phase.

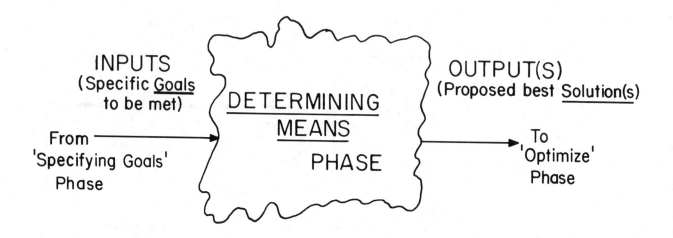

FIG. 6-1 Simple functional view of 'Determining
          Means' phase for the specific system,
          device, process, or engineering
          material to be created. The problem
          solver conceives and proposes the best
          'paper' *solution* to the problem during
          this phase.

"Take seven parts of saltpeter, five of charcoal, and five of sulphur."
  Roger Bacon
  [18, p44]

"A solution is a synthesis of component elements which hurdles the obstructing difficulties and, neither exceeding the available resources nor encroaching on the limits set by the constraints, accomplishes the prescribed goals."
  Morris Asimow
  [12, p45]

through the phase the solution tends to become clearer as symbolized by less irregularity toward the right of the figure. Note also that *something* (the solution!) is to be created during this phase. The implication is that it did not previously exist insofar as I the problem solver knew. Our conception of the interior details of the step will be enlarged in Sec. 6-2.

The Output of the phase is a proposed best solution. Note that it is *proposed*. It is a specific idea for a solution which appears in the judgment of the problem solver to best meet the specified goals. It is a sketch, drawing, schematic, or other symbolic means for conveying that which has been created. It is a symbolization of what "might be"--something *new* perhaps. At this point the problem solver is in effect proposing to "make it (the solution) like this: - - -." It usually is the proposal for something physical, e.g. a circuit, a machine, a system, a bridge, or an apparatus to be physically built. The output is a 'paper solution' proposal. It has *not* at this point been thoroughly and exhaustively tested nor has a solution like that proposed necessarily been built, though it may have. It is thus the embodiment of a *tentative* solution creation that the engineering problem solver judges to have merit and is worthy of carrying to the 'optimize' and following stages of the overall six-step problem solving approach.

It is very important that we realize the output of the 'determining means' phase is *not* the fully completed, finished, polished 'solution' on which no further engineering work is required. It is a major step to that end, however, and clearly a significant improvement over what we had when this phase was initiated.

In an overall sense, for we engineering problem solvers the 'determining means' phase is characterized

"Synthesis is combinatorial."
Thomas T. Woodson
[383, p86]

by deliberate, hard, creative thinking directed

toward *synthesizing* the best solution for the

problem being solved. It is a highly

personalized creative phase requiring exercise of

our full span of problem solving attributes before

a tentatively satisfactory solution can be proposed.

Example 6-1 An engineer has the task of creating the propulsion engine for a 300 MPH surface transportation system for the Boston-Washington corridor. During a 'determining means' phase one alternative he conceives is the idea of a train riding a single aluminum track which is straddled by a linear induction motor shoe which rides with the train but does not contact the rail--a new and unique propulsion means springing out of the well-known induction motor. He works out the theory and geometry of a proposed new type of train 'engine.' His 'output' from the 'determining means' phase is the proposed engine physical configuration. He thinks it is the best long range means of solving the high speed surface transportation propulsion problem. He has created a part of the future *now*! [60, p795]

Example 6-2 While working in a research group I once had the problem "to create a solid state electronic instrument which would be driven by a DC voltage in the 0.3 mv to 10 v range and whose output voltage would be the exact logarithm of the input voltage." Such instruments were not then on the market to my knowledge. Something new had to be created. The 'determining means' phase resulted in the proposal shown in Fig. 6-3 to use an operational amplifier with a special non-linear feedback element. After much subsequent work (in later phases of the problem solving approach) and modification, the basic proposal was proven sound.

Discussion Topics

1. How do you account for the widespread engineering practice of describing the *solution* in technical

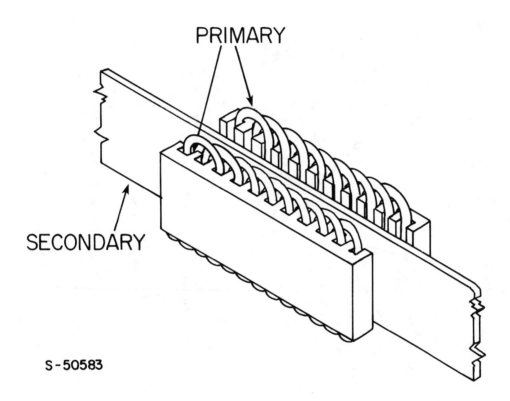

S-50583

FIG. 6-2 Simplified model of a double sided short
         primary linear induction motor for
         propulsion system for high speed railway
         after Chirgwin et al [60].

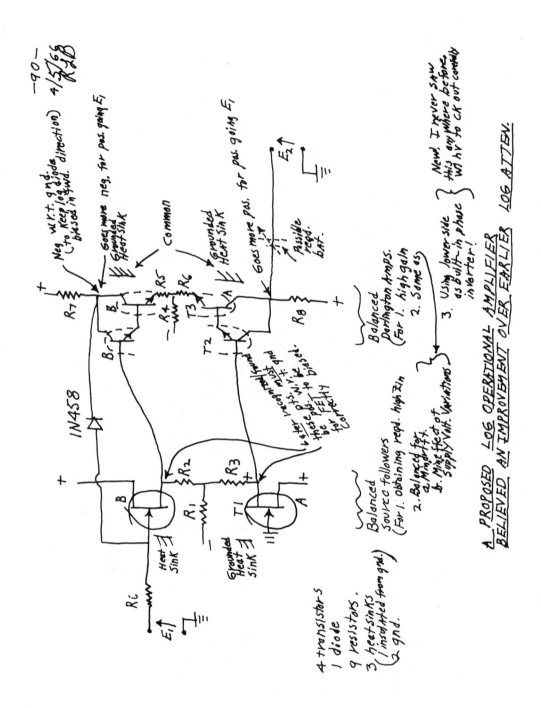

FIG. 6-3 Example of a proposed 'paper' solution taken
from an engineering notebook. A proposed
solution at this stage may have flaws in it.

papers whereas relatively little may be published
on the methodology, including 'failures,' used
by the problem solver in effecting a successful
solution?

2. The purpose of the 'determining means' phase stated
the solution must be satisfactory to the problem
solver. Is satisfying ourselves really enough
or will our solution also have, perhaps later,
to prove satisfactory to others?

3. Constructively criticize the attitude exhibited
by a student: "The phase is trivial. You simply
enter it with a problem and you exit with a
solution. It really is quite simple."

4. How will you know your solution proposal resulting from the phase is 'best?'

5. In a textbook from an engineering course you
especially enjoyed, approximately what percentage
of the problems worked required you to *propose*
a *new* creative solution to the problem? What
percentage were of the 'one answer' type in
which new fresh solution proposal ideas were not
sought? How do you account for this situation?
When you graduate and start practicing engineering
do you expect to have to advance *new* solution
proposals to engineering problems?

6. If the output of the 'determining means' phase
only results in a 'paper proposal,' at what
phase do we get around to construction and
test of the proposal?

7. Based on your understanding to this point of the
'determining means' phase, what personal
difficulties do you see for the problem solver
in this phase?

Exercises

6-E1. Summarize your understanding of the inputs, functions,
and outputs of the 'Problem Inquiry' and 'Specifying
Goals' phases of the six-step creative problem
solving approach.

6-E2. Write out your conception of the input, principal
purpose, and output of the 'determining means'
phase.

6-E3. Propose at least five specific improvement
possibilities to ordinary laboratory clip leads.
Sketch if necessary.

6-E4.   An engineer needs to measure about 50 KV DC
        but has no high voltage meter or funds to buy
        one. He has a 100 v full scale digital volt-
        meter and three bushel baskets full of assorted
        resistors. The HV DC is a low current source,
        so his probe impedance needs to be approximately
        100 megohms or greater. Make a *specific* pro-
        posal for the physical embodiment of a workable
        HV probe he might construct.

6-E5.   A large electric power generator stator
        weighing 800,000 lbs, costing $4,000,000 and
        requiring 24 months for manufacture is being
        delivered to a new power plant site. It is
        within 8 miles of the site after being safely
        transported 1200 miles from the factory when
        the road bed, which is through a swamp,
        collapses because of the combined weight of stator
        and multi-wheel transporting trailer. The
        trailer tips, and the generator stator rolls
        completely off into the swampy water and muck.
        Propose as many solution means to this problem
        as you can. How will you tell which means is
        best?

6-E6.   Electric energy 'leaking' from a high-voltage
        transmission line can be costly and interfere
        with nearby telephones, radio and television
        sets. A portable detector is to be created
        which will quickly and accurately spot the
        'leak.' Propose a means. How will you determine
        whether your proposal is the 'best' solution?

6-E7.   Propose possible ideas for a new or novel
        means for measuring frequency of a wave of
        your choice.

6-E8.   For a military electronics application a $3\mu fd$
        capacitor is required to dump several hundred
        amperes of current for a short time into a
        resistive load. The capacitor must be tested
        for *peak* discharge current capability. Propose
        a specific circuit and a geometrical means of
        physical implementation which you might consider
        suitable for testing this capacitor. (Hint:
        minimize lead inductance.)

6-E9.   It is not so well known among some engineers
        that there are many difficulties with printed
        wiring boards. For example, the edges of the
        'wiring' are far from smooth; some residual
        acid used in the etching process invariably

remains to act on the board and its conductors
on a long term basis; the 'wiring' corrodes;
it is difficult to attach terminals, sockets,
or components in a reliable manner; creepage
and migration of silver or gold adversely affects
leakage resistances between critical points
on the board; establishment of adequate inspection criteria--to name only a few. Suggest
improvement proposal ideas for printed wiring
boards.

6-E10. Suggest idea possibilities for measuring charge
flow of only a few electrons into an electrode structure.

6-E11. If you were creating low-loss, low series inductance variable capacitors in the 0-5
pico farad size suitable for UHF circuits
for the first time, sketch your specific
proposal ideas for how you would physically
structure the capacitors.

6-E12. Consider your engineering discipline on a
macroscopic scale. Propose specific means by
which your discipline potentially could contribute to peace and brotherhood of all nations on
earth. (Example: FM and TV direct broadcast
via satellite to be created by electrical
engineers.)

Creative Problems

6-CP1. A new burglar alarm system is to be conceived
which will warn of a possible intruder at or
through a door. Sketch at least five
alternative solutions which might be
considered.

6-CP2. A tank contains a liquid. The level must be
read out one-half mile away to an accuracy of
0.5 percent. Propose a plausible solution.

6-CP3. A new elegantly simple fail-safe flow-rate meter
is to be created for measuring instantaneous
oxygen flow-rates in a pipe to a rocket engine.
Propose the 'best' solution. How do you know it
is 'best?'

6-CP4. Propose a specific new creative vehicle concept
which would permit manned space flight to
the planet Mars.

6-CP5. A *new* toy is to be created--not a revision
of some existing toy. It is intended for
3-5 year old boys or girls. Propose such a
toy, basing your proposal primarily on
electrical concepts (or mechanical if you are
an ME, etc.) of your choice.

6-CP6. Stealing of objects is a well-known problem of
society. Within your university stealing of
books from the library is most likely a major
problem. It is so in most libraries in spite
of 'check guards' at the doors. Propose a
specific genuinely creative solution which will
positively reduce book stealing in a library to
zero. *After* you have made your proposal, visit
your library and see if you have 'a solution
searching for a problem.' Comment on the
possible dangers, in general problem solving, of
the above methodology where *no* 'problem inquiry'
or 'goal specifying' phases preceded the solution
proposal.

6-CP7. If you were the engineer responsible for
creating a statewide system of identifying where
lightning struck and what the peak discharge
current was in each strike, how would you do it?

6-CP8. Submit an original proposal for a new clever
electrical circuit 'breadboard' for use in
experimental work or teaching.

6-CP9. Focus on an electrical device or system in
the home. Propose a new and radical improvement in the device or function it
performs. Include sketches.

6-CP10. Propose a radically new means of greatly reducing
accidents on Interstate Highways by utilizing
modern electronics and electrical concepts.

6-CP11. Others of a more detailed nature as assigned
by your professor.

6-2 What the Problem Solver Does in the 'Determining
Means' Phase

The discussion in Sec. 6-1 was centered on

clearly understanding the *function* of the 'determining

means' phase. While functional understanding is

essential, it is not enough for successfully

generating new creative solutions to a complex

engineering problem. We need to know more details

of what the problem solver typically does *within*

the phase, i.e. we need a workable model

for a guide in actual problem solving. Note

the word *guide*. The models are intended

to convey a feeling of 'here is what one

might do during this phase.' In modelling it

we do not intend to convey the idea of a hardened

model which the problem solver slavishly follows

in his quest for a new or unique solution. Rather

we adopt the viewpoint of 'here is what this phase

is roughly like. Let's adapt it as seems best

to our particular problem.'

We shall build our understanding of this

important phase by a two-step process, e.g. a first-

order model showing the gross structure within

the phase, and a second-order model showing a

more detailed structure. The latter is the most

useful in actual creative problem solving, but

the former is essential to understand it.

THE FIRST-ORDER MODEL OF THE DETERMINING MEANS

PHASE is symbolically shown in Fig. 6-4. This

figure can be thought of as an exploded view of

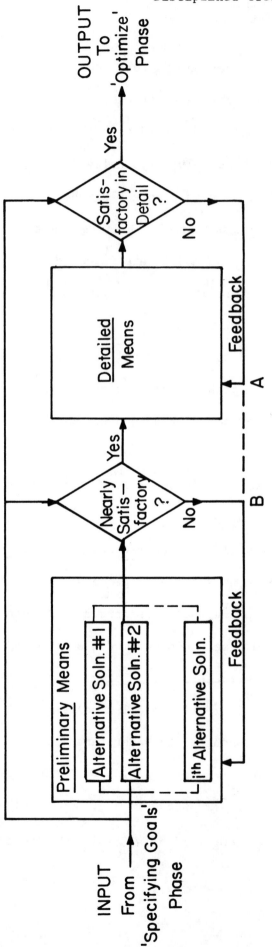

FIG. 6-4 First-Order model of interior of 'Determining Means' phase shown in Fig. 6-1. Note that the specified goals constitute the reference against which the problem solver's proposed tentative solutions are measured in both pre-liminary and detailed sub-parts of this phase.

the interior of Fig. 6-1. As a problem solver, I

enter this phase with a set of goals, hopefully

achievable, which the solution to be created must

meet. I immediately enter the 'preliminary means'

sub-phase. Here I seek to create, recall, or be-

come consciously aware of specific possible alternative

solutions to the problem. Each alternative solution

*" - - there is no
one right answer
to creative
problems."*
John E. Arnold
[10, p252]

requires time for me to think through and arrive

at a specific solution proposal. Alternative solutions

are developed in time sequence and not simultaneously.

Some alternatives I may identify from prior art,

some I may have to create, and some I may simply

recognize exist but appear unworthy of expending

precious engineering effort on them at this time.

The alternative proposals are considered tentative

in nature and identify preliminary 'possibilities.'

Anyone may or may not be wiped out by later

engineering judgment or for some practical reason.

*"Don't kid yourself.
Demand that your
vague ideas be
firmed up to
specific pro-
positions."*
Don C. Hoefler
[152]

Example 6-3

I once chose the problem of creating a
special bed for asthmatic sufferers. The
strategy was to filter the air in the bedroom and
blow a low velocity envelope of clean air over
the sufferer's head while sleeping. Breathing
8 hours of clean air out of 24 later proved
enough to significantly retard onset of asthma
caused by pollens and dusts. For a filter an early
alternative extensively investigated involved
the use of an electrostatic precipitator which
idea was carried to the 'nearly satisfactory'
proposal stage. I was concerned with the possible
side effects any ozone generated by the 5 Kv

"Standard practice
for all problem
solving, then, is
to list all the
possible alternatives
before making a
decision."
    Edward Hodnett
    [151, p64]

charging electrode might have on an asthmatic.
After finding that filter paper with controlled
pore size was commercially available for the
pharmaceutical industry this alternative was
explored and successfully adopted. The
mechanical filter alternative had no ozone
possibility, and the precipitator alternative
was dropped.

The whole important subject of *how* the
problem solver obtains ideas for generating the
alternatives is the subject of Chap. 14, Creativity
Stimulators. There is no magic here, but successful
engineering problem solving indicates the necessity
of identifying the largest possible number of
alternative solutions.

At the output of the 'preliminary means' sub-
phase a decision, represented by the diamond, must
be made **as** to whether each alternative is or is
not nearly satisfactory. The word *nearly* is
emphasized, as in all likelihood even the best
of the proposals will not be wholly satisfactory.
It is here at the decisive phase that each alternative
tentative 'solution' is measured against the set
of specified goals. If the solution proposed appears
to meet most of the primary goals and some of the
secondary goals, then I might, as an engineering
judgment matter, say, "Yes, this solution is nearly
satisfactory" and pass it into the next sub-phase,

" - - the most
important decisions
in a design problem
must often be made
without assistance
from higher mathe-
matics."
    Taylor, et al
    [332, p649]

'detailed means.' If it is not nearly satisfactory,

such as "it appears to be inherently too large to

meet the size goal," then note that a feedback path

exists back to some undefined point near the be-

ginning of the 'preliminary means' sub-phase. This

*"Your criterion
of success of any
solution may be
whether or not
it works."
   Edward Hodnett
   [151, p77]*

path suggests that I may need to go through the

'preliminary means' sub-phase again--to iterate--

performing additional work on the idea, perhaps

working out means to miniaturize it for the

example cited. Each time I iterate a proposed

solution I change, shape, or modify it--perhaps

a little or perhaps a great deal--until finally

I satisfy myself the proposed alternative is

*"Sift through
your hoard and
pick out the
gems."
   Blake King
   [176, p41]*

nearly satisfactory as measured against the

reference of the specified goals. Then and only

then is the preliminary solution proposal ready

to proceed to the 'detailed means' sub-phase.

Assuming a specific solution proposal embodiment

has been created which passes the 'nearly satisfactory'

decision point, I now carry this proposal into

a 'detailed means' sub-phase. Here I examine the

proposed solution more carefully--in more detail--

making modifications and improvements to it. I now

deal with 'practicalities' in effecting an improved

solution proposal. This now improved solution is

measured for acceptability against the same set of

specified goals with which I started. Those

goals which were unable to be met at the

output of the 'nearly satisfactory' decisive

point have been focussed on and suitable modifi-

cations or corrections have been made to the

proposed solution embodiment until the solution appears

to have a high probability of success and should now

pass on to the 'optimize' phase. If it fails to

meet the specified goals, the structure again

includes a feedback path to permit iteration until

the proposed solution *is* satisfactory in detail

and a solution obtained.

Some problems may not be solvable and we may

have to terminate the problem solving process

without a successful output from the phase.

"Never risk your reputation on a single shot for if you miss, the loss is irrepair-able."
  Baltasar Gracian [127, p175]

"In order to minimize the risk it is good policy to hedge against the failure of a new project by providing an alternative, or an 'out' to fall back on, wherever practicable."
  W. J. King [178]

For some types of problems engineering judgment

may indicate the wisdom of carrying two or more

proposed solutions through this phase so that if

one later fails we have a 'second best' proposal on

which to fall back.

Note that Fig. 6-4 shows a dotted feedback

path from point A to point B. It symbolizes

that for some problems the 'detailed means'

sub-phase results in the realization that the entire

principal proposal concept is unsatisfactory--per-

haps because of our having earlier overlooked some

fundamental fact(s)--and we must now start all over

again back near the beginning of the 'preliminary

means' sub-phase.

Example 6-4

Continuing Example 6-3, following the decision to use a large area controlled pore size filter paper the 'detailed means' sub-phase was entered. The details of how many filters were to be used, how to mount them, the type of air mover, whether it should suck or blow, means of eliminating vibration and noise, type fan blade, whether an additional post filter for gaseous contaminants was necessary, whether a pre filter was required to prevent blocking the pores of the main filter, exploring the particle size distributions of dusts and pollens and methods of measuring them—these and other detailed engineering matters were dealt with before a final engineering sketch—a 'make it like this' document—resulted for this new creation, a clean-room bed for asthmatics.

Summarizing, the first-order model of the 'determining means' phase consists of 'preliminary' and 'detailed' sub-phases, both of which contain feedback loops permitting iteration until the proposed solution creation satisfactorily passes the critical decision points. The output of the phase is a well thought-out 'best' solution embodiment to the problem and is in the form of a *specific* proposal on paper.

THE SECOND ORDER MODEL OF THE 'DETERMINING MEANS' PHASE is shown in Fig. 6-5. It is an expansion of the first-order model. (Check it against Fig. 6-4, seeing if it contains all the basic parts of the first-order model.) The figure shows an integrated dis-

" - - ways and means of accomplishing the physical marvels set forth kept me busy thinking."
    Robert H. Goddard
    [121, p30]

"Recognize that every work of man represents an imperfect solution to a problem."
    Blake King
    [176, p41]

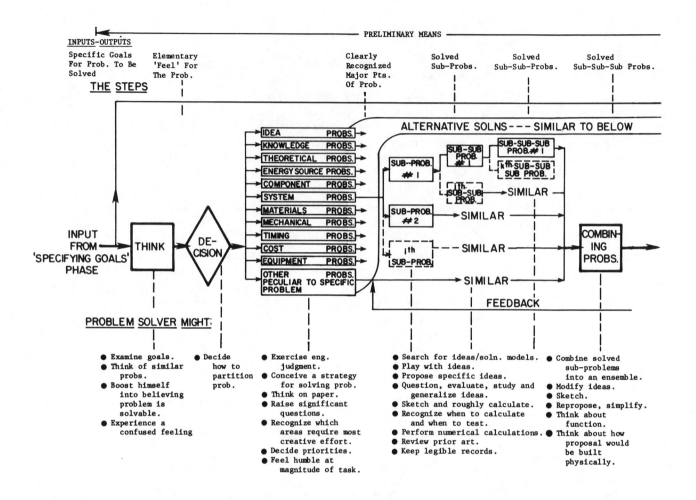

FIG. 6-5 Second-order model of 'Determining Means' phase. It is a more detailed
          view of Fig. 6-4 and shows the morphology leading to a high probability
          of achieving a creative solution to the problem being solved.

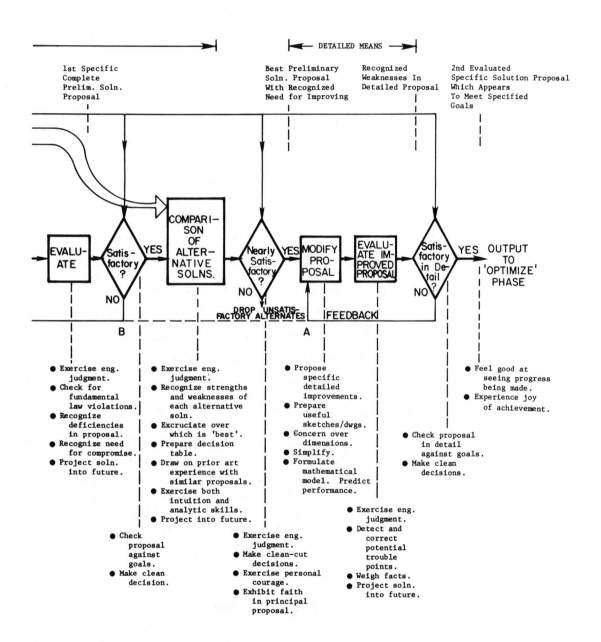

DETAILED MEANS

1st Specific
Complete
Prelim. Soln.
Proposal

Best Preliminary
Soln. Proposal
With Recognized
Need for Improving

Recognized
Weaknesses In
Detailed Proposal

2nd Evaluated
Specific Solution Proposal
Which Appears
To Meet Specified
Goals

EVALU-ATE

Satis-factory? — YES — COMPARI-SON OF ALTER-NATIVE SOLNS. — Nearly Satis-factory? — YES — MODIFY PRO-POSAL — EVALU-ATE IM-PROVED PROPOSAL — Satis-factory in De-tail? — YES — OUTPUT TO 'OPTIMIZE' PHASE

NO   NO   NO

DROP UNSATIS-FACTORY ALTERNATES   FEEDBACK

B   A

● Exercise eng.
  judgment.
● Check for
  fundamental
  law violations.
● Recognize
  deficiencies
  in proposal.
● Recognize need
  for compromise.
● Project soln.
  into future.

● Exercise eng.
  judgment.
● Recognize strengths
  and weaknesses of
  each alternative
  soln.
● Excruciate over
  which is 'best'.
● Prepare decision
  table.
● Draw on prior art
  experience with
  similar proposals.
● Exercise both
  intuition and
  analytic skills.
● Project into future.

● Propose
  specific
  detailed
  improvements.
● Prepare
  useful
  sketches/dwgs.
● Concern over
  dimensions.
● Simplify.
● Formulate
  mathematical
  model. Predict
  performance.

● Feel good at
  seeing progress
  being made.
● Experience joy
  of achievement.

● Check proposal
  in detail
  against goals.
● Make clean
  decisions.

● Check
  proposal
  against
  goals.
● Make clean
  decision.

● Exercise eng.
  judgment.
● Make clean-cut
  decisions.
● Exercise personal
  courage.
● Exhibit faith
  in principal
  proposal.

● Exercise eng.
  judgment.
● Detect and
  correct
  potential
  trouble
  points.
● Weigh facts.
● Project soln.
  into future.

ciplined structure for how, in general, we might
proceed through this phase. Notice that INPUTS-OUT-
PUTS for each of the sub-phases are shown at the top
of the figure. At the bottom are listed some
of the actions we might take at that sub-phase.
The actions indicated are suggestions. For
a given problem it may be necessary to add or
delete actions as seems best for that specific
problem.

This important figure, which is the 'heart'
of the 'determining means' phase of the six-
step problem solving approach, can perhaps best
be understood by means of a sketchy example based
on an actual problem. The example is a summary
of approximately 100 pages of recorded creative
thought all of which cannot be included here.
The example per se is of less importance than
obtaining a 'feel' for how one proceeds
in this phase. Follow the example through by
referring to Fig. 6-5.

<u>Example 6-5</u>

<u>The Problem</u> I am asked to create a 'black box'
instrument whose function is to permit an x-y
recorder to correctly plot on logarithmic
paper on its y axis the voltage V_1.

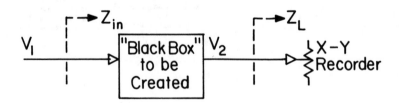

FIG. 6-6

The 'black box' is to be an intermediate instrument between another instrument, a voltage density
function meter, and a recorder and will permit
the voltage V_1 to be 'compressed' on the recorder

paper so that large variations of V_1 may be visually seen without having to change scale ranges on the recorder.

The Specified Goals are:

Primary Goals

1. $V_2 = K \log V_1$

2. $Z_{in} \geq 1$ megohm; $Z_L = 1$ megohm

3. V_1 = DC voltage ranging from 1 mv to 300 mv.

Secondary Goals

4. External power supplies are permissible but it may be desirable to not have any.

5. Frequency response--not considered important as V_1 is so slowly varying as to be considered DC.

6. All active devices to be solid state if possible.

7. Cost not considered important for this problem.

Determining Means With the above goals, which resulted from a 'specifying goals' phase of the six-step problem solving approach, I enter the 'determining means' phase.

"Sometimes you can get started by solving a *part* of the problem." Walter C. Johnson [163, p18]

I first re-examine the goals I have specified, thinking about them. I decide that obtaining the log function will be the most difficult and is crucial to solving the problem. I therefore choose to focus on it. I recall having seen a small commercially available unit of some kind which took the log. Was it of a current or voltage? I am unable to recall, but I do remember where I saw it. This boosts me to believing the problem is solvable! I obtain, after some trouble, a loan of the commercial unit only to discover that it does not cover the desired voltage range, a measured plot of $\log V_1$ vs V_2 is not exactly linear, and the device is in a sealed container unopenable without permanently damaging the device. An X-Ray is not easily obtainable, and no literature is available describing the device. I experience

some frustration that the needed facilities for
X-Ray are not available within our organization.
Also some confusion is present as I think perhaps
someone has already solved problems of this kind,
but there is no easy way to find out.

At this point I clearly decide how to
partition the problem while simultaneously recognizing my major technical problems:

Ideas	I have very few ideas about *how* to solve this problem but here recognize the criticality of generating these.
Knowledge	I recognize the inadequacy of my prior total knowledge. There was no problem like this in any text I had studied. In all my technical reading I had seen nothing published on log type voltage circuits. I recognized surely somebody has worked on a similar class of problems, but the information retrieval problem seems insurmountable just now. I also recognize there will in all likelihood be a severe 'drift' problem which is known for DC amplifiers in the mv level range, and my knowledge of 'drift' isn't all I would like just now.
Theoretical	I recognize that once I obtain an idea for solving the problem which looks promising I shall not be satisfied until I have analyzed it carefully and in detail, including knowing the assumptions involved in the theoretical model. I am particularly concerned about the temperature sensitivity of any type solid state device or system.
Energy Source	Should I plan to run the instrument from standard power supplies or make it self contained with batteries? Oh! Wouldn't it be interesting to make the instrument battery operated and simultaneously have it drift free! *That* hasn't been done to my knowledge and perhaps would result in some contribution to the state-of-the-art!

Components   What kind to use? Clearly the problem solution lies in a piece of 'electronics' containing components. Standard components I can easily obtain. What concerns me is the need for some special component having log characteristics. I recognize clearly that the probability is greater than 0.5 that such a component will be required in the finished solution. Where will I get such a component? What characteristics should it have?

Systems   What basic system configuration will give me 'log characteristics'? What prior-art information is available on such systems? How temperature sensitive are such systems? Do such systems even exist? Do I have to create it? If so, where do I start?

"An invention is never a purely mental product, but is the result of a struggle between thought and the material world."
   Herrn Rudolf Diesel
   [76, p346]

Materials   What kinds of materials will be required to successfully solve this problem? Are they available? Do I have to order them? What delivery times are involved?

"Also I would be glad to have your advice as to a suitable varnish for the cover. I have been using shellac."
   Wilbur Wright
   [393, p22]

etc.

Overall, I feel very humble at the magnitude of the problem before me. I honestly and realistically recognize how *little* I know about solving this kind of problem. An inner voice whispers "you can do it!" I am thankful for that encouragement.

Incidentally, I am recording my thoughts and progress (including 'failures' also) on this problem in my notebook. This practice greatly aids me later in forming new idea combinations and is a legal requirement if any patent action is to be later initiated.

I decide that the best strategy appears to accumulate some ideas for tentative alternative solutions followed by examining the most likely candidates from the systems viewpoint using analytics as necessary.

I conceive a list of 16 potential solution
ideas. Samples are shown in Fig. 6-7.

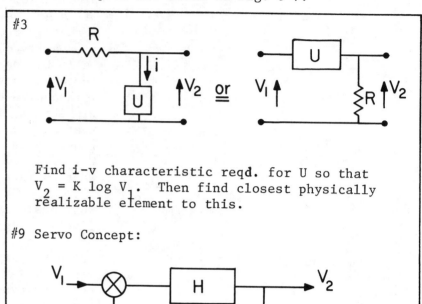

#3

Find i-v characteristic reqd. for U so that
V_2 = K log V_1. Then find closest physically
realizable element to this.

#9 Servo Concept:

Fix up β so
V_2 = K log V_1

#16 Dig up some known logarithmic properties
of circuits and sub-systems--maybe MIT
Radiation Laboratory series?

FIG. 6-7

I decide that of all the alternatives number
3 is elegant by its simplicity and should be
studied further by analyzing it as a system.
Clearly the first sub-problem is what model and
assumptions to use. I decide to try the model
on the left first. I assume that if the unknown
element, U, obeys V_2 = r log i and that no load is
connected, i.e. Z_L = ∞, then I might be able to
solve this nonlinear problem. Also U might turn
out to be a diode! I am uncertain just now however.
My analysis reveals that

$$V_2 = r \log V_1 - r \log R$$

which is the desired form, as the last term is a
subtractible constant. The key assumptions are
that a plot of log i vs V_2 be of constant slope r,
that V_2 is small, and that if a diode is used for

U it be operated forward biased. A sub-problem now is clearly recognized of "what happens if the diode isn't 'perfect' but has some series resistance, as it surely will have in reality?" I set up a 2nd order model, analyze it and find it is desirable for the series resistance to approach zero. How near zero? I decide to make a few simple quick tests of diodes and immediately have the sub-sub problem of what diodes are likely candidates worthy of testing. Then there is the further sub-sub-sub problem of what test circuit to use. I propose one and proceed to test all available diodes, plotting V vs log i. Large differences between diode types are found with some appreciably straighter than others.

It also begins to appear that biasing the diodes may be necessary. I discover with a quick experiment that combining the bias circuitry with the diode must be done with care by setting the diode bias to a precise value. The value influences the straightness of the V_2 vs log V_1 curve. The circuit results in a linear output from 50 mv < V_1 < 60v.

A further 'combining problem' arises with recognition of the need for a DC amplifier to precede the log circuit, opening up the possibility to have the desired log output for V_1 < 50mv. A quick evaluation using an existing DC amplifier proves this concept valid and extends the lower range to 0.2mv for V_1. But *this* combination, while satisfactory as a 'system' fails to pass the 'satisfactory' check against the specified goals, as it is not all one unit. I therefore "feedback"--iterate--and create a DC amplifier to precede the log circuit above. Many detailed sub-problems arise, principally with drift and input impedance. I learn many new things, most of which is not in books I've previously studied. I feel good over reflecting that discipline--to learn--is involved in creative work and that *self* learning is the greatest *inner* delight!

At this point I recognize I have successfully carried one alternative solution quite far. I have a complete schematic diagram of a specific preliminary solution proposal based on a DC amplifier followed by a biased log diode circuit.

" - - the process of
logical engineering
development often
comes to an im-
passe because
the engineer is
following princi-
ples that worked
at the beginning
but have come to
the end of their
utility. - - Thus
inventive insight
often involves see-
ing that the prob-
lem itself is not
what was assumed,
but is of another
sort involving
another angle of
approach."
  Elliott Dunlap
  Smith
  [305, p4]

"For the things of
this world cannot
be made known with-
out a knowledge of
mathematics."
  Roger Bacon
  [17, p94]

I now recognize that there may be better
ways of solving the problem $V_2 = k \log V_1$ and
that I should investigate other promising alternate
solution possibilities. While I am away from
this work visiting in a distant city temporarily
totally forgetting this problem, I suddenly
receive very strong intuitive feelings to pursue
the earlier servo concept, number 9 in Fig. 6-7
and to use a diode as the β element. The
illumination is so strong that I am forced to
sketch out the system configuration on the
program of the musical concert I am attending.
The new system model I have created and almost
instantly analyzed is shown in Fig. 6-8.

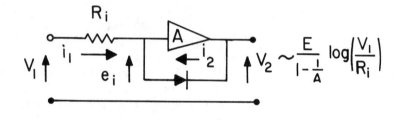

FIG. 6-8

After returning home, I model and analyze
this system more carefully and determine all the
necessary model assumptions for it to correctly
work. I compare this solution alternative
against the one developed earlier and conclude,
after some excruciation, that it is inherently
superior to the earlier solution alternative on
which so much thought had been given and that
the servo system concept is 'nearly satisfactory'
and should be chosen for the 'detailed means'
phase.

I decide to drop the first alternate solution
and proceed with the operational amplifier alternate
as the best preliminary solution.

By utilizing the DC amplifier created for the
first alternative solution as a starting point,
I have the "A" for the operational amplifier. I
decide to make a quick breadboard test and find a
plot of V_2 vs log V_1 is linear from 2 mv to 20 v--
4 decades! The remaining problems of reducing
the total number of separate batteries, reducing
the drift, packaging, retesting, and the fact that
the circuit inherently phase inverts are all
cleanly recognized to require further engineering.

These recognized weaknesses are dealt with
individually, their solutions found possible
with some creativeness. After a considerable
number of 'failures' which I dealt with by
iteration via feedback in the last parts of
Fig. 6-5, I finally emerge from the 'determining
means' phase with a proposed solution in the
form of a specific schematic diagram, shown
in Fig. 6-3, for a system based on a balanced
operational amplifier (to minimize drift) and
a special 'log diode' in the feedback circuit.

I experience a tremendous sense of satisfaction
and internal joy at finally being able to create
what is to me an entirely *new* circuit! A
creation has occurred as a result of deliberately
applying disciplined creativity methods. Incidentally, at this point I also have great
respect for the difficulties of the problem, and
I have reasonable assurance that no knowledgeable
engineer can arise and propose some ultra simple
'solution' to my problem because the most plausible
one has been thoroughly examined and found unsatisfactory.

*" - - we speak
of happiness as
involving a
'striving to-
ward' meaningful
goals, - -."
John W. Gardner
[116, p98]*

Though **Example** 6-5 above was 'electronic,' the

same methodology symbolized in Fig. 6-5 is

generally applicable to creating in other engineering

subject areas. Figure 6-5 is used as the guide.

In closing this Sec., we observe that the

act of synthesizing an idea generally *precedes* the

analysis of that idea.

*"Long lines were
used in electrical
communications for
many years before
any clear con-
ception was
attained re-
garding their
theoretical
behavior."
Ernest A.
Guillemin
[136, p6]*

Discussion Topics

1. Consider Fig. 6-5. Discuss parts of it which
    bother you.

2. Discuss the role of judgment in the 'determining
    means' phase.

3. How will you know when to stop generating
    solution alternatives?

4. An engineer is considering the alternatives of
    a mechanical spring, a battery, and a tank
    of compressed air as sources of energy. Discuss
    specific performance parameters he might use
    for comparison purposes. How will he decide which
    to use?

5. In Example 6-5 **a** special diode was sought
    as a key component in creating a new
    circuit. Explore how, in general, the creative
    problem solver *finds* special components which
    are needed for a new solution concept.

6. Consider the first-order 'determining means'
    model structure of Fig. 6-4. What relationship
    does this structure for solving "creative"
    engineering problems have to the structure you
    have actually *used* up to the present time for
    solving an extended "analytical" engineering
    problem? Particularly explore whether 'alternatives'
    were always clearly identified in your analytical
    work. Also explore the common dogma amongst
    students of "this is *the* way to work the problem!"
    and the effect such dogma has on one's creativity.

7. Discuss the possibility of omitting some of
    the steps in Fig. 6-5 for some engineering
    problems.

8. Will a knowledge of the 'prior art' on a problem
    hinder or help you synthesize new creative
    solution proposals during this phase?

Exercises

6-E13. List as many idea stimulant means as you can
        conceive.

6-E14. If you were the engineer responsible for
        developing a new ultra-compact flight recorder
        for use aboard commercial aircraft to provide
        a permanent record in event of a crash, indicate
        all the major sub-problems you could reasonably
        expect to face during the 'determining means'
        phase.

6-E15. A new solid-state burglar alarm is to be
        created for the consumer market. If you were
        the responsible engineer entering the 'determining

means' phase with this problem, clearly
identify the specific sub-problems you can
see now.

6-E16.   Assume that a storage battery with 100 times
         the capacity of present auto batteries has
         been created and that it has the same size and
         weight. If you were an engineer in a 'determining
         means' phase seeking to create a new all
         electric pollution-free automobile based around
         this battery, identify the specific engineering
         problems you could expect to initially face in
         this phase.

6-E17.   Several military groups have had an 'old
         chestnut' problem around for a long time. They
         simply want a reliable, jam-proof, private
         communication link with an airplane anywhere
         in the world. Suggest potential ideas for means
         to communicate with an airplane.

6-E18.   One creative stimulant makes use of 'similar
         items' for acquiring a fresh viewpoint. Compile
         a list of devices or phenomena which have
         "logarithmic characteristics" which could be
         useful on a problem like 6-5.

6-E19.   A problem which reappears in a wide
         variety of electrical, mechanical, and
         physics investigations is how to transmit
         motion through a wall. Frequently there is a
         pressure differential across the wall. Propose
         a specific means for transmitting translational
         motion through a wall with atmospheric pressure on
         one side and vacuum on the other. Sketch it.

6-E20.   Sketch, as quickly as you can think, ideas for
         how to join two wires together.

6-E21.   Many electronic packages must be hermetically
         sealed. Sealing prevents dust and moisture
         from entering and deteriorating the components.
         The engineer is frequently faced with the
         problem of creating the container. Sketch all
         the separate means you can for making a hermetic
         container for electronic sub-assembiles.

6-E22.   Study the 'selected creative writings' in
         Appendix I. Do they reveal a thought
         pattern anything like Fig. 6-5? What errors
         were made which possibly could have been
         avoided had the problem solver known the
         morphology and principles of this chapter?

Creative Problems

6-CP12.   A new power supply is to be created for an auto-
          pilot for aircraft use. The specified goals
          it must meet are: Input: 28 ± 4v DC; output:
          250 ± 0.5v DC at 1 amp   maximum for specified
          voltage input range; weight: 3 lb   maximum;
          volume: 64 in^3 maximum; vibration: able to
          withstand vibration on a jet airplane when
          the supply is rigidly fastened to the fuselage;
          circuitry: to have no moving parts. Propose
          a *detailed* system block diagram of a supply
          which would appear possible to meet the
          specified goals.

6-CP13.   One of the great problems of civilized societies
          is the possible exhaustion of the world's
          fossil fuel supply. As population and energy
          required per capita continue to increase the
          problem gets more acute. One 'fuel' which by-
          passes fossil fuels is the absorption and
          conversion of solar energy into electric energy.
          Solar energy impinging normally on a surface
          on the earth has an intensity of close to
          1000 watts/M^2 when the sky is clear. Present
          art solar converters are hot water heating
          and photo voltaic direct conversion types.
          The latter, widely used on space vehicles as
          solar arrays, have a conversion efficiency
          of about 13%. The installed cost is approximately
          $1,000/watt. Propose a new creative specific
          possible means of converting sunlight to
          electricity at an efficiency substantially ex-
          ceeding 13% and at a projected cost at least
          an order-of-magnitude below present art solar
          cells. Focus only on 'the converter' problem,
          leaving the obvious energy storage problem for
          later creative work.

6-CP14.   Considering Kw-Hr/ft^3/lb. as an important
          engineering parameter, make a proposal for an
          energy storage means suitable for use in the
          future electric automobile.

6-CP15.   Create a computer program which would permit
          an engineer to implement Fig. 6-5 with relative
          ease for an arbitrary engineering problem. Test
          your program with a *simple* problem, eventually
          building up to complex problems. To be most
          useful, it would indicate to the problem solver
          recognition of problems or potential problems,
          perhaps with outputs "you need to generate ideas

for solving the _____ problem."
Thus the computer could possibly aid in the
basic morphology of this stage, leaving
the engineer additional time to focus on
the problems requiring his creativity.

6-CP16.   Others of a more detailed nature as assigned
          by your professor.

6-3 <u>Some</u> <u>Principles</u> <u>Useful</u> <u>In</u> <u>The</u> '<u>Determining</u> <u>Means</u>' <u>Phase</u>

In this Sec. we formulate and briefly discuss

some of the principles most applicable to the

'determining means' phase. They are presented in

the approximate sequence needed by the disciplined

creative engineer in progressing toward a problem

solution in accordance with Fig. 6-5. A knowledge of

these principles and the ability to apply them

constitutes what the problem solver personally

brings to the morphology for creating shown in the

figure.

"'The weight of
the diesel engine
was in somebody's
head,' Kettering
said. 'Diesel
engines do not
have to be heavy.
We always want
to blame our
ignorance on
the engine.'"
T. A. Boyd
[42, p162]

● <u>Creativity</u> <u>Inhibitors</u> <u>and</u> <u>Stimulators</u>: The
problem solver is both aware and knowledge-
able of these. Inputs from Chaps. 13 and
14 here.

The inhibitors deter our efforts toward
a solution. They occur frequently and
subtly during the 'determining means' phase.
The alert problem solver recognizes
them and consciously seeks out and applies
creativity stimulators as counteractants where
needed.

● <u>Personal</u> <u>Factors</u>: The problem solver recognizes
that his success probability, even with dis-
ciplined methodology applied, largely hinges
on his aggregation of personal factors.
Inputs from Part III of this book here.

Our motivation to solve the problem
and its near relative, persistence, along with
self confidence and the ability to overcome discouragement are all extremely
important factors in our ability to create
any new thing. The environment we are in
may stimulate or depress our creative output. Our intuition may be giving us valuable
signals which we ignore. We may not feel
like creating because of a health problem.
These, and other personal factors, are
elucidated in Chap. 10.

*"Unless the inventor
is willing to re-
lax the step-by-
step procedure of
logical science
and let scientific
clues suggest
generous, or
even extravagant,
technological
conceptions, he
will get nowhere."
Elliott Dunlap
Smith [305, p2]*

● Thinking Flexibility characterized by
thinking, questioning, seeking, and proposal
orientations permeate the entire phase.

When a proposed solution is found to
not be possible to assemble, it is changed
until it *is*. In the process accepted ways
of achieving solutions are challenged and
proposals made for better solutions. No
idea is static! Just because we have always
joined wires by soldering doesn't mean we
must do so now as we flexibly conceive
alternatives, some of which perhaps initially
appear ridiculous.

● Thinking On Paper is essential to stimulate
solutions. Inputs from Chap. 15 here.

By proposing *specific* ideas on paper
we can examine them rationally, identify their
advantages, or find what is wrong with them
and re-propose better ideas. The thinking
may be on scratchpaper, a blackboard, or in
a notebook (preferred). Do be aware of a
pitfall with blackboards! I have seen clever
creative engineers step to a blackboard
and in a short fit of creativity propose some
beautiful solutions, erase them, and on the
following day be unable to recall them!
The creative effort was lost because
the ideas were not recorded in some more
permanent form. The entire subject of
'recording' is elucidated in Chap. 15.
You may want to study it now.

● Clean Decisions are essential for efficient
progress throughout the 'determining means'
phase. Inputs from Chap. 10 here.

"Problems often
boil down to the
simple form of
a dilemma. A
dilemma presents
a choice of two
solutions to a
problem, both
of which are un-
satisfactory."
  Edward Hodnett
  [151, p63]

Decisions are always difficult and
involve the element of choice (discussed
in Chap. 10) by the problem solver.
Decisions are made by the problem solver as
a person. *How* to make a given decision
cannot, in general, be found in books,
though books may help. Most decisions
involve the elements of the unknown, risk-
taking, uncertainty, and commitment. We
choose to record our thinking on paper so
we can, perhaps painfully, examine the
inadequacies of the proposals. We *decide*
to accumulate a set of alternative proposed solutions and to make each alternative
as 'clean-cut' and independent as possible.
We *decide* that a proposed idea probably
could be made to meet the weight goal--
or other goal--and proceed. We *decide*
to modify a proposed idea. We don't make
"half-a-decision" and wishy-washy around
ad nauseum about modifying the idea. We
make a clean-cut decision and *do* the idea
modifying! Wishy-washy 'indecisions' have
a way of multiplying in creative work,
eventually blocking progress entirely.
Incidentally, one of the reasons one or two
creative engineers frequently can progress
so far toward proposing solutions in a given
time period is because of an ability to
make clean-cut decisions whereas groups or
committees may have substantial difficulty
in so doing.

Sometimes it is helpful to prepare a
'Decision Table' as shown by Alger and Hays
[4, p18]   as an aid in decision making.
Those desiring to probe further into decision
theory will find books by Starr [313] and
Asimow [12] relevant.

Frequently our success in proposing new
creative solutions to a problem is related
to our ability to decisively sense quite
early the critical factor(s) in the problem
and decide to address ourselves to these
first. For example in the creation of a new
300 MPH surface transportation system clearly
decisive factors are the propulsion engine,
the energy source, and the means of conveying
the energy to the vehicle. A disciplined
creative engineer would seek solution proposals

"Keep a sharp
lookout for one
or more decisive
factors."
  Edward Hodnett
  [151, p68]

to these fundamental sub-problems before solving the appearance problem which is amenable to solution by known technology.

> ● Strategy Formulation (A Plan) is essential to successfully 'determine means.'

The strategy used to propose new solutions may be rational, as using Fig. 6-5 as a guide, or it may involve strong use of intuition (Chap. 10). Without a strategy of *some* kind the problem solver is left in almost total chaos. Though occasionally new solutions do emerge from chaos, the probability of effecting new solution proposals repetitively appears much smaller than for having a well-thought-out preconceived strategy. The situation is analogous to taking a trip. My goal may be to arrive in Ogallala, Nebraska. The probability of my arriving there is small if I aimlessly wander all over the country. If I adopt a strategy to "buy a used car, drive there and sell it" my probability of actually arriving at Ogallala may be much higher! The point is that in mature disciplined creativity we have *some* overall strategy which we plan to roughly follow in this phase. The strategy may be as simple as "I think an experimental approach is best for this problem" or "I'll conceive some ideas, select the most likely of these to work, model it-- including clearly knowing the assumptions--, analyze it, predict whether it will work, and then modify it until it does work."

"Kettering's plan was to have an electric power unit that would be a satisfactory motor for cranking the engine as well as a generator for feeding electricity back into the battery and keeping it charged."
    T. A. Boyd
    [42, p69]

"It consists in the making every part of them so exactly alike, that what belongs to any- one, may be used for every other musket in the magazine."
    Thomas Jefferson
    [159, p37]

> ● Clearly Recognize Sub-Problems requiring creative effort to solve.

You cannot propose alternative solutions for a problem you don't recognize! It requires genuine alertness to the total problem to apply the principle. Failure here may get us into embarassing trouble later. Imagine the professional embarassment to the engineer who created the electrical power control equipment for a new submarine when he *then* discovered that the finished equipment could not be gotten through the largest hatch on the craft! Because of his

failure to early recognize the sub-problem
of size (which *should* have been 'caught'
in a thorough 'goals' phase) parts of the
submarine hull had to be removed, the
equipment inserted, and the hull plates
rewelded.

Whole books could be written about
costly and embarassing examples of where
the engineer because of a lack of insight into
the *whole* problem during the 'determining
means' phase failed to recognize significant
engineering sub-problems with the result that
a considerably less than 'best' creation is
turned out.

> ● Engineering Judgment and Knowledge are
> needed frequently during the 'determining
> means' phase. Inputs from Chaps. 10
> and 11 here.

While judgment comes with practice
in creative engineering work, the
beginning engineer can accelerate his
judgment development by *exercising* it at
appropriate places throughout the 'determining
means' phase. These are clearly indicated
in Fig. 6-5.

*"Flying machines can
be constructed, so
that a man, sitting
in the middle of the
machine guides it
by a skillful
mechanism and
traverses the air
like a bird in
flight."*
*Roger Bacon
[16, p95]*

It is important to us as disciplined
creative engineers to recognize that
during the idea formation parts of the phase
judgment should be deferred. We are frequently prone by our prior engineering
education to rush in with judgment of a
truly new creative solution proposal and kill
it and its offspring before the idea is
completely 'born.' Such an exercise of
judgment *at the wrong time* may severely hinder
our ability to propose new creative problem
solutions.

Space will not permit us to probe the
interesting areas of bias, prejudice, and
plain resistance to change, all of which,
because of lazy thinking on a given problem, may
pass under the guise of 'judgment.'

In order to exercise engineering judgment knowledge of the specific area is usually
essential. This general subject is treated
in Chap. 11. An engineer cannot create a

new nuclear power plant without general
knowledge of nuclear processes. He cannot
correctly judge the relative merits of two
proposed digital computing facility proposals
without engineering knowledge in the area
of computers. You begin to see *why* the
disciplined creative engineer engages in a
lifetime of learning and self renewal (Chap.
10) so that he can *continue* to create!

" - - every inventor
works amidst an
enormous number of
rejected ideas,
projects and
experiments.
Much must be
attempted for any-
thing to be achieved.
Very little of it
is left standing
at the end."
  Herrn Rudolf
  Diesel
   [76, p346]

● Quantity (Number of Alternatives) Of Ideas is
  to be sought. Inputs from Chap. 14 here.

Extensive evidence indicates that
in creative work "quantity of ideas
begets quality." Almost all could think
of 2 or 3 means for solving a problem, but
this is hardly 'quantity.' Some creative
engineers believe that only the new, the
creative, the clever solutions appear after
8 or 10 proposals. Sometimes, as in 'brainstorming' (Chap. 14), the number of proposed
ideas may exceed 100. Think how much higher
is the probability of your creating the
best solution if you have 100 alternatives
from which to choose instead of 3!

● Fresh Insight into the problem begets
  creative solution proposals.

"Changing the
structure of
the problem is
often the
technique that
succeeds when
all else has
failed."
  Edward Hodnett
  [151, p102]

As we proceed toward developing a suitable problem solution we typically acquire
fresh insight into the problem which, if we
are alert, can foster new more creative
solutions. The engineer creating the low
noise RF amplifier in a radar receiver may,
with fresh insight into the electric and
magnetic field spatial distributions realize
that just because all prior-art RF amplifiers
have been made with microwave 'plumbing' they
don't *have* to be. Fresh insight has occurred.
As a result he conceives the idea of using
strip transmission line elements, greatly
reducing the size, weight, and cost of the
proposed amplifier.

● Drawing On Prior Art is an integral part of
  creating proposed new problem solutions.

New creations in general are not formed
in a vacuum, though it may sometimes *seem*
so to non problem solvers. *Some* prior art

exists, and the disciplined creative engineer wisely uses it to his advantage where he can. He tries to avoid going back and creating things that either already exist or can be bought commercially, choosing to devote his precious creative energies to solving the part(s) of the problem which have not been solved or solved to his satisfaction. The view is one of taking the art at face value in its *present* state and attempting to build on *that*.

A close study of the history of inventors and inventions reveals that virtually all drew on prior art, added a new twist, and created something new, useful and perhaps unexpected. Edison drew on the prior art of electric lamps which *had* been made but would not last before he created the successful lasting carbon filament lamp. Tesla started his conception of the magnificent polyphase motor, generator, and high voltage AC transmission system based on the prior art of DC machines and systems [232]. The Wright brothers drew on the prior art of Lilienthal, Chanute, and others to invent the airplane. More recent cases could be cited.

The engineer should therefore not carry a feeling of guilt because he is 'using prior art' provided he extends it by means of creating something new. Ethics would indicate he give due credit, however, to those who created the prior art which he uses.

"He (an inventor) must resourcefully create out of obscure clues vivid and varied configurations." Elliott Dunlap Smith [305, p2]

● **Spatial Visualization Ability is frequently a necessity.**

Spatial visualization means the capacity to visualize in my mind how a proposed solution *might* be structured or embodied. The ability to reduce the visualization to a sketch or drawing of a *specific* proposal--not something vague and fuzzy--is implied. This ability, along with most others needed to do creative engineering work can be enhanced.

Example 6-6

If I have a new idea for reducing the exhaust emission pollution from an automobile

*" - - what the
scientific know-
ledge first does
is to take the
same hints which
to other men have
no meaning and
intuitively com-
plete them into a
meaningful whole."
Elliott Dunlap
Smith [305, p2]*

I must have the ability to spatially
visualize how the proposed apparatus
should be structured.

Example 6-7

If I conceive an idea for a new integrated circuit proposal I must have the
ability to spatially visualize how the
various deposition and etching layers should
be structured.

Example 6-8

If I conceive of a new idea for controlling the speed of a single phase
squirrel cage induction motor I must have
spatial visualization ability to draw the
schematic diagram of the proposed circuit.

Example 6-9

If I conceive an idea for a new all
solid state digital display wrist watch
I must have spatial visualization ability
in order to propose how the watch might
be physically built.

Example 6-10

If I conceive a new laser radar system
for measuring precisely earth-moon distances,
I must have spatial visualization ability
in order to propose how to assemble the
research apparatus.

This marvelous ability of the human mind
is what enables us to be able to say, "Make
it like this: (sketch of our proposed solution)."

● Order of Magnitude Checks are usually necessary
during early 'preliminary means.' Inputs
from Chap. 16 here.

The idea of these rough numerical checks
is to have a basis for knowing that a proposed
alternate solution is 'within the ball park'
of our sought goals. This subject is so
important to the disciplined creative engineer
that Chap. (16) is devoted to it.

┌───┐
│ ●   Be alert to Marginality and Murphy's Law   │
└───┘

It is extremely easy to create an alternative solution means proposal which initially
looks good but, as further thought reveals,
is basically a very 'marginal' solution proposal [210]. It will work *if* all the parts
are made with absolutely nominal dimensions,
if it is held at absolutely constant temperature,
if the friction that holds it together doesn't
change with temperature, humidity, vibration
or some other variable, *if* all the transistors
have exactly nominal β's, *if* the material of
which the thing is to be made is absolutely
perfect, *if* the pressure in the oxygen tank
doesn't rise too high, and countless similar
'if s'. If evaluation reveals strong evidences
of marginality in the creation, it is a
matter of judgment whether to proceed with
that particular alternate solution proposal.
It may be necessary to establish some limits
for the part(s) that appear marginal.

Murphy's law--'what can happen will happen'--
is closely related to the marginality principle. The disciplined creative engineer, insofar as his problem constraints permit him,
recognizes the reality of Murphy's Law.
Where necessary he takes corrective action
in his solution proposal *before* his proposed
solution gets into later trouble, perhaps
on a large, costly, and embarassing scale.

The disciplined creative engineer also
recognizes the possibility of over-reacting
to this principle by so completely improving
the proposed creation that, perhaps unconsciously,
costs will be so high as to completely eliminate
the creation from ever being constructed. It
takes a truly disciplined creative engineer to
consistently create clever, elegant, simple,
non-marginal solutions to any problem!

┌───┐
│ ●   Elegant Simplicity is worthy of striving toward │
│   in proposed solutions.   │
└───┘

This aesthetic quality, which varies
markedly from problem solver to problem solver,
is probably sought after unconsciously by most
creative people. It is the voice that speaks
to us inwardly saying "that alternative

*"Success depends on
a number of pro-
portional relation-
ships, so that a
small deviation
may decide the
issue. - - a small
change in an indi-
vidual part may
lead to a gross
error in the
production."
   Philo of Byzantium
   circa 200 B.C.
   [249, p35]*

*"Seek the elegant
answer. Don't
settle for just
any solution to
the problem."
   Don C. Hoefler
   [152]*

solution I've created is too complex.
Let me try again for a simpler more clever
solution proposal--one which is elegant and
will stand out above all competition."

Example 6-11

Tesla's conception of a polyphase
generator delivering its power at great
distances to large numbers of polyphase
motors whose individual shaft speed is
in exact synchronism with the generator
is 'elegant simplicity' which had not
been conceived by his predecessors.
[232]

Example 6-12

The use of solid state thermoelectric
elements properly positioned around the
hot exhaust pipe of an automobile as a
replacement for the conventional rotating
alternator is an elegant solution waiting
for some engineer to make a reality.

*"Good design has
an aesthetic
quality--the
quality of
simplicity."
Morris Asimow
[12, p32]*

Other examples could be cited. All
will be found to contain a strong element
of 'beauty' as perceived by the engineer
who created it. We thus sense that the
highly creative engineer, perhaps unconsciously, is a seeker after beauty
which manifests itself in solution
proposals he considers exhibit 'elegant
simplicity.'

● <u>Deficiency</u> <u>Identification</u> in a proposed
alternative solution produces a better
solution proposal.

*"It is possible
that actual trial
will prove the
defects less
serious than they
at first appear."
Wilbur Wright
[396, p22]*

For any single specific solution
I propose, it is wise for me to
realistically and honestly identify
its deficiencies. Raising questions about
the proposed solution here is helpful.
Doing so will permit me to focus on the deficiencies and perhaps take corrective action to minimize
or eliminate them in the proposed solution.
Deficiency Identification is a painful process
for the creator--somewhat akin to recognizing
our own personal faults. Disciplined
creativity tenet would indicate it is *less*

*" - - I conceive
that his (Lilienthal's)
failure was due chiefly
to the inadequacy of
his method, and
of his apparatus."*
  Wilbur Wright
  [392, p16]

painful than to later find the deficiencies
when the created thing is closer to mass
production or large scale implementation
at which point unrecognized deficiencies
have a way of getting white hot for the
engineer! Thus deficiency identification
is a means of minimizing the possibility
of engineering 'failure' and attempting to
maximize our success probability. At the
same time we are realistically aware of the
consequences of failure. [151, p72].

The actual deficiency identification
may be by yourself, a close colleague, your
engineering manager, or others. It is
wise to select others with *care* at this
stage, as too severe adverse criticism of
the proposed new creation by someone un-
skilled or unsympathetic to the difficulties
of creating a truly *new* thing may have a
later psychological strangling effect on the
creativity output of the problem solver.

⬤ Idea Evaluation is an essential part of a
disciplined 'determining means' phase.

The essentialness is shown in Fig. 6-5
by its morphological location. Idea evaluation
is essential because it is the only process
the problem solver has for determining how
near his proposed solution is to the desired
goals. It is one of the important ways a
disciplined creative engineer has of maximizing
the probable later success of his solution
proposals. It is a valuable means of
comparing the relative merits of alternative
solution proposals. All serious new idea
proposals will eventually get evaluated
later by *somebody* The disciplined creative
engineer recognizes that and performs his
own evaluation of his proposals, thus
realistically preparing himself for the time
when his new creation will be scrutinized by
others, perhaps unmercifully.

*"Measuring consequences
must also involve the
question, 'How costly
will failure be?' And
again we distinguish
in degree between
total failure and
partial failure."*
  Edward Hodnett
  [151, p75]

The related topics of engineering judgment and knowledge, clean decisions, and
clear recognition of problem areas have
already been discussed above.

It is important for the disciplined
creative engineer to realize that idea

creation and idea evaluation are two
separate functions. Occasionally
engineering students forget this, mix
the two in their minds, and then discover
they can't create a new idea because the
evaluation concept has a stranglehold
suppressing idea creation almost completely.
By disciplining yourself you can
consciously separate these two functions
and make progress.

> ● Tentative Timing objectives for completing
> the 'determining means' phase generally
> exist. Inputs from Chap. 17 here.

The timing for completing the phase is
generally *not* open-ended for the problem
solver, though in a few instances it may
seem so. Whether an engineer is a salaried
employee or in an independent business
working toward creating a new solution to
a problem, he does not have infinite time
available. The solution must be created
within some time interval in modern indus-
trialized society. The disciplined
creative engineer recognizes this fact and
accepts it. Almost all modern engineering
management insists on pre-programming time
amounts (hence costs) for solving any large
engineering problem of substance. The
artifice of scheduling can be a valuable
tool to the disciplined creative engineer
in maximizing his professional creative
contributions.

The whole topic of timing is
dealt with in Chap. 17.

*"To invent he must
so free his mind
from the influence
and the logic of
his own past and
that of his fellows,
that his unconscious
intuition can see
clues which he and
others have over-
looked, and build
out of them, novel
conceptions."
Elliott Dunlap
Smith [305, p4]*

You will discover other useful principles
as your proficiency in disciplined creative engineering thinking grows through practice. There are
many more than can be included here! Be alert to
those which work best for *you*, become skillful in
their use, and *continue to add new ones* based on
your individual experience with successful problem
solving!

Discussion Topics

1. Select one of the principles cited in this section. Using Fig. 6-5 as a guide, explore the *specific* places in the figure where the principle may enter. Justify your choices.

2. *Why* were *all* the principles needed in a 'determining means' phase not written down and included in this section in a handbook fashion?

3. If you were going to create a new system for permitting a totally blind person to see, what initial strategy would you use upon entering the 'determining means' phase?

4. The 'tentative timing' principle seems to imply that inventions can be created according to a schedule. Discuss.

5. Space did not permit us to deal with some of the difficulties the problem solver may encounter before being able to synthesize a satisfactory solution proposal. Identify some of these and discuss means of minimization. (Example: What do I do when I've run out of ideas?)

6. The 'spatial visualization' principle implied the creative engineer needs skill in graphics. Discuss whether more or fewer graphics courses are being offered in your engineering curriculum than 10 yrs. ago. See if you can determine the reasons in either case.

Exercises

6-E23. List specific topics relevant to the title of this Chap. which were not discussed but which you feel should have been included. What principle cited in this Sec. are you using?

6-E24. Sketch as many means as you can for attaching a nameplate to a piece of equipment.

6-E25. Sketch all the means you can create for getting an electrically insulated conductor through a metallic wall.

6-E26. One of the unsolved problems of modern integrated circuits is how to make an inductance using

well-known deposition and etching technology.
Propose ideas for how it might be done,
including clearly sketching your best idea.

6-E27. Evaluate the advantages and disadvantages
of creating a new system of underground
transmission of large amounts of power using
lasers and fiber optics. Now compare this
alternative with conventional underground
electric energy transmission. Reach a
decision on whether the proposed new alternative
should be pursued further.

6-E28. Choose one of the short papers in Appendix I.
Study it carefully. Does its author reveal
an integrated plan for how he 'determines
means'--perhaps he uses different words--or
does he discuss only a few facets of creating
a new problem solution?

6-E29. The 'recognize sub-problems' principle description
indicated that engineers sometimes fail to
exercise this principle. Can you cite an
example on a specific product created by an
engineer(s)?

Creative Problems

6-CP17. Propose a new means for measuring the current
in one wire of a three phase 1,000,000 volt
60 Hz transmission line.

6-CP18. Propose a new system for eliminating the need
for an electric meterman visiting residences
each month to 'read the meter' so the customer's
bill can be computed.

6-CP19. Reexamine the contents and presentation order
of this Chap. Propose, in outline form, a
better structure in your judgment.

6-CP20. Suppose you were to write an improved version
of this textbook. Retaining the same
educational aims and title as the present book,
identify the *specific* names of the Chaps.
you would use. Now structure these in the
'best' order.

6-CP21. Others of a more detailed nature as assigned by
your professor.

Chapter Summary

● The 'determining means' phase results in the creation by the problem solver of a proposal for a tentatively best means for solving the engineering problem.

● What the problem solver does within this highly creative phase was discussed in some detail. Figure 6-5 was presented as a workable thought guide for proceeding through the phase with any kind of problem demanding a *new* creative solution.

● Some useful principles for proceeding through the phase in a disciplined way were enunciated.

● Engineering examples were given.

CHAPTER 7

DISCIPLINE OF SOLUTION OPTIMIZATION

"We must imagine ourselves to be those who will eventually
use our results - - -"

Eugene K. Von Fange [360, p194]

●   Need for a 'solution optimization' phase.

●   What's done in it.

●   Optimization principles.

●   Possible omission of phase.

7-1 Need and Purpose of Optimization

Kahn's [164] delightful story reveals the

creative engineer's optimization need:

> "Part of my husband's job as a
> research engineer with NASA is to build
> life-size cardboard mock-ups of air and
> spacecraft being considered for production.
> Seated at the control panel of a craft
> that had been approved, he began a
> recheck of the eight listed steps
> required to abandon the craft. The
> first step read: Jettison the canopy.
>
> He did this and, to his amazement,
> discovered that the instructions for
> the next seven steps had been printed
> on the roof of the canopy!"

Impossible? Yet it happened! Fortunately, these

engineers were *looking* for possible user-initiated

failure modes caused by faulty engineering. By

corrective design they averted potential tragedy.

*"Engineering is to
a very large extent
dependent upon
detail."
William LeRoy
Emmet [94, p225]*

The 'details' of solution embodiment, so easily

overlooked by the creating engineer, may have life,

death, or other serious consequences for the
ultimate user(s).

Engineering attention to 'the details' of a
proposed new solution is generally needed in research, development, design, manufacture, and
operations.

Kahn's story, and countless similar ones,
points us toward the need for a distinct *user-
oriented* major phase in an orderly problem solving
approach. We call it *solution optimization*. Its
principal purpose is:

> ● Purpose of 'Solution Optimization' Phase:
> To optimize the proposed solution embodi-
> ment from the *user(s)* viewpoint.

A systems view of this fourth major phase of
creative problem solving is shown in Fig. 7-1.
Its relationship to the other major phases of
disciplined creativity was seen in Fig. 3-1. Note
its critical position in the problem solving approach—
before model construction. Later model construction
of a new solution is usually accompanied by many
difficulties. It is desirable to immediately
precede it with creative engineering activity
insuring that the 'best' model is made, thus
maximizing our contribution probability. Conversely
we minimize the embarrassing possibility of having

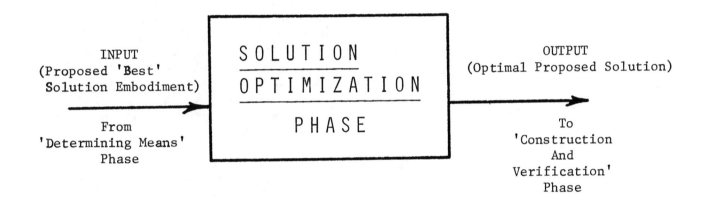

FIG. 7-1 Simple functional view of 'solution
          optimization' phase. The proposed
          solution embodiment is examined from
          the *user's* viewpoint and modifications
          made.

constructed a working model unsatisfactory to the ultimate user(s) and remaking it, perhaps at great cost or inconvenience. The optimization phase also begins to lay the foundation for the later adoption of our new solution.

Observations about this phase:

● Input is a proposed 'best' solution embodiment resulting from the previous 'determining means' phase. Note *embodiment*. It implies a *specific* proposed solution, usually a sketch, drawing or symbolic model. If no such proposal exists here the 'determining means' phase was faulty, and it is not possible to proceed with solution optimization.

● Solution Optimization phase, as its name suggests, emphasizes optimization. Clearly there is:

1. That which is to be optimized (the proposed solution embodiment).
2. The criteria to be optimized (the chosen parameters).
3. The ultimate user(s) for whom all is being done.

Each is important, but here the user(s) is the most important. The engineer's knowledge of the *user(s)* may determine what parameters need to be optimized. Thus while our creative work in previous phases was principally aimed at proposing a new technical solution to the problem satisfactory to *ourselves*, we now shift emphasis toward making the solution satisfactory to the *user(s)* of the proposed solution embodiment. Since the *user(s)* orientation is probably new to you in problem solving, we shall emphasize it in this chapter.

Broadly there are two types of optimization: technical and user.

"Making the gain control automatic--resulted in a constant-output signal when the incoming radio signal varied as fast as 60 times per second. This meant that we now had a receiver that needed no attention when the signal faded."
Harald T. Friis
[113, p22]

They are intertwined in a specific
engineering problem, but all technical
optimization ultimately is aimed
at making the proposed solution
embodiment acceptable to the *user(s)*.
The *user(s)* orientation suggests that
the creative engineer may have to make
some detailed modifications to his
proposed solution to enhance its
acceptability.

● Output of the phase is an optimal (we'll
    define it shortly) proposed solution.
    It is a *specific* proposed solution
    embodiment (sketches or drawings) which
    is probably acceptable to the *user(s)*
    of the new creation.[+]

Overall, the phase is characterized by attention

*" - - a good
exterior is the best
recommendation of
the interior."
Baltasar Gracian
[127, p123]*
to "the details" of the proposed solution embodiment.

The user, for example, may be far more concerned

with the 'detail' of the cabinet color of a new

solid-state Peltier central home air conditioner

being created than with the creatively elegant but

invisible engineering therein.

We define several key terms useful in the

solution optimization phase.

[+]Note that the output is of the same general class
as the input, i.e. we haven't here created an entirely
new basic solution alternative (that should have
been done in 'determining means'). If our input
was a proposed new bridge, we exit it with an
optimal bridge proposal. We do *not* exit with a
new proposal for motor boats!

```
┌─────────────────────────────────────────┐
│  ●   Optimum is the technical best considering  │
│          the state of the art [383, p261]        │
│                                                   │
│  ●   Optimal is the best within the total con-   │
│          straints of the probable user(s).       │
│                                                   │
│  ●   User(s) is the individual(s) or class of    │
│          individuals who will probably use       │
│          the proposed solution embodiment.+      │
└─────────────────────────────────────────┘
```

We enter the phase with what we *thought* was an optimum solution proposal. We exit the phase when we have created an optimal solution embodiment proposal. An example may help.

Example 7-1

" - - the best design is explicitly maximized for the significant desirable, or minimized for the significant undesirable factors."
Joseph P. Vidosic
[357, p18]

Electrical engineers creating the U.S. color television system in the early 1950's knew that the technically 'best' color TV picture was obtained with 3 separate 6Mhz bandwidth channels for red, green, and blue information. The total bandwidth would have been 18Mhz. The receiver costs would have been very great. There also would not have been many TV channel options because of spectrum crowding. Yet the system was 'optimum'. After some very creative engineering involving 'trade-offs' an 'optimal' system proposal was created using only 6Mhz bandwidth, thanks to carefully considering the total constraints of the *user(s)* (cost, color fidelity and number of channels). Millions of people subsequently benefited from this 'solution optimization' accomplished *before* constructing large-scale systems.

Discussion Topics

1. Why have a phase between 'determining means' and 'construction and verification'?

2. "All this is silly. I'll optimize my model as I build it. It's a waste to worry about all these unanswerable things before building a working model." Defend or refute.

+Note that *user(s)* is ultimately *person*-centered and not organization centered! Organizations per se are *not* the ultimate user(s) of the new products engineers create. The *people* therein 'use' them, perhaps for the benefit of themselves and of other people beyond the organization.

3. Reexamine Table 3-1. How do you account for only 3 of the 9 major 'approaches' to problem solving having optimize phases?

4. Does a research engineer ever have to 'optimize' his proposed solutions? Or is 'solution optimization' only important to design engineers close to consumer products?

5. How does a design engineer determine which user criteria are 'the ones' toward which his solution embodiment proposal should aim?

6. Identify a specific marketed technical product which is sub-optimal from the user's viewpoint. What *specifically* are its weaknesses?

7. Consider a portable radio. Did its creator concern himself with 'the big picture', 'the details', or both?

8. Is it *really* possible for the engineer to create a technically optimum new solution but be a user failure? Cite a single specific historically verifiable example.

Exercises

7-E1. An engineer has proposed the following 'electric rug' for elderly people living in cold climates.

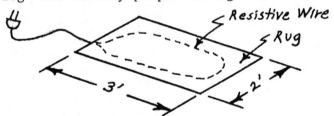

The rug would warm the feet while reading, knitting, etc. It would be offered for sale on the consumer market. Large quantities would be involved. Propose, sketch in *detail*, and label an optimal solution embodiment.

7-E2. Sketch an optimal writing instrument.

7-E3. Consider a flashlight. Cite 3 specific weaknesses you see in this product. Propose an optimal specific solution.

7-E4. Consider the automobile of your choice. Choose an accessory or component part therein. List the specific weaknesses in it from the user viewpoint. Propose an optimal solution.

7-2 <u>What's</u> <u>Done</u> <u>in</u> <u>'Solution</u> <u>Optimization'</u>

   FIGURE 7-2 IS OUR GUIDE for this phase. It,

as the previous phases of disciplined creativity,

consists of discrete manageable functional

blocks.

To convey a feel for the phase we briefly deal

with each function and cite an example.

<u>Input</u>: We start with a *specific* proposed solution

embodiment. It usually is a sketch, drawing, or

symbolic model. The embodiment appears to meet

our specified goals for an acceptable solution of the

second major phase (Chap. 5).

*"It is cheaper to
draw the product
than to make it."
Percy H. Hill
[148, p53]*

Example 7-2

   A creative design engineer has proposed in
his 'determining means' phase a new 'power barge'-
gas turbines driving AC generators all mounted
on a barge. The barge would be towed to a city
nearing electric power brown-out conditions,
temporarily connected to the city's power grid,
and removed after the peak demand passes. The
'power barge' could then be towed to the next
power-short city. The 'power barge' is to be
'solution optimized' before being physically
created. He starts with a set of proposed
sketches.

DEFINE USER(S): If we had done a perfect job

in 'specifying the goals' back in the second major

phase, theoretically we should already know the

user(s) for the new solution being created. We

seldom were so perfect at that stage where many

uncertainties exist. However, we now have a

plausible solution created, on paper at least,

and begin to think about its ultimate acceptability.

To be acceptable we must know "To whom?" "Who

will ultimately use the proposed solution?" What

are his (or her or their) characteristics?" We

seek to learn *in detail* about those who will use our

new creation. The closer the new product being

created is to the production stage, as in design

engineering, the more crucial it becomes for the

engineer to know his user(s) in detail. Many cases

of later 'engineering failures' could be cited

originating because the engineer(s) creating the

product failed to know well the user(s) of his

creation.

<u>Example 7-3</u>

"We are afraid of what we do not understand--a greater under-standing solves problems--there-fore understand the things you work with."
Alexander F. Victor
[356, p116]

When portable electric kitchen dishwashers were first being created by engineers in a large appliance firm, the user was defined as a young housewife in a small home or apartment. A market survey was made to find the desired exterior machine shape. It showed the housewife wanted a *square* machine to match the kitchen cabinets. The design engineer persuaded his manager that the housewife really wanted a *round* machine! His principal arguments were that the round machine would require less steel and be lower in cost. The fact that the company already had several hundred thousand dollars of steel rolling equipment also influenced the decision.

The round dishwasher completed design engineering and pilot production. It was a sales flop. Women didn't like it. They dropped things behind it, and it looked like a round peg in a square hole in the kitchen. A redesign to a *square* exterior was a sales success. Dishwashers since have all been square because it is what the *users* want!

INPUTS—OUTPUTS

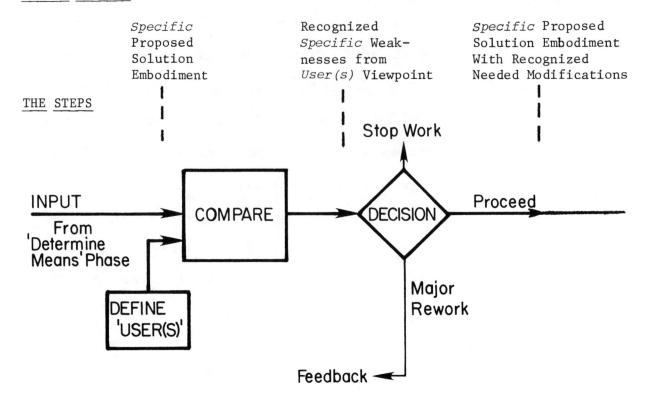

THE STEPS

PROBLEM SOLVER MIGHT:

- Think of all who will ultimately contact proposed solution.
- Identify *user(s)* specifically.
- List *user(s)* characteristics.
- Think why *user(s)* is way he is.
- Consider difficulties in changing *user(s)*.

- Look at proposed solution through eyes of *user(s)*.
- Imagine *user(s)* emotional reactions to proposed solution appearance.
- Identify *user* 'essentials' vs nonessentials for proposed solution.
- Recognize modes of *user*-initiated failure possibilities.
- Recognize, propose, decide new goals criteria the proposed solution must now meet to be acceptable to *user*.
- Analyze/trade-off performance vs cost.
- Excruciate over decision consequences.

FIG. 7-2 'Solution Optimization' phase guide. It is a more detailed
         view of Fig. 7-1 and of this step in Fig. 3-1. Optimization is with respect to the *user(s)*.

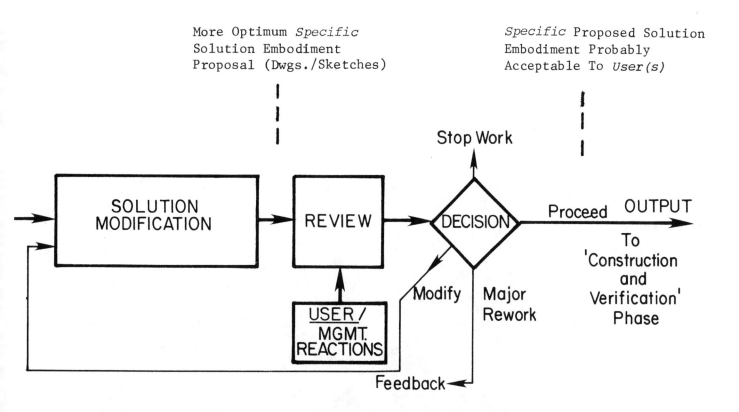

More Optimum *Specific*
Solution Embodiment
Proposal (Dwgs./Sketches)

Specific Proposed Solution
Embodiment Probably
Acceptable To *User(s)*

● Add *user(s)* features.
● Fuss over minute details.
● Perform optimization
   analyses.
● Feel frustrated over
   extreme attention to
   user-oriented detail
   required here.
● Modify sketches or
   drawings. Prepare
   complete ones.
● Make non-operative
   visual-aid model.
● Talk with others.
● Make detailed decisions.

● Carefully determine who reviewers are or
   should be. Arrange.
● Excruciate: Optimized solution really
   acceptable to *user(s)*?
● Think about competing solutions
   (if any).
● Weigh facts and opinions.
● Estimate cost, time, effort, resources
   to construct prototype.
● Excruciate over unknowns and prototype
   success probability.
● Decide whether proposed solution is
   optimal and whether to proceed with
   prototype construction.

FIG. 7-3 Photograph of new 'power barge' capable
of supplying 156 megawatts of electric
power to a city temporarily near
brownout. (Courtesy Newport News
Shipbuilding, a Tenneco Company, and
General Electric Co.)

The example illustrates the costly consequences of not listening to the user. There are many complexities and subtleties here beyond the scope of the text, e.g. how to create a new product for a user(s) who honestly doesn't know what he wants.

For some problems, as in research, *user* may be ourself for an experimental apparatus being created. *COMPARE* the proposed solution embodiment with the user(s) and his characteristics (Fig. 7-2). Spot weaknesses in it from the *user(s)* viewpoint. It is easier said than done, however, for we are here criticizing our own creation--a difficult necessary task. We simply lay aside some personal pride in our creation and attempt to objectively view it through the eyes of those who will use it. If we honestly imagine ourselves the user of what we've created, we may be appalled at the weaknesses we see!

Example 7-4

Early television cameras were packed with components. It was necessary to externally mount the blower motor. Its stream of air kept the critical image orthicon light pick-up tube temperature within acceptable limits. The blower made the camera look bad and it was noisy. I was to engineer the fan inside the camera.

To move it inside and closer to the sensitive orthicon induced 60 Hz pickup in the video picture caused by the magnetic field around the blower motor. I went to great trouble creating a double magnetic shield surrounding the motor. It worked when installed. My peers were satisfied. Later when a customer was using the camera in a critical Chicago TV broadcast the blower motor burned up.

"It may be that there are several criteria in respect to which we would like to optimize the design."
Morris Asimow
[12, p85]

I had focused intently on the magnetic shielding problem ignoring the temperature rise of the blower motor! Had I carefully thought about my design through the eyes of the *user* (the TV station technician) and known that (1) he leaves the cameras on for several hours and (2) he doesn't like smoke pouring from his camera, the trouble would have been prevented. (Vent holes bored in the magnetic motor shield later eliminated the problem.)

Such 'failures' are very humbling to the creative person. My problem solving 'approach' had been faulty in the optimize phase.

Table 7-1 identifies some thought-prodders useful in this initial look at our proposed solution through the *user(s)* eyes.

The object of the questioning and comparison is to clearly recognize the *specific* weaknesses in the proposed solution embodiment. If we as creating engineers fail to recognize solution weaknesses, our later critics most certainly will--probably to the detriment of the new creation. Note we are seeking weaknesses in the proposed *solution--not* in ourselves as creators of it. Performing the comparison may be painful for us, but it is less painful and messy than the alternative of not doing it and later having others severely critical of *both* the faulty proposed solution and its creator, rejecting both. The need for good judgment in realistically identifying

● <u>Appearance</u>   Look right? Too large? Too small? Convey
                functional utility? Harmonious? Aesthetically
                pleasing? Look complex? Too many parts? Parts
                need hiding? *I* like at first sight? Psychological
                reactions to it?

● <u>Features</u>   What does it emphasize? Should these be emphasized?
                Convenience? Utility? Novelty?

● <u>Competition</u> Better than competing solutions? Any exist?

● <u>Cost</u>   Appear much too costly? Appear as pile junk?

● <u>Safety</u>   Basically safe solution? What specifically might
                not be safe? Can it be used in unintentional
                unsafe way?

● <u>Risk</u>   What risks will user incur by having solution?
                Human life affected? How?

● <u>Cultural</u>   Is proposed solution fundamentally opposed to
                ethic-value system of the culture? Will it
                benefit mankind?

● <u>Pollution</u>   Can it pollute the environment? Appearance?
                Noxious gases emitted? Odors? Noise? Solids?
                Liquids? What *else* will it disturb?

● <u>Legal</u>   Legal to use it? Laws require changing? Does
                it infringe on patents? Is it basis for a new
                patent?

● <u>Reliability</u> Will it *always* perform its intended function
                during its useful life? Effect if it doesn't
                once? More? Consequences to user(s)?

● <u>Life</u>   How long will it last? Long enough? Too long?

● <u>Maintenance</u> Nightmare to keep it going? What will probably re-
                quire attention? Can user(s) do it? Can user(s)
                get it done?

● <u>Workmanship</u> Can it be constructed with acceptable workmanship?
                All the time? What is *user(s)* effect if workman-
                ship is faulty?

TABLE 7-1 Some *user*-oriented factors to consider in
           mentally testing a proposed solution embodi-
           ment for weaknesses early in 'solution
           optimization' phase.

solution weaknesses is clear. We also see the
impossibility of modifying a proposed solution
toward later acceptability if we haven't recognized
what specifically is wrong with it.

One of the best ways of detecting weaknesses is
to deliberately force ourselves to do so by recording
our thinking in a notebook (Chap. 15). "Here are the
weaknesses I see in my proposed solution - - -."

From the comparison we may become aware of new
goals criteria--from the user(s) viewpoint--which

*"Many of the
important criteria,
however, are not
technical at all;
- - -"*
*Thomas T. Woodson
[383, p261]*

the proposed solution should now meet. We attempt,
where possible, to quantify these individually.
We may even formulate an analytical 'criterion function'
to be maximized or minimized by differentiation. The

*"- - the choice
of the criterion
profoundly affects
the actual design."
Morris Asimow
[12, p85]*

reader interested will find this useful optimization
tool ably treated by Asimow [12],   Woodson
[383, Chs. 12, 13, 15], and Vidosic [357, Ch. 12].
As a bare minimum we write the new criteria down.
We should recognize some factors important to the
user can't be quantified, e.g. the beauty of a new
vehicle styling. Woodson [383, pp204-262], among
others, has correctly recognized that the value
system of the culture impinges here on both the
creative problem solver and the proposed solution.
(How much armor is added to protect a fighter-plane
pilot?) We shall deal with 'values' in Chap. 10.

*"The engineer uses
all the analysis
and quantification
he can command; but
in the end, the
decisions are
made subjectively;
and there is no
avoiding it."
  Thomas T. Woodson
  [383, p204]*

DECISION excruciation comes next (Fig. 7-2). We
might decide that though the proposed solution
embodiment is technically possible to physically
create, for *user(s)*-oriented reasons we should
stop, e.g. creation of a 'death ray'. Alternatively
we might decide that the solution embodiment
proposed has so many user(s) weaknesses that it
needs a major rework. We might then 'feedback'
and iterate the 'determining means' phase. The
third course is to decide to proceed, incorporating
the needed *user(s)* oriented modifications in the
solution embodiment.

We might want to excruciate here over the
consequences of proceeding and some of the **far-
reaching** responsibilities we engineers have to
society for creating products for the *benefit* of man.
SOLUTION MODIFICATION is now undertaken (Fig. 7-2).
We apply the totality of our abilities to modify
the solution proposal so it incorporates the
user(s)-oriented features previously decided necessary.
We now have to propose *specific* ways of incorporating
each feature. The work inherently involves attention
to 'the details'. The 'broad-brush' approach is
inappropriate here.

Example 7-5

A test equipment engineer is creating a
proposed new apparatus for testing leakage current

*"Trade-offs may be
difficult to make
because some
factors are
difficult to
measure."*
*Ira and Marthann
Wilson [378, p107]*

in 10 KV DC capacitors. It will be used by
inexperienced women in a capacitor factory.
He has decided a weakness in his proposed equipment is the possible electrocution of the
operator. He proposes a detailed specific sketch
permitting the operator to insert a capacitor to
be tested, lower a protective safety shield cover,
and after 30 seconds elapse apply the high
voltage. Appropriate interlocks are incorporated
to protect the user. (Note that the 'broad brush'
view 'the equipment must be made safe' will *not*
propose *how* it is to be done.)

This sub-phase may require informally conferring

with others and seeking opinions on the proposed

solution modifications as the work proceeds. Many

detailed decisions of structure, form, packaging,

materials, colors, processes, availabilities,

trade-offs, and others may be made here.

Perhaps here is the place to make a non-operative

visual-aid model if the proposed solution embodiment

*"We cannot count
on others to have
our vision to see
what could be
done with our
idea."*
*Eugene K. Von
Fange [360, p190]*

is a costly or difficult to envision system. It

may clarify our thinking and be useful later. The

cost of making such models is trivial for many new

engineering solution proposals compared to the

consequences of a faulty solution. One good mock-up

or inexpensive visual aid model may actually save

money by preventing expensive drawings from being

generated for a *user(s)* unacceptable solution.

Complete sketches or drawings are then made from the

acceptable visual-aid model.

Finally, from the modifications a more optimum

specific solution embodiment proposal emerges which

*" - - there will be
one choice among
the gamut of
satisfactory
choices of design
parameters, which
will be as good
as or better
than any other."
 Morris Asimow
 [12, p84]*

we believe to be more acceptable to the *user(s)*

than it was when we started this phase.

REVIEW AND DECISION of the more optimum solution

embodiment proposal is now initiated (Fig. 7-2).

If technicians are to later use the newly created

solution, selected ones are invited to participate

in the review, usually a meeting. The point is, if

possible, to have a representative 'input' here from

the *user(s)* of the proposed new creation. This is

also an appropriate place in the problem solving

process to invite 'inputs' from selected colleagues

and management whose judgment and wisdom, if creatively

exercised, can contribute to the new solution being

created. Also, since construction of the proposed

solution may occur in the next phase, management may

want to be a party to deciding if the proposed

solution should be constructed. The review may be

called a 'Design Review' in design engineering or a

'Project Review' in research or development. These

are similar and aim at enhancing the likelihood of

success for the proposed new solution.

A caution. It is wise, at this phase, for the

problem solver to *carefully* select the reviewers if

possible. Creating a truly new solution always has

high failure risks associated with it. In order to

create the new the problem solver continuously has

to think 'it's possible'. At this crucial point the

proposed new solution is still *not* 'a proven thing'.

If ultra conservative, negativistic, *backw*ard looking,

'it's not possible', attitude people--either user(s)

or managers--are brought to the review process, then

almost certain death to further solution progress

may occur. Such a 'committee' can kill truly new

creations and inventions to the loss of society.

Reserve the 'hard sell' until the last major phase

after the new solution is proven (Chap. 9). History

shows us there will be plenty of skeptics around

even after the solution is *proven*. We don't seek

them at this point, however!

*"It adds up to
making the
correct intuitive
decision about each
minute detail of
the design so the
results will be
the best of all
possibilities."
 Percy H. Hill
 [148, p52]*

The solution optimization phase output is *a
decision* to stop work, proceed, perform a major

rework, or modify (hopefully minor). It is here

at the final checking point we decide whether we

have created the optimal solution embodiment. If

satisfied, we also decide whether to proceed with

prototype construction. Such a decision being complex

may require substantial time and effort to effect,

e.g. the famous case over whether to build a

commercial supersonic transport aircraft proto-

type in the U.S. in the early 1970's.

Example 7-6

Early monochrome TV sets were created with
long cabinets in order to protect the picture tube
(optimum). When placed against a typical room wall
the sets appeared awkward in proportions. Thousands

were sold before television design engineers
became aware that the users wanted a TV set
which *appeared* to not have great depth. Thus it
was decided to create 'thin' sets with part of
the picture tube protruding from the rear of the
set, but protected. The sets appeared pleasantly
proportioned, required less cabinet materials and
the user cost was lower. An optimal solution
was created within the constraints of the users.

The 'proceed' decision generally will not be
made unless there is 'a champion'--the creative
problem solver--for the proposed solution. Once
again the personal importance of the problem solver
to the solution's progress is underscored.

Discussion Topics

1. Assume you have created a new proposed electronic
    package to be installed aboard aircraft to
    warn of impending collisions. Define the *user(s)*.
    Justify your answer.

2. Would you build a 'dummy model' of your proposed
    optimal system in (1)? Cite reasons for *not*
    doing so.

3. Suppose you were Nikola Tesla and had just proposed
    the first nationwide alternating current generation,
    transmission, and distribution system. How would
    you determine the optimal generating frequency
    for the entire system? Of what significance
    is the frequency to the user? He never *sees* it!

4. How can a creative engineer optimize the problem
    solution he has in his mind if he hasn't learned
    the principles of elementary sketching?

5. What difficulties do you see in identifying 'the
    user(s)' for a product to be mass produced and
    used by millions of people?

Exercises

7-E5. Reexamine this chapter. Propose a new outline
       for it which is optimal for *you*, the user.

7-E6.   An engineer, from the 'determining means' phase, has proposed a new compass for aiding blind people. It uses a critically damped compass mounted in a liquid sphere. Orientation information is derived from it and processed by solid state integrated circuits. Read out is by means of small light bulbs as touch sensitive heat sources from which the blind person detects his heading in 10° increments.

  a.   Identify the *user(s)*.
  b.   Sketch your version of this proposed solution embodiment.
  c.   List the *user(s)* characteristics.
  d.   List the specific weaknesses in your embodiment from the user's viewpoint.

7-E7.   Consider a typical controlled urban street intersection with vehicles and people ('the model').

  a.   Define the *users*.
  b.   Determine the *specific* weaknesses in such an intersection from the users viewpoint.
  c.   Propose an optimal intersection embodiment.

7-E8.   Select a new technical idea which you take the most pride for having created. List its weaknesses *specifically* from the user(s) viewpoint.

7-3 Some 'Solution Optimization' Principles

These are collected in Table 7-2. They complement Fig. 7-2 and have been previously touched upon. For brevity we forego exposition of each. For additional details, particularly use of the criterion function and other powerful analytical optimization techniques beyond the scope of this text, refer to books by Woodson [383], Asimow [12], and Vidosic [357].

7-4 Omission of Optimize Phase

On a rare problem we may decide to omit the 'solution optimization' phase in whole or in part.

● It is impossible to perform a 'solution optimization' phase without an a priori specific proposed solution embodiment.

● Attention to details is inherent to the phase.

● Through the user(s) eyes view your proposed solution embodiment.

● Define the probable user(s). Learn all you can about him. Listen carefully.

● All user-important criteria, including constraints, for an optimal solution should be identified and written.

● Probable weaknesses in your proposed solution embodiment from the *user(s)* viewpoint should be identified early.

● Decisions should be clean-cut.

● Methods of optimization include:

    a. Subjective and intuitive
    b. Use of general and engineering knowledge
    c. Graphical
    d. Analytical (criterion function)
    e. Experimental

● Compromise involving trade-offs and conflicts is inherent in choosing the optimal solution embodiment.

● Several optimal solutions may be possible, depending on the initial *user(s)* assumptions made.

● Judgment and vision are needed throughout the phase.

● Failure to optimize a proposed new solution embodiment may later result in personal embarrassment and rejection of the solution.

● Completion of solution optimization occurs only when a decision is made that the specific proposed solution embodiment is optimal.

TABLE 7-2   Some 'solution optimization'
phase guiding principles.

There is a strong attraction to rush in and 'start
building' once a technically optimum solution
proposal has been created. In the rush the user(s)
whom we engineers seek to benefit, may be forgotten.
Before making the omit decision, however, we should
think through the consequences of omission. This
phase, as the previous ones, is intended to enhance
our solution success probability. If we omit it,
we may be courting solution disaster and criticism
of our profession.

Example 7-7

The failure and collapse of the Tacoma Narrows
bridge is well-known. The tragedy possibly could
have been averted had the creating engineers considered
the users' viewpoint of wanting the bridge to remain
firm in a high wind--before having physically built
it. Such 'solution optimization' possibly could
have revealed the potential unstable oscillation
weakness and design modifications made.

*"A central problem
of design is the
fixing of design
parameters at
proper values."
Morris Asimow
[12, p84]*

Careful observation of the role of 'failure'
in engineering problem solving--a relatively mute
subject unfortunately--frequently shows that the
solution optimization phase was either omitted or
improperly executed. Disciplined creative engineers
are aware of the perils of omission.

One of the useful 'signals' engineering case
histories give us is the wisdom of executing a
'solution optimization' phase or its equivalent.

Creative Problems

7-CP1.   Assume you have created a proposed small electronic instrument for warning householders of an impending nuclear attack. Your system can pick up centrally transmitted warning signals by direct radio frequency radiation, over telephone lines or over a carrier on power lines. You have an exact schematic diagram resulting from your 'determining means' phase. Suggest the *specific* criteria this new product must possess to be optimal from the home-owners viewpoint. Propose an optimal solution sketch.

7-CP2.   Assume that from a 'determining means' phase you have created a truly new proposal for converting sunlight directly to DC electricity at an estimated conversion efficiency exceeding 50%. It is based on utilizing the wave properties of light energy. The embodiment would be in a special fabricated sheet form. The sheet is 0.030" thick. Each square meter of sheet exposed normally to the sun is expected to yield 550 watts of useful power. The sheets could be marketed in various sizes depending on the amount of electrical power required by the user. The sheets would be mounted on the roof for sun exposure [20, 23].

    List *specifically* all the characteristics the user would probably want in such a new creation. What advantages, if any from the *user's* viewpoint, would such a system have?

7-CP3.   Others of a more detailed nature as assigned by your professor.

Chapter Summary

● The need was seen for a 'solution optimization' major phase in creative problem solving. It occurs *before* physical construction of the proposed solution embodiment.

● The principal phase purpose is to optimize our proposed solution embodiment from the *user(s)* viewpoint.

● We detect weaknesses and make modifications to our proposed solution, enhancing its later probable acceptance by the *user(s)*. Engineering judgment and vision are much needed here.

● An underlying thesis is that it is cheaper
  and easier modifying here *on paper* than later
  to a physical model.

● The heart of the subject - a guide - is Fig. 7-2.

● A few optimization principles were concisely
  tabulated in Table 7-2.

● Our 'output' is an optimal solution embodiment.
  We shall treat its construction in Chap. 8.

● For eventual solution success and acceptance it
  is generally undesirable to omit the 'solution
  optimization' phase.

● In a broad sense, we are attempting optimization
  of our personal creative contribution throughout
  the entire six-step problem solving approach.

CHAPTER 8

DISCIPLINE OF CONSTRUCTION AND VERIFICATION

" - - - I make a model, being ready then to make a test,
although I never make a model until I feel quite sure I
have something worthwhile, efficient, simple, of low
manufacturing cost and having a good market value."

G. B. Bosco [41, p76]

● Need and purpose of Construction and
  Verification phase in creative
  engineering.

● What is done.

● Some guides.

8-1 <u>Need</u> <u>and</u> <u>Purposes</u> <u>of</u> <u>Construction</u> <u>and</u> <u>Verification</u>

The previous four major steps in the disciplined

creative engineering process have resulted in a

specific new proposed 'paper solution embodiment' for

solving the problem originally defined in the

Problem Inquiry phase. It has been carefully thought

out and appears satisfactory to both us and the

user(s). However, the proposed embodiment is entirely

symbolic. It lacks *physical* presence.

*"Building something
is fun."
  Harald T. Friis
  [113, p29]*

This chap. treats the exciting but difficult

step of reducing our creative idea to practical useful

'*hardware*'[1]. Symbolic ideas are transferred to

reality by constructing a physical model[2] and verifying

---

[1]Review Fig. 3-1 for perspective of how this phase relates to the others.

[2]In this Chap. 'model' implies an assemblage of *physical* hardware. We do *not*
mean theoretical model of analytics.

*"I insist that
the creative process
is not complete
until one has some
tangible evidence
to prove it."
 John E. Arnold
 [11, p259]*

its performance. We shall treat the subject in

some detail because of the importance of this step

in creating a new thing--you will need to know about

it in real-world creative engineering--and because of

the subject's unfortunate omission from most engineering

texts.

THE NEED We logically ask, "*Why* is it necessary to

build and test a model? Why is the step even needed?"

When we *carefully* examine the history of successful

inventors, creative engineers, and projects[1] and

summarize we find the answers in Table 8-1.

Clearly there are many reasons *for* building and

testing a model of our new creation. Since it is *new*

*"The building and
testing of the
least expensive and
most promising de-
sign will often
reveal unsuspected
faults and defects."
 Joseph Rossman
 [279, p62]*

and we may have little prior directly related experience

from which to judge the validity of our new creation;

since we may have doubts about parts of it working

properly; since there may be many perils in forging

ahead without finding factual answers; and finally,

since 'others' have great difficulty accepting and

acting on our new creation without a working model,

the mature creative engineer generally opts for

executing the phase.

Example 8-1

In Research a physical model for studying the

---

[1] Also those which 'failed' from which we learn valuable lessons for proceeding
on future projects!

Satisfy Needs   of:
                     Creating a useful new apparatus for accomplishing a needed
                        function.
                     Our inner creative urge 'To Build.'
Functional Operation
                     Will it work? Does it meet our 'goals'?
                     What technical/non-technical troubles show up?
                     What are its lower and upper safe performance limits based on
                        fact and not symbolic models?
Demonstrate   It in working form for first time.
                     Its questioned performance.
                     Its successful use to 'others' later.
Verify/Check   previous creative thinking for:
                        Correct problems recognized.
                        Rightness of models/assumptions.
                        Order-of-magnitude of effects on which it is based.
                        Practicality of proposed solution embodiment.
                        General correctness.
                        Weaknesses in theory/mathematical modeling/assumptions and to
                           furnish a 'reference point' for theoretical analysis.
                        Criticalities of parts/materials/processes.
                        Mistakes.
                        Unforeseen problems.
Find New Problems   of:
                     Physically making it.
                     Materials/processes needed to make it work.
                     Appearance/aesthetics.
                     Inadequate performance range.
                     Useful life/reliability/incipient failure/failure
                        modes.
                     Safety/unwanted side effects.
                     Unanticipated user modes of operation/malfunctions.
                     Needed revisions/improvements/new theoretical work.
Acquire Experience   of:
                     Working-out successful fabrication/test procedures.
                     Finding what *can't* be done/won't work/isn't successful.
                     Realistically costing it/its operation.
                     Working in a general area.
Minimize Risks   of failure when it is later implemented, as by mass
                     production. Directs future creative work. Provides factual
                     basis for decision-making.
Satisfy Legal Requirements for:
                     Patent ('Reduction to Practice').
                     Firmly establishing who did what, when, and with what specific
                        results ('Diligence').

TABLE 8-1 Reasons for constructing and testing a
            physical model.

"The only thing that will solve that problem is a sample-- a working sample-- people seem to regard the working sample not as a propagandist of any kind because it's an immaterial thing - - - "
  Charles F. Kettering
  [172]

"Before any invention is perfected and marketed a great deal of money must be spent in developing and perfecting the original mental conception."
  F. W. Tausig
  [325]

"If you are going to make thousands or millions of systems, an over-sight cannot be tolerated."
  Ira G. Wilson
  Marthann E. Wilson
  [378, p23]

phenomenon being investigated must be generated to permit testing.

In <u>Development</u> a model is built and tested of the new product family being created.

In <u>Design</u> we don't commit a factory to producing a product, no matter how clever, without first building models and exhaustively testing them.

In <u>Manufacturing</u> we can't know our proposed new process is satisfactory until a model is built and tested under realistic conditions.

In <u>Operations</u> proposed new procedures are tried out on a small-scale basis before large commitments are made.

Thus from research to operations we find the phase of 'Construction and Verification' needed and common. This intensely practical but difficult step is *not* accomplished automatically, as some erroneously assume, but occurs because of our deliberate engineering effort.

PURPOSE

> ● <u>Purposes</u> <u>of</u> <u>Construction</u> <u>and</u> <u>Verification</u> <u>Phase</u>.
>   ▲ Physically create our proposed new solution embodiment.
>   ▲ Demonstrate its reduction to practice.
>   ▲ Use it as a vehicle for acquiring factual information.

Note that the end of the model is to acquire factual information. If beforehand we *knew* without doubt information that our new creation would function as we expect; if we *knew* information it could be built without problems; if we *knew* information that it has no unanticipated or unsolved problems; if we *knew* the information that it solves the problem; if we *knew* information of its performance range and peculiarities; then we *might* not have to go to the considerable trouble of building an initial model.

But in creative work we generally *don't* know

*"Experimental
design---is a power-
ful extension of
paper and pencil
design - -."
 Morris Asimow
 [12, p32]*

the above sets of information beforehand! Thus we

build a model and test it to obtain the information,

first for ourselves and later for 'others', that we

have successfully solved the problem and have a new,

useful and proven creative solution to offer. But the

model's principal purpose remains as a vehicle for

obtaining useful *information*, regardless of how

deep we become enmeshed in 'hardware'.

A *FUNCTIONAL VIEW* of the 'Construction and Verification'

major phase is shown in Fig. 8-1. Our 'input' is

an optimal proposed symbolic solution embodiment model,

e.g. sketches, drawings, schematics, plans. *What* is

to be built is clear and specific in the form of the

carefully conceived 'paper solution embodiment'. It

is the result of all our creative thinking from the

previous four major steps. Our 'output' is to be a

*"The experiment
phase of engineering
design requires that
a piece of hardware
or software be
constructed and
tested to verify
the concept and
analysis of the
design - - -"
 Percy H. Hill
 [148, p46]*

workable proven physical model and information of its

performance, peculiarities, and related facts.

Example 8-2

    Review 'Construction and Verification' part of
Example 3-1.

    The phase consists of:

● Construction A physical model is built of our
   new creation.

● Verification The model is tested and its
   performance verified.

Since during the verification step we usually have

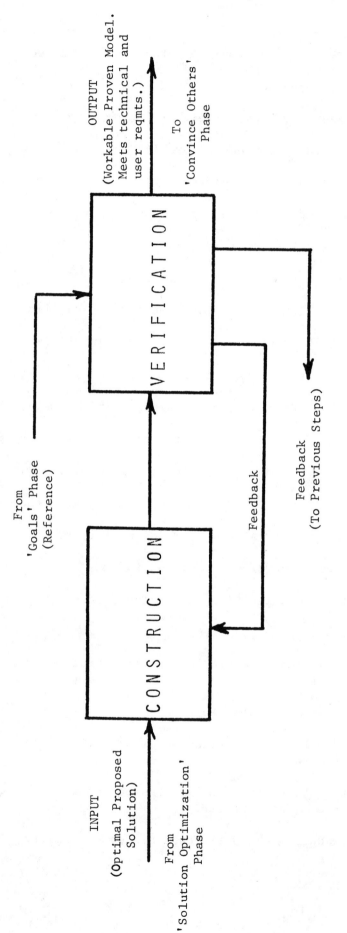

FIG. 8-1 Functional model of 'Construction and Verification' phase. The proposed new creation is physically built and tested.

to modify the physical model, the feedback path to

'Construction' represents this process. Thus

'Construction' and 'Verification' are intimately

linked, and we may iterate this loop many times for a

complex major new engineering creation.

"Without an objective you can't tell when a job is done.
Harald T. Friis
[113, p49]

Note the 'reference' against which we verify the

performance of our new creation is the goals formulated

in the second major step of the six-step approach.

If it meets our goals, the problem is solved. Then

'Convincing Others', Chap. 9, to act on the proven

*"But why can't the critics talk instead about the trial-and-*success* method?"*
Charles F. Kettering
[174, p113]

solution is the remaining major step. If it fails to

meet our goals, it may be necessary to feedback to

appropriate previous steps for re-engineering, as

shown.

Example 8-3

    In the early 50's when we were developing
practical color television receivers, one of the
then very difficult industry goals was "the color
television receiver shall cost the buyer less
than $500." The three major receiver alternatives
were the CBS rotating color wheel system, the
Philco Apple system with vertical color stripes
on the picture tube face, and the RCA shadow mask
system. We made engineering models for each and
costed them. The RCA system came closest to
meeting the $500 goal. That system was finally
adopted. Color television then became a reality
in the United States.

In summary, in the 'Construction and Verification'

phase we find in practical hardware form whether

all our creative ideas leading to this point are

right or wrong. It is an emotionally *exciting*

"I have never been so excited as the day we fired up the complete equipment, looked at the picture on the cathode-ray-tube and found that it gave us the angles of arrival of the signals from Europe."
  Harald T. Friis
  [113, p26]

phase as we see our new creation taking *physical* form! It is generally a difficult step to successfully execute. In short, visible stimulating deliberate *action* occurs during building and testing.

Discussion Topics

1. How do you account for the fact that when confronted with an engineering problem requiring creativity, many students and some practicing engineers rush immediately to 'build something'?

2. Are the previous four major steps aimed at symbolically creating *what* to build really necessary?

3. The author of an engineering text states "--constructing a likely embodiment of the device or system and subjecting it to use and observation-- is so seldom used anymore that the profession has forgotten its possibility." Is this true in *your* engineering discipline? If it is, then what is the useful 'output' to society of the engineer? Is creating symbolic models and analytically solving them the end result of engineering? Has engineering gotten into too much abstraction and removed from 'Hardware'? Why? Can a truly *new* creative engineering idea be verified without building and testing it?

4. Won't we always know whether our proposed new solution embodiment functionally works without building a model?

5. One class of reasons given in Table 8-1 was to 'find new problems.' Haven't we found enough problems in the previous four steps? Why look for more?

6. In great haste a new power circuit breaker embodiment was created on paper and rushed into production. No model was built or tested, since "It's just a new combination of old well-known circuit breaker ideas." Thousands of malfunctioning breakers were later returned to the factory. The manager of engineering and the creating design engineer were fired. Why did they fail?

7. Can one 'Verify' a new creation if he omitted the Specify Goals phase?

8. What problems might a creative engineer encounter working for a 'building type' manager who is unknowing of the need for the previous four steps or how to execute them? Are most engineering managers this type or do they have more mature problem solving approaches?

Exercises

8-E1. Examine your engineering textbooks for physical model building and testing. Do any treat it? Summarize your factual findings.

8-E2. Identify an important engineering product near you. Who created it? Historically and factually did he build and test a model before the product was widely used?

8-E3. As a design engineer assume you have completed the 'optimize' phase for a large new custom-engineered power transformer for Your State Power Co. You are ready to build the first model which is later to be shipped and placed into service. List the probable problems in building the physical model.

8-E4. A development engineer proposes an embodiment for a cigarette-case size electronic slide rule of the future with digital readout. He has pushed all physical dimensions to the limit to get the integrated circuits, batteries and components in the small space. List at least 10 problems he may have in building a physical model.

8-E5. Assume you are a research engineer and have created a paper solution embodiment for the first combined solar heating, cooling, and energy storage system for a home. The cooling is via the ammonia absorption refrigeration system. List the problems you may have in building the first working model.

8-E6. Select an engineering faculty member you admire. Personally visit him. Draw out his opinions on building and testing physical models for a *newly* created engineering product. Prepare a written summary, noting where his ideas agree or disagree with those of this chapter.

8-2 <u>What</u> <u>is</u> <u>Done</u>

THE CREATIVE PROCESS MODEL of the phase is shown in

Fig. 8-2. It is similar to earlier charts and is

the essence of this major step.

"Where possible, it is desirable to split the job into smaller units." Harald T. Friis [113, p48]

The step, as others in the disciplined creative

process, is simply divided into logical manageable

sub-steps. 'Practicality' characterizes this major

step.

A <u>Crucial</u> <u>Decision</u> whether a model is needed for our

particular problem is the first event. Generally a

model *is* needed for reasons cited in Table 8-1. It

is wise here at the beginning to think through and

reach a firm decision, especially if the model to

"Money was an annoying anchor that always seemed to be dragging and hindering (Nikola Tesla's) research activities." John J. O'Neill [232, p217]

be created is large, complex, costly, involves much

new technology, or requires a long time to build.

The decision inherently involves good engineering

judgment based on the facts of our particular model.

It may be made by the creating engineer, his man-

agement, or both.

   <u>Example</u> <u>8-4</u>

     A graduate student and I made the joint
   clean-cut decision to build a model of the new
   Solar Electric Motor whose 'paper embodiment' I
   had created. The resulting model is shown in
   Fig. 8-3.

     In rare cases for an extremely *simple* new

creation which departs little from prior art it may

be possible, at some risk, to bypass the entire phase

as indicated by the upper dotted line in Fig. 8-2.

Example 8-5

A mechanical design engineer decides not to construct a model of a new automobile steering wheel he has created on paper. With some risk, he decides to go directly to production tooling after the overall design for the new car is 'sold' to his management.

Classes of Physical Models we might make should be known before deciding. These are summarized in Table 8-2. Each model class is distinctly different and accomplishes different purposes.

"He may make a rough model in wood or other cheap material in order to determine the practicability of the invention."
Joseph Rossman [279, p62]

For a new creation very early in its technology it may be sufficient to construct only a proof-of-principle model. At an advanced stage we may build a prototype model. Alternatively we might choose to build a proof-of-principle model, verify it; then build an experimental model, verify it; etc. From the creative process viewpoint we are iterating a loop within the phase. Each pass results in a more sophisticated physical model and more useful engineering information.

The class of model we choose to construct naturally depends on the particular creative embodiment and situation.

Factors Against Model Building Though we advocated building a model for a new creation, we should know

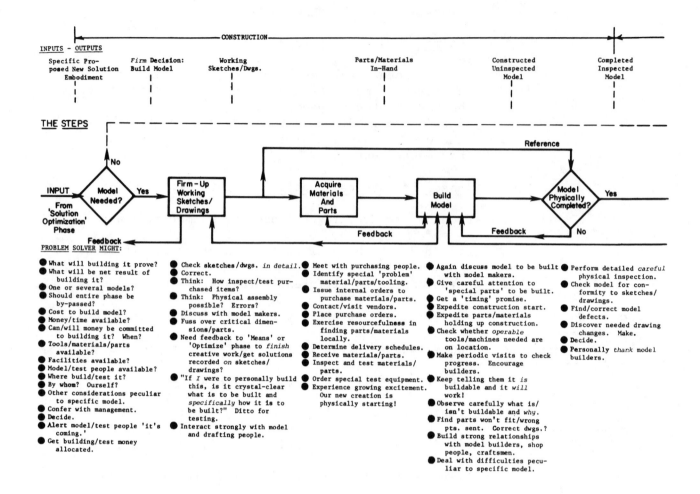

INPUTS - OUTPUTS

CONSTRUCTION

| Specific Pro-posed New Solution Embodiment | *Firm Decision:* Build Model | Working Sketches/Dwgs. | Parts/Materials In-Hand | Constructed Uninspected Model | Completed Inspected Model |

THE STEPS

No

INPUT
From 'Solution Optimization' Phase

Model Needed? Yes → Firm-Up Working Sketches/ Drawings → Acquire Materials And Parts → Build Model → Model Physically Completed? Yes

Reference

No

Feedback   Feedback   Feedback

PROBLEM SOLVER MIGHT:

- What will building it prove?
- What will be net result of building it?
- One or several models?
- Should entire phase be by-passed?
- Cost to build model?
- Money/time available?
- Can/will money be committed to building it? When?
- Tools/materials/parts available?
- Facilities available?
- Model/test people available?
- Where build/test it?
- By whom? Ourself?
- Other considerations peculiar to specific model.
- Confer with management.
- Decide.
- Alert model/test people 'it's coming.'
- Get building/test money allocated.

- Check sketches/dwgs. *in detail.*
- Correct.
- Think: How inspect/test purchased items?
- Think: Physical assembly possible? Errors?
- Discuss with model makers.
- Fuss over critical dimensions/parts.
- Need feedback to 'Means' or 'Optimize' phase to *finish* creative work/get solutions recorded *on* sketches/ drawings?
- "If *I* were to personally build this, is it crystal-clear what is to be built and *specifically* how it is to be built?" Ditto for testing.
- Interact strongly with model and drafting people.

- Meet with purchasing people.
- Identify special 'problem' material/parts/tooling.
- Issue internal orders to purchase materials/parts.
- Contact/visit vendors.
- Place purchase orders.
- Exercise resourcefulness in finding parts/materials locally.
- Determine delivery schedules.
- Receive materials/parts.
- Inspect and test materials/ parts.
- Order special test equipment.
- Experience growing excitement. Our new creation is physically starting!

- Again discuss model to be built with model makers.
- Give careful attention to 'special parts' to be built.
- Get a 'timing' promise.
- Expedite construction start.
- Expedite parts/materials holding up construction.
- Check whether *operable* tools/machines needed are on location.
- Make periodic visits to check progress. Encourage builders.
- Keep telling them it *is* buildable and it *will* work!
- Observe carefully what is/ isn't buildable and *why.*
- Find parts won't fit/wrong pts. sent. Correct dwgs.?
- Build strong relationships with model builders, shop people, craftsmen.
- Deal with difficulties peculiar to specific model.

- Perform detailed *careful* physical inspection.
- Check model for conformity to sketches/ drawings.
- Find/correct model defects.
- Discover needed drawing changes. Make.
- Decide.
- Personally *thank* model builders.

FIG. 8-2 'Construction and Verification' phase creative process model. Our new creation is physically built and tested. This chart is a more detailed view of Fig. 8-1 and of this phase in Fig. 3-1.

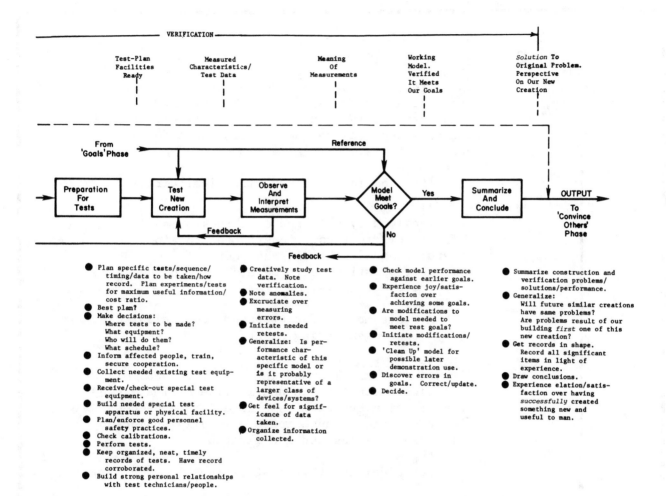

- Plan specific tests/sequence/ timing/data to be taken/how record. Plan experiments/tests for maximum useful information/ cost ratio.
- Best plan?
- Make decisions:
  Where tests to be made?
  What equipment?
  Who will do them?
  What schedule?
- Inform affected people, train, secure cooperation.
- Collect needed existing test equipment.
- Receive/check-out special test equipment.
- Build needed special test apparatus or physical facility.
- Plan/enforce good personnel safety practices.
- Check calibrations.
- Perform tests.
- Keep organized, neat, timely records of tests. Have record corroborated.
- Build strong personal relationships with test technicians/people.

- Creatively study test data. Note verification.
- Note anomalies.
- Excruciate over measuring errors.
- Initiate needed retests.
- Generalize: Is performance characteristic of this specific model or is it probably representative of a larger class of devices/systems?
- Get feel for significance of data taken.
- Organize information collected.

- Check model performance against earlier goals.
- Experience joy/satisfaction over achieving some goals.
- Are modifications to model needed to meet rest goals?
- Initiate modifications/ retests.
- 'Clean Up' model for possible later demonstration use.
- Discover errors in goals. Correct/update.
- Decide.

- Summarize construction and verification problems/ solutions/performance.
- Generalize:
  Will future similar creations have same problems?
  Are problems result of our building first one of this new creation?
- Get records in shape. Record all significant items in light of experience.
- Draw conclusions.
- Experience elation/satisfaction over having successfully created something new and useful to man.

Increasing
Cost,
Complexity,
and
Completeness

● Proof-of-Principle Model
    Minimally operative model of basic principle of our
    new creation. Extremely elementary. *Quickly*
    assembled from readily available parts/materials.
    Known as 'string and chewing gum' model. (Models
    of this type may not be constructable for *all*
    new creations.)
        Example
            'Breadboard' of a new electrical circuit.

● Scale Model
    A dimensionally enlarged or shrunken model
    of our new creation. Constructed to aid
    visualizing it. Usually non-operative. Made
    of wood, plastics, soft metals, or other easy to
    fabricate materials.
        Example
            A scale model of a proposed new nuclear electric
            power generating plant.

● Experimental Model
    Functioning model embodying most new ideas of our
    creation. Constructed nearly like ultimate proposed
    new creation but permits changes where needed. May
    be incomplete in appearance. Usually subjected to
    extensive testing and modification.
        Example
            The model for the first air-cushion vehicle.

● Prototype Model
    Full-scale working model in its most complete
    form. Embodies all ideas of our new creation
    in proposed preferred form. Technically and
    visually complete. Meets our earlier goals com-
    pletely including being probably satisfactory to the
    user. May be constructed of handmade or tooled parts
    or both.
        Example
            The first Saturn rocket.

TABLE 8-2   Principal classes of *physical* models
of new engineering creations.

about some reasons for *not* building one.

Models tend to be costly. Building something

entirely new involves engineering, materials, fabri-

cation, and other problems all of which must be

solved in detail. It takes time and money.

Building even the simplest thing is very

difficult--much more so than is thought from examining

the finished manufactured version years later. In

spite of our careful disciplined creative thinking

" - - progress, im-
provement, and a
higher order of
things are almost
always bred in
adversity."
Phil Simpson
[295, p17]

parts of the model will be ill conceived, won't work,

and modifications needed. Materials may not be what

the model requires. Parts will be made and assembled

wrong. We need special parts we don't have and can

get only with great difficulty. Tests will be run

wrong and inconclusively. The people we have may not

be as skilled as we thought.

The above factors, including risk of 'failure',

and other difficulties peculiar to the particular

model to be built should be weighed before deciding

to build a physical model.

Finally Deciding A *firm* decision to or not to build

a physical model must be reached. The terse actions

"It is senseless to
attempt to make
everyone happy
with our deci-
sions."
Eugene K. Von Fange
[360, p200]

cited in the first column of Fig. 8-2 may help us

decide.

Example 8-6

In the early 50's another engineer and I
were given the challenging job of developing a

FIG. 8-3 'Experimental model' built of first Solar
          Electric Motor. Sunlight from above
          illuminates solar cells on one hexagon
          facet generating current applied to an
          armature coil, left rear, causing rotation.
          It is a light commutated motor and has no
          troublesome brushes. This model ran at
          160RPM in sunlight of 100MW/cm^2 intensity.
          In larger sizes it is potentially useful
          as a water pump in sun-rich countries
          when low cost solar cells become available.
          Such new machines would have vertical
          shafts with cells mounted on an umbrella-
          like rotor.

practical suspension system for the first low
cost home washing machine to be mass marketed by
our company. The manager of engineering made
the *firm* decision we were to build a working model.
That decision was an important motivating ingredient.

The two of us made quite a few models, most
failures, before creating a successful design from
which many thousands were later manufactured.

His decision was an important step toward
making low cost home laundry a reality for the
average worker.

A miserable situation is to be ordering parts or

initially fabricating while vacillating over whether

the model should even be built. Depression and

loss of our morale and that of shop people result .

Both detect somebody hasn't made a decision-needed for

progress to occur.

Assuming a firm decision has been made *to* build

a model, we continue with Fig. 8-2.

CONSTRUCTION starts with the practical act of firming-

up our *working* sketches and drawings. Many 'loose

ends' need attention on them. The object of the

working sketches or drawings is to clearly define the

proposed model embodiment for those who will

build it in our shops and facilities. We as the

creating engineer are responsible for generating

them and their content.

We may need to make a seemingly superhuman

effort to firm-up our sketches and drawings to

definite specific propositions. Our attention to

*"Developmental work
is always a slightly
organized chaos."
Charles F.
Kettering
[42, p71]*

*"The research
worker should not
start work on a
complicated piece
of new equipment
in the precision
shop before he has
had thorough
discussions with
the shop foreman
on the different
ways of doing the
job."
Harald T. Friis
[113, p51]*

*"Some people, the
moment they have
a device to con-
struct or any
piece of work to
perform, rush at
it without
adequate prep-
aration - - -"*
Nikola Tesla
[336]

detail is needed. Effort expended here in generating

complete and accurate parts, sub-assembly, and assembly

sketches and drawings helps avoid difficulties in

later model building.

Sketches or drawings 'sent out' for purchasing

or building constitute 'contract documents' and should

be written with care.

Example 8-7

An engineer generates a sketch for a printed
circuit board to be made. It is 'sent out' to a
vendor specializing in printed circuit fabrication.
When the model board is returned, the engineer
complains because the vendor didn't test it for
voltage breakdown. The engineer failed to specify
testing on the drawing. The vendor performed per
the contract document. The engineer has *himself*
to blame.

There are extremes in sketches and drawings in

*"- - with good liason
the drawings may
be quite sketchy."*
Ira G. Wilson
Marthann E. Wilson
[378, p111]

*"They would not build
the turbines as I
wished."*
Nikola Tesla
[337, p226]

creative engineering work.

● Minimal Drawings: The model embodiment is
   minimally defined. Details communicated
   verbally to model builders. Permits
   moving fast with highly skilled people.
   Much useful information on *how* to make the
   model not recorded. May be lost.

● Maximum Drawings: *Everything* spelled out in
   minute detail. No eventuality overlooked.
   Many very detailed specifications and
   cautions. Requires *very* long to generate
   such documents. Very costly. Many
   arguments occur in the process. Then model
   builders don't follow the drawings or they
   follow them *so* closely that progress occurs
   at a snail's pace.

We should decide where between the extremes to operate

our project. Experience soon reveals the optimum

for our particular environment and model.

A VALUABLE WORK OF ART BY THOMAS A. EDISON

FIG. 8-4   Edison's 1877 working drawing for first phonograph
           made for his machinist, John Kruesi [173, p79].
           Modern engineering working drawings are much more
           detailed and complete. Courtesy of The Henry Ford
           Museum, Dearborn, Michigan. Collections of
           Greenfield Village and The Henry Ford Museum.

Acquiring **The** Parts With a satisfactory set of

definitive sketches or drawings completed we proceed

to acquire materials and parts, Fig. 8-2. This step

can take a long time unless we secure the whole-

hearted cooperation of our purchasing and model building

people. Even then it takes longer than the beginning

engineer realizes for purchase orders to issue, the

vendor to make it--along with all *his* difficulties--,

it to be received, inspected, tested, paid for, etc.

We shouldn't assume that our company, no matter

how large, has infinite varieties of new parts and

materials just for our model and all we have to do is

withdraw them from the stockroom!

Example 8-8

When three or four of us were creating the model
for the first new porous winding high voltage
encapsulated pulse transformer, we needed "some
kind of porous material epoxy will go through and
that is a good high voltage insulator." A purchase
order was issued on a local store for 25 pair of
nylon stockings from which the first successful new
transformer model was made.[1] Nylon cloth was not
available in our stockroom.

Eventually ordered parts arrive, are inspected and

tested if required, the needed materials are in-hand,

and practical model building starts. During this

exciting step as they perform we observe a natural

beauty in the highly skilled artisans who enjoy building

the new.

*"- - they will only
work on those
projects with the
nearest deadline,
and then only if
they are constantly
reminded of its
importance."
  Eugene K. Von
  Fange
  [360, p197]*

*"One of my rules
was to check all
the components:
resistors, con-
densers, tubes,
etc. before
wiring a set
and I then found
that the finished
set worked as
expected."
  Harald T. Friis
  [113, p18]*

---

[1] Surprisingly, auditors didn't make an issue over why stockings were suddenly
charged to engineering!

*"In doing a new
thing, only occa-
sionally does
anything go right.
At least ninety per-
cent of the time is
taken up overcoming
all sorts of new and
unexpected diffi-
culties."*
Charles F. Kettering
[42, p142]

*"Oh, don't the days
seem lank and long
when all goes right
and nothing wrong
and isn't your life
extremely flat with
nothing whatever to
grumble at!"*
King Gama [177]

*"What is important
is unlimited
patience, the ability
to build something
which can be
manufactured as
well as made in a
laboratory."*
Joseph Rossman
[279, p46]

*"- - let every great
master look to it
that his work be
not seen in embryo."*
Baltasar Gracian
[127, p219]

<u>Then Construction Difficulties Crop Up</u> The drawings
weren't clear and the model maker made the part as *he*
thought it should be, and it's wrong--or he made it
right but of the wrong material! Or we didn't design
the part correctly, the model maker completes the job
and drawings must be revised. The parts ordered aren't
what we thought they were--they won't do the job--and
must be expeditiously reordered. The needed machines
or equipment to make the parts are not on hand--or if
they are, they don't work. The machining required
is so tricky because of the nature of our model that
the machinist bitterly complains it can't be made.
Welds that looked simple on paper can't be made without
building special fixtures requiring six months. Or
the model makers don't like our attitude toward them
or the project and they slow down. Glue that is
supposed to stick doesn't. Quick-drying paint requires
days.

Delays appear *everywhere*! In the meantime
management, who is paying for it all, wants progress
reports on the model. We haven't time to generate
them but do anyway. In short "what can go wrong does."

Occasionally things go right.

<u>Example 8-9</u>

When we were creating the new porous winding
high voltage pulse transformer, Example 8-8, in an

"- - every oppor-
tunity should be
afforded to qualify
men in the use of
tools and the making
of their own models."
   G. F. Stratton
   [320, p115]

environment somewhat hostile to the idea, three or
four of us built the first model ourselves in
semi-secrecy overnight. The nylon stockings were
cut into strips and wound without too much difficulty
into a gauze-like transformer winding. A standard
mold was 'borrowed', the winding carefully assembled
therein by a skilled technician, and he and the
mechanical engineer stayed up most of the night
running it through the tricky encapsulating
process. By effort, and considerable luck, we had
a finished new transformer model early the next
morning.

Our high voltage tests showed it so good the
test equipment ruptured rather than the transformer!
We were jubilant!

Thousands of porous winding transformers were
since manufactured using porous dacron. A large
factory previously clogged up with 'rejects' of an
unsuccessful earlier mylar winding design was
changed to a successful operation.

But it started with the first model made in
semi-secrecy.

In the midst of practical construction difficulties

the idealized theoretical models learned in college

which seldom had to be *built* seem far off.

"In 1875 (John
Holland) built his
first model (of a
submarine) but it
was a failure, as
practically all
first models are.
Not discouraged
by this, he kept
working - -"
   Charles F.
   Kettering
   [173, p34]

The above, and many more *specific* problems in

human relations areas, must be cooperatively solved by

the engineer and support people before the model is

realized. Their solution is *not* 'automatic.' We, the

creating engineer, are the catalyst and forcing function

toward their solution.

Inspecting The Model Finally, after much effort,

"Every piece of
equipment was
thoroughly
inspected by
Tesla - -"
   John J. O'Neill
   [232, p183]

perseverance, and surmounted difficulties the model is

assembled, Fig. 8-2 again. But is it completed? We

carefully inspect it, or have others do so, using our

sketches or drawings as the reference. Hopefully

only minor changes are needed which are effected.

Then the model *building* is finished! We have

arrived at the exciting time when our new creation can

"- - it might work and I might go sailing away, without being able to come back."
Robert H. Goddard
[121, p25]

be physically rolled out of the model shop for testing.

For a little while we stand around with those who

built it, reflect on the interesting problems in

getting it built, philosophize on whether it will

successfully pass test, and feel humbly proud at

having made the first model of a truly new creation.

"The thoughtful application of the Golden Rule still pays big dividends."
Eugene K. Von Fange [360, p201]

We *personally* thank those who built it.   The

unsung heroes, the model makers, mechanics, craftsmen,

and technicians made it possible.

VERIFICATION OF THE NEW CREATION, Fig. 8-2, comes

next. Verification is akin to 'checking,' a topic of

Chap. 16, except here we are checking real-world

hardware--the newly created model. From our engineering

laboratory education we are more familiar with practical

"Two minutes' trial was sufficient to prove the efficiency of twisting the planes to obtain lateral balance."
Wilbur Wright [395, p41]

testing ideas and techniques than building. Thus we

only highlight this important subject.

Preparation For Tests is the first important step. The

specific test plan[1] is created in its entirety.

---

[1]The branch of mathematics, Experiment Design, may be helpful here. Schenck's [285, Ch. 6] excellent detailed treatment should be studied by all creative engineers planning test work.

"- - you must have a good set-up. You must do it the best way you can think of. You must make good measurements."
Harald T. Friis
[113, p51]

Equipment and **test** facilities must be collected, or possibly bought or built[1] and readied. The people who will run the tests, either ourselves or technicians, are briefed, special testing problems discussed, and their cooperation sought. Formation of positive attitudes here is extremely important, as a flippant 'these tests aren't very important anyway' attitude can destroy the model we spent months or years building.

"With the aid of technicians the engineer and scientist can be freed to do more creative work."
Albert Spalding
[310, p561]

Much of the preparatory work may be done as the model is being constructed to minimize test time.
Testing and Difficulties   The model of our new creation is then tested. The 'reference' is the set of goals we created back in the second major step of the six-step approach.

In testing we encounter many practical difficulties.

"The [sewing] machine was completed in seven days. About nine o'clock in the evening we tried it; it did not sew. - - -"
Isaac M. Singer
[296, p134]

The technicians don't want to do the tests. The right instruments are not available and must be purchased from short funds. Progress slows to zero while they are shipped. Instruments must be calibrated, but the calibration shop is closed for vacation. Instruments that were certified operative aren't and need repair. The instrument is the right kind but doesn't cover the needed range. The instruments work individually but

---

[1] Special test equipment to be built may require substantial creative engineering in its own right. Don't wait til the day before it's needed to initiate it!

FIG. 8-5   Proof-of-Principle model for a new solid state power circuit of variable frequency output. The variable frequency permits changing the induction motor speed over a wide range without usual auxiliary machines or troublesome mechanical variable speed mechanisms.

"(Nikola Tesla) closed the switch. Instantly the armature turned, built up to full speed in a flash and then continued to operate in almost complete silence."
  John J. O'Neill
  [232, p55]

the total test set-up doesn't work right. The whole test plan has major flaws. The new model doesn't work right or is so good we irreversibly damage our test equipment exploring the limits of the model's performance range. The measurements are dangerous and our company safety specialist won't

"- - (Tesla) always carried experiments to their upper and lower limits."
  John J. O'Neill
  [232, p148]

allow the tests except under highly restrictive conditions. Model components and parts that weren't supposed to fail do and must be replaced before the tests can proceed. We know we must keep timely records (Chap. 15) of the tests, but no record book was provided.

"A careful study and analysis of the unsuccessful device must then be made in order to determine the reasons for its failure."
  Joseph Rossman
  [279, p62]

The above, and many other practical difficulties, must all be solved before the tests are successfully completed. Such difficulties are part of the challenge of being a creative engineer!

Interpreting The Tests The test data are carefully observed and insightfully interpreted by us, Fig. 8-2 again. It is not easy to do. Any engineer can look at a page of data and say, "That's what it measured!" But answers to, "Are these the *right* answers?", "What are these data telling me?" and

"Nobody but myself thought the charring worthy of notice - - -"
  Charles Goodyear
  [122, p128]

"What is the *meaning* of these measurements?" are sought by the creative engineer not satisfied with the obvious. The test data may be telling us[1] that our

---

[1]The interesting subject of 'the data speaking to us' and our creatively listening thereto involves subtleties beyond our space here, unfortunately.

*"Even though the
model performance
meets all of the
objectives and
goals, there is
still a chance of
a slip-up when
production starts."
  Ira G. Wilson
  Marthann E. Wilson
  [378, p170]*

*"We felt that the
model had demon-
strated the
efficiency of our
system of control."
  Orville Wright
  [387, p11]*

*"The man with a
new idea is a crank
until the idea
succeeds."
  Mark Twain
  [349]*

*"The Eagle has
landed."
  Neil Armstrong
  [6]*

new creation works almost as well as we expected but modifications must be made to the model, indicated by the lower feedback path in Fig. 8-2, and we must iterate the process.

WRAPPING IT ALL UP Finally, after considerable patience, effort, insight, money, application of our knowledge, and possibly executing several iterations within this phase for each class of models shown in Table 8-2, we are satisfied the model of our new creation meets our goals. We summarize our experience and draw conclusions about it.

The Problem Is Now Solved! We have the information of how a successful practical working model must be embodied, and we have an actual working model which has been verified to meet the goals for our newly created product. We have the *certain* information our new creation 'works'. We are sure of its performance. We have created something new and useful to offer mankind and have *proven* it performs as we claim. These and similar thoughts are deeply satisfying to us.

Discussion Topics

1. Has your engineering education taught you to sketch? How to generate drawings? How to read them? That you are *responsible* for their content?

2. The possibility of 'failing' to be able to build our model wasn't mentioned. Explore the role of 'failure' in building and testing models of new engineering creations. Discuss effects it may have on your attitudes in this phase.

3. Why iterate the step? Why isn't building *one* model enough?

4. Discuss parts of Fig. 8-2 which bother you.

5. Should we 'get our hands into the act' during building and testing our new model? Or should we depend wholly on others?

6. To what extent is the functional success of our model linked with 'attention to the details' by its builders?

7. Given a sketch of the first model in Fig. 8-3, how long would it take you to build it? Why do we so frequently underestimate the time required to build a new model?

8. Is 'the idea generator' or 'the one who made it work' more important in engineering? How is our motivation related to our capacity to '*make* it work'?

9. How is 'human relations' tied to success in this phase? What problems might we have under great time pressures?

10. Sometimes we find extremely pessimistic model builders or technicians assigned to our project and progress seems asymptotic to zero. What can the engineer do in such situations?

11. "The squeaking wheel gets the grease!" Are there times when we should squeak in this phase?

12. Patience is obviously needed in this step. Can we 'learn' patience? How can we increase it?

13. After construction started on your new model you find your supervisor, without your knowledge, has ordered the model maker to effect a major change in how your model is to be built. The change is technically incorrect. What ethical questions are raised? How will such a situation make you feel?

14. Ask your professor to share experiences in building and testing models of new engineering creations.

Exercises

8-E7.   Select a component on an automobile. Work
backwards in thought to its creation by
engineers. Was a model probably built and
tested? Identify specific problems you
think were probably encountered in building
and testing the first model.

8-E8.   Given the completed inspected model of
Fig. 8-3, propose an effective specific
engineering test plan for it.

8-E9.   Prepare a list of ways we might improve the
efficiency of building and testing a newly
created engineering model.

8-E10. List the ways you might think about to raise
funds to build the first helicopter prototype model.

8-E11. Suppose you were iterating this phase for
the solid state speed control of Fig. 8-5.
You want to construct and test an 'experimental
model'. List the problems you face. Briefly
state what positive action you would take for
each. About how long would it take before you
have a proven working model?

8-E12. Others as assigned.

8-3 Some Guides

A few of these are collected in Table 8-3. We

forego exposition for brevity. Much could be said

about them. These are distillates

from failure and success experiences of many creative

engineers. Following any *one* guide alone will not

insure successful building and testing of our new

creation. We have the task here, as in so much of

creative engineering work, of doing *many* things and

bringing *many* personal skills into use to the end of

*"The inventor must
be persistent and
patient. - - the
experimental stage
involves a rigid
and logical
procedure and hard
work."*
  Joseph Rossman
  [279, p62]

● <u>Initiate</u> <u>Action</u>   yourself in building/testing model.

● <u>Who</u> <u>Builds</u>/<u>Tests</u>   important to success.
                                    ▲ Build yourself (lone inventor) on a 'hands-
                                        on' basis?
                                    ▲ Others build for us (corporate engineer)?
                                    ▲ Select competent people.

● <u>Working</u> <u>Sketches</u>/<u>Drawings</u>:   Attend to them before construction.

● <u>Parts</u>   Order early.

● <u>Test</u> <u>Critical</u> <u>Parts</u>/   components/sub-systems before assembly.

● <u>Details</u>   of the model--give them much attention.

● <u>Human</u> <u>Relations</u>   Work at by:
                                    ▲ <u>Applying</u> '<u>Golden</u> <u>Rule</u>' with compassion and
                                        understanding to model makers, machinists,
                                        technicians, purchasing people, inspectors,
                                        and others.
                                    ▲ <u>Respecting</u> model makers, craftsmen, tech-
                                        nicians of demonstrated ability. Seek
                                        their advice to enhance success.
                                    ▲ <u>Exhibiting</u> <u>Sense</u> <u>of</u> <u>Humor</u> during difficult
                                        times.
                                    ▲ <u>Communicating</u> effectively--verbal and
                                        written--with those helping make our
                                        creation succeed.

● <u>Decisions</u>   Get the facts. Make clean decisions.

● <u>A</u> <u>Test</u> <u>Plan</u>   Create one for the model. Follow it.

● <u>Follow-Through</u>   on promises made to others.

● <u>Written</u> <u>Records</u>   Keep of 'successes' *and* 'failures'.

● <u>Engineering</u> <u>Judgment</u>:   A daily must. No equation can substitute for
                                        it.

● <u>Energy</u> <u>and</u> <u>Effort</u>:   Apply *lavishly* to the many problems only we
                                        can solve.

● <u>Patience</u>,   patience, - - - - - - - - - - - patience!

● <u>Perseverance</u>   succeeds. Don't give up easily or without
                                        knowing <u>why</u> it failed.

● <u>Observe</u>   methods of experienced creative engineers
                                        excelling in successful building/testing.
                                        Learn from them.

TABLE 8-3   Some guides in 'Construction and Verification'
             phase to enhance success likelihood. Other
             more specific suggestions are in Fig. 8-2.

building and testing a successful working physical
model of our new creation. A *single* principle or
skill, in general, won't do the job.

Some engineers excel in this intensely practical
major phase and enjoy it. Others have miserable
experiences of repeated failure, doing nothing right
and having neither interest or inclination in model
building and testing. With engineering experience
in the right creative environment your skill in this
phase may be substantially enhanced so you find some
of its personal rewards.

Unfortunately, space does not permit dealing with
the unique problems of the lone inventor resourcefully
building and testing his own model. We learn much
about success from these courageous independents, who,
against great odds, single-handedly perform most of
the functions in Fig. 8-2, though they are often not
aware themselves of the creative process being used.
Society is very much in their debt.

Nor can we deal with the delights of 'getting
the hands into the act.' Moore [217, Ch. 8] is one
of the few who probes this issue which every creative
engineer who plans to build anything faces.

Nor is there space to probe 'failure', which is
very common in this phase, and what we can do about
it.

*"- - nothing is
followed through,
but everything is
left to itself,
even when well
conceived; - - -"*
Baltasar Gracian
[127, p225]

*"By doing nearly
all the work
oursleves little
money was needed
- - -"*
Orville Wright
[390, p27]

The above and related topics you will have to acquire from experience. As you already sense, 'Construction and Verification' is a profound subject. Only the principal points were treated here.

But the most *difficult* step in the entire creative process lies ahead! We shall see in Chap. 9 that 'Convincing Others' we have solved the problem and to implement our solution on a larger scale may be a great test of our faith, persuasiveness, persistence, and patience.

"A model that works, no matter how crude it is, is an invaluable aid in selling an invention."
Terrence W. Fenner
James L. Everett
[102, p141]

Chapter Summary

● Disciplined creativity tenet demands our created 'paper solution embodiment' be reduced to the construction and verification of a practical working *physical* model.

● The need for and purposes of this major step were presented at some length, since practical model building and testing is omitted or unrealistically minimized in most contemporary engineering text books.

● The sub-steps in the phase from the creative process viewpoint are embodied in the important Fig. 8-2. It is the heart of the subject and was treated in some detail because of its general applicability.

● The 'Construction and Verification' major phase, while emotionally stimulating, was seen to be characterized by practicality and difficulty. Our certain knowledge from 'Problem Inquiry' that the problem is *worth* solving assuages our difficulties. Our total preparation of the previous four major phases of the disciplined creativity approach substantially aids our likelihood of building and testing a successful working model. We now clearly see the chaos of others, less disciplined, trying to build or test *before* creating a suitable embodiment on paper.

● Some guides for enhancing the likelihood of
  successful model building and testing were
  presented (Table 8-3 and Fig. 8-2). These
  are a beginning point in formulating our own
  guides as we acquire experience in this phase of
  creativity.

CHAPTER 9

DISCIPLINE OF CONVINCING OTHERS

"After the invention is perfected to his satisfaction the
inventor must convince the public of its **value**."
                                    Joseph Rossman [279, p48]

● Need and purpose of 'Convince Others', the
   final major phase of creative problem
   solving.

● What is done.

● Some guides.

● Difficulties in this phase.

● Epilogue to morphology of disciplined
   creativity.

9-1 Need and Purpose of 'Convince Others'

The Need Most experienced engineers, inventors, managers,

and other creative people know it is *not* enough to

successfully build and test a new apparatus and

stop. To stop, assuming it will automatically get

transferred to wide scale implementation by some

complex process unknown or little understood by us,

is to commit a serious judgment error.

*"It is much harder
to sell a fairly
good creative idea
than to conceive
the idea."
Myron A. Coler
[65, p74]*

Experience in the world of real creative engineering

quickly convinces one that only *rarely* does 'the world

beat a path to the inventor of the better mouse trap'!

The passive, idealistic, and false view that 'others'

will seek us out seldom gets our new creations into

actual *use*. Such passivism may also lead to considerable

frustration and personal despondency of the undisciplined

creator, especially after spending a fortune developing

the creation only to be unable to get it into *use*.
It may also detract from the engineering profession.

The engineer with such a viewpoint generally
fails, over a time period, to get his new creations
acted upon by anyone or any sector of society. He
labors under the further incorrect assumption that
the hardest part of the creative process is to 'make
the thing technically work'. Having done so, "The
job is finished!" Effectively, all his previous creative
effort and work may be negated and his tangible creative
contribution lost. Unless he changes his attitude or
unless someone else picks up the new creation and
champions it, his valuable creative contribution
may be lost forever. Society may then be the ultimate
loser.

In contrast, the disciplined creative engineer
recognizes the need of 'selling' his matured new
creations to others before any socially beneficial

"Convince: To bring by argument to yield assent or to have belief beyond doubt."
Webster
[373]

action occurs. Such a distinct last step in the
creative process is an *active* one we call 'Convince
Others'.

Purpose

> ● Purpose of 'Convince Others' Phase: To
> get 'others' to accept, act on, and *use*
> our new creation.

Note this phase implies an *active* role by
the creative engineer. We are to be the *initiators*

of 'selling' our new creation(s) to 'others'—actively

disclosing, persuading, advocating, and defending. The

terminus is to have our creation *used* by the 'others'

of society whom we've been trying to aid. There is

none of the pathology of the undisciplined engineer

of the opening paragraphs. Instead this is a phase

of aggressive dynamism—an exciting time when the

totality of our creative thinking and work are coherently

brought forth for 'others' to see, clearly understand,

and *act* upon, perhaps publicly.

Please note we are *not* limiting this phase's

scope to the common mere publication of our creative

work which 'others' may find interesting, promptly

forget, with nothing ever done about *using* our new

creation.

A Functional View of this terminal phase of disciplined

creativity is shown in Fig. 9-1.

Our 'input' is a workable model resulting from the

'Construction and Verification' phase, Fig. 8-2, i.e.

we have a successful *proven* piece of physical hardware

which meets our earlier 'Goals' phase and solves the

problem. We do *not* just have immature concepts and

dreams here! We *know* without doubt our new creation

factually works as intended.

The phase 'output' is our creation being *used*

by 'others', i.e. it is put into service on a small

or large-scale—implemented.

*"He must be enough
of an egotist to
believe that he
and his concept
are not only
right but are
worth fighting
for."*
  Dean L. Gitter
  [119, p94]

*"—not only do you
have to invent, you
have to sell the idea
—to your own staff,
to your superiors,
and to many others."*
  Jacob Rabinow
  [266, p89]

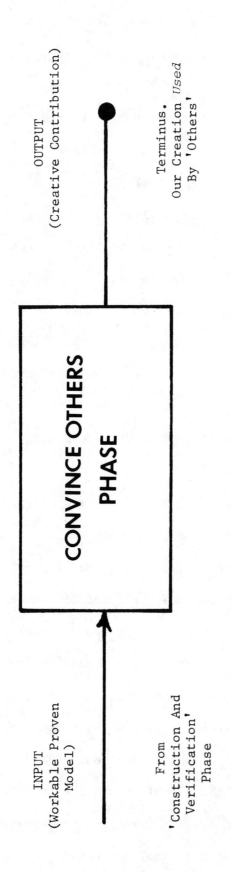

INPUT
(Workable Proven Model)

From 'Construction And Verification' Phase

CONVINCE OTHERS PHASE

OUTPUT
(Creative Contribution)

Terminus. Our Creation *Used* By 'Others'

FIG. 9-1   Functional view of 'Convince Others' phase. It is directed toward getting our creation *used* by others.

Thus in this phase the new creation resulting from weeks, months, or years work generally passes from our creating environment to a larger 'others' environment.[1] It passes from a private to a larger more public social domain.

Example 9-1

Grover, of Los Alamos, after creating the first 'heat pipe' [132] is reported to have had the problem of convincing his peers in Washington to *use* it. He made up small heat pipes about the diameter and length of a pencil and simply placed them in his shirt pocket. A heat pipe has the unique properties of transmitting large quantities of heat very rapidly with nearly zero temperature drop along the pipe.

When his superiors from Washington visited Los Alamos, Grover took them to coffee, inviting them to use his 'stirrer'. Instantly when inserted in the liquid his visitor's fingers got painfully hot. Now that he had their attention(!), he told them all about heat pipes, why and how they should be used.

They subsequently found wide use in space and terrestrial applications.

"The outside inventor's burden--is to demonstrate beyond a reasonable doubt that success will result from this innovation. That takes some doing."
Daniel V. DeSimone [74, p9]

Discussion Topics

1. "I've created this thing, made it work with my sweat and tears and written my engineering report. That's *enough*! Any 'selling', if it's needed, is up to the Sales Department--or Management!" Discuss.

2. Do we really have to 'sell' our new creations in the real engineering world? Why or why not?

---

[1] A seeming exception might be when we, if independent, decide to patent our creation and enter into entrepreneurship. But clearly the new creation will, longer-range, enter the others' environment.

3. Does the engineer have any professional obligation to society to sell his creations to the *use* point? What if the employer's interests conflict with those of society?

4. Compare and contrast the engineer who:
    a. Has *many* creations but can't 'sell' them.
    b. Has *few* creations (perhaps mediocre) but is a real salesman.
    Which, in the long run, has more impact on society?

5. How much effort should an engineer make to sell his ideas? Is there a point of diminishing returns?

6. Can overselling of one's new creation occur?

7. What oppositions can the creative engineer realistica` expect in 'Convince Others'? As a focal point, consider the engineer trying to convince a utility company management, heavily committed to build fossil and nuclear fueled electric power plants, that they should immediately build a demonstration solar thermal-electric plant.

8. Section 9-1 implies all the 'convincing' a creative engineer has to do is in a single concentrated phase. Is this true in reality? Do we need any 'Convincing Others' in *earlier* parts of the problem solving process, **e**.g. how would you convince an overloaded balky supervisor of drafting to give top priority to preparing your set of model drawings?

9. Are there any particular difficulties 'gathering the facts' from our previous creative work? If so, identify them.

10. To what extent is this phase interpretative in nature, i.e. is its role solely to interpret our new creation to others so they just *know* about it?

11. Can we 'convince' without first knowing much about 'others', i.e. who, characteristics, etc.?

12. Is this a relatively easy or difficult phase?

9-2 What's Done In 'Convince Others' Phase

The Creative Process Model is shown in Fig. 9-2. It

is the essence of this final creative process phase.

It consists of:

"The particular group of people for whom the invention is intended must be approached personally in some way. The merits of the invention must be made obvious."
  Joseph Rossman [279, p167]

● <u>Preparation</u> We privately get ready to effectively communicate our new creation to 'others'.

● <u>Communication</u> The new creation is revealed in its entirety to selected 'others' for consideration of acceptance and possible use.

Some overlap exists, as shown at the top of Fig. 9-2.

It is clear our attention is *away* from the creating difficulties and toward gaining acceptance and use of that which has been created. *Here* the details and results of our disciplined thinking and work in previous phases gets 'put together' in a coherent form understandable by 'others'.

"It is, however, a real accomplishment to sell your work to others."
  Harald T. Friis [113, p53]

It should be understood there are numerous subtleties, particularly in the human relations area, to each of these sub-steps. You can best learn of these as you start *practicing* your engineering profession. Figure 9-2 may be a helpful guide at that time.

Since we are familiar with such process model charts, for brevity we forego its detailed discussion and illustrate the sub-steps by examples.

<u>Should The Creation Be Used</u>? is a piercing question we as creator of the new should honestly ask ourselves.

<u>Example 9-2</u>

There is historical evidence Tesla may have created the first 'death ray' [possibly a laser?] as an offshoot of his obsession to transmit power by wireless. He apparently decided, on humanitarian grounds, it should not be used, and he never revealed it. [232, p237]

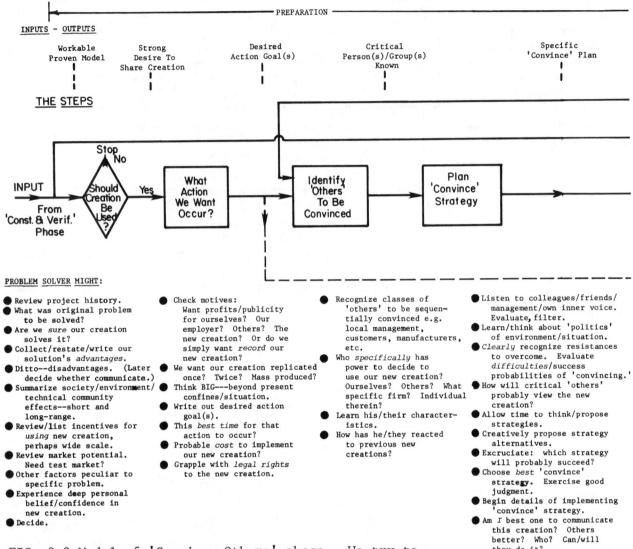

FIG. 9-2 Model of 'Convince Others' phase. We try to
get 'others' to accept and *use* our new creation. This
is a more detailed view of Fig. 9-1 and of this phase
in Fig. 3-1.

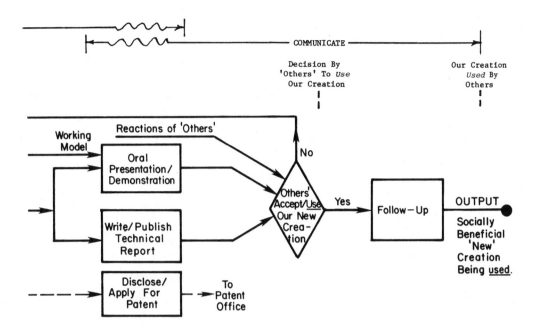

● Seek to understand probable
   viewpoint of 'others' w.r.t. to
   our new creation.
● Select most important ideas from
   our previous work.
● Prepare notes.
● Make outlines. Organize.
● Prepare sketches/charts/slides.
● Work harmoniously with support
   personnel.
● Write/rewrite/condense.
● Select/contact/work with
   patent attorney.
● Visit/travel.
● Make formal/informal pre-
   sentation(s). Interpret
   new creation to 'others.'
   Exhibit enthusiam /confidence
   in it. Defend. Persuade.
   Exhibit patience.
● Feel frustrated at resistances of
   'others' and our failure to
   convince.
● 'Needle' others to read our
   technical report(s).
● Study Chs. 12 and 18.

● Allow time for
   'others' to decide.
● See 'others' exhibit
   courage/risk taking
   in committing to
   our new creation.
● Feel humbled that
   'others' finally
   see what we saw
   long ago.
● Experience rewards
   of disciplined
   creativity (Ch. 2).
● If 'others' decide
   'no', feedback, try
   again with different
   'others'/strategy.
   Don't give up until
   creation is used!

● Implementers use 6 step
   approach, starting
   anew.
● Periodically check on
   progress 'others'
   making toward using
   new creation.
● Resolve difficulties
   /misunderstandings
   w.r.t. the new
   creation.
● Resist pressures to
   become deeply
   involved in less
   creative work
   unless we so choose.
● Possibly receive
   royalties, profits,
   awards, etc.

What <u>Action</u> <u>Do</u> <u>We</u> <u>Want</u> <u>To</u> <u>Occur</u> for our new creation?
It seems fairly obvious we'll not be able to convince
anyone to use it unless we have *clear* action goals
for what specifically we believe should be done with
it.

Example 9-3

Tesla wanted to get his alternating current
electrical system mass manufactured. The
fascinating story of how he sold his alternating
current patents to George Westinghouse for a
million dollars in cash plus a dollar a horsepower,
starting the present giant electrical industry,
is history. [232, pp74-75]

<u>Identify</u> <u>'Others'</u> <u>To</u> <u>Be</u> <u>Convinced</u> is usually easier
said than done. In a corporate environment, is the
critical 'others' our Manager of Engineering? The
ultimate customer? The person who is to actually
operate our new creation?

Example 9-4

When another engineer and I had successfully
created and verified an early suspension system
for our firm's household automatic washing machine,
we identified the 'others' to be sequentially convinced as (1) our local Manager of Engineering
(2) the Division Manager of Engineering.

(We were later successful in 'convincing' them,
and many thousands were manufactured and *used* by
housewives before being superseded by an improved
model.)

<u>Plan</u> <u>A</u> <u>'Convince'</u> <u>Strategy</u> <u>Means</u> is a crucial sub-step
in getting our creations into actual *use*. Is the
best strategy for 'convincing' your company to tool-up
and manufacture your new creation to accost a critical
manager at the fountain and 'lay it on the line'?

Or is a formal meeting best? And if so, will the
newborn creation get 'killed' by a committee? Or
is the best strategy to present a technical paper
at a professional conference?

Obviously considerable excruciation and *careful*
judgment is required here.

Example 9-5

"'You take the apparatus out to Cambridgeport
on the horsecar,' [Bell] said to Watson. 'I'll
stay in the Boston office. We'll see if we can
have a two-way conversation. Take a notebook and
write down what you say and what you hear me
answer. I'll do the same thing. That ought to
convince people that our telephone might be some
use in business.'" [290, p43]

Oral Presentation/Demonstration frequently precedes

"The demonstration
[of Tesla's
induction motor
invention] was a
success from the
technical view-
point but
otherwise a total
loss. Not one
member of the group
showed the slightest
interest."
John J. O'Neal
[232, p56]

formal publication of our new creation. Hopefully
we've been able to get some or all of the critical
decisive 'others' to attend. A presentation *with* a
demonstration of the new creation usually has the
most persuasive effect on objective people. Some
may not be convinced, however, even if they see a
working model. Many effective engineering presentations
are made with carefully prepared slides.

Chapter 12, Communications, treats this especially
important step.

Example 9-6

"In 1831 when he was twenty-two [Cyrus McCormick]
gave his first public demonstration of his reaper
and cut six acres of oats at Steele's Tavern in one
day. - - neighbors - - admitted that it was 'a
right curious sort of thing' but 'nobody ever
believed it would come to much.'" [379, p140]

Write/Publish A Technical Report may go hand in hand

with an oral presentation, though they are *not* the

same.   The engineer has a professional responsibility

"--you must be prepared to defend and explain the engineering decisions you have made."
Guerdon Senswich
[289]

to bring his previous thinking, notes, data,

experimentation, and other creative work to a clear,

organized, written report intelligible to 'others'.

They look to it as a principal permanent output

from our creative work.

See Chap. 12 for suggestions in this important

area.

Example 9-7

Summarizing the results of several years of
creative research work on a new kind of direct energy
converter based on utilizing wave properties of
incident radiation, as sunlight, I published the
technical paper describing it [19].   The writing
and publication had been preceded by formal
presentations at two professional society conferences,
the International Solar Energy Society and the
American Society of Mechanical Engineers.

Disclose/Apply For A Patent may be applicable

to our particular new creation.   'Others', e.g.

corporate managers and those starting a new business

venture usually insist on the protection of a limited

legal monopoly a patent provides.

See Chap. 18 for details in this area frequently

important to creative engineers.

Example 9-8

"The U.S. Patent Office granted Edison 1,093
patents during his lifetime, the largest number
ever given to one man." [379, p294]

<u>Decision</u> <u>To</u> <u>Accept/Use</u> <u>Our</u> <u>New</u> <u>Creation</u> will be

made by 'others' as a 'no' or 'yes'--in time. We

as creators of the new system personally champion it

and normally seek to influence 'others' toward a

'yes' decision. Such a decision may be accompanied

"--there is no force
on earth so power-
ful as a determined
persistent and
imaginative man
with an important
new idea."
  Harry F.
  Guggenheim
  [133, Foreword)

by considerable vacillation, excruciation, emotions,

rationalizations, arguments, alienation, 'politics',

and other intangibles difficult for the creative

engineer to cope with before a decision is finally

made.

Often we are unable to secure a 'yes' decision

to use our new creation. Then we may be forced to

feedback and try another strategy, perhaps on different

'others'. This is frequently the case with independent

inventors.

<u>Example 9-9</u>

In the mid 50's a small group of development
engineers, of which I was privileged to be a part,
had successfully created a new high performance
high frequency ceramic vacuum tube.

There came a specific day when we turned the
development over to the Manager of Design Engineering
for acceptance and a decision to incorporate it into
the firm's product line.

It was eventually accepted, the factory tooled
up, and manufactured as the 6BY4--later the 7077--and
many subsequent product versions. Thousands were
produced and *used* in NASA's worldwide tracking
network as well as in military, civil, and industrial
uses.

<u>Follow-Up</u> is usually required by the creator to assist

'others' in whose hands implementing our new creation

rests. This step is of considerable importance and may

*"If you persevere,
and push, and hang
on long enough, you
will wear down the
opposition."*
  Henry J. Kaiser
  [165]

require great patience, tact, and understanding

by us before our new creation is used on any substantial

scale. It usually takes a long time.

This entire area deals with the subject of

innovation--implementing the new, usually on a mass

scale. It is a complex vast subject beyond our scope

here.

Example 9-10

In Example 9-9 considerable 'follow-up' was
required to get the new ceramic tube into successful
production and use. We created new ultra high
frequency tube testing equipment, created a pilot
plant facility, resolved customer application
engineering problems, and related work. The
'follow-up' extended over several years. Some
engineers transferred from Development to other
organizations to aid the follow-up process.

The steps in total--or some near equivalent--, if

artfully executed, may enhance our likelihood of

living to see the new creation actually *used* by

'others'--with persistence and luck. Additional guides

are in Sec. 9-3.

Exercises

9-E1. An engineer has constructed and tested a new
       vehicle power system. It is on a two and
       one-half ton Army truck. A gasoline engine
       drives an alternator, a silicon controlled
       rectifier and 3-phase frequency changer
       follow, and finally a 3-phase induction motor
       (no brushes!) is in each wheel of the truck.
       Pressing the 'gas' changes the frequency,
       hence vehicle speed. The system is controlled
       by a compact solid state computer. List
       resistances to change the Army might display
       toward this new idea.

9-E2.   Suppose you have created and successfully
        tested a new thermal warning gadget. It
        is about the size of a dime and closes a set
        of electrical contacts when the ambient exceeds
        $212 \pm 1°F$. List at least 10 strategies for
        getting this gadget widely used.

9-E3.   Assume you have created and successfully tested--
        after five years of creative work--a new
        'picture on the wall' color television display
        system. You want to see it widely used
        replacing cumbersome existing picture tubes.
        List potential strategy ideas for 'Convincing
        Others' to use your new system.

9-E4.   Suppose you wanted to introduce into another
        university a new course in Creative Problem
        Solving like you are taking. List strategy
        ideas for getting it into *use* there.

9-E5.   *Outline* the basic steps in preparing a first-
        class oral presentation.

9-E6.   *Outline* the basic steps to get an engineering
        report written and distributed.

9-E7.   Write a carefully thought-out one page 'internal
        memorandum' to your manager seeking to convince
        him the company should manufacture your proven
        new product. (Your Professor will indicate the
        product.)

9-E8.   Engineers frequently use slides in presentations.
        Consider a graph projected to an 8' x 10' screen.
        What size should the letters be for *clear*
        reading at 100 feet?

9-E9.   Choose a technical system or product you
        personally use but have taken for granted.
        Study its history, particularly focusing on
        its introduction to 'others'. Write a one page
        summary of your findings: Cite source(s) of
        information.

9-E10. Think in some depth about 'personal openness'
        and a 'sharing attitude'. Are they desirable
        in this phase? May they get us into trouble
        when presenting our new creation? How? Write
        out your thoughts.

9-E11. Think in some depth about the influence of
        emotions on us during this phase. List their
        possible effects. Briefly discuss each. May
        emotions help or hinder us here?

9-E12.   From a Professor you know who has published
         a book, arrange to privately discuss the
         story of how he convinced a publisher to publish
         his manuscript creation. Particularly search
         out 'resistances' and how they were overcome.
         Summarize the story in writing.

9-3 Some Guides

A few of these are collected in Table 9-1 in

the approximate sequence needed in Fig. 9-2. As with

guides in previous chaps., these are distillates from

failures and successes of many creative engineers.

"It is a great
art to know how
to sell - -"
Baltasar Gracian
[127, p143]

The disciplined creative engineer knows of these and

more. He also knows there is an element of artful

skill in successfully applying both the guides in

Table 9-1 and the steps in Fig. 9-2 to a specific

problem in 'Convince Others'. Truly this entire area

is one where the rest of our professional lives we

must continue to learn and grow through *practice*!

Unfortunately space prohibits us from dealing

with many interesting failures common to the 'Convince

Others' phase. These range from trying to convince

"An outward show
that promises too
much, is sufficient
to make itself
suspect - - -"
Baltasar Gracian
[127, p167]

others to use a new creative idea which has had

little or incomplete application of the previous five

major phases to the case of the engineer who has done

excellent work in the previous phases but reports

it at his professional society with lettering so

small on his slides that even those on the front row

can't see.

● <u>Object</u>   To get our new creation successfully *used* by
                        others.

● <u>Action Goals</u>   ▲ Written.
                        ▲ Clear.
                        ▲ Carefully thought-out.

● <u>'Others'</u>   ▲ Identify critical person(s).
                        ▲ Can't convince 'everybody'.
                        ▲ Only a critical *few* decide use/not use our
                            new creation(s).

● <u>Strategy</u>   Decide whether to:
                            ▲ 'Soft' sell.
                            ▲ 'Hard sell.
                        Think about:
                            ▲ Clever *name* for new creation.
                            ▲ Timing and effects of proposed actions.
                                (Particularly patent action. c.f. Ch. 18)
                            ▲ Whether working model demonstration needed.
                                ● Model flawlessly ready?
                            ▲ Potential objections to new creation.
                                ● Anticipate them specifically/objectively.
                                ● Plan deal with them.
                                ● Propose positive answers *before* 'others'
                                    take irreversible stance against new
                                    creation.
                        Decide *best* way(s) communicate creation to 'others'
                            and by whom.
                        Reduce strategy to definite action *plan*.

● <u>Communicate</u>   A 'presentation' is *different* from a written
                        'report'. Each requires *separate* treatment to
                        be effective.
                        See Ch. 12 for details.

TABLE 9-1   Some enhancement guides for a
            successful 'Convince Others'
            phase. Other guides are in
            Fig. 9-2.

You will have ample opportunity to make 'Convince Others' mistakes in the practicing world! Let us hope they will be a minimum!

Discussion Topics

1. Section 9-1 and 9-2 seem to favor the 'hard sell' approach. When may the 'soft sell' approach of Table 9-1 be needed by the engineer?

2. How do we reconcile personal humility with the aggressive dynamism advocated in the text for this phase? Consider the cases of an engineer with:
    a. Lots of humility.
    b. Almost none, i.e. he exudes confidence, arrogance and an air of superiority.
    Which is most effective in getting his creations into *use*?

3. Explore the role of having a working engineering model in this phase. Can a model 'backfire' on you? Also explore the effects of the *first* impression of the model on 'others'.

4. Table 9-1 says "a presentation is *different* from a written report." Isn't it all right for an engineer to just read verbatum his technical report during a presentation? After all it saves the cost of preparing twice!

5. How is personal enthusiasm related to this phase? *Where* specifically in Fig. 9-2 does it enter if at all?

6. Ditto for persuasiveness.

7. Which will be most effective in this phase?
    a. The technically competent engineer who honestly admits, "I'm not very good with people," or
    b. An engineer who enjoys making presentations, 'has a way with people', but feels weak with the earlier creative phases?

8. How may we give 'others' the important feeling of participation during this phase?

9. Is it possible to *know how* to 'Convince Others' and yet not be able to effectively *do* it?

9-4 Some Difficulties of 'Convince Others'

The previous three Secs. have been cast positively.
There is another side of the coin--difficulties.
These have been placed last to avoid possibly crushing
your spirit during the learning process. As educated
engineers, we should know about these so when we try
to implement the previous suggestions and encounter
failure after failure in selling our new ideas we
don't discard the methodology or become too discouraged.
Several Points should be forcefully made:

"Because it's much more difficult to reverse the thinking of people than it is to give them a new idea."
Charles F. Kettering
[172]

● The Great Difficulty of the 'Convince Others' phase.
In most cases,[1] it is the hardest and most
personally frustrating of *all* the six major phases
in disciplined creative work. Yet its rewards
are sweet when occasional success comes our way.

● Expect To Encounter when trying to get 'others'
to *use* (*Not* just to know about) a truly new
creation:

▲ Prejudice Rossman's study [279] showed
prejudice was ranked the number 3 obstacle
by 710 inventors.
▲ Apathy to your new creation by a majority
who want to maintain the status quo.
▲ Not Invented Here (NIH) attitude with its
implications of rejection, alienation, and
pseudo superiority.
▲ Downright Opposition by those with vested
interests which will be upset if your new
creation is used.
▲ Negativism in an untold number of forms,
frequently to cover-up or protect some
unstated area.

"--all inventors meet with opposition and prejudice even to the point of physical violence. The mass dislikes new things."
Joseph Rossman
[279, p166]

[1]Naturally, there are occasional exceptions. Consider yourself *very*
fortunate to experience an easy 'Convince Others' for your new
creation!

284   Disciplined Creativity

*"--they were all
against me, regard-
ing this undertaking
as a jest."
Admiral Don
Christopher Columbus
[281, p224]*

*"When I was building
my first steamboat
at New York the
project was viewed
by the public with
contempt - - -"
Robert Fulton
[114, p68]*

*"The more people
there are in a
conference, the
less chance that
the really expert
opinion will be
presented, evaluated
and incorporated
into the final
decision."
Ralph K. Means
[212, p476]*

▲ Personal Disparagement by those with small
minds unable to separate our new creation
from our idiosyncrasies and therefore elect
to disparage us personally, being unable
to objectively fault the new creation.
▲ Hostility And Rejection by those around us
and those whom we originally sought to
aid by solving their problem in a unique
way.
▲ Committees ganging up to 'kill' our truly
new creation which, long-range, could be
the organization's salvation. The
relatively poor track record of committees
in accepting any truly new creation is
well-known to inventors and highly creative
engineers. Deep suspicions exist that a
committee usually accepts and acts on
only the most mediocre low creativity
solution. There are of course exceptions.
Count yourself lucky if you encounter
the exceptional committee!
▲ Indecisive Individuals whose business it is
to make clean-cut decisions and who, even
when confronted with the full and complete
story, can't or won't make a decision for
various reasons.

● It Takes Time, frequently *years*, before a truly
new creative solution is accepted and used on
any scale.

Some Historical Cases illustrate the nature of the
difficulties outlined above. These have all been
actually faced by creators trying to 'Convince Others'
to *use* their new creation.

Example 9-11--Ice Making Machine

"Dr. Gorrie's invention [of the first ice making
machine] was proclaimed throughout the South as
the beginning of a new and wonderful industry. But
from New York and New England where the cutting
of natural ice was a profitable business, came
ridicule. A New York daily commented: 'There is
a crank down in Apalachicola, Florida, who claims
that he can make ice as good as God Almighty.'

Neither Dr. Gorrie nor his friends were wealthy.
When the inventor sought capital to commercially
develop his machine he was turned down on every
hand. Four years after patenting his device, ill and

*"Considering the
'ball game' in which
the professional
manager is playing
it is completely
predictible that he
will be hostile to
any money-consuming
project that will
not contribute to
profits in the
short-term."
Louis Soltanoff
[309, p46]*

brooding over his failure to obtain money,
Dr. Gorrie died." [209, p7]

Example 9-12   Automobiles

*"Ironically, this
fact that the
innovator may
come in the role
of savior does
not necessarily
make him any more
acceptable to
those who love
the status quo."*
*John W. Gardner
[116, p28]*

The difficulties of convincing U. S. auto
manufacturers to make significant improvements
to autos is well documented. In the late 1960's
compact cars were finally marketed only *after*
foreign compacts were first introduced placing
convincing economic pressure on U. S. auto firms.

Convincing them to introduce the radically
new Wankel engine hasn't come in the mid 1970's
even after the Japanese successfully introduced
the Mazda car.

And Ralph Nader's whole crusade for anti-
pollution controls, anti-sway bars, anti-whiplash
head rests, inflatable passenger collision
cushions, energy absorbing bumpers and other safety
features is a matter of historical record occasioned
by strong auto industry resistances to changes.

Example 9-13--Xerox

*"And after you have
persisted for three
or four years people
will say, 'Why, it
does begin to look
as though there is
something to
that after all."*
*Charles F. Kettering
[42, p205]*

"When Chester Carlson filed his first
xerographic patent in 1937--no major company
showed more than passing interest in developing
the process commercially. Carlson, unable to
sell the idea himself, had finally given an
exclusive license to Battele Research Institute
- - -." [38]

Example 9-14--Telephone

"Chauncey Depew, president of the Telegraph
Company was offered the purchase of the telephone
patents by Hubbard and Bell in 1876 for a nominal
sum. Depew consulted his technical experts who
rejected the 'utterly unreasonable device - -.'
The technical experts then said: 'Messrs Hubbard
and Bell want to instal one of their "Telephone"
devices in virtually *every* home and business
establishment in the city. This idea is idiotic on
the face of it. Furthermore, why should a person
want to use this ungainly and impractical device
when he can send a messenger to the local telegraph
office and have a clear written message sent to any
large city in the United States? - -

"The introduction [of a new idea] is a time of struggle against stupidity and envy, apathy and evil, secret opposition and open conflicts of interests, the horrible period of struggle with man, a martyrdom even if success ensues."
  Herrn Rudolf Diesel
    [77, p346]

"In such conferences persons who are the most personable or the best talkers may dominate the discussion."
  Ralph K. Means
    [212, p476]

"It is well to affirm your own truth, but it is not well to condemn those who think differently."
  Socrates
    [307, p138]

Hubbard's fanciful predictions, while they sound very rosy, are based upon wild-eyed imagination and a lack of understanding of the technical and economic facts of the situation, and a posture of ignoring the obvious technical limitations of this device, which is hardly more than a toy, or a laboratory curiosity." [191]

Example 9-15--AC Motor

"Did someone steal [Tesla's] invention [of the alternating current motor]? Not the slightest danger. He could not even give it away. No one was even slightly interested." [232, p53]

Example 9-16--Auto Self Starter

"Leland had, in fact, been advised by persons of prominence and influence in the electrical field not to put an electric self-starter on the Cadillac car. It will ruin you, they warned." [42, p75]

Example 9-17--Five Mechanical Inventions

"Resistance took a long time to overcome; but finally the state [of Delaware] promised to grant a patent if [Oliver Evans] could convince a committee that his work [of five mechanical inventions] was really novel. Evans agreed and made his presentation. Seeing that the committee was impressed, he went on in his enthusiasm and described his plans for steam carriages. The committee then decided that he was a lunatic." [379, p57]

Example 9-18--Rocket Missiles

"In May 1940 Harry Guggenheim arranged a meeting in the office of Brigadier General George H. Brett in Washington. It was attended by representatives of the Navy's Bureau of Aeronautics, the Army's Ordinance Department, and the Air Corps. Goddard described his experiments and presented the possibilities, as he saw them, of long-range liquid-propellant rockets for military use.

At the end of the conference the Army representatives said they still felt that 'the next war will be won with the trench mortar'. The Air Corps and the Navy people saw no possibilities in the rocket as a missile weapon, - -" [120, pxx]

Example 9-19--Basic Invention Process

    "It is characteristic of most pioneer inventions that at first people do not believe that it has been done; do not believe it can be done; pay no attention to it; laugh at it. Next, a host of claimants crop up, all of whom have solved the problem, made the invention long ago, and they claim the credit--only nobody knew of their work until the inventor showed the way. Next, people claim that the thing is as old as the hills, is no invention at all; it was long known before the inventor used it, but somehow nobody had used it before. Ultimately, history records that the art did not exist before, that the work of the inventor brought it into existence, and that to him belongs the credit. Usually he gets the credit long after his death.

    This applies to men that produce radical inventions - -." C. P. Steinmetz [318, p544]

The above is only a *small* historical sample selected to give you a quick feel for some of the difficulties in this phase. *Many* other cases could be cited. There is little evidence the task will be any easier for yet to be created new products.

    Small wonder, in view of the *enormous* difficulties of the 'Convince Others' phase, we succeed in injecting *any* truly new creative product into use! We should be thankful the courageous creators of the past persisted *in spite of* the difficulties, for every socially useful man-made object around us at some time passed through a similar phase.

Why People Resist The New Creation is necessary to elementarily understand if we expect repetitive success in the 'Convince Others' phase. Recognize:

"In each instance the tremendous importance of a single 'champion' for the project was clearly established, - -" Richard S. Morse [219, p147]

"There seems to be something in human nature which resists changes."
  Joseph Rossman
  [279, p166]

● People - Not 'Things' - are being dealt with here. It is an entirely different area to the strictly technical with which we engineers are most familiar. People have backgrounds, motivations, emotions, beautiful and not so beautiful sides of their personalities and related humanistic areas.

  Example 9-20

    Corporation managers, who frequently must consider acceptance and possible use of our new creations, are quite human. Their individual humanity is *not* generally at the zero level, as some may think.

● Our Creation Isn't Understood by 'others' and is therefore resisted. From *their* viewpoint, no one has stepped forward with a clear coherent explanation of how it works and what is proposed be done with it, i.e. a story they *understand* is missing.

  Example 9-21

    At an international professional society meeting a young engineer proposed creation and widespread use of solar heated, solar cooled, and solar-electric supplied houses.

    Knowledgeable people present did not understand his fuzzily presented ideas, his ideas were resisted and, unfortunately, he was personally humiliated before an international audience in a moment of high drama.

● Fear Of The Unknown may be grounds for resisting the new creation. To 'others' it is feared because it has little or no history; what is wrong with it is feared; fear is voiced it will cost more than we think when mass produced; there is fear it won't earn a profit; there is fear customers won't buy it. These and other fears may exist in the minds of 'others', causing resistance.

  Example 9-22

    One of my early jobs in Schenectady was to take the engineering report for a new generator coil insulation winding machine down to the Manager of Generator Manufacturing

Engineering. The object was to try to
convince him to use the new machine as a
cost reduction in his factory. They were
hand winding the coils.

After meeting, exchanging pleasantries,
and making my presentation, he enumerated
the fears he had of the new creation and
decided on the spot to *not* use it. "Our
generators have had a handcrafted quality
for years which our customers highly regard."

My mission failed. I did not know how
to cope with resistance and fears of others,
rational or irrational.

● Making A Threatening Change in the way things
have been done heretofore is implied in our
new creation. Changes usually are emotionally
painful to 'others'. They may, depending on
precisely how it is presented and by whom,
view the creation as a threat to be quickly
killed. Risks, accompanied by fears, are
involved in departing from the status quo.

"Great numbers of
corporate executives
consciously are not
aware of their
hostility to new
ideas."
  Louis Soltanoff
  [309, p45]

Example 9-23

The transistor was resisted by vacuum
tube manufacturers who saw the creation
as a threat with the potential for loss of
jobs and security.

If we can get at the roots of *why* our
creation might be viewed as a threat, we
may be able to positively cope with the
threatened 'others' and convince them to
accept and use it.

"When John Kay in-
vented the flying
shuttle, it was
considered such a
threat to labor that
weavers mobbed him
and destroyed his
mold."
  Alex Osborn
  [233, p109]

● Using It Requires Money to implement. 'Others'
may have legitimate responsibilities and
concerns over where the money will come from,
at what rate it will be spent, or even if it
should be spent on our type gadget at all, and
related questions.

Example 9-24

In 1972 I tried to convince the president
of a newly formed small company to incorporate
and use some substantial engineering improvements
to a multi-purpose woodworking machine. I
had created them over a nine year span of

"[The successful
innovator] has to be
willing to risk
his money, his
reputation, and
his career; he
shoots craps
with everything
he's got."
  Jacob Rabinow
  [264, p150]

leisure time creative work on their machine.
He replied, "--there is neither the time nor
the financing to make any changes for sometime."
The improvements, all fully engineered and
proven, still were not in use in 1978.

● Personal Relationships, or lack of them, may be
a resistance factor. Our new creation may be
accepted if 'others' know us, know we are
generally *right*--even if in the minority as
creative engineers usually are, that we have
their best interests at heart, and they like
us, i.e. we have a favorable personal relationship.

Example 9-25

"Mr. Westinghouse, - - you have been
my friend, you believed in me when others
had no faith; you were brave enough to go
ahead and pay me a million dollars when others
lacked courage; you supported me when even
your own engineers lacked vision to see
the big things ahead that you and I saw;
you have stood by me as a friend. The
benefits that will come to civilization
from my polyphase system mean more to
me than the money involved. Mr. Westinghouse,
you will save your company so that you
can develop my inventions. Here is your
contract and here is my contract--I will
tear both of them to pieces and you will
no longer have any troubles from my
[unpaid] royalties [of $12,000,000]. Is
that sufficient?' - - Tesla tore up the
contract - -.

Probably nowhere in history is there
recorded so magnificent a sacrifice to
friendship as that involved in Tesla's
stupendous gift to Westinghouse - -."
[232, p82]

"--more is often
accomplished
through a witty
remark than
through the
gravest argument,
- -"
Baltasar Gracian
[127, p33]

One could make a case for the observation that
acceptance and use of many new things we create
in engineering finally rests on emotional
criteria--not technical--of the 'others', e.g.
they emotionally like us or our creation or both.

● Personal Credentials - educational, legal, level
within organizational hierarchy--may be missing
or sub-optimal. Our new creation is therefore
resisted as suspect.

Example 9-26

An independent inventor approaches a large company to convince them to manufacture his invention. He immediately encounters resistance unless the credential of a patent agreement exists. Alternatively he may be relatively uneducated formally and, unfortunately, is therefore resisted by the educated management of a high technology firm.

"The organizational form of a big oil corporation is not likely to be conducive to innovation. It is not intended to be."
  Dean L. Gitter
  [119, p94]

● It Doesn't Fit Existing Organizational Boxes may be grounds for resistance.

Example 9-27

An engineer proposes a new brushless solar electric motor to a motor manufacturer. Though they know much about motors, they have no one in their organization knowledgeable of solar cells or solar energy conversion, and have never heard of light commutation. The new creation simply fails to 'fit' their existing organizational boxes. It is therefore resisted.

● Pride And Prejudice of 'others' may be the subtle basis for resistance.

Example 9-28

In the late 1950's three of us had, with considerable hard work and luck, created a radically new high voltage pulse transformer design for a military application. The new one withstood test voltages several times that of the transformer we were unsuccessfully trying to manufacture, running about 90 percent rejects. The old one had numerous technical flaws.

"The changes are going to be initiated by the creative people of any age who have the spark and drive it takes to overcome the apathy of the majority."
  Chester M. Sinnett
  [297, p14]

It fell my lot to try to convince the manager of Development Engineering, who had created the unsuccessful design our factory was choked up on, to convert to and use our new porous winding transformer design. It needed only a little more development engineering.

In a meeting of he and my Manager, I demonstrated our successful transformer encapsulated in epoxy resin with a *porous* winding structure side-by-side with his nonporous mylar insulation winding design.

Following the demonstration, the Manager of Development Engineering berated me personally, my "measely crew of engineers" and the new transformer creation against which he was obviously prejudiced.

Over his objections and resistance in every possible way the porous winding transformer was finally used. Many thousands were successfully made in a variety of designs.

The above tabulation is by no means complete.[1]

As an alert creative engineer you will want to add others after you enter engineering practice and attempt to 'Convince Others' to *use* your new creations. Minimizing The Resistance is largely a matter of personal art, skill, and clairvoyance. It is best

"Society is never prepared to receive any invention. Every new thing is resisted, and it takes years for the inventor to get people to listen to him and years more before it can be introduced."
Thomas A. Edison [90]

developed by *practice* coupled with a genuine life-long attempt to observe and learn all you can about other people. Particularly study the 'others' in positions to decide the fate of our new creations. The learning process soon carries one into the important areas of human relations, psychology, and theology, all related to but beyond our scope here.

Two general admonitions can help minimize resistances to our new creations:

---

[1]For example, 'satisfaction' with present solutions to the problem isn't covered. Explore on your own!

● <u>Doing</u> <u>A</u> <u>Thorough</u> Job on the previous five
    major phases of the creative problem solving
    approach--in preparation for 'Convince Others'.

● <u>Honestly</u> <u>Trying</u> <u>To</u> <u>Understand</u> 'Others' viewpoint
    and legitimate concerns in areas such as
    risk taking, profit accountability, marketing,
    environment, and others.

*"--the tribe often
does not welcome
such innovations,
even when it is
clear that they
would be
beneficial."*
A. G. Fredrickson
[110, p125]

But even these, or any other guidelines in this

Chap., will probably *not* reduce resistance to your

new creation to zero! At least you are forewarned of

a few of the awesome 'Convince Others' potential

difficulties ahead. Fortunate and *rare* is the creative

engineer who works in an environment where his new

creations are put into use *without* the travail and

excruciation laid bare in this section!

<u>Discussion</u> <u>Topics</u>

1. Do people resist the specific technical change
    or its social implications when we attempt
    to get our new creations *used*?

2. What part does honest respect of 'others' play in
    this phase?

3. Do the feelings of 'others' play any part in
    resisting our new creations? Explore.

4. Identify principal errors in 'Convince Others'
    phase by proponents of a new product you know of
    that got created but never *used*.

5. What personal effects on the creator may extreme
    resistances and rejection have?

Chapter Summary

●   Our professional need for 'Convincing Others'
     to accept and *use* our new creative solutions
     to engineering problems was made.

●   The principal process steps involved were
     sequentially laid out in Fig. 9-2. Following
     them generally enhances, but does not guarantee,
     the likelihood of successfully 'Convincing
     Others' to *use* our creations. Success is *not*
     always assured, even for experienced engineers--
     an humbling thought.

●   The rather awesome difficulty of the complex
     'Convince Others' terminal major phase of
     disciplined creative tenet was shown. It
     was not fully explored in this limited work.
     There is *much* more to the subject!

●   The ability to successfully 'Convince Others'
     to *use* our new creations varies widely with
     individuals. Some engineers have an easy
     naturalness in this phase. Others are
     frightened and perform poorly. Considerable
     art coupled with our total personality is
     involved here, particularly in ability to
     successfully communicate with and relate to other
     people.

●   The engineer's need for generous amounts of patience,
     understanding, tact, and courage was indicated
     as our creation traverses this phase, probably
     taking a long time.

●   Our lifelong need for observing and learning
     at the one-to-one level from our peers who
     successfully 'Convince Others' was suggested.
     It is doubtful we can ever learn too much
     about how to successfully 'Convince Others'.

EPILOGUE TO

MORPHOLOGY OF DISCIPLINED CREATIVITY

This Chap. completes our Part II presentation of the basic morphological phases of disciplined creativity. The 'Six-Step Approach' is the heart of the creative process for solving complex engineering problems creatively.

The engineer's need for some kind of methodical generalized procedure for solving engineering problems was presented in Chap. 3. A number of alternative problem solving approaches was examined, and the 'Six-Step Approach' advocated was previewed in Fig. 3-1.

Chapters 4 through 9 focused on these six steps, taking them one at a time. For each step we have cited the need, purpose, what is done--including 'postage stamp' creative process charts useful on the job in actual creative problem solving, and revealed some suggested guides for enhancing success therein. Considerable effort has been made to sharpen-up the total process into discrete and not fuzzy ill-defined sub-steps. Unfortunately this 'sharpening-up' is *not* characteristic of most existing creative methodologies many of which tend toward mysticism.

Numerous examples specifically relevant to the practice of creative engineering illustrated the methods of disciplined creativity tenet. Further, we have found considerable reinforcement for the text principles via the marginal quotes taken from a wide spectrum of creative people of past and present.

We have suggested the principal 'Six-Step Approach' may be applied over-and-over to engineering problems requiring new solutions. Thus 'the approach', overall, is a principal tool of the engineer who would *repetitively* create the new ideas, systems, products, components, and other creations of tomorrow's world.

The proper application of these major six steps appears to, in perspective, be what the profession of engineering is all about. It starts with a recognized social need which perhaps can be supplied by technology, proceeds by determining what specific technology and creation solves the problem, and ends with the new creation being *used* for the benefit of society.

We have seen, in retrospect, the general complex nature of creative thinking. In spite of its complexity we have found a systematic order *does* exist which can be taught, learned by others, and put into practice as a means of enhancing our personal creative output. One does *not* have to be 'born a genius' to create! Several thousands of quite ordinary engineers have created amazingly original solutions using the methods advocated.

We have realistically dealt with failure possibilities throughout the creative problem solving process. We have not, however, extensively dealt with the innumerable possibilities of misapplying the principal 'Six-Step Approach'. Major emphasis on all the things that can go wrong appears inappropriate in a positively oriented text.

Finally, we have suggested in many ways that the basic creative problem solving approach is the *same* in research, development, design, manufacturing, and operation areas of engineering. Thus the engineer aspiring to enhance his creativity only needs to master the *one* problem solving approach advocated in Part II.

The subjects treated in Parts III and IV of this work are important auxiliary topics which the practicing creative engineer needs to know about to successfully and repetitively use the 'Six-Step Approach' of Part II. The order in which they are presented is not particularly important. It has already been indicated in the various creative process charts of Part II where the following topics enter or are needed.

PART III

PERSONAL ASPECTS OF

DISCIPLINED CREATIVITY

CHAPTER 10

THE CREATIVE ENGINEER AS A PERSON

"(The Wright brothers) were encouraged to develop themselves
from <u>within</u> and not expect too much help from <u>without</u>."
                    Charles F. Kettering   [173, p17]

- *PERSONAL* nature of Disciplined Creativity.

- His physical and external characteristics.

- His intellectual traits.

- His motivations.

- His formation of ideas.

- His personal work traits.

- His sensitivities.

- His emotions.

- His attitudes.

- His values.

- His environment and relationships to it.

Chapters 3-9 laid out the morphology of

Disciplined Creativity as a sequence of specific

orderly steps which we called the creative process.

If diligently executed the process greatly enhances

our likelihood of creating something new.

In following the process we soon discover the

intense *personal* nature of Disciplined Creativity.

"*We must try to understand our-selves before we try to understand others and their motives.*"
  Chester M. Sinett
  [299, p13]

In a sense we confront ourselves, particularly our

inner selves. We soon find the need for more

understanding about ourselves as creative individuals

--truly unique *persons* with a precious capacity,

the divine gift of being able to create the new.

Thus we are led to examine the *personal* nature
of Disciplined Creativity and to inquire what personal
traits are needed to maximize the likelihood of our
creating the new and are hence worth striving toward.
These are our goals in this Chapter.

10-1 Personal Nature of Disciplined Creativity

AN INTEGRATING PERSPECTIVE, as a starting point,
can be had from the expression for the engineer's
efficiency, η, presented in Chap. 3. There we found
our personal problem solving efficiency to be:

(Eq.1)

$$\eta = (\text{Aptitude})(\text{Intelligence})(\text{Knowledge}) (\text{Problem Approach})^{\alpha}(\text{Motivation})^{\beta} (\text{Personal Factors})^{\delta}$$

where α, β, and δ are real and greater than 1.0
preferably.[1]

Our efforts in Chaps. 3-9 aimed at maximizing
our 'problem approach' abilities. We now address the
latter two important factors, 'motivation' and 'personal
factors'. It is clear that if either or both of these
factors is zero then our useful creative contribution
will also be zero. The fact that their exponents are
greater than 1.0 underscores the powerful exponential
leverage these two factors have on our individual
efficiency in creating the new.

*"Watching is fun.
But at the end of
the day, reflection
upon things accom-
plished by doing
provides more
satisfaction."*
Chester M. Sinnett
[304, p21]

------

[1] According to this simplistic model, α, β, and δ would be different for each
creative person.

At once we meet the inherent intensely *personal* nature of these latter factors. There is no way to avoid the personal aspect. The fact that they are so personal may bother you, as collectively engineers tend to 'look at the objective facts' and pay little attention to 'personal aspects' in problem solving. But creativity is *different*! It demands by its very nature a *personal* input and involvement of considerable degree.

In reality Eq. 1 is a vast oversimplification. Actually, as we shall see in Secs. 10-2 through 10-11 there are *many* personal factors involved in Disciplined Creativity. Further, many of the factors are related to each other--coupled--, and there is considerable overlap between them. Thus, as you've suspected earlier, Disciplined Creativity is both highly personal and *complex*.

Because of the complexity and overlaps the materials of this Chap. inherently *cannot* be as sharply defined as notions of Chaps. 1-9. You are forewarned that the nature of the highly personal subject matter of this Chap. is, in a loose analogical sense, like 'trying to nail jello to the wall'! The engineer tends to worry about the hardness, elasticity, and other characteristics of the jello in an attempt to 'firm it up' whereas our viewpoint *has* to be more like "Do we have any material that has an *identifiable* form at all and if so roughly what is its shape?"

"Now, disciplined thought may take the form of symbols, in which case it is mathematics; or it may take on verbal formulation, in which case it is logic."
Raymond D. Pruitt
[262,p25]

"Creativity is an extraordinarily difficult and elusive research topic - -."
John W. Gardner
[116, p132]

There are many with overly simplistic views of
creativity who in essence demand, "Show me the *one* or
two personal factors, e.g. motivation and initiative,
that I must have to create and *these* are the ones
I'll enhance." An objective view of the research on
creativity turns up about a *hundred* factors! It most
certainly isn't one or two traits.

Finally, we conclude that the 'Gem of Creativity'
shown in Fig. 2-1 indeed has *many* facets--most of them
highly *personal* in nature. In toto, it is truly a
glittering stone of superb beauty!

The above thoughts lead us to the obvious that for
each person there is an:

> ● <u>Outer Life</u> as seen by those around us and an
> ● <u>Inner Life</u> known only to ourselves.

This Chap. principally focusses on the inner life
as it potentially relates to our capacity to create
new products and systems.

The first inner life topic involves the notion
of being a *real* person as distinguished from 'being
like everybody else'. An objective careful study
of many highly creative persons reveals they tend to be
genuine persons.

BEING A REAL PERSON Here we briefly summarize
a few main ideas of psychologists and theologians who
have extensively studied the subject of authentic
personhood.

*"The very word
person owes its
origin to the
masks worn by
the actors to
amplify their
voices (son are--
per)
Paul Tournier
[343, p13]*

Being a real person involves the complex notions

of:

● Knowing Who We Are. It usually involves considerable
  mystery to us--perhaps throughout life.
          The inventor *knows* he is an inventor and
  not someone else.

● Various Masks or as Tournier   [343, p71] says,
  "As you peel an onion, there is always another
  layer, but you never reach the kernel - -."

          The creative person may have one appearance
  to his manager, another to his colleagues, and
  an entirely different one to himself--the kernel.

● Honesty and Sincerity in facing the facts of one's
  total talents rather than repress them.

          For the creative person it may mean
  honestly recognizing we're quite good with one
  or more phases of the six step approach to
  creativity. Yet we're realistically sincere in
  facing the fact we're not much of a salesman
  for our new ideas.

● Continuous Growth or as Fosdick [108, p27] puts
  it, "To be a person is to be engaged in a
  perpetual process of becoming."

          The highly creative person typically finds
  himself engaged in a lifelong learning process
  in which he *knows* he has grown.

● Self Unity "A real person achieves a high degree
  of unity within himself. He does not remain split
  and scattered but gets himself together into wholeness and coherence" [108, p28]. Such wholeness
  promotes one's physical and mental health and tends
  toward avoiding pathology. Such integration
  "cannot be pictured as placidity. It involves
  not only the harmonizing of conflicts but also
  the subjugation of revolts. It involves a
  scale of values" [108, p44]. Maslow [203]
  interestingly extends the unity idea to what
  he calls self-actualization.

*"--when life ceases to
be a fraction and
becomes an integer
- -"*

*Harry Emerson Fosdick
[108, p33]*

● Inner Spiritual Resources "The process by which
  real personality is thus obtained is inward and
  spiritual" [108, p47].

The creative development engineer working against impossible schedules and super difficult technical problems *knows* he will need some kind of inner spiritual resources to see him through his difficulties. He may be free enough to ask for the needed Divine help.

● <u>Self</u> <u>Acceptance</u> complete with all our noble aspirations and regrettable personal short-comings. It leads to self discovery and further personal growth and is a positive active agressive force in a real person's life.

"No well-integrated life is possible, therefore, without an initial act of self acceptance."
  Harry Emerson Fosdick
    [108, p53]

How beautiful to see a creative engineer faced with multiple problems in making his prototype servo mechanism work declare, "I don't know *why* this gear 'runs away'!" He's accepted himself enough to be able to so declare and thus positioned himself for growth to *find* the answer.

● <u>Sense</u> <u>of</u> <u>Selflessness</u>, i.e. an outlook directed at bettering the common lot of mankind as distinguished from a strictly selfish view.

"Thus to pass from a mirror-mind to a mind with windows is an essential element in the development of real personality."
  Harry Emerson Fosdick
    [108, p84]

An engineer creating a new satellite communications system for an underdeveloped country *has* .to be at heart an unselfish person, though he may never have looked at himself in that way.

The theological idea of dying to one's self in order to give one's self away is paramount here. It may translate to losing one's self in his work and thereby later finding himself an important person.

● <u>Inner</u> <u>Feelings</u> and emotions which may be suppressed or expressed. Fear, anxiety, guilt, depression moods, happiness and many other feelings the real person is aware of and in his unique way copes with them.

"--it is plain that without sensitivity there is no creativity."
  Harry Emerson Fosdick
    [108, p166]

The sensitive creative engineer designing an electronics package for a nuclear weapon is aware of his feelings of fear and guilt over the whole activity in which he finds himself. He may be a real enough person to honestly face his feelings and get into some other engineering work where he feels more comfortable. It may take an act of great personal courage to make such a break.

● <u>Believing</u> <u>In</u> <u>Something</u> worthwhile and signif-
    icant in the larger scheme of human affairs
    --even in the face of extreme criticism.

        No great new engineering creation sees
    reality without someone *believing* in the concept.

        This notion is founded on the theological
    concept of faith. Faith in someone or something
    plays a considerable part in creative work and
    in being a genuine person.

● <u>Philosopher</u> <u>At</u> <u>Heart</u> interested in a wide
    variety of things, affairs and ideas and has
    some opinions--right or wrong--on the general
    drift of life's events.

An in-depth treatment of the above and related

topics is beyond our scope here. There are many

interesting volumes [108, 203, 343] written

about being a real person. You are encouraged to

study further in this general area for your personal

growth.

Extending the discussion of being a real person

and applying it specifically to creative persons

leads us to a need to know more about the traits of

the highly creative individual as a unique person

engaged in Disciplined Creative activity. The traits

are the heart of this chapter. But first a few words

about how the traits were found.

FACTUALLY DETERMINING THE TRAITS of the highly

creative person is, in itself, a major problem.

The viewpoint we use here--in an overall sense--

is to ask "What personal traits seem required by

the creative *process* identified in Chaps. 3-9

for us to successfully create the new?" If we

"--the ultimate in creativity derives from and is the lineal offspring of a supremely disciplined mind."
Raymond D. Pruitt
[262, p24]

could identify the desired traits, then, with some

personal discipline, we may be able to optimize

them for ourselves. Some traits are identified on

the various charts. Others are not and are more

subtly implied.

The Methods Used to find the personal creativity

traits identified here in Secs. 10-2 through 10-11

include researching and summarizing:

● What Proven Highly Creative Persons Have Said
   are the personal attributes needed to
   successfully create the new.

   Example 10-1

"Wisdom is better than strength."
Ecclesiastes 9:16

       In 1931 Rossman, a former patent
   attorney turned research psychologist, did
   some of the early significant pioneering in
   creativity research. He surveyed a large
   number of successful inventors asking them
   to identify the traits they thought most
   needed to successfully invent. Some of his
   results are in Table 10-1.

       Additionally creativity traits identified
   in writings of engineers, managers, scientists
   and others were collected, sifted and ordered.

       It is probable that what successful
   creative persons themselves have said are the
   personal traits needed to create constitute
   the most reliable data base.

● What History and Biography Have Said are the
   needed personal traits to successfully create.
   Here the procedure used is to (1) search for
   a highly creative person and then (2) trying
   to identify the creativity traits exhibited.

● The Psychological Research Literature relevant
   to the field of creativity. The aim here was
   to see what psychological researchers who have
   devoted their lives to studying creativity
   have to say about the traits exhibited by
   creative persons.

Perseverance	503
Imagination	207
Knowledge and Memory	183
Business Ability	162
Originality	151
Common Sense	134
Analytic Ability	113
Self-Confidence	96
Keen Observation	61
Mechanical Ability	41

TABLE 10-1 Frequency of Characteristics of A
Successful Inventor Given by
710 Inventors. From Rossman
[279] with permission.

The methods used by research psychologists
in this area involve:

▲ Hypothesizing a certain personal creativity
   trait is probably needed.
▲ Selecting Suitable Subjects to evaluate.
   Test for the characteristic by written
   tests, clinical interviews, and direct
   observations. From these they obtain
   their data base.
▲ Data Analysis is conducted using well-
   known statistical techniques such as
   correlation coefficients.
▲ Conclusions are drawn regarding the validity
   --or lack of it--of how a certain trait
   correlates with creativity.

The psychological literature tends to be very
detailed and, for the engineer, difficult to
interpret. But in general, the research method
psychologists use in studying creativity is
not philosophically unlike the disciplined
rational process used in engineering.

● The Author's Observations from a lifetime of
   informal study of real-life highly creative
   persons I have been privileged to know or work
   with.

*"--creativity rests
on discipline - -"
Raymond D. Pruitt
[262, p26]*

The above four major areas constitute the source

materials for identifying the traits of the mythical

highly creative person as summarized and classified

in following Secs. of this Chapter.

Weaknesses In The Methods Used should be recognized.

There are, of course, many, as all recognize who

have engaged in research in this complex area.

*"Learning without
wisdom is a load
of books on an
Ass's back."
Japanese Proverb*

In the first place the subjects selected may

not be clearly identified--how many, criteria

for selection, whether 'scientists' or 'engineers'

or 'other'--in the reported literature. Then the

testing instrument may not be optimally designed.

Finally, the conclusions may not always be objective

or apply generally. An example from biography is
a study of the life of America's most prolific
inventor, Thomas A. Edison. One can conclude he had
great perseverance. Is this trait needed for *all*
engineers--regardless of discipline--creating
something new? You can easily see there are plenty
of difficulties in researching this general area
where things are considerably less well-defined
(The jello on the wall!) than classical quantities
in engineering.

Ranking The Traits in order of importance, as was
done in Table 10-1 is a natural desire of the engineer.
Unfortunately, the 1976 state-of-the-art in creativity
research is not sufficiently advanced to permit a
rigid unassailable ranking. After all, creativity
has only been researched for about 20 years, and
there is considerable disagreement among research
psychologists even about *what* traits are significant
to creativity. And relatively little serious research
appears to have been done by psychologists on creativity
traits needed by the *engineer*.

In view of the above difficulties (The jello
on the wall *again*!) only a very weak attempt has
been made in the following sections to rank the
traits in order of importance to the practicing
creative engineer.

The Traits Identified from the above research are
briefly cited in Secs. 10-2 through 10-11.

Remember we're talking about *traits*--those attributes which characterize the highly creative person.

The model we're considering is of a mythical person--'his' or 'he' in the following Secs.--who is a *highly* creative individual from a larger parent population. Such a person, naturally, does not exist who has all--or perhaps even most--of these desirable traits. But each is believed to be of importance to engineers aspiring to enhance their creative abilities.

In a larger sense, many of the traits identified may also be applicable to non-engineers engaged in or aspiring to engage in highly creative work.

Finally, remember there are *many* traits which precludes treating any one in detail.

10-2 His Physical And External Characteristics

"I am watching my health closely - -"
Wilbur Wright
[394, p27]

GOOD PHYSICAL HEALTH is one of life's most precious assets. "'Health' is more than the *absence* of disease, defect, disability, pain, or decay; it encompasses the *presence* of vigor and vitality, social well being and a zest for living" [144, p59].

Creativity is certainly easier with good health. Yet many have been demonstrably creative in spite of sub-optimal health. Kettering was nearsighted, and Edison was nearly deaf to name only two.

"There are two rules for remaining healthy: to eat less than one might eat, and to work."
Hippocrates
Quoted by
Paul Tournier
[345, p201]

AGE AND CREATIVITY Wilson and Wilson [378, p192] in an excellent discussion sum it up. "Some excellent research studies have apparently shown that great *inventors* tend to be young. Their performance peaks at mid-career and then drops. But for many *innovators* their greatest achievements come in life's prime years. It seems to be a fact that fewer patentable inventions are made in the older years."[1]

On the other hand there is abundant evidence that creativity may actually increase in our older years. One example is Alexanderson. He received 350 patents in his life, getting two thirds of them beyond age 40. His last patent issued when he was 95 [45, p7]!

The facts appear to substantiate that Disciplined Creativity can be engaged in at *any* age during life provided we have the proper balance of physical and emotional health and other factors.

EXTERNALS Maslow   [202, p102] sees creative people externally as:

Unconventional	Irresponsible
Bit Queer	Wild
Unrealistic	Crazy
Undisciplined	Speculative
Inexact	Uncritical
Unscientific	Irregular
Childish	Emotional.

"A man's wisdom makes his face shine - -"
Ecclesiastes 8:1

Bristol   [44,   p3] indicates that "To many of those around him, the creative person may appear to be a mass of contradictions. Great creative abilities may exist side by side with great individual weaknesses. Strong loyalties and equally strong hatreds may be generated by Creative individuals." And, finally that "the creative person is apt to be a disruptive (even revolutionary) force at times who departs from standard approaches."

In spite of the above indiscipline, it is interesting to note that Rossman's [279,   p40] survey of directors of research ranked the inventors competence number seven in frequency of being mentioned!

FEMININITY VS MASCULINITY Saunders [283] researched engineers with 5-7 years research and development experience with five major U.S. corporations. He found that "Good researchers prefer relatively passive activities and are much more artistic--the creative engineers are mainly masculine - -."

In a more general sense Taylor   [330, p182], a

---

[1]For example see Tuska   [348 , p50] who shows a graph of age at which inventors made their most important invention based on Rossman's [279] data. The bell-shaped curve peaks at age 35-39.

psychologist, sees the creative person as "feminine
in interests and characteristics."

SEXUALITY Barron   [31, p159], also a psychologist,
finds "In addition to unusual endowment in terms of
ego instincts, they have much sexual drive as well
(both pregenital and genital) because they are by
constitution more vigorous organisms and more sensitive
(nervous)."

There are undoubtedly other physical and

external characteristics of the highly creative person,

but the above appear to be the major ones known as of

1976.

10-3 His Intellectual Traits

INTELLECTUALITY AND INTELLIGENCE There is little
doubt that the highly creative person is very
intelligent. Taylor   [328, p386] mentions "--traits
which are found in study after study:[1]

> 10. Superior general intelligence (and)
> 11. An early broad interest in intellectual
>   activities."

Barron   [31, p159] thinks that creative
persons "are born with a greater brain capacity--more
ability to hold a lot of ideas in their head at
once, and to compare more ideas with one another,
hence to make a richer synthesis."

Rossman's study   [279, p40] of 78 Directors
of Research ranked 'reasoning and intelligence'
Number 6 in frequency of being mentioned. He also
found 'common sense' was ranked number 6 in frequency
of mention by 710 inventors.

Finally, we should mention the French have a
'charismatic conception' of creativity, as reported
by Dufresne-Tasse [84] which pays "attention to
the difference between inventive capacity and intelligence."

MEMORY Rossman [279] has numerous prominent

---

[1]On 'productive *scientists*.'

inventors ranking memory as the number one trait
in importance for inventive success. Edison also
placed great emphasis on the memory of a person. A
typical creative engineering project is so complex
that the person with a poor memory is soon lost.

HIGH QUALITY KNOWLEDGE AND EDUCATION of engineering
fundamentals are essential for practicing Disciplined
Creativity. It is so important that it is a separate
factor in Eq. 1. Knowledge and education may or may
not have been attained via formal education. Many
believe that self-acquired knowledge and education is
the most enduring. The important thing is that some-
way the creative person acquired these two important
assets.

> *"You cannot teach a man anything--you can only help him find it within himself."*
> *Galileo*

Rossman's research (Table 10-1) showed "knowledge
and memory" ranked number 3 in frequency of being
mentioned by 710 inventors while "training and education"
ranked number 5 in frequency by 78 Directors of
Research. Rossman [279, p46-47] has prominent
inventors saying:

> "A large fund of facts--are important."
> "He should usually possess a fair knowledge
>   of the art and its requirements."
> "He should have a general knowledge of the
>   art in which he is working - -."

These traits are so patently obvious that they
need no further emphasis.

INSIGHT AND UNDERSTANDING of the problem being
solved and of the knowledge being applied to it are
obvious necessities to the creative problem solver.
A deep-felt need for such insight and understanding
may also serve as one motivation. Some inventors
rank 'hear and comprehend what told' as the number 2
essential for inventive success.

Arnold   [9, p132] points out how we acquire
insight. "The insights we acquire through our own
experiences are more meaningful to us than those we
accept from experiences of others."

Finally, insight may come slowly or quickly--as
the so-called 'flash of insight.' Edel [88, p100]
summarizes the latter. "The flash of insight step
usually occurs at unpredictable times during a period
of relaxed mental condition. It is characterized by
an exhilarating feeling of illumination. New combinations
appear suddenly in the mind with definite awareness

of assured suitability for a particular new development."

ANALYSIS was discussed in Sec. 2-1. In a sense the entire Disciplined Creativity process is one of analysis--a breaking down of the problem into manageable component parts.

"--the primary purpose of analysis is to simplify a problem rather than solve it - -"
E. G. Reed
[273, p144]

Rossman's study   [279, p39-40] of inventors shows analytic ability ranked first in the opinions of 78 Directors of Research. It ranked second in importance as seen by 176 patent attorneys while it rated only number seven in importance by 710 inventors (Table 10-1.) One prominent inventor says [279, p45] "What I consider important is--the ability to analyze the requirements of the problem." Another says the inventor should have an analytical mind.

There is little doubt of the great importance to the engineer of analytic ability, for it is so heavily emphasized in college.

MATHEMATICAL KNOWLEDGE AND ABILITY constitute one kind of analytic ability. As we have repeatedly shown throughout this book, mathematics is of much importance to the creative person.

Rossman   [279, p41] has a famous inventor, Dr. Reginald Fessenden, saying "good working knowledge of mathematics" ranks number three in importance on his list of essentials for inventive success.

Every engineer's education is highly steeped in this area--too much so, many feel, tending to exclude developing synthesizing ability.

APPLICATION ORIENTATION is a very fundamental trait of the highly creative engineer as cited in Sec. 1-2 in the definition of engineering. This trait is so evident as to need no further emphasis other than the fact that we shouldn't forget this foundation trait of our profession as we grow older.

"Fulton--had excellent mechanical ability and, being an artist, he was able to clearly draw all the structural details."
Charles F. Kettering
[126, p25]

MECHANICAL ABILITY is another trait of the highly creative engineer. Rossman [279, p39-40] found mechanical ability ranked number nine in importance by 176 patent attorneys and number ten by 710 inventors (Table 10-1). He has prominent inventors saying [279, p46-47]:

"Mechanical judgment and ingenuity make an inventor."

"He must have creative talent, mechanical
    skill, and knowledge of the prior
    art."
"An inventor should be a draftsman, a
    mechanic and in possession of the broadest
    possible knowledge - -"

Even in highly creative electrical engineering
there is much need for strength in mechanical ability.
An EE will never create a new integrated circuit without
considerable mechanical ability, for example.

THE INTERDISCIPLINARY APPROACH becomes increasingly
important as more and more sophisticated technical
products are being created. Extremely *rare* is the
creative problem which comes to us only in neat
packages of thermodynamics, circuits, fluid mechanics,
engineering economics and others. Rather these are
more like notes on a piano, and the highly creative
engineer has to play the *whole* keyboard to solve the
problem.

*"Specialization
by sinecure
experts--is less
productive of new
and fundamental
combinations of
significant
knowledge than
is broad-based
interdisciplinary
technology."
Harold R. Hay
[142, p2]*

Rossman   [279, p37] succinctly sums it up at
the personal level by saying, "The average inventor
is a man whose early study has fitted him to deal
with mechanical, electrical, metallurgical, or chemical
developments."

CHOICES repeatedly face us throughout the creative
process. First there is the matter of identifying
clear alternatives from which to choose. Then there
are excruciations over risks, consequences--personal
and social--of each alternative, choosing the right
people to do the work, and choosing the right environment in which the work is to be done. Finally, there
is the matter of exercising good personal judgment
in effecting our choices.

GOOD JUDGMENT is a deliberate operation of the mind
involving comparison and discrimination. From it
knowledge of values and relationships are mentally
formulated so that wise choices can be made between
factual alternatives.

Rossman   [279, p46] found 'common sense' ranked
number six in importance by 710 inventors (Table
10-1). He also has a prominent inventor saying,
"The inventor should show discrimination as between
the theoretical or the fantastic and practical." He
quotes Dr. Elihu Thomson as saying "sound judgment"
is the first essential for inventive success.

Taylor   [330, p182] sees the creative person
as "more independent in judgment," a notion reinforced

by Barron's research   [28,   p147] on 100 U.S.
Air Force Captains. Barron   [26,   p387] amplifies,
"If such a person then embarks on the risky business
of seeking and putting forth new theories, he must
be prepared to stand his ground against outcries
from the proponents of the previous but in his view
no longer tenable consensus. He must possess
independence of judgment and hold to his own opinion
in the face of a consensus which does not fit all
the facts."

*"Where did you get
your good judgment?"
"From my experience."
"And where did you
get your
experience?"
"From my poor
judgment."
    Anon*

        Finally Taylor   [331, p22] sees "other traits
that should be tested include--to foresee consequences,"
an important ingredient of good judgment.

RISK-TAKING, frequently on a grand scale, is associated
with the intellectual traits of the highly creative
person. Taylor   [330, p181-182] summarizes it as
"willingness to take greater and more long-range
risks" and "more radical." In another place
[328, p86]   he says that creative scientists have
"a special interest in the kind of 'wagering' which
involves pitting oneself against uncertain circumstances
in which one's own effort can be a deciding factor."

        Kettering   [173, p86] cites a significant
historical example of the type risk-taking creative
people commit to. "In 1798 our government was in
great need of rifles. It was then that Eli Whitney
suggested an idea that has completely changed
American industry. He offered to make 10,000 rifles
for the government in two years - -." His risk-
taking resulted in proving for the first time the
concept of interchangeable component parts [379, p82].

DECISIVENESS is the intellectual ability to reach
a clean-cut decision for a projected course of action.
Its ingredients were summarized in Sec. 4-2. We
only add here a thought pointed up by Rossman
[279, p45].   ("The inventor) must be willing to
throw away years of endeavor and research, without
regret and completely redesign the idea to fill
certain demands "--an obvious potentially heart-
breaking aspect of 'decisiveness.' In such a
decision the creative person clearly brings together
his choices, good judgment, and risk-taking abilities--
all of which are clearly interrelated.

THOROUGHNESS appears to not turn up in many
psychological studies as a prominent trait of the
creative person. Yet close observation of real life
highly creative engineers reveals the presence of the

"(Roger Bacon) knew his methods of careful experimentation were at odds with the superstition and guesswork of his time because he was often thrown into jail."
  Charles F. Kettering
  [173, p45]

thoroughness trait--some might even call it craftsmanship.

While the low creativity person is wringing out two or three ideas, the highly creative person generates 80 or more ideas, i.e. he *thoroughly* 'covers the field' of possibilities in order to miss no overlooked idea.

Thoroughness may involve interest and patience, both yet to be discussed in Secs. 10-4 and 10-6. Once again we see how these personal traits are interrelated.

SELF RENEWAL AND LIFETIME LEARNING is another intellectual characteristic of highly creative persons who--long ago--have discovered that learning is fun. Virtually all educated men at least render lip service to the concept of continuing education. Some even practice it. The highly creative individual finds himself engaged in *continuous* learning *beyond* college for the remainder of his life. Further, he finds himself being renewed by the experience and thereby placed in a position to create ever newer needed things.

Gardner's [116] treatise is one of the more thoughtful writings on this subject and worthy of intensive study by engineers. The study of biography and autobiography can also be an inspiring source of renewal, learning and lifting of our fatigued creative spirits.

Thus we increasingly see there are *many* intellectual traits exhibited by the highly creative person. Clearly there are many subtleties, complexities, and downright unknowns in these complex areas.

We now move to personal traits in the important general area of motivation.

10-4 His Motivations

MOTIVATION is a dominant factor of eq. (1). Taylor [330, p181] states that it is the "belief of practically everyone that motivation is a strong component of creativity." Arnold [9, p129] says the creative person "---must have great emotional, mental and physical *drive* and the ability to channel this drive." Motivation clearly is of *major* importance in Disciplined Creative activity.

Motivation is that which animates. It is of two principal kinds:

●	External Motivation	Determined by the total environment in which the creative person works.
●	Internal Motivation	Basically determined by the creative person himself.

"The creative process is not a comfortable thing. It involves urge, pressure."
   A. D. Moore
      [217, p2-3]

Engineering management spends much time trying to optimize the first; the individual must supply the second type, though it can be substantially influenced by externals. Either are the result of some kind of stress application to the person.

Motivation, when thoroughly thought through, leads--ultimately--to religion with psychology as a way stop.

"What motivates man to great adventures? --I can say quite definitely that they sprang more from intuition than from rationality, and that the love of flying outweighed practical purposes - -"
   Charles A. Lindbergh
      [194]

There are myriads of complex internal motivations. Rossman [279, p152] found from studying the stated motives of 710 inventors that love of inventing, desire to improve, financial gain, necessity or need, desire to achieve, part of work, and prestige--in decreasing order of importance--were principal incentives which caused them to invent. Many other motives exist, naturally. You will find a good condensed discussion of motivation in Wilson and Wilson's book [379, p187]. There are many articles and volumes written on this popular subject.

Finally, we close by pointing out there is such a thing as overmotivation; but most of us operate so far below that limit most of the time for it to be of little importance to us.

CHALLENGE and responding positively to it appears to be a trait of the creative person. Some might even call it a motivation. Numerous engineers seek active challenges in their creative work. Bristol [44, p3] says of *The 100 Most Important People In The World* they "tend to thrive on, often actively seek challenges."

Without significant work challenges the highly creative engineer soon moves to other work where challenge exists.

CURIOSITY AND INQUIRINGNESS is one "generalized personality impression of the creative person" according to Rossman [279, pxx]. Taylor [330, p181] classifies curiosity as a motivational characteristic while Gough [126, p217] calls it "inquiringness as a habit of mind."

"--an individual needs--curiosity, namely the desire to know the answer to how, why, when, where of each experience, to have the inventive attitude. "
  Igor Sikorsky
    [293, p8]

Curiosity leads the creative person into a "diversity of activities" as found by Bristol [44, p4]   from studying The 100 Most Important People In The World. Such diversity frequently leads the highly creative person to form new combinations of ideas that would not have been created had not curiosity served as the catalyst.

INTEREST repeatedly turns up as an observed motivational trait of highly creative people.

Ask a highly creative research engineer how he got started on his new line of research and he'll probably reply he was first curious about such-and-such a thing, then he began playing with the idea some more and finally discovered he was intensely interested in that area.

Interest is a powerful motivator and channeler so that all our activities and energies follow a coherent or consistent pattern.

Frequently the creative person's interest is initially sparked by hobbies, travel, chance conversations with colleagues and other means.

We should finally recognize the interests of highly creative persons usually change with time--a perfectly normal phenomenon in keeping him alive and vital.

"Many companies can blame their downward trend to a lack of encouragement of their creative people."
  Chester M. Sinnett
    [301, p19]

ENCOURAGEMENT, DISCOURAGEMENT AND CRITICISM The highly creative person is ultra sensitive to encouragement. Its positive effects are exactly the opposite of discouragement and criticism which are all too common. What a nearly magical motivational effect encouragement has on us! It can pull us out of the doldrums and inject new motivation to ourselves, our project and those around us. All it takes is a few kind words from someone whose opinions we respect. They can infuse our spirit with a new energy we may not have known we had.

The highly creative person especially appreciates encouragement when things are generally going badly

*"And just as every-
one was becoming
absolutely dis-
couraged, an
experiment
produced a bare
teaspoonful of a
rare compound
called--tetra-ethyl
lead."*
  Charles F. Kettering
     [173, p77]

on his project. It engenders the deepest long-range respect, strengthened relationships, and is a positively healthy thing. Unfortunately some small men find it expedient to pass out encouragement only when things are going *well* on our creative project but remain silent as stones during the *dark* times when encouragement is most needed. The highly creative person sees through this modus operandi. Perhaps to counteract it he finds joy and satisfaction in encouraging other creative persons around him during their dark times.

Though an environment of encouragement of the creative person's efforts is a desirable one, many new creations are born surrounded by discouragement and criticism. The creative person has simply decided to rise above these effects. Such cases strongly suggest that, in the final analysis, the motivational or demotivational effects are determined by the person himself independent of externals.

*"Honors were con-
ferred upon (Thomas
Midgley, Jr.) from
many directions."*
  Charles F. Kettering
     [173, p77]

RECOGNITION AND REWARDS are essential motivational ingredients for many highly creative persons. We explored rewards earlier in Sec. 2-2. The noblest creative person accepts whatever recognition and rewards the world bestows on him in a spirit of considerable humility.

Discussion Topics

1. Does creative thinking cause greater personal mental strain than non-creative thinking? Why? Might it have any effects on your body?

2. Is it possible to put each distinguishing trait of the creative person in a neat well-defined box and avoid the 'jello on the wall' problem?

3. List ideas for how you might become 'a real person.'

4. Is there an emotional element involved in creativity? If so, is this good or bad in your opinion?

5. List ways *you* might identify the traits of higly creative persons.

6. Does this whole area appear to be 'hard science' or 'soft science?'

7. Why aren't the traits of Secs. 10-2 and 3 ranked according to importance to the engineer?

8. List the externally visible traits of a
    generalized highly creative engineer.

9. How do you account for the fact that many useful
    inventions were made by persons *not* 'classically
    intellectual?'

10. How do you account for why highly creative
    persons tend to take large risks?

11. List ways you might engage in a lifetime of
    self-renewal.

12. Is it better psychologically for a person to be
    externally or internally motivated?

13. How do you account for the high motivational
    effects of 'interest' in something?

14. When were you last encouraged? Describe it.
    How did it leave you feeling?

10-5 His Formation Of Ideas

Idea formation obviously constitutes the major

'output' of a highly creative person. It is natural,

therefore to group a family of personal traits around

this theme as we continue our characterization.

IMAGINATION AND IDEAS are absolutely essential to
create the new. Rossman   [279, p39] found imagination
ranked second in importance by 710 inventors (see
Table 10-1), third by 176 patent attorneys and fourth
by 78 directors of research. Dufresne-Tasse [84]
also points out the French under their charismatic
concept of creativity have great respect for imagination.

Taylor   [330, p182] sees the creative person as
having a "liking for ideas vs people vs things." He
also sees   [330, p181] the creative person's "liking
to manipulate and toy with ideas" as one motivational
characteristic. Finally, he sees   [331, p22] "we
lack a test for determining capacity to manipulate
ideas."

VISUAL ABILITY permits the creative person to tangibly
express his imaginative ideas. It has two principal
parts:

●   Mental Conception of the idea.

● The Sketch or Drawing embodying the idea.
   This is the important "make it like this"
   document. By it our ideas can be communicated
   to others.

Rossman   [279, p44-47] shows 'ability to visualize,'
'ability to perceive a definite object,' and 'spatial
visualization' are essentials for inventive success.

It is unfortunate for the creative engineer
that sketching and drawing courses have been de-
emphasized in many U.S. engineering colleges since
World War II, for ability to sketch repeatedly crops
up from actual creative projects, biography, and
history as an important trait of the highly creative
person.

OWN VS OTHERS' IDEAS Many creative people tend to like
their own ideas best. Call it egotism or dogmatism
if you wish. Carried too far it becomes an inhibitor,
and we acquire a 'mother complex' over our ideas as
discussed in Sec. 13-2. Yet there is among many a
deep reverence for the ideas of others. One example
is cited by Rossman [279, p42] where he reports
Dr. Miller Reese Hutchison saying to abstain from
infringing on ideas of others is the number five
essential for inventive success on his scale of values.

*NEWNESS, ORIGINALITY, NOVELTY, CLEVERNESS, INGENUITY
AND RESOURCEFULLNESS* and similar terms are important
to the creative person struggling with new ideas.

Rossman   [279, p39-40] showed that originality
ranked first in importance by 176 patent attorneys,
third by 78 directors of research, and a surprising
fifth by 710 inventors. He also mentions [279, p36]
native ingenuity as one important characteristic of
inventors. He has other prominent inventors citing
'shrewdness,' 'resourceful mind,' 'resourcefullness,'
and 'ingenuity' as essential also.

Guilford   [134, p158], summarizing 10 yrs.
research on creativity, identifies 'originality' as
one major result characterizing the creative person.

Lowenfeld   [197, p13], in discussing originality,
says that "creative students give *uncommon* responses
to questions and *unusual* solutions to problems."

Dufresne-Tasse [84]   reports the French
charismatic conception of creativity involves emphasis
on newness. Bristol [44]   mentions that 'uniqueness'
is one creative characteristic those had in *The 100*

Most Important People In The World Today.

　　Finally, Arnold　　[9, p129] succinctly sums the matter up with "--invention involves taking an idea from one field and combining it, oftentimes with an idea from a completely unrelated field in order to form this new creative combination."

FIRSTNESS is of course one of the joys of engaging in creative work in a virgin area of technology. Being *first* is one requirement of obtaining a patent. In the scientific area being *first* to publish something new has its rewards to the creative person.

"--you embody it, and during that period of embodiment you have a feeling of almost divine guidance."
Edwin H. Land
[185, p151]

　　Note that it frequently happens that the engineer creates a truly original--to him--idea; but it may not be the *first* time that idea was created. Originality does not necessarily imply firstness! But firstness implies originality!

　　Bristol　　[44, p5] has the right perspective when he says "Often the creative person is the first to establish important relationships, the first to see the need for a new invention, the first to promote an entirely new industry, or the first to employ a new way of thinking"--all based on his study of *The 100 Most Important People In The World.*

FOCUS AND CONCENTRATION of a deliberate kind on the creative task to be solved has characterized virtually all great creations in any field. Without focus and concentration brought into play by the personal efforts of the creative person nothing useful results. It is especially true in the application of Disciplined Creativity in engineering.

　　Rossman　　[279, p43] records Henry Wood Wise as saying one essential for inventive success is concentration on a single objective. Bristol [　44, p4] remarks that "A single-minded approach to life has been a characteristic of significant numbers of creative persons," and, finally, that "creative people may often find themselves involved in crusades."

"Decide what your real dreams are-- then reach for them. They are closer than you think."
Henry J. Kaiser
[165]

SYNTHESIS, VISION AND GOALS have characterized all the great creative engineers of the past, or as Rossman　　[279, p47] records one inventor saying, "He must be a dreamer - -." Marconi dreamed of communicating across the Atlantic via wireless. Westinghouse dreamed of preventing wrecks on trains because of faulty brakes, and the astronauts had

a vision of walking on the moon--all of which
'visions' eventually came true to the benefit of
mankind.

Bristol   [44, p3] says that "ability to see
possibilities unnoticed by others" is one common
characteristic of creative minds." On the same thought,
Rossman [279, p46] records a prominent inventor
as saying "--ability to combine facts to create something
new are important."

That such vision capabilities are not beyond our
grasp is seen in Rossman's [279, p37]   comment that
"the more prolific inventors ordinarily are simply
superior mechanics and engineers of active mind and
vision somewhat beyond the usual run of men of the
same general class and occupation."

Finally, Bristol   [44 , p4] correctly indicates
that "creative people and organizations are apt to
set very high goals for themselves."

ABILITY TO REDEFINE AND REARRANGE has been found
by Guilford [134, p163]   in a 10 yr. study of
creativity to be characteristic of a creative person.
He identifies symbolic redefinition and figural
redefinition and evolved tests for both. Bristol
[44, p3]   found that a common characteristic of *The
100 Most Important People In The World* is their
"skill to rearrange and/or combine things for greater
success."

Hardly a day passes in the life of the Disciplined
Creative engineer when he doesn't have to use this
trait.

GENERALIZING is a trait seldom mentioned in the
psychological research literature on creativity.
Yet observation of real engineers and a careful study
of other sources repeatedly turns up the fact that
the highly creative individual has a strong capacity
to generalize and thereby arrive at new idea
combinations.

*"If I have seen
further than
others, it is
that I have
stood on the
shoulders of
giants."
Sir Isaac Newton
[224, p54]*

This trait is undoubtedly coupled to the previous
trait--ability to redefine and rearrange--as well as
problem understanding and ability to simplify.

The ability to generalize is especially needed
in the early parts of the 'Problem Inquiry' phase of
Disciplined Creativity and to some extent in succeeding
phases, as during the Verification Phase when the
engineer is trying to summarize his results and draw

meaningful conclusions.

FLUENCY is the facility with which ideas can be
generated. Guilford [134, p157-158] identifies
specific types of fluency characterizing creative
persons:

● <u>Word</u> <u>Fluency</u> is the ability to rapidly think of
words satisfying prescribed requirments, as
containing a stated letter or syllable.

● <u>Ideational</u> <u>Fluency</u> is the rapid listing of
meaningful words in a specified category or
the listing of ideas to meet meaningful
requirements.

● <u>Associational</u> <u>Fluency</u> is the ability to list
words bearing some relation to a given word,
as naming synonyms to the word 'dark'.

● <u>Expressional</u> <u>Fluency</u> is the ability to put words
into organized phrases and sentences.

The well-known brainstorming technique is one example
of fluency widely applied by creative persons.

The highly fluent person has, according to
Arnold [9,   p129], "more ideas per unit time and
ideas cover a greater range of human experience than
those of persons who are more prosaic."

FLEXIBILITY OF THINKING is explained by Guilford
[134, p157].   "Some individuals are rigid or set
in their ways of thinking and this shows up particularly
where problems call for the rejection of habitual,
conventional, or previously successful ways and the
striking out in new directions." He found there are
two kinds:

● <u>Spontaneous</u> <u>Flexibility</u> where the thinker is
flexible even when he has no need to be.
● <u>Adaptive</u> <u>Flexibility</u> where he would fail to solve
the problem if he were not flexible.

Bristol [44] observes that "adaptability to
changing conditions" is one characteristic of *The
100 Most Important People In The World Today*.

There is little doubt about the importance of
flexibility of thinking to Disciplined Creativity.
It is somewhat related to the earlier fluency quality,
though technically not quite the same.

DIVERGENT THINKING is defined by Guilford   [134, p160]
thus: "In divergent-thinking operations we think
in different directions, sometimes searching, sometimes

"(Alexanderson's)
practice of adapting
old apparatus to
novel ends is said
to have given him
the reputation
around the company
as a 'Master
Salvager'."
James E. Brittain
[45, p9]

seeking variety." He classifies divergent thinking
as one of five fundamental intellectual operations
and mentions it is one major result of his 10 year
research on creativity.

Divergent thinking is widely used throughout the
Disciplined Creativity process where we seek to
identify alternatives—alternative problem definitions,
solutions, test methods, strategies, and the like.

CLOSURE RESISTANCE is defined by Taylor   [330, p181]
as the "resistance to closing up and crystallizing
things." In a sense it represents the hope that 'one
more truly great idea might be born next and we shouldn't
stop quite yet'. Finally, though, the creative person
realizes he must stop generating ideas and converge
on the best solution from the ideas generated. It is
well-known in creative methodology, however, that too
early closure can severely limit the problem solution.

CONVERGENT THINKING tends to converge on the answer.
According to Guilford   [134, p160], "in convergent
thinking the information can and does lead to one
right answer or to a recognized best or conventional
answer."

We should not lose sight of the fact that convergent
thinking is one trait of the creative person. Naturally
one cannot engage in divergent thinking and convergent
thinking simultaneously. They are used at *different*
times during the Disciplined Creativity process.

This type thinking is so well ingrained in the
engineer as to require no further comment.

DATA INPUT is a seemingly endless flow into the highly
creative person and is another of his traits. He has,
as Taylor   [330, p181] says a "tendency to accumulate
an overabundance of raw stuff plus a willingness
ultimately to discard." See Chap. 11 on Information.

Data input is a lifelong process for the creatively
viable person who always is alert to take advantage
of new ideas, products, materials, and systems.
Kettering   [173, p63] cites an example. "In a
laboratory in New Jersey another inventor was working
with photography. He wanted to take 15 or 20 pictures
a second on a strip of film, but he had been unable
to find any such material until one day he heard of
Eastman's work. So he immediately wrote a letter to
Rochester enclosing $2.50 for a sample strip of the
new material to be sent to T. A. Edison, Orange, New
Jersey."

CRITICALNESS both of his own ideas and creations
as well as those of others seems to be a common
trait of highly creative persons. Rossman [279, p46]
quotes a prominent inventor who says "pitiless criticism
of one's own conceptions and creations" is essential.

This trait may irritate others coming into contact
with the highly creative person who fail to understand
that finding what is wrong is the beginning of the
creative process of generating new ideas and improving
things. Thus criticalness is akin to Constructive
Discontent discussed in Sec. 10-9.

ESCAPISM AND HOBBIES Every healthy person recognizes
the need for occasional escapes from the rigors of
work--even if one loves his work. Such escapes
provide both physical and mental renewal, the latter
being particularly important to the highly creative
person trying to generate new ideas. It is a well
established principle in creative thinking that when
the mind and body are relaxed new idea combinations
occur which we wouldn't likely have generated otherwise.

The matter is as Edel   [89, p100] has said.
"Some form of mental relaxation is needed to replace
the previously established thought patterns that have
formed confining ruts in the conscious part of the
brain."

Hobbies, reading, and travel constitute a few
major 'escapes' via which the highly creative person
comes away with new fresh ideas. This topic is
coupled in some complex way with the next trait.

SEEK ADVENTURE AND NEW EXPERIENCES seems to also be
a characteristic of the highly creative person. Taylor
[330, p181]   mentions the creative person's "need
for variety" and that he is "--more adventurous" while
Bristol   [44, p6] says that "Desire for new
experiences is a characteristic shared to some extent
by creative people." Tournier [344   ] makes an
impressive case for man's inherent need for adventure.

Such adventure may be found in travel, attending
engineering conferences, sharing ideas with others,
reading, and actual work on our creative project--to
name only a few.

Whether the activity is or is not 'an adventure'
is determined entirely by the attitude of the creative
person.

From such adventure and new experiences it is fairly common to return to our creative work both renewed and with many fresh ideas.

THINKING AND ABSTRACTNESS of that thinking is a trait which Taylor   [224, p386] says has been found in study after study on productive scientists. Saunders [283] in studying engineers with 5-7 years research and development experience with 5 major U.S. corporations found that, predictably, the research group ranked highest and the sales group lowest in 'liking to think'.

Thinking--often hard and excruciating--is an interwoven vital part of the Disciplined Creative process of Chaps. 3-9. Without it no ideas of importance get generated and carried to a state of usefullness.

There are several different levels of abstraction in thinking. The higher the abstraction level the more compact are the tangible results of the highly creative person's thinking and the more use is made of symbolic representations. Abstractness and symbolism is an interesting subject beyond our scope here.

VICARIOUS THINKING is frequently used by the highly creative engineer to generate new ideas, and it is one more trait of the highly creative person.

"In addition to creator he is also audience." Morris I. Stein [316, p89]

In essence he simply imagines he is someone else using his proposed new gadget in which case he may see whole new vistas needing improving. Vicarious thinking particularly enters into the Optimize Phase (Chap. 7) of Disciplined Creativity.

An interesting useful application of vicarious thinking has been pointed up by Gordon [123] who suggests we imagine ourselves as *being* the object we're trying to create as, "How would I feel if I were a spring?"

SENSE OF TIME AND TIMING has several dimensions for the highly creative person. First, and very fundamental, in the words of Wilson and Wilson   [379, p181] "You must have the necessary time to complete and carry out the design task. --Many good ideas are never carried out simply because time is not available to do the necessary work."

Then there is the matter of having so much to do that is enjoyably creative that many creative people become ultra time conscious, trying to not waste a minute in unproductive activity.

Finally, there is the uncanny sense of correct timing which some highly creative individuals possess for introducing a new idea.

There are probably other traits characterizing the highly creative person's formation of ideas. You may want to explore this on your own.

We next examine his work traits and see how they differ from the ordinary.

10-6 His Personal Work Traits

INITIATIVE AND ACTIVITY are traits of major importance to the highly creative person. There is little room for laziness in Disciplined Creativity!

"Initiative is doing the right thing without being told."
Victor Hugo
[157, p54]

Rossman [279, pxx] cites initiative as one of the top "generalized personality impressions of the creative person." He also quotes [p42] Emile Berliner as saying that "more than the industry of the bee" ranks the number 3 essential for inventive success.

An integral part of initiative is 'follow-through' ability--especially important for the creative engineer who would achieve useful results.

From observations of creative engineers it is clear there are *large* differences between individuals on these traits, especially when placed in an open-ended situation demanding Disciplined Creative effort. The highly creative person thrives on initiative and activity while those at the other end of the spectrum flounder around seeking someone to *tell* them what to do.

ENTHUSIASM AND EXCITEMENT about his work characterizes the highly creative person. He genuinely *enjoys* his work, looks forward to coming to work each day, and may even hate to leave it at the end of the day. Highly creative work to him is an exciting activity and his enthusiasm and excitement frequently--but not always--are contagious to those around him. It shows--almost radiates!

Enthusiasm and excitement--properly channeled on a useful creative engineering project--are very beautiful things. The very etymology of the word enthusiasm springs from the idea of being spirit-filled --having God within us. It is the source of much of the highly creative person's energy.

"Obsessed with the idea Morse neglected his painting, using it only as a means of providing funds for his experiments."
Charles F. Kettering
[173, p65]

INVOLVEMENT AND COMMITMENT are somewhat related to the previous trait. The creative person tends to get involved at a deep personal level with his work because he *believes* in what he is doing and is committed to it. The subject of personal commitment to the problems is implicit in the "Should I/we solve it?" question of the Problem Inquiry Phase, Fig. 4-2. The commitment motivates and sustains us through the difficult times.

Once we're committed to the problem it's like being afflicted by a disease--we can't turn it loose. Meals are forgotten, sleep is lost, and the problem becomes our principal waking thought. Everything we look at is seen through the problem before us.

ENERGY AND WORK are both obviously highly necessary to practice Disciplined Creativity. Both depend principally on the creative person--as all these traits we've been identifying. We identify energy as the inherent potential energy of the creative person to do useful tasks. Work is the rate at which we use our personal energy on the task.

"For three years Eastman worked on this problem--night and day in his spare time."
Charles F. Kettering
[173, p62]

Bristol [44, p3] found that one common characteristic of *The 100 Most Important People In The World* is their "drive and effort to make needed improvements." He also mentions hard work. Rossman [279, p41] records Dr. Reginald Fessenden as saying the "ability to work 18 hrs./day" ranks number four on his list of essentials for inventive success. Another inventor [p53] says "His energy never flags."

Space does not permit us to explore why the creative person has such boundless energy. It is related to his commitment, enthusiasm, his inner spirit and other personal factors, however.

PATIENCE, IMPATIENCE, PERSISTENCE AND PERSEVERANCE are all related.

It is helpful in creative work to think of patience as the quality which sees us through the *short*-term difficulties and troubles--the experiment that is fundamentally sound but something was wrong with one instrument kind of thing.

Impatience tends toward emotional instability, irrationality and indiscipline and cannot endure even short-term troubles.

"But Goodyear found
that his battle had
only begun. He
became poverty
stricken trying to
get a patent, and
fighting legal
battles."
  Charles F. Kettering
  [173, p59]

Persistence and perseverance in creative work
imply a *longer* term thrusting--the overcoming of many
smaller difficulties to achieve a larger end, usually
at considerable personal sacrifice.

Note from Table 10-1 that perseverance ranked
number *one* in importance by 710 inventors!

These qualities are obviously required in high
measure throughout the 6 Step Approach to creativity
of Chaps. 3-9. Kettering   [173, p58] has the right
viewpoint when he says, "--patience is not an isolated
thing. It is an intelligent desire with a willingness
to work and an understanding of how much effort and
time will be required."

These attributes of creative work, as with so
many of these important traits we are identifying,
can be enhanced by first working with some highly
creative person who has patience and perseverance in
goodly measure. These qualities, also, are like a
disease--they can be 'caught' provided we're willing.

Too much cannot be said about the importance
of patience and persistence if our creative work is
to have a successful outcome.

OBSTACLES, DIFFICULTIES, AND HARDSHIPS constitute
an integral part of most highly creative work. Most
of the time our project goes askew. Once in awhile
things go right. Murphy's Law is omnipresent.

The difficulties may be because of the sub-optimal
environment, technical troubles with our project which
seem insurmountable, or we may have some personal
trouble as excessive worry, little money, or others.

"In the next two
months (Sikorsky)
built an experi-
mental (helicopter),
then the tests and
real trouble
began--the engine
was too small."
  Charles F. Kettering
  [173, p26]

Rossman   [279, p41] has the famous inventor
Dr. Elihu Thomson saying, "obstacles are regarded as
things to be overcome" and Henry Wood Wise [p43] says
one essential for inventiveness is to be prepared to
undergo hardships. Many past inventors have had to
undergo extreme personal hardships because of their
work. Some of the worst include poverty, alienation,
loneliness, and others. Finally, Bristol   [44, p4]
observed that 'ability to overcome obstacles' is often
mentioned with respect to The *100 Most Important
People In The World Today*.

It may require great courage, patience and
perseverance for us to overcome the numerous obstacles

encountered throughout the Disciplined Creative
process laid out in Chaps. 3-9.

SELF-CONTROL AND DISCIPLINE constitute important
work traits of the highly creative person. Taylor
[328, p386] says that psychologists have found
in study after study of productive scientists that
they have "A high degree of control of impulse,
amounting almost to over control." Bristol   [44, p6]
says of Dr. Charles Townes, the maser/laser inventor,
that "he has a tremendous self-discipline," and
Rossman   [279, pxx] mentions self-discipline as one
"generalized personality impression of the creative
person."

"*By emulation of
discipline, we shall
not destroy
creativity.*"
 Raymond D. Pruitt
 [262, p26]

The self-discipline theme is so implicitly woven
throughout the creative process revealed in Chaps. 3-9
that no further emphasis is needed.

ORDER-DISORDER AND CONFUSION are other work traits
which stand out for the highly creative person.
Taylor   [328, p385] finds that in study after study
of productive scientists psychologists have found
a "liking for method, precision, exactness." Barron
[26, p386]   studied doctoral candidates in the
sciences and found "the more highly regarded young
scientists are marked by a strong need for order and
for perceptual closure, combined with a resistance
to premature closure and an interest in what may appear
as disorder, contradiction, imbalance, or very complex
balance whose ordering principle is not immediately
apparent."

The disciplined engineer usually prefers to proceed
in his creative work in an orderly way. Those who do
usually--but not always--get the problem solved and
make a larger contribution than their more chaotic
colleagues. But we should recognize there is inherent
in the Disciplined Creative Process a certain amount
of personal chaos and confusion. This is perfectly
normal, but the process laid out in Chaps. 3-6 seeks
to minimize the confusion by always giving us some
definite action to engage in next.

COMPLEX ORDER PREFERENCE It appears that the creative
person's work traits are a dichotomy in the area of
complexity. His personal world and thinking is generally
quite complex compared to those less creative. It's
almost as if the creative person prefers a complex
order of things. Yet most creative persons have high
regard for the beauty and elegance of simplicity--*simple*
circuits, mechanisms, and the like.

The dichotomy is that his thinking encompasses both complex and simple orders. Frequently it is necessary to first create the complex to arrive at and appreciate the simple. A genuine paradox! The Disciplined Creative engineer recognizes it and tries to work toward simple things inasmuch as is possible for his particular problem. Simple things have a tendency to cost less initially and have better service and reliability records than more complex apparatus.

COHERENCE OF ORGANIZATION has been identified by Lowenfeld [197, p13] as a trait of a highly creative person's work. By it he means an integration or unity of organization both for how the work is to proceed and in its final result--"the ultimate harmony by which good books are written and good houses are built." The Greek word telikos--tending toward an end, purposive--appears to best capture the coherence of organization idea in our creative work.

10-7 His Sensitivities

SENSITIVITY is an important trait of highly creative persons who, according to Lowenfeld [197, p12] tend to be "unusually sensitive to what they see, hear, touch, etc." We are sensitive both to what is right and what is wrong with a given creation. Arnold [9, p129] breaks it down into sensitivity to problems and ability to verbalize this awareness into a problem statement.

"--these people have the faculty of looking around and being able to find problems - -"
Chester M. Sinnett [300, p21]

Rossman [279, p36-45] is more specific for inventors, pointing out "one of the important characteristics of the inventor is his ability to recognize industrial problems and needs - -" and that inventors "Are quick to see a need and just as quick to supply the means for fulfilling that need." He reveals via Emile Berliner [p42] some of the subtleties involved in sensitivity. Berliner says inventors have "the ability to appreciate the possibilities of phenomena that less observing would pass by without seeing." It is precisely this kind of sensitivity which has been the genesis of many inventions.

Common observation of highly creative persons also reveals they are, as Taylor [330, p182] indicates, "more emotionally sensitive."

In short the highly creative person is unusually and delicately sensitive to *everything* around him and therefore is more capable of reacting positively than

his less sensitive colleagues. The sensitivity
notion has many implications in practical creative
engineering work. You will have to pick up this
trait from the more creative engineers and managers
around you in your actual work.

OBSERVATION capacity is one kind of sensitivity.
Edel [89,   p99] gives us the historical perspective
that "Famous creative individuals are known to be
keen observers of the environmental conditions in
which they live." Barron   [30, p159] elaborates
for us.

> "1. Creative people are more observant and
>   they value accurate observation, truth
>   telling to themselves, more.
> 2. They often tell or express only part truths,
>   but vividly, and the part they express is
>   the generally unrecognized--they point to
>   the usually unobserved.
> 3. They see things others do, but also others
>   do not."

The capacity for keen observation ranked number
9 in importance by 710 inventors (Table 10-1).

Observation, as most other traits we're identifying
in this Chap., has a thousand facets, depending on the
individual problem. Be especially sensitive to the
observational skills in those highly creative engineers
around you. Your own sensitivity and capacity to
astutely observe will grow with practice.

ERRORS AND WHAT IS WRONG constitute another kind of
sensitivity based first on observation. Rossman
[279, p45]   has a prominent inventor saying he
must have "ability to see errors in present-day
devices, and to correct them."

*"--progress is made
through failure as
well as through
success."*
*John E. Arnold
[9, p21]*

This trait is particularly called for in the
Optimization Phase of Disciplined Creativity. Its
subtleties were explored in Chap. 7.

The typical engineer is quite adept at detecting
"what's wrong" with a product--more so than detecting
what is *right* about it--so that we needn't say more
on this topic.

CAPACITY TO TOLERATE AMBIGUITY is another sensitivity
of a highly creative person. Stein [316, p87]
summarizes this trait. "He has the capacity to
exist in a state in which he does not comprehend

all that he perceives or feels. Nevertheless, he
continues to seek resolution of the problem confronting
him. Some persons find this lack of structure intolerable
and when they experience it they become too anxious
for constructive work. They either retreat from the
ambiguity or they impulsively grasp hold of any means
that provides them with structure."

Taylor [331, p21]   mentions that "the capacity
to be puzzled--may be very important." Saunders [283]
researched engineers with 5-7 years research and
development experience with 5 major U.S. corporations
and found the research group found it easiest to
sympathize with a person who is doubting and unsure
about things.

Finally, Taylor and Barron [326, p387] opine
that "As discoveries occur which cannot be assimilated
to current conceptions of orderliness in nature,
increasing effort must be made to understand the
unordered and to find a new principle which will restore
order. The person who pays close attention to what
appears discordant and contradictory and who is
challenged by such irregularities is therefore likely
to be in the front ranks of the revolutionaries."

Clearly considerable personal sensitivity is
involved in detecting and coping with ambiguities.

Discussion Topics

1. How do you form a new idea?

2. Are sketches and drawings important to the
    creative engineer?

3. Highly creative persons appear to prefer *novel*
    solutions to problems. How do you account for
    this?

4. How does one get *time* to 'focus and concentrate'
    in the real engineering world?

5. Have you been taught how to think divergently?
    Why or why not?

6. Can hobbies enhance personal creativity? How?

7. Why is personal initiative of great importance
    to the engineer?

8. Can enthusiasm be 'taught'?

9. List ways we can increase our personal energy
    and work output.

10. How do you account for why creative persons
    emphasize patience and perseverance so heavily?

11. List ways we might develop our creative sensitivities

10-8 His Emotions

The whole emotional area is so complex that,

like previous traits, we must break it into discrete

subareas. Their individual relevance to creativity

will be evident after a little thought.

*"--everyone makes
his life through
the emotions--
through loves and
hates, faith and
hope, jubilations
and disappointments.
They are the vital
parts of life."
William Menninger
[213, p18]*

PERSONAL PSYCHOLOGY Barron   [27,   p147] found from
his psychologic research on 100 USAF captains that
original persons are more complex psychodynamically
and have a greater personal scope. "Hence they also
have more apprehensions of unconscious motives,
fantasy life, etc. They note or observe their impulses
more and allow them expression in the interest of
truth." Finally, he found that "creative people have
exceptionally strong egos. The self is strongest when
it can go far back regressively (allow primitive
fantasies, tabooed impulses into consciousness and
behavior) and return to a high degree of rationality.
The creative person is both more primitive and more
cultured, more destructive and more constructive,
crazier and saner, than the average person."

Virtually all psychologists who have done research
on the creative person agree that we are very complex
as persons--which introduces our next topic.

COMPLEXITY Taylor   [330,   p182] finds the creative
individual "more complex as a person." Barron
[31, p159]   says "Their universe is thus naturally
more complex, and in addition they usually have more
complex lives leading them to prefer much tension in
the interest of the pleasure they obtain from its
discharge."

There appears little reason for doubting the
complexity argument, particularly in light of the
large number of traits we've identified so far of
the highly creative person--and we're *not* yet through!

FEELINGS, EMOTIONS AND INNER TENSION To say that
the highly creative person is a wide range feeling
person is an understatement. He typically experiences
the *full* range of human emotional feelings, and he is
aware of these feelings--perhaps because of his
sensitivity.

*"The creative
individual knows
his own feelings
better than the
average person."
S. I. Hayakawa
[143, p4A]*

He can appreciate exhilaration in his work
because he has experienced depression. He appreciates
'riding loose' because he has experienced anxiety.
He appreciates the joys of satisfaction with a finished
piece of creative work because he has experienced
inadequacy. He appreciates relaxation because he has
experienced the rigors of strain and hard disciplined
effort (see Fig. 17-6), and, finally, he appreciates
what it is to be "in the working mood" because he
has experienced--perhaps most of the time--not being
in the mood to do serious creative work.

AN INNER FREEDOM SENSE has been recognized by many
creativity researchers and writers. It too is basically
a feeling experienced by the highly creative person.
Like all feelings, it varies with time. Today we may
have a strong feeling of inner freedom while later in
the day we may feel constrained and unfree.

*"These men were
working under
conditions of
substantial
freedom and
leisure."
Arthur Holly
Compton
[66, p23]*

Barron [27,   p150] tells of freedom's importance
and its relation to organization. "Thus the ability
to respond in an unusual or original manner will be
greatest when freedom is greatest.

Now freedom is related in a very special manner
to degree and kind of organization. In general
organization in company with complexity, generates
freedom."

Finally, he sums it up. "Freedom of expression
and movement, lack of fear of dissent and contradiction,
a willingness to break with custom, a spirit of
play as well as a dedication to work purpose on a
grand scale; these are some of the attributes which
a creative social entity whether vast or tiny, can
be expected to have."

*"And you will know
the truth, and
the truth will set
you free."
Jesus
[John 8:32]*

As everybody knows, freedom has a thousand
different dimensions. However one interprets it, the
emotional feeling of freedom is extremely important
to most highly creative persons.

SELF-ACCEPTANCE was briefly discussed in Sec. 10-1
under the title Being A Real Person. The psychological
research data on the creative person's self-acceptance
appear contradictory. We have Taylor [330,   p182]

saying the creative person is "more self-accepting" while Saunders [283] finds among engineers with 5-7 years research and development experience with 5 major U.S. corporations that the "researcher seems to be a little more critical, a little less self-accepting."

The route to the best personal mental health appears to be via self-acceptance. Otherwise we are placed in the high entropy generating position of using so much of our psychic energy fighting ourself with little leftover to apply to creative engineering activities.

SUPPRESSION VS EXPRESSION of emotions is, of course, an important issue for the highly creative person. If he suppresses his emotions completely ("I have this feeling here's the way we should solve this problem - -") then obviously his creative output may tend toward zero.

Barron's [27, p148] research on 100 USAF Captains shows "original persons reject suppression as a mechanism for the control of impulse. This would imply that they forbid themselves fewer thoughts, that they dislike to police themselves or others, that they are disposed to entertain impulses and wild ideas that are commonly taboo - -."

The ability to express our emotions in positive senses is both good mental health and can be productive of new creative ideas in our work. But expressing our true feelings may demand a high degree of personal courage to overcome the ingrained suppression tendency. It demands great personal discipline, a subject we've explored numerous times in this book.

THE UNCONSCIOUS MIND is without doubt operative in the creative process, as virtually everyone knows who has studied the creative process in any depth. While it is true most of our ideas form at the conscious level, many solutions to the most difficult problems occur to the creative person via the unconscious mind first and may be first felt emotionally as a vague feeling before it reaches consciousness.

Dufresne-Tasse [84] states that the French attach "Great importance to unconscious forces in the creative process."

"One is constantly
aware that the
conscious mind
does not provide
these solutions."
E. G. Reed
[273, p145]

Sometimes in sleep or semi-sleep the mind at the unconscious level forms new idea combinations. The alert person is aware of this little understood phenomenon and tries to ask himself upon awakening what his emotions and unconscious mind are trying to tell him. He does all within his power to court the process.

DOMINANCE turns up in psychological study after study, according to Taylor [328, p386], who finds that creative persons have "A high degree of personal dominance - -." Barron's [27, p147] research on 100 USAF captains also showed original persons are more self-assertive and dominant.

Dominance, many would say, is an emotional characteristic. Carried too far it can run over into arrogance which some creative people exhibit. Dominance--the "this is the way things will be" attitude--probably is a result of the strong ego possessed by creative persons.

A SENSE OF DESTINY seems to be an emotional trait of many highly creative persons. Tesla felt that it was his destiny to bring into being the entire alternating current power system, the induction motor, resonant circuits and many other useful inventions. Significant numbers of other inventors appear to also have this emotional trait, as a study of biography and history shows.

Bristol [44, p2] observes that "creative people often demonstrate a deep 'sense of mission' and are not as easily deterred from their course of action as their less creative peers."

This emotional trait is obviously coupled to his sense of commitment and perhaps other traits as well, including our next topic.

A SENSE OF SIGNIFICANCE about the work and the product being created seems to permeate the emotions of the highly creative individual. He has a sense of broad perspective and may have some very strong feelings about where his new creation 'fits' in the larger scheme of things. While he may explore significance on the conscious level as indicated in Fig. 4-2 in the Problem Inquiry Phase, there is also a decided emotional tone he exhibits regarding his work.

Rossman [279, p38] observes that "inventors know the value of an improvement." Bristol [44] would measure the significance by the lives it touches. "One way to judge creative ability is to determine how far-reaching the results of a single creative act may be" and "one measure of a person's creativity may be the number of lives he influences through his efforts."

Finally, it is obvious that a creation that directly affects the lives of 200 million people is more significant than one which touches only 10 people.

"(Samuel Morse) had the courage to go through all the hardships, poverty, and discouragement necessary--to demonstrate the commercial possibilities of the telegraph."
Charles F. Kettering [174, p651]

COURAGE is repeatedly a strong emotional characteristic of highly creative people. Bristol [44, p3] finds "creative men and women tend to be highly courageous, unusual and interesting." Rossman [279, p53] observes that "the inventor is therefore courageous and optimistic."

It takes substantial courage to progress through the creative process of Chaps. 3-9, especially if the work is done in a hostile environment or if one is laying out his own funds for the execution of the work. One has to genuinely *believe* in himself, his new ideas, and his problem solving approach to exhibit the noble trait known as courage.

In the final analysis the highly creative person pits himself against existing ways and systems for solving the problem. He is all alone in the rightness of his beliefs and convictions.

Courage has many dimensions as many poets and writers have shown. Kennedy [170] and Woods [382] expose some for those caring to dig deeper.

A SENSE OF AWE AND WONDER--at a deeper personal emotional level--appears present in many--but not all --highly creative persons. It is like an awe that one exists in a universe where one can--seemingly out of nothing (though, we now know that notion is not strictly true, as all ideas are combinations of previously known facts)--create a new product; awe that one lives in a land where freedom to create exists and the process is encouraged; a sense of profound wonder that one can heat houses, cook, and generate electricity from just *sunshine*; a sense of both awe and wonder over why some of the apparatus we create even works in the first place; and a thousand other dimensions it has!

It is surprising most psychologists researching creativity appear to have not identified awe and

"I now see scientific accomplishment as a path, not an end; a path leading to and disappearing in mystery."

Charles A. Lindbergh
[194, p60B]

wonder--that childlike quality--as a trait of creative persons. Only Bristol [44] mentions from his study of *The 100 Most Important People In The World Today* that they had a "sense of wonder" and this was their chief characteristic.

PSYCHIC DISTURBANCES is one aspect of creativity that, fortunately, appears to be waning in recent years in the United States. An earlier view held that a person had to have some kind of psychic disturbance--i.e. tend toward being crazy--in order to create anything new. The French appear to still have this outdated notion, for as reported by Dufresne-Tasse [84], they see "Acceptance of psychic disturbance as an almost inevitable condition or price for genius." As we have shown throughout this entire book, so-called genius and the capacity to create the new is basically a disciplined rational process. It would seem that mental disturbances, therefore, can only impair--and not enhance--the process.

"Worrying is just like running the mill when there is no grist to grind. All that does is to wear out the mill."

Charles F. Kettering
[174, p18]

While it is true that the highly creative person with his wide breadth and scope experiences worry, frustrations, mild depressions from time-to-time, guilt occasionally and many other pathologic signs common to all humanity he manages to keep them under control by exercising good personal discipline. Even a cursory search of the psychology literature turns up volumes dealing with such subjects. We have deliberately not emphasized such pathologic areas in this book, leaving these for the specialist in curing mental disease.

We have thus seen that a person's emotions have a marked effect upon his ability to create the new.

We now explore a related area, his attitudes.

10-9 His Attitudes

THINGS VS PEOPLE 'Things' are generally preferred over 'people' by the highly creative person, as Taylor [326, p385] observes has been found in study after study on productive scientists: "A preference for mental manipulations involving things rather than people: a somewhat distant or detached attitude in interpersonal relations and a preference for intellectually challenging situations rather than socially challenging ones."

The engineer suffers from the same malady for which he has been roundly criticized in recent decades.

The methods of Fig. 4-2 in Problem Inquiry and of
Fig. 7-2 Solution Optimization phases seek to help
us over our blind spots by raising 'people type'
issues important to our creation.

INTEGRITY, HONESTY, AND SINCERITY are usually assumed
present in the highly creative person. We may not
have realized their importance as traits until we
meet someone who has little of these qualities.
Rossman   [279,   p41] records Dr. Elihu Thomson
as saying "strict integrity" is no. 3 in importance to
inventive success on his list.

*"Personal integrity
implies an intrinsic
honesty."
  J. Kenneth Salisbury
  [280, p18]*

HONESTY is required in the creative process
starting with Problem Inquiry--honesty in facing
the initial situation and honestly defining the
problem therein, honesty in assessing the potential
social impacts our new creation may have, honesty
in committing ourselves to solve the problem, and so
on throughout the remaining five steps.

Note that honesty and sincerity was cited in
Sec. 10-1 as one of the attitudes of being a real
person.

OPENNESS AND FOLLOWING TRADITION There is an attitude
of beautiful openness among highly creative persons.
Taylor [330,   p182] observes they are "more open
to the irrational in themselves." Taylor and Barron
[326, 388]   opine that "such a person in science--
must be able to open himself to sources of information
which others deny to themselves."

This openness leads the creative person to
reexamine traditional ideas and ways as Rossman
[279,   p44] observes when he has a prominent
inventor saying it is essential for the inventor to
not be hampered by tradition.

*"Why is the grass
green?"
  Charles F. Kettering
  [174, p190]*

QUESTIONING AND CONFIDENT DOUBTING Arnold   [9, p130]
says that "Questioning is basic and fundamental." It
goes hand-in-hand with confident doubting--we believe
what others are telling us but we doubt them just
enough to check up on the truthfullness of what they
say. This attitude turned up in Rossman's [279,   p39]
study where 176 patent attorneys ranked 'suspicion'
as the number 7 attribute needed in invention.

Note that the questioning attitude has been
woven throughout the various creative process charts
in Chaps. 3-9 as a spur to us and a means for obtaining
needed information.

CONSTRUCTIVE DISCONTENT means we're discontented with things as they are, but we don't stop with dissatisfaction alone. We go beyond to propose *constructive* improvements.

"But Marconi was not satisfied. He still dreamed of sending messages across the seas."
Charles F. Kettering
[174, p53]

The world is full of discontents. It takes that extra something, which the highly creative person has characteristically, to propose improvements. The constructive discontent attitude seems to permeate such persons.

Bristol [44] mentions constructive discontent as one characteristic those had in *The 100 Most Important People In The World Today*. Rossman [279, p44] has a prominent inventor indicating one essential to success is having a desire to better conditions generally.

"A sympathetic friend said to him 'It's too bad to do all of that work for nothing.' 'But it's not for nothing,' said Edison. 'We have got a lot of good results. Look now, we know 700 things that won't work."
Charles F. Kettering
[174, p79]

POSITIVE OUTLOOK AND OPTIMISM Creative people are great optimists. Kettering [174, p3] says "research men are always optimistic - -," and Rossman [279, p39] shows 'optimism' ranked number 8 in importance by 176 patent attorneys. A prominent inventor [p46] believes ability to improve on former inventions is important. Finally, Rossman [279, p36] says the inventor is characterized by 'this-is-the-way-to-do-it" attitude, basically a positive response.

Without optimism and a positive outlook we are doomed, for there are simply too many places in the creative process of Chaps. 3-9 where gloom and despair can enter and conquer our spirits.

This and the previous trait are clearly coupled.

SELF-CONFIDENCE also characterizes the highly creative person--sometime to the point of objectionable arrogance. It is founded on faith--in one's ideas and his ability to execute them successfully. It is what Arnold [9, 129] means by saying "--he must have confidence in himself as one qualified to bring about these improvements." Recall from Table 10-1 self-confidence ranked number 8 in importance by 710 inventors.

Finally, Edel [89,p102] nicely sums it up. "Practice with creative thinking procedures leads to more confidence in their use."

HUMILITY seems the very opposite of self-confidence. Yet it is possible to be both confident and humble. We are confident in our own abilities to solve the problem; yet we're humbled by how little we really know.

All the truly great highly creative persons appear
--if we look deep enough--to have an identifiable
streak of humility in them. The Wright brothers are
an inspiring example.

Humility is one of mankind's more nobler
attitudes or traits.

DETERMINATION is a characteristic attitude of most
highly creative persons. Without it we tend to 'fold
up' when the first difficulties crop up on our creative
project.

*"Howe was determined
to make the demon-
stration so he set
up a shop and
offered to sew
free of charge,
the work brought
to him."
  Charles F. Kettering
  [174, p61]*

Rossman   [279, p47] has a prominent inventor
saying he must have the determination to attain the
objective. And Kettering's   [174, p55] wisdom
on the matter is summed up in "And one thing that the
experiences of Hyatt can teach us is that opportunities
are almost completely controlled by the determination
of the man--and not by his surroundings or the things
with which he has to work."

The trait is obviously related to others, e.g.
motivation, patience, perseverance, and courage.to
name a few. Again we see the difficulties in attempting
to draw hard and fast lines between the traits because
of the overlaps which exist.

There may be other attitudinal traits which also

come into play in the creative process, but the above

appear to be the main ones known as of 1976.

Since one's attitudes are frequently founded on

his values, we explore that topic next.

10-10 His Values

PERSONAL VALUES for the highly creative person appear
to be considerably different from those of their less
creative parent population. The things important to
the creative person tend to have an intangible esthetic
character such as independence, autonomy, and others
which we shall briefly list.

Barron   [31, p159] is speaking of values when
he says "They are thus independent in their cognition
and also *value* clear cognition, so that they will
suffer great personal pains to testify correctly."

"If a man does not keep pace with his companions, perhaps it is because he hears a different drummer. Let him step to the music which he hears, however measured or far away."
        Thoreau

Because he *values* safety for others the disciplined creative engineer thinks through his new product thoroughly to be sure it will be safe under ordinary-use conditions. Because he *values* creative effort, he carefully thinks through 'the need' before plunging into the details of solving a trivial problem. Because he *values* manufacturability, he thinks his design through to the simplest possible state. Because he *values* the feelings of others he seeks their inputs to the design before it is finally firmed up--and so on throughout the process laid out in Chaps. 3-9.

INDEPENDENCE, AUTONOMY, NONCONFORMITY AND LONELINESS are traits valued by the highly creative. Rossman [279, pxx]   says that, in general, creative persons are nonconformists and independent thinkers while Taylor   [330, p182] finds them "more devoted to autonomy" and "more self-sufficient." He also finds [p386] "marked independence of judgment, rejection of group pressures toward conformity in thinking." Finally, Wilson and Wilson   [379, p184] are of the opinion that "By necessity, a good innovator is an independent thinker and doer. He can't be one of the crowd. He must be a lone wolf."

Underneath, perhaps these remarks tell us that the highly creative person *values* his personal freedom very much.

INTUITION AND HUNCHES are other traits valued by the highly creative. Barron   [29, p386] studied Doctoral candidates in the sciences and found "the more highly regarded young scientists are unusually appreciative of the intuitive and nonrational elements in their own nature." Rossman   [279, p47] records a prominent inventor saying "He must possess--feeling for the dynamic and kinetic relations directly rather than through mathematical analysis."

An intuition or hunch is a vague feeling that a certain way is the right way to solve the problem even though it obeys none of the well-known rules of logic. Some of the world's greatest creative giants have had great respect for the role of intuition in the creative process. They *value* it!

"(Hyatt) found a way under heat and pressure, to mold gun cotton together with alcohol and camphor--something no educated chemist would have done at that time. --out of the mold came a hard clear substance he called 'celluloid'--the first of the great family of plastics - -"
        Charles F. Kettering
        [173, p54]

Intuition is related to prior personal history, knowledge, personal sensitivity, emotions, and faith ("It's possible!" idea) among others.

ESTHETICS is an especially valued trait among highly creative persons. It involves an esthetic sensitivity,

as observed by Gough [126].   Taylor   [330, p181]
mentions that creative people have an "intense,
esthetic and moral commitment to their work." Rossman
[279,   p50] says that "we sometimes find an
interesting streak of the artistic and poetic
temperament in inventors" and he goes on to show that
Morse was a landscape painter, Fulton a portrait
painter, Awkwright wrote verses, Watt was a rhymer,
Cartwright wrote poetry, and Da Vinci was an artist.

"The requirement that a product be 'aesthetically pleasing' leaves much room for individual interpretation."
R. J. Rhine
[275, p163]

Perhaps it boils down to the creative person
valuing beauty--in whatever medium he is working. But,
as everyone knows, beauty is in the eye of the beholder.

ELEGANCE may be a kind of esthetics. It implies harmony,
wholeness, and great beauty. Creative people value
it--whatever we call it. Taylor   [328, p386]
mentions that "A drive toward comprehensiveness and
elegance in explanation" are traits which are found in
study after study of productive scientists. Interestingly
in another place   [331, p20] he finds that
"compactness of thinking and expression may be related
to the elegance of the final product"--a testimony to
the importance of language and symbols.

For some, simplification is the pinnacle of
elegance and the term 'elegant simplicity' captures
this notion. Rossman   [279, p44] has a prominent
inventor indicating one essential to inventive success
is "eliminate all unessential details" and another one
emphasizes the "ability to simplify."

The elegance trait may influence the creative
engineer from beginning to end of the creative process.

"--we call it a practical joke. --you will notice that we have no name for its possible counter- part, the theoretical joke."
A. D. Moore
[217, p7]

HUMOR, perhaps surprisingly to some, is a valued trait
among many highly creatives. It helps immensely in
human relationships, as oil helps minimize frictional
losses in an engine.

Appreciation for high quality good humor is so
universal as to need no amplification here, other than
to mention the fact that highly creative persons are
not a humorless lot!

10-11 His Environment And Relationships To It

ENVIRONMENT and how he relates to it are extremely
important matters to the engineer who would create.
He typically works in a corporate environment with all
this implies. It is a highly competitive environment
where it is absolutely *essential* a profit be made for

the enterprise to survive. Thus the principal
larger emphasis is on fiscal matters, a subject with
which many sensitive highly creative persons are
uncomfortable. Others thrive on the excitement
abounding in such an environment.

It is an environment founded on a formal organization, authority of key persons, and the delicate matter
of relationships--including respect and trust--between
the various persons within the organizational hierarchy.

*"Some credit for a
successful job,
perhaps more than
50 per cent, belongs
to the laboratory
employing him."
Harald T. Friis
[113, p55]*

If the organization is too formal and rigid,
creativity perishes. If it is entirely loose little
useful work results from the majority of the people.
It is largely the role of management to get the right
organizational balance. Bristol   [44, p4]
correctly observes that "--a certain minimum amount
of freedom is necessary for creativity to flourish."

There is the matter of having adequate facilities
in the environment for doing the creative work. The
creativity of an engineer may be taxed to the limit
to find ways his creative project can be executed
using available--however inadequate--facilities. Most
significant creative work in engineering is done with
considerably less than ideal facilities, to the surprise
of the typical engineering student. But as Taylor
[331, p29]   correctly affirms, "The creative
individual tries to adjust the environment to him,
to improve it in ways he feels are urgently needed."

Then there is the matter of the physical environment.
Wilson and Wilson   [379, p188] point out that
"Everyone knows that the activity of the mind is
affected by the physical environment. Excessive
heat, excessive cold, or high humidity can lead to
lowered physical and mental activity." The ideal
physical environmental conditions for creativity to
flourish occur within a rather narrow band for each
person.

*"All you have to
do to encourage
inventors is to
love them."
Jacob Rabinow
[266, p90]*

Finally, there are environments which encourage
creativity and those which discourage it both by
words and actions. In this book we have repeatedly
pointed up the important role of encouragement to the
creative process and the person. Fortunate indeed is
the person who is immersed in an environment encouraging
his creativity. The highly creative person relates
well to such an environment and performs at his
highest level.

BUSINESS ABILITY ranked fourth in importance by 710
inventors (Table 10-1). But Rossman   [279, p39]

also showed that the *lack* of business ability by inventors was the fourth most frequent characteristic mentioned by 176 patent attorneys! Thus inventors recognize the importance of business ability but acknowledge they aren't very good at it, even though inventors like Henry Wood Wise [p43] indicate one essential for inventive success is to "have a business mind."

"My Lords are displeased that he thus occupies himself with contrivances, and doth not attend to his trade - -"
  Nuremberg Council Decree, 1569
  [404, p155]

This general area, like so many of the decades of other creative traits we've exposed in this Chap., is another where we engineers must work at improving ourselves the rest of our lives--lifelong learning again. Ideally the highly creative person would exhibit much business acumen--in addition to all the *other* traits we've identified.

PRACTICALITY at the personal level ought to be a hallmark of the highly creative engineer. Unfortunately, we're collectively frequently less than ideal on this trait, especially when the new creative project nears the manufacturing stage. Rossman   [279, p46] succinctly mentions that "ability to build something which can be manufactured as well as made in a laboratory" is important. Finally, he has a prominent inventor saying that ability to determine manufacturing costs is important.

"It is one thing to produce something in the laboratory test tubes and another to manufacture it by the ton."
  Charles F. Kettering
  [173, p121]

It is on the practicality issue that the important notion of a proposed embodiment--"make it like this"-- comes to the forefront. Creation of practical embodiments was treated in Chap. 6.

HIS SHARING ABILITY comes into play with the relationships the highly creative person has with selected colleagues. We cited in Sec. 10-9 the 'openness' trait. Its natural outgrowth is the desire to share problems and results with friends and selected colleagues. The desire to share just seems to gush out when a person has created something new which works as intended.

The opposite of sharing, naturally, is to remain secretive and suspicious of all around one and to turn inward. Carried far enough such traits lead to a form of mental illness. How *beautiful* is its opposite--to share one's creative treasures! It also tends to promote good personal relationships with one's colleagues; but it may get us into trouble in patent matter if we share with others too soon.

SALESMANSHIP, TALKATIVENESS AND COMMUNICATIONS are natural outgrowths from one's sharing trait except that with salesmanship there is a specific goal--to

'sell' someone our creative idea(s) to the point
they will *act* on them.

Rossman   [279, p45] has a prominent inventor
saying 'salesmanship' is second on his list of
essentials to the inventor. Another [p46] says he
must "have the ability to demonstrate the value
of his invention." It translates to salesmanship.
As everyone knowns, salesmen tend to be talkative.
Saunders   [283] found on 'talkativeness' some
tendency for engineers with 5-7 years research and
development to be rated higher when they are more
talkative and can express their ideas. Finally,
Wilson and Wilson   [379, p187] emphasize that
"--a good innovator must be able to communicate. He
must present his ideas clearly and defend them
against attack. Almost always, ideas are attacked
(at least in the beginning)."

These traits particularly enter into the
Disciplined Creativity process at the end of the
Problem Inquiry Phase (Chap. 4) and throughout the
Convince Others Phase (Chap. 9).

RELATIONSHIPS WITH OTHERS involve, as Taylor [330,
p182] indicates "socialization and interpersonal
involvement tendencies." But as Rossman [279,
pxx] observes "In general, the truly creative person
is not a good organization man." Nevertheless the
creative person has *some* kind of relationships--good
or bad--with those who are a part of his environment.

Perhaps needless to say, one key element of good
relationships with others is genuine and honest
respect. Because we respect the opinions of a
component engineer we ask his advice and comments
on a circuit problem we have. He gives it to us, and
we establish a relationship between us based on
respect.

Then the engineer has some kind of relationship
with those in administrative authority over him--his
supervisor or manager. He also has to relate to
people working for him, as secretaries, technicians,
and model makers. Then he must relate well to people
from other organizations who have a legitimate interest
in his new creation. Such people are frequently met
for the first time in meetings and conferences.

All of these people to whom we relate--in some
strong or weak form--react to our total personality.
They can, and usually will, sense rather early whether
we are facade or 'a real person' discussed in Sec. 10-1.

*"These men who
have turned the
world upside down
have come here
also."*
   [Acts. 17:6]

*"In my humble
opinion, however,
the best tool
available for
human engineering
still is, and will
continue to be, the
Golden Rule."*
   Samuel R. Sapirie
   [282, p3]

A good sense of honest humor can be an enormous personal asset in our relationships with others.

Discussion Topics

1.   Do emotions really have any place in the objective profession of engineering?

2.   How will you deal with having a strong emotional feeling to 'go fishing' when there is much creative work needing doing?

3.   How do you get 'in the mood' to do serious creative work?

4.   Is there any 'best time of day' for you when creative work seems easiest?

5.   How might you react upon receiving word that higher management has cancelled all work immediately on your significant project?

6.   Is courage related to awareness? Explore.

7.   How would you react if your Manager told you derogatorily, "The trouble with you is you have *convictions* and you *live* by them instead of fitting in with everyone else."?

8.   What role, if any, does 'positive outlook' play in solving a well defined difficult engineering problem?

9.   What is a 'pet idea'? How do you relate such 'irrational' ideas to the concept of a *disciplined* creative engineer?

10. What is 'a hunch'?

11. Where do we get hunches?

12. Are hunches of any real value to the creative engineer?

14. Do emotions influence hunches in anyway?

15. Can we stimulate our ability to conceive hunches?

16. What, if anything, can be done about the mountains of uncreative 'paper work' we get bogged down with in some environments?

17. Overall, this Chap. cited many traits of the highly creative person. Not much was said about *how* we might acquire some of these traits. How might we go about it?

Exercises

10-E 1. Search out John Gardner's excellent little book [116].   Read it. Write a two page abstract of your principal findings.

10-E 2. Reread this entire Chap. in one sitting. Write a brief essay on the kind of person you honestly aspire to be after studying this Chapter. Make it *personal*.

10-E 3. Prepare a list of environmental factors that tend to stifle your creativity in a corporate environment.

10-E 4. Ditto but for an independent inventor.

10-E 5. The Chap. presented nearly a hundred traits of the highly creative person. Select five which you think are the *most* important to being an engineer. Justify *why* these are most important.

10-E 6. Next time the telephone rings in your environment, pause to consciously decide whether you *feel* like answering it. Make a specific decision. Afterwards write down how you *felt*. What, if anything, does this exercise say about automation negating us as persons?

10-E 7. Here are four specific practical ways I intend to continue my lifelong learning process after graduating: (List. Briefly discuss each).

Chapter Summary

● An integrating perspective via Eq. 1 tied the important motivation and personal factors to our efficiency in solving creative engineering problems.

● We explored what it means to be a real person.

● Then we identified nearly a hundred personal traits that ideally the highly creative person would possess. These were the heart of the Chapter. Other traits undoubtedly exist; but we have the main ones in hand here.

●   We saw that there are *many*, *many*, specific
traits that a highly creative person either
exhibits or has above average skill in and
that those possessing the simplistic view that
only a *few* personal factors must be optimized
are badly misinformed or labor under a delusion.

●   We close by marveling that we are endowed by
the Creator with so many divine-like intensely
personal traits which permit us to actively
participate in the beautiful creative process as
we traverse this life. What majestic gifts we
possess!

●   The Chap. has been somewhat longer than other
Chaps. because of both the vastness of the subject
and its inherent delicate personal nature.

Thus we close Part III--Personal Factors--and

enter Part IV which deals with Other Facets of

Disciplined Creativity. These are less personal.

They along with Part III materials, all relate back

to the Six Step Approach methodology of Part II and

seek to reinforce our ability to successfully apply

it.

PART IV

OTHER FACETS OF
DISCIPLINED CREATIVITY

CHAPTER 11

INFORMATION AND DISCIPLINED CREATIVITY

"The engineer uniquely creates systems and products
based on his information."
Thomas T. Woodson [383, p37]

● Relations between information and problem
solving approach.

● Identifying the information needed.

● Sources of information.

● Finding the information.

● The information.

● Using it.

● Omission of information gathering.

11-1 <u>Introduction</u>

The words 'information', 'knowledge', and
'truth' are akin. Flesch [106, p119] shows that
originally "*Truth* means simply and merely--that
which is trowed... . It is the past participle
of the verb *to trow--to think*, *to believe firmly*,
to be thoroughly persuaded of ... . Truth presupposes
mankind - - -." Knowledge, Webster [373] says,
implies acquaintance with fact or the state of being
aware of something or of possessing information. He
also says information implies knowledge, intelligence,
facts, or data of an event or situation.

For our purposes we define 'information' as
intelligence, facts, data, or knowledge, particularly
as these relate to the problem and its solution being
created. A further implication is that we need

*"Facts are obser-
vations that
competent observers
will agree upon."
Joseph H. Simons
[294]*

356   Disciplined Creativity

"It is possible to fly without motors, but not without knowledge and skill."
  Wilbur Wright
  [391, p15]

information we trust. We instinctively realize our general need for information and that in some vague way its possession may aid us in engineering problem solving. Conversely its absence may impair our creativity.

Information may be classified as verbal, written, symbolic, and graphic.

The relationship between information and the disciplined creative problem solving approach is shown in Fig. 11-1.

At each major phase we require the personal 'input' of information. The kind and amount of information we need varies from phase to phase. If we are creating a new solar heater for homes, we might need information in 'problem inquiry' on types of houses, living patterns of occupants, acceptable costs and similar information. Later in 'construction and verification' our need might be for specific information on the life of materials exposed to sunlight or how to motivate craftsmen and technicians.

We may also have a need for information, perhaps from our notebook (Chap. 15), in connection with patents (Chap. 18) and communicating (Chap. 12).

"The mind of him who has under-standing seeks knowledge, inquires after and craves it, - - "
  Proverbs 15:14
  [5]

Our insatiable personal need for information is of an on-going lifetime nature and vitally linked to our creative self renewal (Chap. 10). Obviously,

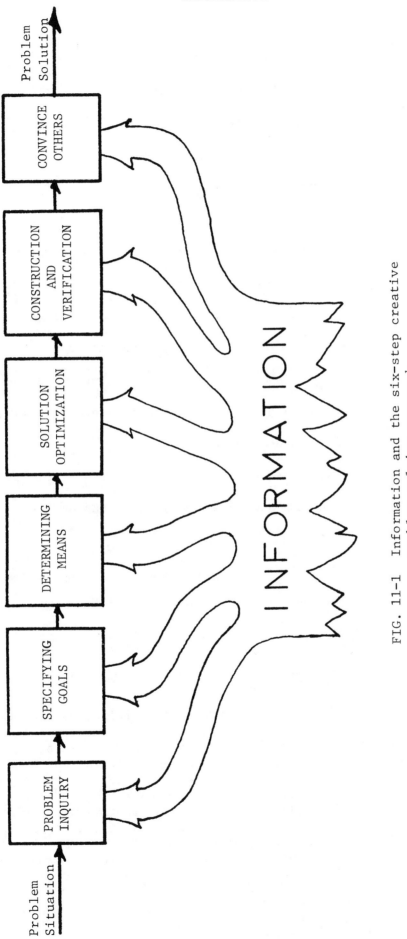

FIG. 11-1   Information and the six-step creative
problem solving approach.

we can only scratch the surface here of the

enormous subject of 'information'. Additional

viewpoints are in Woodson [383], Wilson [378],

Hawkins [141] and others.

11-2 Identifying The Information Needed

One of our first problems is to identify the

general or specific information we *think* we need to

help us get on with creating the new solution.

There are two extremes: (1) the engineer who needs

no new information; (2) the engineer who needs to

know 'everything about everything'. Neither extreme

gets the problem solution created optimally, if at

all. One misses the needed key facts. The other

fails to recognize the need for selectivity, i.e.

identifying the *specific* information needed and

going after *it* only.

The sequence of relevant questions suggested

in Table 11-1 may help identify the information

needed for our specific problem.

Example 11-1

*"He usually realizes
there are a great
many things he
doesn't know."
Thomas T. Woodson
[383, p67]*

A mechanical engineer in the 'problem inquiry'
phase is thinking about creating an all solar
powered house (heating, air conditioning, electricity)
as a means of reducing pollution and conserving
precious fossil fuel. He recognizes he needs
specific factual information on sunlight intensity
vs time of day and year for his particular location.
Intensity is a vital parameter strongly influencing
his new solution proposals. The problem is not
solvable without the intensity information. If
he 'guesses', he risks creating an unworkable

- Do I need additional information? Why?

- Is the problem solvable without it?

- What risks are entailed if I don't get it?

- What will having it probably contribute
  to the solution?

- Specifically, what information is needed?

- Does it probably exist?

- What will it cost to get it?

- How long will it probably take?

- Would I believe and act on it if I had it?

TABLE 11-1   Helpful questions for identifying the
             information needed at a specific point
             in the creative problem solving process.

solution. Having it will determine the required
solar collector area and the system cost.
Specifically he needs to know normal intensity
vs time curves for sunlight for clear days and
for a range of cloud cover conditions. Such
information probably exists, he thinks, and could
be obtained most authoritatively, quickly, and
at low cost from NASA, the US weather service,
or the International Solar Energy Society.

It is axiomatic that information needed to help

solve the problem cannot be retrieved, if it even

exists, unless it is first identified. Thus the

problem solver's creative role is again underscored.

Only *after* it has been identified do we proceed to

determine the likely sources.

We should realize, particularly when we create

in newer areas, that the information sought may

not exist and cannot be retrieved.

Example 11-2

The Wright brothers searched for trustworthy
information on a maximum lift aircraft wing.
The information existing was wrong, correct
information did not exist, and the need for generating
their own experimental information is history [388].

We may not *know* the information doesn't exist, however,

unless we perform a search for it.

11-3 Sources of Information

Assuming the information needed has been

identified and that it probably exists, we face the

problem of "what source(s) most probably has it?"

Our thinking is to first examine the source(s) having

the highest probability of success, since our time

and effort are precious.

Some factors to consider in choosing where to look include:

- Kind of information needed.

- Scope of information needed.

- Ease of initiating the request and using the source.

- Reputation for truthfulness, accuracy, and clarity of the source.

- Whether the source agency, company, or person is known to be active in the area of information sought.

Example 11-3

A mechanical engineer needs theoretical information on the maximum heat flux a 'heat pipe' can carry. He wants to use the heat pipe as a component in a larger system he is creating. Since the information sought is theoretical in nature and the heat pipe is relatively new, he might consider looking in the physics literature, e.g. the *Journal of Applied Physics*, or in some of the engineering literature dealing with new advanced energy conversion methods e.g. the *Intersociety Energy Conversion Engineering Conference Proceedings*. Both sources likely contain reliable technical papers by workers active in heat pipes.

"You need the ability to locate the right source - - -"

Ira G. and Marthann E. Wilson [378, p64]

When trying to decide where to look for the needed information, it is helpful to have a collection of the principal sources available. Otherwise we tend to get lost in detailed branches of the information storage hierarchy. Such a collection is in Table 11-2.

● Yourself
    Prior experience.
    Previous observations.
    Memory.
    Personal files, notebooks,
      publications.
    Prior experiments.

● Colleagues
    Talk with them.
    Their technical reports.
    Private correspondence (letters).

● Management
    Past and current developments.
    Who is doing what and results.
    Confidential sources.
    General guidance.

● Technical Journals and Magazines
    These are largest single major
      source of current information
      in any field. Many exist.
    Information in interest sphere
      of its readers.

● Newspapers
    General interest.
    Technical digests.

● Technical Books
    Related to specific
      areas.

● Professional Societies
    Abstracts.
    Relevant technical papers.
    Specialized indexes.
    Search services.
    Translations.

● Other Firms
    Competitors.
    Manufacturers.
    Vendors
      Catalogs.
      Samples
      Trade literature.
    Known experts.
    Plant visits.

● Conferences/Seminars/Institutes
    Attendance.
    Personal contacts established.
    Published Proceedings.

● Library
    Catalog.
    Reference work.
    Engineering indexes.
    Repository of much
      information.

● Government
    Technical Reports
      (From many agencies).
    Patents.

● Foundations and Institutes
    Technical papers,
      periodicals.

● Universities
    Faculty publications
      in specific areas.

● Consultants
    Technical specialists.

● Client
    Proprietary information.
    Problem facts.

TABLE 11-2   Broad classification of some sources
             of information frequently useful
             to the creative engineer.

*"Develop a honeybee
mind, gathering
ideas everywhere
and associating
them fully."
  Don C. Hoefler
  [152]*

The source[1] choice is a matter of judgment, and there are no hard and fast rules. On a large engineering problem spanning several years we might draw from all the sources. For a short duration small problem we might use only one source. We should be alert, however, to the possibility that information from a single source may have a limited view whereas information from multiple sources may be more objective.

Example 11-4

An aggressive engineer with a well-known company proposed that his department create and manufacture the solenoid valves for its new washing machines. Management agreed and the creative processes were initiated. After many months, major technical difficulties, and expending thousands of dollars the project floundered and was stopped. Solenoids were bought from a vendor specializing in this type component. Had both the engineer and his manager initially obtained information from several existing sources on the technical and manufacturing problems of such valves, they would have arrived at the objective view of buying the valves. Thus their creative effort was wasted--largely because of inadequate initial information.

*" - - the lack of
necessary information
can be disastrous."
  Ira G. and Marthann
  Wilson [378, p59]*

Disciplined problem solvers culminate this initial part of information retrieval with crisp decisions, e.g. "I think the best source is probably examining the catalogs of companies manufacturing

_____."

---

[1]A study of known laws and effects [150] has been a helpful source for some problem solvers in evoking new idea combinations.

11-4 <u>Finding</u> <u>the</u> <u>Information</u>

Finding the specific information we want is

"*I advise you to
- - - reading
everything in the
original and not
in translations.*"
*Thomas Jefferson
[158, p33]*
generally difficult, tedious, frustrating, and time

consuming. The creative engineer frequently wishes

for an idealized centralized worldwide data bank

from which he could obtain instant and complete recall

of desired information. Since such facilities are not

yet created[1], we must use sub-optimal present methods.

" - - *information
costs time and
money* - - "
*Thomas T. Woodson
[383, p69]*
From the beginning we should realize that *time* is

required to find the information we want. We should

therefore not expect the impossible, e.g. a copy of the

technical paper we want in the Library of Congress to

be on our desk today. With skill in knowing your way

around with a specific information source you will

find ways of speeding up the acquisition process.

We now briefly treat means of retrieving the

needed information. The details are best found by

each problem solver.

THE TELEPHONE is one of the best means of quickly

finding general and specific information--if you or

your project can afford it. Many engineers need to

rediscover it! Why should you spend costly effort and

time running extensive tests to determine specific

properties of a material when the information

could be had by a five minute telephone conversation

---

[1]
Computer techniques are advancing in this area.
Some organizations are, in 1971, able to perform
limited computerized literature searches complete
with abstract print-outs.

with an expert in the materials field? Using it

effectively is predicated on finding, from some

source, the name of a specific individual within an

organization most likely to have the desired infor-

mation. He may be within our own firm, the author of

a paper we studied, a person we met at a conference,

an individual our management or colleagues suggested,

or someone whose name we found in an organization

chart whose title indicates he may have information

in the desired area. Woodson [383, p72] identifies

helpful strategy to use in the actual call.

KNOWING THE SYSTEM for where the information is stored

is essential.

Example 11-5

" - - *knowing your way around a library is a valuable part of your training as a problem solver."*
Edward Hodnett
[151, p48]

In a library 'the system' involves looking
in a catalog (itself a large, complex, and detailed
index), finding the identifying numbers, and
physically locating the book or article. Alternatively
we may start by examining one of the large number
of engineering indexes available in book form,
many with helpful abstracts.

Example 11-6

To retrieve information from some government
agencies, 'the system' is to first subscribe to an
indexing service or list of current publications.
From these the specific documents we want may be
ordered by number for a small fee.[1]

Example 11-7

In technical journals and magazines 'the system'
involves finding the subject or author index (usually
published annually in one issue of the journal),
locating the year and month of the sought article,
and finding the article.

---

[1] Another useful source for finding unclassified technological information
available from the Federal government is Olken's book [230].

Sometimes knowing 'the system' is itself such

a complex task that specialists are necessary. The

U.S. Patent Office is an example. Large companies have

their own staffs of specialists skilled in performing

patent searches for the creating engineer back in a

company division.

USING ASSISTANCE of others frequently is best in

finding the information we seek. The librarian is

there to assist you. They want to do so! When we

make our specific need known we may be pleasantly

surprised to learn their suggestions put us on the

trail of finding the information we want. Such

assistance can save fruitless and costly searching.

Example 11-8

While creating a new concept for a solar-
electric energy converter [19, p73   ] at Goddard
Space Flight Center, I felt the need for information
on the structure, lengths, diameters, wavelength
response, and other information on human eye retinas.
A helpful librarian said that information was not
available in that fine library! She mentioned where
I would find it. I would have spent hours vainly
searching had I not sought competent assistance.

"Our prospecting should also cover duds, for good ideas are often un-covered by digging into causes of failure."
  Alex F. Osborn
  [234, p143]

Talking over our problems of finding the desired

information with colleagues and friends may also be

helpful. They may be aware of hints on finding it

which we don't know about.

SOME BARRIERS may exist once we've found the desired

information. It may be in a journal and the library

policy is to permit no journals to be checked out.

It may need to be duplicated but the machine is

broken down today. It may cost money to obtain a

copy and we don't know the correct account number

to use--or only cash is accepted and we have no means

of such direct payment in our organization. It may be

on microfiche[1] and a 'reader' is not available. It may

require excessive paperwork because of the specialness

of the document. It may be 'classified' and we are

not qualified to examine it--or we may have the wrong

type of clearance. These and many more barriers

may trip us up before we have *in hand* the needed

information. There is no magic for solving these, but

patience, persistence, and courtesy will enable us

to surmount such barriers. They seem larger at the

moment than they really are.

STOPPING THE RETRIEVAL process usually has to be

reached as a clean-cut decision. Either we realize

we have found enough information for our problem and

can stop or there is endless more possible to find

but we cannot justify continued searching.

11-5 The Information

ITS FORM may not be most immediately useful. It may

be printed with faint type or wrong color ink to

reproduce well. It may be stored verbally (records,

tapes, etc.) so we have to listen to chaff to get

at what we need. It may be in a foreign language

----

[1] A means of photographically shrinking a dcoument.

we can't read and have no one who can. It may

be microfilm or microfiche and our reader is difficult

to use and even more difficult to obtain a reproduction

of the specific sketch or part we want. It may be

an intensely theoretical paper much over our head

and we need a good abstract and summary; but none

was included. The page sizes may be too large or

small for reproduction of the part we want. It,

overall, may be "soft" information and we need "hard"

information[1]. These difficulties, and more, have all

been experienced by creative engineers preceding you.

We simply accept the information in the form published

and go from there as seems best.

ITS CONTENT CLAIMS may be most important in solving

our problem.

*"Reading provides
far better creative
exercise when we
make notes as
we go."
  Alex F. Osborn
  [234, p77]*

> Does its author claim: The information
> is fact? Opinion? An untried concept?
> He built and verified it? He is first to
> create it? It's patented? It only works
> over some range of parameter values?
> It has been optimized? He has solved
> all the problems--or even the principal
> ones? He has the correct model and
> assumptions?

It can be an eye-opener to examine the retrieved

information from the view "What does this author

claim?" Such a scholarly thoughtful examination

---

[1]
Woodson [383, p44]   defines 'soft' information as
generally nebulous, qualitative, verbal, transient,
not necessarily verifiable or some combination
of these. 'Hard' information is verifiable,
unambiguous, permanent, documentable, numerical,
checked by several sources, or it has some combination
of these attributes.

requires time but can yield rich rewards and aid

in avoiding failure possibilities on the problem

solution we are trying to create.

CHECKING may be essential before we use it in

"Much of what we 'know' is untrue." Edward Hodnett [151, p42]

solving our particular problem. We may take the

position of 'confident doubters'--we are initially

confident the author's information is correct but

we doubt it just enough to check it by raising

private questions and seeking satisfying answers.

Checking is treated in Chap. 16.

11-6 <u>Using It</u>

RELEVANCE TO MY PROBLEM for the retrieved information

"However, knowledge alone, - - never gives rise to new inventions or industries. It is usually left to the inventor to utilize the facts and principles of science, and to apply them for practical purposes." Joseph Rossman [279, p19]

can be established best by the creative problem

solver arriving at that precious new combination of

ideas. Some questions I might deal with after finding

and studying the retrieved information include:

- ● Do I really understand the principal point(s) made by the authors of this information?

- ● Are the assumptions made in the newly found information the correct ones? Why? Which ones, if any, need challenging

- ● Do I have *all* the facts?

- ● Do I have too little information?

- ● What information is missing?

- ● Do I need to retrieve and study any references cited in the new information?

- ● Am I saturated with too many and possibly irrelevant 'facts'?

> ● When the information is applied to my
>   particular problem will it violate any
>   known engineering principles or physical
>   law?
>
> ● Can I creatively twist the information
>   into a new mode or regime, not envisioned
>   by the information's author, permitting its
>   use in *my* problem?

We should be aware that even mature creative
engineers go through the entire information acquisition
chain, and may after studying a piece of new information discard it as irrelevant to their problem.
There is generally much chaff.

MY ATTITUDES TOWARD IT may significantly affect my
use of the new information. If I am destructively
critical, the new information probably won't be of
much help on my problem. Conversely, if I exhibit
constructive open attitudes the probability of my
forming new useful idea combinations from it is enhanced. Attitudes are treated in Chap. 10.

*" - - education
is not knowledge."
Charles F.
Kettering
[172]*

LEGAL PROBLEMS possibly may result from using the
new information. The informed engineer is aware
of the need for paying royalties to the rightful
owner of an invention if he decides to appropriate
the information of its content into solving his
own problem. For some information acquired we may
feel ethically bound--legal in some cases--to obtain
'permission' of the owner as for copyrighted materials
before we use the new information. The problem solver

also occasionally acquires proprietary information
for which there may be legal problems if used
intentionally or unintentionally in his new creation.

Just because a piece of information has been
published does not necessarily imply we may use it
without possible legal ramifications. Patents (Chap. 18)
may cover the rights. Copyrights may cover other
information.

11-7 Omission of Information Gathering

We have, to this point, suggested that the
creative problem solver has a general need for
acquiring new information with which to form new idea
combinations for solving problems. There may be
rare exceptions, however, when information gathering
is deliberately *not* done.

Example 11-9

When one is creating in an entirely *new* area
in which he, from his general knowledge of the
area, knows there is no prior art, he may decide
it is pointless to spend major time and effort
searching for prior information. After I created
the concept for the first Solar Electric Motor
(SEM) and, with the aid of a graduate student, was
reducing it to practice, I felt from my knowledge
of motors and solar cells nothing like SEM had been
created previously. A literature search verified
no publication of a similar motor.

Example 11-10

In the early 50's the 6AJ4 RF amplifier tube
was created by several of us in a development
engineering organization [154]. It was the
first low cost tube of its kind capable of operating
up to 1000 Mhz for the UHF Television band. When
we started, our manager whom we greatly respected
called us in and said, "You men are going to create

*"This is like a
group of fellows
who are going on
a long **trip** and
don't want to
start out with
packs on their
backs which con-
tain a lot of things
they will not
use... . Let's you
and me go up and
survey the road
first without any
packs on our backs."
Charles F. Kettering
[174, p101]*

the first low cost RF amplifier tube for the new
UHF band. I place two constraints on you:
(1) it shall be capable of being mass produced
on existing tube manufacturing machines and (2) you
are not to look in *any* books!" Several months
later and after many failures we brought back the
first successful model we had created. He replied,
"Fine! *Now* you may look in the books!" We did and
found to our amazement statements made to the
effect that the upper frequency limit of glass
type tubes was about 250 Mhz. Had we known this
information *before* starting the developments,
it is doubtful we would have been able to create a
new tube type. The opinions of 'the experts' would
have weighted us down. We didn't know beforehand it
couldn't be done! So we generated our own information
and created it!

"What you call a
fact may with
good reason not
seem a fact to
the other fellow."
Edward Hodnett
[151, p50   ]

We cite these exceptions for the purpose of

showing there *may* be rare situations when creativity

is enhanced by *not* acquiring previous information! The

risks of acquiring vs not acquiring information should

be appraised by you and your management in light of your

particular problem situation.

Discussion Topics

1. "I can create new ideas without 'information'.
    The topic is irrelevant to creativity." Discuss.

2. In view of the information explosion what techniques
    do you propose to use in future practice of
    engineering to make information more accessible
    to you?

3. A colleague has specific information on integrated
    circuits needed by you in creating a new electronic
    system. He is reluctant to give it to you and is
    downright obnoxious. How will you obtain the
    information?

4. Discuss the pros and cons of obtaining engineering
    information verbally vs in writing. Especially
    discuss the case where things later go wrong
    and the verbalizers say, "I **never** told you that
    information."

5. Discuss where engineering knowledge comes from, how it is reported, stored, and how current textbooks are. Are journals and magazines more current?

6. Cite an engineering project where inadequate information was accumulated early in the project. What were the consequences?

7. From Table 11-2 select one source. What difficulties may you have with it getting the information you want? How can these be minimized.

8. How will you know when to stop retrieving information?

9. How can an engineer rapidly test information to divide fact from opinion?

Exercises

11-E1. Fig. 11-1 showed we need information in each of the six major phases of creative problem solving. Select one phase, go back to its detailed chart guide (e.g. Fig. 4-2), and prepare a written list of *all* the places where the creative engineer needs 'information'.

11-E2. Focus on a professional journal in your discipline. Find and abstract a single problem which was solved in a new, unusual, or novel way.

11-E3. Prepare a list of names of *all* the assignee companies in the calendar year _____ to whom patents on burglar alarms were assigned by their inventors. (Hint: *Official Gazette* of the U.S. Patent Office.)

11-E4. Prepare a list of patent numbers, titles, and issue dates for fire detection means during the calendar year _____.

11-E5. Prepare or obtain a neat list of titles of *all* the journals in your engineering discipline area which most interests you and which may be helpful in future creative work therein.

Chapter Summary

● The role information plays in orderly creative problem solving was briefly explored.

●   The engineer has the problems of identifying
the needed information, finding the most
likely source, retrieving, interpreting, and
finally--the most important--creatively *using*
the information.

●   Engineers who repetitively create truly *new*
things make information acquisition a lifelong
dynamic activity, providing fuel for further
new ideas.

CHAPTER 12

TECHNICAL COMMUNICATING

"Engineering investigations evidently are of no
value, unless they can be communicated to those
to whom they are of interest."
           Charles Proteus Steinmetz [317, p290]

● Our communications need.

● The communications process.

● Inquiry into our communications.

● Communication goals.

● Means of communicating.

● Optimizing communications.

● Reproduction and distribution.

● Follow-up.

● Common errors.

12-1 Our Need For Effective Communications

        Whether we work with a large firm or an independent

engineering business we'll certainly have to frequently

communicate before the new product is created and

used. The disciplined engineer finds himself communicating

throughout the six-step creative process of Fig. 3-1.

        We need information about the problem situation

*"But he who
practices truth
--comes out into
the light; so
that his works
may be plainly
shown to be what
they are - -"
 John 3:21
 [5]*

from others; we discuss our early creative concepts

with selected colleagues; a written proposal (it later

becomes a legal contract) may have to be generated

for management or a sponsor communicating the proposed

creative work; management wants to know and participate

in the setting of the goals or specifications for what

is to be created; we may communicate with people

inside and outside our firm about our proposed means
for solving the problem; we communicate with purchasing
and suppliers for catalogs, parts, materials, instrumentation
and orders; we communicate with machinists, craftsmen,
and technicians how we want our model built, modified,
and tested; we communicate with patent people; we may
write operation and service manuals, thereby communicating
with installers, users, and service people; managers,
sponsors of the work and colleagues must be kept
informed of our progress; we communicate with ourselves
via past records, tests, and data taken on our new
creation; finally, we communicate to 'others' the worth
of our ideas and the need for *using* the new creation.

Clearly we have a *daily* need for effective **two-way**
communications in creative problem solving! In them
we are attempting to *reveal* thought--both ours and others--
so ideas become tangible and *understood*.

Effectiveness in our engineering communications
may:

● Maximize our contributions

● Minimize confusion and costly wasted effort

● Significantly improve the technical state-of-the-
art

● Improve our reputation

● Engender personal peace and harmony with colleagues

● Increase our value to the firm

*"--he should rush
to the boss
immediately with
all good news."
Harald T. Friis
[113,   p52]*

*"Engineering
students should
understand early
in their formal
training that
written and oral
communications
are as much an
engineering tool
as a basic
engineering
fundamental."
Martin J. Caserio
[55]*

● Open promotion doors:

    ▲ In our technical field
    ▲ In management

● Increase our lifetime earnings.

Obviously we have a considerable *personal*

stake in our ability to communicate well!

"--what is called style in writing or speaking is formed very early in life, - -"
Thomas Jefferson
[160]

Communications expertise, as seen for so many

other facets of creativity, is an intensely *personal*

matter. Knowledge, art, and skill acquired through

practice are the essential personal ingredients.

Some communications knowledge can be acquired here--a

few of the more important aspects; but you only get

introduced to practicing in the university. You have

the rest of your professional life to *practice*

effective communications!

"The ability to communicate, orally or on paper, is conspicuously lacking in most engineers. The rewards for those engineers who have this skill are almost unbelievable."
Howard F. Peckworth
[244, p1113]

Historically engineers have been collectively

and individually criticized by managers and others

outside of engineering for sub-optimal ability to

communicate effectively. Engineering communications

breakdowns are sometimes widely manifest to others

in the form of failures, seriously detracting from

the individual engineer and the profession.

12-2 The Communications Process

THE ELEMENTARY MODEL of the basic communications

process is in Fig. 12-1.

The model is adapted from communications theory

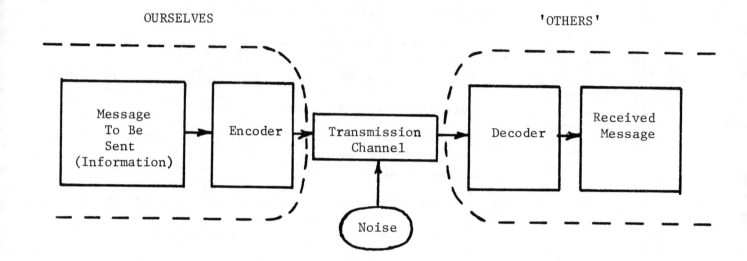

FIG. 12-1 Simplified model of the basic communications
          process and its relevance to ourselves and
          'others'. A more complete model would
          include the reverse process from 'others'
          back to ourselves, adding the vital element
          of feedback and making it a bilateral
          process. A still more sophisticated
          model would include information storage.

"Communicate to impart, bestow, or convey; to make known; to give by way of information."
  Webster
  [373]

"One must have feedback if communications are to mean anything."
  Chester M. Sinnett
  [303, p20]

well-known to electrical engineers. It's the functional basis of many operative physical communications systems of the non-storage class, e.g. television, radio, telemetry and others. From the physical model we can learn much by analogy about our interpersonal communications.

We may have a new thought ('message' or 'information') to communicate to someone else, i.e. 'others'. We encode it verbally in our mind, engage our speech organs and transmit* an audible signal launched toward 'others'. The transmission channel is air. External noises, e.g. a jet aircraft, may enter the transmission channel polluting the original signal. In spite of the 'noise pollution', if the signal-to-noise ratio is high enough the decoder of 'others' can detect and intelligibly decode it as the received message, perhaps filtering some but not all the noise.

A similar system from 'others' back to ourselves is operative for providing feedback, i.e. determining errors and making it a two-way process.

A similar model could be constructed for visual communications where the transmission channel is in a shorter wavelength range, i.e. visible light. The

---

* We are using the term 'encoder' here loosely to also include the 'transmitter'. It would naturally show up in a more detailed model.

functional ideas are similar to Fig. 12-1, however.

Naturally the actual models for the communication

process between people are much more complex. They

are being researched by scientists and engineers and

involve modeling the human brain [378, Ch. 9].

But the simple ideas of Fig. 12-1 are enough, by

analogy, for us to more effectively *use* the communication

process in our creative engineering work, particularly

if we explore the system limitations.

SOME PRACTICAL LIMITATIONS in the communications process

may be gleaned by analogy from the theory of such

systems. We may encounter:

- Too Complex A Signal to be transmitted. The
  system can't pass it or passes it poorly.
  ("Why doesn't he use words and symbols I can
  understand?")

- Distortion within the system occurs at one or
  several places because of imperfect encoders,
  transmission channel, or decoders. ("I've
  had this eye trouble.")

- Information Rate is too high or low for the bandwidth
  of the system causing a distorted received
  signal. ("He's lecturing so *fast*, I'm lost!")

- Noise enters the system, either as shown or at
  other places, e.g. within the message. ("This
  man's thinking isn't very clear.")

- Magnitudes of signal and noise may be too large,
  blocking the system and causing it to not work.
  Conversely the signal may be small and undetectable.
  ("I can't hear him.")

- Part(s) Not Turned On, i.e. some part(s) of the
  system may, for various reasons, not be on
  and operative. ("I'm *tired* of listening to
  him.")

Clearly for effective communications the above

effects must be minimized. Also equally clear is that

the *entire* system must be functionally optimized and

not just a single sub-system.

Example 12-1

A beautifully done 'message' on a slide sequence
clearly describing our newly created product has
been generated but 'others' are 'turned-off' from
tiredness. They've been sitting through three days
of technical paper presentations with ours the last
one on Friday afternoon at 5:30 P.M.

Timing, noise, prior history, tiredness--all
contribute to failure of the *system*.

We sense what experienced creative engineers have

long known--that making a formal technical presentation

requires simultaneous optimization of *many* variables

to get our message across!

12-3 Inquiry Into Our Communications

*"If you would
  not be forgotten
As soon as you are
  dead and rotten,
Either write things
  worth reading
Or do things worth
  the writing."
Poor Richard*

Before racing off 'communicating', first it is

wise to *think*. The disciplined engineer's thinking

proceeds along the lines of Fig. 12-2.

An example illustrates the thinking.

Example 12-2

In the early 1950's I had created a new design
for a microwave amplifier tube (6BY4) test jig. It
was to be used later in the new ceramic tube
operation in my firm's factory. I had made careful
engineering drawings for the first model to be
built and had communicated these to our model shop.
A skilled model maker, Joe* whom I knew and respected,
was assigned the job.

---

*Fictitious name.

● Is There A Need for 'others' to know about this?
    ▲ Identify/study/know 'others'.
    ▲ Seek *why* 'others' need to know.

● Is The Basic Communications Problem one of:
    ▲ Informing our management?
    ▲ Informing 'others' of progress toward solution?
    ▲ Personal relationships?
    ▲ Technicians/craftsmen/suppliers not knowing
        how we want our new device built?
    ▲ 'Others' not knowing of our new creation?
    ▲ Persuading others to *use* our new creation?
    ▲ Something peculiar to this problem?

● Is It Worth Communicating?
    ▲ Why?
    ▲ *What* is to be communicated?
        ● Write out in one thesis sentence.
    ▲ What will it probably cost?

● Is It Probably Communicable?

● Should I/We/Someone Else communicate it?

● When Is The Best Time to communicate it?

FIG. 12-2 A suggested outline for inquiring into
          engineering communications situations.

"While it is not
necessary for the
individual to
actually build
his invention with
his own hands, he
must design it on
paper or transmit
his thoughts to
someone who can."
  James M. Lafferty
  [184, p94]

After several weeks Joe came to my desk and loudly proclaimed, "You've got an *ultra* precision micrometer in your gadget which can't be built!"* (The micrometer moved a 'capacitive finger'—a common practice in microwave 'plumbing'.) "When you figure out how to build it, come back to see me!" He left.

After some thinking and a little amateur's luck on a lathe I was fortunate enough to have made 'the impossible micrometer barrel'. It had several more times the turns-per-inch of a standard micrometer—a necessity for this particular model.

I then had a problem: *How* to communicate this micrometer to Joe. My thinking went:

- Does He Have A Need To Know of its existence? Yes, for without it the new amplifier model couldn't be made. But he didn't need to know I had built it and proven him wrong.
- The Basic Communication Problem I defined as one of personal relationships. Joe had said it *couldn't* be built which now wasn't factually so. To rudely 'cram it down his throat' would adversely affect our relationships on this and all future projects and would hardly be practicing the Golden Rule.
- Is It Worth Communicating? Yes, without it the model progress halts. What is to be communicated is to get into his hands the newly built 'impossible micrometer' without injuring his craftsmanship pride or our relationship.
- Is It Probably Communicable? Yes, especially since I had in hand the physical gadget he needed.
- Should I/Someone Else communicate it to Joe? I could give it to Joe's supervisor and have him order Joe to use it on my model. But that gives Joe grounds for discontent. No, *I* should communicate this 'impossible micrometer' to Joe.

*"It can't be built" is heard frequently on creative projects. Technicians and craft people, unfortunately but not always without justification, look upon engineers as creators of impossible to build designs.

● When Is The Best Time to communicate it?
I decided that afternoon was best.

*"For the ear
tries words as
the palate
tastes food."
Job 34:3
[5]*

(Later taking it to the Model Shop, I found Joe,
put an arm around his shoulder, and said, "Joe,
you'll never guess what I stumbled on in the hall
returning from coffee break!" "What?" Opening
my hand, I showed him 'the impossible micrometer'.
He faintly smiled, picked it up, and tried it on
the partly finished model. It fit. He smiled
more. Our communication had been effective. He
never knew who built it. The model was finished
and extensively *used* until a better one was created.)

Example 12-2 also illustrates the delicacy of

our communications with others and points up the

important part 'personal relationships' play in

communications.*

If the engineer *omits* thoughtful inquiry from

the communications process possible misunderstandings,

hard feelings, demoralization of support and higher

level people, and literal halting of the creative

work may result. Such unsavory situations may

generally be anticipated and avoided with *thoughtful*

inquiry.

12-4 Goal(s) Of Our Communication

The disciplined creative engineer thinks through

the *specific* goal(s) [purpose(s) or objective(s)]

of his communication. He gets beneath the surface

by asking himself "What *specific* action are we after?"

---

*It also says something about Moore's thesis [217] of 'Getting the hands
into the act' of creative work! Explore on your own.

"What *meanings* (i.e. 'signals') do we wish to
communicate?" and related questions earlier identified
in Chap. 9, Fig. 9-2.

Example 12-3

    In 1971 two senior EE students had done an
exceptionally nice 'project' job of creating a new
apparatus for testing solar cells in sunlight. The
apparatus was finished, it looked extremely nice,
it had been carefully thought-out and constructed,
it met the project's goals, and it *worked*. We
mutually felt the need for sharing and communicating
this work with other research and development
engineers and scientists in the growing solar
energy movement.

    We established our communication goal as
"Prepare a first-rate technical paper describing
this apparatus for presentation at the International
Solar Energy Society Meeting, Goddard Space Flight
Center, Greenbelt, Md., May 10-14, 1971."

    (One student subsequently prepared it. I took
him to the meeting where he presented it--his first
professional paper--to an international audience.
Thanks to disciplined preparation, he did a superb
job, it came off well, our goal was met and *effective*
communication to 'others' occurred.)

In Chap. 5 we dealt with the general subject of
establishing technical goals. We can translate some of
these ideas to establishing communications goals.

● Primary Communications Goal Now

    Example 12-4

        "To *get* the contract for _____
    by writing an effective proposal thereby
    communicating with our potential customer/sponsor."

● Secondary Communications Goal Now

    Example 12-5

        "To communicate to the larger engineering
    and business community *specifically* how to build
    _____ based on our having successfully
    done the creative work communicated in the earlier
    proposal."

In the 'heat-of-battle' of active creative

engineering work we don't always write out goals

for each communications case. Thinking them through is

faster. But for more important communications, as in

the 'Convince Others' phase, experienced creative

engineers usually *write* out goals as an aid to

sharpening up thinking.

12-5 <u>Means Of Communicating</u>

Whatever means we choose for communicating, it is

*"Don't use
hydrochloric
acid. It eats
the hell out
of the pipes!"*

desirable to have clarity, conciseness, simplicity,

wholeness, objectivity, sincerity, veracity, the facts,

accuracy, and related qualities. It is *not* generally

an easy task to achieve them!

One of the best means of communicating used

repeatedly by effective engineers and others has come

to be known as 'the preacher principle'.

●   The <u>Preacher Principle</u> For Communicating:
     ▲ Tell 'em what you're going to tell 'em.
     ▲ Tell 'em.
     ▲ Tell 'em what you told 'em.

This powerful, simple, but not-so-obvious principle

is widely used in both mundane and sophisticated

engineering communications. It works for both oral

and written communicaton means.

<u>Example 12-6</u>

A manufacturing engineer writes an internal

"--the important
thing is to state
the crux of the
matter as
succinctly as
possible first."
W. J. King
[178, p2]

"--at times it pays
to mark a third
party for a copy
of the memo as
a witness."
W. J. King
[178, p2]

letter to his manager:

▲ Telling him this is about a major problem
   currently occuring in the factory. It
   potentially could shut the factory down.
▲ Stating concisely what the problem is, what
   he has done about it so far, and what should
   be done immediately.
▲ Summarizing in one paragraph what he said and
   what specific action the manager should
   take.

We now identify more specifically principal

communication means important to creative engineers.

Alternative Communication Means are identified in

Fig. 12-3.

It is a matter of engineering judgment which means

is best for our particular project at a given point

in the problem solving process. A detailed discussion

of each is inappropriate here.

It is clear we principally communicate orally and

visually (in its many forms). We now briefly examine

these broader classes of communications means.

ORAL COMMUNICATIONS occur most frequently on a typical

creative engineering project. Oral communications may

be informal or formal. We may communicate with

individuals (face-to-face, telephone, video, or other)

or groups (company meeting, professional society

presentation, lectures, etc.).

Oral communications have the distinct disadvantage

that no permanent record is made of them generally.

"Replies show that
management regards
both older and
newer engineering
graduates as weak
in oral reporting."
E. A. Walker
[364, p22]

● Oral

● Graphical
   ▲ Sketches
   ▲ Engineering Drawings/Specifications

● Letters

● Informal Notes

● Technical Memorandum

● Mathematical Calculation(s)

● Engineering Report:
   ▲ Proposal
   ▲ Interim Progress Reports
   ▲ Final Project Report
   ▲ Technical Paper

● Slides and Films

● Articles for Magazines, Books, News Media

● Combinations of Above

FIG. 12-3 Principal means of communicating
          used by engineers in creating
          a new product.

Formal oral communication with groups is so
important in creative work that a few general suggestions
for effective ways to do it are collected in Fig. 12-4.
Much more could be said [364, Ch. 18] about the
details, but there is no substitute for learning from
actual practice on a creative project you are involved
with. You may find study of Sec. 12-9 helpful in
preventing common pathologies from creeping into your
presentation.

WRITTEN COMMUNICATIONS in its various specific forms
identified in Fig. 12-3 is the second major class of
communications means.

Written communications have the distinct advantage
of a more permanent character.

A few suggestions for preparing in this area are
in Fig. 12-5.

"Writing is a
personal
thing."
Richard W. Dodge
[80]

There are many details you'll pick up as you gain
experience and acquire writing skill; but the principal
steps you'll need are in Fig. 12-5.

THE ENGINEERING PROPOSAL/REPORT, a subclass of written
communications, is a very important communication
'output' of the creative engineer. It:

●   Is the recognized first step in establishing
    a firm 'bench mark' on our creative contribution.

● <u>The Outline</u>

▲ Make one.
▲ Keep it:
  ● Punch line.
  ● Short.
  ● Clearly structured.

● <u>Prepare Visuals</u>

▲ Decide on charts, slides, or other means.
▲ Think out concise titles, word choices, letter sizes, and graphic details.
▲ Double or triple time estimate to get them made.

● <u>Prepare Demonstration</u>(s)

▲ Tidy up working model.
▲ Be sure it *works--every* time.
▲ Decide how integrate with rest of presentation.

● <u>Prepare Speech Notes</u>

▲ Tell audience what this will cover.
▲ *Clearly* describe the new creation.
▲ *Clearly* cite its:
  ● Advantages
  ● Benefits
  ● Incentives for using it.
▲ *Say* you advocate using it or what *specific* action you advocate with respect to the new creation.
▲ Summarize your essential message.
▲ Excruciate over right word choices.

● <u>Rehearse</u>

▲ Before a carefully selected friend/critic.
▲ Seek rough spots.
▲ *Listen* carefully.
▲ Modify as needed.

● <u>Present It</u>

▲ Optimize your *appearance*.
▲ Relax. Be your natural self--at your best.
▲ *Show*:
  ● Enthusiasm
  ● Confidence
  ● Faith
  in your new creation.
▲ Give a forceful delivery.

FIG. 12-4 Steps and suggestions for making an effective formal oral presentation of our new creation.

● Preparation   ▲ Secure:
                      ● Time.
                      ● Place.
                      ● Satisfactory physical facilities (quiet, no telephones,
                          no/few interruptions).
                      ● Writing mood.
                 ▲ Think about why/to whom you will write. Mentally place
                     ourselves in their shoes.
                 ▲ Decide on single/multiple authorship.
                 ▲ Collect/study relevant materials.
                 ▲ Roughly organize materials/ideas.
                 ▲ Rough outline (plan) what is to be written.
                 ▲ Lay outline aside for awhile.
                 ▲ Discuss with our manager.

● Writing   ▲ Set a *definite* date with yourself to start
                     writing.
                 ▲ Optimize our personal mood for writing.
                 ▲ Think about 'others' who will receive/act on what
                     we write.
                 ▲ Modify outline.
                 ▲ Think about format. Decide.
                 ▲ The language:
                      ● Excruciate over meanings, sentence structure,
                          words, simplicity, and clarity.
                      ● Frequently consult dictionary.
                      ● Try develop *own* writing style in boundaries
                          of technical rightness, objectivity,
                          accepted English, professional ethics,
                          good taste, and company policies.
                 ▲ Illustrations. Anticipate/deal with problems of:
                      ● Drafting
                      ● Photography
                      ● Reproduction
                      ● Permissions/copyright.
                 ▲ References
                      ● Choose relevant ones.
                      ● Cite specifically.
                 ▲ Rewrite until satisfied.
                 ▲ A *definite* rough draft should result.

FIG. 12-5   Some steps and suggestions for
            obtaining effective written
            communications.

● Establishes who did what, when, and with what
   results.

● May serve as the technical basis for decision
   and action by 'others'.

● Is valuable to others and ourselves for future
   reference.

● May settle later arguments.

● Is sometimes useful in patent litigation.

● May build professional statue and respect.

"The word 'report' means to 'carry back', to bring back information about something seen or investigated."
Ralph J. Smith
[306, p212]

There are innumerable ways of classifying engineering

reports. One can quickly get lost in details of format,

computerized access numbers, and the like. To avoid

this, we choose the classification so clearly stated

by Steinmetz years ago.

"The Scientific Record of the investigation.
   This must be so complete as to enable another
   investigator to completely check up, repeat
   and further extend the investigation. It thus
   must contain the original observations, the
   method of work, apparatus and facilities,
   calibrations, information on the limits of
   accuracy and reliability, sources of error,
   methods of calculation, etc., etc.

"Some technical reports are so dry and dusty--that if you put a pile of them in a hydraulic press and apply millions of pounds of pressure to it, not a drop of juice will run out."
Charles F. Kettering
[174, p215]

   It thus is a lengthy report, and as such
   will be read by very few if any, except other
   competent investigators, but is necessary as
   the record of the work, since without such
   report, the work would be lost, as the conclusions
   and results could not be checked up if required.

   This report appeals only to men of the
   same character as the one who made the
   investigation, and is essentially for record
   and file.

The General Engineering Report. It should be
   very much shorter than the scientific report,
   should be essentially of the nature of a
   syllabus thereof, avoid as much as possible
   complex mathematical and theoretical considerations
   but give all the engineering results of the

*"Every manager
interviewed said he
read the summary or
abstract - - -; only
a few managers read
the body of the
report or the
Appendix material."*
*Richard W. Dodge
[80]*

investigation, in as plain language as possible.
It should be addressed to administrative
engineers, that is, men who as engineers are
capable of understanding the engineering
results and discussion, but have neither
time nor familiarity to follow in detail
through the investigation, and are not
interested in such things as the original
readings, the discussion of methods, accuracy,
etc., but are interested in results.

This is the report which would be read
by most of the men interested in the matter.
It would in general be the form in which the
investigation is communicated to engineering
societies as paper, with the scientific report
relegated into an Appendix of the paper.

The General Report. This should give the
results, that is, explain what the matter
is about, in plain and practically nontechnical
language, addressed to laymen, that is,
non-engineers. In other words, it should be
understood by any intelligent nontechnical
man.

*"--the solution is
condensed to a
single data sheet
with explanatory
drawings and not
described in a
long memorandum."*
*Harald T. Friis
[113, p42]*

Such general report would be materially
shorter than the general engineering report,
as it would omit all details, and merely
deal with the general problem, purpose
and solution.

In general, it is advisable to combine
all three reports, by having the scientific
record preceded by the general engineering
report, and the latter preceded by the
general report. Roughly, the general report
would usually have a length of 20 to 40
percent of the general engineering report,
the latter a length of 10 to 25 percent
of the complete scientific record." [317, p291-292]

Creative engineers in research and development

may generate reports roughly of the 1st and 2nd kind.

Engineers in design, manufacturing, or operations tend

to generate those of the 2nd and 3rd kind.

How Do You Structure an engineering report?

Each firm usually has its own structure and format for engineering reports. You'll want to become familiar with your company's system soon after starting work. There are semmingly endless details from paper color and texture up.

"Good writing is clear thinking made visible."
Unknown

Beneath the facade one finds structures along the lines shown in Figs. 12-6 and 12-7. There is no *one* best structure for *all* reports.

Note these classical outlines implicitly incorporate 'the preacher principle' cited earlier.

Such outlines are enough for us to get started and prepare a draft of the engineering report[1] on our particular new project. But we finally come down to the disciplined business of taking pen in hand and actively *writing*! We rapidly learn by practice and experience, picking up details of this vast subject as needed.

"--a wrong answer is worse than no answer."
W. J King
[178, p2]

A well-written engineering report is *right* from both technical *and* grammar viewpoints.

12-6 <u>Optimizing Our Written Communications</u>

There are hastily written poorly thought-out

---

[1]Those insisting on details will find them along with many examples in Woodson [383] and Hicks [147]. Helpful advice is also in Buhl [50, Ch.8], Edel [89, Ch. 4], any many other sources.

●   Title Page
      ▲ Title
      ▲ Author
      ▲ Organizational Affiliation
      ▲ Date
      ▲ Report Identification Number(s)

●   Abstract

●   Introduction

●   Report Body

●   Discussion

●   Summary or Conclusions

●   Recommendations

●   Bibliography

FIG. 12-6 Outline for a short engineering proposal, report, or paper for publication.

●   Front Cover

●   Notices

●   Title Page

●   Foreword or Preface

●   Abstract

●   Table of Contents

●   List of Illustrations

●   List of Tables

●   List of Mathematical Symbols

●   List of Abbreviations

●   List of Appendices

●   Introduction

●   Report Body

●   Results

●   Discussion and Projections

●   Summary or Conclusions

●   Recommendations

●   Acknowledgment

●   Bibliography

●   Glossary of Terms

●   Appendices

●   Index

●   Distribution List

●   Back Cover

FIG. 12-7 Outline for a more complete engineering
report. Such reports require
substantially more costly preparation
time than those of Fig. 12-6.

"After investigating the actual design problems incountered I have chosen to redefine by my direction a small amount."
  From a student's engineering report.

communications and there are *optimal* communications.

The latter usually is more effective in getting our

new creation across, into *use*, and with a minimum of

misunderstanding and hard feelings.

Whether written or spoken, optimal communications

say precisely what we mean, are concise, consider both

reader or audience and what is technically best,

convey *meanings* instead of superfluous trivia, and

achieve our communications goals.

It's usually necessary to optimize any written

form of communication *before* we issue instructions

to reproduce and distribute it. A few time proven

suggestions are in Fig. 12-8.

A carefully optimized communication document is a

beautiful creation.

"---words come to assume meaning and carry emotional content quite apart from their dictionary definitions."
  E. S. Taylor
  [332, p646]

Space does not permit dealing with the ill

effects on men and organizations of unoptimized engineering

communications. You will see many examples when you

enter practice.

12-7 <u>Reproduction</u> <u>and</u> <u>Distribution</u>

Having decided specifically what our communication

document is to say, we now have the problem of getting

it reproduced and in the hands of 'others'. It may

be a complex engineering report or a simple customer

warranty card we've written. Whatever the communication,

●   <u>Secure</u> <u>Time</u>   to think/write our draft.

●   <u>Anticipate</u>   weaknesses/probable/legitimate questions of
                                        'others'. Deal with:
                                        ▲ Why do what we propose at all?
                                        ▲ Why do it this way?
                                        ▲ Why do it now?

●   <u>Revise</u>   /review/revise *before* 'others' see it.

●   <u>Check</u>   whether it meets our communications goals.

●   <u>Lay</u> <u>It</u> <u>Aside</u>   for awhile.

●   <u>Friendly</u> <u>Critic</u>(s)   Find one. Listen/weigh carefully.

●   <u>Revise</u>   manuscript as necessary.

●   <u>Definite</u> <u>Optimized</u> <u>Document</u>   Bring it to this stage.

FIG. 12-8   A few general guide lines in optimizing
            our written communications. Effective
            engineering reports and recommendations
            on which 'others' *act* are the result of
            careful disciplined creative thought.
            They are seldom, if ever, generated in
            a single 'moment of genius'.

"Be careful about whom you mark for copies--when the interests of other departments are involved."
W. J. King
[178, p4]

it does *not* "just automatically come out of 'the system' in a finished form."

It is a common mistake to assume that "all the *hard* work is done now that it's written. It's *no* trouble to get it cranked out in quantity!" Any real-world engineer who has issued a major engineering report through an overloaded secretarial pool, an inadequately staffed drafting group, or a nonexisting photo lab will attest to the non-triviality of the reproduction and distribution phase.

We usually have to work through and with support people in this phase. The roles are outlined in Fig. 12-9.

Our output here, indeed a *major* output from our previous disciplined creative effort, is finished copy versions of our engineering report. It may be a large stack of documents.

12-8 Follow-Up

As a disciplined engineer we follow-up on our communications. We don't naively assume that just because *we've* gotten over the hurdle of getting our report issued or oral presentation made no further action is needed. Instead we question as shown in Fig. 12-10 for our specific communications problem.

ENGINEER'S ROLE

● Determine Number of copies to be made for 'others'.
     Identify recipients.

● Estimate Costs and money availability.

● Initiate reproduction/distribution process.

● Periodically Check support-people's progress.
     Follow-up/needle/coordinate.

● Proofread/correct report 'Masters'.

● Secure Approval signature(s) (if needed) on 'Masters'.

● Write Transmittal letter.

● Personally Deliver issued report/communication to 'others'
     (where/if possible).

SUPPORT ROLE

● Secretary ----------- Translate our draft to polished
                                 document.

● Drafting/Artists ---- Prepare drawing/illustration
                                 'originals'.

● Photo Lab ----------- Make photographs/slides.
                                 Prepare for reproduction.

● Reproduction -------- Required number of copies are made
                                 (Xerox, printed, or otherwise) from
                                 our 'Masters'.
                                 Copies checked.

● Distribution -------- Issued report, with transmittal letter
                                 is sent to intended 'others'.

FIG. 12-9 Outlined roles of engineer-support
           people in getting an engineering
           report draft reproduced and
           distributed to the intended 'others'.
           Time is required to have a professional
           quality report emerge.

- Did he/they *receive* our communication?

- Did they *hear/read* it?

- Did they *understand* it?

- Did it *achieve our intended goal*?

- Have we *listened* to what they say about it?

- Further specific action indicated?

FIG. 12-10 Check list for following-up
on our communications.

Example 12-7

*"--but we don't
have the time to
read all that
interests us."*
 Chester M. Sinnett
 [302 , p16]

For three years I worked for a colorful Manager of Engineering. He was overloaded.

My first engineering report to him contained crucial recommended changes to the product which required his approval before being placed into *use* in our factory.

Several days passed. I heard nothing. Finally I visited him regarding the report, asking, "Did you get it?" (A *check* on our distribution system.) He fumbled around in a two-foot stack of papers, reports, and memoranda on his desk and finally fished out the report. He explained he used the 'Napoleonic Filing System'. Napoleon had discovered a large percentage of the paper work fed to him 'took care of itself'. Of the remaining part if anything of importance was therein, someone wanting it done would 'follow-up' on it and press for a decision!

*"[A manager] wants
to know right away
whether he should
read the report,
route it, or skip
it."*
 Richard W. Dodge
 [80]

After reading the abstract, conclusions, and recommendations *only* of my issued report, he then approved the recommendations on the spot. They were subsequently placed into *use*.

I had learned an important lesson of the necessity of communications 'follow-up'.

12-9 Common Errors In Oral Presentations

The previous sections have emphasized written communications, though oral communications were mentioned in Sec. 12-5. Because of the importance of oral presentations in creative work and because one repeatedly sees so many errors at various internal company and professional society conferences, Table 12-1 is included.

*"Many an idea has
gone untried all
because of poor
or improper
presentation."*
 Daymond J. Aiken
 [2, p18]

The hope is that, being forewarned, perhaps your generation can improve the general quality of oral presentations in the engineering profession, profiting

PHYSICAL FACILITY

- Room too small/large
- Temperature/humidity wrong
- Uncomfortable seats
- 'Dead Spots' in room

- Spots on projector screen
- Noise/distractions
- Lighting/other controls don't work
- Translator problems

PRESENTER

- Fails to show up
- Shows up late
- Appearance:
  - Dirty
  - Poor grooming
  - Inappropriate clothing
  - Overdue haircut
- Audience background/needs incorrectly assessed
- Our work presented by someone else not knowledgeable

- Speaking:
  - Accent
  - Too slow/fast
  - Too soft-spoken/loud
  - Monotone voice
  - Reading paper
  - No enthusiasm/spirt/confidence
  - Tense/unrelaxed
  - No audience eye contact
  - No humor/humanness exhibited
  - No emphases
  - No hand motions
  - Unacceptable mannerisms
  - Treating audience with contempt
  - Overtime

TECHNICAL CONTENT

- No coherent pattern/story
- Faulty creative thinking in problem solving process
- Overlooked basic technical flaw
- No experimental verification
- Demonstration doesn't work
- Important technical points glossed over/omitted

- Too much technical detail
- No numbers
- Wrong numbers
- Irrelevant data
- Failure to anticipate/answer obvious technical questions about the creative work

SLIDES/CHARTS

- None. Words only
- Wrong set slides
- Slides backwards/upside down
- No/poor focus
- Slide operator asleep
- Projector bulb burns out
- Lettering too small
- Poor quality drafting/photography:
  - Slide made from Xerox of Xerox, etc.
  - Slide made from typed page
  - Can't see white letters on black
  - Improper lighting
  - Color/contrast poor
  - No standard of reference visible (photographs)

- Too much/little information/slide
- Slide filled with long detailed eqs.
- Error(s) in slide content
- Slide content not thought-out
- No/poor title
- Hurried presentation--no/little explanation
- Failing say what's plotted against what
- No pointer
- Light gun doesn't work
- Failure to point to specific place on slide, i.e. pointer waving
- Projected slide so large we 'get lost' in it

CHALK BOARD

- Unorganized
- Lots details-no main points
- Piling material without erasing
- Thin chalk lines

- Wrong color chalk/board
- Lettering/sketches too small
- Poor sketches

QUESTIONS

- Using all time on presentation, avoding questions
- Failing to stimulate questions
- Failing to answer legitimate questions
- Not knowing answers to reasonable questions
- Fuzzy answers
- Berating questioner

TABLE 12-1 Common errors made in oral presentations. The effective engineer knows of and minimizes them.

from the errors of those preceding you.

Discussion Topics

1. Discuss *where* in the six step problem solving
    approach of Fig. 3-1 you will orally communicate.

2. This chapter emphasized communication with 'others'.
    Do we have any need to communicate with *ourselves*?
    Where in Fig. 3-1?

3. Choose an engineer in your field whom you respect
    for creative contribution. Was he an effective
    communicator? Cite examples.

4. Does pride and arrogance influence ability to
    effectively communicate?

5. Ask your professor to show from creative engineering
    practice an actual example of:
    a. A typical letter written by an engineer.
    b. A sketch made while creating a new product--
        not the published version.
    c. An engineering drawing in your field.
    d. An engineering drawing that *failed* to communicat
        and what the consequences were.
    e. A well-written engineering report in your
        field.
    f. A half-baked engineering report that somehow
        got issued or published. Identify
        how it fails to communicate and *specifically*
        what is wrong with it.
    Discuss each.

6. Are engineering reports *really* needed in actual
    practice? They are painful to generate, very
    costly, and in view of the communications
    alternatives of Fig. 12-3 may not even be
    needed!

7. What part(s) of a formal engineering report does
    a middle-manager read? Why? Ditto for top
    management. What 'feedback signal' does this
    give in writing our next report?

8. You need a special permanent magnet made for
    your new device being created. You *must* have
    it in-hand in 14 days or less.
    a. How will you find the name and address of
        a permanent magnet supplier you'll
        communicate with?

    b. How will you find a single 'right man'
        within the large company to talk with?

    c. What will you say in 6 minutes or less
        via long distance telephone?

    d. Does telephoning pose any unique communications
        problems?

    e. What communications 'follow-up' will you
        initiate?

9. Can severe management-imposed time constraints on us impair communications? Consider the case where your manager tells you, "Mr. _____, you have exactly five minutes to tell this group about your new creation and what you propose be done with it!"

10. Explore relationships between an engineer's ability to communicate and his making tangible long-term creative contributions in a modern corporate environment.

11. Is there the possibility of choking-up an otherwise creative engineering organization with too many 'communications'? What, if anything, can be done about it?

12. Managers frequently 'measure' an engineer's output by examining his communications or the effects they have on others. Discuss whether the practice is fair, consequences, effects on us and others, and related topics.

13. Is 'engineering communications' an easy or difficult subject to personally master? Has this chap. covered *all* the subject? Is there more to it?

Exercises

12-E1. Review creative process flow charts in Figs. 4-2, 5-1, 6-5, 7-2, 8-2, and 9-2. List sequentially *where* you will probably need to communicate and in what form.

12-E2. Refer to Example 12-3. Assume you were an engineer on that project. You need to *quickly* purchase a standard telescope mount. Find the name and address of the principal company selling such an item. Write an optimized letter requesting technical information, availability, price, delivery, and anything else you deem necessary. Be specific.

12-E3. You are president of a concern that
        manufacturers expensive wave guides, primarily
        for the military. At the Flamingo Hotel in
        Las Vegas you 'accidentally' run into the
        presidents of the other principal manufacturers
        of wave guides for the military and learn that
        a basement scientist in Cairo, Illinois, has
        developed a wave guide out of two coat hangers
        that out performs all your 500-dollar models.
        You agree to investigate the problem.

        Write a letter to the Cairo intruder
        (Mr. I. S. Clever), requesting information
        and possibly suggesting a meeting to discuss
        his invention. [354, p25]

12-E4. Write a *one* page personal resume communicating
        to a potential employer your principal
        professional assets.

12-E5. Examine a telephone. Mentally turn back in
        time to when it was a series of sketches or
        drawings conceived by a creative engineer.
        You want to have the first model built. Write
        out the *specific* instructions you would give
        to the model shop supervisor.

12-E6. Write a one paragraph interim progress report
        to your professor of progress made in the past
        week on your major creative problem in this
        course.

12-E7. a. Arrange to visit several engineering
            professors not connected with this
            course. Choose ones with industrial
            experience.
        b. Discuss common errors made in writing formal
            engineering reports. Take notes.
        c. Compile your findings concisely similar
            to Table 12-1. Be *specific*.
        d. Will *you* make such errors in your future
            practice?

12-E8. List the personal problems an engineer may
        have in getting an engineering report written
        and issued.

12-E9. An engineer submits a hastily-written (0.2
        baked--*less* than 'half-baked'!) invention
        disclosure letter to his firm's patent
        attorney. List/discuss the possible consequences
        of such an incomplete communication.

12-E10.   Select an already created gadget or idea
          in your field of interest which is *new* to
          you.
          a.   Write a description suitable for your
               professional society journal's readers.
          b.   Write a description for a newspaper article.

12-E11.   Prepare and deliver an oral presentation as
          directed by your professor of your solution
          to a creative problem.

Chapter Summary

● The engineer creating new products has a need to
  be an effective communicator with others.

● The complex communication process between ourselves
  and others, and vice versa, is analogous to an
  electrical communication system. The analogy
  suggested insights which can enhance our ability
  to communicate with 'others'.

● The 'Six-Step Approach' was seen applicable to our
  communications problems, i.e. inquiring, setting
  communications goals, etc.

● Principal communication alternatives were identified
  in Fig. 12-3.

● Some suggestions were made for effective oral
  presentations and engineering reports.

● A plea was made for attempting to optimize our
  communications, regardless of kind.

● Finally, recognition was made that effective
  communication involves a follow-up process.

CHAPTER 13

CREATIVITY INHIBITORS, $C_o e^{-\alpha\tau}$

"Throughout the long history of the human race, we
find that creativity has nearly always had to
struggle against anything from discouragement to
violent rejection."

A. D. Moore [217, p140]

● The role of creativity inhibitors in problem
solving is briefly treated.

● Common inhibitors are concisely tabulated.

13-1 <u>Role</u> <u>of</u> <u>Creativity</u> <u>Inhibitors</u>

*"Inhibit: to
hold back; to
check; restrain;
hinder."*
[373]

The engineer actively engaging in serious
creative problem solving soon becomes vaguely aware
of factors which deter his creativity. We call this
class *creativity inhibitors*. The terms 'stifler'
[360, p28], 'block' [7, p95], 'pitfall' [279, p160],
'barriers' [148, p28] and others are used in creativity
literature to convey the same concept.

*"In mathematics,
however, there was
my previous dis-
taste of the
subject to
overcome."*
*Robert H.
Goddard
[121, p35]*

Inhibitors may seriously impair our ability to
successfully solve the problem and reduce our net
creativity contribution over a time period. The
impairment, in a loose analogical sense, may be roughly
according to the exponential

$$C(\tau) = C_o e^{-\alpha\tau}$$

where:

$C(\tau)$ = One's net creative contribution
at any time τ.

C_o = One's potential creative contribution.

α = Creativity inhibitor coefficient,
a real number.

τ = Time.

Clearly a large α may markedly lower one's potential

creative contribution. Since, as discussed in

Chap. 3, we seek to maximize our creative contri-

butions, then the individual problem solver must

seek means for minimizing his inhibitor coefficient(s).

*"The army of demons
is always there,
ready to move in,
---"*
*John C. Stedman
[315, p40]*

Creativity inhibitors, even if unrecognized,

are omnipresent and active throughout *all* the major

phases and sub steps in the problem solving approach

advocated in Chaps. 3-9. It is therefore proper

to consider them as a separate topic. The topic is

closely linked with the pathology of creativity--the

complex areas of disease and failure of the creative

processes.

Example 13-1

A research engineer who hungers for encouragement by his supervisor fails to receive even one
encouraging word for an exciting new concept he
has. He suffers inwardly, nothing is done, and the
concept is lost from society.

*"---the creative
personality must
be highly resis-
tant to dis-
appointment."*
*Guy Suits
[322, p30]*

Inhibitors and their subtle influences on an

individual's ability to produce new creations appear

to have been grossly minimized in most engineering

books. Anyone who has engaged in real-world engineer-

ing problem solving activity will attest to their

reality.

*"We dragged the
pieces back to
camp and began
to consider
getting home.
The next morning
we had cheered up
some and began to
think there was
some hope of
repairing it."*
*Orville Wright
[389, p30]*

We shall attempt in this Chap. to collect and

order some of the known creativity inhibitors. The

expectation is that foreknowledge of them may enhance

*"A man of the stuff
of which great
inventors are
made will invent
under any cir-
cumstances and
conditions."*
J. A. Haddad
[138, p237]

the probability of successfully solving a given

engineering problem which requires a creative

solution.

Discussion Topics

1. "The whole inhibitor subject is a sick one and
   has no place in an engineering curriculum or
   text. The engineer doesn't need to know
   this subject." Discuss.

2. A design engineer is 'creating new means for
   fastening two copper wires together'. He is
   entering the 'determining means' phase.
   Identify and discuss some creativity inhibitors
   he may encounter before arriving at useful new
   ideas.

13-2 Some Creativity Inhibitors

Many people have reported and expounded upon

inhibitors to creative work. [202] [346] [269] [271]

[81] [8] [380] [234] [267]. A typical reported work

deals with a small number of inhibitors. The reader

may be left with the impression, "That's all there

is to inhibitors." Actually the engineering

problem solver encounters many inhibitors. An

articulation of what is believed to be an acceptable

total view of this profound subject as it affects

*"--come, let us meet
together---. But
they intended to
do me harm.
And I sent
messengers to them
saying, I am doing
a great work and
cannot come down.
Why should the work
stop while I leave
to come down to you?"*
Nehemiah [221]

the individual engineer is shown in Table 13-1.

It contains the more common creativity inhibitors

encountered by your creative predecessors. The

probability of encountering some, all, or others on

your future engineering problems is large. The

CREATIVITY

OF PROBLEM SOLVER

OF PROBLEM SOLVER

Attitudes Of:

- Conformity
- Unquestioning
- Disorderliness
- Conservatism
- Pessimism
- Timidity
- Making excuses to stop work
- Applying group effort at wrong time

Inner Feelings Of:

- Inertia
- Discouragement/Depression
- No Confidence
- Little Courage
- Not truly wanting to contribute
- Lack of life purpose
- Excessive self criticism
- Laziness
- Frustration
- Resentment
- Anxiety
- Conflict/alienation toward others
- Inadequate imagination

Rebellion Against:

- Self
- Management
- Colleagues
- Supporting help
- Environment
- The problem
- Intuition

Health

- Impairment/partial/complete loss
- Tiredness
- Worry
- Inability to relax and free ideas

Fear Of:

- Questioning
- New Ideas
- Using imagination
- The problem
- Making mistakes
- Failure
- Ridicule/criticism
- Risk taking
- Anticipation of idea by others
- Losing job

Loss Of:

- Perspective of problem importance
- Motivation/confidence problem is solvable
- Patience and persistence
- Financial support
- Communication with management
- Curiosity
- Ability to 'play' with new ideas
- Self respect/honesty
- Desire for continuous self renewal

Satisfaction With:

- Self/environment
- Rationalizations for not creating
- Status quo
- Prior solutions
- Deliberately avoiding the problem

Habits Of:

- One problem-one solution dogma
- Old secure ways when new ways needed
- Familiarity with the problem
- Cultural/technical origin

Technical:

- Implication(s) all worth-while has been created
- Obscuration of problem(s) by analytics
- Insensitivity to recent advances
- Inadequate knowledge/information
- Inability to find/focus on true problem(s)
- Not understanding problem
- Failure to astutely observe
- Overspecialization/refusal to cross disciplines
- Incorrect/incomplete model/assumptions
- Destructive criticism of need/goals/proposed means/model/implementation
- Difficulty caused by not recording previous work
- Refusal to explore alternate solution possibilities
- Routines/standards inflexible
- 'Giving up' after first un-successful experiments

Excessive

- Pressure to create
- Supervision
- Meetings
- Emphasis on cost at wrong time
- Practicality emphasis at wrong time
- Analysis at wrong time
- Judgment of truly new creation at wrong time
- Hope of riches/quick success
- Unjustified enthusiasm/confidence
- Haste in judging creators/creations
- Reporting
- Perfectionism
- Legal difficulties
- Marketing problems

TABLE 13-1   Tabulation of some creativity inhibitors. The engineer may encounter these and others while inquiring into and solving 'the problem'.

INHIBITORS

AND ENVIRONMENT

OF ENVIRONMENT

Lack Of:

- Encouragement
- Funding/sponsorship
- Motivation/enthusiasm/ initiative
- Knowledge of an ordered problem solving approach
- Time allocation to do creative work
- Awareness/sensitivity to a true need/challenge
- Correct problem definition
- Incentives to create
- Hope/faith problem is solvable
- An action plan to create
- Commitment to solve problem
- Persuasiveness
- Specific goals
- Decisiveness at critical points
- Proper materials
- Thoroughness at all phases
- Adequate recognition/rewards for creating
- Adequate patent protection
- Confidence in patent attorney

Wrong

- Decisions
- Information/facts

Limitations On:

- Abilities
- Freedom to create
- Experimental facilities
- Hiring engineers 'not like our group'

Restraints Of

- Management unsympathetic/ prejudiced/distrustful of creativity/creators
- Indifference to new creations
- Deliberately created obstructions to frustrate creative work
- Resistance to change/new ideas
- Frequent changes of key decisions
- Sanctions against questioning/study/exploring
- Excessive routine work
- Unnecessary secrecy
- Ill conceived policies
- Unenlightened committees
- Spirit of dogmatism
- Emphasizing *today's* problems
- Unrealistic time schedules
- No responsibility to creative engineer
- Inadequate supporting help
- Refusal to truthfully recognize problem
- Procrastination/delays
- Over concern with who gets credit for idea
- Non-implementation of creations
- Militaristic obedience to 'authorities'
- Excessive emphasis on competition
- 'Harmony' at any cost
- Others stealing one's ideas
- Dishonest promoters

Remarks Of Others

- "It will cost too much."
- "We don't think it's a good idea."
- "That's ridiculous."
- "That's the silliest idea I ever heard."
- "Only an eccentric would propose such a thing."
- "That's too radical."
- "It will make our system obsolete."
- "We're not ready for it."
- "It won't enhance our prestige to propose it."
- "You're years ahead of your time."
- "We don't have time, money or manpower."
- "Precisely what profit is in it?"
- "We think your specifications are no good."
- "Let our committee consider it."
- "It won't work."
- "We tried that years ago."
- "We've always done it this way."
- "It's contrary to company policy."
- "It hasn't been tried."
- "It's too obvious to be considered."
- "It's out of our field."
- "Your model is superficial."
- "What we have *works*. Leave it alone!"
- "It's not practical."
- "It can't be done."
- "Make a pre-production run with orangutang operators, and if we get 110% yield we'll try it next year."

table is self explanatory. It is clear the

inhibitors may be within ourselves, the environ-

ment, or both.

"He (Igor Sikorsky)
spent months at the
flying fields talk-
ing to the experts,
particularly Captain
Ferber who offered
him the following
advice: 'Don't
waste your time on
the helicopter--
the airplane will
be far more
valuable."
  Charles F.
  Kettering
    [175, p26]

  Some inhibitors are capable of being reversed

to become stimulators.

Example 13-2

  Unrealistic time schedules may inhibit
creativity severely. Realistic time goals for
completing parts or all of the problem may be a
vital creativity stimulant.

  There are two frequently occurring inhibitors

requiring brief explanations.

> ● Functional Fixation is the ascribing of
> a familiar function to a specific object
> so that its single function becomes firmly
> fixed in our minds while we remain mentally
> blind to other possible uses, extension, or
> modification possibilities.

Example 13-3

"And then some
amateur comes in
and looks at the
obvious. He
doesn't know what
is obvious, ob-
viously, and he
says, 'Why don't
we do something
about this over
here.' And a
new invention
is born."
  John E. Arnold
    [7, p95]

  'Functional fixation' may cause one to
think of a relay as 'a current interrupter/
starter'. That fixation may inhibit my
creative exploration of its possible uses
as a source of wire, a means of achieving
limited angular/linear motion, a source of
light (arc), an object of art, a thermo-
dynamic illustration of a time varying system,
and others.

If you are interested in studying functional
fixation further, explore the references
[360, p31] [284].

> ● Mother Complex of an idea is capsulized by
> Von Fange [360, p85] as "I don't care what it
> looks like, how complex it is, it's mine,
> mine, MINE!" While emotional pride in one's
> new idea is understandable, excessive emotion-
> alism may inhibit either improving the idea
> or creating superior alternative means of
> solving the problem.

Example 13-4

As a still 'wet-behind-the-ears' development engineer, I once had the problem of creating a light weight 400 Hz to DC power supply for a new autopilot in one of the Navy's first delta wing fighter aircraft. The supervisor asked me specifically to attempt the solution by means of creating a voltage doubler circuit using gas thyratron tubes. Such a circuit had not been successfully created to our knowledge. After several months I demonstrated an operable circuit. It involved two thyratrons, two oil filled capacitors, a filter, and a separate regulating circuit. In my naïvity I was emotionally proud of the complex completed circuit, for it was mine, mine, MINE! I had been completely blinded to the alternative circuit of a simple bridge rectifier--the system finally used.

I *also* learned from this experience that a prejudiced initial solution means advanced by one's management may, in the end, be a severe creativity inhibitor!

"If we are going to progress in any line we must learn to fail intelligently so we won't become discouraged at the 99.9 per cent failure."
Charles F. Kettering [175, p11]

The reader interested in details of inhibitors is referred to the cited prior art literature. All is *not* yet known about creativity inhibitors! Hopefully future research will continue to add to knowledge in the area, further enhancing our problem solving effectiveness.

The question naturally arises, "What can the individual problem solver do to *overcome* some or all of his creativity inhibitors?" It suggests creativity stimulators, the subject of the next chapter.

"--the things you will probably need most are infinite patience and persistence. Few people realize the difficulties of doing any new thing."
Charles F. Kettering [175, p11]

Exercises

13-E1.   Look over all your engineering textbooks. Bring one to class which specifically mentions 'creativity inhibitors' or equivalent terms. Share findings with your class.

13-E2.   Prepare a list of ten major *specific* items which you feel have inhibited your net creativity in solving previous problems.

13-E3.   Identify *specific* features you would build into a classroom to make it the *best* possible means for inhibiting creativity. (After C. W. Taylor [329, p59].)

13-E4.   Prepare a list of specific creativity inhibitors, not in Table 13-1, which may be encountered in your first year of engineering employment.

Chapter Summary

● A vast array of creativity inhibitors exists. The engineer seeking to create significant *new* concepts should be aware of them.

● Inhibitors, if we let them, can reduce our problem solving creative output to zero in one or all parts of the six step approach!

● Some major creativity inhibitors were identified and articulated in Table 13-1.

CHAPTER 14

CREATIVITY STIMULATORS, $C_o e^{+\beta\tau}$

"The stimulus accompanying an idea might be looked
upon as a gift from Divine Providence to help us
over the rough obstacles and hurdles - - - "
Eugene K. Von Fange [360, p86]

● Creativity stimulators in problem solving.

● Useable creativity stimulators.

14-1 Role of Creativity Stimulators

We identified some creativity inhibitors in

Chap. 13. Awareness of inhibitors is necessary but not

sufficient for successfully solving engineering

problems requiring *new* clever solutions. Something

more positive is needed at the personal level to

stimulate thinking and enhance our creativity. We

call it a *creativity stimulator*. The terms 'creative

technique' and 'ideational technique' are also widely

used. We adopt Von Fange's definition.

● Creativity Stimulator - "Anything that will give *us* a fresh viewpoint." [360, p41]

Example

One creativity stimulator from Table 14-1 is
Alternative Approaches. Its essence is: "You ask,
"What are the alternatives?" and you " - - make a
list of all our ideas." Both the question and the
act of thinking up the list can, and usually does
stimulate us toward fresh solution viewpoints.

Note the *personalness* aspect. Creativity

stimulators may markedly enhance our ability to succ-

fully solve the chosen problem. This enhancement,

to continue the loose analogy of Chap. 13, may be

roughly according to the exponential

$$C(\tau) = C_o e^{+\beta\tau}$$

where:

B = Our net creativity stimulator coefficient, a positive real number.

"Shockley concluded that small differences in the idea associating abilities of individuals make a tremendous difference in their creativeness."
Jacob Rabinow
[266, p77   ]

Clearly a large β is desirable for maximum net contribution. The β coefficient is related in some undefined way to our *personal* knowledge of and ability to apply creativity stimulators at a given time τ into our problem.

An idealized useful creativity stimulator should:

● Aim us toward acquiring fresh viewpoints and *new* ideas.

● Be specific, clearly stateable (i.e. not vague and fuzzy), and reasonably simple.

● Be practical and useful by engineers in solving *new* problems without having to go into the details of why it works.

● Be generally applicable and consistent with the basic six step problem solving process of Chaps. 3-9.

● Suggest action by its name.

● Have been tested by the experience of others and found helpful in actual creative work.

Since we may need one or more creativity stimulators at many points in the problem solving process of Chaps. 3-9, it is appropriately a separate topic. Only we personally can identify *when* we feel the need for an idea stimulator. *Which* one(s) we choose to use is related to our total knowledge of them. Many problem solvers know of only a few but use them well. More

"Unfortunately, many inventors, writers and other innovators tend to 'cleanup' their description of the process so that it sounds either quite neat and orderly or highly mystical. In fact the mind often proceeds in quite a disorderly and non-logical route to new ideas - - - "
M. O. Edwards
[92, p24]

mature problem solvers use a larger number, perhaps

unconsciously, and are able to bring significantly

more new useful ideas into consciousness.

We shall acquire a more specific feel for creativity

stimulators in Sec. 14-2.

Discussion Topics

1. Defend or refute: "I feel like I only need to know the 'fundamentals' of EE and as many circuits and how they operate as I can absorb. All this esoteric bit about 'creativity stimulators' is useless to my future as a circuits engineer with the Circutronics Co."

2. Does an engineer *really* need creativity stimulators? Isn't it enough to just mechanically follow the various charts and procedures in Chaps. 3-9?

3. Identify the creativity stimulators you have used, perhaps unconsciously, in the past when faced with a new engineering problem.

4. Defend or refute: "I can't use any creativity stimulator unless I thoroughly understand *why* it works!"

5. Explore possible relationships between creativity stimulators and inhibitors via the more realistic relation:

$$C(\tau) = C_o e^{+(\beta - \alpha)\tau}$$

What relation between β and α would you want? Are β and α time invariant constants under realistic engineering problem solving conditions?

14-2 Some Creativity Stimulators

" - - one needs to know that aids in the form of princi-ples, procedures and operative mechanisms can be quite useful, and this writer urges you to experiment with those which stimulate your curi-osity or interest."
M. O. Edwards
[91, p24]

THE SUBJECTIVE NATURE OF CREATIVITY STIMULATORS

is inherent, an important point we must initially

realize. Not everyone can use a given stimulator with

identical results because of differences in personal

make up and background. Stated another way, if one

creativity stimulator fails to give us a fresh viewpoint

on our engineering problem or fails to stimulate to

truly new ideas, we discard it and try others which

do 'work' for *us*.

    GOOD JUDGMENT AND 'FOLLOW UP' are required for

the new ideas created from using any creativity

stimulator. This important point is sometimes missed

in the excitement of having created a dramatic new

idea or fresh insight, and we may feel, "That's it!

It's *complete*!" A new idea is rarely complete at its

birth, refinement being necessary by application of

good judgment and 'follow-up'. Acquisition of the

fresh new viewpoint or idea is only *one* step in a

total disciplined process described in Chaps. 3-9 and

not an end in itself. Edwards [91, p24] has the correct

perspective:

> "The creative methods or techniques described
> here are not designed to replace more
> orthodox methods of problem solving, such
> as the use of logic and the scientific
> method, nor are they guaranteed to work in
> all circumstances; rather they should be
> considered as additional approaches which
> should be used in combination with traditional
> problem solving methods."

    SOME CREATIVITY STIMULATORS are in Table 14-1 in

a form useful to engineers. The literature on creative

stimulators has suffered from fragmentation. A typical

book or article elucidates only a few techniques

though others have long been known. This first collection

"A great deal of polishing and re-polishing will be needed before the ideas suggested by these techniques end up as finished products."
John E. Arnold [11]

from many sources is probably not complete in itself, but it potentially gives you considerably more new idea-acquiring tools than heretofore.

Some stimulators have been extensively written about by pioneers such as Rossman, Osborn, and others. You will meet in the references some of those who initially recognized a given stimulator's relation and value to creative thought.

Some stimulators may seem intuitively obvious to us but we may not have considered the possibility of repetitively using them.

"There is no fool-proof procedure for getting good new ideas."
Ira G. and
Marthann E. Wilson
[378, p125]

Examine all of Table 14-**1** and adopt those which help the most in solving your problems. You can hardly be expected to master all these now, or even an appreciable fraction. Rather, you may want to refer to and later use Table 14-1 in your industrial practice of engineering, especially when you get 'hung-up', as all engineers do, and need a fresh viewpoint or a new idea.

Discussion Topics

1. Why are creativity stimulators subjective rather than objective in nature?

2. How will you determine *which* stimulator from Table 14-1 you will use on a given engineering problem? Is knowing *where* to use it in the problem solving process of any importance?

3. Just because one creativity stimulator worked

TABLE 14-1
COLLECTION OF CREATIVITY STIMULATORS

● **ABANDONMENT, TEMPORARY** (Laying it aside, stopping work, sleeping on it)

"Long since, I learned the trick of 'walking away from it'."
A. D. Moore
[217, p91]

    Essence Temporarily decide to stop project activity.
    Akin To Flash of Insight, Illumination, Incubation, Sleep, Escaping.
    Example While trying to create a low drift battery operated DC amplifier using conventional transistors, after little success I temporarily abandoned it. Later the fresh viewpoint of using field effect transistors occurred and was successful.
    Ref. [234, Ch. 15] [151, p84]

● **ADAPTING**

    Essence Are there other areas where similar problems existed and have been solved? Will the same solutions apply here? What could be copied?
    Akin To Modify, Copy, Rearrange, Restructure.
    Example Adapting the gas turbine to the helicopter, replacing the piston engine cast a fresh outlook on helicopter use.

● **ADDITION TO**

    Essence Questions Osborn suggests [234, p258]: How can we add more strength? How could this be reinforced? How can I add more value? Extra feature?
    Akin To Multiplication. Use of auxiliary.
    Example Creation of ultrasonic remote control for TV sets was an addition. Millions were sold.
    Ref. [234, Ch. 23]

● **ALTERNATIVE APPROACHES**

"I usually make a list in the order of their importance of all devices which I think might accomplish the result."
E. C. Loetscher
[196, p73]

    Essence "You ask, 'What are the alternatives?'" [151, p60]
               " - - make a list of all your ideas." [234, p154]
    Akin To Brainstorming, Check Lists, Listing.
    Example An engineer creating the power supply for an unmanned space probe initially considers all known power generation means from conventional turbine-generators to direct energy conversion.
    Ref. [268] [234] [151, Ch. 8] [Ch. 6]

● **ANALOGY** (Metaphorical Analogies)

"Analogy suggests rather than proves."
Edward Hodnett
[151, p143]

    Essence Possible likeness(es) of the familiar and the present problem. Gordon [123, p37] identifies classes: personal analogy, direct analogy, symbolic analogy, and fantasy analogy.
    Akin To Nature's Way, Imagining/ Visualizing, Similarity/Contrast, Gordon Technique. Metaphors, Association.
    Example Rabinow invented the electromagnetic particle clutch by analogy to an earlier electrostatic clutch.
    Ref. [378, p154] [151, Ch. 18] [279, p74] [123]

● **ANALYSIS** See 'Mathematics'.

● **ANOMALY STUDY**

    Essence Observe and study phenomena which are deviations from the usual.
    Akin To Curiosity, Special Range Study.
    Example The anomaly of 'voltage breakdown' in the I-V curve of semiconductor diodes led to creation of families of stable voltage reference zener diodes.

● **ASSOCIATION**

"Association is a very important component in getting a new idea."
Ira G. and Marthann Wilson
[378, p127]

    Essence " - - the phenomenon by which imagination gears itself to memory and causes one thought to lead to another." Alex F. Osborn [234, p120]
    Akin To Memory, Combining, Analogy, Imagining/Visualizing.
    Example John Alby Spencer's invention of the Klixon bimetal switch (U. S. Patent 1,448,240) resulted from associating his boyhood observation of a snapping furnace door with controlling an electric iron temperature. Moore tells the fascinating story [217, p83].
    Ref. [234] [378] [217]

● **ASSUMPTION CHALLENGING**

    Essence Raudsepp suggests we "Question every accepted assumption about your problem. How did they emerge? Who made them? How valid are they really?" [272, p208]
    Akin To Questioning, Observation, Curiosity.
    Example By challenging the assumption that all space vehicles must move with respect to the earth's surface, 'stationary' satellites were created and launched forming communication links between continents. (Incidentally, it also challenged the popular assumption microwaves couldn't be sent beyond the horizon!)
    Ref. [272] [151, Ch. 7]

● **ATTRIBUTE LISTING**

    Essence "Crawford lists the attributes - - - -, and then by changing or modifying one or more of the attributes or specifications, he brings originally unrelated objects together to form a new combination - - - -." John E. Arnold [11, p255]
    Akin To Morphological Analysis.

TABLE 14-1 (CONT.)
COLLECTION OF CREATIVITY STIMULATORS

● ATTRIBUTE LISTING (CONT.)
    Example "Wooden-Handle screwdriver attributes:
             1. Round Steel Shank
             2. Wooden handle riveted to it
             3. Wedge shaped end
             4. Manually operated
             5. Torque provided by twisting action
             The round shank was changed to a hex shank, so that a wrench could be used to
             increase the torque. The wooden handle has been replaced by a molded plastic
             handle, and thereby cutting down on breakage and danger from electrical shock.
             The end has been modified to fit all kinds of screw heads. [11]"
    Ref.   [91] [11]

● AUXILIARY, USE OF
    Essence "An additive that makes the solution possible without - - - becoming a
             substantial part of it." Hodnett [151, p95]
    Akin To Imaging/Visualizing. Addition, Subtraction.
    Example A die for a drawn metal electric motor enclosure.
    Ref.   [151, Ch. 13]

● BIG DREAM
    Essence "a. Think the biggest dream possible - - -
             b. Read, study, and think about every subject connected with your
                 big dream - - -
             c. Drop down a dream or so, then engineer your dream into reality" [91, p231];
                 [333].
    Akin To Imagining/Visualizing, Flash of Insight, Illumination, Wishing, Intuition.
    Example Creation of the safety razor by King Camp Gillette [11, p258].
    Ref.   [91] [11] [232] [333] [Ch. 10]

● BLAST AND REFINE
    Essence 1. Blast the problem
             2. Create ideas
             3. Refine them
    Akin To Competition, Cost Reduction
    Example c.f. [216].
    Ref.   [216]

● BLOCK DIAGRAM MANIPULATION
    Essence 1. Identify function blocks for thing to be created.
             2. Creatively 'play' with combinations.
             3. Propose a plausible system.
    Akin To Input/Output Study.
    Example A computer 'flow chart' prepared before the detailed program is written.

● BRAINSTORMING
    Essence 1. A selected group of creative individuals (5-10 is ideal) is assembled by a
                 skilled leader.
             2. A clear problem is posed.
             3. Multiple 'brainstorm' ideas are proposed by the group.
             4. Ideas are recorded in some way.
             5. An evaluation session is held later.
             6. Success guides include [233, Ch. 33]:
                 a. A skilled leader is required.
                 b. Problem should be a specific single problem.
                 c. Judgment is deferred (no fault-finding).
                 d. Uninhibited 'wildness' is welcomed.
                 e. Quantity of ideas is sought.
                 f. Combination and improvement of ideas is sought.
                 g. Spirit of mutual encouragement pervades group.
             7. 'Brainstorm Sessions' may also be conducted *individually*.
    Akin To Alternative Approaches. Imagining/Visualizing.
    Example "Suggest ideas for storing energy"
             1. High C capacitors   5. Water tower
             2. Convert to high energy   6. Large flywheel
                 chemical bonds   7. Large L
             3. Batteries
             4. Compress spring   101 ideas were created by 8 seniors in 25
                                            minutes in this particular session.
    Ref.   [233] [360, p46] [252] [238] [204] [11, p60] [4, p44] [357, p84] [399, p64]

● CAN'T BE DONE
    Essence 1. Find precisely what 'can't be done.'
             2. Apply deliberate creative effort to propose ways it *can* be done.
    Akin To Impossibility, Abandonment, Delaying.
    Example Creation of Gillette safety razor [11, p259]
    Ref.   [11, p251] [229].

"Mr. Tesla will accom-
plish great things,
but he certainly
never will (create an
AC generator)."
 Prof. Poeschl
 [253, p41]

TABLE 14-1 (CONT.)
COLLECTION OF CREATIVITY STIMULATORS

● CASE HISTORY See 'Historical Review.'

● CATALOG STUDY
  Essence Browse through catalogs directly or peripherally related to our problem.
  Akin To Reading, Play, Cost Reducing.
  Example Browsing through a catalog on strip recorders, an idea for a new laboratory
           experiment to teach students the interaction of thermodynamics and electric
           motors occurred.
  Ref.   [91]

● CHALLENGING ACCEPTED SCIENTIFIC THEORIES
  Essence 1. Dig out what has been taken for granted by others who have attacked the
              same invention problem.
           2. Challenge it.
           3. Set up a line of attack. [229, p152]
  Akin To Questioning, Curiosity.
  Example By challenging iteration of the mechanical-to-electrical energy conversion
           theory of telephone amplification, DeForest realized that telephone currents
           could be amplified directly by a grid-controlled electron current in an
           evacuated chamber. The triode vacuum tube was born. [229, p152]
  Ref.   [229]

● CHECK LIST

"Probably the best
check list---is
the one he makes
up for himself."
John E. Arnold
[11, p254]

  Essence Own Check List
           Prepare a specific list of problems needing solutions and possible solution
           ideas needing follow-up.
           Prepared Check Lists
           Many of these are scattered throughout this book. They can prod us into the
           desired new viewpoint. Others are in [234, p217, 284]; [89, p107]; [378, p135];
           and periodically in engineering journals.
  Akin To Listing, Formula, Approach.
  Example See Ch. 4 and following chapters.
  Ref.   [234] [89] [378] [11]

● COMBINING

"A creative thinker
evolves no new
ideas. He actually
evolves new combi-
nations of ideas
that are already in
his mind."
Elmer C. Easton
[86, p173]

  Essence " - - the act of bringing things together into new combinations - - "
           [234, p116, p280, also Ch. XVI]
  Akin To Synthesis, Matrix of Ideas, Associating, Forced Relationship, Morphological
           Analysis.
  Example " - - (Edison) speculated what the result would be if these (phonograph and
           kinetograph) were somehow combined, and the combination led to talking
           pictures." [357, p87]
  Ref.   [86] [357]

● COMPETITION (Profit Motive)
  Essence "What can my competitor do to go me one better?" Osborn [234, p279].
  Akin To Incentive, Vicarious Thinking, Cost Reducing, Empathetic Involvement.
  Example The pioneering 6BY4 ceramic triode vacuum tube was created partially from the ini-
           tial stimulus of thinking "If I were an engineer with the competing company how
           would I come at this problem better than we are now doing?"
  Ref.   [234, p278]

● COMPUTERS
  Essence Computer Programming.
  Akin To Focusing Deliberately, Mathematics, Graphics.
  Example From the theoretical formula for torque of an induction motor, an engineer
           writes a program. The print out plots the torque-speed curve for several supply
           frequencies. A fresh view of controlling the motor speed by a variable
           supply frequency resulted.

● CONCENTRATING See 'Focusing'.

● CONFERENCE/MEETING ATTENDANCE
  Essence 1. Selecting the conference/meeting.
           2. Getting to go/going.
           3. Attentive listening/notetaking.
  Akin To Listening, Notetaking, Talking With Others.
  Example While attending a Southeastern Electric Exchange Conference in Atlanta and
           hearing a paper on air pollution, a new idea (later proven successful)
           was instantly born for solving a problem on a bed with filtered air for
           asthmatics which I was developing.

● CONTRAST
  Essence 1. Determine what exists now for solving the problem.
           2. Ask, "What is the contrast of this?"
  Akin To Reversal, Similarity/Contrast
  Example I created and successfully built the first coaxial amplifier for testing
           6BY4 tubes at 900 Mhz. Tube removal was manual. The 'contrast' was

TABLE 14-1 (CONT.)
COLLECTION OF CREATIVITY STIMULATORS

● CONTRAST   (CONT.)
  Example   automatic ejection which was easily incorporated.
  Ref.   [360, p42]

● COURSE TAKING
  Essence   Take formal course(s) related to the problem area.
  Akin To   Listening, Notetaking, Talking With Others.
  Example   Many engineers participate in company and Graduate courses. Fresh creative
            viewpoints of their on-the-job engineering problems generally result.
  Ref.   [Ch. 10]

● CURIOSITY
  Essence   Inquire, perhaps with care, into that which excites us [37].
  Akin To   Playing, Directing Interest.
  Example   Moore's creation of the new electrospherics and magnetospherics [217, p76].
  Ref.   [217] [37]

● DEADLINE SETTING   (Scheduling, Programming)

"I got myself in
a spot where I
had to finish
it on time."
  Walter Chrysler
  [61, p218]

  Essence   " - - - Establishment of firm deadlines and numerous subdeadlines in the course
            of a project." [360, p82].
  Akin To   Planning
  Example   President Kennedy's setting of a deadline to have a man on the moon within the
            decade lead to many fresh scientific and engineering viewpoints and creation of
            entirely new systems in the 1960's.
  Ref.   [360] [234, p218] [217, p119] [Ch. 17]

● DECISION(S)

"Professionals know
that they can't create
unless they make a
start." A. Osborn
  [234, p215]

  Essence   To reach a clear-cut planned course of action.   (Crisp decisions may free us
            from doubt and lead to entirely new viewpoint(s).
  Akin To   Starting, Choices, Judging.
  Example   C.f. Ch. 4, Section 4-2.
  Ref.   [234, p215] [Ch. 4] [Ch. 10]

● DEFICIENCY IDENTIFICATION   (Weaknesses)

"After noting a
deficiency, I set
out to determine
what it is, - - - "
  H. M. Friendly
  [112, p110]

  Essence   1. " - - find its defects - - - " W. H. Carrier [54, p75].
            2. Let them suggest improvements to us.
  Akin To   Criticism, Tear Down Sessions, Observation, Focusing Deliberately, Listing,
            Reverse Brainstorm.
  Example   Tesla, over the objections of his Professor, identified arcing on a DC machine
            as undesirable. He later invented the new polyphase machine
  Ref.   [54] [232] [112] [Ch. 7]

● DELAYING   See 'Abandonment'.

● DIRECTING INTEREST

"These things are
found by the persons
who are interested
in them."
  Seneca
  [287, p23]

  Essence   Deliberately guiding our initial small interest toward a subject or problem
            to see if it grows and gives us a fresh viewpoint.
  Akin To   Focusing, Curiosity, Talking With Others.
  Example   The late Professor W. F. Fagen initially directed my interest toward direct
            energy conversion. It subsequently grew and resulted in an entirely fresh
            viewpoint of 'energy conversion'.
  Ref.   [287] [Ch. 4]

● EDISONIAN METHOD   (Try Everything, Random Search, Trial-and-Error)

"Its heart and
soul - - is
perseverance."
  Osborn
  [234, p210]

  Essence   "The Edisonian theory called for trying everything." [234, p156]
  Akin To   Experimentation.
  Example   Edison's search for a satisfactory incandescent lamp filament.
  Ref.   [234] [91, p23] [378, p153] [151, Ch. 16] [279] [217, p104]
            [Ch. 16]

● EMPATHETIC INVOLVEMENT
  Essence   "One imagines himself to be the problem; he then tends to acquire a closer
            feeling for the problem, which can provide a new outlook and in turn a
            preferable concept and solution" [357, p86].
  Akin To   Vicarious Thinking, Analogies.
  Example   If I were this amplifier active device, what source impedance would I want to
            see for minimum noise figure? (The answer gave a fresh view to noise testing
            actual amplifiers!)
  Ref.   [272, p213] [357]

● ENCOURAGEMENT

"We should do
anything possible
to encourage people
to get more and
better ideas."
  Ernest Berger
  [35, p102]

  Essence   1. Find someone needing encouragement.
            2. Find ways to encourage him.
            3. Observe how it stimulates you, perhaps in an entirely different area.
  Akin To   Motivation, Emotion, Talking With Others.
  Example   " - - I esteem greatly the experiments which you have lately made."
            Octave Chanute [58, p128].
  Ref.   [58] [234] [Ch. 10]

TABLE 14-1 (CONT.)
COLLECTION OF CREATIVITY STIMULATORS

● **ESCAPING**

"Often some of the best things we do in this world are an escape."
Paul Tournier
[345, p107]

Essence	Temporarily escape from a given situation, problem, or environment to renew ourselves.
Akin To	Retreating, Walking, Solitude, Nature, Travel, Illumination, Flash of Insight, Abandonment.
Example	While engaged in research on a logarithmic attenuator device, I felt the need for a new fresh idea. 'Escaping' to my wife's hometown for a weekend, the needed idea suddenly came in the midst of watching a high school play.
Ref.	[345] [Ch. 10]

● **EXAGGERATION** See 'Magnify'.

● **EXPERIENCE**

Essence	"The inventor must have this ability to search through everything he has ever experienced that may have some bearing on a problem - - -." Jacob Rabinow [266, p83].
Akin To	Memory.
Example	Based on his unfavorable experience of adjusting his watch for a year, Rabinow invented the widely used self-regulating watch. [266, p87]
Ref.	[234, p68] [151, Ch. 20] [266] [Ch. 3]

● **EXPERIMENT**

Essence	1. Think what should be done. 2. Assemble needed apparatus. 3. Conduct the experiment. 4. Record/interpret results.
Akin To	Edisonian Method, Verification.
Example	" - - (Tesla) had planned the experiment so that the first bolts of man-made lightning ever created would shoot from the top of the 200-foot-tall mast." [232, p183]
Ref.	[232] [Chs. 8, 16]

● **EXPLAINING IT**

" - - I remember when I was working at my electric motor what a help it was to talk it over."
Joseph Henry
[145, p18]

Essence	"One explains the problem, the difficulty, to a good listener and then carefully attends the listener's reactions and statement; - - - what he says could well stimulate the poser of the problem with a good idea" [357, p83].
Akin To	Talking With Others, Listening.
Example	While engaged in research on thermionic energy converters, I had a difficult problem designing the containing envelope. Explaining the problem to a technician friend resulted in four new ideas.
Ref.	[360] [357] [145]

● **FACT ACCUMULATION**

Essence	Find all the facts you can relevant to the problem.
Akin To	Information Retrieval, Observation, Notetaking, Recording, Study.
Example	Engineers and scientists accumulated facts on the environmental constraints of the human body and were led to fresh viewpoints resulting in creation of practical space suits for astronauts.
Ref.	[234, p145] [151] [Ch. 4, 11]

● **FANTASY**

Essence	" - - imagine the best of all possible worlds, a helpful universe permitting the most satisfying possible viewpoint leading to the most elegant of all possible solutions." William J. J. Gordon [123, p51]
Akin To	Imagining/Visualizing, Play, Nature's Way, Analogy, Similarity/Contrast.
Example	An inventor has the task of creating a system for heavy army tanks to get over bottomless crevasses up to 10 feet wide. He observes two ants crossing a chasm. He entertains fantasy constructs resulting in the idea of welding special hitches to the front and rear of each tank so that like ants, they could be connected to form their own bridge at will - - - [123, p131].
Ref.	[123] [Ch. 10]

● **FLASH OF INSIGHT** See 'Illumination'.

● **FOCUSING DELIBERATELY**

"I finally concentrate on what appears to be the best idea - - - "
R. B. Bryant
[48, p115]

Essence	Deliberately address ourselves to the problem or idea, thinking of it exclusively.
Akin To	Concentration, Thinking, Meditation, Choices.
Example	Robert Goddard's inspiring creation of rockets. [120]
Ref.	[48] [120] [360, p80] [234, Chs. 12, 18] [279] [Ch. 10]

● **FORCED RELATIONSHIP**

Essence	1. Isolate the elements of the problem. 2. Find the relationships between/among these elements. 3. Record the relationships. 4. Analyze/find the patterns (or basic ideas present). 5. Develop new ideas from patterns [91, p22].
Akin To	Matrix of Ideas, Mathematics, Alternative Approaches, Morphological Analysis.
Example	The idea for the first solar electric motor (SEM) was created from considering the possibilities of forcing a relation between the new solar cells and old known DC motor concepts [257]

TABLE 14-1 (CONT.)
COLLECTION OF CREATIVITY STIMULATORS

● FORCED RELATIONSHIP (CONT.)
   Ref. [91] [257

● GENERALIZE
   Essence " - - mental feedback of a series of observations or experiences leading to an improved judgment." [360, p104] We may generalize deliberately (conscious mind) or accidentally (unconscious mind working). [234, p158]
   Akin To Flash of insight, Reflection, Review, Relaxing, Summarizing, Simplifying, Observation, Experience.
   Example James Watt's steam engine creation [87].
   Ref. [360] [87] [234]

● GORDON TECHNIQUE (Synectics)
   Essence A group attacks the underlying concept rather than the problem itself. Concepts are explored at length. Concentrating on the underlying concept prevents early closure on the problem and encourages radical applications of old techniques [225].
   Akin To Encouragement, Brainstorming.
   Example To find a new way to park automobiles in a crowded city, the group might focus on 'storing things'. [11, p265]
   Ref. [225] [91] [11] [123] [324] [192] [89]

● GRAPHING
   Essence Plot (manually or computer) theoretical or experimental curves. This simple powerful technique for obtaining a fresh viewpoint is frequently overlooked.
   Akin To Mathematics, Special Range Study.
   Example Plotting a transistor's curves gives fresh insight into why our circuit behaves as it does.

"A man's capacity as an inventor depends upon his faculty of making guesses which have some semblance of possibility - - -" Casper L. Redfield [279, p111]

● GUESSING (Hunch)
   Essence Tentative ideas, frequently radically new, are proposed which may not be initially founded on facts. Verification and modification is later done.
   Akin To Alternative Identification, Intuition.
   Example Land's invention of the Polaroid camera was the result of, among other factors, correctly guessing there was a market for such a product in the face of extensive market research to the contrary. [270, p133]
   Ref. [279] [270] [Ch. 10]

● HISTORICAL REVIEW (Prior Art, Case History)
   Essence 1. Accumulate relevant prior art documents or apparatus.
         2. Study/review.
   Akin To Literature Search, Patent Search, Competition.
   Example Powerful numerous factual engineering examples are accumulated in Stanford University's Engineering Case Program.
   Ref. [Ch. 11]

" - - constructing and building hobbies are more stimulating creatively than collecting hobbies." Eugene Raudsepp [272, p207]

● HOBBIES
   Essence Engaging in a spare time activity solely because we enjoy it.
   Akin To Play, Relaxation, Flash of Insight, Illumination, Recreation, Self Renewal.
   Example "I saw one such in the glassmaking department of General Electric's research laboratory. During his lunch hour, a young scientist was at 'work' making a ship model out of glass." [234, p74]
   Ref. [234] [272] [Ch. 10]

"Be on the alert for hunches, - - " Guy Suits [234, p128]

● HUNCH (Intuition)
   Essence A strong recurring intuitive feeling about a problem or solution idea.
   Akin To Guess, Intuition, Illumination, Flash of Insight.
   Example Long's creation of video tape recording at Ampex was a result of his strong 'hunch' about the success of such a product [270, p134].
   Ref. [234] [270] [Ch. 10]

● IDEA NEEDLER LIST
   Essence Use a prepared list of 'idea needlers' as a stimulator.
   Akin To Check List, Approach, Formula.
   Example "How much of this is the result of custom, tradition, or opinions? Why does it have this shape? How would I design it if I had to build it in my home workshop?"
   Ref. [359] [234, p 284]   [See frequent lists throughout this text.]

● IDEA QUOTA SETTING
   Essence Set ourselves a quota of ideas to be thought up. In thinking them up, others beyond the quota may occur [234, p219].
   Akin To Brainstorming, Imagining, Focusing Deliberately.
   Example Fifteen EE students, with the goal of proposing 100 ideas for disposing/reusing of solid garbage in homes reached the goal in 22 minutes.
   Ref. [234]

● ILLUMINATION (Flash of Insight, Leap)
   Essence " - - the sudden insight or understanding that comes to us some time after we

TABLE 14-1 (CONT.)
COLLECTION OF CREATIVITY STIMULATORS

● ILLUMINATION (CONT.)

"My best inventions always come to me in a flash; - - -"
Howard Parker
[236, p103]

Essence have stopped concentrating on a problem." Von Fange [360, p93].
It consists of stages [85, p30]:
1. Preparation
2. Frustration/Incubation
3. Sudden Insight
4. Verification
This phenomenon because of its personal drama, frequent appearance, and importance has been reported or studied by many. [234, Ch. 15];[151, p173, 179ff]; [279, p101];[254, p387]; [305, p5]; [369, Ch.4] and others.
Reported conditions favoring the flash include: A do-nothing period; yoga, bath, shaving, sleeping, chopping wood, theatre, sermons and many others.

Akin To Imagining/Visualizing, Graphics, Subconscious.

Example Tesla's 1882 creation of the AC motor based on the new idea of a rotating magnetic field. [232, p48]

Ref. [360] [85] [234] [151] [279] [254] [305] [232] [236] [369]

● IMAGINING/VISUALIZING

"I regard the imaginative faculty as chief in value to the inventor - - -"
Elihu Thomson
[279, p73]

Essence "Imagination is the association in new relations of ideas already possessed by the mind." Edwin J. Prindle [259, p522]. Osborn [234, p112]identifies three classes:
1. Visual Imagery: The power to see things in the mind's eye.
2. Reproductive Imagination: Enables us to deliberately bring pictures *back* into our minds.
3. Structural Visualization: An instinctive ability to construct in the mind's eye from a flat blueprint a clear picture of a solid object.
Other classifications exist [179]; [104, p13].

Akin To Illumination, Flash of Insight, Graphics Conscious Mind.

Example "Tesla visualized a power-and-broadcasting station which would employ thousands of persons" [234, p203].

Ref. [234] [151, Ch. 21] [279, p212] [232] [368] [217, p82] [259, p579] [179] [104]

● IMPROVEMENT SEARCHING

"About 50,000 patents are now issued every year, and about 40,000 of them are nothing but improvements on ideas already patented."
Malcolm Buckley
[234, p176]

Essence 1. Select an embodiment of the present art.
2. Search for improvement ideas.

Akin To Imagining, Deficiency Identification.

Example The automobile is the composite result of the thousands of engineers' and inventors' searching for improvements.

Ref. [234, p178] [379]

● INCUBATION See 'Abandonment'.

● INVERSION See 'Reversal'.

● LACK OF KNOWLEDGE

Essence "We like to take people who are not educated in their line and put them on to research because then they don't know what can't be done and they'll try." Charles F. Kettering [172]

Example See Ch. 11, Examples 9 and 10.
Ref. [172]

● LAWS AND EFFECTS STUDY

Essence Examine descriptive lists of known physical laws and effects [150].   Let them suggest possible new ideas for our problem.
Physics texts may be helpful stimulators.

Akin To New Uses.

Example From studying the 'pinch effect' an engineer created a new idea for a contact-less means of switching current in an auto radio power supply, replacing the trouble prone mechanical vibrator.

Ref. [150]

● LISTENING

Essence Riveting our mind and ears on what is being said. May involve reception, comparing with what we already know, and formation of new idea proposals.

Akin To Focusing deliberately, Conference/Meeting Attendance, Talking With Others.

Example From listening to advice on electromagnets given by Henry, Morse invented the telegraph [379, p120].

Ref. [379] [Ch. 12]

● LISTING See 'Check Lists'.

● LITERATURE SEARCH See 'Historical Review'.

TABLE 14-1 (CONT.)
COLLECTION OF CREATIVITY STIMULATORS

● MAGNIFY

Essence   Scaling up. Osborn suggests helpful questions [234, pp259, 261, 284]: What if this were blown up to the nth degree? What if this were preposterously *over*-stated? How about doubling it? More time? Greater frequency? Stronger? Higher? Longer? Thicker? Extra value? Plus ingredient? Duplicate? Multiply? Exaggerate?

Akin To   Division

Example   "Gang drills are one of the many manufacturing steps based on multiplication" [234, p261].

Ref.   [234]

● MATHEMATICS

"(Analysis) knowledge exposes shortcomings which lead to ideas for improvements." John R. M. Alger Carl V. Hays [4, p43]

Essence   1. A model is proposed.
2. Assumptions are made.
3. Equations written and calculations made.
4. Answer is found and checked.
5. Result is 'interpreted' for new insight.

Akin To   Logic, Systemized Approach, Graphics.

Example   "Knowing the theoretical design equations for an electric generator, it is possible to use calculus of variations or iterative mathematical methods to design a lowest-weight generator for given power and efficiency requirements" [4, p43].

Ref.   [137] [4] [232]

● MEDITATION

Essence   To be thoughtfully alone with ourself.

Akin To   Flash of Insight, Illumination.

Example   Can be practiced anywhere. Reported instances favoring new idea generation involved: walking, church attending, mountain tops, in bed, flying, pullman, bathing, shaving, sailing, and concert attendance [234, pp166-167, 223-225] [279].

Ref.   [234] [279]

● MEMORY

" - - the inventive process relies mainly on past experience for the material out of which it forms the new patterns. Memory is, there-fore, highly important for invention." Joseph Rossman [279, p96]

Essence   Recalling past experiences potentially relevant to this problem.

Akin To   Meditation, Reflection, Generalizing.

Example   "Tesla depended entirely on his memory for all details" [232, p295].

Ref.   [357, p82] [151, p49] [279] [232] [217, Ch. 11]

● MINIFY

Essence   Scaling down. Osborn suggests helpful questions [234, pp264-266]: What if this were *smaller*? What could I *omit*? How about dividing? How could this be made more *compact*? Lower? Shorter? Lighter? Streamline? Why does this have to be so heavy?

Akin To   Division, Subtraction.

Example   The entire microelectronics field was created by minifying the transistor.

Ref.   [234]

● MODIFY

Essence   To change or reshape an idea, concept, or apparatus. Osborn suggests helpful questions [234, p284]: New twist? Change meaning, color, motion, sound, odor, form, shape? Other changes?

Akin To   Adapting, Questioning, Imagining/Visualizing.

Example   "Roller bearings go back to about 1500 and Leonardo da Vinci. For four centuries they were straight-sided cylinders, of less use than ball bearings. The revolutionary improvement came in 1898 when Henry Timken first patented his *tapered* roller bearing. This entailed but a slight modification of shape in the cylinder type. But the new design took care of both radial and thrust loads, and thus surpassed all other forms of bearings" [234, p247].

Ref.   [234]

● MORPHOLOGICAL ANALYSIS (Morphological Box, Function Matrix, Matrix of Ideas)

"I recommend it to you very highly." John E. Arnold [11]

Essence   The method attributed to Zwicky [403, p118] and described by Arnold [11] consists of:
1. State problem broad and generally.
2. Define independent variables broad and generally.
3. Each independent variable becomes an axis on a 'morphological chart'. For n independent variables, we have a chart of n dimensions. (Two dimensional charts are called idea matrix.)
4. Each independent variable is expressed in a number of ways. These are laid out with unit dimensions on each of the n axes.
5. Each 'drawer of idea combinations' is examined for problem solution possibility. Some will be already invented. Some will be impractical. Some no one may have thought of before.

Akin To   Attribute Listing, Association, Forced Relationships, Check Lists, Brainstorming.

Example   Problem [11]: Getting something from one place to another via a powered vehicle. Independent variables: Type vehicle, power source, operating media.

TABLE 14-1 (CONT.)
COLLECTION OF CREATIVITY STIMULATORS

● MORPHOLOGICAL ANALYSIS (CONT.)
   Example

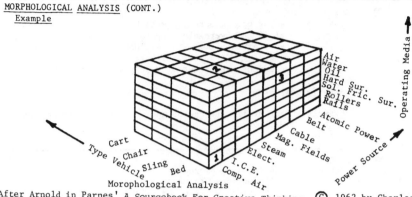

Morphological Analysis

(After Arnold in Parnes' *A Sourcebook For Creative Thinking*. Ⓒ 1962 by Charles
Scribner's Sons. Used by permission.)
         Drawer #1 is characterized by a bed-type vehicle, moving over rails, powered
         by compressed air. Similar for other 'drawers'.
   Ref.   [403] [11] [91, p22] [357, p83] [4, p39]

● MULTIPLE PROJECTS
   Essence   Carry several projects. When one goes sour for need of new ideas, temporarily
           drop it. Work on another project. When we come back we may have the needed
           fresh viewpoint or new idea.
   Akin To   Abandonment, Scheduling, Planning.
   Example   "Edison habitually switched from one project to another and worked on several
           simultaneously." [234, p165]
   Ref.   [234]

● MULTIPLICATION   See 'Magnify'.

● NATURE'S WAY

"Nature's scheme of
things is revealed
to those who search."
M. O. Edwards
[91, p23]

   Essence   Astutely look around in nature and find a basically similar problem. Observe
           how solved. Let it suggest new viewpoints.
   Akin To   Observation, Analogy, Synectics, Alternative Approaches.
   Example   Creation of honeycomb structural insulation material, originally for the B58
           bomber, was by analogy to bee honeycombs.
   Ref.   [357, p82] [4, p42] [192, p71] [279] [91] [123]

● NECESSITY   See 'Needs Identification'.

● NEED IDENTIFICATION

"The inventor experi-
ences a need which
he wishes to satisfy."
Joseph Rossman
[279, p81]

   Essence   A need, perhaps previously not specifically recognized, is brought into
           consciousness. See Ch. 4, Section 4-2.
   Akin To   Observation, Necessity.
   Example   See Section 4-2.
   Ref.   [279] [Ch. 4]

● NEW EXPERIENCE SEEKING
   Essence   Deliberately seek out new experiences likely to evoke new idea combinations
           for us.
   Akin To   Experience, Travel, Self Renewal.
   Example   As a result of a desire to have new fresh creative experiences in solar energy
           conversion, I worked a summer at Goddard Space Flight Center in the Space
           Power Technology branch. Many new ideas resulted.
   Ref.   [Ch. 10] [Ch. 3]

● NEW USES (Other Uses)

" - - the very life
of a new product
depends on thinking
up many new uses."
Alex F. Osborn
[234, p233]

   Essence   " - - discovering a fact, then imagining what it could be useful for,
           - - - " [137]
   Akin To   Imagining, Brainstorming, Vicarious Thinking.
   Example   "In refining petroleum to get kerosene they had a troublesome by-product--
           gasoline. They could find no use for gasoline, or even a way to get rid
           of it" [173, p21].
   Ref.   [234, p178ff] [279] [137] [173]

● NEW SCIENTIFIC FACT STUDY
   Essence   Inform yourself of new scientific facts from research. Creatively probe how
           to use these on your problem.
   Akin To   Study, Informing Yourself.
   Example   Slepian's creation of Westinghouse's line of De-ion power circuit breakers
           was made using this technique [229, p157].
   Ref.   [229]

● NOTETAKING
   Essence   Simply jot down on paper what we are thinking about, feeling, seeing, or
           hearing for later use and idea stimulation.

TABLE 14-1 (CONT.)
COLLECTION OF CREATIVITY STIMULATORS

● NOTETAKING (CONT.)

"I carry with me at all times a pad for putting down these ideas - - -."
R. S. Bassett
[279, p68]

Akin To   Writing, Notebook Writing, Check Lists.
Example   See Ch. 24.
Ref.   [279] [234] [Ch. 15]

● NOTEBOOK WRITING (Journal)

" - - the fresh start made with these note- books was worthwhile."
Robert Hutchings Goddard
[121, p41]

Essence   Simply write down our thoughts and ideas in a notebook. The act of writing or sketching frequently suggests other new ideas, reveals gaps in our thinking, exposes unsolved problems, and uncovers weaknesses.
Akin To   Notetaking, Writing, Sketching.
Example   See Ch. 24.
Ref.   [121] [360, p173] [234, p168] [217, p144] [Ch. 15]

● OBSERVATION

" - - - observation of the flight of buzzards leads me to believe that they regain their lateral balance - - - by a torsion of the tips of the wings."
Wilbur Wright
[391, p18]

Essence   To inspect, take note of, watch, or pay attention to. Implies a keen awareness, perhaps seeing what others missed.
Akin To   Curiosity, Interest.
Example   "Dr. Willis R. Whitney - - - - observed that the short-wave radio operators maintaining contact with Admiral Richard E. Byrd during his South Pole Expedition developed fever while on duty. Because fever had been found promising as a therapeutic agent, Dr. Whitney built a shortwave device based on that observation to generate fevers. He called it a 'radiotherm'." [260, p178]
Ref.   [391] [260] [234] [279, p93] [232, p181] [217, p176ff]

● OMISSION See 'Subtraction'.

● ORDER OF MAGNITUDE

Essence   Make a 'ballpark' calculation or estimate of magnitude.
Akin To   Mathematics, Educated Guess.
Example   See Ch. 27.
Ref.   [Ch. 16]

● OTHER USES See 'New Uses'.

● PARTITIONING (Sub-Dividing, Factoring the Problem)

Essence   " - - subdivide the objective into discrete elements. Generate ideas for each element separately." Von Fange [360, p171].
Akin To   Division.
Example   Henry Kaiser saw his problem of wanting to build ships as no steel, no shipyard, no experienced personnel, no plans, and no money. He proposed an original method of ship construction based on prefabrication. He became the most successful shipbuilder in the world in World War II. [188, p142]
Ref.   [360] [188, p142] [234, p135] [151, p28] [378, p138] [Chs. 4, 6]

● PATENT GAZETTE STUDY

" - - over a million patents have expired and are free to anyone."
M. L. Clevett, Jr.
[63, p27]

Essence   Thumb through issues of *Official Gazette*, a weekly publication of the United States Patent Office. Contains drawings and abstracts of patented inventions. [63, p27]
Akin To   Reading.
Example   To develop an idea for an easier less painful way to inject fluids in the body than the standard needle, you browse through the *Gazette*. You find a picture of a high-pressure cutting tool using a small water jet to cut solid materials. You instantly see fluid might be injected into humans via a high pressure microjet.
Ref.   [63]

● PLAY

" - - - combinatory play seems to be the essential feature in productive thought ---"
Albert Einstein
[93, p16]

Essence   "Play - - - means the activity of floating and considering associations apparently irrelevant to the problem at hand [123, p118]. It " - - - consists of random manipulation and experimentation" [279, p93]. It is pleasurable, satisfying, and exercised for amusement.
"Boys at play show the whole inventive process at work. There is a flash of inspiration or the development of some need, the search through experiences, and the hope for some method of achieving it, the swift assembling of scraps of knowledge, ideas and dreams from which a method is evolved, and finally there is tireless energy in carrying out the plan." G. Marconi [199].
Akin To   Curiosity, Relaxing, Recreation, Self Renewal, Experimentation.
Example   Rabinow was 'playing' with the electrostatic clutch in his lab when the new idea of an electromagnetic particle clutch was born [266, p85].
Ref.   [123, Ch. 5] [279] [199, p5] [266] [234, p71] [217, p92] [93]

● PRIOR ART STUDY See 'Historical Review'.

● QUESTIONING

"Why could he (Tesla) not produce lightning?"
[232, p30]

Essence   "First you isolate the subject or problem you want to think about. Then you ask a series of questions - - - ." Osborn [234, p228]
Akin To   Idea Needler, New Uses, and others.

TABLE 14-1 (CONT.)
COLLECTION OF CREATIVITY STIMULATORS

● QUESTIONING (CONT.)
  Example Why does an offshore oil drilling structure have to be erected at sea over
           the site? The question led R. G. Letourneau to create the idea of prefabricated
           floatable triangular platforms with three legs extensible to the ocean floor.
  Ref.   [234, Ch. 21] [232] [151, Ch. 5] [311, p398] [Ch. 10]

● RANDOM SEARCH See 'Edisonian Method'.

● READING - RELATED AND NON RELATED FIELDS
  Essence Set aside time to read in other fields. Start with related fields. Gradually
           spread to areas further removed from your specialty [272, p207].
  Akin To Relaxing, Curiosity, Interest, Self Study, Technical Paper Study.
  Example Product design engineers frequently read in materials and process magazines,
           forming new ideas for a problem as they read.
  Ref.   [272] [234, p77] [Chs. 10, 11]

● REARRANGE (Restructure)
  Essence Questions Osborn suggests [234, Ch. 24] How else can this be arranged? What if
           the order were changed? Should this come before that? What layout might be
           better? Where should this part be placed in relation to that? What other
           time would be best for that? Interchange components?
  Akin To Questioning, Imagining/Visualizing, Modify, Adapt.
  Example " - - in the early days of airplanes, a heated controversy developed over
           the question of whether the pusher type--or--the tractor type was better,
           with the propeller out ahead. The latter type won out. In the new jet
           planes, however, the power comes from behind;" [234, p272]
  Ref.   [234] [151, Ch. 14]

● RECORDING See 'Notebook Writing'.

● REFLECTION See "Generalize".

"Ideas come in
periods of relax-
ation, such as
riding home on a
train."
 Spencer Miller
 [279, p104]

● RELAXING
  Essence Deliberately or accidentally we temporarily physically and emotionally 'let-
           up'. Many specific ways exist to relax. Be alert to the arrival of new idea
           combinations while relaxing. Record them.
  Akin To Illumination, Flash of Insight, Play, Recreation.
  Example "Next morning, while he (Kettering) was shaving, the conception came to him
           of just how he could fit the principle of the differential gear into the
           (cash) register to subtract or add at will." [260, p60]
  Ref.   [271] [279] [260] [Ch. 10]

● RESTATEMENT OF PROBLEM
  Essence " - - to change our way of looking at (the problem)" [151, p103].
  Akin To Restructuring.
  Example "Our problem is not to design machines that will operate successfully. Our
           problem is to design machines that can also be sold for a profit." [151, p16]
  Ref.   [151] [234]

" - - contrast can
be a source of
ideative fluency."
A. F. Osborn
[234, p277]

● REVERSAL (Contrast, Inversion)
  Essence Do the opposite of present art. Helpful questions to get us started on this
           powerful technique have been posed by Osborn [234, p277]: Transpose positive
           and negative? What are the opposites? What are the negatives? How about
           up-ending? Should we turn it around? Why not up instead of down? Why not
           down instead of up? What is the opposite of the conventional? How about
           saying it in reverse? How about doing the unexpected? What can be done by
           way of surprise? Reversing the obvious? Why not try it on the other end?
           How about building it upside down?
  Akin To Rearrange, Restatement of Problem, Alternative Approaches.
  Example Early in the U.S. space program engineers had the problem of preventing
           capsule burn-up on reentry into the earth's atmosphere.

   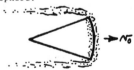

           Old Capsule   New Capsule
  Couldn't create materials to stand   Temperatures on broad base more
  high temperatures at pointed end.   controllable. Ablating materials
                                        were created.
           Use of the new capsule for manned space flights was extensive.
  Ref.   [234] [279, p72] [217, p108]

● REVIEW See 'Generalize'.

● RIDICULOUS, USING THE
  Essence Pluck the most 'ridiculous' idea from our list of ideas. Reflect upon its
           characteristics, how apply to our problem, or what it suggests.

TABLE 14-1 (CONT.)
COLLECTION OF CREATIVITY STIMULATORS

● RIDICULOUS, USING THE (CONT.)
Akin To   Play, Curiosity, Reversal, Alternative Approaches, Brainstorming.
Example   Idea of a helicopter picking up an entire field hospital and transporting
          it to where wounded are--a 'ridiculous idea' extensively used in the
          Viet Nam war.
Ref.   [360, p54]

● SCHEDULING IT   See 'Deadline Setting'.

● SELF STUDY   See 'Reading'.

● SIMILARITY/CONTRAST
Essence   Similarity
          "What is this like? What attribute has this in *common* with that? Isn't this
          the *same* as that? What about the *component* parts?" [234, p149]
          Contrast
          "What is this *unlike*? What is the point of *difference*? What about the
          opposite? How about *vice versa*? [234, p149]
Akin To   Reversal, Analogy.
Example   "Diesel wanted to burn fuel directly in the cylinders but did not know how to
          ignite it. - - - - Then the answer came from an experience with a cigar
          lighter invented by someone else and offered to Diesel to light a cigar. The
          essential features of the cigar lighter were (a) air and fuel in a cylinder,
          (b) the air in the cylinder is suddenly compressed by a piston, (c) results
          in ignition of the fuel. The similarity is striking and the principle of the
          Diesel engine is invented." K. K. Paluev [235]
Ref.   [234] [235] [360, p41]

"Engineering is an art
of simplification, and
the rules--when and
how to simplify--are
a matter of experience
and intuition."
Olle I. Elgerd

● SIMPLIFYING
Essence   Strip off non essentials, usually for purposes of (a) lowering cost, (b) making
          it easier to make, (c) improving reliability, (d) promoting acceptance.
Akin To   Subtraction, Division, Intuition, Beauty.
Example   "The early English railways had a complex, costly scheme of fastening the rails
          down to granite blocks. Along came the American, Robert Stevens, who invented
          the T-rail, the fishplate, the hooked spike, and the wood tie laid on a
          crushed rock roadbed. Much simpler, much cheaper, much better--and adopted
          worldwide within ten years." [217, p108]
Ref.   [217] [234, p267] [279, p267]

"What you do to a
situation when you
use a formula approach
is to schematize it.
You impose a pattern
on it - - - "
Edward Hodnett
[151, p89]

● SIX STEP APPROACH USE
Essence   An ordered problem solving approach is applied. [Ch. 3ff]
Akin To   Approach, Methodology, Formula
Example   "'Many people think of inventions as coming on a man all in one piece,'
          said Edison. 'Things don't happen that way, much. The phonograph, for
          example, was a long time coming, and it came step by step. For my own
          part, it started way back in the days of the civil war, when I was a young
          telegrapher in Indianapolis.' That was 1864. It took him til 1877 to work
          out his first crude model." [234, p176]
Ref.   [234] [151, Ch. 12] [Chs. 3-9]

"A great number of the
inventors sketch their
solutions as fast as
they come without
regard to their
practicability."
Joseph Rossman
[279, p61]

● SKETCHING (Drawing)
Essence   Simply use your pen and start rough sketching your ideas on paper. They do
          not initially have to be complete or neat.
Akin To   Imagining/Visualizing, Recording.
Example

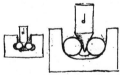

Sketches of first ball and roller bearings by Leonardo da Vinci [190, p26].

Ref.   [190] [279] [89, p32] [Ch. 15]

" - - my heart in-
structs me in the
night seasons."
Psalms 16:7
[5]

● SLEEPING
Essence   Go into the state of sleep. Record new ideas during semi-sleep or upon
          arising.
Akin To   Relaxing, Illumination, Escaping, Abandonment, Subconscious.
Example   "Have you not worked on a mathematics problem in vain for hours, gone to bed,
          and waked up with the answer neatly worked out?"[151, p179]
Ref.   [234, p163, p221] [279, p110] [5] [151] [Ch. 10]

● SPECIAL RANGE STUDY
Essence   "Is there a special range of physical conditions within which a particular
          phenomenon takes place?" [229, p158]
Akin To   Anomaly, Observation, Experimentation, Graphing.

TABLE 14-1 (CONT.)
COLLECTION OF CREATIVITY STIMULATORS

● SPECIAL RANGE STUDY (CONT.)
   Example The negative-resistance region of the tunnel diode current-voltage curve has
            resulted in many new product applications.
   Ref.   [229]

● SUBDIVIDE See 'Partitioning'.

● SUBSTITUTE
   Essence Search for a substitute. Ask: What other material, process or device could be
            used to solve or eliminate the problem?
   Akin To Modification, Adaptation, Alternative Approaches.
   Example Langmuir's substituting argon for vacuum in light bulbs, doubling the lamp
            efficiency. [234, p251]
   Ref.   [234]

● SUBTRACTING
   Essence Osborn suggests [234, p267]: What can we *eliminate*? Suppose we leave this out?
            Why not *fewer parts*? Eliminate objectionable? How can this be *streamlined*?
   Akin To Leaving it Out, Omission, Simplifying.
   Example Automotive design engineers' elimination of unnecessaries from an automobile,
            offering them as accessories only to those wanting them.
   Ref.   [234]

● SUMMARIZING/CONCLUDING
   Essence 1. Think over the totality of a situation.
            2. Force ourself to write out a specific summary or set of conclusions.
   Akin To Meditation, Reflection, Focusing, Generalizing, Simplifying.
   Example I conclude:
            1. Theoretically a circuit of form:

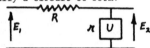

            can be made a logarithmic voltage attenuator obeying
                 $E_2 = r \log E_1 - r \log R$
            2. I know requirement on U is:

            etc. (From my research notebook.)

● SYNTHESIS See 'Combining'.

● SYNECTICS See 'Gordon Technique'.

● TALKING WITH OTHERS
   Essence 1. Search out someone we respect and trust.
            2. Talk with him about our creative work.
            3. Observe and record new viewpoints stimulated.
   Akin To Explaining it, Relationships, Listening.
   Example Samuel Morse's seeking Joseph Henry's advice and explaining his idea of the
            telegraph is well known [379, p120].
   Ref.   [379] [378] [234] [Ch. 12]

*"An intelligent
visitor with rel-
atively little
familiarity with the
subject may
contribute a great
deal."
 Ira G. and Marthann
Wilson
 [378, p132]*

● TECHNICAL PAPER STUDY See 'Reading'.

● TESTING
   Essence Conceive and physically run a controlled test to verify expected performance
            and detect weaknesses. Frequently results in fresh viewpoints. Don't
            overlook mentally testing a new idea either!
   Akin To Experimentation, Imagining/Visualizing, Vicariousness.
   Example "The mental constructs (for the polyphase machine) were built with meticulous
            care as concerned size, strength, design and material; and they were tested
            mentally, he (Nikola Tesla) maintained, by having them run for weeks--after
            which time he would examine them thoroughly for signs of wear." [232, p51]
   Ref.   [232] [Ch. 8]

● TIME ALLOCATION
   Essence Set aside a definite period for creative thinking about a specific problem.
   Akin To Deadline Setting, Scheduling, Programming.
   Example Many management 'programs' for engineering a new product, as PERT, are based
            on the concept of time allocation for thinking and working on a problem or its
            parts.
   Ref.   [234, p220] [Ch. 17]

TABLE 14-1 (CONT.)
COLLECTION OF CREATIVITY STIMULATORS

● TRAVEL
  Essence   Personal exposure to new places, people, things, and ideas by taking a trip
            for pleasure or business.
  Akin To   Observation, Accident, Illumination, Adapting and others.
  Example   The invention of negative feedback by Black occurred while he was travelling
            on the Lackawanna Ferry. Moore records the interesting story [217, p131].
  Ref.   [217] [234, p68] [233, p57] [Ch. 10]

● VALUE ANALYSIS
  Essence   Edwards [91, p23] capsulizes Miles' original work [216]:   It may be
            defined as an objective, systematic and formalized method of performing a
            job to achieve only necessary functions at minimum cost. Six questions are
            evoked concerning each part:
            a. What is it?   d. What did it cost?
            b. What must it do?   e. What else will do the job?
            c. What does it do?   f. What will that cost?
  Akin To   Competition, Cost Reducing.
  Example   See [216]   for numerous specialized examples.
  Ref.   [91] [216]

"By thinking in terms   ● VICARIOUS THINKING
of their wants, I   Essence   " - - a bridge by which we put ourselves into another's place" [234, p113].
have arrived at some   Akin To   Gordon Technique, Analogy, Empathetic Involvement.
of my best ideas."   Example   " - - were you ever a piston in a Diesel engine?" C. F. Kettering [174, p163]
E. M. Statler   Ref.   [234, p113, 278] [174]
[234, p278]

● WALKING See 'Meditation'.

● WEAKNESS IDENTIFICATION See 'Deficiency Identification'.

● WISHING
  Essence   To desire or crave creating something. Many inspired engineering inventions
            started with 'a wish' by an individual.
  Akin To   Motivation, Emotion, Needs Identification.
  Example   "Fulton said 'I wish I could run a boat with an engine; and did it."
            G. Marconi [200, p202].
  Ref.   [200] [232, p24] [Ch. 10]

● WRITING THOUGHTS See 'Notebook Writing'.

for you on your last engineering problem, will
it necessarily be *the* one to use the next time
you are stuck for a new idea?

4. Explore the problems you see in acquiring
    proficiency in applying creativity stimulators to
    real-world engineering problems.

5. Focus on a stimulator of your choice from Table
    14-1. Cite an example in your engineering area
    of a device or apparatus which was probably
    created by the originating engineer's use of that
    stimulator.

6. From Table 14-1, consider Nature's Way. Identify
    created devices having functional counterparts in
    nature. Discuss similarities.

7. Describe the circumstance leading to one of your
    personal instances of Illumination. Do they
    check with Table 14-1? Suppose illumination
    gives you the wrong answer. What do you do then?

8. Is Table 14-1 really complete or do you expect to
    be able to add to it later?

9. Identify personality characteristics best and least
    suited for successful use of creativity stimulators.

Exercises

14-E1. An engineering professor wants to dramatically
        demonstrate to his students the effect of the
        'Curie Temperature' on the behavior of magnetic
        circuits. Recall it is the temperature at
        which a material ceases to have magnetic properties.
        Propose a specific circuit or apparatus which
        might work.

14-E2. Electrical engineers are mostly taught linear
        circuit principles. Select a *non* linear device
        and propose a new or novel product or application.
        What creativity stimulator was used in arriving
        at this problem statement? What stimulator(s)
        did you use in arriving at a proposal?

14-E3. Consider the Combining stimulator. Take the ideas
        of a transistor, battery, capacitor, resistor,
        and home. Propose a new, novel, and potentially
        useful new product idea.

14-E4.   Focus on a technical magazine of your choice.
         Find a specific product advertised which interests
         you. Propose a major improvement or a new and
         unique use for it. List the creativity stimulator(s)
         used.

14-E5.   To illustrate the Reversal creativity stimulator,
         focus on a home appliance of your choice. Propose
         a new, novel, useful product.

14-E6.   To illustrate the Modify stimulator, focus on an
         electrical or mechanical component of your choice.
         Propose a new novel improvement to it.

14-E7.   Consider a typical engineering textbook. Propose
         a major new, novel, and improved idea ('a *fresh
         viewpoint*') for an ideal textbook such that
         learning is enhanced. Cite principal creativity
         stimulators used in arriving at your new idea.

14-E8.   To illustrate the Deficiency Identification stimu-
         lator, select an electrical or mechanical component
         of your choice. Identify its principal faults.
         Propose a new or novel significant improvement.

14-E9.   To illustrate the Deficiency Identification
         stimulator, go to a hospital and find the most
         modern wheel chair available. As a well person,
         sit in it and use it for a while. Think about
         its intended use for *sick* persons. Prepare a
         list of specific deficiencies you see in this
         product. Is this well-known product in need of
         numerous small improvements or a major creative
         rethinking and restructuring? Make sketches of
         specific proposed improvements. List all the
         creativity stimulators used throughout the exercise.

14-E10. List New Uses for power transistors scrapped
         during the manufacturing process for failure to
         meet mechanical and electrical specifications.

14-E11. List 5 creativity stimulators you might use for
         'getting started' on an initially unappealing
         engineering problem which has to be solved by you.

14-E12. Consider a 3 kw home electric oven. If a 10 lb
         turkey requires 3 hrs. to bake, compute the
         electrical energy input. Now assume the 10 lb
         turkey is 10 lb of water and that it undergoes
         a 300°F temperature change. Compute the energy
         required for baking this 'turkey' 3 hrs. Suggest

ideas for improving baking efficiency. What creativity stimulators did you use?

14-E13. A new 'bug type' vacuum cleaner is to be created for automatically cleaning a household floor. Using the Morphological Analysis stimulator, draw the morphological box. Expand the most promising 'drawer'.

14-E14. If you were performing a Problem Inquiry phase on the possibility of utilizing solar energy for the home, list the creativity stimulators you find helpful in approaching this particular problem.

14-E15. Others based on Table 14-1 as suggested by your professor. (There are endless possibilities!)

Chapter Summary

● The real-world engineer creating the products of the future needs *personal* creativity stimulators at many points throughout the six step problem solving process of Chaps. 3-9.

● Creativity stimulators, when we find those which 'work' for us, tend to enhance our likelihood of making a net contribution provided good judgment and follow-up are applied later.

● Many known and tested creativity stimulators were collected for the first time in a concise form useful to engineers.

● A detailed understanding of *why* a given creativity stimulator 'works' for us may never be known until we understand much more about how the human mind forms new ideas.

CHAPTER 15

RECORDING CREATIVE WORK

" - - I bought a number of green cloth-covered notebooks with
numbered pages, and started to make a systematic record of
suggestions, setting down the date of each as it occurred."
Robert Hutchings Goddard   [121, p40]

● Need for recording.

● Principal recording means.

● Notebook recording.

15-1 The Need For Recording Creative Work

The need for recording creative work in some

way may be intuitively evident. It's not to most

beginning engineers who also don't know *how* to

permanently record. Even some practicing engineers

think recording their work isn't important or don't

know how to do it--or both. They repeatedly are in

*"--the contestant
who can prove that
he was the first
one to make the
invention will
win the contest
- -"*

*Robert A. Buckles
[49, p152]*

trouble over poor or no records; and they may well

get their firm in serious legal trouble if a patent

contest over their new creation later enters the courts.

As we creatively push through the disciplined

problem solving process of Chaps. 3-9 progressing

toward solving our problem, we find it necessary to

make records. Let's get a perspective on *why* records

of creative engineering work are needed by ourselves and

others. The reasons are identified below.

Records Are Needed By Ourselves To:

● Show Tangible Progress evidence toward solving the
   problem--our job.

● Reveal and Explore our thoughts and help develop

*"For the purpose
of moving our
minds, pencils can
serve as crowbars."*
  Alex F. Osborn
  [234, p216]

our creative potential. The act of *thinking*
is involved, preceding recording by microseconds
or years. Records help reveal our further
thinking and are a tool for effective disciplined
thinking of the highest order.

● Stimulate:

  ▲ Generating new ideas and creations.
  ▲ Recognizing Flaws in our ideas, designs, or new
    creations.
  ▲ Recalling forgotten ideas, data, or details
    when the need arises. It frequently does
    when engineering is practiced.
  ▲ Organizing our thinking and progress toward
    solving the problem. The larger the
    problem the greater the need for organizing
    ourselves, avoiding getting lost on some
    interesting but unneeded detail.

● Store Information, ideas, facts, and data having
  present or potential relevance to the problem.

● Prepare Progress Reports for management. They
  have legitimate needs for knowing the problems
  solved, the problems being experienced, work
  remaining, etc.

● Document Our Thinking at a given time.

● Prepare Patent disclosure letter(s) [Chap. 18] on
  our new creations.

● Protect Ourselves against possible later attacks
  by others for:

*"--the great value
of invention records
is when you have
your day in
court, - -"*
  Damien Start
  [314]

  ▲ Who created specifically what.
  ▲ When specifically it was *first* conceived and
    'reduced to practice'.
  ▲ Proving achieved performance or results.
  ▲ Proving non-abandonment of the invention.

    Such attacks may become particularly acute in
patent litigation cases, particularly if our
invention is being contested in court by someone
claiming *he* invented it first and is therefore
entitled to the legal rights a patent bestows.
Our records, or lack thereof, then come into
full view and are *the* principal evidence
determining the case's outcome.

Our Records Are Needed By Others:

● Managers frequently want to check progress, find

facts, answer questions, or find some important detail of our creative work.

It is emphasized that in the highly competitive business world it is absolutely necessary for the manager or entrepreneur to have firm legal ownership of the patent rights for the new product he is to manufacture. Our original records are the keystone for obtaining those rights.

"Witnessed notebook entries are invaluable in connection with patents."
Harald T. Friis
[113, p52]

● Patent Attorneys for validating your patent disclosure letter, preparing the patent application, processing it through the Patent Office, and following up on the case even after the patent issues, especially in patent inter- ference cases.

● Implementers of your new creation. They may want to check how we *actually* made the model that works, performance, and other details-- all of which we did long ago; but they need the *detailed* records of that work to quickly resolve their implementation problems. *Caution*: Don't show your original records to others outside your organization without first checking with your manager and patent attorney! Important ethical, legal, and business issues are involved.

Finally, if we as creators of the new--and obviously most interested in it--don't record our work, *who* will? Failure to record our creative work inevitably results in it being *lost* to both ourselves ("I can't remember exactly how I built that.") and future generations. Those who follow may have to redo the work and possibly never hit on the unique creation we did. The resulting costly wasted effort and loss to society of potentially useful new creations and inventions is tragic.

Most of the creative giants of the past--Faraday, Edison, the Wright brothers, Goddard and *many* others-- instinctively knew to record their work. They left us, in addition to useful new creations, a valuable

legacy of detailed records of their work. Recording

gave their work a *permanent* character.

Example 15-1

  Goddard at the time of his death had collected
and left: four complete rockets; numerous notebooks
spanning his pioneering creative rocketry work from
1899 to 1943; reports to his sponsors; several book
length and shorter manuscripts; papers on 214 patents
on rockets and rocket apparatus granted him between
1914-1956; motion picture films, slides, and photographs;
and many other items including diaries and correspondence
In toto they comprise 'the record' of his creative
work which all subsequent space vehicle technology
and explorations built on [120]. He clearly knew
the need to permanently record his creative work.

*"You should also
keep a carefully
dated record of
other steps you
take in working
on the invention."*
[240]

Our thinking and emphasis in this Chap. will be on

recording our *early* creative work--before patent action

is initiated, formal engineering reports issued, or

technical papers published. These more formal reporting

methods were treated in Chaps. 9 and 12. Thus we'll

focus on recording *prior* to the 'Convince Others' phase

of Fig. 3-1--the part of disciplined creative engineering

work behind the scenes, seldom made public, and usually

secret for patent, competitive, or security reasons.

You are expected to have some skill in recording

your creative work. Unfortunately, with the exception

of 'Laboratory Notebooks', relatively little exists on

the subject in the curricula of most engineering schools

in 1977.

We now identify the principal recording options.

15-2 Principal Recording Means

The major alternatives for recording creative

engineering work are collected here.

"Record: To commit to writing, to printing, to inscription, or the like; to make an official note of; to write, transcribe or enter in a book or on parchment, for the purpose of preserving authentic evidence of - - -"
Webster
[373]

● Notebook in which we record our thoughts, new ideas, new creations, tests, and the like. Easy to use, versatile enough to apply to any creative project, it is the most widely used recording method and the most enduring. The durability of the written word is well-known.

They tend to get lost if not safeguarded.

Example 15-2

Goddard kept many notebooks during his years of work creating rocketry [120].

● Physical Embodiment, i.e. a model, of the new creation. A well constructed model may endure hundreds of years. Models of new creations have a mystique all their own.

A model may rust, have parts removed for later 'more important' work, be vandalized, destroyed by fire, stolen, sold into oblivion, and otherwise disappear or deteriorate unless given special care. The original models of many significant new creations are kept in museums as a record.

Example 15-3

The Egyptian pyramids are well-known creative monuments to an ancient high technology civilization. They are one of the most permanent records man has devised, standing in spite of deteriorating influences.

● Photographs/Slides/Movies of a new creation sometimes are the most appropriate recording means. If later widely disseminated such records can be quite enduring.

Deterioration with age of the films is a problem.

Example 15-4

The photograph of the Wright brothers' first flight of the airplane [388] is well-known.

It was recorded with a simple box camera.

● __Notes__ of new ideas, thoughts, evaluations, decisions, etc. made 'on the run' during the creative problem solving process are a record.

"You should keep correspondence about the invention, sales slips of materials you buy for use in working on it, and any models or drawings, so that these can be on hand if needed to help you prove the facts and dates of the steps you have taken."
  [240]

Notes are 'weak' records because of forgery possibilities and other legal reasons.

Example 15-5

"Soon Bell had a patent on the telephone, and scores of inventors and pseudo-inventors claimed that they had preceded him in making the simple discovery. In all Bell was involved in more than five hundred patent suits, but again and again the courts ruled that he was the inventor, and only the patent system protected his invention from being pirated. Probably no patent was ever the center of more legal dispute. Once a diagram on the back of a sheet of paper, inadvertently sent to a school for the deaf, giving advice on teaching methods, was resurrected as evidence to prove that Bell had preceded another inventor in developing a vital detail."
[241].

● __Dictation__ is sometimes used to record ideas, tests, and other creative thoughts, particularly on fast moving projects.

Transcribing is a problem along with corroborating the date. Also in a civil court case the possibilities of falsification of a dictated record would not be overlooked by the opposition.

Example 15-6

Gordon, in an interesting treatment [123, p16] on basic creative processes says, "The problem - - was to devise a dial [for an aircraft instrument] which would abolish both the psychological reading error and the mechanical friction error. As [the inventor] worked on this dual problem he made notes and talked into wire recorders and dictaphones - -."

● __Recordings__ of 'brainstorm sessions' are sometimes made and later transcribed to a written list.

Recordings have the same disadvantages

as dictation. Also establishing precisely
who created what idea is a problem--a general
problem with this method of group ideation.

Example 15-7

In the early 1950's I lead a brainstorm
session on the problem of assembling, exhausting,
and sealing the new ceramic tube [later the
6BY4, 7077 and many other offshoots] being
created for our firm. I tape-recorded the
session. The ideas were transcribed to a
written list. One idea was later used as a
successful proprietary process for making the
tube in quantity.

● Letters describing part or all of our new creations
  are frequently written by creative people--not
  so much with the idea of 'recording' at the time
  as to 'communicate'. Later it is seen the letters
  constituted some or all the records made.

Letters have the disadvantages of falsification
possibilities and not being part of a *continuous*
record, as in a notebook.

Example 15-8

"---It is seldom that mankind's epochal
achievements on the history-making and history-
changing scale of practical aerial flight
have ever been recorded, discussed, and
elucidated with such clarity, candor and simple
charm as are found in the Wright-Chanute
letters - - -" [208, pp22-24]

● Diaries jotting down work and problems are kept
  by many creative people. Their content may
  range from highlight to minute detail. Some
  diaries are so complete as to be notebooks
  in their own right. Such diaries, if later
  widely disseminated, become as enduring as the
  printed word.

Diaries frequently evolve toward non-detailed
listing of events, impressions, etc.--as Edison's
diary [90],   use cryptographic notes known
only to the writer, and usually aren't a complete
record as a seriously kept notebook.

Example 15-9

Faraday's seven volume diary [98]
is a masterpiece of creative work, permitting
us to follow his thoughts through hundreds of

significant experiments and observations
on magnetism. His work and records laid the
foundation for modern experimental methods.

Of the recording alternatives, the notebook is by

*"The research
worker should
record his results
in detail in a
notebook."*
 Harald T. Friis
 [113, p52]

far the most important in creative engineering practice.

The other recording means will be used less frequently.

Some students have the erroneous idea a notebook

is to be used *only* in a laboratory. Some also think

it's only a patent notebook. Actually it is used in

the *entire* creative problem solving process and can

be another helpful tool enhancing our creativity.

Notebook recording is emphasized here. We now

detail *how* to do it correctly.

15-3 Notebook Recording

SOME GENERAL MATTERS should first be mentioned.

● Behind It is the imperative to make a *legally*
   acceptable record of our creative work--a
   record which would be admissible into and would
   stand up in court should later events make it
   necessary. A very long history of patent cases--
   contested inventions, pirated ideas, and many
   other facets--clearly shows the necessary
   procedures to follow for the creator to *clearly*
   document his case and have it upheld by the
   courts. We can only cover the more important
   aspects here--what we need to do in creative
   work to protect ourselves and our firm.

      Buckles [49, Ch. 5] has an excellent
   treatment of legal aspects of recording.

● Who Makes Entries in a notebook? *You* and *ONLY*
   you do! A notebook is not a group effort or
   something 'they' do. It is the record made
   by you as the *individual* solving the problem.
   Hence a notebook is a highly *personal* professional
   record of thoughts and events occurring throughout the *entire* creative problem solving process
   for your particular problem.

● Sensing When To Record is a problem. High
   creativity disciplined engineers make daily
   entries *as* thoughts and ideas occur. To
   delay recording ("I'll write that down
   tomorrow.") is to frequently lose the thought.
   There is no one 'best' time of day or 'best'
   place in the creative process for recording,
   though more obvious places are shown in the various
   charts in Chaps. 4-9.

   The disciplined engineer knows enough about
   the recording subject to sense when to record.
   ("I must write these tests up *now*!") Your skill
   in sensing when to record will come with practice.

*"The best time to
record an
invention idea
is when it
occurs - -"
 Damien Start
 [314]*

● Truthfulness in matters great and small is the
   only policy worthy of following in recording
   creative work. If we only thought of 11 ideas
   in truth, *say* so. If we define the problem
   one way while others define it totally differently
   and if it is true, *say* so. If we made an error
   in thought, construction, or tests, *say* so.
   If we honestly believe this new idea is a first,
   say so.

   One hallmark of most outstanding creative
   people is their intrinsic love of the beauty of
   truth.

   In case of a later civil action involving
   your new creation you may have to swear in court
   to the truthfulness of your notebook entries.
   It's best to be prepared!

*"In many cases he
(Huffaker) puts
down data as
though from
observation when
in reality they
are only estimates
made while seated
at a distance."
 Wilbur Wright
 [398]*

● Clarity and Specificness is to be sought in our
   entries. The entry should be so *clear* and
   specific that years later a knowledgeable person
   could pick up your notebook, read it, and know
   specifically what was being done, i.e. your
   thoughts and steps toward problem solution can
   be reconstructed. Your record should stand on
   its own.

● Completeness of the notebook record should be our
   goal. For new ideas it is important we record
   them as *complete* as we know *at* the time we
   were thinking and *when* we were thinking it. There
   may come a time later--when and if a patent is
   applied for--when we'll certify under oath that
   'this is the *full*, clear and exact description
   of this invention'

   It can help us greatly to have--throughout

*"The greatest
difficulty occurs
in bringing the
idea into a clear
and concise form
so that it can be
transferred to
paper for record.
The first records
are generally
very sketchy and
sometimes
inaccurate."
 Russel S. Ohl
 [227, p110]*

our records--attempted to be complete. Where we recognize incompletenesses, there is nothing wrong with our saying so if it is true.

● Qualitative *AND* Quantitative thinking is to be recorded. Both classes are important. A notebook filled with page after page of analysis of some sub-problem on a new apparatus may be nearly useless in proving the conception date and inventor of the new creation. A notebook filled with new creative ideas but no analysis or follow-up aimed at reduction to practice is equally ineffective. *Both* are necessary, as has already been said in Chaps. 3-9. Ideally *all* our qualitative and quantitative thinking throughout the creative process of Chaps. 3-9 would be recorded in our notebook.

You will learn more about these matters from

senior engineers, managers, and your firm's patent

attorney after you get on the job practicing disciplined

creative engineering.

We now examine details of notebook recording.

THE NOTEBOOK itself is our first problem.

"A far better practice is to keep written records of all research and development work in bound notebooks."
Robert A. Buckles
[49, p69]

● *A BOUND Notebook* is very important. Loose leaf, spiral bound, or any other type permitting page removal or insertion is *not* acceptable. If we elect to record our precious creative efforts in such, we've made a serious judgment error. Obtain a high quality durable leather or cloth bound notebook. Cheap notebooks that fall apart after a few months use may result in expensive wasted creative effort and are legally shaky.

The legal reason for it being *bound* is simply to minimize fraud possibilities. A creator can't later remove a page and reinsert a fraudulent one with 'an earlier date of conception' to predate competitors. While no engineer would ever do such a thing on ethical grounds--no matter how much is at stake--such a phenomenon has been seen by patent attorneys.

● A <u>Separate</u> <u>Notebook</u> for each of your major projects
  avoids getting things 'mixed-up'. It results
  in a clearer record than if we just chronologically
  record our thoughts on *all* our projects in one
  notebook.

● <u>Identify</u> <u>The</u> <u>Notebook</u> inside the front cover.
  Proper identification may be extremely important
  in a court case.

Example 15-10

THERMIONIC CONVERSION
RESEARCH NOTES — '62

Robert L. Bailey
UNIVERSITY OF FLORIDA
Department of Electrical Engineering

● <u>Number</u> <u>The</u> <u>Pages</u> sequentially is very important.
  Imagine the suspicion an opposing attorney could
  throw on your record in court if it has missing
  pages (or doubly numbered pages) right at the
  place and date where 'proof of first conception'
  is trying to be legally established in a contest
  between two inventors!

MAKING ENTRIES is our next problem.

*"If an error is
made in any
entry, it should
not be erased but
should be crossed
out."*
  Robert A. Buckles
    [49, p70]

● <u>Permanent</u> <u>Black</u> <u>Ink</u> is preferred. It doesn't fade with
  age and can't be changed without being obvious.

● <u>Legible</u> entries are to be clearly made in your
  own handwriting so others *unfamiliar* with your
  eccentricities can read it.

● <u>Sign</u> <u>And</u> <u>Date</u> every entry and page. This may be
  very important to a patent attorney in court
  trying to establish that *you* invented your gadget
  on such-and-such a date. Cultivate this important
  practice at the beginning of your professional
  career!

Example 15-11

From a notebook on improving a woodworking machine:

be modified to include A boss on the left side Also for A set screw similar to the one now on the right side
Robert L. Bailey 7/19/72

Robert L. Bailey 7/24/72
IMPROVEMENTS TO SPEED CONTROL PARTS
The Problem. On July 17, 1972 the speed control mechanism on my Shopsmith jammed. It would not go to

Note how an entry on one date ends and a later entry beings.

⬤   No Skipped Pages or spaces left. Let your entries be *continuous*. Your integrity may be open to question if, at a *later* date, you make an entry into such a blank page or skipped space even though you correctly date that later entry; but if you *must* skip a space, fill it with x's or crosshatching.

⬤   Frequent Entries are preferred. Such entries establish you were *continuously* working on the problem ('establishes diligence' in legal terminology) and did not abandon the work. 'Abandonment' may have serious legal and business consequences. In a patent contest case an opposing attorney possibly could win the case for his client--even though his client invented the gadget *after* you did--if he can show by your record you abandoned the invention.

"The invention must not have been abandoned at any time."
Robert A. Buckles
[49, p22]

Example 15-12

April 18, 1969   Robert L. Bailey
SUMMARY OF CONCEPTUAL STAGES -- EYE-LIKE CONVERSION

Date	Action/conception	Described On P. No. in 65 FC notebook of mine
6/24/68	*First began to think about eyes as power converters*	35
6/27/68	*Explored prior art on knowledge of Eye retinas. Recognized possible connection between Anechoid chambers, eyes, and solar conversion. Began thinking of protuberances and conical like energy absorbers.*	40 — 44

6/28/68   Statement of problem: get light   47-49
          quanta *into* volume. Proposed
          specific geometries applicable to silicon
          technology based on conical like absorbers.

7/8/68   I advanced a possible plausible theory,   68-78
          based on antenna theories, of *how* conical
          shaped absorbers might work.
          Proposed first elementary model.
          Incompletenesses recognized. Related
          to surface absorption phenomena. I
          proposed specific conical converter
          containing flexible base and *no*
          semiconductors (except a series
          diode)

7/19/68   Basic idea for crucial experiment   93
          advanced (Explore at RF)

8/16/68   Recommended Research follow-up by   *P2 of my final*
          NASA Office Univ. Affairs on this idea   *Report "A summer*
                                                    of research at
                                                    GSFC, Greenbelt, Md."

          Robert L. Bailey 4/18/09

● <u>Identifying</u> <u>Titles</u> help logically structure
   your record and make later use of the notebook
   easier for you and others. Titles by subject
   facilitate quick recovery of information and
   ideas.

   A record that flows on and on from entry
   to entry without titles or subtitles, while
   better than *no* record, is very difficult to
   later use.

<u>Example</u> <u>15-13</u>

                                    Mon. July 8, 1968
FURTHER THOUGHTS - "EYE-LIKE" SOLAR CONVERSION
   The "eye idea" advanced on p35 repeatedly comes
back to me. Friday the following line of reasoning
occurred to me at end of a day of hard
thinking:
   First-Order Hypothesis for "eye-like" conversion:
   The duality of "wave-like" and "particle-like"
   properties -----

● The <u>Problem</u>, as you see it, should be clearly
   stated. Fortunes have hung, in patent court

cases, on whether the inventor in *fact* had
the insight to recognize the problem correctly
--probably in a different way from how it was
seen by less perceptive people.

Example 15-14

THE IMPROVEMENTS

Headstock Assembly
  Shopsmith's original design for Cooling:

Read And Understood
Erwin J. Brien
Date March 7, 1972

The major Air inlet WAS Around the jointer power
take off. Clearance holes Around the sander take off
&, the bed WAYS, the end pan where it joins the
Aluminum Casting, leaks Around the motor pan where
it joins the aluminum Casting, leaks through
the Adjustable speed control dial, and leaks
through the electrical switch, All furnished places
where cooling Air could and did enter.
The Problem: Sawdust in the cooling Air eventually
              clogs up the motor, seriously impairs

Robert L. Bailey March 4, 1972

Robert L. Bailey March 4, 1972
  its cooling and the motor burns up!
  (I had one burn up on me this WAY. Cost
  me ~$45.00 And lots time to get it rewound
  and replaced.) Also the sawdust
  clogs up the VARiable speed mechanism
  and the teeth in the quill feed. The
  result is that every 4-6 months
  the headstock ASSY must be completely
  disAssembled, the sawdust cleaned out
  and reassembled --A genuine nuisance!
My Early Attempts consisted of:
  a. Placing felt washers Around the Aholes where the
     bed WAYS enter the headstock. Ditto for

"--sometimes he may
discover thereby
that the crux of
the problem is
really quite
different from
what it was at
first thought
to be."
  Robert A. Buckles
    [49, p72]

● Our Purpose(s) or Goal(s) should be clearly
    stated. Otherwise those who later read the
    record have no way of knowing what *specifically*
    we were striving toward.

Example 15-15

*"They need not
be a lengthy
dissertation
- -"*

*Robert A. Buckles
[49, p72]*

Goddard's notebook repeatedly shows succinct
purpose statements. A sample [120, p27] under
September 29, 1931 date:

"The purpose of this test was to obtain
a flight with a remotely controlled rocket
of about 180 lb. lift with a copper-tube jacket,
pressure regulator and streamline casing."

● The Strategy or Plan for attacking the problem
    should be clearly shown.

Example 15-16

Early strategy for verifying the Electromagnetic
Wave Energy Converter concept was recorded as:

Experimental vs Analytical Verification
    Is clear these two main routes exist for
exploring this new idea. Also is clear to me
that the analytics are/maybe very involved
and complex and possibly unsolvable. Also it may
not be worth solving the analytics if the device
I propose fundamentally is not sound/doesn't work.
Experimental approach will be relatively easy and
can in reasonable time tell whether proposed system will
or will not work.
Robert L. Bailey 4/18/69

● The *FIRST* Conception, no matter how embryonic,
    is *very* important to record. *Clearly* state
    whether you believe it entirely new or only
    some aspects new.

Example 15-17

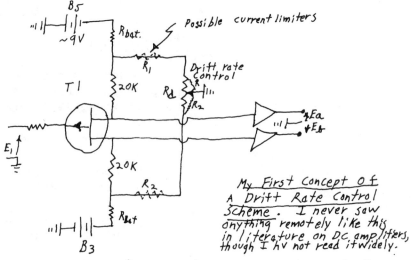

My First Concept of A Drift Rate Control Scheme. I never saw anything remotely like this in literature on DC amplifiers, though I hv not read it widely.

Decreasing R_1 ⟹ increases drift rate in <u>neg dir.</u> on E_a & E_b
Decreasing R_2 ⟹   "   "   "   " <u>pos dir.</u>   "

I should thus be able to set the drift rate control so as to compensate for imperfect batteries B_3 & B_5.

"In his application for a patent he must make an oath that he verily believes himself to be the first person to make the invention which he claims as his, - -"

    Robert A. Buckles [49, p16]

● *Who* <u>Conceived The Idea</u> is very important to specifically identify. Avoid phrases like: "The idea evolved of - - -" (*who* created it?); "It was suggested that - - -" (*who* suggested it?); "The new idea was generated of - - -" (*who* generated it?); "The management proposed the concept of - - -" (*what* was his *name*?). A patent attorney must know who *specifically* the inventor was. It is not always an easy task, especially with a fuzzy record!

Example 15-18

TUESDAY, sept. 20, 1966   9/20/66
                                             R 1B
    Thought about above problem and analysis method overnight. <u>It is correct.</u> Overnight, the idea occurred to me that I should be able to combine the ideas of (1) the drift rate compensator control
                        (2) the imperfect voltage reference diodes
so that now the drift rate control would give a precision control on the drift rate out of the FET's.
    My conception is as follows:

● Advantages of the proposed new creation or
  solution embodiment should be *clearly* and
  forcefully made in the record. The more
  significant the advantages the greater the
  long-term potential value of the new creation.

  A *clear* record of the advantages may
  later be used for drafting important patent
  claims.

Example 15-19

*"The claims are
the most
important part
of the patent
application."*
[240]

Read and und'de
Erwin J. ??
Date March 7

Advantages of this arrangement now include:
a. The motor is supplied with clean filtered
   air and will not burn up due to sawdust
   choking.
b. The interior is pressurized now so that
   sawdust cannot enter and clog up the
   various mechanisms —A serious nuisance in the past.
c. The previous 'leak problem' fades into
   insignificance now, since if small air leaks
   occur, as around shafts, no harm is done
   even long term.
Thus with these changes the air flow pattern has
been completely reversed over what the original
Shopsmith design was!

Robert L. Bailey March 4, 1972

● Discussions With Others. Identify who *specifically*
  you talked with about your new creation. *Don't*
  talk with anyone *outside* your firm about your
  new creation.

Example 15-20

Another important change in the direction of
this research occurred about Nov 1, 1967. I was
talking with Mr. Scott Wann, computer technician,
who had considerable trouble with a peculiar
kind of asthma and acquired a body of lore
connected therewith. We exchanged lore. He
said he had tried some tests using an activated
charcoal (which is made from (coconut shells) as a
means of absorbing some gasses from the air. He
showed me a Barnebey Cheney (Columbus, Ohio) brochure.
On Nov 7, 1967 I wrote them and asked for additional
information, esp. on flat filters. In my discussion
with Wann the idea of incorporating an activated
charcoal filter in Betty's bed design was instantly
conceived by me. I don't know why I had not
previously thought of this idea, as activated charcoal
odor absorbers for refrigerators is well known.
Robert L. Bailey 11/14/67 Read and understood
Erwin J. Arum
Date Oct. 21, 1968

● Distinguish <u>Proposed</u> <u>From</u> <u>Actual</u>, i.e. make
   very *clear* in the entry whether your new
   creative idea is envisioned or you have
   constructed it.

   Fuzzy thinking merges what *actually* exists
   at the time of making the entry with *proposed*
   better ways of solving the problem. An unbiased
   observer of the record then can't tell whether
   an imaginative creative act necessary for
   an invention has occurred or whether one is
   simply recording actual prior art solutions
   to the problem.

Example 15-21

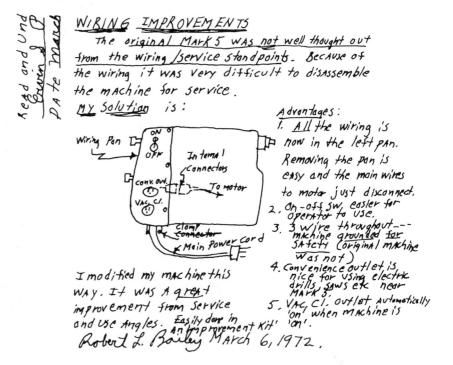

WIRING IMPROVEMENTS

The original MARK 5 WAS not well thought out from the wiring /service standpoints. Because of the wiring it WAS Very difficult to disassemble the mAchine for service.

MY Solution is:

Wiring Pan

ON
OFF
conv. ovt.
VAC. Cl.
Internal Connectors
To motor
Clamp Connector
Main Power Cord

Advantages:
1. <u>All</u> the wiring is now in the left pAn. Removing the pan is easy and the main wires to motor just disconnect.
2. On-off sw. easier for operAtor to use.
3. 3 wire throughout--- mAchine grounded <u>for</u> sAfety (original mAchine <u>WAS not</u>)
4. Convenience outlet is nice for using electric drills, saws etc near MARK 5.
5. VAC, Cl. outlet Automatically 'on' when mAchine is 'on'.

I modified my mAchine this wAy. It WAS A greAt improvement from Service and use Angles. EAsily done in An 'Improvement Kit'.

Robert L. Bailey March 6, 1972.

ReAd and Und Erwin J B DAte MArch

● <u>Sketches</u> should be liberally used to describe
   your new creation. A sketch of the proposed
   preferred physical form your gadget should take
   is better than pages of words.

   Sketches are particularly important in
   creative work. In a sense they are the end
   products of our creative thinking. In essence
   we are here saying 'make it like this', i.e.
   an embodiment. It may have taken considerable
   disciplined thought to arrive at this important
   state. Record it, even if the idea is incomplete.

The Patent Office or the courts may consider it the basis for a 'constructive reduction to practice'.

Example 15-22

"The drawings were not dated, and, hence, such drawings as were introduced by the party, Long, depend for their dates upon the memory of the witnesses. As a consequence, the evidence furnished by such drawings is unsatisfactory and inconclusive."
Day V. Long and Evans
[71]

Leonardo da Vinci's sketches of link chains [352, p228]--the world's first.[1]

● Calculations, especially 'Order of Magnitude Calculations',[2] showing general technical feasibility of your new creation, are especially important to record. Show the formulas, their sources, and numerical calculations for your creation. If one or more parameters must be optimized for your proposed new creation to work properly, indicate which parameters, the approximate range they must have, and show the calculation.

---

[1]Source: F. M. Feldhaus, *Leonardo, der Techniker und Erfinder*, p 81, [Jena, 1913].

[2]This subject is so important in creative work that Chap. 16 is devoted to it.

Such calculations may later be important in establishing that on such-and-such an early date--*ahead* of competing inventors--you *clearly* recognized and showed your new creation to be technically feasible.

Example 15-23

From a notebook on a difficult DC amplifier sub-problem while creating a new logarithmic voltage attenuator:

Wednesday, May 4, 1966   -140-
ORDER OF MAGNITUDE CHECK   5/4/66   RJB

For Dickson type CC FET:

$g_m \sim 240\ \mu mhos$

$r_d \sim 130 \times 10^3\ ohms$

$\mu \sim 240 \times 10^{-6}\ 130 \times 10^3 = 312 \times 10^2 \times 10^{-3} = 312 \times 10^{-1} = 31.2$

① $R_A = \dfrac{1}{g_m} = \dfrac{1}{240 \times 10^{-6}} = .00417 \times 10^6 = \boxed{4.17K}$

② $\dfrac{E_A}{E_b} = -\left(\mu + 1 + \dfrac{r_d}{R_b}\right) = -\left(31 + 1 + \dfrac{130K}{1K}\right) = \boxed{-162}$

Assumed value (is not a sensitive parameter) --evident

As the phase splitter is grossly unbalanced insofar as its sensitivity to E^+ variations is concerned.

③(p135) $E_2 \sim +E\left(\dfrac{4K}{1K} + 1\right) \log E_1$

$\boxed{E_2 \sim 5 E \log E_1}$

A *significant* improvement over the *balanced* design which gave 2!

Above design would be:

1. Have *equal* channel outputs from phase splitter due to E^+ supply Variations

$E_a = + A E^+$
$E_b = + A E^+$ Don't need to know, Just need to know they are equal in magnitude & sign.

Thus troublesome effect of E^+ Variations would be completely eliminated theoretically, assuming perfectly balanced amplifiers following the phase splitter. This would be a major improvement over present prototype.

2. Unbalanced by a factor of ~ -162 $\left(\dfrac{E_a}{E_b} = -33\right)$

3. Sensitivity to E^- supply Variations (eqns p137)

$E_a = -\left[\dfrac{4170}{1000 + 4,170 + 130,000 + 31 \times 1,000} - 1\right] E^-$ ③+④

$\boxed{E_a \sim +97\% \ E^-}$

$E_b = +\left[\dfrac{1,000}{166,170}\right] E^-$

$\boxed{E_b = +[.6\%]\ E^-}$

Essentially no worse than present prototype cf. p129 for comparison.

A *considerable* improvement over present prototype (.6% vs 2.7%)

*"The notebooks of
Newton and Leonardo
da Vinci are full
of good ideas that
were never carried
out to a useful
conclusion."
  Ira G. and
Marthann E. Wilson
  [378, p126]*

● Reduction To Practice And Tests are especially
   important to record. Such a record establishes
   the fact your new creation was carried beyond
   the idea stage to something specific, practical,
   and useful.

   Let your records clearly show:

   ▲ Purpose of building or testing it.

Example 15-24

   Goddard wrote in his notebook [120, p95] in
1936: "The object of this test was to obtain a flight
with a rocket having a large thrust, at the same time
avoiding the possible tendency for large chambers to
burn out because of reduced centrifugal cooling. - -"

   ▲ Expected Results from building or testing.

Example 15-25

   From a notebook on travelling wave tube research:

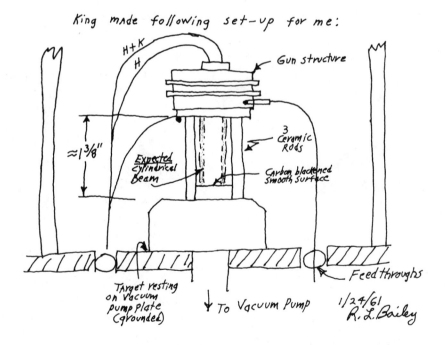

   ▲ Model Composition that was *actually* built
      and tested.

Example 15-26

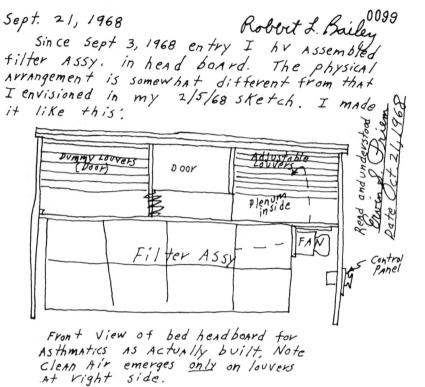

Sept. 21, 1968   Robert L. Bailey   0099
    Since Sept 3, 1968 entry I hv Assembled
filter Assy. in head board. The physical
Arrangement is somewhat different from that
I envisioned in my 2/5/68 sketch. I made
it like this:

Dummy Louvers (Door)   Door   Adjustable Louvers
                                Plenum inside
Filter Assy   — —   FAN
                              Control Panel

Read and understood
Gloria S. Griem
Date Oct 24, 1968

Front view of bed headboard for
Asthmatics as Actually built. Note
clean Air emerges only on louvers
At right side.

▲ Be Specific in showing how this model
   was made or tested differently to other
   models, crucial materials it was made
   of, or the specific process by or through
   which it was made or tested.

Example 15-27

    From Goddard again: "The arrangement differed
from that used with the Karavodine chamber in that
a spray of gasoline was produced close to the intake
valve. The spray device employed was the result
of a number of tests. The gasoline passed from a
No. 80 hole under a pressure of 2 to 5 lb. and
impinged upon the end of a rod, which was flat except
for a very narrow rim. The spray, in the form of
a cone, was directed toward the inflowing air."
[120, p48]

▲ Photographs should be made of the new
   creation and permanently glued in the
   notebook. Photographs show the new
   creation factually was built or tested.
   They can be important elements in proving
   'reduction to practice' of an invention.

"By all means
keep the actual
apparatus, device,
or material in
its original
condition."
C. D. Tuska
[348, p142]

Label the photograph, *clearly* showing
what it is. Date and sign it.

Example 15-28

*"All photographs
should show clearly
all essential parts
and their relation
to one another."*
C. D. Tuska
[348, p142]

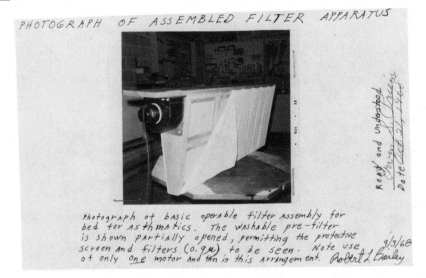

PHOTOGRAPH OF ASSEMBLED FILTER APPARATUS

Read and Understood
[signature]
Date Oct 24, 1968

photograph of basic operable filter assembly for
bed for asthmatics. The washable pre-filter
is shown partially opened, permitting the protective
screen and filters (0.9μ) to be seen. Note use
of only one motor and fan in this arrangement. Robert L. Bailey   9/3/68

▲ Data in the form of meter **readings**, oscillograms,
   computer print-outs of test results, or other
   data appropriate to your model or tests
   should be recorded in your notebook. These,
   along with notations of calibrations,
   checks, etc. constitute the technical
   proof your new creation did or did
   not perform as expected.

Example 15-29

Sept. 23, 1968   Robert L. Bailey
    Today the 2 pr. special hinges arrived from
Constantine. Installed.
    The basic construction of "Happy-Night" bed
is now completed.

AIR FLOW TESTS — FINAL PROTOTYPE

Purpose: To determine air flow in ft3/min vs motor
         speed control setting.

Test Conditions. Air T ~ 70°F
        Plastic bag over outlet — same as Sept 21 entry.
        Finished prototype including filter-fan assy.
        motor speed control, activated charcoal
        final filter, cotton cloth pre-filter,
        0.9 micron main filter (16 8"x10" filters)
        leak proof ducting, & air directing
        louvers.

"The inventor should
exercise care that
his invention is
operable."
C. D. Tuska
[348, p145]

DATA

Control Setting	Normal line voltage Time To fill ~3.5ft3 plastic bag (Bag initially collapsed)	Clean Air ft3/min	Notes
115	60 Sec.	3.5	All times include time for motor to Accelerate from Standstill.
100	68 Sec.	3.1	
90	72	2.9	
80	75	2.8	⌐Motor start-up time becomes noticeable ~3-4 secs.
70	78	2.7	
60	80	2.6	⌐Motor would not self start @ 60. Turned on then to 115v quickly then back to 60. Ditto for lower voltages.
50	85	2.4	
40	125	1.7	
35	>180	~0	3 Motor tends to slowly "run down" in speed at this low voltage.

Read and Understood.
Erwin J. Green
Date Oct. 21, 1968

DATA plotted next page

Conclusions
1. Operate control in range 50 – 115V is OK. Flow velocity doesn't fall off rapidly. Set control for Acceptable noise level at night. Run @ 115 during day to clean roomair.
2. Finished prototype Appears to hv Acceptable Air flow volume.
                                                    Robert L. Bailey 9/23/68

▲ Accuracy. If the model wasn't built
to the physical accuracy required, *say*
so. Show *specifically* where the inaccuracy
lies. If there was something wrong with
the test set **up** causing inaccurate readings
say so, showing what *specifically* was wrong.
Critical performance tests should have
some statement indicating the degree of
accuracy of the measurements.

Example 15-30

BUSHING PROBLEMS
    I machined out of bronze stock a new bearing
B 2980 for the speed control mechanism. I paid
special Attention to the clearance between its I.D.
and the O.D. of B 2980 worm shaft. I made
clearance ~ 0.001" and this appears work well.
    I also made a new larger bushing of brass
brass like that described on p18. When I
made that earlier version I had made the
fit between the bushing and B2979 too loose.
I made it right this time being more careful
of the fit.

It is clear these parts on the speed control Assy.
must be made to close tolerances by Shopsmith
to Avoid mechanism jamming. They, undoubtedly,
will be able to do a better job than I can do.

   I noted the wear on B2979 quadrant control
gear, again. As observed on p18, this part should
be made of A different material to Avoid gear
tooth wear.

Robert L. Bailey 7/24/72

▲ <u>Calculated</u> <u>vs</u> <u>Measured</u> results should be
clearly compared where possible. Such
comparisons serve as our basis for model
improvement and demonstrate to readers
we know what we are doing and can predict
our creation's performance.

Example 15-31

   In May 20, 1966, performance testing a new
logarithmic voltage attenuator being created:

8. The slope of 70mv/decade checks vy close
to the measured E = 72mv/decade for IN458.
This in turn <u>checks previous analyses</u> which
predicted

$$E_t = -E \log E_1$$

         ↳ diode slope = +72mv/decade

9. The slope of 145 mv/decade appears to
<u>verify</u> ③ P133

   ③ $E_2 \sim +E \left(\frac{|Aa|}{|A\phi|} + 1 \right) \log E_1$

            ↳ ≈ equal from data, p181

   $\sim 72 (2) \log E_1$

<u>Excellent</u> → 144 mv predicted
<u>Agreement</u> → 145 mv measured

▲ <u>Successes</u> in building parts or all the
model, successes in testing and any
other successes tending to verify our
earlier expectations should be recorded.

   It is very important to make such
entries *on the day* you actually experience

such successes to establish the earliest
possible date for 'reduction to practice'.

Successes may be the result of *years*
of disciplined creative work--years with
many failures encountered.

Example 15-32

From a notebook on travelling wave tube research:

Wish I had been able to make a colored movie
of this. The action was beautiful! Everything
seemed to work according to theory!

I tried to get some typical beam diameters
under different voltage conditions so that when
the helix is installed later I will know approximate
electrode potentials needed to get a good cylindrical
beam. Took following data:

1/24/61   R. L. Bailey

▲ Failures should also be recorded. These
tend to show how the new creation should
not be made. Say what *specifically* was
wrong and *why* you think it failed. Show
specifically how you propose the 'failure'
be fixed or avoided on future models.

Example 15-33

Goddard's tenacity in dealing with early rocket
failures [120, p3] is well-known. A sample under
December 3, 1929 entry date:

"Test. In the test of December 3, no
flame appeared until a short time after
pressure had been applied, when the chamber
exploded. This explosion was found to
have been due to the long gasoline pipeline

from the tank to the chamber. In order
to avoid the use of a valve and at the
same time to avoid siphoning, this line
had passed over the gasoline tank and hence
had delayed the admission of the gasoline
until a consdierable amount of oxygen
accumulated within the chamber."

▲ Observing <u>Astutely</u> and recording what we
   observe and what we believe its significance
   is important. It may show we have an insight
   into the problem, previous investigators
   missed or 'failed' to correctly assess
   and therefore did not arrive at the successful
   'reduction to practice embodiment' we've
   created.

   Record your observations carefully
   even though you may not, at the time of
   entry, fully understand 'the why' of what
   you are seeing.

*"--but Goodyear was
alert and recognized
a small uncharred
area that later
withstood extremes
of temperature."*
C. D. Tuska
[348,   p85]

Example 15-34

Goddard's notebook [120] under a July 12, 1935
entry shows for the flight test of his A-10 rocket:

"<u>Test</u>. When tested the rocket rose practically
vertically during the entire 14 sec. of
propulsion period. The oscillations from
side to side were of less extent than for
previous tests during the first part of the
flight but were of larger extent toward
the end of the period of propulsion.
According to Mr. A. W. Kisk, who observed
the flight from the 50 ft. shelter, the
rocket did not move more than 40 ft. from
a vertical line through the center of the
tower for the first 1000 ft."

▲ <u>Uncertainties</u> <u>and</u> <u>Unknowns</u> should be clearly
   identified in your record.

Example 15-35

From a notebook on travelling wave tube research:

At the collector the beam appeared to have the highest current density, J, close to where the last turn ended as:

To V_N

To V_p

End of bifilar helix

Red glow from carbon

End of bottom most turn

No indication of current on this side

View of collector as seen from gun end of helix

If ~~the~~ any turns get red on any helix I couldn't tell it but there were many phenomena happening inside to mask this. Above 1200V V_o there is evidence that current leaves the helix like this (remember V_L could not be adjusted properly above 1500V)

Appears to be glow serious of in tube of this design RLB

This can be seen on some portions of outer helix & not others.

Tells me beam entry conditions on a structure like this are very critical. (Desire to enter parallel to axis) Very complicated phenomena happening inside! Wish I had a movie of it!

▲ <u>Conclusions</u> about models built or tested should be clearly shown. You learned some things. What are they? *Specifically* what do you conclude?

Example 15-36

July 9, 1969   Robert L. Bailey
CONCLUSIONS <u>FROM</u> <u>THESE</u> <u>TESTS</u>

1. It is <u>clear</u> now that the essentials (<u>not 'details'</u>) of the hypotheses I advanced on pp 68-78 of GSFC notebook of mine are at least conceptually and qualitatively <u>valid</u>. In particular, I now know that conical-like wave absorbers of geometry shown and consisting of metallic elements (<u>not</u> semiconductors!) <u>are</u> capable of absorbing energy from an incoming wave. The 'details', as optimum l/d ratio, optimum absorber shape, relating peak response to geometry, etc, are <u>not</u> clear yet.

2. These tests furnish me with a tremendous <u>boost</u> in believing, more than ever, now in the possibilities of building highly efficient (>>13% for photovoltaic solar arrays) absorbers of the sun's energy and converting this to <u>useful</u> power. I have earlier described such arrays.

So far as I know, this is the first such energy absorber of this kind in the world. I do not recall ever having seen anywhere or in any publication an "antenna" predicated on principles like those herein advocated.
July 9, 1969   Robert L. Bailey

Read And Understood
[signature]
Date   2-25-70

Tests Witnessed
Bruing J. Bruin
Date July 11, 1969

● <u>References</u> studied or having a bearing on
the problem should be *specifically* cited.
These are later useful in writing engineering
reports. They also establish the legal fact
we *were* familiar with prior art devices in
the area of our problem, reinforcing the
case we've gone *beyond* the prior art in our new
creation.

Example 15-37

From a notebook on solar energy research:

T. Hagemann, E.R., "R.H. Goddard and Solar Power
1924-1934", Solar Energy, Vol. 6,
No. 2, pp 47-54, 1962
Comments:
Interesting history on Goddard's
Attempts w hot water heaters—nothing
on DEC.
                    Robert L. Bailey 6/18/68

*"--he is presumed
to have knowledge
of, or access to,
all of the printed
literature of the
world which
comprises the
'prior art'."*
  Robert A. Buckles
  [49, p17]

CORROBORATION of your notebook entries is very

important to legally establish.

● <u>What Is Corroboration</u>? It simply means we must
have critical entries in our notebook witnessed
by some competent person who *understands* what
we have done and its significance. He must
sign and date our notebook entries. Should
later events make it necessary, the corroborator
may have to appear in court and under questioning,
substantiate the date, that you were in fact
the person who showed him your new creation, what
he saw, answer questions about the record of
your invention, etc.

*"--the uncorroborated
word of an inventor
as to when he first
conceived an
invention will not
be accepted in
evidence - -"*
  Robert A. Buckles
  [49, p67]

● <u>Who/How Many Corroborators</u>? The person you
choose to corroborate your creative notebook
entries is generally a colleague, manager,
or knowledgeable friend *with* your firm whom
you trust. It is very necessary you make him
understand what you are showing him. A 'witness'
can be almost any person whereas 'a corroborator'
must not only see but understand what he sees.
There is a great difference!

Select a young person in good health as
your corroborator; but he must *not* be the

*"This apparent
inability of the
witness to under-
stand the method
of operation
or to testify that
the machine
operated in
accordance with
the claimed
method, was a
fatal defect in
White's proof
and resulted in
his loss of the
interference to
Graham."*
  *Robert A. Buckles
    [49, p159]*

co-inventor. In case court action on your
invention follows years later, you want someone
who will be around!

One corroborator is the minimum. Two are
preferred. If one later dies, you still have
someone who can appear in court if necessary.

● When To Corroborate? The ideal is to have *every*
  notebook page corroborated; but a corroborator
  will soon not want to see us coming if we do
  it that often! Crucial places, short of the
  ideal, are:

  ▲ When the problem to be addressed is clear
    enough to be defined and written.
    (Problem Inquiry Phase).
  ▲ When the goals are specified for what constitute
    an acceptable solution. (Specify Goals
    Phase).
  ▲ When the '*first* conception' occurs (either
    in Problem Inquiry or Determining Means
    phases) for what you believe to be a
    new, unique, and useful way to solve
    the problem. It is *here* that 'the act
    of invention' occurs in a legal sense.
  ▲ When your new creation is 'reduced to
    practice', i.e. Construction and Verification
    phase.

Have a corroborator sign and date your notebook
entries on pages recording the above events.

*"The records of the
Patent Office and
the courts are
replete with cases
of 'inventors' who
have lost inter-
ferences because
they were unable
to produce
corroborating
testimony of their
dates of invention
or reduction to
practice."*
  *Robert A. Buckles
    [49, p158]*

● Getting A Corroborator To Read And Sign is a
  problem in a busy engineering office where each
  man has too much to do. It's also a problem
  for the independent inventor. If you have a good
  working relationship with your corroborator, the
  problem is easier. Even then you may have to follow
  frequently until you eventually get his signature.
  It helps to open your notebook where you have prepar
  them for signing and dating. Some creative
  colleagues simply exchange notebooks, corroborating
  each.

● Signing And Dating. Get your corroborator to sign
  as below. You can have a rubber stamp made for
  the form or copy it on each page.

Example 15-38

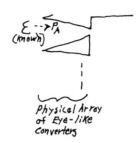

Read And Understood
Date E-25-70

Physical Array
of Eye-like
Converters

1. Design array for use near f = 1000 MHz (eppt. available
to instrument here or near here. Low enough to hv buildable
geometries, not high enough to get into severe skin effect
losses/other peculiar μwave effects.)

● Safekeeping your notebook is very important.
It contains complete and clear descriptions of
valuable technical creative work. Your firm
may insist its contents remain secret for
competitive reasons. Also for patent reasons
it is very important your notebook not be
made public prior to the time a patent application
is filed, i.e. your creative work must remain
essentially secret until the proper time for
revealing it. That time is when a patent application
is made.

Don't leave your notebook where it can
accidentally fall in the trash can and be
carried away by unknowing janitors. *Don't*
leave it in a large laboratory where it can
get accidentally carried away by someone.
Don't lose it. Keep it away from fire, liquids,
children, and animals. Keep it in your desk or
a safe where it will be physically secure.

*"Many persons believe
that they can
protect their in-
ventions against
later inventors
merely by mailing
to themselves a
registered letter
describing the
invention. This
is not true."*
[240]

Having exposed a few principal aspects of recording

creative engineering work, you may think it a frightening

and unwieldy part of disciplined creativity. But recording

soon becomes second nature when you do significant

creative work. Such serious recording then becomes no

great burden.

You should consult with your patent attorney when

in doubt. There is *much* in this whole area beyond the

material in this Chap. which he can help you with--
probably for a fee though. If you work for a large
firm the patent attorney will periodically review
your notebook for possible company patent action.

You've probably gotten new insight into the *depth*
and *detail* required to generate a 'record' useful in
furthering your creative work and which is legally
defensible. The depth and detail is considerably
beyond what you've probably done in 'Laboratory Notebooks'
to date. It penetrates to our thoughts.

Finally, we should mention the recording suggestions
of this Chap. embrace the ideal. Things are seldom
ideal, which is one reason we need good engineering
judgment and patent attorneys.

In striving toward the ideal, be forewarned there
is such a thing as *over* recording--we spend one hour
solving the problem and seven recording every nit we
did then. Not *everything* needs to be recorded! It
simply isn't possible, practical, or necessary for
a satisfactory record. Most of us tend to *under*
record and fall far short of the ideal notebook record.
Practice and good judgment will soon show you how far
to go.

Discussion Topics

1. An aggressive young corporate R&D manager advises
    his engineers starting a new major 'rush project':
    "Spend *all* your time working *on* the project. I
    don't want to see you wasting time endlessly writing
    in notebooks." What will be the probable state of
    this project in 10 months?

2. A new product is in design engineering. The design
    engineer invents an improved product embodiment
    and properly records it. Later the man who did
    the early research sees the improved version. He
    complains to his manager, "That guy stole my
    idea! I had that idea three years ago. I even
    built one like that and threw it away!" A
    seething rivalry ensues between the two company
    divisions and the two engineers. Can 'records'
    help resolve the schism? How?

3. Nikola Tesla, a great past creative engineer,
    had an obsession for *not* keeping records. Yet
    he created many electrical inventions we use
    today. Discuss this anomaly in light of the
    emphasis of this Chap. *to* record.

4. Why, in the business environment, so much emphasis
    on *legal* aspects of 'recording'?

5. "Why should I bother recording my ideas? Management
    isn't ever going to *do* anything about them anyway!"
    Discuss and explore this attitude.

6. Why, if it's true for you, have you been given so
    little formal instruction in how to record creative
    engineering work?

7. An engineer works for a firm as a member of a small
    team creating a new product. He is *not* issued a
    notebook. What, if anything, should he do?

8. "I do all my creating in my head and then build
    the gadget. All this recording bit is a farce
    and a waste!" Discuss this attitude.

9. How does a busy design engineer find *time* to
    record his thinking and ideas in a notebook?

10. Why record 'failures'?

11. What problems may you have in getting your notebook
    record corroborated?

12. What specific recording methods will you probably
    use in *your* future engineering work?

13. In Section 15-1 it was said we need records to
    stimulate generation of new ideas and creations.
    How can this be?

14. Can excessive emphasis on 'recording' actually
    inhibit creative thinking?

15. Does an independent inventor have any advantages over his corporate counterpart in recording his work?

Chapter Summary

● We have a need to record our creative engineering thinking in some permanent manner. We need the record for further progress in solving the problem. Others, particularly patent attorneys, also need it--perhaps years later.

● The principal recording alternatives were identified and briefly assessed. The notebook was found to be the most practical means for recording creative work.

● How to keep a legally acceptable notebook record of our creative work was shown in some detail. Such a record firmly legally establishes who created what invention, when and with what results. We may find favor with ourselves, our patent attorney, our management, and potential users of our new creation as a result of well kept records.

● Clearly 'recording', is another major helpful tool to the disciplined creative engineer seeking to create better products for tomorrow's world.

CHAPTER 16

ORDER-OF-MAGNITUDE AND CHECKING TECHNIQUES

" - - no architect wanted his temple to collapse because
he had dared to break away from known shapes."
L. Sprague de Camp   [73, p44]

● Order-of-magnitude and checking defined.

● Why and where needed in creative work.

● Mathematics and heuristics.

● Order-of-magnitude techniques.

● Checking techniques.

16-1 <u>Why and Where Needed in Creative Work</u>

DEFINITIONS We **start** by defining:

● <u>Order-of-Magnitude</u> Associates a parameter
with its most probable magnitude decade.

---

*"The good design-
er - - makes
many rough
estimates to
establish the
importance of
various factors."
E. S. Taylor
[332,   p650]*

An order-of-magnitude calculation is similar to an

estimate. An estimate is based on partial or

incomplete information. It may involve using a

large set of diverse facts, knowledge, assumptions,

simple mathematics, and a creative extension of

present-art.

<u>Example 16-1</u>

What is the order-of-magnitude of possible
solar generated electrical energy in relation to
the earth's total electrical energy requirements?

Assume: 1.   1 KW/M^2 = solar radiation
intensity normal to
earth's surface under
clear conditions.
2.   3960 Mi. = earth's radius.
3.   0.1% of earth's surface could be
covered with solar-
electric converters.
4. η = 5% conversion efficiency
for the solar-electric
converters.

Then the total solar power arriving at sea
level is approximately

$$\frac{1 \text{ KW}}{\text{M}^2} \times \pi \times (3960 \text{ Mi.} \times 1610 \text{ M/Mi.})^2 = 1.28 \times 10^{14} \text{ KW}$$

The total annual electrical energy generated would
be

$$\textbf{1.28} \times 10^{14} \text{ KW} \times .001 \times .05 \times 24 \times 365 = 5.6 \times 10^{13} \text{ KWH}$$

The latter is about 40 times the present annual
electrical energy consumption of the whole world.
[57, p3]

Our order-of-magnitude calculation places the
probable potential for solar generated electricity
in the decade of 10 - 100 times present generation
based on reasonable assumptions. Whether it is
35 times or 50 times is immaterial at this point.
We quickly determine solar-electric energy potential,
for the assumptions made, is *not* just 4 times
(1 - 10 decade) the need. We also **imply** it is *not*
400 times (100 - 1000 decade) present needs. We
have thus calculated the approximate order-of-
magnitude consistent with the creative assumptions.
If we change the assumptions, a new order-of-
magnitude calculation would be made.

'Order' is used in the mathematical sense as the

degree of exponentiation. We are not 'guessing' but

are making a reasonable *simple* mathematical estimate

based on known plausible assumptions. By *simple*

means we obtained a 'feel' for the technical potential

of the creative idea of solar generated bulk

electricity.[1]

A related definition is checking.

> ● <u>Checking</u> tentatively verifies a calculation
> or proposed embodiment of new ideas.

_____

[1]Perhaps future creative engineers will make this idea, and others cited
in this Chap., a reality.

"There is a logical sequence associated with invention and that is to check to see if the conception is good."
  Jacob Rabinow
    [266,   p93]

Checking starts with a proposal--a calculation already made or a proposed physical apparatus. The act of creating the proposal precedes the act of checking it. Checking may be done on the whole or a sub-part of the problem. In general we apply our *total* engineering expertise to checking and not just our mathematical expertise.

Example 16-2

A new man-powered aircraft embodiment is proposed as a creative means of eliminating jet aircraft air pollution. Check whether the idea of man-powered aircraft can succeed technically for sustained flight.

Assuming a single-place aircraft, from the extensive prior art it is known the smallest man-carrying craft requires an engine of at least several tens-of-horsepower (1 HP = 746 W) to take off and sustain flight. Check on how much power a man in good health can deliver. Find it is about 100 W at best for short times. The check clearly shows a man-powered aircraft for sustained flight would, at best, be a marginal proposition. Major engineering effort should probably not be expended on it.

"--estimation and order-of-magnitude analysis are the hallmarks of the engineer."
  Thomas T. Woodson
    [383,   p107]

From the Examples we see that order-of-magnitude and checking are closely linked and are often inseparable in actual creative problem solving. The techniques may aid us in *quickly* deciding whether to 'proceed' or 'stop' on a creative idea.

WHY NEEDED Order-of-magnitude and checking techniques are needed since there are no uniquely 'right answers' to most real-world engineering problems requiring creativity. The 'reference' of the college answerbook is missing. We need shortcuts for *quickly* determining 'ball-park' values of important

engineering parameters and checking them. A more

exact value can be found later. Also the engineer's

time is money. We may not have enough time or

money to justify spending months or years studying

a parameter for a new idea in detail when a clever

simple 'back-of-the-envelope' few minutes calculation

is sufficient to determine if the proposed new idea

is potentially feasible. An order-of-magnitude

calculation and check would be adequate, saving time

and money. Further, we may not have enough knowledge,

especially early in a new problem, to perform detailed

"--there is a vast difference between merely possessing a great amount of knowledge and knowing how to use it."
Ira G. and Marthann E. Wilson [378, p183]

calculations. Finally, close observation of repetitively

creative engineers shows they intuitively perform

such calculations and checks. They are able to move

fast and far into new technology areas, making

significant contributions. They leave behind

plodders who insist on accurate tenth-order models

before progressing.

WHERE NEEDED Where orders-of-magnitude and checking

techniques are needed in the disciplined creative

problem solving process is shown in Fig. 16-1.

In the various steps the problem solver might:

● <u>Problem Inquiry</u> In 'Estimate of Problem
   Solvability' sub-phase (Fig. 4-2) perform
   order-of-magnitude calculation on new
   concept proposed. Estimate order-of-magnitude

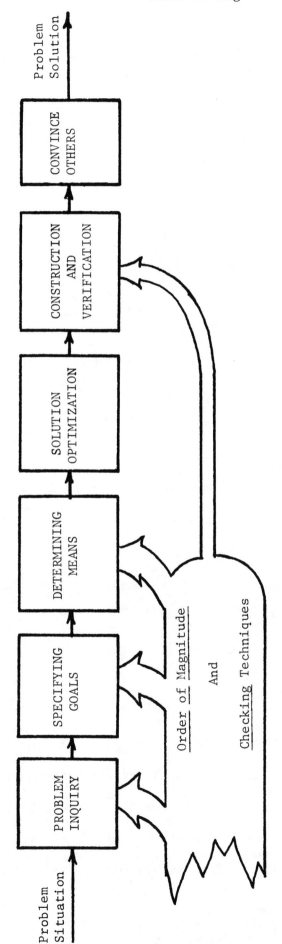

FIG. 16-1 Where order-of-magnitude and checking techniques are principally needed.

of market for new concept, device, or system.
With checking techniques verify the estimates.

● Specifying Goals Perform order-of-magnitude
   calculations to determine parameter numerical
   goals (Chap. 5) for new device or system to
   be created. Verify with checking techniques.

● Determining Means In preliminary means sub-phase
   (Fig. 6-5) perform order-of-magnitude calculation
   on each alternative solution proposal. Verify
   with checking techniques.

● Construction and Verification In testing sub-
   phase (Fig. 8-2) verify physical embodiment
   of solution created with checking techniques,
   particularly experimentation. Order-of-
   magnitude calculations are less important
   here, as by now we need exacting answers
   based on more sophisticated models.

We bring our personal skill in order-of-magnitude

calculations and checking to the principal steps above.

The success of the new idea being created may hinge

on our execution of these techniques. As in earlier

Chaps., we again meet the *personalness* of disciplined

creativity.

Before we present the techniques we should

discuss the role of mathematics.

16-2 Mathematics and Heuristics

MATHEMATICS AS A HELPFUL TOOL is recognized in all

areas of engineering analysis. Note the word,

analysis, a topic broached in Sec. 2-1. Is mathematics

needed or at all helpful to the creative engineer?

Some creative people would emphatically **say**, "No!"

Disciplined creativity tenet answers, "Yes--with

conditions." The conditions are that we recognize it

*"Educated common
sense, with all its
weaknesses, is still
the basis of final
judgments."*
 Thomas T. Woodson
 [383, p98]

as a tool only--one among many the creative engineer

has, that it may be appropriate and helpful at

some places in the creative problem solving process

and totally inappropriate at others, and that we

recognize its limitations.

Some of the powerful analytical tools available

to us include:

●   <u>Simulation</u>   Operating a mathematical model representative of the proposed new system, device or product.

●   <u>Analogs</u>   Going from the equations of a proposed model to equivalent electrical equations which can be simulated on a computer,

●   <u>Computers</u>   Either analog or digital.

●   <u>Statistics And Probability</u>   Helpful in tolerance problems to determine nominal values, worst cases and permissible spread. May be related to perturbation theory.

●   <u>Non-Linear Analysis</u>   Helpful, *if* it can be done, when systems and components must be operated under high stress conditions.

These, and others, have undoubtedly been emphasized

in your engineering education. They may be powerful

aids in the problem solving process where *analysis*

of a proposed new idea is required. They may not be

helpful, for example, in the act of *synthesizing* a new

idea.

Wilson [378 , p156] has shown mathematics is

useful in design engineering only if:

*"Smart creative
workers are those
who are quick to
see the limitations
of mathematical
calculations."*
  *George F. Nordenholt
  [226]*

"1. The problem is so well constructed that
     meaningful equations can be written.

2. Adequate input information is available.

3. A method of computation is known.

4. Computations can be made in acceptable time
    and at an acceptable cost."

In much creative **engineering** work these severe

limitations force us to simpler, quicker, short-cut

methods such as order-of-magnitude and checking

techniques. These invariably involve heuristics--

probably a new term to you.

*Heuristics: "The
logic of discovery."*
  [373]

HEURISTICS **is** a way of creatively thinking using the

knowledge, logic, *and* mathematics we already know.

Example 16-3

Farber [100, p2] states that "--in Egypt
camels are used in treadmills to irrigate the
land. If an engine were to convert 0.8 percent
of the energy from the sun falling upon the circle
in which the camel walks, the camel could be
replaced. In addition, the three acres that are
used to raise food for the camel then **could** be
used for other purposes."

Note the simpler less rigid approach he uses. He

did not get wrapped in intricacies of modeling camels

or solar engines. He used knowledge, logic, and

simple mathematics and concluded a new solar irrigation

engine is worth creating.

Guillemin [135, p28] says of heuristics:

"It may seem to the reader that the heuristic
method of attack spoken of in this chapter is
nothing more than a guess and patchwork process

guided more or less by intuition and reasoning
based upon past experience and familiar
mechanical analogies. This is exactly what
it is. Most students do not seem very well
satisfied with such a process of obtaining a
solution. They rather prefer a so-called
rigorous straightforward integration process.
But if they will take the trouble to look into
the latter in connection with some of the
matters discussed in this chapter they will
find that the operations involved are a mere
manipulation of mathematical symbols in accordance
with prescribed rules. The entire process is
as dry as a desert and as translucent as the
proverbial clay. It lacks the spirit of
initiative and adventure that attends the
heuristic method. The latter is so much more
intelligent because it requires so much more
insight and understanding of the physical principles
involved. It requires also a certain 'instinct'
or 'feeling' which comes only with intimate
acquaintance with various physical processes
and the usual mathematical functions by which
they may be described. In short the heuristic
method is an inspirational method, and carries
with it all the color and enthusiasm which
comes from real mental activity. It forms the
basis of the true research spirit.

It is true that the real significance
of this sort of mental research is hard for
the student to develop. Its mainspring is
composed of experience and initiative--."

"Good inventors
do this first,
before their
enemies do it,
- -"

Jacob Rabinow
[266, p93]

In creative engineering work we are venturing into

new areas. Risks and uncertainties are involved,

and heuristics--the combination of knowledge, logic,

and mathematics--helps us minimize these and rapidly

converge toward the best problem solution. In

Secs. 16-3 and 16-4 we shall see heuristics in both

order-of-magnitude and checking techniques. It is

here we assemble our engineering knowledge and

start to use what we already know. The techniques

are so simple you will be calling them 'common sense'

after you learn to use them well!

Discussion Topics

1. What relations, if any, exist between orders-of-magnitude and 'rules-of-thumb'?

2. "Order-of-magnitude estimates are useless, as they depend on your assumptions which, everybody knows, can be *anything*!" Discuss.

3. What assumptions would you make in estimating how far a crow can fly on a spoonful of corn? How is this problem related to creating a new worldwide air transportation system?

4. What differences exist between an order-of-magnitude calculation and a detailed calculation, e.g. the stress in a new structural member? Which do you know the most about?

5. Nothing was said about information. What does the creative engineer do when he has insufficient information to make an order-of-magnitude calculation?

6. What mental resistances might we throw up to neither start nor perform an order-of-magnitude calculation on a specific creative problem?

7. Why do many engineers have the idea that 'to check' something means to check the mathematics only?

8. How would you check 'the need' for creating a new product?

9. Fig. 16-1 showed these techniques are not used in two principal steps. Why?

10. "Heuristics brings into the problem solving process an infinitude of experience--which I don't have--and a 'fuzzy logic'--which isn't nearly as clear as my mathematics--, and I just don't think creative engineers think this way!" Discuss.

11. Is the subject of 'modeling' related to Secs. 16-1 and 16-2? How?

16-3 Order-of-Magnitude Techniques

We cite examples for communicating the type thinking involved. The title topics frequently recur in creative engineering work.

●   <u>Physical</u>   What order-of-magnitude is the
                                physics?

Example 16-4

     Domenico Fontana, engineer-architect, in
1586 successfully performed the creative feat
of raising the obelisk in St. Peter's Square in
Rome. Hear his thinking: "Before I prepared for
the undertaking of the removal, I wished to ascertain
the weight of this obelisk that is nearly 75 feet
6 inches high. I therefore caused to be hewn
out a palmo [8 · 7 inches] in a cubical block of
the same stone; I found this block weighed
86 pounds. . . . I deduced that the obelisk
weighed 963,537 $\frac{35}{48}$ pounds . . . .

     I reflected accordingly that a capstan
with good ropes and pulleys will raise about 20,000 lb.
and that therefore 40 capstans would raise 800,000
lb. For the remainder (of 163,537 lb.) I proposed
to use five levers of strong timber each 42 · 65
feet long; so that I should have not only a
sufficiency but an excess of power. Moreover,
according to my dispositions, more light machines
could always be added, if the first prove inadequate."
[180, p199]

●   <u>Size</u>   What is the size order-of-
               magnitude?

Example 16-5

     In 1968 I created the electromagnetic wave
energy converter concept for a new solar-electric
means [19], later patented by NASA. The concept
was analogous to the cones in a human eye with
each pair acting as an energy absorber. I needed
to know the physical size order-of-magnitude of
the cones in an eye. My thinking was they must be
several wavelengths of light long. If the light
wavelength is of the order of 1 micron (10^{-6}M),
I deduced the cones must be several times this
long. A quick check of Helmholtz's original
observations on the eye showed the cones to be
about 60 microns long with bases of about 2 microns
diameter. I felt that large area structures
composed of millions of cones this size could

probably be man-made for practical solar
converters.

```
┌─────────────────────────────────────────────┐
│  ●    Energy   What energy order-of-magnitude │
│                is required?                   │
└─────────────────────────────────────────────┘
```

Example 16-6

Cherry has proposed covering large areas of
U. S. desert with solar cells, obtaining bulk
electrical power from the sun. Note his simple
rationale for estimating the order-of-magnitude
of the energy storage required for such a new
system.

"By providing an electrical storage system
for the station...around the clock power would
be available. Using lead acid storage batteries
similar to those installed in telephone exchanges,
a storage capacity of 2.6 KWH/ft^3 can be obtained.
A 1 million KWH storage capacity would require
about 400,000 ft^3 or a building approximately
115 x 115 x 30 ft. high. This storage could provide
around the clock power to the 10,000 homes in the
winter time for 4 full days, should this be necessary
or it could be used to handle peak power demands."
[59, p79]

```
┌─────────────────────────────────────────────┐
│  ●    Power    What power order-of-magnitude is │
│                needed?                        │
└─────────────────────────────────────────────┘
```

Example 16-7

In considering creating a new national electrical
system based on extracting power from the wind,
Heronemus uses order-of-magnitude calculations.

"If aeroturbines to the total of 2 x 10^{10} KW
were installed at all favorable sites [in the
world], if the annual production were 500 KWH
per annum per installed KW, total energy extracted
would be 10^{14} KWH per year (100 x 10^{12} KWH).

The 1964 Energy R & D panel projected a
year 2000 U. S. requirement in an 'all-electric
economy' for 31 x 10^{12} KWH generation per year.
If thirty percent of the world's favorable
wind sites were in the U. S., the total generation
requirement for the U. S. for year 2000 could
be met by wind power alone with an installed plant
of 6.2 x 10^9 KW.

*"But it is sense-
less, in many cases,
to use precise
quantities."*
Eugene K. Von Fange
[360,   p176]

But there is the rub: the largest feasible wind turbine appears to be about a 6 megawatt unit, and 2 Mw units are even more desirable: one million to three million new aerogenerators would be required!"   [146, pS20778]

●   <u>Cost</u>   What is the cost order-of-magnitude?

Example 16-8

Cherry's new 'solar farm' concept beautifully illustrates how an engineer makes rough cost order-of-magnitude estimates early in the creative process.

"---thousands of sq. ft. of solar array might be produced at costs around $50 per KW--or $.50 per sq. ft. Thus a square mile of array would cost about $14 million. Construction of the necessary ground support structure and conductor might amount to $1.00 per sq. ft. or $28 million per sq. mi. Batteries for a 1,000,000 KWH storage facility might cost $10 per KWH or $10 million when purchased in large quantities, and the necessary buildings and switching gear might add another $20 million over a 20 yr. period, including 2 battery replacements.

"Would any of you think of building a tower without first sitting down and calculating the cost, to see whether he could afford to finish it?"
Jesus
[222, Luke 14:28]

Since the solar array is a direct energy conversion system and has no fuel costs associated with it, its operating costs should be considerably less than any of the dynamic systems, perhaps as low as $1.00/ft^2 over 20 yr. or $28 million per sq. mi. which would include 2 array replacements. ---a 1 sq. mi. solar array power station, built after techniques are developed to produce low cost solar arrays and batteries, would cost about $100 million to build, operate and maintain over a 20 yr. period. A solar array in the sunny south-western part of the U. S. using a 70 percent sunshine factor, would generate at least 2.1×10^8 KWH/Mi^2 yr. If the power were sold for 3¢/KWH, about twice today's rates, the gross return over a 20 yr. period would be 1.26×10^8/Mi^2. Subtracting the installation, maintenance and operating costs of 1.0×10^8/Mi^2 leaves about $26 million net income per sq. mi. over 20 yr. This land is then producing a 'crop' which yields about $2000 per acre per year. Farm land yielding such a net return is considered premium."   [59, p81]

Additional details on the important area of engineering cost estimating will be found in [13   ] and in other publications.

● <u>Market</u>   What is the market order-of-magnitude?

<u>Example 16-9</u>

Assume we would like to know the market potential order-of-magnitude for a new type electric generator concept we've created for an automobile.

We proceed by estimating there are approximately 200 million people in the U. S. An average family is about 3.3 persons, or about 60 million families. Assume every family obtains one new car within the next fifteen years. This takes into account the average life of the car and the fact of many families purchasing new autos every few years. Commercial firms buy large quantities of new cars and trucks each year. Thus a potential market of approximately 75 million auto generators appears a possibility in 15 yrs. If they could be sold for $50 each retail, a total sales market of about $3.7 billion would exist. If about half of the retail price is the manufacturing cost, then a *total profit potential exists of about $1.8 billion* over a 15 yr. span. The profit would be available for manufacturer, distributor, dealer, etc.

A rough market order-of-magnitude calculation aids us in deciding which new concepts should be further pursued. A cost calculation may give creator and management strong motivation in the ensuing creative work.

"--surprisingly quick and accurate (presumably) estimates of engineering situations can be obtained in a few minutes."
Thomas T. Woodson
[383, p107]

● <u>System</u>   What order-of-magnitude will the system have?

<u>Example 16-10</u>

Estimate the collector area order-of-magnitude required for the system of propelling a small automobile by solar electric power.

*"From the tables
of Lilienthal we
calculated that
a machine having
an area of a little
over 150 square
feet would support
a man when flown
in a wind of 16
miles an hour."*
Orville Wright
[388, p12]

Assume the auto requires 7 KW at the wheels for 60 MPH and electric motors of 70 percent efficiency are to be used. Then 10 KW input power will be required at the motors which must be supplied by the solar array, assuming no losses in motor speed control apparatus. Further assume solar-electric arrays are about 10 percent efficient. To get 10 KW electrical power out of the array will require a sun power input of 100 KW. Since the sun's intensity is about 1 KW/M^2, about 100 M^2 of collector area would be required which we have assumed is, by unspecified means, oriented perpendicular to the sun's rays. Clearly the 100 M^2 collector area is much too large to be practical for mounting on an automobile. Even if the solar-electric converters could be made 100 percent efficient, the required 10 M^2 collector area is still too large. Thus a simple order-of-magnitude calculation quickly reveals this creative system is impractical.

● <u>Efficiency</u> What is the efficiency
                order-of-magnitude?

Example 16-11

Estimate efficiency order-of-magnitude of a proposed method of generating bulk electric power based on using warm tropical ocean surface water, a boiler, a turbine driving a generator, and cool ocean water to condense the working fluid.

Assume the power plant would be on a floating platform. Further assume surface water temperature = T_h = 82°F = 27.8°C and bottom water temperature = T_c = 36°F = 2.3°C. Without the need to know any details of the boiler, turbine, or generator, we quickly estimate the maximum efficiency is the Carnot efficiency or

$$\eta \leq 1 - \frac{T_c}{T_h} = 1 - \frac{2.3 + 273}{27.8 + 273} = 9.1\%$$

Actual efficiency would be less because of losses. Since 'efficiency' is of most importance when non renewable fuels are being used and since the 'fuel' for this ocean thermal difference system is free solar energy, the *exact* efficiency value isn't important in the early phases of creating such a system. [308]

+---+
| ●   <u>Time</u>   What time order-of-magnitude will |
| it take? |
+---+

See Chap. 17 for how to make time estimates.

In each of the above examples we note the problem solver's rationale is based on using general engineering knowledge,[1] logic, and *simple* mathematics-- heuristics. We also observe the impreciseness of the calculations. Precision in the quantity being estimated comes later as details and more sophisticated modeling of the new idea evolve.

"The art and science of estimation is very under-developed and needs much attention."
Morris Asimow
[12, p34]

With experience we develop confidence in our ability to make rapid order-of-magnitude calculations as we creatively *use* our general and engineering knowledge.

<u>Exercises</u>

16-E1. What numerical order-of-magnitude of bricks will be required to create your future home? List your assumptions.

16-E2. What order-of-magnitude energy storage would be required to propel a 4000 lb. surface vehicle 300 mi. at 60 MPH? List your assumptions.

16-E3. Estimate the order-of-magnitude energy conversion efficiency of a man doing physical labor.

16-E4. For a 20 watt lunar telemetry transmitter to be created, estimate the order-of-magnitude of electric field strength at the earth. What order-of-magnitude voltage gain receiver will be required to see the pulses on a 10 inch picture tube? List your assumptions.

---

[1]We may have to acquire information (Chap. 11) new to us to proceed with such calculations, however.

16-E5.   Recalculate Ex. 16-1 for $\eta = 50\%$. Do such
         converters exist? What creative problem does
         this suggest? What order-of-magnitude land
         area would be required to supply all U. S.
         electricity by this means?

16-E6.   Others of a more detailed nature as assigned
         by your professor.

16-4 Checking Techniques

Since a creative engineer is professionally

responsible for his work, it is essential we have

some means of checking it. Checks may be made on

a running basis during the individual six-steps

in the problem solving process or on a physical

embodiment, i.e. a model. We may want to check our

order-of-magnitude calculations or we may want to

check a formula or calculation of someone else's

before using it in our solution.

To check implies error may have entered. Woodson,

in an excellent treatment of the subject [383, Ch. 14],

has shown "the more clear-cut sources of error

include:

> "In practice reliability turns out to be much more important than speed."
> Ver Planck and Teare [355, p229]

> "--it is safe money to wager that an unproven answer is wrong."
> Thomas T. Woodson
> [383, p240]

Original misunderstanding of the problem;
Erroneous data;
Invalid or over-extended assumptions;
Faulty reasoning; illogical conclusions;
Incorrectly stated principles or laws;
Improperly set-up or conducted experiments;
Typographical or copying errors; erroneous
   table look-up, etc;
Slips in the routines of arithmetic, algebra,
   slide rules, or calculator."

Sometimes in creative work we may propose a solution

which intuitively appears satisfactory but is

impossible to build or assemble. These and other

sources of error enter truly creative work.

Checking may enable us to minimize them.

As before, we classify checking techniques

and cite short examples.

● <u>Fact Check</u> Are the facts right?

Hodnett [151,   p46] has shown the ways to

check facts are:

1. Watch how they are assembled.

2. Review or test the procedure used for assembling
    the facts.

3. When you cannot check your facts **directly**,
    at least question the source.

Example 16-12

An electrical engineer, watching technicians
take experimental performance data on his newly
created telemetry system, observes the instruments
were calibrated 8 yrs. ago! Thus all the 'facts'
accumulated are suspect.

● <u>Assumption Check</u> Do the assumptions
                          individually and collectively
                          appear correct?

Example 16-13

*"Certain assumptions
can be validated at
the outset of a
design; others must
await the final
numerical answer
for their
justification."*
Thomas T. Woodson
[383,   p242]

In the early days of television, I was assigned
the job of cost-reducing a video amplifier for a
commercial television receiver. It involved
redesigning. I calculated the passband based on
formulas from my engineering textbook. The
constructed amplifier had no resemblance to the
predicted passband! I later found the textbook
model had been set up on the wrong assumption that
video peaking inductors have no resistance. The
text author apparently had never checked his
assumptions!

<u>Logic Check</u> Is the logic pattern wrong or
                    incomplete?

Example 16-14

A new means of capturing solar energy via a large area satellite, beaming the microwave power to earth, collecting it in desolate terrestrial areas and converting it to 60 Hz power was proposed in the mid 60's. Thus solar generated bulk electricity would be made available at the earth's surface.

A logic check shows the sun's energy is available *already* at user need sites in up to 1 KW/M^2! It would therefore appear more logical to create new solar-electric converters useable at the need site, as homes. Such an approach avoids the severe cost, reliability, and transmission problems of the proposed new system.

> ●   <u>Physical Law Check</u>   Does it violate any known physical law?

Example 16-15

A beginning engineer has proposed a seemingly clever new high speed mechanical trip-mechanism for a circuit breaker. A careful check shows the mechanism cannot be built because of interference fits. Two bodies cannot occupy space simultaneously.

> ●   <u>Experience Check</u>   Is the result reasonable in the light of experience --mine, my colleagues, or 'experts'?

Example 16-16

Two creative scientists in the early '70's proposed a new thin film for coating metallic surfaces, yielding characteristics which absorb solar radiation but greatly attenuate reradiation. They proposed its use in a flat-plate solar energy collector. Their contention was that it could heat fluids to 500°C.

An independent check by a heat transfer expert showed that on the basis of past experience as well as simple heat transfer analysis 500°C couldn't be achieved.

"Poor arithmetic will make the bridge fall down just as surely as poor physics, poor metallurgy, or poor logic will."
  Thomas T. Woodson
  [383, p245]

"The possibility of success in solving a problem may be increased by consulting an expert."
  Edward Hodnett
  [151, p47]

The proposed collector was modified to a focussed type where such temperatures can be achieved, as is known from solar energy past experience.

+---+
| ●   Mathematical Check   Should the mathematics |
| be checked? |
+---+

These are so well-known we simply list them as

"With the most brilliant engineering design, however, if in the numerical calculation of a single structural member an error has been made and its strength thereby calculated wrong, the rotor of the machine flies to pieces by centrifugal forces, or the bridge collapses, and with it the reputation of the engineer."
Charles P. Steinmetz [317, p293]

reminders:

    Homogeneous Check
    Units and Dimensions Check
    Math Rules Check
    Limiting Case Check
    Symmetry Check
    Alternate Solution Method Check
    Numerical Check
    Graphical Check

These can be powerful checking tools when competently used. Details are in [355, Ch. 6], [383, Ch. 14], [317, p293], and other sources.

+---+
| ●   Experimental Check   Is it best to experimentally |
| check it? |
+---+

Experimental checks are made to:

1. Prove or disprove ideas, particularly new ones.

2. Verify an analysis or check for:

    a. Wrong assumptions
    b. Overlooked factors or conditions
    c. Conditions unsimulatable analytically

3. Discover improvements and new ideas.

4. Demonstrate principles and settle arguments.

5. Evaluate performance, particularly for systems so complex we can't calculate performance.

6. Determine future course of action.

*"--if you really
wish to learn, you
must mount a
machine and be-
come acquainted
with its tricks
by actual trial."*
Wilbur Wright
[397, p100]

Experimental checking, usually involving tests

of a physical system, apparatus, or material is an

important area of engineering. It undoubtedly has

been emphasized in your laboratory education.

Experimentation involves considerable knowledge,

judgment, and art. Failure is more common than

success. It is a breeding ground for many creative

ideas. Unfortunately, details of the subject are

beyond the scope of the present work.

We cite only one creative example.

Example 16-17

In the early days of creating the torpedo there
were major disagreements among theoreticians
about the optimum shape of the torpedo. The
issue was settled when a creative individual
proposed casting a *large* slender block of soap
with a cable in it, towing it behind a ship
for a long time, pulling it up and looking at the
shape it 'wanted to be'. It was reportedly done
and torpedos subsequently were shaped based on the
experimental check.

We close by observing the importance of

engineering judgment, in addition to imagination, in

both order-of-magnitude calculations and checking.

Exercises

16-E7. Example 16-10 was impractical. Check whether the
conclusion changes if a hybrid system is created,
e.g. solar arrays at fixed locations that charge
vehicle batteries while it is not used.

16-E8. An engineer wants to create a refrigerated
hangar in which an entire military airplane can
be placed for -60°F testing. What order-of-
magnitude calculations should he make? Checks?

16-E9. An engineer asserts that electrical energy is
only about 20 percent of the total energy required

to run the U. S. Check his 'facts'. What form
is the remaining energy?

16-E10. Others of a more detailed nature as assigned
by your professor.

Chapter Summary

● Order-of-magnitude calculations furnish the
creative problem solver with a powerful tool
for quickly getting new creations or sub-parts
thereof in 'the right ball-park', especially
in the early steps of the creative process.

● Checking is another powerful toolset enabling
one to verify the reliability of his work.

● How these are related to the six-step disciplined
approach for creatively solving problems was
shown.

● With practice in actual creative problem
solving our skill and confidence in applying
such techniques grows.

CHAPTER 17

DISCIPLINE OF PROGRAMMING THE SOLUTION

"In real life inventing the future is
the province of planning and programming."
Robert U. Ayres   [14, p160]

● Why programming is needed.

● How to program creative projects.

● Effects of programming on the creative person.

17-1 Why 'Programming' Is Needed

PROGRAMMING is the total process of deliberate planning,

scheduling, budgeting, selling, and implementing a

creative project. It is an ordered rational process

widely used by practicing engineers and managers.

It is akin to technological forecasting [14] and

aims toward making the forecast come true.

"If you fail to
plan you plan
to fail."
Anon

Programming ability is another important useful

tool to the disciplined creative engineer. We shall

make a beginning here by exposing programming fundamentals;

but ability in programming creative work can best be

acquired by doing it when you enter engineering practice.

TIME AND COST to create a new product, i.e. solve the

initial problem, are extremely important in the business

world where you will work. Managers, sponsors, customers,

and others need to know "How long it will take and how much

will it cost?" to create an acceptable new solution.

Only when a program for the proposed creative work

is in clear written form can rational decisions be made

on whether it's the best way to use stockholder's or

our resources profitably. Wasted effort and money is

thus avoided.

Because businesses intend to make a profit it is crucial that some workable logical procedure exist for estimating probable times and costs (both total project cost and expenditure rate) to create our proposed new

"--more than half of the 500 largest corporations in the United States now have formal long-range planning programs."
Robert U. Ayres
[14, p14]

product, system, or process. Such estimates are standard practice in modern Research and Development (R&D) where high risks always exist and we desire to maximize our success probability in solving the problem. Such estimates are also daily tools in design engineering, manufacturing engineering, construction, and operations areas. Modern industry would be chaos without programming; progress would cease.

PROGRAMMING AND THE SIX STEP APPROACH of Chs. 3-9 are related as illustrated loosely in Fig. 17-1 and more explicitly in Fig. 17-2.

We need *time* for each of the six steps. Some steps may need more time than others.

Because of our humanness, we tend to follow curve

"Between the conception and the completed invention there lies always the time spent by the inventor in work and suffering."
Herrn Rudolf Diesel
[76, p346]

A without a formal program. With a program and specific sub-deadlines we might follow curve B, resulting in substantially greater energy--hence presumably progress-- being applied to the project.

Since other people and organizations may later be affected by our plans and schedules for executing the six

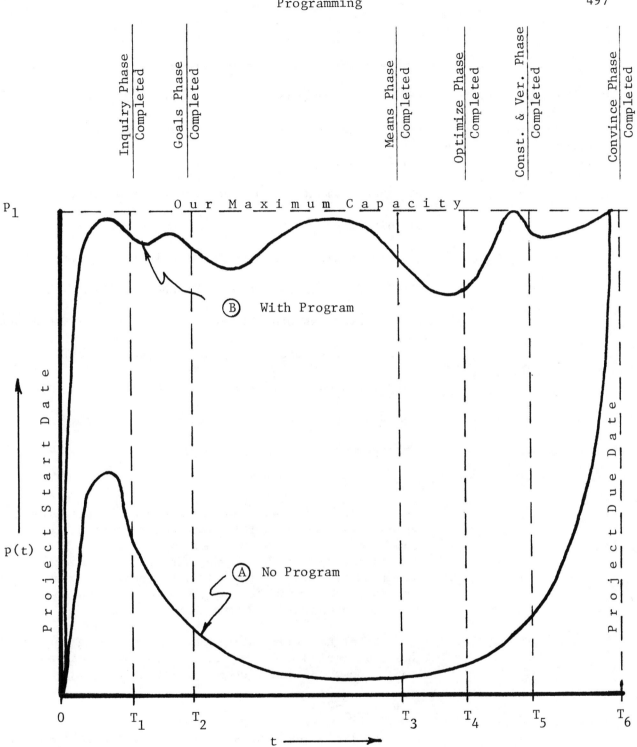

FIG. 17-1   Problem solver's energy expended per time increment,
            p(t), without and with programming. Area under each
            curve is total energy applied to the project. The
            disciplined creative engineer sub-deadlines each phase
            of the six step approach. Adapted from Eugene K.
            Von Fange, *PROFESSIONAL CREATIVITY*, © 1959. By
            permission of Prentice-Hall, Inc., Englewood Cliffs,
            N.J. [360, p115].

steps and since the creative process requires time and

resources--both translate to money--then programming

the solution via the six steps permits us, after more

creative thought, to finally confidently answer, "It'll

take about x months and y dollars to complete this project

and solve the problem."

Programming is logically done in the latter part
of the Problem Inquiry phase, as shown in Fig. 4-2. It
is also sometimes done at the beginning of the Construction
and Verification phase, Fig. 8-2, if the project
construction and test is to be extensive.

PROGRAMMING ORIGINATES with either the problem solver

or management.

Example 17-1

A mechanical engineer recognized the need for creatir
commercial apparatus for solar house heating. He has
completed most of the Problem Inquiry phase, Fig. 4-2.
In its latter part he thinks through and prepares a
specific program of project tasks to be performed,
schedules, and proposed budget. He proposes them to
his management.

Later he finds satisfaction from having generated
and implemented his program--a step toward making
solar house heating a commercial reality.

Example 17-2

In 1961 President Kennedy formally established a
United States goal to put a man on the Moon by the end
of the decade.

NASA engineers and managers, in a superb planning
and scheduling exercise on project Apollo, subsequently
programmed the technology to be created to make Neil
Armstrong's historic July 20, 1969 first step on the
Moon a reality.

Successful creative projects may be done either
way. A desirable motivating excitement occurs, though,
when programming originates with the problem solver.

Discussion Topics

1. Does the business world *really* need engineers who
    can 'program the new' into creation? Can't we just
    start creative work without programming?

2. "It's *management's* job to program! The engineer has
    nothing to say about it and shouldn't get involved!
    Also everything about 'programming' appears about as
    firm as jello nailed to a wall!"

3. "Invention is entirely unpredictable. It's futile
    to try 'programming' it!"

4. Identify rationalizations *against* 'programming' the
    creation of a new product.

5. Compare on-the-job contributions of (a) an engineer
    who works on what he wants to, quickly accepts
    responsibility to solve any problem anyone asks him
    to (The 'nice guy' image!), and operates with absolutely
    no program with (b) an engineer who carefully chooses
    goals, programs his activity, and tells other people
    "No!" when asked to take on deflecting tasks.

6. Reexamine Fig. 17-1. Why does our power typically
    tend to decay shortly after starting a project? Why
    is curve B irregular? Which curve have you mostly
    followed?

7. Consider Example 17-2. Had you been NASA's project
    chief in 1961 what specific technical areas would you
    have programmed?

8. Explore compatibility of programming the solution with
    the concept of freedom of creative inquiry for the
    problem solver.

9. To what extent has your education to date been
    programmed?

17-2 Planning And Scheduling Alternatives

PRINCIPAL CLASSES of planning, the first step in programming, are:

"--a firm plan and
schedule are
essential."
  John R. M. Alger
  Carl V. Hays
     [4, p58]

● **Policy Planning**: Formulating broad desirable goals or future objectives.

● **Strategic Planning**: Identifying plausible alternative options for achieving the chosen policy goal(s).

● **Tactical Planning**: Proposing the sequence of actions to implement a specific stragegy.

They progress from the general to the specific. The creative engineer uses tactical planning most, and emphasis here is on it.

Tactical planning may be subclassed as:

● **Normal Program**: The plan proposed is based on a normal effort for all people involved.

● **Crash Program**: Based on a supernormal effort. Involves overtime work, abnormal schedules, shortcuts, high emotions, etc.

Here we deal only with normal programming. Crash programming is an extension of it.

PRINCIPAL PLANNING AND SCHEDULING METHODS are:

● The Gantt Chart

● Milestone Chart

● Program Evaluation And Review Technique (PERT)

All three can be manually done; but PERT, in its most sophisticated form, uses modern computers. We examine these methods individually.

THE GANTT CHART was developed by Henry L. Gantt [62]. It's also called a bar chart.

To make a Gantt chart:

● Subdivide the project into specific manageable
   steps, problems, or tasks. The more precisely
   they are defined--from broad to detailed--the
   more accurate your final time estimate can be
   for the project. Write the tasks down.

● Sequence the tasks. The six step approach can
   guide. List the tasks in some logical order in
   a column on a large sheet of paper.

● Schedule, by a horizontal bar opposite each task,
   the estimated time to do that specific task.
   It requires good judgment, decisiveness, and
   discipline. Time estimates frequently depend
   on the assumptions made. Indicate these in
   a suitable way (footnotes or separate explanatory
   sheet). Alger and Hays   [4, p59] neatly
   summarize the factors to consider in making time
   estimates:

   ▲ Task complexity
   ▲ Number of people involved
   ▲ Experience and caliber of people
   ▲ New knowledge or techniques that must be
      learned
   ▲ Other projects in which the assigned people
      are also engaged
   ▲ Vacations and holidays
   ▲ Incomplete information
   ▲ Material procurement delays
   ▲ Dependence on facilities or manpower
      beyond your control

The method is easy to see from an example.

Example 17-3

   See Fig. 17-2. Each step could be further
subdivided and scheduled as desired into more detailed
sub-steps from the charts in Chs. 4-9. The level
of detail on a Gantt chart is entirely a matter of
engineering judgment.

   Large desk pads, pencils, and much scratchwork
are normal starting points for preparing Gantt charts.

   Planning and scheduling via Gantt charts has the

advantages of:

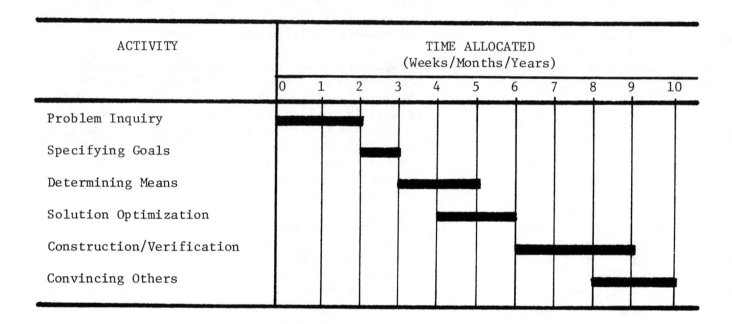

FIG. 17-2 Illustrative simple *Gantt* (Bar) *Chart*
          for planning and scheduling the prob-
          lem solution with the six step
          approach. Note scheduling overlap
          between some phases minimizes total
          solution time.

● Forcing <u>Terse</u> <u>Definitions</u> to be made by us as
  specific propositions.

● Removing <u>False</u> <u>Notions</u> that "There isn't much
  to be done" by clearly identifying tasks.

● Encouraging <u>Sensible</u> <u>Planning</u> and scheduling at
  the *beginning* of a project before senseless
  and perhaps costly mistakes are made.

● <u>Documenting</u> our plan as of a specific time. Gantt
  chart documents are frequently used in presentations
  to management.

● Measuring <u>Project</u> <u>Progress</u> At any time, t, a
  glance shows what's been done and what's to
  be done if auxiliary "actual progress" bars
  are plotted as the project progresses.

Vidosic [357] cites its disadvantages:

● <u>Difficult</u> <u>To</u> <u>Apply</u> effectively to large complex
  systems.

● <u>Progress</u> of a job is difficult to follow.

● <u>Critical</u> <u>Activities</u> that actually determine cost
  and time-to-finish cannot be singled out and
  analyzed on bar charts.

● <u>Effort</u> <u>Is</u> <u>Wasted</u> on noncritical activities.

In spite of its limitations, Gantt charts are widely

used by engineers engaged in creative work and have proven

to be a useful planning tool.

MILESTONE CHARTS seek to define desirable milestones in

our problem solving progress and predict their timing.

'Milestone' is defined as the occurence on the project

of a desirable discrete major event--a checkpoint.

Precisely what constitutes 'a milestone' is a matter

of engineering judgment. In planning creative projects

it's normal to excruciate--either with ourselves or others--

over *what* the milestones should be, their desirability,

*"--we have so much
to do and so little
time to do it."
K. A. Kesselring
[171, p15]*

*"A good schedule
will contain
numerous check-
points."
John Dustin
Kemper
[168, p138]*

necessity, their relationship to the larger project, and
similar items before finally deciding them.

Final project success may hinge on carefully
programming the *right* milestones. Considerable creativity
may be required to identify them.

Milestone planning and scheduling is a simple
addition to a Gantt chart for a typical project.

Example 17-4

> See Fig. 17-3. The desirable milestones are
> listed and each scheduled in some rational order.
> This example, from the government's NSF/NASA Solar
> Energy Panel Report, also illustrates the idea that
> programming must extend over many years in complex
> interdisciplinary R&D.

> The program shown, if competently implemented,
> may eventually make low cost solid state solar-electric
> converters a reality for houses and buildings. Such
> a creation would have enormous beneficial social
> impact.

*"The activities of
the moment are
linked in time
with the outcome
of events months
or years ahead."
Edward Hodnett
[151, Ch. 11]*

Milestone planning and scheduling has essentially
the same advantages and limitations as the Gantt chart
method.

PROGRAM EVALUATION AND REVIEW TECHNIQUE (PERT)

This important method of planning and scheduling originated
as a management tool in the late 1950's on a weapons system
project, the Navy's Polaris submarine [255]. It permitted
the complex Polaris project to be completed well *ahead*
of schedule. The PERT method was subsequently imposed
on Polaris contractors. The use of PERT later spread
widely in industry.

*"When the Polaris
submarine was
conceived, four
major inventions
were needed for
its success:--.
As a fifth one
can add 'PERT'."
Dennis Gabor
[115, p6]*

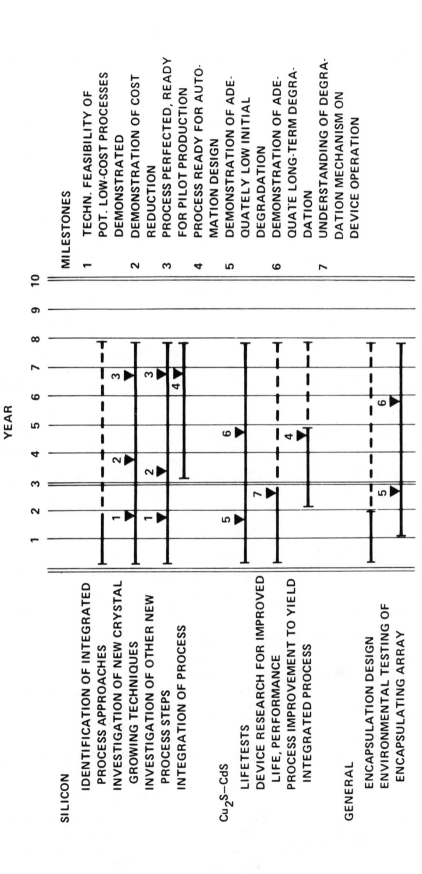

FIG. 17-3 A *Milestone Chart* for planning and scheduling
the development of low cost solar array
technology [308, p66].

In 1974 many U. S. firms contracting with the
government must, as one of the contract terms, use
PERT programming from start to end of the project.

There is a large literature on PERT, a sample
being   [14] [245] [246] and [255]. We can only
touch the main ideas here.

PERT programming centers around a PERT network,
also called an arrow diagram. The key ideas of a
PERT network are captured in Fig. 17-4.
The network is composed of 'events' symbolized by circles
and 'activities' symbolized by arrows. Arrow length isn't
significant. Events are defined as recognizable points
in time at which specific tasks or activities start or
end. An 'event' is like a milestone discussed earlier.
'Activities' represent work required between two consecutive
events. These are like the tasks of our earlier bar
charts.

To be useful the network must indicate the timing
from event to event. To find it, three estimates are
recorded for the activity.

*"Even the most un-
certain case can be
narrowed down by
first asking, 'Will
it be done in a
matter of a few
hours or a few
months--a few
days or a few
weeks?'"
W. J. King
[178, p4]*

● Optimistic The shortest time, t_o, in which an
   activity can be completed with good luck.
   (Everything falls in line the first time
   through, but no breakthrough contemplated.)

● Most Likely The best estimated time, t_m, required
   to complete the activity under expected conditions
   of work accomplishment.

● Pessimistic The longest time t_p, an activity would
   take if significantly worse luck (major redesign,
   major reshuffling of planned action, etc.) occurs
   (excluding Acts of God).

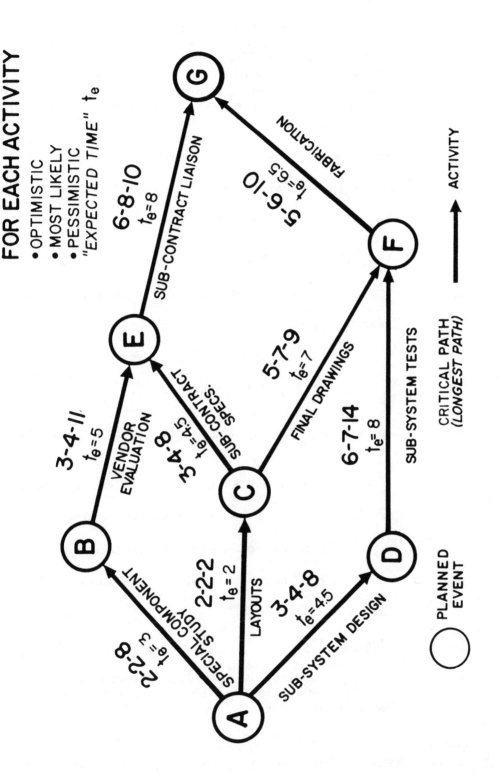

PERT NETWORK

3 TIME ESTIMATES FOR EACH ACTIVITY

- OPTIMISTIC
- MOST LIKELY
- PESSIMISTIC

"EXPECTED TIME" t_e

SPECIAL COMPONENT STUDY 2-2-8 $t_e = 3$

LAYOUTS 2-2-2 $t_e = 2$

SUB-SYSTEM DESIGN 3-4-8 $t_e = 4.5$

VENDOR EVALUATION 3-4-11 $t_e = 5$

SUB-CONTRACT SPECS. 3-4-8 $t_e = 4.5$

SUB-CONTRACT LIAISON 6-8-10 $t_e = 8$

FINAL DRAWINGS 5-7-9 $t_e = 7$

SUB-SYSTEM TESTS 6-7-14 $t_e = 8$

FABRICATION 5-6-10 $t_e = 6.5$

 PLANNED EVENT

→ ACTIVITY

CRITICAL PATH *(LONGEST PATH)*

FIG. 17-4 A *PERT Network* for planning and scheduling [245].
To find the longest (critical) path through the
network, the series sums of t_e values are compared.
PERT networks are widely used on complex projects.

Example 17-5

Activity BE in Fig. 17-4 was optimistically estimated as 3 weeks, the most likely estimate was 4 weeks, and the pessimistic estimate was 11 weeks. These numbers would ordinarily be obtained from the person(s) responsible for performing that activity. The numbers may reflect both experience and good judgment.

Using these estimates the 'expected time,' t_e, for completing the activity may be computed from[1]:

$$(\text{Eq. 1}) \quad t_e = \frac{t_o + 4t_m + t_p}{6}$$

At t_e the probability is 0.50 the activity will be completed earlier and 0.50 it will be completed later than t_e.

Example 17-6

For activity BE in Fig. 17-4,

$$t_e = \frac{3 + 4 \times 4 + 11}{6} = 5 \text{ weeks}$$

Expected times for other activities shown are computed the same way.

It is clear a PERT network realistically accounts for the statistical nature of a task completion.

The total expected time to complete any one path through a PERT network is simply the sum of all t_e for that path.

Example 17-7

To complete layout, final drawings, and fabrication of the example in Fig. 17-4 (path ACFG) requires 15.5 weeks expected time.

---

[1] Equation (1) is based on a beta distribution, but such details--including actually plotting the curve--are *not* necessary to use PERT.

Since *all* the activities shown on a PERT network must
be completed for the project to end, it follows we
should investigate which path requires the *longest*
estimated time. It's the 'critical path,' since it
limits project completion.

Example 17-8

Again referring to Fig. 17-4, path ADFG is the
critical path since it requires 19 weeks. Other
paths require less time.

A good programmer would focus on the critical path,
seeking ways to shorten it.

PERT networks for major projects tend to become
large complex charts. For this, and other reasons the
entire procedure is frequently processed on computers,
permitting rapid computation, direct response to our
questions ("At 15 weeks what is the probability path
ADFG will be completed?"), and others. The details--
including the role of feedback--are beyond us here but
can be quickly learned in industry built on the fundamental
concepts presented here.

Planning and scheduling creative projects with
PERT has the advantages of:

● Imposing Discipline to consider *all* the elements
   of effort required to achieve the desired
   objectives and the interrelationships among
   the elements.

● Communication Means for quickly and effectively
   transferring plans and their substance.

● Structured Planning lending itself to systematic
   determination of the total estimated time which
   can then be compared to a directed or desired
   completion date.

● Visible Proof that a planning job *has* been done.

"Where hundreds of non-repetitive inter-dependent tasks are to be accomplished, as in building construction, new plant or product development, and research, the technique is most beneficial."
  Joseph P. Vidosic
  [357, p104]

● <u>Means</u> <u>For</u> <u>Appraising</u> Progress against approved plans and forecasting problems in meeting a schedule.

On the other hand PERT is not well suited for highly repetitive tasks, as occur in manufacturing.

In closing this section on planning and scheduling, we observe that (a) all methods involve identification and itemization of each manageable task followed by estimating the time to do it; (b) all result in creating a specific written document--the project program; (c) the charts can also be made by starting from the due date, if one is thrust upon us, and working *backwards*, juggling times and overlaps until everything 'fits'; (d) it is wise to allow contingency time--it usually takes longer than we initially think to do *anything*; and finally (e) one planning and scheduling a project excruciates over the many unknowns, uncertainties, assumptions, and risks involved in attempting to creatively program future progress

"An inexperienced engineer commonly believes that he can accomplish about twice as much as he can in fact accomplish in a given time."
  John R. M. Alger
  Carl V. Hays
    [4, p58]

PERT and other planning and scheduling techniques will undoubtedly continue to evolve.

17-3 <u>Program</u> <u>Budgeting</u>--<u>The</u> <u>Next</u> <u>Step</u>

Assume we've generated a specific plan and schedule for our proposed creative project.[1] We now know about how *long* it will take to solve the problem; but how much will it *cost*?

---

[1] Caution: A budget prepared *without* a specific plan and schedule is strictly a shot in the dark!

We can:

●   <u>Have</u> <u>Others</u> <u>Cost</u> <u>It</u>, as cost estimaters, planners, accountants, managers, or the appropriate person within the organization.

●   <u>Cost</u> <u>It</u> <u>Ourselves</u>, since we are most familiar with the project. Our knowledge may be limited, though, and we may not have all the cost facts, they may not be current, others may not believe our final figures, etc.

●   <u>A</u> <u>Combination</u> of the above, proceeding ourselves to obtain the correct cost figures from the most authoritative source and prepare a proposed budget.

In general the cost of each activity or groups of activities on our plan and schedule must be estimated. The summation of all activity costs is the estimated project cost.

Also in general the estimated cost[1] of an activity, C_A, is:

"The account code structure consists of numbers which are used for charging (charge numbers) and summarizing (summary numbers) the costs of a program."

    [246, p40]

(Eq. 2) $C_A = C_m + C_p + C_e + C_L + C_o + C_{pr}$

where:

    C_m = Material Cost

    C_p = Parts Cost

    C_e = Equipment/Tooling Cost

    C_L = Labor Cost

    C_o = Overhead Cost

    C_{pr} = Profit

The calculation of each parameter inherently involves the details of your firm's accounting system ("What's our current overhead rate for projects similar

---

[1] Remember there are two kinds of cost: (a) <u>Retail</u> <u>Cost</u>--the cost to the customer, and (b) <u>Manufacturing</u> <u>Cost</u>--may or may not include C_{pr}, depending on our motives in preparing the cost estimate. Manufacturing cost may be only 20-50% of retail cost for mass produced consumer type goods.

to mine?"). We may also have to make order-of-magnitude

cost estimates and check them (see Ch. 16). One simply

acquires the best cost *facts* he can for the activity

and totals.

Broadly, the project cost, C_T, is:

(Eq. 3) $C_T = \displaystyle\sum_{\text{All } A} C_A.$

On many projects it is convenient to group costs into

major categories, as:

(Eq. 4) $C_T = C_D + C_I$

where:

C_D = Direct Costs

C_I = Indirect Costs.

Each may then be itemized for the project, using an

appropriate format.

<u>Example 17-9</u>

See Fig. 17-5. For higher management use
it's generally desirable to get a project budget on
a *single* sheet.

A technique exists for joining cost estimating with

*"The level of
detail to which
to apply PERT
COST is largely
a matter of
judgment."
[246,   p40]*

planning by PERT networks. It is called PERT/COST   [245]

and is a computerized version of the above concepts.

The method is beyond our present scope.

You will have opportunity to probe deeper into cost

estimating and expenditure rate control once you are

doing engineering or management work. Adopt a learning

attitude toward those older and skilled in this area.

INFORMAL ROUGH BUDGET FOR

Proposed UF-GSFC EWEC Research Program
(UF's Part Only)

Grant Period: Oct. 1, 1974 - June 30, 1975

A. SALARIES AND WAGES
    1. Senior Personnel
        a. Professor A (Princ. Inv.)   50% - 3 Quarters $ 8,000
        b. Professor B   0+
        c. Fields & Waves Prof.   25% - 3 Quarters   4,000
    2. Other Personnel
        a. 2 Grad. Students   33% - 3 Quarters   9,000
        b. 2 Pre-Bacc. Students   25% - 3 Quarters   1,800
        c. 1 Secretary   25% - 3 Quarters   1,500
        d. 1 Technician (Electronic)   100% - 3 Quarters   8,250
B. STAFF BENEFITS   4,114
C. TOTAL SALARIES, WAGES, AND BENEFITS   36,664
D. PERMANENT EQUIPMENT   0
E. EXPENDABLE EQUIPMENT AND SUPPLIES   2,000
F. TRAVEL (2 men, 15 total trips @ $300/trip)   4,500
G. PUBLICATION COSTS (3 papers, $600/paper)   1,800
H. COMPUTER TIME COST (6 Hrs. @ $500/hr.)   3,000
I. OTHER COSTS   0
J. TOTAL DIRECT COSTS   47,964
K. INDIRECT COSTS 49.42% of C   18,119
L. TOTAL COSTS   66,083

+Dr. B's salary is paid by USDA. No part of it may be paid by any other
agency.

FIG. 17-5 Sample project budget for a proposed
university research project. It was
prepared from a Gantt chart for this
project.

Exercises

17-E1. Prepare a Gantt chart for your major course
        problem chosen from 4-CP1 through 4-CP10.

17-E2. Ditto for a Milestone chart.

17-E3. Ditto for a PERT chart.

17-E4. Prepare a *one* page budget covering the construction
        and verification phase for the gadget proposed in
        your major course problem. Clearly indicate all
        assumptions on a separate page.

17-E5. Assume you had decided to create this textbook.
        Prepare a Gantt chart for getting the manuscript
        written. Cite assumptions on a separate page.

17-E6. Assume the largest power transformer ever to be built
        for an electric power generating plant has been
        designed. The first one is now to be built and
        tested. List the tasks requiring time.

17-E7. Consider Example 17-1. Assume you were the engineer
        designing a solar water heater to be manufactured
        by your small company. List the tasks requiring
        time before a definite design is in hand.

17-4 Getting The Program Accepted

Inexperienced engineers think that once planning,

scheduling, and budgeting are completed the project

programming chore is finished. Actually the hardest

job lies ahead in getting managers, potential sponsors,

or others in authority to accept and implement our proposed

program. This reluctance is higher if our program

proposes creating a radically new product, system, process,

or gadget, especially if someone is to put money into

the project.

Suggestions for how to convince others to act on our

creative proposals were cited in Chapter 9. A few

additional helps for getting others to accept a program

*"--the money to
pay for research
and development
is not auto-
matically available
when it is wanted."
John Dustin
Kemper
[168, p138]*

are:

● <u>Be</u> '<u>A</u> <u>Champion</u>' for your proposed program.
If no single person 'champions' the creative
project its death is almost certain, thereby
negating all your careful programming effort.
A little exhibited *enthusiam* for the project
based on honestly believing in it can
frequently--but not always--get the program
accepted.

● <u>Document</u> <u>The</u> <u>Program</u> in some suitable way
(see Ch. 12--Communicating). People respond
most favorably to a *written* document laying
out the proposed program.

*"Ideally another
man's promises should
be negotiable instru-
ments, like his
personal check, in
compiling estimates."
W. J. King
[178, p4]*

● <u>Credible</u> <u>Dates</u> proposed are vital to project
success and our reputation. Whether we like
it or not, much of the world judges us by our
reputation for meeting schedule promises.
Take every step possible *before* any formal
presentation of your program to obtain credible
dates.

● <u>Informal</u> <u>Program</u> <u>Acceptance</u> of key people who
will work on your proposed project is generally
important to obtain *before* its presentation
to management. The program may have obvious
errors which they will spot, saving embarrassment
and enhancing the likelihood of program acceptance.

● <u>Secure</u> <u>Approval</u> of higher management (or sponsor)
of the program, preferably over a signature.
It is extremely helpful to the creative engineer
later, when the project gets assailed, as it
surely will, to have the active support of the
manager who initially approved the program.

Finally recognize that unless you can get your program

accepted by the crucial people it will not progress to

implementation.

17-5 <u>Implementing</u> <u>The</u> <u>Program</u>

Having 'sold' your program, it's again tempting to

sit back and think all the *hard* work is done. Actually

we are now only ready to *begin* implementing the plans we've so carefully laid for creating the new project.

Some suggestions:

*"It is always diffi-
cult at the start of
a long development
cycle to instil the
sense of urgency
necessary to insure
on-time delivery."*
John R. M. Alger
Carl V. Hays
[4, p58]

● Implementation Is Not Automatic A creative
program usually gets started by one person--the
project leader, champion, or principal
investigator--with high initiative.

● *Work* Your Plan now that you've so carefully
conceived it. If the project wanders into
other areas without solid reasons[1], the project
goal(s) may never be reached.

● Constant *Follow-Up* is required to detect extreme
difficulties, unanticipated problems, schedule
slippages, personnel problems, bureaucratic
blocks and any other hindrances to the program.

● Modify Your Program and update it as the project
proceeds. Programming is *not* static!

*"A magnificent
motto: to make
haste slowly."*
Baltasar Gracian
[127, p58]

Since implementing the proposed program normally follow

the six step approach, we reenter it at the appropriate

place (Chs. 4-9) and find detailed guidance for continuing.

17-6 Effects Of Programming On The Creative Person

Because the subject of 'programming creativity'

has been historically controversial[2], it is appropriate

to close this Ch. with a brief appraisal of some effects

of programming on the individual(s) actually doing the

creative work.

---

[1]Such side investigations are quite ordinary in creative research, however; but
there are usually solid reasons for making them. Such side investigations
sometimes open up new creative possibilities unknown before.

[2]The undisciplined say it can't be done and shouldn't be attempted; disciplined
engineers have been programming for years in modern industry!

*"The people at the
conference asked
me to develop a
high-frequency
neutrodyne amplifier
type of broadcast
receiver with
loop antenna for
the top level
people in the
AT&T companies
and they gave
me three weeks
to do it."*
  Harald T. Friis
   [113, p19]

*"A sense of time
and timing is
part of your
equipment as a
problem solver."*
  Edward Hodnett
   [151, Ch. 11]

Programming increases psychological strain on an individual. Von Fange sees the problem solver's efficiency related to strain on him as in Fig. 17-6. Without some strain we are in a low efficiency creatively dormant state while with too much strain our efficiency goes negative and we go into depression and nervous breakdown.

Realistic project programming can help us operate in or near the ideal state. A program puts enough strain on us--but not too much--to keep us operating near peak efficiency. It is truly a sad spectacle to see an engineer on a fast moving creative project who has too much strain on him. He may not know about Fig. 17-6, work harder, only to have his efficiency *de*crease. A wise project leader senses this frequently observed phenomenon in both himself and those on the project. A brief 'time off' temporarily relieves the strain.

Programming when realistically done and compassionately administered has the beneficial effects on us of motivating and building confidence in our ability to create. It is genuinely beautiful and inspiring to participate on a carefully programmed well-managed creative project. Programming also helps us avoid the psychological pitfalls of bitterness and grief over having not met our milestones and project completion dates--especially if they were

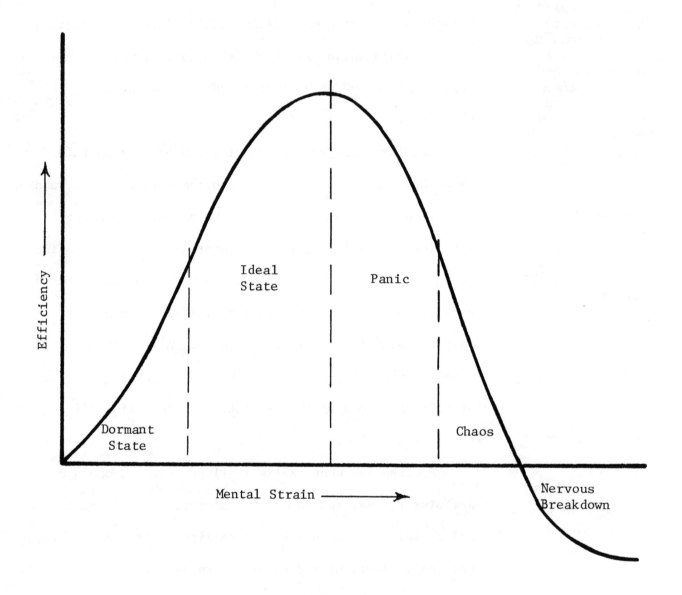

FIG. 17-6   Efficiency-mental strain picture for a
            problem solver. Psychologists have
            measured related curves in studying
            mania and mental depression [181].
            From Eugene K. Von Fange, *PROFESSIONAL
            CREATIVITY*, © 1959. By permission of
            Prentice-Hall, Inc., Englewood Cliffs,
            N.J. [360, p111].

arrived at earlier by the well-known dart and calendar method.

But for the undisciplined creative person ("I progress best in chaos and *no* programs!") programming is looked upon as an unnecessary evil, another useless time consumer created by management, and a psychological straight jacket to creativity.

On balance, programming for creative work--when properly done (It requires discipline and *time*!)--can be a useful tool for the creative engineer or manager seeking to make tangible professional contributions. Finally, such an ordered method for thrusting into the future is an absolute necessity to modern engineering and business managers. Because of its usefullness it appears extremely unlikely programming will vanish from the business world in which engineers work.

Discussion Topics

1. Your engineering manager asks, "When can you have me a transformer turns ratio test set operative?" Without thinking you reply, "By 4:00 PM day after tomorrow." Later the equipment is not operative. The manager says nothing, but you sense what he is thinking about you. How might this unsavory situation been avoided?

2. Programming appears to require precious time. How does the engineer *find* time to do it?

3. Can a person unfamiliar with the product to be created adequately program it?

4. How do you decide which programming method to use on a specific engineering project?

5. What difficulties do you see in generating a proposed budget for a new engineering project?

"It is seldom that one achieves more than he plans."
[261, p93]

"Education should help men and women to understand how implacably the problems of the world are bracketed in time."
Edward Hodnett
[151, Ch. 11]

6. In implementing a creative project, how firmly
    should you stick to the program?

7. Are most programmed engineering projects completed
    on time? Cite an example. What are the consequences
    of late completion?

8. Cite an example of a proposed engineering project
    which was programmed but never implemented. Why
    was it not put into use?

9. Does the emphasis programming places on *time* affect
    the problem solver's health?

10. How will you react when everything on your carefully
    programmed project seems to go wrong?

11. What other effects--beyond those of Sec. 17-6--might
    programming have on the problem solver?

Chapter Summary

We've tried to show why programming is vitally needed
in the business world in which you will work. We saw
programming as a total disciplined process consisting of
planning, scheduling, budgeting, acceptance, and implementi
We examined a few major concepts in each area.

Finally, we briefly looked at the effects programming
can have on us.

Obviously there is much more to programming than
can be treated here--as we've seen in other areas of
creativity.

CHAPTER 18

PATENTS

"Patents are the key to our technology;
technology is the key to production."
Franklin D. Roosevelt [278]

● Importance and brief history of patents.

● Nature of a patent.

● Requirements for patentability.

● Steps in securing a patent.

● Marketing and developing it.

● Inventor's rewards.

18-1 Disciplined Creativity And Patents

Disciplined creativity aims at generating

*"Almost every
engineer is
affected by the
patent system."
John R. O'Malley
[231]*

a useful embodiment. We must then communicate it.

One means of conveying our technical creations to

society is via patents.

One who secures a patent is generally recognized

to have engaged in the pinnacle of creative technical

work.

We focus on patents[1]; but don't lose the perspective

that many results of disciplined creativity may *not*

be patentable. Yet they may be socially beneficial.

So patents constitute only *one* means of getting our

creations eventually in use by society. Other means--

---

[1]Emphasis is on United States patents; patent laws vary in other countries.

"Ideas must be revealed if they are to be of much benefit."
  Joseph P. Vidosic
    [357, p271]

perhaps more effective in some cases--also exist,

e.g. publishing our new creation, giving it to

society.

18-2 Why Are Patents Important?

The United States Constitution provides the

answer: " - - to promote the *progress* of the useful

arts." The public benefits from the patent system

because:

- ● It induces the inventor to make the invention by offering patent protection.

- ● It gives the public the opportunity to use it if the inventor succeeds with the help of the patent in developing and marketing the invention.

- ● It makes knowledge of the invention available to everyone. The inventor must describe the invention in the patent, and patent copies may be purchased by the public for a nominal cost.

If it weren't for the patent law many inventors

"In general, an employee has the right to keep his invention a secret - -"
  F. J. Benasutti
    [33, p8]

wouldn't develop their inventions, abandoning their ideas

instead of going forward with them. Others would keep

them secret.

A patent is valuable 'intellectual property.'

Because a patent is useful others may want it; it has

monetary value. A patent is owned. It may be kept,

sold, licensed (royalty), mortgaged as collateral for

a bank loan, given away, dedicated to the public,

bequeathed or otherwise disposed of, e.g. by contract

(assignment), as property.

A patent protects risk capital investments in new processes and products. It protects the inventor or investors in the new venture for a limited time without fear of others stealing costly research and development, thus reaping an unfair competitive advantage.

Example 18-1

In developing Nylon, the duPont Corporation spent about $45,000,000 on research and thereafter invested an additional $196,800,000 in plants and facilities for nylon production [351].

"Each patented invention in any industry may spur competitors into increasing inventive activity, in the constant jockeying for business advantage."
Robert A. Buckles
[49, p10]

A patent held by company A may stimulate inventors in company B to create an even better useful product. Thus company B engages in invention and patent activity out of competitive necessity. From it new beneficial industries may be created.

Because of the business importance of patents, most firms have the newly hired engineer sign a "patent agreement" as a condition of employment. Thus any invention made while employed by the firm may be its property. The engineer should carefully study the language and understand it before signing.

Discussion Topics

1. Consider the "patent agreement." Are such agreements 'fair?' Discuss pros and cons.

2. What alternatives exist if one refuses to sign a "patent agreement?"

3. Suppose an engineer creates a potentially patentable new product but keeps it secret. Does society benefit long-range from his creativity?

4. Explore the importance or unimportance of
    patents to the lone inventor.

5. A patent is property. Can it be pirated?
    How? Cite an example.

6. Securing a patent requires much effort. Why
    bother?

18-3 How Did Patents Arise?

In ancient times when a man made a discovery or
an invention he tried to keep it secret. He passed it
on from father to son, keeping it a family matter--or

"The ancients also thoroughly under-stood the great importance of inventions and discoveries. They honored their inventors by making them gods."
Joseph Rossman [279, p1]

he died taking the invention to the grave. The result
was a general failure to promote progress in the useful
arts. Only in comparatively recent times has the idea
arisen to encourage inventors from secrecy toward public
disclosure of their invention. In exchange society
guarantees a limited time monopoly to exploit the
invention. This idea we call a patent. The word has
connotations of openness.

In Europe the British Statute of Monopolies was

" - - England was, until we copied her, the only country on earth which ever, by a general law, gave a legal right to the exclusive use of an idea."
Thomas Jefferson [161, p291]

passed by Parliment in 1623. It asserted the common-law
principle that patents may only issue to the true and
first inventor. This historic act was the prototype
of modern patent statutes in the western world.

In early America there were no general laws providing
for the granting of patents. The inventor appealed to
the governing body of his Colony or State. The first
such patent was granted in 1641 by the Massachusetts

General Court to Samuel Winslow for a novel method

of making salt.

When the delegates met in Philadelphia in 1787

to frame the Constitution, one problem was to protect

inventors and authors. From their deliberations came

the Constitutional provision which enabled Congress to

enact the first patent law. From it the modern

United States system evolved [319].

Example 18-2

"Jefferson, besides being the first supervisor of the Patent Office, was in effect the first patent examiner."
[319, p1]

"Congress shall have power--to promote the progress of science and useful arts by securing for limited times to authors and inventors the exclusive right to their respective writings and inventions." [350]

The American patent system has become the model

adopted by numerous countries.

Today most civilized countries issue patents.

An exception is China which is still without a patent

system.

18-4 What Is A Patent?

'Patent' may mean to different individuals:

● The act of applying for a patent.

● The issued patent document.

● A time limited monopoly granted by the government to the inventor.

● A grant from the government in exchange for public disclosure of the invention.

● A contract between the government and the inventor.

Buckles [49, p3] shows that a patent is a *contract* between the Government and the inventor. The inventor's part of the 'consideration' is his public disclosure of the invention. In exchange the Government gives the inventor exclusive 'rights' to his invention for a limited time. While the contract is in force the public has access to the invention disclosure and may obtain permission from the patent owner to practice the invention by entering into a separate contract. When the contract terminates, i.e. when the patent expires, the public then has free access to the invention.

In the United States a patent:

- ● Is granted by law through the Patent Office.

- ● Is valid for 17 years from its issue date. It is *not* renewable except by special act of Congress.

- ● Has invention for its subject matter.

- ● Is received by the inventor (or his heirs or assigns).

- ● Confers rights which extend throughout the United States and its territories and possessions.

- ● Confers "the right to *exclude* others from making, using or selling" the invention. What is granted is *not* the right to make, use, or sell, but the right to *exclude* others. This important legal distinction has implications beyond our present purposes. It entitles the inventor to sue infringers and win, if such action is necessary.

" - - it is the giving birth to a new idea capable of physical embodiment.
H. C. Merwin
[214, p10]

Example 18-3

See Fig. 18-1. Note the only 'right' granted is *excluding*.

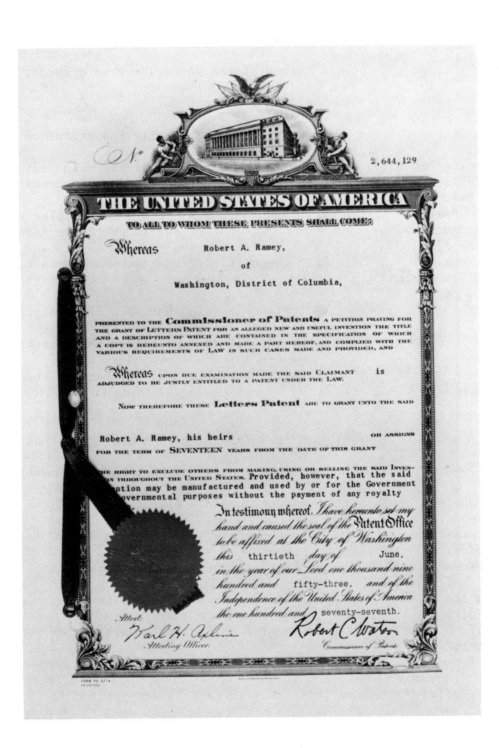

FIG. 18-1 Example of a United States patent letter.

18-5 <u>What</u> <u>Can</u> <u>Be</u> <u>Patented</u>?

United States patents may be granted, according

to law, for a *new* and *useful*:

● <u>Process</u> -- primarily industrial or technical.

● <u>Machine</u> -- any apparatus with moving parts.
          Also includes electronic apparatus.

● <u>Manufacture</u> -- refers to articles without moving
          parts which are made.

● <u>Composition</u> <u>Of</u> <u>Matter</u> -- relates to chemical
          compositions.

● <u>Plant</u> -- which has been asexually propagated.

These classes of subject matter collectively include

practically everything made by man and the processes for

making them.

It is interesting to observe a patent is granted

on the *embodiment* of the new machine, manufacture, etc.

and *not* upon the idea or suggestion of the new machine.

" - - note that
patentable inven-
tions also include
new and useful
improvements to
the foregoing
categories."
F. J. Benasutti
[33, p4]

The above are sometimes classed as 'utility patents.'

Patent laws also provide for the granting of 'design

patents' to any person who has invented a new, original

and *ornamental* design for an article of manufacture.

A design patent protects only the *appearance* of an

article. Design patents are granted for 3 1/2, 7 or 14

year terms.

"Its conception
must require
that exceptional
talent which is
beyond the
skill of the
ordinary
designer."
Albert Woodruff
Gray
[128, p114]

18-6 <u>What</u> <u>Cannot</u> <u>Be</u> <u>Patented</u>

Not all inventions are patentable. Alleged

perpetual motion machines are refused patents. Inventions

useful solely in the utilization of special nuclear

material or atomic energy for atomic weapons are

excluded. Mental processes, systems of logic, or

methods of doing business may not be patented. Products

of nature are not patentable since presumably they

existed earlier.

18-7 <u>Requirements</u> <u>For</u> <u>Patentability</u>

        To be granted a patent the inventor must have engaged

in invention. 'Invention' may mean either the act of

"An invention within the mean- ing of patent law must involve conception plus reduction to practice." John R. O'Malley [231]

inventing or that which is invented. It is interesting

that the word 'invention' has never been *positively*

defined by congress or the courts. Instead it's defined

negatively, i.e. by statements of what is *not* invention!

Such thinking has lead to 'negative rules' of invention

collected in Fig. 18-2.

        The closest patent law comes to a positive stance

is summarized in Fig. 18-3. Both Figs. 18-2 and 18-3

may be helpful in screening potential 'inventions.' There

are so many legal nuances, though,--and patent law as

interpreted by the courts continually changes--that

when in doubt one should consult a competent patent

attorney.

"It is not neces- sary to have a 'flash of genius' in order to make an invention." F. J. Benasutti [33, p5]

        It is wise to be able to produce 'proof of conception'

of an invention when and if later needed, as in a patent

● IF OBVIOUS is not invention. If it is merely a result of
  routine engineering or design or if it would have been
  obvious to anyone "ordinarily skilled in the art," then it
  does not rise to the dignity of invention.

● MERE 'AGGREGATION" of elements is not invention whereas a
  valid 'combination,' even if it includes old elements, may
  be patentable if all the elements contribute in some way
  to a unitary end and the contribution of each element is
  more than a mere additive effect.

● SUBSTITUTION OF AN EQUIVALENT ELEMENT in an old combination is
  not invention unless a new and unexpected result is obtained.

● SUBSTITUTION OF A NEW ELEMENT in an old combination is not
  invention even if the substituted element is novel.

● SUBSTITUTION OF MATERIALS, whether superior or inferior,
  is not invention unless a new function or result is
  obtained.

● CHANGING SIZE, SHAPE, DEGREE, OR SPEED of a thing is not
  invention unless it produces a new mode of operation or a
  new function.

● ADDING PARTS is not invention unless the added parts produce
  a new function or result.

● DUPLICATING PARTS, elements, or subcombinations of prior art
  is not invention unless a new function results.

● OMISSION OF PARTS from a prior art device is not invention
  unless, by the omission, an unexpected result is obtained.

● COMMERCIAL SUCCESS of a new development, device or product
  does not necessarily prove its concept amounted to
  invention.

● MAKING IT PORTABLE is ordinarily not invention.

● WORKMANSHIP EXCELLENCE is not invention.

FIG. 18-2 Illustrative 'Negative Rules' of invention.
Such 'rules,' growing out of U. S. court
interpretations, have many exceptions in
patent law. They also continually change.
Adapted from Buckles [49, Ch. 3].

The 'invention' must be:

● ORIGINAL – with the inventor applicant.

● NEW – as defined in the statutes.

● USEFUL – to mankind, not frivolous, contrary to public
  policy, or inimical to the public welfare.

● NONOBVIOUS – at the time the invention was made to a
  person having ordinary skill in the art to which the
  invention pertains.

● NOT PREVIOUSLY KNOWN OR USED – by others in the U. S. or
  patented or described in a printed publication in the U. S.
  or a foreign country.

● NOT PATENTED OR DESCRIBED – in a printed publication in the
  U. S. or a foreign country more than one year prior to
  applying for a U. S. patent.

● NOT USED OR SOLD – publicly in the U. S. more than one year
  prior to applying for a U. S. patent.

● NOT ABANDONED – at any time prior to applying for a
  patent. Diligence by the inventor is implied.

● NOT DESCRIBED – in a U. S. patent granted to a competing
  inventor while 'the inventor's' patent application
  is pending. The first filed and issued patent
  is a bar to the granting of a patent to the second
  'inventor.'

FIG. 18-3 Principal legal requirements for
           patentability in the United States.
           Adapted from Buckles [49, Ch. 2].

interference case. It translates to keeping good

records (Ch. 15).

Discussion Topics

1. Congress and the courts define invention negatively.
    Why?

2. The 'non-obvious' rule for invention seems to imply
    the inventor must be exceptionally skilled in the
    technical area of his invention. Explore.

3. What does 'first' in Fig. 18-3 mean?

4. Can a computer program be patented?

5. An engineer convinces management to manufacture his
    unpatented invention. Eighteen months after the
    first one manufactured is sold they decide to apply
    for a patent, since its commerical success is certain.
    Can a patent be granted?

6. An engineer works for three years perfecting his
    'invention.' Elated at success, he writes a technical
    paper describing it, submits it to his professional
    journal, and it is published. Thirteen months after
    the first journal copies are sold he decides, after
    receiving favorable mail regarding his invention,
    to apply for a patent. Will he encounter a
    'statutory bar?' What?

7. A new valid combination of old elements is one require-
    ment for patentability. Consider the popular spray
    can. Explore whether its elements were 'old' when
    the first one was invented. Why was the spray can
    an invention according to the laws?

8. Explore specific historical examples in your
    engineering area of the 'negative rules' of Fig. 18-2.

9. A patent only entitles one to 'exclude others.'
    What value, if any, does this have for the corporate
    inventor? The lone inventor?

10-8 Principal Steps To Secure A Patent

Assume an 'invention' has probably been created and

that we've carefully thought through the need for obtaining

a patent.   How do we proceed?

The principal steps are in Fig. 18-4.   The details
are in [117], [240], and [405].

Buckles' [49]   excellent treatment is also a must for
the serious inventor.

The importance of being guided by a competent
patent attorney through the legal complexities of these
steps cannot be overestimated.

18-9   The Patent Disclosure Letter

At the end of the records step of Fig. 18-4 one
generates a 'patent disclosure letter.'   This important
act:

*"The law requires
the disclosure
to be clear
enough to enable
a person skilled
in the art to
employ the inven-
tion without the
necessity of
'reinventing' to
make it
operable."
Robert A.
Buckles
[49, p74]*

● Puts together the main features of your invention.

● Puts the invention in a permanent written form
   capable of being understood by others.

● May be of considerable later legal importance
   as the inventor's first tangible step of
   'revealing,' i.e. coming out of secrecy.

The letter is usually addressed to the firm's
patent department or the inventor's attorney.   A patent
disclosure letter should include:

● Statement of Objects of the invention.

● Drawing(s) or Sketch(es) showing the elements
   of the invention.

● An Identification of the several elements.

● A Complete Description of the invention
   referenced to the drawing(s).

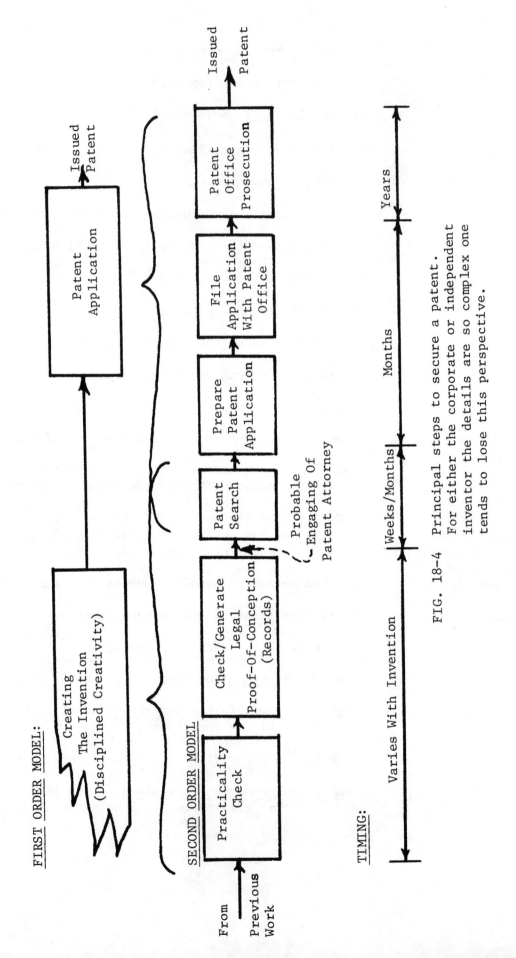

FIG. 18-4   Principal steps to secure a patent.
For either the corporate or independent
inventor the details are so complex one
tends to lose this perspective.

● Reduction To Practice statements if applicable. They should be factually supportable from your patent notebook.

● Novelty Statement, i.e. how the invention differs from prior art and in what respects it is believed an improvement over prior art.

● Date of Conception of the invention--if it is clearly defined--should be stated based on *provable facts*, i.e. records (Ch. 15).

● Disclosure Circumstances, names, and dates-- if applicable--the invention has been described to others.

● Inventor's Signature at the end of the letter or on *every* page.

● Date of the disclosure should be *clearly* indicated.

● Witnesses to the disclosure should *clearly* sign and date it, preferably on each page. Such witnesses are 'corroborators,' as discussed in Ch. 15.

The disclosure letter may be one or several pages long. It is used by your patent attorney to perform a 'novelty search' of prior patents and to prepare the patent application.

Example 18-4

See Fig. 18-5.

Because a patent disclosure letter is so important, it should be written with care.

18-10 Requirements For Filing A Patent

The application for a patent is made to the Commissioner of Patents. The formal filing documents

Page 1 of 6 pages

COLLEGE

OF

ENGINEERING

UNIVERSITY OF FLORIDA

GAINESVILLE, FLORIDA 32601
AREA CODE 904 PHONE 392-0911

DEPARTMENT OF ELECTRICAL ENGINEERING

March 2, 1970

Dr. M. E. Forsman, Chairman
University Patent Committee
Room 308 Weil Hall
University of Florida

Subject: Patent Disclosure

The purpose of this letter is to disclose what is believed to be
a new invention I have made of potential usefullness and value.

Invention Name

Electromagnetic Wave Energy Converter

Intended Function of This Invention

My invention proposes a means of converting the energy in a plane
polarized electromagnetic wave incident on the invention into a useful
unidirectional current, hence energy, in an output load. Thus it is
an apparatus for converting the radiant power in an electromagnetic
wave into a Direct Current (DC) electrical power. It is intended
principally for "power" conversion as opposed to "signal" conversion
in the somewhat related antenna art. The invention is believed
potentially useful as a power absorber and converter in the fields of
wireless microwave power transmission, laser power transmission, and
solar energy conversion. The latter area is the principal intended
application, though the invention is not to be construed as limited
to solar conversion only.

Witnessed and Understood:

Erwin S. Priem   Date *March 2, 1970*   *Robert Leo Bailey*
                                               Inventor

Ce. J. Sige   Date *March 2, 1970*   *March 2, 1970*
                                               Date

FLORIDA'S CENTER FOR ENGINEERING EDUCATION AND RESEARCH

FIG. 18-5   Sample first page of a patent
            disclosure letter. U. S. Patent
            No. 3,760,257 was granted Sept.
            18, 1973 on this invention [21].

required are:

● A <u>Petition</u> amounting to a request for a
   patent.

    Example <u>18-5</u>

      See Fig. 18-6.

● An <u>Oath</u> or declaration stating the inventor
   believes himself to be the original and
   first inventor, among other allegations.

● A <u>Specification</u> consisting of:

▲ A <u>Written</u> description "in such full,
  clear, concise, and exact terms as to
  enable any person skilled in the art
  to which the invention pertains--to
  make and use the same." [117, p13]
▲ <u>Claim(s)</u> distinctly claiming the subject
  matter the applicant regards as his
  invention. [117, p14]

    Example <u>18-6</u>

      See Fig. 18-8.

*"The claim or claims
of a patent are the
most important part
of the patent."
Frank Wattles
[372, p22]*

● A <u>Drawing</u>--if the invention can be illustrated--
  which shows every feature specified in the
  claims.

    Example <u>18-7</u>

      See Fig. 18-7.

● A <u>Filing Fee</u> for the application.

The above documents are usually prepared by a patent
attorney from your patent disclosure letter and consul-
tations with you. He sends them to the Patent Office.
Their form and language is very legalistic. Each word
may have hidden legal implications.

1. PATENT APPLICATION, SOLE INVENTOR; PETITION, POWER OF ATTORNEY, OATH

To the Commissioner of Patents:

Your petitioner, _____, a citizen of the United States and a resident of _____, State of _____, whose post-office address is _____, prays that letters patent may be granted to him for the improvement in _____, set forth in the following specification; and he hereby appoints _____, of _____, (Registration No. _____), his attorney (or agent) to prosecute this application and to transact all business in the Patent Office connected therewith. (If no power of attorney is to be included in the application, omit the appointment of the attorney.)

[The specification, which includes the description of the invention and the claims, is written here.]

_____, the above-named petitioner, being sworn (or affirmed), deposes and says that he is a citizen of the United States and resident of _____, State of _____, that he verily believes himself to be the original, first, and sole inventor of the improvement in _____ described and claimed in the foregoing specification; that he does not know and does not believe that the same was ever known or used before his invention thereof, or patented or described in any printed publication in any country before his invention thereof, or more than one year prior to this application, or in public use or on sale in the United States more than one year prior to this application; that said invention has not been patented in any country foreign to the United States on an application filed by him or his legal representatives or assigns more than twelve months prior to this application; and that no application for patent on said invention has been filed by him or his representatives or assigns in any country foreign to the United States, except as follows: _____.

```
                                    _____
                                             (Inventor's full signature)
State of _____
County of _____
ss:
    Sworn to and subscribed before me this _____ day of _____, 19__.

    [SEAL]                          _____
                                          (Signature of notary or officer)


                                    _____
                                              (Official character)
```

FIG. 18-6   A petition form for a patent [117].

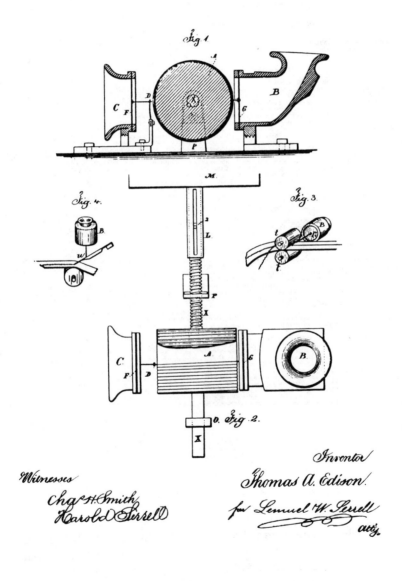

T A. EDISON.
Phonograph or Speaking Machine.

No. 200,521.   Patented Feb. 19, 1878.

FIG. 18-7 A patent drawing for a famous
           invention.

UNITED STATES PATENT OFFICE.

THOMAS A. EDISON, OF MENLO PARK, NEW JERSEY.

IMPROVEMENT IN PHONOGRAPH OR SPEAKING MACHINES.

Specification forming part of Letters Patent No. **200,521**, dated February 19, 1878; application filed December 24, 1877.

To all whom it may concern:

Be it known that I, THOMAS A. EDISON, of Menlo Park, in the county of Middlesex and State of New Jersey, have invented an Improvement in Phonograph or Speaking Machines, of which the following is a specification:

The object of this invention is to record in permanent characters the human voice and other sounds, from which characters such sounds may be reproduced and rendered audible again at a future time.

The invention consists in arranging a plate, diaphragm, or other flexible body capable of being vibrated by the human voice or other sounds, in conjunction with a material capable of registering the movements of such vibrating body by embossing or indenting or altering such material, in such a manner that such register-marks will be sufficient to cause a second vibrating plate or body to be set in motion by them, and thus reproduce the motions of the first vibrating body.

The invention further consists in the various combinations of mechanism to carry out my invention.

I have discovered, after a long series of experiments, that a diaphragm or other body capable of being set in motion by the human voice does not give, except in rare instances, superimposed vibrations, as has heretofore been supposed, but that each vibration is separate and distinct, and therefore it becomes possible to record and reproduce the sounds of the human voice.

In the drawings, Figure 1 is a vertical section, illustrating my invention, and Fig. 2 is a plan of the same.

A is a cylinder having a helical indenting-groove cut from end to end—say, ten grooves to the inch. Upon this is placed the material to be indented, preferably metallic foil. This drum or cylinder is secured to a shaft, X, having at one end a thread cut with ten threads to the inch, the bearing P also having a thread cut in it.

L is a tube, provided with a longitudinal slot, and it is rotated by the clock-work at M, or other source of power.

The shaft X passes into the tube L, and it is rotated by a pin, 2, secured to the shaft, and passing through the slot on the tube L,

the object of the long slot being to allow the shaft X to pass endwise through the center or support P by the action of the screw on X. At the same time that the cylinder is rotated it passes toward the support O.

B is the speaking-tube or mouth-piece, which may be of any desired character, so long as proper slots or holes are provided to re-enforce the hissing consonants. Devices to effect this object are shown in my application, No. 143, filed August 28, 1877. Hence they are not shown or further described herein.

Upon the end of the tube or mouth-piece is a diaphragm, having an indenting-point of hard material secured to its center, and so arranged in relation to the cylinder A that the point will be exactly opposite the groove in the cylinder at any position the cylinder may occupy in its forward rotary movement.

The speaking tube is arranged upon a standard, which, in practice, I provide with devices for causing the tube to approach and recede from the cylinder.

The operation of recording is as follows: The cylinder is, by the action of the screw in X, placed adjacent to the pillar P, which brings the indenting point of the diaphragm G opposite the first groove on the cylinder, over which is placed a sheet of thick metallic foil, paper, or other yielding material. The tube B is then adjusted toward the cylinder until the indenting-point touches the material and indents it slightly. The clock-work is then set running, and words spoken in the tube B will cause the diaphragm to take up every vibration, and these movements will be recorded with surprising accuracy by indentations in the foil.

After the foil on the cylinder has received the required indentations, or passed to its full limit toward O, it is made to return to P by proper means, and the indented material is brought to a position for reproducing and rendering audible the sounds that had been made by the person speaking into the tube B.

C is a tube similar to B, except that the diaphragm is somewhat lighter and more sensitive, although this is not actually necessary. In front of this diaphragm is a light spring, D, having a small point shorter and finer than the indenting-point on the diaphragm of B. This spring and point are so arranged as to fall

exactly into the path of all the indentations. This spring is connected to the diaphragm F of C by a thread or other substance capable of conveying the movements of D. Now, when the cylinder is allowed to rotate, the spring D is set in motion by each indentation corresponding to its depth and length. This motion is conveyed to the diaphragm either by vibrations through a thread or directly by connecting the spring to the diaphragm F, and these motions being due to the indentations, which are an exact record of every movement of the first diaphragm, the voice of the speaker is reproduced exactly and clearly, and with sufficient volume to be heard at some distance.

The indented material may be detached from the machine and preserved for any length of time, and by replacing the foil in a proper manner the original speaker's voice can be reproduced, and the same may be repeated frequently, as the foil is not changed in shape if the apparatus is properly adjusted.

The record, if it be upon tin foil, may be stereotyped by means of the plaster of paris process, and from the stereotype multiple copies may be made expeditiously and cheaply by casting or by pressing tin foil or other material upon it. This is valuable when musical compositions are required for numerous machines.

It is obvious that many forms of mechanism may be used to give motion to the material to be indented. For instance, a revolving plate may have a volute spiral cut both on its upper and lower surfaces, on the top of which the foil or indenting material is laid and secured in a proper manner. A two-part arm is used with this disk, the portion beneath the disk having a point in the lower groove, and the portion above the disk carrying the speaking and receiving diaphragmic devices, which arm is caused, by the volute spiral groove upon the lower surface, to swing gradually from near the center to the outer circumference of the plate as it is revolved, or vice versa.

An apparatus of this general character adapted to a magnet that indents the paper is shown in my application for a patent, No. 128, filed March 26, 1877; hence no claim is made herein to such apparatus, and further description of the same is unnecessary.

A wide continuous roll of material may be used, the diaphragmic devices being reciprocated by proper mechanical devices backward and forward over the roll as it passes forward; or a narrow strip like that in a Morse register may be moved in contact with the indenting-point, and from this the sounds may be reproduced. The material employed for this purpose may be soft paper saturated or coated with paraffine or similar material, with a sheet of metal foil on the surface thereof to receive the impression from the indenting-point.

I do not wish to confine myself to reproducing sound by indentations only, as the trans-

mitting or recording device may be in a sinuous form, resulting from the use of a thread passing with paper beneath the pressure rollers t, (see Fig. 3,) such thread being moved laterally by a fork or eye adjacent to the roller t, and receiving its motion from the diaphragm G, with which such fork or eye is connected, and thus record the movement of the diaphragm by the impression of the thread in the paper to the right and left of a straight line, from which indentation the receiving-diaphragm may receive its motion and the sound be reproduced, substantially in the manner I have already shown; or the diaphragm may, by its motion, give more or less pressure to an inking pen, u, Fig. 4, the point of which rests upon paper or other material moved along regularly beneath the point of the pen, thus causing more or less ink to be deposited upon the material, according to the greater or lesser movement of the diaphragm. These ink marks serve to give motion to a second diaphragm when the paper containing such marks is drawn along beneath the end of a lever resting upon them and connected to such diaphragm, the lever and diaphragm being moved by the friction between the point being greatest, or the thickness of the ink being greater where there is a large quantity of ink than where there is a small quantity. Thus the original sound vibrations are reproduced upon the second diaphragm.

I claim as my invention—

1. The method herein specified of reproducing the human voice or other sounds by causing the sound-vibrations to be recorded, substantially as specified, and obtaining motion from that record, substantially as set forth, for the reproduction of the sound-vibrations.

2. The combination, with a diaphragm exposed to sound-vibrations, of a moving surface of yielding material—such as metallic foil—upon which marks are made corresponding to the sound-vibrations, and of a character adapted to use in the reproduction of the sound, substantially as set forth.

3. The combination, with a surface having marks thereon corresponding to sound-vibrations, of a point receiving motion from such marks, and a diaphragm connected to said point, and responding to the motion of the point, substantially as set forth.

4. In an instrument for making a record of sound vibrations, the combination, with the diaphragm and point, of a cylinder having a helical groove and means for revolving the cylinder and communicating an end movement corresponding to the inclination of the helical groove, substantially as set forth.

Signed by me this 15th day of December, A. D. 1877.

THOS. A. EDISON.

Witnesses:
GEO. T. PINCKNEY,
CHAS. H. SMITH.

FIG. 18-8   The description and claims of Edison's phonograph patent. Claims are written for as broad coverage as possible. Buckles [49, p187] analyzes Edison's claims.

18-11 Who May Apply For A Patent?

"More than 50 percent of all patents are issued to private inventors."
  David L. Ladd
  [183, p7]

Only the true inventor(s) may generally apply for a patent. The true inventor is the person who furnishes the ideas--*not* the employer or the person who furnishes the money. There are no limitations of age or sex. A foreign citizen may obtain a U.S. patent under exactly the same conditions as a United States citizen. Your patent attorney acts as your agent in applying for a patent.

To a corporate engineer whose invention is 'assigned' to the firm it may appear that the firm is applying for the patent; but in a legal sense the application is from the engineer. The firm's patent attorney acts as his agent. The 'rights' to the invention belong to the firm.

18-12 Is Filing Time Important?

"Diligence is the key word here."
  John R. O'Malley
  [231]

Yes! Assuming no other complications, the Patent Office grants a patent to the *first* inventor. We can't know whether a competing inventor has worked diligently and filed his application first. Therefore there is urgency in filing for a patent.

There is also, in some circumstances, the need to delay filing, e.g. until demonstration tests are completed on the invention. The *latest* a patent application can be filed is one year after the invention has been made public in a printed form. Also an application cannot be filed if the invention has been in public use or

sale for more than a year. Beyond a year it's presumed

the inventor gives it to the public.

Discussion Topics

1. Identify likely personal difficulties in writing
    a patent disclosure letter.

2. Approximate the cost to file an application and
    secure a patent.

3. Why does it typically take some time to secure a
    patent after the invention has been made? Is this
    good or bad from society's view?

4. What happens when two inventors file co-pending
    patent applications on the same thing?

18-13 Is A Model Necessary?

For a normal patent *application*[*] at the Patent

Office models are no longer generally required, since

the description of the invention in the specification

and drawings must be sufficiently full and complete, and

capable of being understood, to disclose the invention

without the aid of a model. A model will not be admitted

unless specifically called for, e.g. applications for

alleged perpetual motion machines.

However, in the event of an 'interference' at the

Patent Office, i.e. two inventors file on the same

invention, to win the 'interference proceeding' the

---

[*] The act of filing the patent application constitutes "constructive
reduction to practice" which is sufficient unless "an interference" is
declared by the Patent Office.

inventor--through his attorney--must *prove* 'actual
reduction to practice.' It can only be achieved from
having earlier built and tested a working model.

" - - if the device is inoperable, the patent is invalid."
John R. O'Malley [231]

Also it is sometimes impossible to make a full and
complete specification and drawing for the patent
application without having built a working model. So
good judgment may insist on building and testing a working
model before filing; but note there is no *legal* requirement
this be done to file for a patent. In fact many patents
are issued without a model having been made.

18-14 What A Patent Attorney Does

The patent attorney is a communicator between the
inventor and the Patent Office. He helps the inventor
by:

"Thus, the inventor should seek the aid of a patent attorney before the patent application is filed."
John R. O'Malley [231]

- Making Patent Searches to see if someone earlier
  patented the same invention. This step is
  important in determining what is patentable
  in the inventor's disclosure.

- Preparing The Application documents in the precise
  form required by the Patent Office. An important
  service here is making the claims as broad as
  possible--but not so broad as to be invalid--on
  behalf of his inventor-client.

- Helping Decide whether to file in U.S. only,
  foreign countries, or both.

- Filing The Application for the patent with the
  Patent Office including paying the required
  filing fees.

- Follow-Up on the patent application as it proceeds
  through the Patent Office. The Patent examiner
  may reject the application on one or more
  specifics. The patent attorney, after consultation
  with the inventor, responds to these positively.

He acts as the inventor's advocate before
the Patent Office.

● Counselling his client so as to avoid possible
costly or disastrous patent litigation.

Enlightened inventors have patent attorneys. Corporat

inventors have the services of a patent attorney. For

independent inventors selection of a patent attorney is

a problem and is best done by reputation. Inventor-attorne

personal relationships may be a problem in either case.

18-15 What The Patent Office Does

Patent applications are assigned to a patent examiner

who takes applications rigidly in the order received.

In time he studies your application for compliance with

the legal requirements. He also makes a far-reaching

search through prior U.S. and foreign patents and other

publications to see if your invention is new. He reaches

a decision--an 'office action'--which is mailed to your

patent attorney. In it he may reject your application

because of: unpatentability, earlier patents have the

*"Though this
be madness, yet
there is a
method in't."*
Shakespeare

same features, its features would be obvious to a person

skilled in that field, or one or more of your claims

may be disallowed.

If the invention is rejected, you and your attorney

may decide to either abandon the application or to

proceed--after study--by responding in writing to the

examiner's specific reasons for rejection. After several

such interactions the patent may be finally granted.

Patents are granted for about two-thirds[*] of the
applications. When granted a notice and an abstract
of the new patent is published in the *Patent Gazette*.

Additional information on Patent Office proceedings
is in references [49], [117], and [240].

18-16 <u>Can</u> <u>I</u> <u>'Do-It-Myself?'</u>

" - - if he
tries, the
Patent Office
will usually
politely suggest
that he hire
a patent
attorney."
 John R.
 O'Malley
 [233]

The inventor may prepare his own application and
file it in the Patent Office and conduct the proceedings
himself. However it requires substantial knowledge
of patent law and Patent Office practice. Unless the
inventor is familiar with these matters or studies them
in detail, he may get into considerable difficulty. Also
there is no assurance the patent obtained would adequately
protect the invention.

Most inventors employ the services of a patent
attorney or agent who are authorized to represent inventors
before the Patent Office.

18-17 <u>Marketing</u> <u>And</u> <u>Developing</u> <u>The</u> <u>Patent</u>

Patents seldom promote themselves. Introducing

" - - marketing
their patent is
sometimes a
more difficult
job than making
the invention in
the first place."
 Robert A.
 Buckles
  [49, p137]

the invention to the marketplace usually hinges on the
inventor or his firm. The Patent Office cannot help in
this area. One is unlikely to profit from his patent
unless he either uses it himself or persuades others to
use it (Ch. 9) by pointing out the advantages it provides,
perhaps enabling him to sell or license the patent.

---

[*]The fraction changes with time.

Buckles   [49, Ch. 8] gives helpful advice on what to do with the issued patent.

18-18 Inventor's Rewards

It would be inappropriate to close patents without mentioning positive and negative rewards.

The inventor receives the initial rewards of a patent certificate and the patent itself. Issuance of these generate public acclaim and prestige which is a reward to some. Many firms award their inventors small honorariums, stock shares, certificates of recognition, and similar tangibles.

"Even though the greatest and immediate reward of the inventor is the sheer joy of the work, inventing is a business undertaking with a hope of profit."
Joseph Rossman
[279, p159]

For the inventor-entrepreneur his reward may be the profit or royalties from the manufacture or licensing of his invention. One of the greatest rewards is within the inventor, i.e. the sense of adventure and satisfaction from having generated new businesses and contributed to society's progress.

But a patent may be a Pandora's Box for the inventor when others infringe his invention. Then legal proceedings with their cost, emotions, and notoriety--may be instituted The patent field is also strewn with inventors who went bankrupt for various reasons. So troubles, disparagements, headaches, possible financial loss, and others may be the 'negative rewards' of securing a patent!

" - - Edison had spent more money in obtaining patents, litigating them, and preventing infringements of them than he had received from his patents as such."
F. L. Vaughn
[353, p181]

Exercises

18-E1. Order personal copies of references [117] and
        [240].

18-E2.   Secure a *Patent Gazette* copy. Peruse it.
         Write a one page summary of your findings and
         reactions to this document.

18-E3.   Choose a specific invention. Explore who invented
         it and whether, factually, he had 'smooth' or
         'rough' sailing after the patent was granted.

18-E4.   A team of five engineers successfully creates a
         new invention. Explore the problem of identifying
         the true inventor(s) when the time comes to write
         the patent disclosure letter. Write a summary.

18-E5.   Select one of your better creations. Write
         your professor a disclosure letter. Consider
         him your firm's patent attorney.

18-E6.   Arrange to visit a faculty member who has a
         patent. Record the story of its creation,
         securing the patent, and its subsequent use.

18-E7.   Carefully study Edison's phonograph patent,
         Figs. 18-7 and 18-8. Analyze his claims,
         particularly their breadth or narrowness.

Chapter Summary

A large literature exists on patents. The salient
points needed by the engineer practicing disciplined
creativity were summarized. Hopefully we now have a
better perception of what a patent is and how to obtain
it.

Finally, the Ch. suggests consulting a patent
attorney for specifics with respect to your particular
invention.

APPENDICES

I. SELECTED CREATIVE WRITINGS

CREATIVITY TRAINING FOR ENGINEERS--ITS PAST

PRESENT AND FUTURE[1]

Hyman Olken, Senior Member, IEEE

Summary--The significant fact about creativity training for engineers in the past is that it was retarded by the widely held concept that creative aptitude could only be born, not developed. This attitude was largely dispelled by Osborn's intensive campaign to promote "Brainstorming," his recommended technique for developing creativity.

The significant thing about creativity training at present is that our understanding of the mental processes involved is developing rapidly with the current advances in computers, psychology, and bionics. This will provide solid foundation for developing effective curricula in creativity training.

In the future technological advances will become more and more complex, and more and more scientifically sophisticated. To cope with this, it will not be enough to train engineers in the whole mental process of creativity. It will also be necessary to train specialists in each stage of that mental process: conceptual design, feasibility study, system design and development, subsystem development, etc.

This paper develops the above points in detail and concludes with the framework for a suggested on-the-job creativity training program.

THE PAST

THE SHAPE of things in creativity training for engineers in the past, in the present, and in the future is largely the result of a few significant factors which can be surveyed adequately, even within the space limitations imposed here. These factors will be reviewed briefly, and with these as a setting a program for on-the-job creativity training of engineers to meet the working conditions of the present day will be outlined.

The earliest suggestion for creativity training of engineers dates as far back as 1906, when E. J. Prindle presented a paper at a meeting of the AIEE on "The Art of Inventing" [1]. He was a patent examiner who came in close contact with the mental processes of inventors, and so came to realize that there is more method to it than most people realize. He therefore felt it would be practical to train technical people, particularly engineers, in a methodical procedure that would help them to create valuable inventions for industry.

The Prindle paper is significant not only for making this proposal, but also for the very good examples he gave of a methodical, step-by-step procedure for devising inventions. One of these is the procedure followed by the inventor in creating an elapsed time meter for recording the duration of long distance telephone calls. These steps are illustrated by a good series of figures, two of which are included here (Figs. 1, 2).

Prindle's thesis was that each invention is the result of a series of small inventive steps, and that the completion of one of these steps leads to and provides the cue for solving the next one.

The next significant factor in the history of creativity training for engineers occurred in 1931 with the publication of a book called "The Psychology of the Inventor" by J. Rossman, also a patent office examiner [2]. Rossman's book is a thesis presented for a Ph.D. in psychology.

He sent out questionnaiares to over 700 of the most prolific inventors known to the Patent Office, and from the answers contained in these questionnaires, he compiled this book. He was mainly interested in the mental procedures of inventors, which are detailed in a good chapter on "The Actual Methods of Inventing" (Ch. V) and one on "The Mental Processes of the Inventor" (Ch. VI).

From this table of contents (Fig. 3) one can gain an idea of the comprehensive nature of his study, which had the virtue of being the first one founded on firsthand information from the inventors themselves.

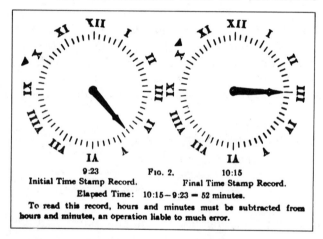

Fig. 1--Start of the step-by-step invention process for elapsed-time recorder, as pointed out by Prindle in 1906. See Prindle [1].

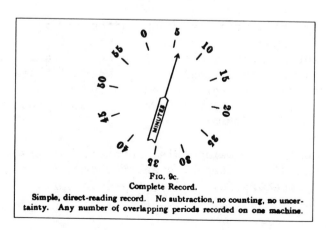

Fig. 2--End of the step-by-step invention process for elapsed-time meter as pointed out by Prindle in 1906. See Prindle [1].

TABLE OF CONTENTS

Fig. 3--Comprehensive nature of Rossman study is indicated by Table of Contents of his book, Psychology of the Inventor. See Rossman [2].

The factor of greatest significance about creativity training at that time and for almost a generation afterward was the attitude, then almost universally prevalent, that creative ability is something you are born with and therefore not something that can be developed by training. Hence it was senseless to try to train people to be better inventors. This attitude was so widely and deeply held that it almost completely smothered any attempts to set up creativity training courses.

A good example is my own experience in trying to get the Massachusetts Dept. of Education to let me set up (in Boston) a course in inventing in 1933. The objection was that "the newspaper reporters would make a laughing stock of its University Extension Division for supporting the idea that persons could be trained to improve their creative or inventing ability." This same objection was made in 1934. Finally, in 1935, they said that if I could get endorsement of the idea from a leading scientist at Harvard or Massachusetts Institute of Technology, Cambridge, they would allow me to set up such a course.

Fortunately, a former professor of mine at that time at the Harvard Engineering School was Prof. A. E. Kennelly, after whom the Kennelly-Heaviside layer was named. He had been president of the AIEE and IRE, and so was regarded as an engineering authority beyond question. It also happened that he had for a long time been Edison's mathematician, so he wrote a convincing endorsement and I was allowed to set up the course which ran for several years, until I left Boston. His endorsement (Fig. 4) states the case for creativity training of engineers as concisely and convincingly as I have ever seen it put.

> We all realize that good singers are born and that we cannot hope to produce a Caruso out of a person with congenitally inferior vocal organs. Nevertheless, the study and training of the voice not only greatly enhances the powers of a Caruso, but also develops the capacity for good singing in the community. We certainly gain by aiding the teaching of the art of singing.
>
> Similarly, we recognise that great inventors are born, and that we cannot hope to produce an Edison out of persons with congenitally inferior scientific imagination. Nevertheless, the study and training of the inventive powers not only strengthens the inventiveness of an Edison, but also develops the capacity for usefully inventing in the community. We certainly stand to gain by aiding and teaching of the inventive art.

Fig. 4--Arthur E. Kennelly's endorsement of creativity training of engineers as feasible. (From letter by A. E. Kennelly to Mass. Dept. of Education, Univ. Extension Division.)

The next significant landmark occurred about 1956 with Osborn's campaign for training in creativity by his "brainstorming" method.

Courses for creativity training of engineers had cropped up here and there (in General Electric, M.I.T., etc.) after 1935, but they were quite rare, widely scattered, and all were established in the face of deep seated opposition based on the idea that creativity was a faculty inherited at birth, and so could not be developed by training.

Osborn's campaign for promoting "Brainstorming" was a monumental effort. He published a series of books that popularized the technique [3], set up a foundation for it,[1] and organized a campaign of institutes, seminars, and workshops on it that penetrated into all areas of industry, the armed services, and

---

[1] Creative Education Foundation, Buffalo, N.Y.

the field of education.

The technique of brainstorming itself was useful only in simple problems in creativity, such as ideas for promoting the rental of colored telephones by the phone company and soon after declined in use and importance. But the campaign to get it adopted was immensely successful in overcoming the attitude that creativity training was not feasible. Thereafter courses in creativity training were an accepted thing, just as much so as training in physics or mathematics.

To summarize, the significant thing about the past in creativity training for engineers was the universal opposition to such training based on the belief that it was not feasible, and the complete obliteration of that attitude by Osborn's campaign for Brainstorming.

THE PRESENT

The most important and significant thing about creativity training in the present is this: we are getting closer to a good understanding of the mental process involved in creativity and therefore to a sound basis for developing creativity training curricula.

The basis of the mental process of creativity was to a considerable extent made clear by the Rossman study. This showed that:

1) Creativity is essentially a trial-and-error matching of mental images to fit a desired idea combination. This is well expressed by the typical quotation from Rossman shown in Fig. 5.

2) The creative mental process is carried out by breaking the problem into small inventive steps and solving these one at a time.

3) We start the solution of the invention problem by setting up, intuitively, a line of attack (nowadays known as "heuristic" but formerly called a "hunch"), and this line of attack leads to the pattern for breakdown of the problem into smaller inventive steps.

4) It is an iterative process. The solution of one of the smaller invention steps many suggest a different breakdown into smaller steps and a new sequence for solving them. We then go through the mental process loop all over again.

> "The actual inventing becomes more or less a problem in mental mathematics — the addition and subtraction of materials, energy, motion...If a peculiar movement is required, all the known movements are brought to the mental picture and, one by one, are added or subtracted which may result in a combination of old ideas and new....
>
> "...the interesting aspect of this inventive process is that most of the efforts are first made mentally. The inventor manipulates the symbols of his past experience mentally, and only after a satisfactory solution is obtained by mental trial-and-error behavior does he actually attempt to satisfy the need."

Fig. 5--Typical inventors' concept of creativity
as disclosed by Rossman study. See Rossman [2],
pp. 77, 82.

Recent work on simulating the creative problem solving process by computers, particularly the work of Simon and his school, quite strongly supports this picture of the basic nature of the creative mental process [4]. One example of an invention that very well illustrates these characteristics of the creative mental process should be cited.

This is the Astron machine for producing power by controlled nuclear fusion. In this invention, the general scheme is to provide a powerful magnetic field to act as a "magnetic bottle," in which the multimillion-degree fusion reaction takes place; but to create this bottle not by the usual heavy currents in a conductor coil, but by a cylindrical "E" layer of high energy electrons [5]. This layer produces both the necessary containment and the necessary heating of the gasses to produce the fusion reaction, as is seen in Fig. 6. This is the main line of attack for solving the fusion-reactor problem which was conceived by the inventor, Christofilos. Its physical embodiment is shown in Fig. 6 (a). However, to accomplish the desired effect, the E layer requires 200 a of electrons and these must be accelerated to an energy level of 5 million volts. This made it necessary to invent an electron gun capable of generating this huge electron current. And once these huge currents were available it was seen that, to accelerate them to 5,000,000 volts, the then known accelerators, all based on electrostatic forces, would be grossly inadequate, and that those huge currents made practical a new "induction" principle accelerator [6] (Fig. 7).

Thus, the fusion reactor invention is solved by a chain of smaller inventive steps, and the line of attack selected (E-layer) sets the pattern for the breakdown of the problem into the smaller steps. In fact, each of these major parts of the over-all invention: electron gun, accelerator, was in fact solved by a chain of smaller inventions, and making them involved going around the whole mental process loop for the Astron invention again and again. In other words, it was eminently an iterative process [7].

Two other phases of the mental process of creativity in engineering are highly significant and have to be borne in mind if we are to develop successful curricula for creativity training. The first of these is what I would call "the wrong approach barrier," and the other is the method of arriving at an original line of attack for solving a major invention problem, or what might be called "the technique of originality."

When one sets out to solve a major invention problem, the line of attack first selected may very well be the wrong one. Then the longer one works along this line, the more it gets built up as a barrier to keep you from getting back onto the right one. This presents one of the most costly and distressing difficulties in achieving an invention.

This "wrong approach barrier" is ultimately broken by one of these three occurrences taking place.

First, some accident may occur which suddenly makes the inventor aware that he is following the wrong line of attack and points out to him the right one. Goodyear's accidental invention of heat plus sulphur as the means for producing vulcanization of rubber when he accidentally dropped some crude rubber mixed with sulfur onto a hot stove is a case in point. This road to overcoming the "wrong approach barrier" has been a common one, particularly in the chemical field, as is attested by an extensive literature on "accidental invention."[2]

---

[2] See Rossman [2], Ch. VII.

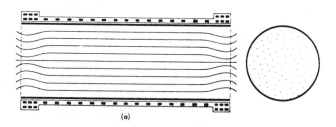

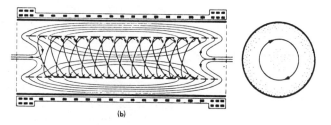

THE ASTRON MACHINE. (a) An axial magnetic field is produced in an evacuated cylindrical tube. The current-carrying coils are so wound that there is a small bump in the field lines at each end of the cylinder. (b) High-energy electrons are then injected into the cylinder and form a circulating layer of current about the central axis. This current produces a magnetic field which modifies the original field to give a configuration of field lines that close upon themselves. (c) Deuterium or tritium gas at room temperature is then admitted into the chamber and is heated as a result of collisions with the electron layer, producing a high-energy plasma.

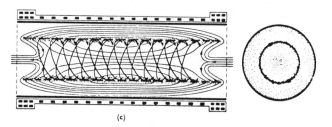

(a)

Fig. 6-(a)--The Astron concept of nuclear fusion reactor. (b) The Astron nuclear fusion reactor under construction. Reaction chamber is long cylinder at left; accelerator is at right foreground.

(b)

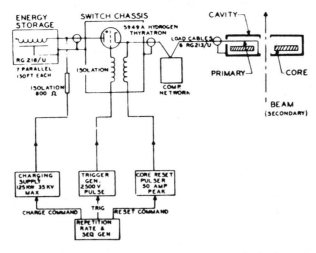

Fig. 7--Principle of operation of induction
type accelerator used in Astron.

Another route by which the "wrong approach barrier" is often surmounted
is the practice of abandoning work on an invention and "letting it lie fallow,"
so to speak. The literature on creativity cites a number of eminent cases of
this [8].

Still another road to surmounting the "wrong approach barrier," and one
commonly experienced but seldom mentioned in texts on creativity, is one mentioned in Rossman and illustrated in Fig. 8. This is the procedure for carrying
on the development of the invention along the same line of attack, but this line
gradually veers around until one is headed in a decidely different, even the
opposite direction from the one you started out on. In this case, the inventor
set out to conceive an automatic food can soldering machine. What he wanted was
some way of bending the ends of the can down so they would dip into a soldering
bath, or to project the solder bath surface up to reach the ends of the can. However, he could not see any approach for reaching this goal, so he started off with
the manual approach of using a soldering iron, but curved to fit the end of the
can. By a chain of small inventive steps that led logically from one to another,
he ultimately reached the hoped for solution by having a roller in a solder bath
with ridges which carry the solder up to meet the ends of the can.[3]

As mentioned earlier, selecting the line of attack for solving an invention
problem is probably the most crucial step in the whole creative mental process
because it in effect sets off a chain reaction of mental activity by which the
solution to the problem is finally achieved. In particular, the line of attack
selected determines the pattern of breakdown of the problem into smaller parts,
and the iterative loops or "chain of events" by which they will be solved. A
good technique or procedure for selecting the right line of attack at the outset
is therefore vital.

The history of many major inventions suggests this basic principle for doing
that. First, dig out what has been taken for granted by others who have attacked
the same invention problem, challenge it, then set up a line of attack in accordance
with the results of that challenge.

One of the most striking examples of this is the invention of the three-element
(triode) vacuum tube. Transmission of speech over long telephone lines requires
an amplifier every few miles. When the quest for such an amplifier first began,
a well-known example of an amplifier existed in the form of the telegraph relay.

---

[3]See Rossman [2], pp. 63-67 for details.

In this device the basic principle of operation is that you convert the received electrical energy into mechanical energy (i.e., attracting the relay armature), and this is converted back again into electrical energy (by the armature closing the relay output circuit) (Fig. 9). A great many inventors, including even Edison, took this approach for granted and proceeded to invent devices that would put it into effect (Fig. 10). That is, they had the receiver at the distant point speak into a microphone of the next circuit. Finally DeForest (or probably more correctly von Lieben [9]) realized that telephone currents could be amplified directly by a grid-controlled electron current in an evacuated chamber. This was immediately recognized as *the* solution to the problem, as attested by the speed and eagerness with which the American Telephone Co. bought up the DeForest patents.

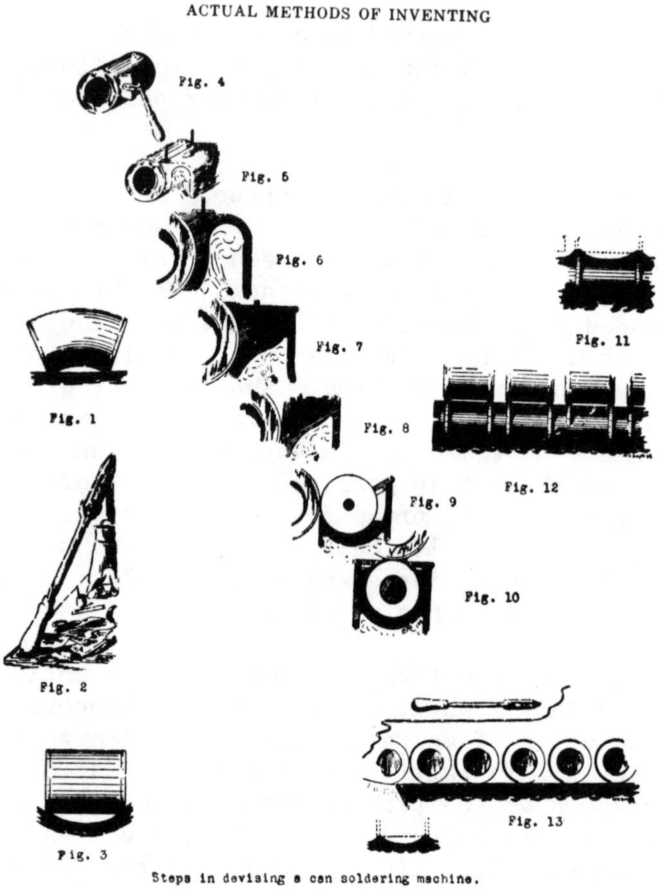

ACTUAL METHODS OF INVENTING

Fig. 8--Procedure for surmounting "wrong approach barrier."

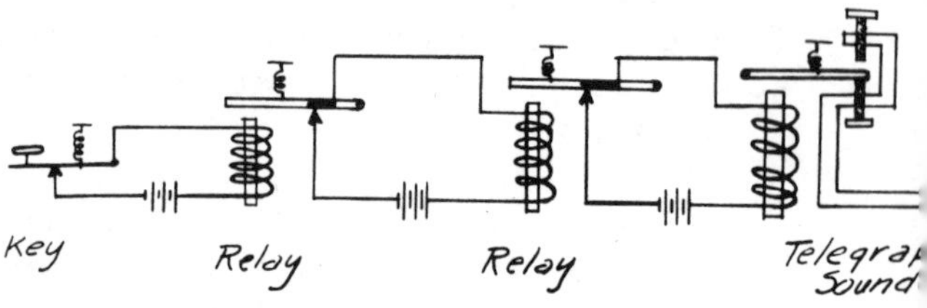

Fig. 9--Telegraph relay principle of amplification: convert from electrical to mechanical energy, then back again, at each stage.

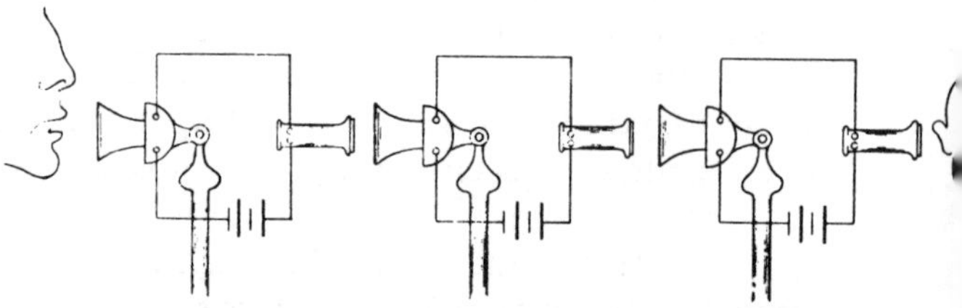

Fig. 10--The mechanical-to-electrical energy conversion principle applied to telephone amplification.

A dramatic example of this occurred in more recent times in what is known as the Tri-Ergon patent case. At the time when the motion picture industry turned to talkies and location of the sound track on the motion picture film became standard practice, this technical problem arose: to project the picture, the film is held stationary for a fraction of a minute, then is moved until the next frame is in position for projection. It is then held there until the next frame is projected. This means constant stop-and-go motion of the film. However, the sound track must move continuously, at a very constant speed, otherwise the sound will be distorted in pitch, to which distortion the human ear is highly sensitive.

Consequently there was a veritable blizzard of inventions for film drives with highly refined speed regulators to keep a loop of the film moving at uniform speed. Finally, however, someone realized that all these speed controls were unnecessary and he merely looped the film tightly around a flywheel. Because of its inertia, the flywheel's speed remains quite constant and thus stabilizes the motion of the film so that reproduction of sound from the sound track can take place correctly. The patent battle which took place over this invention was epochal and demonstrated handily that the right solution to this invention was the one which recognized what others were taking for granted and departed from it [10].

This principle, or what one might call "the technique of originality," is so vital to successful invention that I would like to give a working example of how it can be applied in a current, practical, invention problem.

Consider, for example, the many recent inventions in the printing, or more properly, the graphic arts industries. There have been many electronic inventions to automate what the linotype operator does: compose, justify lines, etc. Also, there have been many inventions of new processes for putting an impression on a page: ozalid processes, and dry (electrostatic) processes, such as Xerox. But despite this proliferation of graphic arts inventions, one thing is still being taken for granted in all of them. That is, that one must perform one impression operation for each copy produced. Only in the case of producing carbons in a typewriter do we produce multiple copies with each impression operation.

Suppose then, that we do not take this for granted. Why not have printing machines that will produce large quantities of copies--say a thousand or ten thousand--at one impression operation? Then we will not need the extremely costly and elaborate high-speed presses now required for mass production in printing.

One line of attack immediately suggests itself, the use of X-rays. A strong X-ray beam could be projected through a stencil forming the desired copy, to penetrate a whole stack of coated sheets, and thus converting each one into a copy of the desired page. This line of attack automatically points to the breakdown of the problem into these smaller parts:

1) How to keep the beam from spreading and making the letters thicker as it goes through the stack.

2) How to form a coating that is sensitive to X-rays, yet is cheap and not affected by light, heat, etc.

3) Since the X-ray beam would affect both sides of the sheet, how would you produce printing of different material on different sides of the sheet?

To summarize, we already recognize certain characteristics of the mental process of creativity which can serve as the basis for framing creativity training curricula. These are:

1) Matching mental images.
2) Initial line of attack.
3) Breakdown into parts.

4) Reiterative loop.
5) Familiar approach barrier.
6) Technique of originality.

With all these characteristics of the creative mental process recognized, one is in a position to develop an effective curriculum for creativity training of engineers. A suggestion for such a curriculum is presented later. At this point it is worth noting that the curricula for creativity training now widely used, those proposed in Osborn's book and the books by von Fange and the other well-known writers on creativity, all rest heavily on a different concept of the creative mental process [11]. That is the concept which considers the creative mental process to consist of four major parts:

1) *Preparation*, during which one gathers a background of ideas on the invention problem to be solved;

2) *Incubation*, during which these ideas are stewed over in the subconscious;

3) *Illumination*, during which the ideas fuse into a desired combination; and

4) *Verification*, during which stage one determines that this combination in effect fulfills what one started out originally to achieve.

This is a very appealing concept which was stated in a book by an English psychologist, G. Wallis, called "The Art of the Thought," published in 1926, but was probably originated by a French author in 1900 [12].

Others, particularly psychologists, like Woodworth, liked it so much they popularized it widely until it now pervades most of the literature on creativity, many of the writers who use it not even being aware of where it stems from.

This concept is attractive but very superficial, because it explains away the mental mechanics of creativity by relegating everything to "the subconscious." However, the current investigations into mental creativity are based more on the characteristics first pointed out by Rossman. Studies by Simon, simulating (by computer) the trial-and-error manipulation of mental images in creative problem solving, have added emphasis to the points made by Rossman [13]. More recently, the basic nature of concept formation, which underlies all creative thought, has been studied by Harlow and others [14]. As a result, one can summarize the present in creativity training by saying that we have got started on the road that leads to clarification of the mental processes involved, and this will provide a good basis for practical curricula for creativity training.

THE FUTURE

When we start to think about creativity training in the future, we have to stop briefly and make some clarifying definitions so that the same words will mean the same things to all of us. In particular, there are three specific but related activities which we will be referring to constantly: engineering, invention, and research. Let us explain their meanings so that we can use them with clarity and precision.

Let us first consider what is signified by the terms "engineering" and "invention." Suppose, for example, that you ask an engineer to design a conventional soaring airplane to meet a specified speed, rate of climb, ceiling, pay load, etc. The engineer will analyze the group of physical principles which, in combination, make flight in heavier-than-air, soaring type of aircraft possible. That is, each principle is taken apart by itself (angle of incidence, angle of lift, etc.) and proportioned to suit the specification requirements. Then all the different elements, each properly proportioned, are grouped together to provide the complete design. What we have done here is essentially an analytical function of breaking down a combination of ideas into its component elements. This is engineering.

But suppose that only the conventional soaring type of airplane is known, and you ask the design engineer to devise a new type of airplane, one that rises by flying straight up instead of by soaring, and that can stay put or "hover" at any desired point above ground. The known combination of scientific principles which produces soaring flight will not do. His problem now is to provide a new combination of physical principles that makes possible vertical flight. This is a problem of invention.

But invention and engineering alone are not enough to bring about the industrial success of any technical development. For example, DeForest combined the physical principle of a thermionic current flowing between the plate and filament to control the thermionic current. He thus invented a highly sensitive amplifier.

Engineers knew the laws of thermionic emission so could proportion the filament to produce any specified current. They also knew the laws of space charge, so knew how to proportion the space between filament, grid and plate, and how much voltage to put on each. In other words, they knew how to take apart the combination of physical principles that made up the three-element vaccum tube, proportion each, then put them together again to produce a tube of any desired capacity.

However, it was found that only small, weak tubes, those that used less than about 45 volts on the plate, would work. In higher power tubes (using more than 45 volts on the plate) the thermionic currents to the plate became very erratic, and everything the tube amplified was highly distorted. Thus the combination of principles for the thermionic amplifier was known, the design principles were known, but only tubes of very small power could be built.

Irving Langmuir of the General Electric Company (and also Arnold and Campbell of American Telephone and Telegraph) then did some systematic investigating or research and found the cause of this irregular behavior of three-element tubes at more than 45 plate volts [15]. Langmuir discovered that the irregularity was due to ionization of the gas inside the tube by the stream of electrons flowing toward the plate. So he removed the gas until a high vacuum existed inside the tube. Then the tubes behaved smoothly as amplifiers in sizes up to those having thousands of volts on the plate. High power amplifiers could then be built.

Thus we have clear definition of the three functions necessary for the industrial success of any technological development. They are:

1) *Invention*. Forming a combination of scientific principles which makes possible the desired machine or process.

2) *Engineering*. Breaking down this combination of principles into its elements, proportioning each to suit the specifications, then combining all to produce the final design.

3) *Research*. Systematic investigation to discover unknown scientific facts or new scientific principles.

As we have just noted, invention is the mental process of forming a group of lesser ideas, or idea elements, into a single idea combination or pattern. But the essence of the process is this: the idea elements are not merely stuck together, retaining their individual identities, as in a mosaic or a mixture. Instead, during the inventing process a mental fusion or synthesis takes place and one resultant idea compound, one single, unifying concept, is formed out of the separate idea elements.

It is important to note that idea compounds, like chemical compounds, differ considerably from their constituent elements. The principal difference is that things can be done with the idea compound that cannot be achieved with the idea elements themselves. Thus Morse combined the idea of distant transmission of dots and dashes over an electrical circuit and the idea of using the dots and dashes in an alphabetic code to effect distant transmission of intelligence. With neither one of these ideas, by itself, is this result possible.

We should also note that the result of the inventing process does not always have to be a concrete material thing such as a machine, a product or a process. An invention may be an abstract, intangible thing, often a useful mental tool, such as a mathematical technique or a scientific theory.

For example, Newton synthesized the idea element of algebraic procedure with another idea element, the theory of limits, into a single idea compound, a single unifying concept, the calculus. He thus produced a powerful mathematical tool for solving the problems of science and engineering.

Now training in engineering and applied science has for many years been concentrated on analytical procedures, the breaking down of known idea combinations into their component elements. This does not help to develop the opposite mental capability of synthesis. Hence many an engineering student comes out of his engineering course with whatever creative aptitude he had originally impaired by neglect, if not positively retarded by overemphasis on the opposite faculty of analysis.

Some schools, like M.I.T., Harvey Mudd College, Claremont, Calif., and a number of others, are becoming aware of this and are attempting to revise their curricula so as to add courses specifically designed to promote development of creativity, or to reorient existing courses so as to provide more stimulus to idea-compounding mental activity. However, as our inventions become more technical and more complex, it will take a high order of analytical ability to evaluate an idea element for match or fit into the desired idea combination. For example, to achieve the Astron invention, a highly theoretical analysis was necessary to see if the *E*-layer idea would be feasible. Hence, an engineer, to be an inventor, will have to have more and more advanced analytical training to perform the basic operation of the creative mental process, the matching of ideas for fit in a desired new combination. This is already strongly evident in such fields as solid-state devices, lasers, nuclear reactors, etc.

If our inventors of the future are to have the higher analytical abilities needed to cope with our increasingly technical inventions, the present over-emphasis or unbalance of analytical training relative to training in creativity will increase even more rapidly than our present creativity training courses will be able to correct it. We will therefore need much greater development and expansion of creativity training in engineering schools than are now planned, merely to keep the imbalance at its present level. In short, as far as the future is concerned in creativity training of engineers, we will have to run much faster just to stand still.

Another prospect in the future of creativity training is this: as our technological developments become more technical and more complex, the job of evaluating an idea for fit in a desired combination is an extensive mental operation, often beyond the capacity for one mind alone to carry out. So we have to break the whole invention process into a division of labor among people devoted to special functions. We call these: 1) conceptual design, 2) feasibility study, 3) system design, and 4) subsystem design.

This separation of steps in the creative process among separate individuals makes the process much more difficult to carry out and it begets new problems, in communication, organization, etc. It will also lead to narrow fields of specialization within the creative mental process, and creativity training programs will have to be developed to fit each of these specialities.

To conclude this section of the discussion: the need for creativity train-ing of engineers is slowly being realized and met, but for a long time to come the need will far outrun what is being done to meet it. Also, we will in the future not only have to train engineers in the whole mental process of creativ-ity, but also specialists in each stage of it: conceptual design, feasibility study, system design and development, and subsystem design and development.

SUGGESTED ON-THE-JOB CREATIVITY TRAINING PROGRAM

With this quick glance at the past, present, and future in creativity training as a setting, a creativity training procedure which could be applied and made practical in both large and small concerns will be proposed.

Essentially, the creativity process is composed of two main phases:

1) A concept-formation or conceptual stage, in which one conceives the invention problem and a line of attack for solving it.

This is the nascent stage of the inventive mental process, and one that sets the entire course of mental activity for the achievement of the desired invention.

2) A developmental phase, in which the problem and line of attack are already known, and one carries out the breaking down of the problem into parts, and the iterative repetition of the mental loop until all these parts are solved.

This is the "concrete" stage, in the inventive process, one might say, because it is carried out by consciously and deliberately carrying out each step in the chain.

A training procedure for this developmental stage can be easily developed by following the steps recommended by most of the leading creativity schools like Osborn, von Fange, Gordon, etc. These steps are:

1) Defining the inventive problem.
2) Listing the parts into which the problem can be divided.
3) Listing all possible solutions for each part, etc.

A good procedure for on-the-job training in this developmental phase of invention is to place the student under a more experienced person skilled in this developmental phase and to have the student carry out the different steps listed under his supervision.

The conceptual phase is the more imaginative or insightful part of the creative mental process. This phase can also be developed by on-the-job training, but requires a different approach, as follows.

1) Have the student study a number of reports or articles in the technical literature, and for each one have him write out, in 3 sentences or less:

    a) What technological advance does this paper present?
    b) What is the key idea by which this advance is brought about?

Good examples of carrying this out are provided in Figs. 11-14. Then have the student write out, for each paper:

    a) What new invention problem does this paper suggest?
    b) What line of attack for a known invention problem does it suggest?

Have all these things written out and then reviewed by a more experienced man who is capable in this conceptual phase of the invention process.

A good example of what could then be done is shown in Figs. 15 and 16.

August 1963 IEEE PROCEEDINGS

THE DETECTION OF CHIRPED RADAR SIGNALS BY MEANS
OF ELECTRON SPIN ECHOES

W. B. Mims

Summary -- The application of the electron spin echo phenomenon to the detection of chirped microwave pulses is considered. The attainable time resolution is determined by the width of the paramagnetic resonance line, and the length of the received waveform is limited by the phase memory time of the spin packets in the active material. Pulse compressions of 1000:1 appear to be feasible. A typical device of this kind would require to be operated at liquid helium temperatures. It could be adapted so that in itself it provided maser amplification of the compressed pulses.

August 1963 IEEE PROCEEDINGS

The Detection of Chirped Radar Signals by Means of Electron Spin Echoes (Mims, p. 1127) -- In a typical chirped radar system the transmitted pulse is subjected to a linear frequency sweep and the returned pulse is then passed through a frequency dispersive network in the receiver which delays one end of the pulse more than the other in such a way as to compress the pulse in time. This pulse compression technique makes it possible to transmit longer pulses with correspondingly more energy and yet maintain short pulse widths in the receiver for a high degree of radar resolution. In this paper the author shows that in the microwave region these frequency swept pulses can also be compressed--as much as 1000 to 1--by making use of the electron spin echo phenomenon in certain paramagnetic materials. The result is a highly original and important contribution to a practical radar problem.

Fig. 11--Typical author's abstract of technical paper; fails to give cues for inventive application of technical ideas contained in the paper. (Note: From W. B. Mims, "The detection of chirped radar signals by means of electron spin echoes," Proc. IEEE, vol. 51, p. 1127; August, 1963.)

Fig. 12--Author's abstract (Fig. 11) rewritten to point out: what technological advance does the paper present? and what is the key idea by which this advance is brought about? (Note: From "Scanning the Issue," Proc. IEEE, vol. 51, p. 1082; August, 1963

N-DECADE COUNT-RATE METER WITH AUTOMATIC
SCALE CHANGE FEATURE AND RESOLUTION OF ONE DECADE

ABSTRACT

The circuit described was designed for space flight application and is therefore transistorized and was laid out on two 4-inch square cards. Three decades were used but stacking the individual decade count rate circuits would permit coverage of any number of decades. Two channels of the telemetry system are needed; one for the count rate meter outputs and one for an indication of which count rate meter is being read out.

Pulses in our case from a BF$_3$ counter, after being shaped into quantized pulses are fed simultaneously into the inputs of all count rate meters being used. For a good part of the curve of output voltage vs. input rate, the output voltage is proportional to the log of the input rate. This portion of the curve is used when the response of the various CRM's is being selected such that the range to be covered is covered in only slightly overlapping stages. The output of each CRM can be gated off. After the gates the outputs are fed through "or" circuits and then all run into a summer circuit. All gates are open when the count rate is in the range of the first or lowest rate CRM, but no output is observed from any CRM except the first because of the "or" circuit since all other CRM have higher rate sensitivities. When the output of the first CRM reaches the end of the log portion of the curve, a special circuit closes the gate, disconnecting CRM number one from the system output. Now the second CRM can be read out. This process continues through n stages of CRM's.

A circuit senses which CRM's have reached the end of their range. This circuit provides telemetry information indicating which CRM is being read out.

Range changes are made in less than 1/2 ms which was compatible with CRM time constants. With minor modifications switching ranges could be done in a few μs.

The advantages of covering a large number of decades while still maintaining resolution of a single decade and automatically changing ranges are obvious to the fields of hazards control, chemistry and other areas.

Fig. 13--Another example of author's abstract which does not reveal contents of the paper useful in creativity.

ABSTRACT

The most efficient use of telemetry channels is always a paramount problem of space flight projects. Monitoring radiation fields in space often requires coverage of large ranges of count rate which, if count rate meters are to be used, means either a decrease in resolution due to coverage of the entire range with one rate meter or use of several telemetry channels if several different rate meters are used.

This paper describes a unique method permitting the desired resolution to be obtained by use of as many count rate meters as required while limiting the number of telemetry channels needed to two. A circuit switches one telemetry channel from one rate meter to the next as the input rate changes, while the other telemetry channel is used to monitor which rate meter is being read out.

Fig. 14--Rewrite of author's abstract in Fig. 13 to bring out ideas contained in the paper in a manner to stimulate creativity. (Note: From S. Thomas, "N-decade count-rate-meter with automatic scale change feature and resolution of one decade," IEEE TRANS. ON NUCLEAR SCIENCE, vol. NS-10, pp. 36-41: January, 1963.

ABSTRACT

Experimental work on the flashover characteristics of a 300-kw Diesel-driven dc generator is described and the effects of certain parameters and a theoretical explanation are given. The observations reveal the effects of initial speed, load, and commutating ability on the susceptibility of a dc machine to flashing. Additional work is necessary, however, in order to correlate more fully the observations from high-speed motion pictures with the theoretical analysis and to develop means of reducing the tendency toward flashover.

Fig. 15--Author abstract typically fails to indicate how contents of report suggest new invention problem, or suggest new line of attack for known invention problem. (Note: Taken from "Flashing of DC Machines caused by short circuits," NRL Report 3735, Naval Research Lab., Washington, D.C.)

To produce faster submarines requires more power output from direct current electric motors of a given size than is currently practical. One of the limiting factors in size reduction of motors is "flashover" effect. Flashover is an electrical flame which spreads over the commutator of a dc motor when the motor is overloaded. The report gives an analysis of the physical phenomena underlying "flashover" and so points the way to its elimination. More horsepower per cubic inch of dc motor is therefore in prospect.

The report also describes how flashover was produced experimentally in a dc machine in which the flashover was detected from oscillograms taken of voltage and current in the armature. A comparison of oscillograms with photographs of the commutator obtained with a high-speed motion picture camera substantiated the use of the oscillograph data as a measure of flashover. A schematic of the electrical connections and instrumentation is included.

Fig. 16--Author abstract of Fig. 15 rewritten to indicate how contents of report suggest new invention problem.

Usually, important invention problems are "in the air," so to speak, for a long time. The critical need is for new lines of attack to solve them. The ability to conceive new lines of attack for invention problems can be developed by the procedure of studying research reports just outlined, and asking, "What new line of attack does this suggest?" This training approach for the conceptual phase of invention can be still further exercised and developed by certain preferred practices which some great inventors have evolved for themselves and found useful as cues for readily recognizing a new line of attack for the solution of invention problems.

For example, Dr. Slepian, the great inventor of electrical power devices for Westinghouse, watches out for new scientific facts discovered by research, and considers each of these a cue to a successful line of attack on some invention problem [16].

A particularly good illustration of this occurred during the 1930's, when power networks were expanding rapidly in extent and in power output, but switching devices lagged in development and explosions of circuit breakers became a common occurrence. Dr. Slepian then conducted an extensive program of research on the electric arcs in circuit breakers and found out these new facts [17]:

1)   Immediately after the arc is formed, a thin layer of high insulation strength (i.e., free of ions) formed near the electrode, and

2)   If the arc is swept quickly over the electrode it rapidly cools and becomes deionized (i.e., insulation across the air gap recovers quickly).

He immediately asked how these two facts could be used to improve high-power switches and realized this line of attack for the high-power switching problem:

a)   Break the arc into many smaller ones by a succession of metal plates, at each of which the thin high insulation layer will be formed (Fig. 17), thus greatly increasing the insulation recovery across the switch gap.

b)   Spin the arc over these metal plates by magnetic forces, thus producing rapid cooling at the electrodes, which also increases rapid recovery of insulation across the switch gap (Fig. 18).

The result was the highly successful line of "De-ion" circuit breakers which made a valuable addition to the Westinghouse line of switchgear.

Other such pointers which the inventor could be trained in using, to make him proficient in conceiving a line of attack for solution of invention problems, are:

1)   *Special range.*

Is there a special range of physical conditions within which a particular phenomenon takes place? Often this phenomenon offers a valuable approach to the solution of an invention problem.

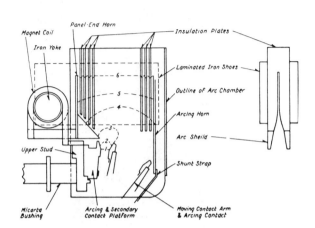

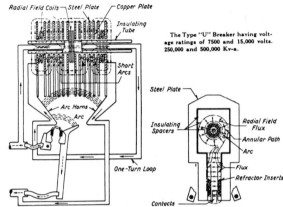

Fig. 17--Break a switch arc into many smaller ones by a succession of metal plates across arc gap, at each of which a thin, high insulation layer is formed, thus greatly increasing the insulation recovery across switch gap.

Fig. 18--Shaping metal plates to produce rapid spinning of arc by magnetic forces causes cooling at the arc, thus also helps rapid insulation recovery across switch gap.

For example, whenever one finds a reverse-slope region in a current-voltage curve, this indicates a negative-resistance range (Fig. 19). This negative resistance can be used for creating an electronically controlled oscillator and other valuable "active" electrical and electronic devices. A particularly good illustration of this is the negative-resistance region of the tunnel diode current-voltage curve and the many applications that have been made of it.

  2) *Upset of widely accepted scientific or engineering theory.*

A good example of this is another invention of Dr. Slepian which he made when he investigated the arcs which occur in high power oil type circuit breakers. Up to that time the arc blast in the oil-filled breaker was considered a necessary evil that one had to live with [17]. He found that the vaporization of oil by the arc created a blast which restored the insulation strength across the switch gap, so the oil blast was what made the switch work and should be enhanced, rather than eliminated. This resulted in a modification of the de-ion breaker which added the oil blast effect to the de-ion principle and so created a line of circuit breakers for the very highest (230 kv) voltage power lines then in use (Fig. 20).

To conclude this section, it may be summarized thus:

  1) The critical part of the inventive process is the conceptual
      phase, during which the inventor conceives the invention
      problem to be solved and a line of attack for solving it.
      These concepts trigger and set the stage for the whole
      inventing process.

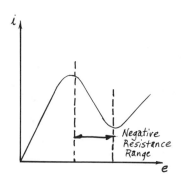

Fig. 19--Negative-resistance (reverse-slope) region in current-voltage curve; useful characteristic for inventing "active" electrical and electronic devices.

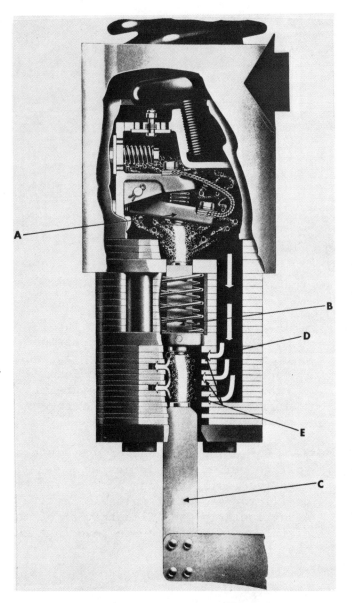

Fig. 20--Oil blast generated by switching arc (upper) is used to create additional oil blast (lower) that rapdily restores insulation strength across switch gap. Switching arc "nuisance" is thus utilize to increase capacity of circuit breaker.

2) Engineers can be trained to develop their capability in this conceptual phase by having them review current research reports, and in each report,
    a) Pick out the technological advance that was made.
    b) Pick out the key idea by which it was achieved.
    c) Then ask
        (1) What invention problems does this suggest?
        (2) What new line of attack on a known invention problem does it present?
3) These things should all be written out and reviewed by a supervisor of recognized creative ability.

4) The capability for generating new lines of attack to invention problems can be further developed by practicing the employment of these cues for finding such concepts that have been discovered and proven effective by eminent inventors. Among these are
   a) New scientific facts.
   b) Special range.
   c) Upset of accepted scientific theory.

To conclude, one may summarize the over-all picture on creativity training for engineers as follows:

1) The strong psychological barrier against creativity training that existed in the past has been swept away.
2) At present we are learning more about the creative mental process and thus forming a solid foundation for developing creativity training curricula.
3) In the future, inventions will be more technical and complex. As a result, the comparison of concepts done by trial-and-error matching of ideas to form new idea compounds will require greater analytical training in the person who does it, hence even more deep seated cultivation of engineers in the opposte mental faculty to the one needed for idea synthesis. The future need for creativity training of engineers will therefore far outrun the measures being developed for providing it.
4) Finally, it is possible to provide on-the-job training even in the imaginative, conceptual phase of creativity, by using known procedures and putting the learner under the supervision of a person of demonstrated creative ability.

ACKNOWLEDGMENT

The author is grateful to the following sources for the use of their illustrations in this paper: The Institute of Electrical and Electronic Engineers for Figs. 1 and 2 from *AIEE Transactions*, for Figs. 11 and 12 from *IEEE Proceedings*, and for Figs. 7 and 14 from *IEEE Transactions on Nuclear Science*; Inventors Publishing Co. for Figs. 3, 5, and 8 from J. Rossman, Psychology of the Inventor; Addison-Wesley Publishing Co., Inc. for Fig. 6 from A. Bishop, Project Sherwood; Benwill Publishing Co. for Figs. 9 and 10 from *Electromechanical Design*; and Westinghouse Electric Co. for Figs. 17, 18, and 20.

REFERENCES

[1] E. J. Prindle, "The art of inventing," *Trans. AIEE*, vol. 25, pp. 519-547; May, 1906.
[2] J. Rossman, "The Psychology of the Inventor," The Inventors Publishing Co., Washington, D. C.; 1931.
[3] A. F. Osborn, "Your Creative Power," Charles Scribner's Sons, New York, N. Y., 1948; and "Applied Imagination," Charles Scribner's Sons, New York, N. Y.; 1957.
[4] A. Newell and H. A. Simon, "Computer simulation of human thinking," *Science*, vol. 134, pp. 2011-2017; December, 1961.

[5] A. S. Bishop, "Project Sherwood: The U. S. Program in Controlled Fusion,"
     Addison-Wesley, Reading, Mass.; 1958.

[6] W. A. S. Lamb, "Design features of a high-current pulsed electron accele-
     rator," IRE TRANS. ON NUCLEAR SCIENCE, vol. NS-9, pp. 53-56; April, 1962.

[7] V. L. Smith, "Development of 36-Megawatt Modulators for the Astron 1000
     Megawatt Electron Accelerator," IRE TRANS. ON NUCLEAR SCIENCE, vol. NS-9,
     pp. 57-67; April, 1962.

[8] W. Platt and R. A. Baker, "Relation of scientific hunch to research,"
     J. Chem. Educ. vol. 8, pp. 1969-2002; 1931.

[9] E. Hawkes, "Pioneers of Wireless," Methuen and Co., Ltd., London, England,
     pp. 274-276; 1927.

[10] "Text of Supreme Court Ruling on Tri-Ergon," Motion Picture Herald, pp. 57-64;
     March 9, 1935.

[11] W. S. Woodson, "Creative techniques--a comparative analysis," *J. Indust.
     Engrg.*, vol. 15; pp. 60-66; March-April, 1964.

[12] T. Ribot, "Essai Sur L'imagination Creatrice," Alcan, Paris, France,
     pp. 222-223; 1900.

[13] M. Minsky, "Steps toward artificial intelligence," PROC. IRE., vol. 49,
     pp. 8-30; January, 1961. See especially pp. 21-30.

[14] R. Hyman, "Creativity," *International Science and Technology*, no. 20
     pp. 51-58; August, 1963. See especially references on p. 87.

[15] W. R. MacLauren, "Invention and Innovation in the Radio Industry,"
     The Macmillan Co., New York, N.Y.; 1949.

[16] L. A. Kilgore, "Creative engineering--and engineer's viewpoint," *Westinghouse
     Engineer*, vol. 20, No. 5, pp. 136-139; September, 1960.

[17] "Circuit Interruption," *Westinghouse Engineer*, vol. 7, inside front cover
     page; July, 1947.

THE PROCESS OF INVENTION[1]
Jacob Rabinow

It is fitting that I expound on the process of invention in relation to
education, because I flunked every speech course I took in college,
and upon graduating during the Great Depression and trying to become
a teacher in New York City, I flunked all the oral-speech exams.

Let me begin by asking what appears to be a rhetorical question:
How much creativity does the world really want? We take the need for
creativity as a matter of faith. We assume people want more and more
creativity--more new art, music, poetry, inventions, everything.

I have asked several economists if there is any limit to the amount
of creativity that is good for a nation. The experts are not sure.
They think that there isn't enough in the United States, that other
countries seem to have more. We hear the experts say that productivity
is rising at a rate of some 3 to 6 per cent per year, depending on
how you slice the statistics. But the question is, how much is good?
Is 100 per cent good? Obviously not, because we would obsolete our
equipment faster than we could use it. Is 20 per cent good? 3 per cent?
6 per cent?

It may be true that we do not need much more creativity although, as an
inventor, I certainly hope we do. In any case, the question of how much
creativity we want has a direct bearing on what society offers in the way
of inducements to inventors and other creative people. It is reflected
in the way we educate people and in the way we reward their behavior.

SOCIETY AS A MASS

I think of society, as a whole, as a kind of ponderous mass. This
is also true of business, government, and the universities as sub-
systems. You try to sell a new idea and you find you are fighting
tremendous inertia. This inertia means that the social system has a
built-in lag. Electrical engineers know that the presence of mass
results in a lagging system and that no matter how hard you drive it,
it always succumbs to the force a little late.

The job of the inventors is to provide the lead for a lagging system.
We are supposed to recognize needs ahead of the rest of society, to see
how to do things before society is quite ready to do them. This is the
penalty of being an inventor. If you invent something when everybody
wants it, it is too late; it's been thought of by everybody else. If you
invent too early, nobody wants it just because it is too early. If you
invent very late, after the need has passed, then it is just a mental

---

[1]Reprinted from Daniel V. DeSimone's *Education For Innovation*, Pergamon
Press, Ltd., Elmsford, N. Y., Copyright 1968. Used by permission. Mr. Rabinow
is a retired reemployed engineer at the National Bureau of Standards in
Gaithersburg, Maryland.

exercise. I assure you that it is very hard to invent just at the right
time.

   We inventors therefore have to push individuals and companies and
governments into doing things and using things before they are ready, and
if we push hard enough against the social lagging network, maybe things
work out about right. In my more sober moments I think we don't come out
quite even, but we do get someplace.

   Now this inertia is, in a sense, a good thing. Society's inertia acts
like a built-in filter. It cuts out some of the "baloney" that inventors
like to dish out. We inventors love new ideas for their own sake, and
if you listen carefully to us, you'll find that a great many ideas aren't
worth implementing. Often this is because they weren't thought through to
the end, or they weren't tested thoroughly, or there wasn't enough time.
In any case, while I detest most of the inertia I have to fight, I have
to admit that, when I am on the other end of the scale and ideas are submitted
to me, I often have to take a questioning and critical attitude. The
ideas have to be proved, and it is usually very difficult to prove in
advance that a new idea is good.

THE NATURE OF INVENTION

   By what process does one invent? There are big differences of
opinion on the subject. I believe inventors invent in a completely random
fashion. In order for a computer to do the same thing, it would have to
be provided a program by which it could try things without knowing where
it is going and evaluate each new and unexpected result. It's as if you
put on cards all the knowledge you have in your brain, throw the cards
into the air, and then look at the arrangement after they all fall down.
Sometimes you may get something new.

   I don't believe one can truly invent logically. I have tried to find
out what a "morphological" approach is, and I have never gotten a
straight answer. I have heard people tell me that the way to invent is
to take all the known facts, put them in a logical order, and the answer
will be apparent. To this, all I can say is "Bunk." Occasionally, we do
approach things logically and get logical answers and we even get patents
on the logical answers. But these are not the great inventions. These
are not--forgive me for the expression--"flashes of genius".

   What you have to do in mating new ideas is to try to put together things
which you don't know in advance will go together. In other words, if you
can do something logically, you can program a computer to do it, or you can
have a group of people do it. But the good inventions aren't made this way.
I'll try to give you some examples.

   The best article I've ever read in this connection was written by
Bill Shockley.[1] This was a study of a peculiar phenomenon of human nature.

---

[1] William Shockley, On the statistics of individual variations of productivity in research laboratories, *Proceedings of the IRE*, March 1957,
pp 279-290.

In it Shockley says that in most particulars human beings are about equal.
The average runner, in decent health, can run perhaps 50 per cent slower
than a champion; we can all memorize about the same amount; or we can lift
about the same weight. We are about equal in most abilities, but not in
creativity. Here Shockley finds the differences are very, very large.
He studied several laboratories, Bell Laboratories, the National Bureau of
Standards, and others, and he found each contained one or two men with a
great many patents. Some men had a few each and, finally, there was just
a scattering. He found that this is so in all creativity--in music there
are a few who write great music, and a great deal of it, and then the curve
falls off.

Shockley surmised that creativity must not have a simple functional
relationship to the workings of the brain; if it did, it would be more or
less equal among most people. He postulated that if an invention requires
the combination of four ideas, and a man can put the four together, he may
get it. A man who can only put together three ideas at a time will never
get it. And so, Shockley analyzed this phenomenon mathematically and showed
that if a man can put together twelve ideas, and a second can do only six,
he's not just twice as good as the second fellow; he's some hundred or a
thousand times better. Consequently, Shockley concluded that small differences
in the idea-associating abilities of individuals make a tremendous difference
in their creativeness.

Inventive ability is dependent upon how many ideas one can put together
at one time. I think this is also true of poetry. One has words in his
head, tries different combinations and picks those that sound poetic.
Perhaps you can get a computer to try all the words in the English language,
but its selections won't be very good compared to those of a human being.

I imagine musicians write music by a random process. They try notes
mentally or play them on a piano to see how they sound, and then select
those which sound good together. I think this is the way all creative
processes have to be done--by random trial and error. I don't think
creativity can be approached in any other way. I may be wrong, but I can't
imagine anybody writing great music by a logical process. I've observed
people compose music; they try and discard, try and discard, and if they
are very good at it, they try a great many times.

This means, if the theory is correct, that the amount of information
you have available to play with is most important. I disagree with those
who say that too much knowledge is bad for an inventor because it biases
him. It may indeed, but I think that without a great number of facts, one
can't invent. I recall that Kettering once said that education is bad
for a man because it teaches him too many things that he can *not* do. This
may be partially true, but I think education has two facets, (1) the things
it teaches you, and (2) what it teaches you to do with them. I think
that education is absolutely necessary, for otherwise people would invent
the same things over and over again. You must know what has been done by
others in your field: indeed, in quite different fields as well. From
this knowledge you have to conceive combinations that other people have
never thought of, and I submit that this must be done by a crazy random
process--by pure luck, if you like.

TRY EVERYTHING

It is very difficult to explain to people about the number of trials you have to make, how often you beat your brains out, and try one thing after another. Either you discard the results because you are a severe critic of your own ideas, or your friends demolish them because they are more severe than you are. But you keep trying and eventually you may get something that goes together. And if it doesn't go together, you've got to try another technique which I call the "606" approach. This is to try everything, and see what works. During the war we had some tough problems, and when we couldn't come up with bright ideas, we just tried everything. It is not a very cheap way of solving problems, but it did produce Salversan and other things. When I use it, I consider this method somewhat degrading. I do it because a customer wants something, and I have no clear way of doing it, except trying everything; so I do.

I think Edison used the "606" approach in his search for a satisfactory filament. He even tore hairs out of the beards of his visitors, so the story goes. He tried everything until he found the carbon filament. Most of the time, of course, Edison didn't have to resort to this--he was far too bright. But it's a workable method; if you have to tear hair out of a visitor, and the hair works, the process is just as good as getting an idea out of thin air.

FIX IT BUT DON'T CHANGE IT

Let me give you some examples of my approach to invention to illustrate some of the points I have tried to make. Concrete examples, especially simple ones, are better than talking in generalities.

A man came to me once and said, "I have a problem." This is the opening sentence of many visitors. "I have a gadget that arms a bomb after the propeller turns a few hundred times. A screw moves out of a hole and the bomb goes into the armed condition. My problem is that my factory girls tighten the screws too much and the propeller can't start turning. The air stream isn't strong enough, when the bomb is falling, to make the screw turn. Give me a simple way to stop a girl from tightening the screw too much."

I said, "Simple! There is a whole class of mechanisms that prevent a screw from turning more than a fixed number of times. For example, a set of stacked washers and other such devices will do this."

He said, "If I wanted to use a standard mechanism I wouldn't come to you. You are supposed to be a bright guy who can fix the fuse without changing anything." This is another expression that inventors hear often: "Fix it, but don't change a thing!"

So I said, "Well, let me think about it." This meeting was at my home and I suddenly got an idea. I went downstairs and got a Shake-Proof lock washer. It's a washer that goes on the screw to prevent it from

loosening.   It has teeth all around, bent in such a way that as you tighten
the screw, the teeth jam and the screw locks in position.   I softened
this lock washer in a gas flame over the kitchen stove, turned the teeth
the other way and now I had a very interesting washer, which my wife called
the "unlock washer".   Now, you couldn't tighten the screw, but you could
loosen it very easily.   I was very proud of this device.   Then the question
was, could I get a patent, and the answer was, "No."   They already sell
left-handed lock washers.   I was very proud of the washer.   It's very easy
to design a guided missile system, but it's quite another thing to invent
a new lock washer.   Try it.

I would like to point out that this kind of invention can't be done
by a logical approach.   Perhaps there is a kind of inverting logic that we
can at times use: "Let's try it backwards."   Why should I have done that
to a lock washer?   Well, one can see that there's a connection between a
screw and a washer and that's how the idea is born.   One begins to think
of all the things one knows about screws, or about things that have something
to do with screws.   One thinks of a washer, then a backwards lock washer,
and suddenly everything fits.

I'd like to tell you about another trivial invention, because I'm
proud of the trivial ones.   It's like loving more those children who have
the greatest problems.   I'd like to tell you about a speed reducer that
no one ever used commercially.   The problem, again, was in connection with
ordnance.   We were developing a rocket fuse during World War II.   The fuse
had a pre-wound spring that drove a little escapement, a clockwork so
arranged that a few seconds after firing the rocket the fuse was armed.
The Air Force wanted us to design a mechanism into the fuse so that if
it didn't hit a target within a few more seconds after firing (it was an
air-to-air missile) the rocket was to destroy itself.   And the interesting
limitation was stated again: "The device is in production; don't change
anything, but give us the new feature of self-destruction at the end
of x seconds."

So, I invented a speed reducer.   I needed something which had to fire
the detonator at the end of ten turns of the arming escapement and explode
the rocket.   Let me describe the invention.

A helical spring drives a wheel attached to the end of a spring.
The wheel drives a clock.   (We were asked not to add anything to this basic
mechanism, which was already a part of the fuse.)   Now, if you wind this
spring ten turns and watch the spring unwind, you'll notice a very interesting
action.   The end of the spring that is fixed stands still, while the end
attached to the wheel makes ten turns.   The middle section of the spring,
during this time, will make five turns.   The section one-tenth of the way
from the fixed end will make one turn and so on along the spring.   Thus,
if you attach a contact to the spring one-tenth of the way from the fixed
end, the contact will make one revolution while the clock-driving end makes
ten revolutions.   By fastening such a movable contact to the spring and
providing a corresponding stationary contact on the frame, I had the
necessary mechanism to fire the fuse at the end of the desired period.
This device is a speed reducer which is not good for anything else.   As

you see, it is not really a good gadget, but I am very proud of it.

Again, how does one do this logically? By what logical process can you look at a fuse clockwork and decide that you can get a speed reducer out of the spring itself? Since the time when this was conceived, I found one other mechanism that resembles this clock spring. I had never noticed this device before. It's curious, but once you think of a mechanism, you can easily recognize its relatives elsewhere. I'm not particularly proud of designing the first guided missile control system because that was a lot of different hardware put together. Perhaps some parts of the assembly were quite clever, but most of it was just assembled in a conventional manner. I'm much more proud of the spring speed reducer.

SHORT LETTERS ARE MUCH HARDER

I want to tell you about another gadget, again trivial, because it illustrates particularly well how an inventor works. In this case I was very conscious of the process of invention. My patent attorney and I were driving from Cleveland. We had just demonstrated a good headlight dimmer, a safety device which the automobile industry didn't want because it cost an extra dollar. Anyway, we were driving back to Washington.

My friend said to me, "Jack, I have a problem. I subscribe to an answering service, and when I'm out of the office they take messages. Every time I come back to the office I have to call them to find out whether there's a message. Often I forget, and that's the time when there is a message. If I call and there is no message, I waste their time and mine. Can you build me something so that when my phone rings it will turn on a light and I will know there is a message?" I said, "Well, that's simple. Take a microphone and a two-stage audio amplifier, put a latching relay on the output, and connect a light to the relay." He said, "Look, if I wanted to use an audio amplifier and a latching relay, I don't need you; I'm an electrical engineer, myself. I want something simple."

"Well," I replied, "if you want something simple and cheap, it will require more thought." There's a famous story about President Lincoln having written a very long letter to a friend, and the friend later asking how the beleaguered President had time to write such long letters. The President replied that he did not have time to write short ones.

Anyway, as we were driving back to Washington, a solution occurred to me. When I came to America in 1921 (I was eleven years old), I saw a toy and that toy was the answer to the telephone problem. A small celluloid dog was placed into a small cardboard dog house. If you clapped your hands, or yelled, "Rex," the dog jumped at you. The mechanism consisted of a battery and a magnet, and at the back of the box were two contacts against which lightly rested a hanging pendulum. As the back of the box was vibrated by a loud sound, the circuit became intermittent, and the magnet released a spring which caused the dog to jump. The whole thing sold for a half-dollar.

I had remembered the toy dog after a lapse of some thirty-five years, and I said to my friend, "I know how to make your telephone device very cheaply." When I came home, I built a contact that opened easily when vibrated. To this I connected a neon light which has a curious characteristic that can make it stay lighted once it is triggered. I gave the gadget to my friend and showed him that it could be easily built for less than a dollar.

He called me back a day later and said, "Yes, I have it on my desk and you're still a lousy inventor." I said, "What's the matter now?" He said, "I can't sneeze, I can't close the door, I can't even open a window because of the traffic noise." So, we incorporated a time delay into it so that the sound had to last for at least two seconds. I obtained a patent on the device, but about the same time the telephone company came out with a device that lights a red light whenever your phone rings. You can now get it as standard equipment and you don't need my silly gadget.

A RUSSIAN MEMORY STORE

I mention this episode because I believe it illustrates a significant point. I once told this story at an information retrieval meeting and was told that it is perfectly obvious what went on in my brain. It went back and looked up an index entitled "Sound-operated devices". Then it went through the file and found "A toy dog". My answer was: "Now that's very interesting, except that in 1921 I had no way of knowing that some silly patent attorney would ask me, some thirty years later, for a sound-operated device." If I were filing the toy dog, I'd file it under "Toys", "Dog", "Rex", but certainly not under "Sound-operated devices". Moreover, there's a more difficult problem. I spoke only Russian when I came to the United States and I would have had to file it under a Russian listing. I don't think my brain could have translated my whole memory into English. In general, there's no way of filing things under the titles or in the order in which you're going to need them later. This is why, when I hear people talk about automatic retrieval of significant information in the Patent Office, I believe they are talking nonsense. You can certainly set up automatic retrieval of trivial information. Until computers can file things without any order of preference, and not know in advance what is important and what is not important about a subject, and until they are able to look up the information later in any order and in any context, including by pictures, smell, and sound, we shall not have creative machines. I don't say this will not be done some day, but not in the immediate future.

The difficulty is this: The human brain apparently can remember our experiences, whether they are smells or sounds or pictures, and the brain can "re-live" them later. We have all had the experience of smelling something and saying, "I smelled this thirty years ago under some specific circumstances," and then the whole scene flashes back. The inventor must have this ability to search through everything he has ever experienced that may have some bearing on a problem, and extract the needed items out of this peculiar thing we call the brain. The items are recalled in connections which were not foreseeable because there's no way of foreseeing now what one will need in the future.

Perhaps people like myself have a warped intelligence. For example,
I can't remember the names of people. I meet them and two minutes later
I can't introduce them to anyone else. This is a useful thing to tell
audiences; then I'm not so embarrassed later on. I really am very poor
at it. Someone I know says I don't like people, but that's not true. I
happen to like people; I just can't remember their names. I can, however,
remember technical things without any effort at all.

ASKING THE RIGHT QUESTIONS

Let me relate to you a few other samples of the kind of thinking
one does when one invents. I once conceived an idea of which I'm very
proud and, again, which nobody wants. This is a process of taking blurred
photographs and later de-blurring them. You may laugh, but the Air Force
spends big money on this sort of thing. I took a picture of the New York
skyline with a Leica while riding across one of the bridges. The picture
has a slight vertical blurr because it was taken late in the evening.
The exposure had to be quite long even with an F-2 lens. I had it hanging
in one of our rooms and as I was sitting across the room and looking at
it, I was saying to myself, "It looks good as an eleven by fourteen enlargement, but I know it's blurred horizontally." No one noticed this but it
bothered me. Having nothing to do--I often have nothing to do, because
I'm lazy--I began to wonder whether one could remove the blur from a
blurred picture without "fudging", that is, by rigorous processing.

Once I asked the right question, the wheels began to turn, and the
answer was "Yes." It seemed a rather straight-forward process, although
the mathematics of it are too much for me. David Gilbarg, who is head
of the math department at Stanford, later did the theory. He pointed out
that a blur is a type of an integration process and that by taking the
correct derivatives one can almost always solve the problem of deblurring,
providing certain boundary conditions are present.

The problem interested me because it illustrated the kind of invention
which I like, one which nobody asked me for. You're not sure there's any
good reason for it, but suddenly you begin to question "Can it be done?"
And when you ask the question, the solution follows. One of the big tricks
in inventing is not so much to invent the "how", but the "what". In other
words, the creating of the problem is as big an invention as the solving
of the problem--sometimes, a much greater invention.

Many years ago I invented a magnetic clutch and it received considerable
publicity and I received many invitations to speak. This is why I can
do it now without dying a thousand deaths, as I did before the clutch.
One of the talks was before the Optimists' Club of Washington. A man came
to me afterwards and said, "I'm head of the biggest diaper wash service in
Washington. We'd like to be able to count them without opening them."
I didn't ask him why. He asked, "Is this a difficult problem?", to which
I said, "Medium." I suggested that they sew into the corner of each
diaper a small bead of metal, then X-ray the batch of diapers from two
directions. From the resulting picture we should be able to tell how
many diapers there are in the bag. He thought that my suggestion was too
sophisticated a solution for his unsophisticated business. As far as I

know, nothing was ever done with it.   The point is that once the problem
is posed, most competent engineers will think of some kind of solution.
They will vary from brilliant to stupid, but they will be solutions.

RE-INVENTING THE WHEEL

When I came to Washington, nearly thirty years ago, I thought of a
stereo motion picture system.   I went to the Patent Office Search Room
and told an attendant that I was going to look for the idea.   He said,
"That's multiplex photography.   Don't bother looking.   Since you work at
the Bureau of Standards and they're part of the Department of Commerce,
as we are, go directly up to the Examiner in Chief.   He'll help you find
it."

I found the division and the right examiner.   He sat in a small
office surrounded by little drawers, called "shoes", which were full
of patents in his particular art.   I explained to the venerable gentleman
that I had a system of three-dimensional movies where one eye sees the
odd pictures and the other eye the even pictures as the successive pictures
are projected on the screen.   I had a revolving shutter in front of the
face of the viewer to select the pictures.   The examiner listened and
then, without looking, picked up a patent and said, "Like this?"--and
there was my invention, with my exact drawing, dated 1910, the year I was
born.   I never got over the shock.   What left me thunderstruck was that the
drawing was identical with my sketch.   If I hadn't seen the date, I would
have sworn that the other inventor stole it from me.

INVENTION BY ANALOGY

Some of my inventions have made money and are important at least,
economically.   One is the magnetic particle clutch for which I received
immense rewards--a gold medal from the Department of Commerce, and a
steep raise in salary.   As a result of this I was making more money than
my boss, which raised many non-technological problems.   Anyway, the clutch
invention came about in a curious way.   There was an accidental discovery
of an electrostatic particle clutch by a man named Winslow when he was
playing with a Johnson-Rhabek clutch.   I won't give you the whole history
of clutches.   Winslow was playing with another clutch and discovered a
curious effect: if particles of starch or limestone were embedded in a
film of oil between two plates and if he applied a high voltage across the
mixture, the particles chained up into a kind of conglomerate that made
the two plates bind together.   He applied for a patent on this device and
the Patent Office, of course, rejected it as unworkable.   So he came down
to the Patent Office in Washington and demonstrated the electrostatic clutch
and got the patent.   The patent was tested at the Massachusetts Institute
of Technology.   They played with it and didn't like it very much.   It
finally reached one of the consulting firms to my group at the National
Bureau of Standards.   One one occasion, while playing with it in our
lab, it suddenly occurred to me that if electrostatic attraction could be
made to do the job, electromagnetic attraction should be very much better.
The Mu of iron is about a thousand or two thousand, while the K of starch

is about two, so that for the same field stress, if you like, one should be able to get a thousand times more sheer force. Besides, one doesn't have high voltage problems, and a lot of other things should be easier.

So we tried it, and about an hour later we had the first magnetic particle clutch. And then the roof caved in. Apparently, clutches had been a pain in the neck for a long, long time. Apparently, they still are. This was the first new, efficient, different clutch in many years. It didn't wear out, didn't need adjustments and had several other virtues.

The U.S. patent rights were vested in the U.S. Government, while I retained the foreign rights. I mention this because people have often asked me, "How many millions did you make on the magnetic clutch?" In the United States I earned nothing but a grade step raise and a lot of glory, and I learned how to speak in public after a fashion. After five years of great effort and forty-four foreign patents in twenty-two foreign countries, I earned a little over twenty thousand dollars. That is the total.

However, the feeling of accomplishment was very sweet. Very many people knew about the clutch, and to this day people talk about it. It has become a familiar, commercially available device. It found its way into the Hillman car, the Peugeot, the Renault. It is used in many IBM machines and in all Control Data tape drives. But I must say that even engineers in my own company don't know that I invented it.

The clutch illustrates the "invention by analogy" method. Inventors do this very often. The Patent Office is sometimes unsophisticated enough to issue patents when one invents something by using analogous art. If it's "too analogous", they won't let one get away with it, but if it's not obviously analogous, one can get away with it. This is one of the tricks patent attorneys pull out of their hats. What surprised me in the particular case of the particle clutch is that it wasn't done before me. I had occasion to tell of the clutch to J. Presper ("Press") Eckert, who is one of the inventors of the electronic digital computer--you may remember the Eckert and Mauchly Corporation. He thought a minute and said, "You know, Jack, I have an idea for another invention. I can make an electrostatic clutch similar to your gadget." "Press, you just closed the loop," I said, and told him about Winslow's original electrostatic clutch. Here you see Press, a very brilliant inventor, doing exactly what all inventors do. They immediately start beating their brains out to see if they can improve on what you just said. After a while this becomes a way of life. You see something that bothers you or interests you, and you invent.

THERE MUST BE A BETTER WAY

My automatic watch regulator was another useful invention. If you have an American car with a clock in it, you've paid me three-quarters of a cent because all American car clocks use it. Now, if the clock doesn't run, that's not my fault. But if it runs incorrectly, that is my fault, and I'll give you back the three-quarters of a cent.

It all began in 1945, when my wife gave me a present of a Gruen

wrist watch. It was a good watch and waterproof, too. Have you ever
tried to adjust a waterproof watch? You just unscrew the back, but you
need a special tool. And if you don't have the tool, you wreck the case.
Nevertheless, you unscrew the back and you find the gadget marked "F"
and "S" (fast and slow) and you move it a little bit in the right direction.
The correct amount is a "little bit", but the correct amount varies and
no one knows how much is correct. You just move the F-S lever a little
bit, depending on your eyesight. Then you screw the cover back on, if you
can. After wearing it a while, you discover that it's now adjusted a little
too far, so you open it again and move it "half a little bit" in the other
direction. Finally, if you're very careful and don't get dirt into the
watch and don't hurt the mechanism, you get it regulated. For six months
you have a good watch and then it starts drifting in some other direction,
because by now it's winter. The average temperature is lower, so the oil
inside is a little thicker, or thinner, or dryer. After having done this
for about a year, being an inventor, I said, "Nuts to this! There must
be a better way." And so I invented the self-regulating watch. I'm
wearing one of them. When you pull at the stem and move the hands forward,
the rate speeds up a little. If you move them back, the rate slows down.
In a clock this is a very simple device. It makes the clock actually cheaper
and better because it eliminates the regulating stem and the act of
regulation, which most people can't perform anyway.

The device is actually a form of an integrating servo system.
This I didn't know when I invented it, but people pointed it out to me
later. You know, most inventions are later analyzed by the theoreticians,
and people enjoy explaining to us what it was that we really did, and why
it was obvious.

IMPROVING PERFECT WATCHES

You need to play "Hearts and Flowers" as background music when I tell
the story of the watch regulator. My attorney and I tried to sell it to
the president of one of the large watch manufacturers and he said, "It's
a beautiful idea but we can't use it."

I said, "Why not?", and he said, "Because we advertise a perfect watch
and how could we advertise anything better?"

I said, "Well, can't you do what Cadillac does and forget what you
said last year and start all over again each year?" He said, "No, we
won't."

I said, "Is your watch perfect?" He said, "No, just a good watch,
like any other good watch, but we say it's perfect and for most people it's
good enough."

"How do you set them?" I asked. He replied, "We always set them
a little fast in the factory because no watch can be set correctly. The
rate will depend on how you wear it, whether you sleep with it under a
blanket or above the blanket, whether you keep the watch on a window or
the window open, whether you sleep in a cold or hot room, whether you are
active or sit still all day, and so on. All these things affect a watch."

And finally he said, "A fast watch is psychologically all right and a slow watch is psychologically out of order. So, we set them fast and most people don't mind; if they mind, the watch dealer will regulate it for them."

Anyway, I couldn't sell the regulator for nine years, and then I had dinner with an engineer from Chrysler who told me that his boss "hated inaccurate clocks". The boss thought the regulator was a pretty good idea and so the Chrysler people asked the clock industry to incorporate it, and eventually all the other companies fell in line.

So on this invention I did make money--about one hundred and fifty thousand dollars over a period of some ten years. But I did not succeed in selling it to the watch industry. Benrus put it into one of their watches for a while and gave it up because the sales people didn't want to sell it. But, again, customers should never be told that a watch needs regulation. You always tell people that the jeweled watches are perfect. Benrus stopped making watches incorporating my regulator, but I kept a few samples for sentimental reasons.

SELLING IDEAS

This problem of selling inventions is generally far more difficult than the invention itself. The clock regulator is almost an ideal invention in the sense that it makes the clock *better* and at the same time makes it *cheaper*. Still, it took nine years and a lot of disappointments before I could sell the idea. This is true about many of the things I do. But I do them anyway. This is my work and I can think of nothing better to do.

This brings me to the question of incentives. Even if you're crazy like me, you have to have incentives. They are what keeps you trying and you have to try very hard, indeed. Not only do you have to invent, you have to sell the idea--to your own staff, to your superiors, and to many others. Unless you're a dictator, you have to get your own staff enthusiastic about one of your ideas for them to work on it. You've got to sell all the time. In my case I have to sell to my wife and children, and they sometimes are very negative. They have been living with this invention business for a long time and they are not easily impressed. You have to sell to your friends, to your own patent attorney and, of course, you have to sell to the Patent Office, and that's an art in itself. You do **sell** all the time because you are the kind of guy you are and you have to do it because this is a way of life.

It started when I was very young. I wanted to be an engineer all my life. After graduating from high school, I was talked out of taking an engineering course. I went to the City College of New York and, after a short time, went back to engineering because in 1933 you starved even with a degree. I thought I might just as well starve at something I liked, so I became an engineer. I sold hot dogs at Coney Island, helped to clear snow off the streets of New York, and worked at all sorts of jobs. I

worked in factories for ten to twelve dollars per week. Then the National
Recovery Administration came in and, as a radio trouble-shooter, I made
fourteen dollars per week and my boss complained that he was going to
go bankrupt if he had to pay me fourteen dollars a week. It was good
experience.

When I tell young engineers how things were then, they seem to think
I'm lying, because they can't believe that a man with two degrees could
work for twelve to fourteen dollars a week. Even for me, it's hard to
remember those days. I learned what it was like to work in a factory and
I was surprised that so many people not only don't mind, but actually like
routine work. When I was very young I worried as to who was going to do
all the dirty and monotonous work in the world. I found that most people
don't want to be inventors, or foremen, or leaders. They just like to do
a routine job and go home and forget about it. There have been many times,
since I've been in business for myself, when I wanted to go home and forget
about it too; but for other reasons.

JUST LOVE THEM

How do you fire up students to want to invent? I submit that the most
important requirement is teachers who admire inventions. Some time ago
I attended a meeting where the speaker was wondering how to set up a
good laboratory. I posed the following question: "If the government wanted
to hire, create or discover great artists to create great paintings, how
could it build up a stable of people who could create great art? Whom
would you appoint as chief and how would he recruit great artists?"

I suggested that the way to do this is like setting up a good laboratory.
Get a man who loves art, who understands it, and let him decide. Just give
him plenty of funds and tell him to get an organization of artists. If
he loves art, he will find his people. If, in addition, he happens to be
a good manager and a fine human being, he'll do wonders.

This approach should hold for encouraging inventors. All you have to
do to encourage inventors is to love them, to love inventions for their
own sake, not necessarily because they make an immediate buck for the
corporation. Encourage those things which are emotionally exciting. If
you get a man who feels like this, his people will invent.

Very recently I was attending a celebration of the 175th anniversary
of the Patent Office's founding, and another speaker remembered my
analogizing inventors to women and saying that when the king in Camelot
was asked, "How do you make a woman happy?", he replied, "Just love her,
love her, nothing else." The speaker continued with his story and said
that the trouble with inventors is that it would be nice to "just love
them", but that's impossible because "they are such bastards". I don't
believe this. We're no more so than any of the rest of the human race.
Perhaps we are difficult at times, but then, who isn't?

The way to encourage creativity in school is to get teachers who

are better than most of the teachers we have today. This is no exaggeration.
High school and undergraduate teachers today, by and large, are terrible,
and the reason they're terrible is because their salaries are terrible.
My thinking about this is very simple. Double the average salary of the
American school teacher and cut his classes in half. This will mean that
we will need four times as much money. This will be a lot of money,
but it will enable us to hire the kinds of teachers that we need. The
government has recently raised the salaries of engineers and it can now
get the kinds of engineers it wants. If we have good teachers who love
science or love music or love art, the students would love these subjects,
too.

We can talk forever about how to increase creativity in school, but
unless we get teachers who love creativity, who get fired up, and get a
twinkle in their eye when they see a good idea, we're not going to get it
from the students. I believe this is true in industry, too. If you have
a research director who likes inventions, who respects original work,
who can rise above the direct buck-benefit to the company and who can look
the other way when a researcher is stealing time to work on something he
really likes--and all directors of research, including myself, do this--
then you have the kind of boss whose people will invent. And if you have
the other kind of boss who doesn't like inventions, for whatever reason,
you're not going to get inventions, because people are very practical.
They will not beat their brains out for somebody who doesn't want them
to do original thinking.

I've heard teachers complain that students don't ask enough interesting
questions. I suspect that the trouble is that by the time a bright kid
gets to college, he knows that most teachers are afraid of difficult questions,
so he gets wise and doesn't ask them. The young children in kindergarten
don't know this yet. Also, the questions they can ask are probably answerable
by the teacher.

In industry, people who say that they would like to have very active
inventors, would like to encourage them, and to pursue their ideas in
any area, really don't mean this. Most managers in industry want inventors
who invent in a very narrow field. In other words, most managers want an
inventor who will solve their problems, not his problems. This is typical
and normal. They want an inventor who is specialized in their business and
doesn't invent anything else. Harry Diamond, who at one time was my boss,
and after whom the ordnance laboratory in Washington is now named, used to
say--I'll clean up his statement a little bit--"Everybody wants a southern
Negro from as far North as possible."

In summary, what I want to say about the difficulty an inventor faces
is this: Nobody wants his inventions. They want his brains. He can get
a good salary, but you can't interest people in his really original inventions.
The way to improve that, perhaps, is to get industry leaders and heads of
laboratories to really want inventions for their own sake.

I was once talking about this to Sherman Fairchild, who is both an inventor and a very successful businessman, and what he said was, "You know, Jack, the trouble is that inventions aren't worth a damn, but inventors are very valuable people!"

DISCUSSION

Inventing Within Relevant Missions

Jack Morton: Could an inventor increase the probability of invention-- loading the dice one might say--by knowing what business he is in and, therefore, being better able to identify the sources of information he needs? For example, like a miner who knows where to look for gold.

Jacob Rabinow: When one narrows his specialization, he probably comes up with fewer ideas. If one loads the dice in favor of a certain art, one cuts off analogous arts, which I think are important. The more an inventor can pull out of related *and* unrelated arts, the more original his ideas are likely to be.

Jack Morton: You mentioned the very difficult problem of not only selling the invention, but also finding the capital to support its development. If an invention is therefore to be part of a modern business, it must be relevant, I should think, to the goals of that business.

Jacob Rabinow: You are talking about the needs of the entrepreneur or the manager, and there is no question that he cannot blindly support research, no matter how beautiful it is, in fields which have no relevance to his enterprise. But the question I am addressing myself to is, how do we bring out inventiveness in individuals, and I feel that we should encourage them if at all possible. I have asked people at Bell Laboratories what they do when an employee invents something which is not remotely connected with telephones--like a cure for cancer. The answer was, "We'd support it." I said, "That's very nice, but what would you do if he did something not quite so spectacular?" And the answer was, "We would probably give him a little money, or give him some time to work on it, but not encourage it too much." But, you see, even a little bit of encouragement shows you care.

Emanuel Piore: I'm inclined to agree with Jack Rabinow regarding the need to give some encouragement to inventors, even when their activities are irrelevant. We had an employee in one of our labs whose child died of leukemia. He wanted to do something about this problem and got involved in the development of blood separators, offering his assistance to the National Institutes of Health. Well, the local management gave him time off, but wouldn't even pay his travel expenses to Washington--until the upper management heard about it and raised hell with the local people. This illustrates some of the difficulty that top management has in the area of encouraging its employees. The problem is how to get the word down below. This is a very basic problem.

Employee Rights in Inventions

     Calvin Taylor: I hear from some inventors that we need to straighten
out the incentive system in industry before we move back into the schools
to encourage creativity. They say that by and large, inventors have to
sign away all of their rights in their future inventions before they can
get a job in a corporation.

     Jacob Rabinow: There are other kinds of incentives, such as salary
increases, prestigious titles, fringe benefits, elegant laboratories and
equipment, and they are, I think, reward enough. I don't think the patent
rights make much difference.

The Randomness of Invention

     Robert Dean: If it is felt that invention is a random process, does
this mean that systematic logic has no role in the development of new
ideas?

     Jacob Rabinow: No, there are many problems you attack logically. In
life, in economics, in technology, there are many problems for which the
logical approach works beautifully, because you don't have to invent.
If you come to me and ask, "How do you stabilize an oscillating car on the
road?", I can tell you logically how to take the oscillation problem and
lick it by proper damping. If you ask me how to guide an airplane or a
missile, I can give you logical approaches. There's nothing wrong with a
pure, straight, logical approach, but this is not invention.

     There *is* a logical sequence associated with invention and that is to
check to see if the conception is good. You get a crazy idea, and then
you start going logically through the ABC's of physics or chemistry and
find that the idea will or will not work. Good inventors do this first,
before their enemies do it, which is one of the things that distinguishes
the crackpot from the inventor.

     Emanuel Piore: Conant wrote a book on science using case histories.[1]
He took some case histories in chemistry, of people who were very creative
chemists. The book shows that for all the ballyhooing about the scientific
method, no creative scientist uses it. This is one of the problems that
some of the operational researchers, who look over the shoulders of engineers
and scientists, would like to structure.

     Jacob Rabinow: At the end of World War II we had a great many engineers
and scientists, in our laboratory at the National Bureau of Standards with
lots of time. One of the things we did with our time was to analyze
proximity fuses logically: What kind of targets were there, what kinds of
forces were available to "feel" the target, and so on. (A proximity fuse
is a device that "feels" the target at a distance.) We took the whole
range of factors and possibilities and analyzed them exhaustively. In
the matrix of boxes we would place a plus if the possibility was realistic
and zero if it could not be done. This was a logical, methodical approach
aimed at covering the whole spectrum of energy, versus targets, versus sources.

---

[1] James Bryant Conant (ed.), *Harvard Case Histories in Experimental Science*.
Harvard University Press, Cambridge: 1957.

There was one box which was zero, because it was logically impossible.
I invented a fuse that used that possibility very effectively, though I
can't tell you about it because it's still classified.

L. M. Boelter: You said that teachers are needed in our schools who
have a fondness and respect for creativity. Did you mean all kinds of
teachers, or only teachers in the technical fields?

Jacob Rabinow: All kinds of teachers--in poetry, in English, in
languages, in writing, in art, in the sciences, in anything where
originality is important.

II REFERENCES

1. "Accredited Curricula Leading to First Degrees in Engineering in the United States - 1965-1966," 33rd Annual Report Engineers' Council for Professional Development, pp 38-40.

2. Aiken, Daymond J., *Human Spark Plugs Wanted* (Pamphlet), [New York, N. Y.: Prentice-Hall, 1945].

3. Alexander, Jerome, Quoted in Rossman.

4. Alger, John R. M. and Carl V. Hays, *Creative Synthesis In Design*, [Englewood Cliffs, N. J.: Prentice-Hall, Inc., 1964].

5. *The Amplified Bible*, [Grand Rapids, Michigan: Zondervan Publishing House, 1965].

6. Armstrong, Neil, Verbal report from Apollo 11 Lunar landing to NASA Mission Control, Houston, Texas, TV live broadcast, July 20, 1969.

7. Arnold, John E., "Personal Development," *Machine Design*, January 12, 1956.

8. Arnold, John E., "The Creative Engineer," in *Creative Engineering* (Pamphlet), by American Society of Mechanical Engineers, Circa 1956.

9. Arnold John E., "Education For Innovation," pp 127-138 in Parnes, *A Sourcebook*.

10. Arnold, John E., quoted in Parnes, *A Sourcebook*.

11. Arnold, John E., "Useful Creative Techniques," *Creative Engineering Seminar Report*, Stanford University, 1959. Reproduced in Parnes, *A Sourcebook*.

12. Asimow, Morris, *Introduction To Design*, [Englewood Cliffs, N. J.: Prentice-Hall, Inc., 1962].

13. Atkins, William J., "An Engineering Approach To Cost Estimating," *Electronics Industries*, Nov., 1964, pp 52-55.

14. Ayres, Robert U., *Technological Forecasting and Long-Range Planning*, [New York, N. Y.: McGraw-Hill, 1969].

15. Bacon, Francis, Quoted in Klemm.

16. Bacon, Roger, *Epistola de Secretis Operibus Artis et Naturae*, Quoted in Klemm.

17. Bacon, Roger, *Opus Maius*, translated by Robert Belle Burke, Univ. of Pennsylvania, 1928. Quoted in Klemm.

18. Bacon, Roger, Quoted in Kettering, Charles F., *Short Stories of Science and Invention*.

19. Bailey, Robert L., "A Proposed New Concept for a Solar-Electricity Converter," *Transactions of the ASME, Journal of Engineering for Power*, Vol. 94, Series A, No. 2, April, 1972.

20. Bailey, R. L., "Electromagnetic Wave Energy Conversion," NASA Technical Memorandum No. NASA TM-X-62, 269, *Proceedings of NASA Laser-Energy Conversion Conference*, Moffet Field, California, Jan. 18-19, 1973.

21. Bailey, R. L., (Assigned to NASA under Fletcher's name.) U. S. Patent No. 3,760,257, issued Sept. 18, 1973.

22. Bailey, R. L., "Disciplined Creativity - One *Key* To The Future," *PROCEEDINGS*, 1974 IEEE Southeastcon, Orlando, Fla., April 29 - May 1, 1974, pp 2-5.

23. Bailey, et al, "Final Report. Electromagnetic Wave Energy Conversion Research," Grant No. NSG-5061, Sept. 30, 1975, to NASA, GSFC, Greenbelt, Md.

24. Barr, H. F, Foreword in *Typical Problems In Engineering*, Set 1, No. 1, *General Motors Engineering Journal*, General Motors, Technical Center, Warren, Michigan.

25. Barr, John H., Quoted in Rossman.
26. Barron, Frank, in Taylor and Barron's *Scientific Creativity*, Copyright
     © 1963 John Wiley & Sons, Inc., Reprinted by permission of John
     Wiley & Sons, Inc.
27. Barron, Frank, "The Disposition Toward Originality," in Taylor and
     Barron, *Scientific Creativity*, Copyright © 1963 by John Wiley &
     Sons, Inc., Reprinted by permission of John Wiley & Sons, Inc.
28. Barron, Frank, "The Disposition Toward Originality," pp 139-152 in
     Taylor and Barron.
29. Barron, in Taylor and Barron.
30. Barron, Frank, "The Needs for Order and for Disorder as Motives in
     Creative Activity," in Taylor and Barron's *Scientific Creativity*,
     Copyright © 1963 by John Wiley & Sons, Inc., Reprinted by permission
     of John Wiley & Sons, Inc.
31. Barron, Frank, "The Needs for Order and for Disorder as Motives in
     Creativity Activity," pp 153-160 in Taylor and Barron.
32. Bassett, R. S., Quoted in Rossman.
33. Benasutti, F. J., "The Patentable Invention-Respective Rights of
     Inventor and Owner," *Synthesis*, No. 13, 1973.
34. Bergantz, Joseph A., "The Creative Problem-Solving Process," *Chemical
     Engineering Progress*, Vol. 59, No. 12, December, 1963.
35. Berger, Ernest, Quoted in Osborn, *Applied Imagination*.
36. Berliner, Emile, Quoted in Rossman.
37. Beveridge, W. I. B., *The Art of Scientific Investigation*, [New York,
     N. Y.: Random House, 1957].
38. Bjornsson, E. S., Editorial, *Synthesis*, No. 2, January, 1972.
39. Bollay, William, "New Directions In Engineering Education," in DeSimone,
     Education.
40. Bolz, Ray E., and Robert C. Dean, Jr., "Strategies and Teaching
     Methods," Chap. 11 in DeSimone, *Education*.
41. Bosco, G. B., Quoted in Rossman.
42. Boyd, T. A., *Professional Amateur, The Biography of Charles Franklin
     Kettering*, [New York, N. Y.: E. P. Dutton and Co., Inc., 1957].
43. Bradley, F. W., "Things Scholastic," *Phi Kappa Phi Journal*, Vol. XXIX,
     No. 2A, 1949.
44. Bristol, Benton K., "Observed Creative Characteristics As Recorded
     in One Book," *The Journal of Creative Behavior*, Vol. 5, No. 1,
     First Quarter 1971, pp 1-6.
45. Brittain, James W., "The Remarkable Career of An Engineer-Inventor,"
     The Bent of Tau Beta Pi, Summer 1976, pp 7-11.
46. Brody, Boruch, and Nicholas Capaldi, *Science: Men, Methods, Goals*,
     [New York, N. Y.: W. A. Benjamin, Inc., 1968].
47. Brown, Gordon S., "Engineer-Scientist," *Electronics*, Vol. 32, No. 47,
     November 20, 1959.
48. Bryant, R. B., Quoted in Rossman.
49. Buckles, Robert A., *Ideas, Inventions, And Patents*, [New York, N. Y.:
     John Wiley & Sons, Inc., 1957].
50. Buhl, Harold R., *Creative Engineering Design*, [Ames, Iowa: The Iowa
     State University Press, 1960].
51. Burdell, E. S., "General Education in Engineering," *Journal of Engineering
     Education*, Vol. 46, No. 8, April, 1956, pp 619-750.
52. Burnham, Daniel, "Make Big Plans," *Words of Inspiration*, [Chicago,
     Ill.: J. G. Ferguson Pub. Co., 1963].

53. Bush, Vannevar, "The Gentleman of Culture," *Wiley Bulletin*, Fall, 1959.

54. Carrier, W. H., Quoted in Rossman.

55. Caserio, Martin J., "Some Comments on the Importance of Effective Technical Communications," in *Characteristics and Organizations of the Oral Technical Report* (Pamphlet), General Motors Corp., 1959.

56. Chandler, Charles DeForest, and Frank P. Lahm, *How Our Army Grew Wings*, [New York, N. Y.: The Ronald Press Co., 1943], pp 144-148.

57. Chang, Sheldon S. L., *Energy Conversion*, [Englewood Cliffs, N. J., Prentice-Hall, Inc., 1963].

58. Chanute, Octave, Letter to Wilbur Wright, October 12, 1901, in McFarland.

59. Cherry, W. R., "The Generation of Pollution-Free Electrical Power From Solar Power," *Transactions of the ASME*, *Journal of Engineering for Power*, Vol. 94, Series A, No. 2, April, 1972.

60. Chirgwin, K. M., C. H. Lee and P. J. Larsen, "Linear Induction Motor For High-Speed Tracked Vehicles," *Proceedings of The 4th Intersociety Energy Conversion Engineering Conference*, Washington, D. C., September 22-26, 1969, pp 795-806. (Copies of *Proceedings* available from American Institute of Chemical Engineers, 345 East 47th St., New york, N. Y. 10017).

61. Chrysler, Walter, Quoted in Osborn, *Applied Imagination*.

62. Clark, W., *The Gantt Chart*, [New York, N. Y.: The Ronald Press Co., 1922].

63. Clevett, M. L., Jr, "Someone Has Probably Tried It," *Engineer*, March-April, 1970.

64. Colclaser, R. G., "A Design School for the Young Engineer in Industry," *Engineering Education*, March, 1968.

65. Coler, Myron A., "The Two Creativities," *Chemical and Engineering News*, August 15, 1966, pp 72-84.

66. Compton, Arthur Holly, "Case Histories: Creativity In Science," in *The Nature of Creative Thinking* (Pamphlet), Industrial Research Institute, Inc., based on a May 5-7, 1952, Conference at Skytop, Pa.

67. Cottrell, Alan H., "Technological Thresholds," in *The Process of Technological Innovation*, [Washington, D. C.: Nat'l Academy of Sciences, 1968].

68. "Courses in Creative Problem-Solving," *Stanford Research Institute Journal*, No. 15, June, 1967.

69. Crawford, Robert P., "The Techniques of Creative Thinking," [New York, N. Y.: Hawthorne Books, 1959].

70. *Creative Engineering* (Pamphlet), [New York, N. Y.: American Society of Mechanical Engineers, Circa 1956].

71. Day V. Long and Evans, 1935 C. D. 445, 448.

72. Dean, Robert C., Jr., "Trade-Offs and Constraints," Chap. 8 in DeSimone, *Education*.

73. de Camp, L. Sprague, *The Ancient Engineers*, [Cambridge, Mass.: The MIT Press, 1960].

74. DeSimone, Daniel V., "The Innovator," *Engineer*, Engineer's Joint Council Publication, January-February, 1967.

75. DeSimone, Daniel V., *Education for Innovation*, [Elmsford, N. Y.: Pergamon Press, Ltd., Copyright © 1968].

76. Diesel, Herrn Rudolf, "Die Entstehung des Dieselmotors," Berlin, 1913, Quoted in Klemm.

77. Diesel, Herrn Rudolf, Quoted in Klemm.

78. Diller, N. Richard, "Problem Solvers Are Made--Not Born," *Automation*, March, 1966, pp 22-23.

79. Dodge, A. Y., Quoted in Rossman.

80. Dodge, Richard W., "What To Report," *Westinghouse Engineer*, July-September, 1962.

81. Doyle, Lauren B., "Seven Ways to Inhibit Creative Research," *Datamation*, February, 1965, pp 52-60.

82. Draper, C. Stark, "Education For Creativity," Chap. 8 in DeSimone, *Education*.

83. Drucker, Peter F., *Managing For Results: Economic Tasks and Risk-Taking Decisions*, [New York: Harper and Row, 1964].

84. Dufresne-Tasse, "Insight, the Troublemaker: The French Writers of the 20th Century Before Creativity," *The Journal of Creative Behavior*, 2nd Quarter 1975, pp 137-146.

85. Easton, Elmer C., "An Engineering Approach To Creative Thinking," *Ceramic Age*, Sept., 1955.

86. Easton, Elmer C., Quoted in Osborn, *Applied Imagination*.

87. Easton, William, "Creative Thinking and How to Develop It," *"Mechanical Engineering*, Vol. 68, No. 8, August, 1946.

88. Edel, D. Henry, Jr., INTRODUCTION TO CREATIVE DESIGN, Copyright ©️ 1967. Reprinted by permission of Prentice-Hall, Inc., Englewood Cliffs, New Jersey.

89. Edel, D. Henry, *Introduction To Creative Design*, [Englewood Cliffs, N. J.: Prentice-Hall Inc., 1967].

90. Edison, Thomas Alva, *The Diary and Sundry Observations of Thomas Alva Edison*, ed. by Dagobert D. Runes, [New York: Philosophical Library, Inc., 1948].

91. Edwards, M. O., "Solving Problems Creatively," *Systems & Procedures Journal*, January-February, 1966. Reprinted by permission, *The Journal of Systems Management*, January, 1966.

92. Edwards, M. O., "Solving Problems Creatively," *Systems & Procedures Journal*, January-February, 1966.

93. Einstein, Albert, Quoted in Mead.

94. Emmet, William LeRoy, *The Autobiography of An Engineer*, 2nd Ed., [New York, N. Y.: The American Society of Mechanical Engineers, 1940].

95. *Encyclopedia Americana* (1964), Vol. X.

96. Fabun, Don, et al, *The Dynamics of Change*, [Englewood Cliffs, N. J.: Prentice-Hall, Inc., 1967].

97. Fabun, Don, "You and Creativity," *Kaiser Aluminum News*, Kaiser Aluminum & Chemical Corp., Vol. 25, No. 3, 1968.

98. Faraday, Michael, *Faraday's Diary* (7 Vols.), [London: G. Bell and Sons, Ltd., 1932-1936].

99. Farber, Erich A., "The Teaching and Learning of Engineering," *Journal of Engineering Education*, Vol. 45, No. 10, June, 1955.

100. Farber, E. A., and J. C. Reed, "Practical Applications of Solar Energy," *Consulting Engineer*, Vol. 8, No. 3, Sept., 1956.

101. Farber, Erich, "Engineering Analysis In Education," *Journal of Engineering Education*. Vol. 49, No. 3, December, 1958.

102. Fenner, Terrence W., and James L. Everett, *Inventor's Handbook*, [New York, N. Y.: Chemical Publishing Co., Inc., 1969].

103. Field, Crosby, "Mechanical Invention As A Form of Expression," *Mechanical Engineering*, Vol. 50, 1928, pp 447-453.

104. Field, Crosby, "Creative Engineering," p 13-15 in *Creative Engineering*.

105. Fleischmann, Walter L., "Specifications . . . Their Preparation and Use," *Metal Progress,* Vol. 19, Nos. 4-6, April-June, 1967.

106. Flesch, Rudolf, *The Art of Readable Writing*, [New York, N. Y.: Harper & Brothers Publishers, 1949].

107. Forshee, F. F., Quoted in Rossman.

108. Fosdick, Harry Emerson, *On Being A Real Person*, [New York, N. Y.: Harper & Brothers, Publishers, 1943].

109. Frazier, A. W., "The Practical Side of Creativity," *Hydrocarbon Processing*, Vol. 45, No. 1, January, 1966, pp 167-170.

110. Fredrickson, A. G., "The Dilemma of Innovating Societies," *Chemical Engineering Education*, Summer, 1969, p 124ff.

111. Freund, C. J., "Creativity Is a Task, Not a Trait," *Machine Design*, May 25, 1967, p 161-162.

112. Friendly, H. M., Quoted in Rossman.

113. Friis, Harald T., *Seventy-five Years in an Exciting World*, [San Francisco, Calif.: San Francisco Press, 1971].

114. Fulton, Robert, Quoted in Wilson, Mitchell.

115. Gabor, Dennis, *Innovations*, [New York, N. Y.: Oxford University Press, 1970].

116. Gardner, John W., *Self-Renewal: The Individual And The Innovative Society*, [New York, N. Y.: Harper & Row Publishers, 1963, 1964], Harper Colophon Books.

117. "General Information Concerning Patents," U. S. Dept. of Commerce, [Washington, D. C.: U. S. Government Printing Office, January, 1966].

118. Gilmer, Ben S., "Times Demand As Goal: Education For Creativity," *Auburn Alumnews*, (Auburn, Ala.), July, 1961.

119. Gitter, Dean L., "Creative Sparks To Kindle Oil Industry," *Petroleum Management*, April, 1965, pp 92-96.

120. Goddard, E. C., and G. E. Pendray, *Goddard Rocket Development*, [Englewood Cliffs, N. J.: Prentice-Hall, Inc., 1948].

121. Goddard, Robert Hutchings, *Autobiography of Robert Hutchings Goddard*, [Worcester, Mass.: Achille J. St. Onge, 1966].

122. Goodyear, Charles, Quoted in Wilson, *American Science And Invention*.

123. Gordon, J. J., *Synectics*, [New York, N. Y.: Harper and Row, 1961].

124. Gordan, T. J. and Olaf Helmer, "Report On A Long-Range Forecasting Study," [Santa Monica, California: Rand Corporation], Rand publication P-2982, September, 1964, pp 39-41. Also published in Helmer, Olaf, *Social Technology*, Basic Books, 1966.

125. Gordan, William J. J., Quoted in Raudsepp, "Removing Barriers To Creativity".

126. Gough, Harrison G., "Imagination-Undeveloped Resource," pp 217-226 in Parnes, *A Sourcebook*.

127. Gracian, Baltasar, *A Truthtelling Manual and the Art of Wordly Wisdom*, Trans. Fischer, [Springfield, Illinois: Charles C. Thomas Publisher, 1934].

128. Gray, Albert Woodruff, "Fundamentals Of Design Patents," *Machine Design*, January 12, 1956.

129. Grinter, L. E., "Report of The Committee on Evaluation of Engineering Education - 1952-1955," American Society for Engineering Education, June 15, 1955.

130. Grinter, L. E., "Report on Evaluation of Engineering Education (1952-1955), *Journal of Engineering Education*, Vol. 46, No. 1, September, 1955, pp 25-63.

131.   Grosvenor, W. M., Quoted in Rossman.

132.   Grover, G. M., "Structures of Very High Thermal Conductance,"
       Journal of Applied Physics, Vol. 35, June 6, 1964, pp 1990-1991.

133.   Guggenheim, Harry F., Foreword in Goddard, *Goddard Rocket Development*.

134.   Guilford, J. P., "Creativity: Its Measurement and Development,"
       pp 151-168 in Parnes, *A Sourcebook*.

135.   Guillemin, Ernest A., *Communications Networks*, Vol. I., [New York,
       N. Y.: John Wiley & Sons, Inc., 1931].

136.   Guillemin, Ernest A., *Communication Networks*, Vol. II, [New York,
       N. Y.: John Wiley & Sons, Inc., 1931].

137.   Hadamard, J. S., *An Essay on the Psychology of Invention In the
       Mathematical Field*, [Princeton, N.J.: Princeton Univ. Press,
       1945].

138.   Haddad, J. A., *175th Anniversary of the U. S. Patent System*, Vol. 1,
       [Washington, D. C.: Patent Office Society, 1966].

139.   Hammond, H. P., et al, "Report of Committee on Aims and Scope of
       Engineering Curricula," *Journal of Engineering Eudcation*, 30,
       No. 7, March, 1940, pp 555-566.

140.   Hammond, H. P., "Engineering Education After the War," *Journal of
       Engineering Education*, Vol. 34, No. 9, May, 1944, pp 589-614.

141.   Hawkins, George A., *Student's Engineering Manual*, [New York, N. Y.:
       McGraw-Hill Book Co., 1968].

142.   Hay, Harold R., "Internationalized Solar Technology," *Sunworld*,
       No. 1, July, 1976.

143.   Hayakawa, S. I., "We Need Creative People," commentary, *Gainesville
       Sun*, Aug. 23, 1973.

144.   Hayman, H. S., "An Ecologic Model of Health and Disease," *Phi
       Kappa Phi Journal*, Vol. XLIX, No. 4, Fall, 1969, pp 52-61.

145.   Henry, Joseph, Quoted in Shippen.

146.   Heronemus, William E., *Congressional Record-Senate*, December 7, 1971,
       pp S20776-S20780.

147.   Hicks, Tyler G., "Communications In Engineering," Ch. 2 in Hawkins.

148.   Hill, Percy H., *The Science of Engineering Design*, [New York, N. Y.:
       Holt, Rinehart and Winston, Inc., 1970].

149.   Hix, C. F., and D. L. Purdy, "Creativity Can Be Developed," *GE Review*,
       May, 1955.

150.   Hix, C. F., and R. P. Alley, *Laws and Effects*, [New York, N. Y.:
       John Wiley & Sons, Inc., 1958].

151.   Hodnett, Edward, *The Art of Problem Solving*, [New York, N. Y.,
       Harper & Row, Publishers, 1955].

152.   Hoefler, Don C., "But You Don't Understand The Problem," *Electronic
       News*, July 17, 1967.

153.   Holloman, J. Herbert, "Creative Engineering And the Needs of Society,"
       Chap. 1 in DeSimone, *Education*.

154.   Horton, C. E., "Development of a UHF Grounded-Grid Amplifier,"
       Proc. IRE, Vol. 41, No. 1, pp 73-79, January, 1953.

155.   *How To Solve Problems*, Pamphlet AFP 50-2-21, Conference Outline 21,
       Management Course for Air Force Supervisors, 1 June, 1955, [Washington,
       D. C.: U. S. Govt. Printing Office].

156.   Howard, G. E., Quoted in Rossman.

157.   Hugo, Victor, Quoted in *Quotations To Remember*, Compiled by editors,
       [Kansas City, Missouri: Hallmark Cards Inc., n.d.].

158.   Jefferson, Thomas, August 19, 1785 letter to Peter Carr from Paris,
       in Whitman.

159. Jefferson, Thomas, Letter to John Jay, August 30, 1785, in Whitman.

160. Jefferson, Thomas, October 15, 1785, letter to J. Bannister, Jr.,
      in Whitman.

161. Jefferson, Thomas, letter to Isaac McPherson, August 13, 1813, in
      Whitman.

162. Jefferson, Thomas, Quoted by Sinnett, Chester M., "The Challenge
      of Personal Professional Development," *Research and Development*,
      April, 1970.

163. Johnson, Walter C., "Creative Problem-Solving," *IEEE Student Journal*,
      September, 1968, pp 17-20.

164. Kahn, P., Reprinted with permission from the January, 1968, *Reader's
      Digest*.

165. Kaiser, Henry J., Quoted in Lederer.

166. Keeler, Harper Brown, "Freedom and Control: The Dilemma of Creativity
      in the Organizational Environment," Doctoral Thesis, MIT, June,
      1966, Defense Documentation Center document AD 635 261.

167. Kelvin, Lord (Sir William Thomson), *Popular Lectures and Addresses*,
      Vol. I, Second Edition, [London: Macmillan and Co., 1891].

168. Kemper, John Dustin, *The Engineer And His Profession*, [New York,
      N. Y.: Holt, Rinehart and Winston, Inc., 1967].

169. Kennedy, John R., *Parade Magazine*, Sept. 23, 1962.

170. Kennedy, John F., *Profiles In Courage*, [New York, N.Y.: Harper
      & Row, Publishers, 1964].

171. Kesselring, K. A., "Responsible Creativity," *The Monogram* (Intra-
      Company publication of General Electric Co.), Campus Digest
      Edition, 1967.

172. Kettering, Charles F., "Remarks on receiving Award of Merit of The
      American Alumni Council at Ann Arbor, Michigan, July 13, 1948."
      Transcribed from a radio broadcast by station WJR, Detroit,
      Michigan.

173. Kettering, Charles F., *Short Stories of Science and Invention*,
      [Detroit, Michigan: General Motors Corp., 1959].

174. Kettering, Quoted in Boyd.

175. Kettering, Charles F., Quoted in *Words of Inspiration*, [Chicago,
      Illinois: J. G. Ferguson Publishing Co., 1963].

176. King, Blake, "Object: Creativity," *Mechanical Engineering*, November,
      1963, p 38-41.

177. King Gama's "Grumbler Song," from *Princess Ida*, by Gilbert and Sullivan.

178. King, W. J., "The Unwritten Laws of Engineering," *Mechanical Engineering*,
      June, 1944, pp 398-402.

179. Kirkpatrick, E. A., *Imagination and Its Place in Education*, [New
      York, N. Y.: Ginn, 1920].

180. Klemm, Friedrich, *A History of Western Technology*, Trans. Dorothea
      Waley Singer, [New York, N. Y.: Charles Scribner's Sons, Copyright
      © 1959 by George Allen & Unwin Ltd, Book Publishers, London,
      England].

181. Kraines, Samuel Henry, *Mental Depressions And Their Treatment*, [New
      York, N. Y.: Macmillan, 1957].

182. Krick, E. V., *An Introduction To Engineering* and *Engineering Design*,
      [New York, N. Y.: John Wiley and Sons, Inc., 1965].

183. Ladd, David L., "So You Think You've Got A Million Dollar Idea,"
      Family Weekly, Sept. 7, 1961.

184. Lafferty, James M., Quoted in Moore.

185. Land, Edwin H., "Addiction As a Necessity and Opportunity," *Science*,
      15 January 1971, p 151-153.

186. Larson, Gustave E., *Developing And Selling New Products*, [Washington, D. C.: U. S. Government Printing Office, 1955].

187. Lear, William P., "Lear: Searching for Plausible Solution to Smog," *Gainesville Sun*, Wednesday, Oct. 8, 1969.

188. Lederer, William J., "Henry Kaiser's Seven Keys To Success," *Reader's Digest*, November, 1961, pp 142-146.

189. Leonard, George B., *Education and Ecstasy*, [New York, N. Y.: Delacorte Press, 1968].

190. "Leonardo's Lost Notebooks," *Life*, March 3, 1967. Originally from Madrid Manuscripts, National Library, Madrid, Spain.

191. Levine, R. C., *IEEE Trans. On Engineering Management*, July, 1968. Copyright © 1968 by The Institute of Electrical and Electronics Engineers, Inc.

192. Lincoln, John W., "Developing a Creativeness In People," in Parnes, *A Sourcebook*.

193. Lindbergh, Charles, "A Letter From Lindbergh," *Life*, July 4, 1969. Reprinted by permission of Harcourt Brace Jovanovich, Inc.

194. Lindbergh, Charles, "A Letter From Lindbergh," *Life*, July 4, 1969.

195. Linus, in Schulz, Charles M., *Linus On Life*, [Kansas City, Missouri: Hallmark Cards Inc.], n.d.

196. Loetscher, E. C., Quoted in Rossman.

197. Lowenfeld, Viktor, "Creativity: Education's Stepchild," pp 9-17 in Parnes, *A Sourcebook*.

198. Mann, C. R., "A Study of Engineering Education," Bulletin No. 11, The Carnegie Foundation for the Advancement of Teaching, 1918.

199. Marconi, G., "Every Man His Own Inventor," *Colliers*, 1922, 70, 5-6.

200. Marconi, G., Quoted in Rossman.

201. Marvin, Philip R., "Successful Product Dvelopment," *Machine Design*, January 26, 1956, pp 56-60.

202. Maslow, A. H., "Emotional Blocks To Creativity," pp 93-103 in Parnes, *A Sourcebook*.

203. Maslow, Abraham H., Toward A Psychology of Being, 2nd Ed., [Princeton, N.J.: D. Van Nostrand Co., Inc., 1968].

204. Mason, Joseph G., "Suggestions for Brainstorming Technical and Research Problems," in Parnes, *A Sourcebook*.

205. Mathews, B. E., and R. L. Bailey, "A Course In Creative Problem Solving," *IEEE Transactions On Education*, Vol. E-8, No. 4, December, 1965, pp 85-90.

206. McCune, Francis K., "Elements of Competitive Engineering," before the 1965 Engineering Deans' symposium, (Pamphlet), [New York, N. Y.: General Electric Co., n.d.].

207. McFarland, Marvin W., Editor, *The Papers of Wilbur and Orville Wright*, *Vol. I*, [New York, N. Y.: McGraw-Hill Book Co., Inc., 1953].

208. McFarland, Marvin W., and Arthur G. Renstrom, *The Library of Congress Quarterly Journal of Current Acquisitions*, Aug. 1950, As quoted in McFarland.

209. McKnight, Blanche S., "A Floridian Gave Ice to the World," *All Florida - TV Week Magazine*, n.d.

210. McMillin, John C., "Designing Marginal Circuits," *IEEE Student Quarterly*, December, 1961, pp 23-25.

211. Mead, Margaret, "Where Education Fits In," *IBM Magazine*, Vol. 28, No. 10, Nov.-Dec., 1962.

212. Means, Ralph K., "Engineering Sense," *Naval Engineers Journal*, June, 1967.

213. Menninger, William C., M.D., A PSYCHIATRIST FOR A TROUBLED WORLD, Copyright © 1967 by the Menninger Foundation. Reprinted by permission of The Viking Press.

214. Merwin, H. C., *Patentability of Invention*, [Boston, Mass.: Little, Brown & Co., 1883].

215. Middendorf, W. H. and G. T. Brown, Jr., "Orderly Creative Inventing," *Electrical Engineering*, Oct., 1957, pp 866-869.

216. Miles, Lawrence D., *Technique of Value Analysis and Engineering*, [New York, N. Y.: McGraw-Hill Book Co., Inc., 1961].

217. Moore, A. D., *Invention Discovery, and Creativity*, [Garden City, N. Y.: Doubleday and Company, Inc., 1969].

218. Morse, Richard S., "Innovation and Entrepreneurship," in DeSimone, *Education*.

219. Morse, Richard S., "Preparing Innovators and Entrepreneurs," in DeSimone, *Education*.

220. Morton, Jack A., 'Discussion' of Richard S. Morse' paper, "Innovation and Entrepreneurship," in DeSimone, *Education*.

221. Nehemiah 6:2-3, *The Amplified Bible*.

222. *The New English Bible*, Oxford University Press, Cambridge University Press, 1970.

223. "New Uses and Management Implications of PERT" (Pamphlet), Booz-Allen Applied Research, Inc., 1964.

224. Newton, Isaac, Quoted in Gordon D. Friedlander, "The Burndy Library: Window On The History of Science," *IEEE Spectrum*, March, 1970.

225. Nicholson, Scott, "Group Creative Thinking," *Management Record*, Vol. 18, No. 1, July, 1956. Published by the National Industrial Conference Board.

226. Nordenholt, George F., editorial: "A Graduate Can Measure A Bottle," *Product Engineering*, April, 1953.

227. Ohl, Russel S., Quoted in Rossman.

228. Olken, H., "Invention--A Coming Profession," *Scientific American*, January, 1933.

229. Olken, Hyman, "Creativity Training for Engineers--Its Past, Present, and Future," *IEEE Transactions On Education*, December, 1964, pp 149-161.

230. Olken, Hyman, *Technology Transfer: How To Make It Work*, [Livermore, Calif.: Olken Publications, 1972].

231. O'Malley, John R., "Patents And The Engineer," *Engineering Facts From Gatorland*, Vol. 4, No. 5, Dec., 1967. (Published by University of Florida Alumni Association).

232. O'Neill, John J., *Prodigal Genius - The Life of Nikola Tesla*, [New York, N. Y.: David McKay Co., Inc., 1944], Tartan Book Series.

233. Osborn, A. F., *Your Creative Power*, [New York, N. Y.: Charles Scribner's Sons, 1950].

234. Osborn, Alex F., *Applied Imagination*, [New York, N. Y.: Charles Scribner's Sons, 1953].

235. Paluev, K. K., Comments on the paper by Igor Sikorsky, "Creative Engineering, Inventiveness and Intuition," published by ASME, July 1944, in a pamphlet, *Creative Engineering*.

236. Parker, Howard, Quoted in Rossman.

237. Parnes, Sidney J., *A Sourcebook for Creative Thinking*, [New York, N. Y.: Charles Scribner's Sons, 1962].

238. Parnes, Sidney J., "Do You Really Understand Brainstorming?," in Parnes, *A Sourcebook*.

239. Parsons, William Barclay, *Engineers and Engineering in the Renaissance*, [Cambridge, Mass.: The M.I.T. Press, 1939].

240. *Patents & Inventions: An Information Aid For Inventors* (Pamphlet), U. S. Dept. of Commerce, 1967.

241. Patterson, John C., *America's Greatest Inventors*, [New York, N. Y.: Thomas Y. Crowell Co., 1943].

242. Paulson, Richard, "Creative Specialist?," *Product Engineering*, November 25, 1963, p 80-81.

243. Peake, Harold J., "Difference Between Engineers and Scientists," *IEEE Transactions On Engineering Management*, Vol. EM-16, No. 1, February, 1969, pp 50-53.

244. Peckworth, Howard F., "Relevance of Engineering Education to the Needs of the Practicing Engineer in Business and Industry," Session III in *Report of the World Congress On Engineering Education* (pub. by ASEE), Ill. Inst. of Techn., Chicago, Ill., June 21-25, 1965.

245. *The PERT/COST System*, Navy Special Projects Office, [Washington, D. C.: U. S. Government Printing Office, Oct., 1961].

246. "PERT Guide For Management Use," Government's PERT Coordinating Group, [Washington, D. C.: U. S. Government Printing Office, 1963].

247. Peterson, Wilfred A., "The Art of Perspective," in *The New Book of The Art of Living*, [New York, N. Y.: Simon and Schuster, Inc., 1962].

248. Peterson, Wilfred, "The Art of Action," in Peterson, *The New Book*.

249. Philo of Byzantium, Quoted in Klemm.

250. Piaget, Jean, Quoted in Dean, Thomas C., "Challenges in Higher Education," *Phi Kappa Phi Journal*, Vol. L, No. 3, Summer, 1970.

251. Pickering, William H., "The Engineer-1968," *The Bridge* of Eta Kappa Nu, May, 1968, pp 5-7.

252. Pleuthner, Willard, "Brainstorming," *Machine Design*, January 12, 1956.

253. Poeschl, Quoted in O'Neil.

254. Poincaré, Henri, *The Foundations Of Science*, Trans. George Bruce Halsted, [New York, N. Y.: The Science Press, 1929].

255. "Polaris Management," A pamphlet prepared by Special Projects Office, Department of the Navy, Wash., D. C., [Washington, D. C.: U. S. Gov't Printing Office, 1961].

256. Polya, György, *How To Solve It*, [Princeton, N. J.: Princeton Univ. Press, 1945].

257. Potdar, Vasanth Kumar, "Construction and Evaluation of A Novel Solar Electric Motor," Master's Thesis, University of Florida, 1971.

258. Powell, W. F., Speech at General Electric Co., Owensboro, Ky., February 13, 1956.

259. Prindle, Edwin J., "The Art of Inventing," *AIEE Trans.*, V 25, May, 1906.

260. From *Professional Amateur: The Biography of Charles Franklin Kettering* by T. A. Boyd. Copyright © 1957 by T. A. Boyd. Reprinted by permission of the publishers, E. P. Button.

261. *Professional Management in General Electric*, Volume Three, General Electric Co., Schenectady, N. Y., 1954, p 139.

262. Pruitt, Raymond D., "Creativity and Discipline," *The Mayo Alumnus*, January, 1966.

263. Rabinow, Jacob, Concluding Discussion in DeSimone, *Education*.

264. Rabinow, Discussion on Morse's Paper, in DeSimone, *Education*.

265. Rabinow, Jacob, Quoted in DeSimone, *Education*.

266. Rabinow, Jacob, "The Process of Invention," Chap. 6 in DeSimone, *Education*.

267. Raudsepp, Eugene, "Removing Barriers To Creativity," *Machine Design*, May 24, 1962.

268. Raudsepp, Eugene, "Develop Your Inventing Ability," *Popular Mechanics*, June, 1962.

269. Raudsepp, Eugene, "Stimulating Invention," *Machine Design*, April 1, 1965, pp 87-89.

270. Raudsepp, Eugene, "Learn To Play Your Hunches," *Machine Design*, April 15, 1965.

271. Raudsepp, Eugene, "Creativity and the Critical Attitude," *Machine Design*, May 26, 1966.

272. Raudsepp, Eugene, "Try These Six Steps to More Ideas," *Hydrocarbon Processing*, Vol. 45, No. 10, October, 1966.

273. Reed, E. G., "Developing Creative Talent," *Machine Design*, Nov., 1954, pp 142-146.

274. Reel, Herbert C., "Thinking Unlimited," *Mechanical Engineering*, February, 1964.

275. Rhine, R. J., "Engineering Design and Social Value," *IEEE Trans. On Educ.*, Dec., 1964, pp 161-165.

276. Rhoads, C. P., Quoted in Boyd.

277. Roberts, Benjamin W., and Walter Lowen, "VITA Solving Technical Design Problems Throughout the World," *Engineering Education*, March, 1968.

278. Roosevelt, Franklin D., Quoted in Buckles.

279. Rossman, Joseph, *Industrial Creativity: The Psychology of the Inventor*, [Secaucus, N. J.: University Books, 1964], 288 p.

280. Salisbury, J. Kenneth, "Qualities Industry Wants In Its Engieers," *General Electric Review*, May, 1952, pp 16-19.

281. Sanderlin, George, *Across the Ocean Sea*, [New York, N. Y.: Harper & Row, Publishers, 1966].

282. Sapirie, Samuel R., "Human Engineering," *The Bent* of Tau Beta Pi, Summer, 1972.

283. Saunders, David R., "Some Measures Related To Success and Placement in Basic Engineering Research and Development," pp 321-327 in Taylor and Barron.

284. Scheerer, Martin, "Problem Solving," *Scientific American*, April, 1963, pp 118-128.

285. Schenck, H., Jr., "Experimental Measurements and Data Analysis," in Hawkins, *Student's Engineering Manual*.

286. "Scientific Method," *Encyclopaedia Britannica*, Vol. 20, [Chicago, Ill.: Encyclopaedia Britannica, Inc., 1949].

287. Seneca, Letter to Lucilius, A.D. 65, Quoted in Klemm.

288. Senswich, Gordon, "Fourteen Ways To Sell An Invention," *Synthesis*, No. 5, April, 1972.

289. Senswich, "Fourteen Ways to Sell An Invention," *Synthesis*, No. 6, May, 1972.

290. Shippen, Katherine B., "Mr. Bell Invents the Telephone" (Pamphlet), Bell Telephone System, 1955.

291. Shockley, William, "On the Statistics of Individual Variations of Productivity in Research Laboratories," *Proceedings of the IRE*, Vol. 45, No. 3, March, 1957, pp 279-290.

292. Shockley, William, quoted in DeSimone, *Education*.

293. Sikorsky, Igor, "Creative Engineering, Inventiveness and Intuition," presented at ASME annual meeting Nov. 30-Dec. 4, 1942, and Nov. 29-Dec., 1943. Published July, 1944.

294. Simons, Joseph H., "Scientific Research In The University," *American Scientist*, Vol. 48, No. 1, March, 1960.

295. Simpson, Phil, "Order Out of Chaos," *Phi Kappa Phi Journal*, Spring, 1970.

296. Singer, Isaac M., Quoted in Wilson, Mitchell.

297. Sinnett, Chester M., "The Challenge of Personal Professional Development," *Research And Development*, April, 1970.

298. Sinnett, Chester M., "The Challenge of Personal Professional Development," reprinted from RESEARCH/DEVELOPMENT magazine, copyright © August, 1970 by Technical Publishing Company.

299. Sinnett, Chester M., "The Challenge of Personal Professional Development," *Research and Development*, Dec., 1970.

300. Sinnett, Chester M., "Observations Regarding Leadership," *Research and Development*, April, 1971.

301. Sinnett, Chester M., "Cultural Blocks To Creativity," *Research and Development*, May, 1972.

302. Sinnett, Chester M., "Are Your A Communicator?," *Reserch and Development*, July, 1972.

303. Sinnett, Chester M., "Management/Employee Communications," *Research and Development*, September, 1972.

304. Sinnett, Chester M., "Are you a 'doer' or a 'watcher'?"

305. Smith, Elliott Dunlap, "Some Psychological Factors Favoring Industrial Inventiveness," presented at annual meeting of the American Society of Mechanical Engineers, New York, N. Y., Nov. 29-Dec. 3, 1943.

306. Smith, Ralph J., *Engineering As A Career*, Second Edition, Ch. 2, [New York, N. Y.: McGraw-Hill Book Co., Inc., 1962].

307. Socrates, Quoted in *Words of Inspiration*, [Chicago, Ill.: J. G. Ferguson Publishing Co., 1963].

308. *Solar Energy As A National Energy Resource*, NSF/NASA Solar Enrgy Panel, December, 1972. (Available from National Technical Information Service, Springfield, Va. 22151, as PB 221-659).

309. Soltanoff, Louis, "The Innovation Myth," *Industrial Research*, Aug., 1971, pp 44-46.

310. Spalding, Albert, "The Engineer, A Professional," Chapter 9 in Hawkins, *Student's Engineering Manual*.

311. Speeth, Sheridan Dauster, "The Rational Design of Toys," *The Journal of Creative Behavior*, Vol. 1, No. 4, Fall, 1967.

312. Starkey, W. L., "The Ingredients of Design," *Mechanical Engineering*, May, 1966, p 16-18.

313. Starr, Martin Kenneth, *Product Design and Decision Theory*, [Englewood Cliffs, N. J.: Prentice-Hall, Inc., 1963].

314. Start, Damien, "Getting It Written Down," *Synthesis*, No. 2, January, 1972.

315. Stedman, John C., "Engineering and the Many Cultures," in DeSimone, *Education*.

316. Stein, Morris I., "Creativity a Intra-and Inter-Personal Process," pp 85-92 in Parnes, *A Sourcebook*.

317. Steinmetz, Charles Proteus, *Engineering Mathematics*, [New York, N. Y.: McGraw-Hill, 1917].

318. Steinmetz, C. P., Quoted in Prindle.

319. *The Story Of The United States Patent Office*, 4th Ed., Feb., 1965.

320. Stratton, G. F., "A College of Invention," *Scientific American*, 96-97, August 17, 1907, p 115.

321. Stuber, Paul J., "Synergism: 2 + 2 = 5," *C & EN*, Nov. 14, 1955.

322. Suits, Guy, "Creativity in Research," Research Laboratory *Bulletin*, General Electric Co., Schenectady, N. Y., Winter, 1959-60.

323. Suits, Guy, "Selectivity--A Modern Research Necessity," Address before American Management Association, Chicago, Ill., September 15, 1964, GE Publication GP-0300A 9-64(M).

324. "Synectics: Inventing By The Madness Method," *Fortune*, August, 1965.

325. Tausig, F. W., *Inventors and Money-Makers*, [New York, N. Y.: Macmillan, 1915], 50.

326. Taylor, et al, "A Look Ahead," in Taylor and Barron's *Scientific Creativity*, Copyright © 1963 by John Wiley & Sons, Inc., Reprinted by permission of John Wiley & Sons, Inc.

327. Taylor, Calvin W., and Frank Barron, *Scientific Creativity*, [New York, N. Y.: John Wiley & Sons, Inc., 1963].

328. Taylor, et al, "A Look Ahead," pp 372-389 in Taylor and Barron.

329. Taylor, C. W., "Factors Influencing Creativity," in DeSimone, *Education*.

330. Taylor, Calvin W., "Tentative Description of the Creative Individual," pp 169-184 in Parnes, *A Sourcebook*.

331. Taylor, Calvin W., *Creativity Progress And Potential*, [New York, N. Y.: McGraw-Hill, Inc., 1964].

332. Taylor, E. S., et al, "Report on Engineeering Design," *Journal of Engineering Education*, Vol. 51, No. 8, April, 1961.

333. Taylor, Jack, "How To Create Ideas," [Englewood Cliffs, N. J.: Prentice Hall, 1961].

334. Teare, B. Richard, et al, "Educational Objectives In The Preparation of Engineers," Chap. 9 in DeSimone, *Education*.

335. Teller, A. J., "Fundamentals, the Fulcrum, Creativity, the Objective," *Transactions* of the Chemical Engineeering Division, American Society for Engineering Education, (1960).

336. Tesla, Nikola, *American Magazine*, April, 1921, Quoted in O'Neill, *Prodigal Genius*.

337. Tesla, Nikola, Quoted in O'Neill, *Prodigal Genius*.

338. Tesla, Nikola, Source unknown.

339. "Thomas A. Edison, Inventor," *Electrical Engineering*, Vol. 66, Feb., 1947.

340. Thomson, Elihu, Quoted in Rossman.

341. Thring, M. W., "On The Threshold," *Proceedings of Institution of Mechanical Engineers*, Vol. 179, Pt. I, (1964-65), pp 1089-1096.

342. Torrence, E. Paul, "Scientific Views of Creativity and Factors Affecting its Growth," *Daedalus*, 94 (Summer, 1965), 663-681.

343. Tournier, Paul, *The Meaning of Persons*, [New York, N. Y.: Harper & Row, Publishers, 1957].

344. Tournier, Paul, *The Adventure of Living*, Trans. by Edwin Hudson, [New York, N. Y.: Harper and Row, Publishers, 1965].

345. Tournier, Paul, *The Healing of Persons*, Trans. Edwin Hudson, [New York, N. Y.: Harper & Row Publishers, 1965].

346. Tumin, Melvin, "Obstacles To Creativity," pp 105-113 in Parnes, *A Sourcebook*.

347. Tung, Au, "Heuristic Approach to Systems Design," *Engineering Education*, March, 1969.

348. Tuska, C. D., *Inventors and Inventions*, [New York, N. Y.: McGraw-Hill Book Co., Inc., 1957].

349. Twain, Mark, Quoted in *Think*, an IBM Magazine, Vol. 28, No. 10, Nov.-Dec., 1962.

350. United States Constitution, Article 1, Sec. 8, Sept. 17, 1787.

351. United States V. Imperial Chemical Industries, Ltd., 105F. Supp. 215, 222.

352. Usher, Abbott Payson, *A History of Mechanical Inventions*, Revised Edition, [Cambridge, Mass.: Harvard University Press, 1966].

353. Vaughn, F. L., *Economics Of Our Patent System*, [New York, N. Y.: MacMillan, 1925].

354. Venezky, Richard L., "A Small-Scale Experiment In the Application of Creativity to the Teaching of Technical Communication," *IRE Trans. On Eng. Writing and Speech*, Vol. EWS-5, No. 1, August, 1962.

355. Ver Planck, D. W. and B. R. Teare, Jr., *Engineering Analysis*, [New York, N. Y., John Wiley & Sons, Inc., 1954].

356. Victor, Alexander F., Quoted in Laird, Donald Anderson, *The Technique of Personal Analysis*, [New York, N. Y.: McGraw-Hill Book Co., Inc., 1945].

357. Vidosic, Joseph P., *Elements of Design Engineering*, [New York, N. Y.: The Ronald Press, Inc., 1969].

358. Vollmer, James, "Engineering, Growing, Steady State, or Evanescent," *Bridge* of Eta Kappa Nu, Vol. 65, No. 4, August, 1969.

359. Von Fange, "Developing A Useful Imagination," *General Electric Review*, Sept., 1955.

360. Von Fange, Eugene K., *Professional Creativity*, [Englewood Cliffs, N. J.: Prentice-Hall, Inc., 1959].

361. Von Karman, Theodore, quoted in Freund, C. J., "Creativity Is A Task, Not A Trait," *Machine Design*, May 25, 1967, p 161-162.

362. Walker, E. A., et al, "Past Appraisals of Engieering Education And Related Studies," *Goals of Engineering Education Information Document No. 2*, American Society for Engineering Education, December, 1963.

363. Walker, E. A., Keynote Speaker, "Engineering Education Around The World," *Report of the World Congress on Engineering Education*, (Published by American Society of Engineering Education), Illinois Institute of Technology, Chicago, Ill., June 21-25, 1965.

364. Walker, E. A., et al, *Goals of Engineering Education - The Preliminary Report*, American Society for Engineering Education, October, 1965.

365. Walker, E. A., et al, *Final Report: Goals of Engineering Education*, American Society For Engineering Education, January, 1968.

366. Walker, Eric A., "Our Tradition-Bound Colleges," *Engineering Education*, October, 1969.

367. Walkup, Lewis E., "Individual Creativity in Research," *Battelle Technical Review*, Battelle Memorial Institute, Columbus, Ohio, August, 1958.

368. Walkup, Lewis E., "Creativity in Science Through Visualization," *The Journal of Creative Behavior*, Vol. 1, No. 3, July, 1967.

369. Wallas, G., *The Art of Thought*, [New York, N. Y.: Harcourt, Brace, 1926].

370. Warren, H. E., Quoted in Rossman.

371. Watkins, J. Elfreth, "The Beginnings of Engineering," *Transactions American Society of Civil Engineers*, Vol. 24, No. 472, May, 1891, p 332-333.

372. Wattles, Frank, "Claiming Your Invention - Part I," *Synthesis*, No. 13, 1973.

373. *Webster's New International Dictionary*, 2nd ed., [Springfield, Mass.: G. & C. Merriam Co., Publishers, 1956].

374. Western Electric Graduate Engineering Education, 1966, Western Electric Co., Inc., 10 Columbus Circle, New York, N. Y. 10019.

375. Whinnery, John R., *The World of Engineering*, [New York, N. Y., McGraw-Hill Book Co., 1965].

376. Wilson, *Jefferson's Letters*, [Eau Claire, Wisconsin: E. M. Hale and Co., n.d.].

377. Wickendon, W. E., "Report of the Investigation of Engineering Education, 1923-1929," Pittsburgh, Society for the Promotion of Engineering Education, Vol. I: 1930, Vol. II: 1934.

378. Wilson, Ira and Marthann, *From Idea To Working Model*, [New York, N. Y.: John Wiley & Sons, Inc., 1970].

379. Wilson, Mitchell, *American Science And Invention*, [New York, N. Y.: Simon & Schuster, Inc., Copyright © 1954].

380. Wilson, Robert Q., "Expanding Creative Capabilities," *Battelle Technical Review*, Vol. 11, No. 4, April, 1962, pp 11-15.

381. Wilson, W. E., *Concepts of Engineering Systems Design*, [New York, N. Y.: McGraw-Hill Co., 1965].

382. Woods, Ralph L., *Courage Is ...*, Essandras Special Editions, [New York, N. Y.: Simon & Schuster, Inc., 1968].

383. Woodson, Thomas T., *Introduction To Engineering Design*, [New York, N. Y.: McGraw-Hill Book Co., 1966].

384. *Words Of Inspiration*, [Chicago, Illinois: J. G. Ferguson Publishing Co., 1963].

385. *Workbook for Military Creative Problem Solving*, [Ft. Belvoir, Va.: U. S. Army Management School, 1964].

386. Wright, Orville, "On The Problem of Flight," in McFarland.

387. Wright, Orville, "On the Wright Experiments of 1899," in McFarland.

388. Wright, Orville, Quoted in McFarland.

389. Wright, Orville, Letter to Katharine Wright, Oct. 14, 1900, Quoted in McFarland.

390. Wright, Orville, Letter to Alexander Klem, April 11, 1924, In McFarland.

391. Wright, Wilbur, Letter to Octave Chanute, May 13, 1900 in McFarland.

392. Wright, Wilbur, Letter to Octave Chaute, May 30, 1900 in McFarland.

393. Wright, Wilbur, Letter to Octave Chanute, August 10, 1900 in McFarland.

394. Wright, Wilbur, Letter to Bishop Milton Wright, Sept. 23, 1900, in McFarland.

395. Wright, Wilbur, Letter to Octave Chanute, November 16, 1900, in McFarland.

396. Wright, Wilbur, Letter to Octave Chanute, July 1, 1901 in McFarland.

397. Wright, Wilbur, Lecture before Western Society of Engineers, Chicago, Ill., Sept. 18, 1901, in McFarland.

398. Wright, Wilbur, Letter to Octave Chanute, Oct. 18, 1901 in McFarland.

399. "Yale Study: Brainstorm Blocks Creativity," *Printer's Ink*, February 21, 1958.

400. Yerazunis, Stephen and Arthur A. Burr, "A Modern Approach To Design Education," *Engineering Education*, March, 1968.

401. Young, J. F., "Developing Creative Engineers," p 9-12 in *Creative Engineering*.

402. Zener, C., "Engineering in the Future," talk given at 17th Annual College-Industry Conference at Carnegie Institute of Technology, February 4 and 5, 1965. Published in *Florida Engineer*, October, 1965, p 18ff.

403. Zwicky, Fritz, *Discovery, Invention, Research*, First American Edition, [New York, N. Y.: The MacMillan Co., 1969].

404. Quoted in Klemm.

405. Write: Office of Invention and Innovation, National Bureau of Standards, U. S. Department of Commerce, Washington, D. C. 20234.

INDEX

Of Subjects